Acknowledgments appear on page T520, which constitutes an extension of this copyright page.

Copyright © 2011 Pearson Education, Inc., or its affiliates. All Rights Reserved. Printed in the United States of America. This publication is protected by copyright, and permission should be obtained from the publisher prior to any prohibited reproduction, storage in a retrieval system, or transmission in any form or by any means, electronic, mechanical, photocopying, recording, or likewise. For information regarding permissions, write to Pearson Curriculum Group Rights & Permissions, One Lake Street, Upper Saddle River, New Jersey 07458.

Pearson, Prentice Hall, Pearson Prentice Hall, and MathXL are trademarks, in the U.S. and/or other countries, of Pearson Education, Inc., or its affiliates.

ExamView® is a registered trademark of eInstruction Corporation.

TI-Nspire™ is a trademark of Texas Instruments Incorporated. SAT® is a trademark of the College Entrance Examination Board. ACT® is a trademark owned by ACT, Inc. Silly Putty® is a registered trademark of Crayola Properties, Inc. Use of the trademarks implies no relationship, sponsorship, endorsement, sale, or promotion on the part of Pearson Education, Inc., or its affiliates.

PEARSON

ISBN-13: 978-0-7854-7020-5
ISBN-10: 0-7854-7020-4
4 5 6 7 8 9 10   V057   13 12 11 10

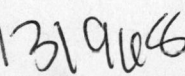

Teacher's Edition

FOUNDATIONS SERIES

Prentice Hall

Algebra 2

Randall I. Charles
Basia Hall
Dan Kennedy
Allan E. Bellman
Sadie Chavis Bragg
William G. Handlin
Siegfried Haenisch
Stuart J. Murphy
Grant Wiggins

PEARSON

Boston, Massachusetts • Chandler, Arizona • Glenview, Illinois • Upper Saddle River, New Jersey

Algebra 2 *Teacher's Edition Contents*

Series *Authors*

Randall I. Charles, Ph.D., is Professor Emeritus in the Department of Mathematics and Computer Science at San Jose State University, San Jose, California. He began his career as a high school mathematics teacher, and he was a mathematics supervisor for five years. Dr. Charles has been a member of several NCTM committees and is the former Vice President of the National Council of Supervisors of Mathematics (NCSM). Much of his writing and research has been in the area of problem solving. He has authored more than 75 mathematics textbooks for kindergarten through college.

Dan Kennedy, Ph.D., is a classroom teacher and the Lupton Distinguished Professor of Mathematics at the Baylor School in Chattanooga, Tennessee. A frequent speaker at professional meetings on mathematics education reform, Dr. Kennedy has conducted numerous workshops and institutes for high school teachers. He is coauthor of calculus and precalculus textbooks, and, from 1990 to 1994, he chaired the College Board's AP Calculus Development Committee. He is a 1992 Tandy Technology Scholar and a 1995 Presidential Award winner.

Basia Hall is currently Manager of Instructional Programs for the Houston Independent School District. Ms. Hall has been a department chair, instructional supervisor, school improvement facilitator, and professional development trainer. She has developed curricula for high school mathematics and co-developed the Texas state mathematics standards. A 1992 Presidential Awardee, Ms. Hall is past president of the Texas Association of Supervisors of Mathematics and is a state representative for NCSM.

Consulting *Authors*

Stuart J. Murphy is a visual learning author and consultant. He is the author of *MathStart*, a series of children's books that presents mathematical concepts in the story contexts. A graduate of the Rhode Island School of Design, Mr. Murphy has worked extensively in educational publishing and has been on the authorship teams of a number of mathematics programs. He is a frequent presenter at meetings of the National Council of Teachers of Mathematics and the International Reading Association.

Grant Wiggins, Ed.D., is the President of Authentic Education in Hopewell, New Jersey. Dr. Wiggins consults with schools, districts, and state education departments on reform matters; organizes conferences and workshops; and develops materials on curricular change. With Jay McTighe, he is co-author of *Understanding by Design* and *The Understanding by Design Handbook*, published by ASCD. His work has been supported by the Pew Charitable Trusts, the Geraldine R. Dodge Foundation, and the National Science Foundation.

Siegfried Haenisch, Ed.D., has taught mathematics from elementary to graduate school, most recently as Professor in the Department of Mathematics and Statistics at the College of New Jersey. Dr. Haenisch was the site director for the training of teachers in the New Jersey Algebra Project. Dr. Haenisch currently serves as a mathematics curriculum consultant to school districts. The Mathematical Association of America granted him the 1995 Award for Distinguished Teaching of Mathematics.

Program *Authors*
Algebra 1 and Algebra 2

Allan E. Bellman, Ph.D., is a Lecturer/Supervisor in the School of Education at the University of California, Davis. Before coming to Davis, he was a mathematics teacher for 31 years in Montgomery County, Maryland. He has been an instructor for both the Woodrow Wilson National Fellowship Foundation and the T^3 program. He has been involved in the development of many products from Texas Instruments. Dr. Bellman has a particular expertise in the use of technology in education and speaks frequently on this topic. He was a 1992 Tandy Technology Scholar and has twice been listed in Who's Who Among America's Teachers.

Sadie Chavis Bragg, Ed.D., is Senior Vice President of Academic Affairs at the Borough of Manhattan Community College of the City University of New York. A former professor of mathematics, she is a past president of the American Mathematical Association of Two-Year Colleges (AMATYC), co-director of the AMATYC project to revise the standards for introductory college mathematics before calculus, and an active member of the Benjamin Banneker Association. Dr. Bragg has coauthored more than 50 mathematics textbooks for kindergarten through college.

William G. Handlin, Sr., is a classroom teacher and Department Chairman of Technology Applications at Spring Woods High School in Houston, Texas. Awarded Life Membership in the Texas Congress of Parents and Teachers for his contributions to the well-being of children, Mr. Handlin is also a frequent workshop and seminar leader in professional meetings throughout the world.

Geometry

Laurie E. Bass is a classroom teacher at the 9–12 division of the Ethical Culture Fieldston School in Riverdale, New York. A classroom teacher for more than 30 years, Ms. Bass has a wide base of teaching experience, ranging from Grade 6 through Advanced Placement Calculus. She was the recipient of a 2000 Honorable Mention for the Radio Shack National Teacher Awards. She has been a contributing writer for a number of publications, including software-based activities for the Algebra 1 classroom. Among her areas of special interest are cooperative learning for high school students and geometry exploration on the computer. Ms. Bass is a frequent presenter at local, regional, and national conferences.

Art Johnson, Ed.D., is a professor of mathematics education at Boston University. He is a mathematics educator with 32 years of public school teaching experience, a frequent speaker and workshop leader, and the recipient of a number of awards: the Tandy Prize for Teaching Excellence, the Presidential Award for Excellence in Mathematics Teaching, and New Hampshire Teacher of the Year. He was also profiled by the Disney Corporation in the American Teacher of the Year Program. Dr. Johnson has contributed 18 articles to NCTM journals and has authored over 50 books on various aspects of mathematics.

Reviewers *National*

Tammy Baumann
K-12 Mathematics Coordinator
School District of the City
 of Erie
Erie, Pennsylvania

Sandy Cowgill
Mathematics Department Chair
Muncie Central High School
Muncie, Indiana

Kari Egnot
Mathematics Teacher
Newport News High School
Newport News, Virginia

Sheryl Ezze
Mathematics Chairperson
DeWitt High School
Lansing, Michigan

Dennis Griebel
Mathematics Coordinator
Cherry Creek School District
Aurora, Colorado

Bill Harrington
Secondary Mathematics
 Coordinator
State College School District
State College, Pennsylvania

Michael Herzog
Mathematics Teacher
Tucson Small School Project
Tucson, Arizona

Camilla Horton
Secondary Instruction Support
Memphis School District
Memphis, Tennessee

Gary Kubina
Mathematics Consultant
Mobile County School System
Mobile, Alabama

Sharon Liston
Mathematics Department Chair
Moore Public Schools
Oklahoma City, Oklahoma

Ann Marie Palmeri Monahan
Mathematics Supervisor
Bayonne Public Schools
Bayonne, New Jersey

Indika Morris
Mathematics Department Chair
Queen Creek School District
Queen Creek, Arizona

Jennifer Petersen
K-12 Mathematics Curriculum
 Facilitator
Springfield Public Schools
Springfield, Missouri

Tammy Popp
Mathematics Teacher
Mehlville School District
St. Louis, Missouri

Mickey Porter
Mathematics Teacher
Dayton Public Schools
Dayton, Ohio

Steven Sachs
Mathematics Department Chair
Lawrence North High School
Indianapolis, Indiana

John Staley
Secondary Mathematics
 Coordinator
Office of Mathematics, PK-12
Baltimore, Maryland

Robert Thomas, Ph.D.
Mathematics Teacher
Yuma Union High School
 District #70
Yuma, Arizona

Linda Ussery
Mathematics Consultant
Alabama Department of
 Education
Tuscumbia, Alabama

Denise Vizzini
Mathematics Teacher
Clarksburg High School
Montgomery County,
 Maryland

Marcia White
Mathematics Specialist
Academic Operations,
 Technology and Innovations
Memphis City Schools
Memphis, Tennessee

Merrie Wolf
Mathematics Department Chair
Tulsa Public Schools
Tulsa, Oklahoma

Contents *in Brief*

Welcome to Pearson's *Prentice Hall Algebra 2* student book. Throughout this textbook, you will find content that has been developed to cover all of the American Diploma Project's (ADP) math benchmarks. The End-of-Course Assessment is modeled after the ADP Algebra 2 test and can serve as practice before taking the actual ADP test.

ADP END-OF-COURSE EXAM CONTENT STANDARDS
for Algebra 2

The following chart shows the alignment of the ADP Core and Module Content to the lessons and features in Pearson's *Prentice Hall Algebra 2* text.

Content Standards		Where to Find
Operations on Numbers and Expressions		
O1.a	Convert between and among radical and exponential forms of numerical expressions.	Lessons: 6-1, 6-4
O1.b	Simplify and perform operations on numerical expressions containing radicals.	Lesson: 6-2
O1.c	Apply the laws of exponents to numerical expressions with rational and negative exponents to order and rewrite them in alternative forms.	Lesson: 6-2 Concept Byte: p. 380
O2.a	Represent complex numbers in the form $a + bi$, where a and b are real; simplify powers of pure imaginary numbers.	Lesson: 4-8 Concept Byte: p. 278
O2.b	Perform operations on the set of complex numbers.	Lesson: 4-8
O3.a	Convert between and among radical and exponential forms of algebraic expressions.	Lesson: 6-4
O3.b	Simplify and perform operations on radical algebraic expressions.	Lessons: 6-1, 6-2, 6-3, 6-4, 6-5, 6-7
O3.c	Apply the laws of exponents to algebraic expressions, including those involving rational and negative exponents, to order and rewrite them in alternative forms.	Lesson: 6-4 Concept Byte: p. 380
O3.d	Perform operations on polynomial expressions.	Lessons: 5-2, 5-4, 5-5
O3.e	Perform operations on rational expressions, including complex fractions.	Lessons: 8-4, 8-5, 8-6
O3.f	Identify or write equivalent algebraic expressions in one or more variables to extract information.	Lessons: 4-7, 8-5, 10-2, 10-4, 10-5
Equations and Inequalities		
E1.a	Solve equations and inequalities involving the absolute value of a linear expression.	Lesson: 1-6
E1.b	Express and solve systems of linear equations in three variables with and without the use of technology.	Lessons: 3-5, 3-6, 4-3
E1.c	Solve systems of linear inequalities in two variables and graph the solution set.	Lessons: 3-3, 3-4 Concept Byte: p. 175
E1.d	Recognize and solve problems that can be represented by single variable linear equations or inequalities or systems of linear equations or inequalities involving two or more variables. Interpret the solution(s) in terms of the context of the problem.	Lessons: 1-4, 1-5, 3-1, 3-3, 3-6
E2.a	Solve single-variable quadratic, exponential, rational, radical, and factorable higher-order polynomial equations over the set of real numbers, including quadratic equations involving absolute value.	Lessons: 4-5, 4-6, 4-7, 5-2, 5-5, 6-5, 7-5, 8-6
E2.b	Solve single variable quadratic equations and inequalities over the complex numbers; graph real solution sets on a number line.	Lessons: 4-5, 4-6, 4-7, 4-8 Concept Byte: p. 279
E2.c	Use the discriminant, $D = b^2 - 4ac$, to determine the nature of the solutions of the equation $ax^2 + bx + c = 0$.	Lesson: 4-7
E2.d	Graph the solution set of a two-variable quadratic inequality in the coordinate plane.	Concept Byte: p. 279
E2.e	Rewrite nonlinear equations and inequalities to express them in multiple forms in order to facilitate finding a solution set or to extract information about the relationships or graphs indicated.	Lessons: 4-1, 4-2, 5-3
Polynomial and Rational Equations		
P1.a	Determine key characteristics of quadratic functions and their graphs.	Lessons: 4-1, 4-2, 4-8
P1.b	Describe and represent the effect that changes in the parameters of a quadratic function have on the shape and position of its graph.	Lessons: 4-1, 4-2, 4-3

Content Standards		Where to Find
P1.c	Describe the effect that changes in the parameters of a quadratic function have on the shape and position of its graph.	Lesson: 4-1
P1.d	Recognize, express, and solve problems that can be modeled using quadratic functions. Interpret their solutions in terms of the context.	Lessons: 4-3, 4-5, 4-6, 4-7
P2.a	Determine key characteristics of power functions in the form $f(x) = zx^n$, $a \neq 0$, for positive integral values of n and their graphs.	Lessons: 5-1, 5-9
P2.b	Determine key characteristics of polynomial functions and their graphs	Lessons: 5-1, 5-2, 5-3
P2.c	Represent polynomial functions using tables, graphs, verbal statements, and equations. Translate among these representations.	Lessons: 5-1, 5-2, 5-8, 5-9
P2.d	Determine key characteristics of simple rational functions and their graphs.	Lessons: 8-2, 8-3
P2.e	Represent simple rational functions using tables, graphs, verbal statements, and equations. Translate among these representations.	Lessons: 8-2, 8-3
P2.f	Recognize, express, and solve problems that can be modeled using polynomial and simple rational functions. Interpret their solutions in terms of the context.	Lessons: 5-8, 8-3
Exponential Functions		
X1.a	Determine key characteristics of exponential functions and their graphs.	Lessons: 7-1, 7-2
X1.b	Represent exponential functions using tables, graphs, verbal statements, and equations. Represent exponential expressions in multiple forms. Translate among these representations.	Lessons: 7-1, 7-2, 7-5
X1.c	Describe and represent the effect that changes in the parameters of an exponential function have on the shape and position of its graph.	Lesson: 7-2
X1.d	Recognize, express, and solve problems that can be modeled using exponential functions, including those where logarithms provide an efficient method of solution. Interpret their solutions in terms of the context.	Lesson: 7-2
Function Operations and Inverses		
F1.a	Combine functions by addition, subtraction, multiplication, and division.	Lesson: 6-6
F1.b	Determine the composition of two functions, including any necessary restrictions on the domain.	Lessons: 6-6, 6-7
F2.a	Describe the conditions under which an inverse relation is a function.	Lesson: 6-7
F2.b	Determine and graph the inverse relation of a function.	Lesson: 6-7
F3.a	Determine key characteristics of absolute value, step, and other piecewise-defined functions.	Lesson: 1-6
F3.b	Represent piecewise-defined functions using tables, graphs, verbal statements, and equations. Translate among these representations.	Lesson: 1-6
F3.c	Recognize, express, and solve problems that can be modeled using absolute value, step, and other piecewise-defined functions. Interpret their solutions in terms of the context.	Lesson: 1-6
Data and Statistics		
S1.a	Summarize and compare data sets using statistical methods.	Lessons: 11-5, 11-6, 11-7
S1.b	Determine, use, and identify potential misuses of weighted averages.	Lesson: 11-5
S1.c	Use a computer or calculator to find a linear regression equation (least squares line) as a model for data that suggest a linear trend, and determine the correlation coefficient.	Lesson: 2-5
S2.a	Analyze the strength of the linear relationship indicated by the regression line.	Lesson: 2-5
S2.b	Interpret data and communicate conclusions effectively.	Lesson: 11-7 Concept Byte: p. 744
S2.c	Make judgments regarding accuracy, reasonableness, and bias in the use of data.	Lesson: 11-7
S2.d	Critique and justify various methods of sampling and data collection used in real world problems.	Lesson: 11-7

Content Standards		Where to Find
Probability		
R1.a	Determine the number of ways events can occur using permutations, combinations, and other systematic counting methods.	Lessons: 11-1, 11-2
R1.b	Relate the expansion of $(x + y)^n$ (i.e., the binomial theorem) with the possible outcomes of a binomial experiment and/or the nth row of Pascal's triangle.	Lesson: 11-8
R1.c	Apply probability concepts to calculate the probability of events and to make informed decisions in practical situations.	Lessons: 11-2, 11-3, 11-4
R1.d	Analyze and interpret actual data to estimate probabilities and predict outcomes, including those involving relative frequency.	Lessons: 11-2, 11-3, 11-4
R1.e	Compare theoretical probabilities with the results of simple experiments (e.g., tossing number cubes, flipping coins, spinning spinners).	
R1.f	Compute and graph cumulative frequencies.	
R2.a	Identify and distinguish between discrete and continuous probability distributions.	Lesson: 11-9
R2.b	Identify the principal characteristics of the normal distribution and use them to estimate probabilities.	Lesson: 11-9
R2.c	Identify and describe the key characteristics of and create frequency distributions of both discrete and continuous data.	Lessons: 11-8, 11-9
Logarithmic Functions		
L1.a	Apply the properties of logarithms and use them to manipulate logarithmic expressions.	Lessons: 7-4, 7-5
L1.b	Solve logarithmic equations, paying attention to the possibility of extraneous roots.	Lesson: 7-5
L2.a	Determine key characteristics of logarithmic functions.	Lesson: 7-3
L2.b	Represent logarithmic functions using tables, graphs, verbal statements, and equations. Translate among these representations.	Lesson: 7-3
L2.c	Describe the effect that changes in the parameters of a logarithmic function have on the shape and position of its graph.	Lesson: 7-3
L2.d	Recognize, express, and solve problems that can be modeled using logarithmic functions. Interpret their solutions in terms of the context of the problem.	Lessons: 7-3, 7-5
Trigonometric Functions		
T1.a	Recognize periodic phenomena and determine key characteristics of such phenomena.	Lesson: T-5
T1.b	Use the relationship of the sine and cosine functions to a central angle of the unit circle to determine the exact trigonometric ratio of angles on the unit circle (0° to 360°, 0 to 2π).	Lesson: T-3
T1.c	Explain and use both degree and radian measure for angles.	Lessons: T-3, T-4
T1.d	Represent trigonometric functions using tables, graphs, verbal statements, and equations. Translate among these representations.	Lesson: T-5
T1.e	Determine key characteristics of trigonometric functions and their graphs.	Lesson: T-5
T1.f	Describe the effect that changes in the parameters of an equation of a trigonometric function in the form $f(x) = A \sin B(x - C) + D$ (or the similar cosine function) have on the shape and position of its graph.	
T1.g	Recognize, express, and solve problems that can be modeled using trigonometric or other periodic functions.	Lessons: T-1, T-5, T-6
Matrices		
M1.a	Perform addition, subtraction, and scalar multiplication of matrices.	Lesson: 12-2
M1.b	Perform matrix multiplication.	Lesson: 12-3
M2.a	Find the determinant of a 2 × 2 or 3 × 3 matrix.	Lessons: 12-3, 12-4
M2.b	Determine the inverse of a 2 × 2 or 3 × 3 matrix or indicate that no inverse exists.	Lessons: 12-3, 12-4

	Content Standards	Where to Find
M2.c	Represent 2-variable and 3-variable systems of linear equations using matrices and use them to solve the system.	Lessons: 3-6, 12-4
M2.d	Solve a matrix equation.	Lessons: 12-1, 12-4
M3.a	Use matrix tools to represent and transform geometric objects in the coordinate plane.	
M4.b	Add, subtract, and compute the dot product of two-dimensional vectors; multiply a two-dimensional vector by a scalar.	
	Conic Sections	
C1.a	Identify a parabola, circle, ellipse, or hyperbola from its equation, description, or key characteristics.	Lessons: 10-1, 10-2, 10-3, 10-4, 10-5
C1.b	Represent conic sections whose axes are parallel to the x- and y-axes using graphs, verbal statements and equations. Translate among these representations. Represent the equations of conic sections in multiple forms to extract information about the parabola, circle, ellipse, or hyperbola.	Lessons: 10-2, 10-3, 10-4, 10-5
C1.c	Describe the effect that changes in the parameters of a particular conic section have on its shape and position.	Lessons: 10-2, 10-3, 10-4, 10-5
C1.d	Recognize, express, and solve problems that can be modeled using conic sections. Interpret their solutions in terms of the context of the problem.	Lessons: 10-2, 10-3, 10-4, 10-5
	Sequences and Series	
I1.a	Represent the general term of an arithmetic or geometric sequence and use it to generate the sequence or determine the value of any particular term.	Lessons: 9-2, 9-3, 9-4, 9-5
I1.b	Represent partial sums of an arithmetic or geometric sequence and determine the value of a particular partial sum or sum of a finite sequence.	Lessons: 9-4, 9-5
I1.c	Recognize when an infinite geometric sum can be determined and determine the sum when possible.	Lesson: 9-5
I1.d	Convert the recursive model for linear growth ($a_1 = a$, $a_{n+1} = a_n + d$, where a is the first term and d is the constant difference) to a closed linear form ($a_n = a(n - 1)d$).	Lesson: 9-1
I1.e	Convert the recursive model of geometric growth ($p_1 = a$, $p_{n+1} r p_n$ where a is the first term and r is the constant growth rate) to a closed exponential form ($p_n = ar^{n-1}$).	Lesson: 9-5
I1.f	Recognize, express, and solve problems that can be modeled using a finite geometric series. Interpret their solutions in terms of the context of the problem.	Lesson: 9-5
I2.a	Use recursion to generate and describe, analyze, and interpret patterned relationships other than arithmetic or geometric sequences.	Lesson: 9-1
I2.b	Use iterative methods to solve problems.	Lessons: 7-1, 7-2, 9-1

Algebra 2 Leveled Pacing Chart

This Leveled Pacing Chart will help you customize your course to include topics in discrete math or trigonometry and to provide for differentiated instruction.

The suggested number of days for each chapter is based on a traditional 45-minute class period and on a 90-minute block period. The suggested number of days for instruction leaves time for assessments, projects, assemblies, or other special days that vary from school to school. The chapter pacing guides will need to be adjusted for courses taught with Discrete Math or Trigonometry and for the Comprehensive Course.

KEY

✓ = Algebra 2 Content
○ = Reviews the previous year
❏ = Content for Enrichment

	Regular Course	Course with Trigonometry	Comprehensive Course
Chapter 1 Expressions, Equations, and Inequalities	T = 12 B = 6	T = 12 B = 6	T = 10 B = 5
1-1 Patterns and Expressions	○	○	○
1-2 Properties of Real Numbers	○	○	○
1-3 Algebraic Expressions	○	○	○
1-4 Solving Equations	○	○	○
1-5 Solving Inequalities	○	○	○
1-6 Absolute Value Equations and Inequalities	✓	✓	✓
Chapter 2 Functions, Equations, and Graphs	T = 18 B = 9	T = 17 B = 8	T = 15 B = 8
2-1 Relations and Functions	○	○	○
2-2 Direct Variation	✓	✓	✓
2-3 Linear Functions and Slope-Intercept Form	✓	✓	✓
2-4 More About Linear Equations	✓	✓	✓
2-5 Using Linear Models	✓	✓	✓
2-6 Families of Functions	✓	✓	✓
2-7 Absolute Value Functions and Graphs	✓	✓	✓
2-8 Two-Variable Inequalities	✓	✓	✓
Chapter 3 Linear Systems	T = 14 B = 7	T = 12 B = 6	T = 10 B = 5
3-1 Solving Systems Using Tables and Graphs	✓	✓	✓
3-2 Solving Systems Algebraically	✓	✓	✓
3-3 Systems of Inequalities	✓	✓	✓
3-4 Linear Programming	✓	✓	✓
Concept Byte: Linear Programming		❏	❏
3-5 Systems With Three Variables	✓	✓	✓
3-6 Solving Systems Using Matrices	✓	✓	✓
Chapter 4 Quadratic Functions and Equations	T = 22 B = 11	T = 20 B = 10	T = 19 B = 9
4-1 Quadratic Functions and Transformations	✓	✓	✓
4-2 Standard Form of a Quadratic Function	✓	✓	✓
4-3 Modeling With Quadratic Functions	✓	✓	✓
Concept Byte: Identifying Quadratic Data	✓	✓	✓

	Regular Course	Course with Trigonometry	Comprehensive Course
Chapter 4 (continued) Quadratic Functions and Equations	T = 22 B = 11	T = 20 B = 10	T = 19 B = 9
4-4 Factoring Quadratic Expressions	✓	✓	✓
Algebra Review: Square Roots and Radicals	○	○	
4-5 Quadratic Equations	✓	✓	✓
Concept Byte: Writing Equations From Roots	✓	✓	✓
4-6 Completing the Square	✓	✓	✓
4-7 The Quadratic Formula	✓	✓	✓
4-8 Complex Numbers	✓	✓	✓
Concept Byte: Powers of Complex Numbers	✓	✓	✓
Concept Byte: Quadratic Inequalities			✓
Chapter 5 Polynomials and Polynomial Functions	T = 22 B = 11	T = 20 B = 10	T = 18 B = 9
5-1 Polynomial Functions	✓	✓	✓
5-2 Polynomials, Linear Factors, and Zeros	✓	✓	✓
5-3 Solving Polynomial Equations	✓	✓	✓
5-4 Dividing Polynomials	✓	✓	✓
5-5 Theorems About Roots of Polynomial Equations	✓	✓	✓
5-6 The Fundamental Theorem of Algebra	✓	✓	✓
Concept Byte: Pascal's Triangle			❑
5-7 The Binomial Theorem	✓	✓	✓
5-8 Polynomial Models in the Real World	✓	✓	✓
5-9 Transforming Polynomial Functions	✓	✓	✓
Chapter 6 Radical Functions and Rational Exponents	T = 22 B = 11	T = 20 B = 10	T = 18 B = 10
Algebra Review: Properties of Exponents	○	○	
6-1 Roots and Radical Expressions	✓	✓	✓
6-2 Multiplying and Dividing Radical Expressions	✓	✓	✓
6-3 Binomial Radical Expressions	✓	✓	✓
6-4 Rational Exponents	✓	✓	✓
6-5 Solving Square Root and Other Radical Equations	✓	✓	✓
6-6 Function Operations	✓	✓	✓
6-7 Inverse Relations and Functions	✓	✓	✓
Concept Byte: Graphing Inverses			❑
6-8 Graphing Radical Functions	✓	✓	✓
Chapter 7 Exponential and Logarithmic Functions	T = 14 B = 7	T = 13 B = 6	T = 11 B = 5
7-1 Exploring Exponential Models	✓	✓	✓
7-2 Properties of Exponential Functions	✓	✓	✓
7-3 Logarithmic Functions as Inverses	✓	✓	✓
Concept Byte: Fitting Curves to Data		❑	❑
7-4 Properties of Logarithms	✓	✓	✓

	Regular Course	Course with Trigonometry	Comprehensive Course
Chapter 7 (continued) Exponential and Logarithmic Functions	**T = 14 B = 7**	**T = 13 B = 6**	**T = 11 B = 5**
7-5 Exponential and Logarithmic Equations	✓	✓	✓
Concept Byte: Using Logarithms for Exponential Models			❑
Chapter 8 Rational Functions	**T = 14 B = 7**	**T = 13 B = 6**	**T = 11 B = 6**
8-1 Inverse Variation	✓	✓	✓
Concept Byte: Graphing Rational Functions	✓	✓	✓
8-2 The Reciprocal Function Family	✓	✓	✓
8-3 Rational Functions and Their Graphs	✓	✓	✓
8-4 Rational Expressions	✓	✓	✓
8-5 Adding and Subtracting Rational Expressions	✓	✓	✓
8-6 Solving Rational Equations	✓	✓	✓
Chapter 9 Sequences and Series	**T = 11 B = 5**		**T = 7 B = 4**
9-1 Mathematical Patterns	✓		✓
9-2 Arithmetic Sequences	✓		✓
9-3 Geometric Sequences	✓		✓
9-4 Arithmetic Series	✓		✓
9-5 Geometric Series	✓		✓
Chapter 10 Quadratic Relations and Conic Sections	**T = 11 B = 5**	**T = 10 B = 5**	**T = 7 B = 4**
10-1 Exploring Conic Sections	✓	✓	✓
Concept Byte: Graphing Conic Sections	✓	✓	✓
10-2 Parabolas	✓	✓	✓
10-3 Circles	✓	✓	✓
10-4 Ellipses	✓	✓	✓
10-5 Hyperbolas	✓	✓	✓
Chapter 11 Probability and Statistics			**T = 17 B = 8**
11-1 Permutations and Combinations			✓
11-2 Probability			✓
11-3 Probability of Multiple Events			✓
11-4 Conditional Probability			✓
11-5 Analyzing Data			✓
11-6 Standard Deviation			✓
11-7 Samples and Surveys			✓
Concept Byte: Describing Data			✓
11-8 Binomial Distributions			✓
11-9 Normal Distributions			✓

	Regular Course	Course with Trigonometry	Comprehensive Course
Chapter 12 Matrices		T = 11 B = 6	T = 8 B = 4
12-1 Adding and Subtracting Matrices		✓	✓
Concept Byte: Working With Matrices		✓	✓
12-2 Matrix Multiplication		✓	✓
12-3 Determinants and Inverses		✓	✓
12-4 Inverse Matrices and Systems		✓	✓
Chapter T Trigonometry Concepts		T = 11 B = 6	T = 9 B = 4
T-1 Right Triangles and Trigonometric Ratios		✓	✓
T-2 Special Angles		✓	✓
T-3 The Unit Circle		✓	✓
T-4 Degrees and Radian Measure		✓	✓
T-5 Graphs of Sine, Cosine, and Tangent Functions		✓	✓
T-6 Basic Identities		✓	✓
Total Number of Days	**160**	**158**	**160**

BIGideas

These Big Ideas are the organizing ideas for the study of important areas of mathematics: algebra, geometry, and statistics.

Algebra

Properties
- In the transition from arithmetic to algebra, attention shifts from arithmetic operations (addition, subtraction, multiplication, and division) to use of the *properties* of these operations.
- All of the facts of arithmetic and algebra follow from certain properties.

Variable
- Quantities are used to form expressions, equations, and inequalities.
- An expression refers to a quantity but does not make a statement about it. An equation (or an inequality) is a statement about the quantities it mentions.
- Using variables in place of numbers in equations (or inequalities) allows the statement of relationships among numbers that are unknown or unspecified.

Equivalence
- A single quantity may be represented by many different expressions.
- The facts about a quantity may be expressed by many different equations (or inequalities).

Solving Equations & Inequalities
- Solving an equation is the process of rewriting the equation to make what it says about its variable(s) as simple as possible.
- Properties of numbers and equality can be used to transform an equation (or inequality) into equivalent, simpler equations (or inequalities) in order to find solutions.
- Useful information about equations and inequalities (including solutions) can be found by analyzing graphs or tables.
- The numbers and types of solutions vary predictably, based on the type of equation.

Proportionality
- Two quantities are *proportional* if they have the same ratio in each instance where they are measured together.
- Two quantities are *inversely proportional* if they have the same product in each instance where they are measured together.

Function
- A function is a relationship between variables in which each value of the input variable is associated with a unique value of the output variable.
- Functions can be represented in a variety of ways, such as graphs, tables, equations, or words. Each representation is particularly useful in certain situations.
- Some important families of functions are developed through transformations of the simplest form of the function.
- New functions can be made from other functions by applying arithmetic operations or by applying one function to the output of another.

Modeling
- Many real-world mathematical problems can be represented algebraically. These representations can lead to algebraic solutions.
- A function that models a real-world situation can be used to make estimates or predictions about future occurrences.

xxii

Statistics and Probability

Data Collection and Analysis

- Sampling techniques are used to gather data from real-world situations. If the data are representative of the larger population, inferences can be made about that population.
- Biased sampling techniques yield data unlikely to be representative of the larger population.
- Sets of numerical data are described using measures of central tendency and dispersion.

Data Representation

- The most appropriate data representations depend on the type of data—quantitative or qualitative, and univariate or bivariate.
- Line plots, box plots, and histograms are different ways to show distribution of data over a possible range of values.

Probability

- Probability expresses the likelihood that a particular event will occur.
- Data can be used to calculate an experimental probability, and mathematical properties can be used to determine a theoretical probability.
- Either experimental or theoretical probability can be used to make predictions or decisions about future events.
- Various counting methods can be used to develop theoretical probabilities.

Geometry

Visualization

- Visualization can help you see the relationships between two figures and connect properties of real objects with two-dimensional drawings of these objects.

Transformations

- Transformations are mathematical functions that model relationships with figures.
- Transformations may be described geometrically or by coordinates.
- Symmetries of figures may be defined and classified by transformations.

Measurement

- Some attributes of geometric figures, such as length, area, volume, and angle measure, are measurable. Units are used to describe these attributes.

Reasoning & Proof

- Definitions establish meanings and remove possible misunderstanding.
- Other truths are more complex and difficult to see. It is often possible to verify complex truths by reasoning from simpler ones using deductive reasoning.

Similarity

- Two geometric figures are similar when corresponding lengths are proportional and corresponding angles are congruent.
- Areas of similar figures are proportional to the squares of their corresponding lengths.
- Volumes of similar figures are proportional to the cubes of their corresponding lengths.

Coordinate Geometry

- A coordinate system on a line is a number line on which points are labeled, corresponding to the real numbers.
- A coordinate system in a plane is formed by two perpendicular number lines, called the x- and y-axes, and the quadrants they form. The coordinate plane can be used to graph many functions.
- It is possible to verify some complex truths using deductive reasoning in combination with the distance, midpoint, and slope formulas.

1 Expressions, Equations, and Inequalities

2 Functions, Equations, and Graphs

Visual See It!

Reasoning Try It!

Practice Do It!

3

Linear Systems

4 Quadratic Functions and Equations

Visual See It!

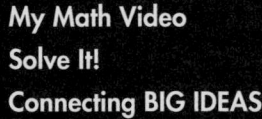

Reasoning Try It!

Practice Do It!

5

Polynomials and Polynomial Functions

6 Radical Functions and Rational Exponents

Visual See It!

Reasoning Try It!

Practice Do It!

Exponential and Logarithmic Functions

8 Rational Functions

Visual See It!

Reasoning Try It!

Practice Do It!

9 Sequences and Series

10 Quadratic Relations and Conic Sections

Visual See It!

Reasoning Try It!

Practice Do It!

Probability and Statistics

12 Matrices

Trigonometry Concepts

Visual See It!

Reasoning Try It!

Practice Do It!

Are you ready for your training?

Visit **myPearsonTraining.com** and learn how you can attend an instructor-led Webinar or view a step-by-step tutorial whenever you want! We offer a comprehensive Web site of self-paced Adobe® Flash® tutorials that show teachers step by step how to get started using their Pearson textbooks and technology products.

As a teacher, your time is valuable. So we've developed just-in-time training that's available on your schedule, when you need it.

At **myPearsonTraining.com,** you can watch step-by-step tutorials or connect with one of our online trainers for a virtual seminar (Webinar) about your textbook and technology. We're ready when you are!

Get Ready!

 Evaluating Expressions

Lesson 1-3

Evaluate each expression for $x = -2, 0,$ and 2.

1. 10^{x+1} **2.** $\left(\frac{3}{2}\right)^x$ **3.** -5^{x-2} **4.** $-(3)^{0.5x}$

Lesson 2-5

Using Linear Models

Draw a scatter plot and find the line of best fit for each set of data.

5. $(0, 2), (1, 4), (2, 6.5), (3, 8.5), (4, 10), (5, 12), (6, 14)$

6. $(3, 100), (5, 150), (7, 195), (9, 244), (11, 296), (13, 346), (15, 396)$

Lessons 4-1
and 5-9

Graphing Transformations

Identify the parent function of each equation. Graph each equation as a transformation of its parent function.

7. $y = (x + 5)^2 - 3$ **8.** $y = -2\,(x - 6)^3$

Lesson 6-4

Simplifying Rational Exponents

Simplify each expression.

9. $\left(x^{\frac{1}{5}}\right)^{10}$ **10.** $\left(-8x^3\right)^{\frac{4}{3}}$

Lesson 6-7

Finding Inverses

Find the inverse of each function. Is the inverse a function?

11. $y = 10 - 2x^2$ **12.** $y = (x + 4)^3 - 1$

Looking Ahead Vocabulary

13. In advertising, the *decay factor* describes how an advertisement loses its effectiveness over time. In math, would you expect a decay factor to increase or decrease the value of y as x increases?

14. There are many different kinds of growth patterns. Patterns that increase by a constant rate are linear. Patterns that grow *exponentially* increase by an ever-increasing rate. If your allowance doubles each week, does that represent linear growth or exponential growth?

15. The word *asymptote* comes from a Greek word meaning "not falling together." When looking at the end behavior of a function, do you expect the graph to intersect its asymptote?

Get Ready!

Assign this diagnostic assessment to determine if students have the prerequisite skills for Chapter 7.

Lesson	Skill
1-3	Evaluate Expressions
2-5	Use Linear Models
4-1 and 5-9	Graph Transformations
6-4	Simplify Radicals
6-7	Find Inverses

To remediate students, select from these resources (available for every lesson).
• Online Problems (PowerAlgebra.com)
• Reteaching (All-in-One Teaching Resources)
• Practice (All-in-One Teaching Resources)

Why Students Need These Skills

EVALUATING EXPRESSIONS
Evaluating expressions is essential to determining the values of logarithms and exponents.

USING LINEAR MODELS
Students extend their skill of using linear models to finding exponential and logarithmic models.

GRAPHING TRANSFORMATIONS
Graphing transformations is an essential skill when graphing certain logarithmic and exponential functions.

SIMPLIFYING RADICALS
Simplifying radicals is essential to simplifying exponents when solving exponential equations.

FINDING INVERSES
Understanding how to find inverses is essential in understanding the relationship between exponential and logarithmic functions.

Looking Ahead Vocabulary

DECAY FACTOR Ask students for other examples of decay. How does decay change things?

EXPONENTIALLY Ask students to choose an allowance, doubling it at regular intervals. Ask them what a graph of the allowance over time would look like.

ASYMPTOTE Ask students to consider what it means to intersect something.

Answers

Get Ready!

1. $0.1; 10; 1000$

2. $\frac{4}{9}; 1; \frac{9}{4}$

3. $-\frac{1}{625}; -\frac{1}{25}; -1$

4. $-\frac{1}{3}; -1; -3$

5.
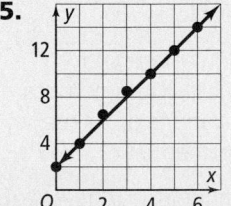
$; y \approx 1.98x + 2.20$

6.
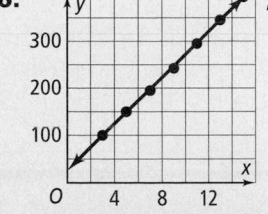
$;$
$y \approx 24.66x + 24.77$

7. $y = x^2$
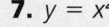
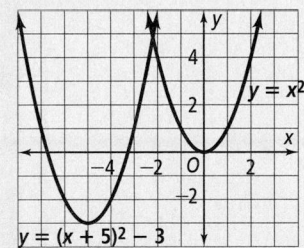

8. $y = x^3$
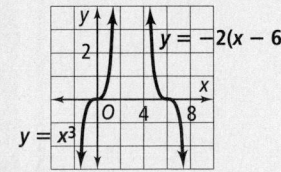

9. x^2

10. $16x^4$

11. $y = \pm\sqrt{\frac{10 - x}{2}};$ no

12. $y = -4 + \sqrt[3]{x + 1};$ yes

13. decrease

14. exponential

15. no

Chapter 7 Overview

UbD Understanding by Design

Chapter 7 expands on student understandings and skills related to exponential and logarithmic functions. In this chapter, students will develop the answers to the Essential Questions posed on the student page as they learn the concepts and skills bulleted below.

BIG idea Modeling

ESSENTIAL QUESTION How do you model a quantity that changes regularly over time by the same percentage?

• Students will model situations with exponential functions.

BIG idea Equivalence

ESSENTIAL QUESTION How are exponents and logarithms related?

• Students will use exponents to solve logarithmic equations and logarithms to solve exponential equations.

BIG idea Function

ESSENTIAL QUESTION How are exponential functions and logarithmic functions related?

• Students will show that exponents and logarithms are inverse functions.
• Students will graph exponential and logarithmic functions.

PowerAlgebra.com

Your place to get all things digital

Download videos connecting math to your world.

VIDEO

Math definitions in English and Spanish

VOCABULARY

The online Solve It will get you in gear for each lesson.

SOLVE IT!

Interactive! Vary numbers, graphs, and figures to explore math concepts.

DYNAMIC ACTIVITIES

Download Step-by-Step Problems with Instant Replay.

ONLINE PROBLEMS

Get and view your assignments online.

ONLINE HOMEWORK

Extra practice and review online

MathXL FOR SCHOOL

Logarithms provide a way to work with the inverses of exponential functions.

Exponential functions model what some might call "explosive" growth, but logarithmic values grow very slowly. Decibels are logarithms that measure sound, and when sound energy increases dramatically, the decibel values creep upward. A few extra decibels can bust your eardrums!

Vocabulary

English/Spanish Vocabulary Audio Online:

English	Spanish
asymptote, *p. 463*	asíntota
Change of Base Formula, *p. 493*	fórmula de cambio de base
common logarithm, *p. 482*	logaritmo común
exponential decay, *p. 463*	decremento exponencial
exponential equation, *p. 498*	ecuación exponencial
exponential function, *p. 462*	función exponencial
exponential growth, *p. 463*	incremento exponencial
logarithm, *p. 480*	logaritmo
logarithmic equation, *p. 503*	ecuación logarítmica
logarithmic function, *p. 483*	función logarítmica

PowerAlgebra.com

Chapter 7 Overview

Use these online assets to engage your students. These include support for the Solve It and step-by-step solutions for Problems.

 Show the student-produced video demonstrating relevant and engaging applications of the new concepts in the chapter.

 Find online definitions for new terms in English and Spanish.

 Start each lesson with an attention-getting Problem. View the Problem online with helpful hints.

My Math Video

00:04:04   VIDEO ►

BIG ideas

1 **Modeling**
   Essential Question How do you model a quantity that changes regularly over time by the same percentage?

2 **Equivalence**
   Essential Question How are exponents and logarithms related?

3 **Function**
   Essential Question How are exponential functions and logarithmic functions related?

Chapter Preview

PowerAlgebra.com | Chapter 7 Exponential and Logarithmic Functions | 461

My Math Video
Use this photo to introduce the concept of logarithmic functions.

Q What is being shown in the photo? **[a DJ spinning a record]**

Q What do decibels measure? **[sound]**

Q If someone told you that the music is just a few decibels louder than what is safe, should you be concerned? Why or why not? **[Yes; an increase of just a few decibels is dramatically louder.]**

EXTENSION
Have students research other types of logarithmic models, such as the Richter scale or the pH scale.

 Increase students' depth of knowledge with interactive online activities.

 Show problems from each lesson solved step by step. Instant replay allows students to go at their own pace when studying online.

 Prepare students for the Mid-Chapter Quiz and the Chapter Test with online practice and review.

Modeling

BIG idea Many real-world mathematical problems can be represented algebraically. These representations can lead to algebraic solutions. A function that models a real-world situation can then be used to make estimates or decisions about the situation, or predictions about future occurrences.

ESSENTIAL UNDERSTANDINGS

7-1 You can represent repeated multiplication with a function in the form of $y = ab^x$ where b is a positive number other than 1.

7-4 Logarithms and exponents have corresponding properties.

Equivalence

BIG idea A single quantity may be represented by many different expressions. The facts about a quantity may be expressed by many different equations (or inequalities).

ESSENTIAL UNDERSTANDINGS

7-1 You can represent repeated multiplication with a function in the form of $y = ab^x$ where b is a positive number other than 1.

7-3 The exponential function $y = b^x$ is one-to-one, so its inverse $x = b^y$ is a function. To express "y as a function of x" for the inverse, write $y = \log_b x$.

7-5 You can use logarithms to solve exponential equations. You can use exponents to solve logarithmic equations.

Function

BIG idea A function is a relationship between variables in which each value of the input variable is associated with a unique value of the output variable. Functions can be represented in a variety of ways (such as graphs, tables, equations, or words). Each representation is particularly useful in certain situations. Some important families of functions are developed through transformations of the simplest form of the function.

ESSENTIAL UNDERSTANDINGS

7-1 You can represent repeated multiplication with a function in the form of $y = ab^x$ where b is a positive number other than 1.

7-2 The factor a in $y = ab^x$ can stretch or compress, and possibly reflect the graph of the parent function $y = b^x$.

7-3 The exponential function $y = b^x$ is one-to-one, so its inverse $x = b^y$ is a function. To express "y as a function of x" for the inverse, write $y = \log_b x$.

7-5 You can use logarithms to solve exponential equations. You can use exponents to solve logarithmic equations.

Exponential and Logarithmic Models

Exponential Models

The function $y = ab^x$, represents
• exponential growth if $a > 0$ and $b > 1$
• exponential decay if $a > 0$ and $0 < b < 1$

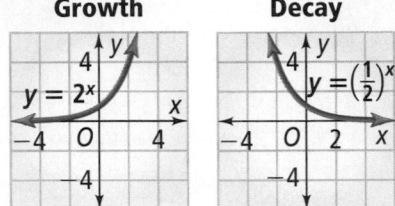

The factor a can stretch, compress, or reflect the graph of the parent function $y = b^x$.

The function $y = ab^{(x-h)} + k$ is translated horizontally for nonzero values of h and vertically for nonzero values of k.

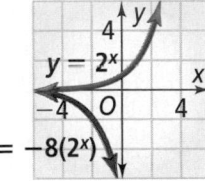

Logarithmic Models

The equation $y = \log_b x$ is the inverse of the exponential function $y = b^x$. The common log is a logarithm with base 10. It is commonly written without the base. So $\log_{10} x = \log x$.

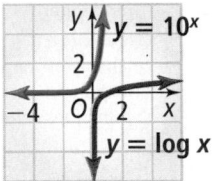

The fact that exponential and logarithmic functions are inverses can be used to find values of logarithms.

Common Errors When Using Exponential and Logarithmic Models

Exponential Models Students may make errors when converting the factors for growth and decay from percent to decimal. For example, a growth rate of 3% indicates that the value b should be 1.03. Remind students to check the first few terms to be sure their models are correct.

Logarithmic Models Students sometimes confuse the domain and range of logarithmic models. Point out that because the functions are inverses of each other, the domain and range of the exponential model is the range and domain of the logarithmic model.

Solving Logarithmic Equations

The properties of logarithms can be used to solve logarithmic equations.

For any positive numbers m, n, and b where $b \neq 1$:

Product Property $\quad \log_b mn = \log_b m + \log_b n$

Quotient Property $\quad \log_b \frac{m}{n} = \log_b m - \log_b n$

Power Property $\quad \log_b m^n = n \log_b m$

Example: What is the solution of $\log 3 + \log 2x = 2$?

$$\log 3 + \log 2x = 2$$
$$\log (6x) = 2 \qquad \text{Product Property}$$
$$10^{\log 6x} = 10^2 \qquad \text{Exponential Form}$$
$$6x = 100$$
$$x = \frac{50}{3}$$

Common Errors When Solving Logarithmic Equations

Quotient Property Students sometimes mistakenly apply the Quotient Property in the reverse order. Point out that the log of the numerator is the first term in the subtraction expression.

Exponential Form Errors occur when students write logarithmic equations in exponential form. Encourage them to write steps as needed.

Solving Exponential Equations

Solve Algebraically

Exponential equations can be solved by taking logarithms of each side. Although logarithms to any base can be used, common logs are generally used.

Example: Solve $13^{n+10} = 80$.

$$13^{n+10} = 80$$
$$\log 13^{n+10} = \log 80$$
$$n + 10 \, (\log 13) = \log 80 \qquad \text{Power Property}$$
$$n + 10 = \frac{\log 80}{\log 13}$$
$$n \approx -8.9216$$

Example: What is the solution of $5^x = 30$?

$$5^x = 30$$
$$x \log 5 = \log 30$$
$$x = \frac{\log 30}{\log 5}$$
$$x \approx 2.113$$

Solve Graphically

Both exponential and logarithmic equations can be solved using a graph or table.

Example: Solve $3^{4x} = 500$.

Enter $3^{(4x)}$ in Y_1 and 500 in Y_2. Find the intersection.

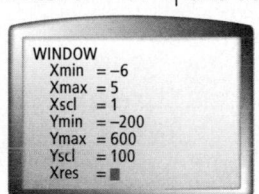 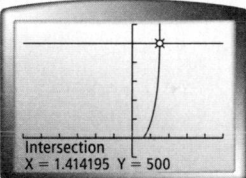

Solve using the table.

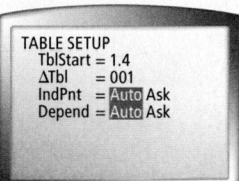 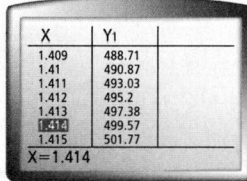

Common Errors When Solving Exponential Equations

Same Bases: A method for solving exponential equations involves equating the exponents if the bases are the same. Students may try to equate the exponents when the bases are not the same. Different bases require the use of logarithms. Have students check their answers to be sure their solution is correct.

Logs of negative numbers: Students can often be confused as to the restrictions for the variables and logarithmic equations. Point out that a positive number to any power can never been negative. Therefore, it is not possible to find a logarithm of a negative number. For example, there is no solution to the equation $10^x = -100$.

CHAPTER
7

EXPONENTIAL AND LOGARITHMIC FUNCTIONS
Pacing and Assignment Guide

		TRADITIONAL		BLOCK
Lesson	Teaching Day(s)	Basic	Average	Block
7-1	1	Problems 1–2 Exs. 10–19, 42–53	Problems 1–2 Exs. 10–21, 42–53	**Day 1** Problems 1–4 Exs. 10–32, 35–53
	2	Problems 3–4 Exs. 22–27, 35, 37–41	Problems 3–4 Exs. 22–32, 35–41	
7-2	1	Problems 1–3 Exs. 6–11, 13–19, 21, 22	Problems 1–3 Exs. 6–19, 21–24	**Day 2** Part 1 Problems 1–3 Exs. 6–19, 21–24 Part 2 Problems 4–5 Exs. 5–33
	2	Problems 4–5 Exs. 5–12, 15–33	Problems 4–5 Exs. 5–15, 16–33	
7-3	1	Problems 1–3 Exs. 12–17, 19–25, 29–31	Problems 1–3 Exs. 12–31	**Day 3** Problems 1–5 Exs. 12–45, 48, 50, 51, 65–77
	2	Problems 4–5 Exs. 32, 33, 36–40, 50, 65–77	Problems 4–5 Exs. 32–45, 48, 50, 51, 65–77	
7-4	1	Problems 1–2 Exs. 9–16, 50–65	Problems 1–4 Exs. 9–28, 30–33, 36–42, 46, 48–65	Problems 1–4 Exs. 9–28, 30–33, 36–42, 46, 48–65
	2	Problems 3–4 Exs. 17–19, 23–25, 36		
7-5	1	Problems 1–3 Exs. 5–16, 19–23, 25, 29	Problems 1–3 Exs. 5–25	**Day 4** Part 1 Problems 1–3 Exs. 5–25, 27–33 Part 2 Problems 4–6 Exs. 5–32, 35–50, 35–50
	2	Problems 4–6 Exs. 5–10, 12–17, 19–21, 29–31, 35–50	Problems 4–6 Exs. 5–32, 35–50, 35–50	
Review	1	Chapter 7 Review	Chapter 7 Review	**Day 5** Chapter 7 Review Chapter 7 Test
Assess	1	Chapter 7 Test	Chapter 7 Test	
Total		**12 Days**	**11 Days**	**5 Days**

Note: Pacing does not include Concept Bytes and other feature pages.

Resources

	For the Chapter	7-1	7-2	7-3	7-4	7-5
Planning						
Teacher Center Online Planner & Grade Book	I	I	I	I	I	I
Interactive Learning & Guided Instruction						
My Math Video	I					
Solve It!		I TM	I TM	I TM	I TM	I TM
Student Companion (SP)*		P M	P M	P M	P M	P M
Vocabulary Support		I P M	I P M	I P M	I P M	I P M
Got It? Support		I P	I P	I P	I P	I P
Dynamic Activity		I	I	I		
Online Problems		I	I	I	I	I
Additional Problems		M	M	M	M	M
English Language Learner Support (TR)		E P M	E P M	E P M	E P M	E P M
Activities, Games, and Puzzles		E M	E M	E M	E M	E M
Teaching With TI Technology With CD-ROM		✓ P	✓ P			
TI-Nspire™ Support CD-ROM		✓	✓	✓	✓	✓
Lesson Check & Practice						
Student Companion (SP)*		P M	P M	P M	P M	P M
Lesson Check Support		I P	I P	I P	I P	I P
Think About a Plan (TR)*		E P M	E P M	E P M	E P M	E P M
Practice Form K (TR)*		E P M	E P M	E P M	E P M	E P M
Standardized Test Prep (TR)*		P M	P M	P M	P M	P M
Practice Form G (TR)*		E P M	E P M	E P M	E P M	E P M
Extra Practice	E M					
Find the Errors!	M					
Enrichment (TR)		E P M	E P M	E P M	E P M	E P M
Answers and Solutions CD-ROM	✓	✓	✓	✓	✓	✓
Assess & Remediate						
ExamView CD-ROM	✓	✓	✓	✓	✓	✓
Lesson Quiz		I TM	I TM	I TM	I TM	I TM
Quizzes and Tests Form K (TR)*	E P M			E P M		E P M
Quizzes and Tests Form G (TR)*	E P M			E P M		E P M
Reteaching (TR)		E P M	E P M	E P M	E P M	E P M
Performance Tasks (TR)*	P M					
Cumulative Review (TR)*	P M					
Progress Monitoring Assessments	I P M					

(TR) Available in All-In-One Teaching Resources   * Spanish available

1 Interactive Learning

Solve It!

PURPOSE To express an exponential pattern in algebraic terms

PROCESS Students may
- sketch simpler models and extrapolate results to apply to more complex models.
- write an equation for the model.

FACILITATE

Q How many times does the original bottom ring move? **[once]**

Q How many times does the smallest ring move from its original position to its final position if there are n rings? Explain. **[2^{n-1} times; the smallest ring gets every second move. In between moving it, there is only one legal move that is not moving it again.]**

Q Is there a post you have to move the smallest ring to as the first move if you want the final stack on a specific post? Explain. **[Yes; for n odd, move it to the post where you want the stack, and for n even, move it to the post where you do not want the stack.]**

ANSWER See Solve It in Answers on next page.

CONNECT THE MATH The Solve It introduces an exponential expression as part of a solution to a problem. In the lesson students will write and use exponential equations to solve problems.

2 Guided Instruction

Problem 1

Q What would happen to the graph of 2^x if the 2 was replaced by a 5? **[The graph would be steeper.]**

Objective To model exponential growth and decay

This is a famous puzzle. Variations of it show up in many video games.

Getting Ready!

You are to move the stack of 5 rings to another post. Here are the rules.
- A move consists of taking the top ring from one post and placing it onto another post.
- You can move only one ring at a time.
- Do not place a ring on top of a smaller ring.

What is the fewest number of moves needed? How many moves are needed for 10 rings? For 20 rings? Explain.

Lesson Vocabulary
- exponential function
- exponential growth
- exponential decay
- asymptote
- growth factor
- decay factor

The number of moves needed for additional rings in the Solve It suggests a pattern that approximates repeated multiplication. You can represent repeated multiplication with a function of the form $y = ab^x$ where b is a positive number other than 1.

Focus Question What is an exponential function?

An **exponential function** has the general form $y = ab^x$, $a \neq 0$, with $b > 0$, and $b \neq 1$. In an exponential function, the base b is a constant. The exponent x is the independent variable with domain the set of real numbers.

Plan

How does making a table help you sketch the graph?
The table shows coordinates of several points on the graph.

Problem 1 Graphing an Exponential Function

A What is the graph of $y = 2^x$?

Step 1 Make a table of values.

x	2^x	y
-4	2^{-4}	$\frac{1}{16} = 0.0625$
-3	2^{-3}	$\frac{1}{8} = 0.125$
-2	2^{-2}	$\frac{1}{4} = 0.25$
-1	2^{-1}	$\frac{1}{2} = 0.5$

x	2^x	y
0	2^0	1
1	2^1	2
2	2^2	4
3	2^3	8

Step 2 Plot and connect the points.

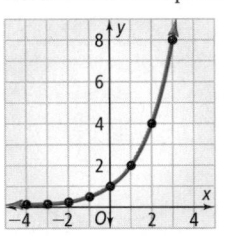

BIG ideas **Equivalence**
Function
Modeling
UbD

ESSENTIAL UNDERSTANDINGS
- Repeated multiplication can be represented with a function in the form of $y = ab^x$ where b is a positive number other than 1.
- An exponential function is a function with the general form $y = ab^x$, $a \neq 0$, with $b > 0$, and $b \neq 1$. In an exponential function, the base b is a constant. The exponent x is the independent variable with domain of all real numbers.

Math Background

Exponential notation is a simplified way to represent repeated multiplication. For example, $2 \cdot 2 \cdot 2 \cdot 2 \cdot 2 \cdot 2 \cdot 2 = 2^7$. Repeated multiplication by the same factor can be represented by an exponential function.

Such functions have the form $y = ab^x$ where b is greater than 0 and not equal to 1, and x is any real number.

For $a > 0$, the value of b determines whether the function grows or decays exponentially:
- When $b > 1$, the function *grows* exponentially.
- When $0 < b < 1$, the function *decays* exponentially.

Note that if $b = 1$, the function would simplify to $y = a$, which is a constant function.

Exponential functions can be used to model many real-world situations, including half-life, radiometric dating, interest-bearing savings accounts, population growth, and a bouncing ball.

Support Student Learning

Use the **Algebra 2 Companion** to engage and support students during instruction. See Lesson Resources at the end of this lesson for details.

PowerAlgebra.com

1 Interactive Learning

Solve It!
Step out how to solve the Problem with helpful hints and an online question. Other questions are listed above in Interactive Learning.

Dynamic Activity Students can use this interactive graph to explore exponential growth and decay. They can manipulate the sliders to vary the values of a and b in the equation $y = a \cdot b^x$.

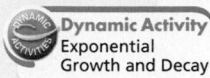

B What is the graph of $y = \left(\frac{1}{2}\right)^x$?

Step 1
Make a table of values.

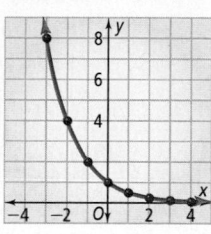

x	$\left(\frac{1}{2}\right)^x$	y
−3	$\left(\frac{1}{2}\right)^{-3}$	$2^3 = 8$
−2	$\left(\frac{1}{2}\right)^{-2}$	$2^2 = 4$
−1	$\left(\frac{1}{2}\right)^{-1}$	$2^1 = 2$
0	$\left(\frac{1}{2}\right)^{0}$	$2^0 = 1$

x	$\left(\frac{1}{2}\right)^x$	y
1	$\left(\frac{1}{2}\right)^{1}$	$\frac{1}{2} = 0.5$
2	$\left(\frac{1}{2}\right)^{2}$	$\frac{1}{4} = 0.25$
3	$\left(\frac{1}{2}\right)^{3}$	$\frac{1}{8} = 0.125$
4	$\left(\frac{1}{2}\right)^{4}$	$\frac{1}{16} = 0.0625$

Step 2
Plot and connect the points.

 Got It? 1. What is the graph of each function?

a. $y = 4^x$ **b.** $y = \left(\frac{1}{3}\right)^x$ **c.** $y = 2(3)^x$

d. Reasoning What generalizations can you make about the domain, range, and y-intercepts of these functions?

Two types of exponential behavior are *exponential growth* and *exponential decay*.

For **exponential growth**, as the value of x increases, the value of y increases. For **exponential decay**, as the value of x increases, the value of y decreases, approaching zero.

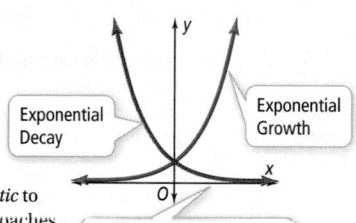

Exponential Decay

Exponential Growth

The x-axis is an asymptote.

Hint
Asymptote comes from the Greek word *asymptotos*, meaning "not meeting."

The exponential functions shown here are *asymptotic* to the x-axis. An **asymptote** is a line that a graph approaches as x or y increases in absolute value.

take note

Concept Summary   **Exponential Functions**

For the function $y = ab^x$,

- if $a > 0$ and $b > 1$, the function represents exponential growth.
- if $a > 0$ and $0 < b < 1$, the function represents exponential decay.

In either case, the y-intercept is $(0, a)$, the domain is all real numbers, the asymptote is $y = 0$, and the range is $y > 0$.

PowerAlgebra.com   Lesson 7-1   Exploring Exponential Models   463

Got It?

Q How do you know what numbers to select for the x values? **[You should select values that are positive, negative, and zero.]**

Take Note
The graph of an exponential growth function, $y = ab^x$ when $a > 0$ and $b > 1$, is a curve that rises from left to right. It gets steeper as x increases.

The graph of an exponential decay function, $y = ab^x$ when $a > 0$ and $0 < b < 1$, is a curve that falls from left to right. It gets less steep as x increases. In both types of exponential functions the x-axis is a horizontal asymptote of the graph.

---

2 Guided Instruction

Each Problem is worked out and supported online.

Problem 1
Graphing an Exponential Function

Problem 2
Identifying Exponential Growth and Decay
Animated

Problem 3
Modeling Exponential Growth
Animated

Problem 4
Writing an Exponential Function
Animated

Alternative Problem 4
Writing an Exponential Function

Support in Algebra 2 Companion
- Vocabulary
- Key Concepts
- Got It?

Answers

Solve It!

31; 1023; 1,048,575; The number of moves follows the pattern $2^x - 1$.

Got It?

1. **a.** 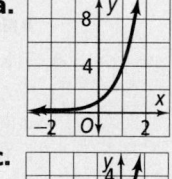   **b.**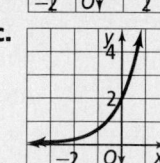

c.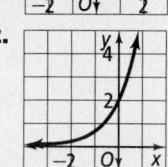

d. domain: all real numbers, range: $y > 0$; y-intercept: $(0, a)$ where $y = ab^x$

Lesson 7-1   463

Problem 2

Q In the exponential growth function represented by $y = ab^x$, what represents the y-intercept? [a]

Got It?

Q You are not given a value for a in an exponential function. What is the y-intercept of the function? Explain. [(0,1); answers may vary. Sample: The function $f(x) = b^x$, is the parent function for the family of exponential growth functions with base b. To determine the y-intercept, evaluate b^x when x is set equal to zero: $b^0 = 1$. Therefore, the y-intercept is the ordered pair (0, 1).]

Take Note

Q Does t always represent time in years? Explain. [No; time may need to be calculated in units other than years, for example, some bacteria grow exponentially in hours or minutes.]

Think
What quantity does the y-intercept represent?
The y-intercept is the amount of money at $t = 0$, which is the initial investment.

Hint
Growth rate refers to the value of r. Growth factor refers to the value of b, or $1 + r$.

Problem 2 Identifying Exponential Growth and Decay

Identify each function or situation as an example of exponential growth or decay. What is the y-intercept?

Ⓐ $y = 12(0.95)^x$

Since $0 < b < 1$, the function represents exponential decay. The y-intercept is $(0, a) = (0, 12)$

Ⓑ $y = 0.25(2)^x$

Since $b > 1$, the function represents exponential growth. The y-intercept is $(0, a) = (0, 0.25)$.

Ⓒ You put $1000 into a college savings account for four years. The account pays 5% interest annually.

The amount of money in the bank grows by 5% annually. It represents exponential growth. The y-intercept is 1000, which is the dollar value of the initial investment.

✓ **Got It? 2.** Identify each function or situation as an example of exponential growth or decay. What is the y-intercept?

 a. $y = 3(4^x)$　　　　　b. $y = 11(0.75^x)$

 c. You put $2000 into a college savings account for four years. The account pays 6% interest annually.

For exponential growth $y = ab^x$, with $b > 1$, the value b is the **growth factor**. A quantity that exhibits exponential growth increases by a constant percentage each time period. The percentage increase r, written as a decimal, is the *rate of increase* or *growth rate*. For exponential growth, $b = 1 + r$.

For exponential decay, $0 < b < 1$ and b is the **decay factor**. The quantity decreases by a constant percentage each time period. The percentage decrease, r, is the *rate of decay*. For exponential decay, $b = 1 + r$, so r is a negative quantity.

take note
Key Concept　Exponential Growth and Decay

You can model exponential growth or decay with this function.

| Amount after t time periods | Rate of growth ($r > 0$) or decay ($r < 0$) |

$$A(t) = a(1 + r)^t$$

| Initial amount | Number of time periods |

For growth or decay to be exponential, a quantity changes by a fixed percentage each time period.

Additional Problems

1. What is the graph of $y = 3.1^x$?

ANSWER

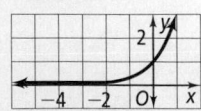

2. Identify $y = 0.7^x$ as an example of exponential growth or decay. What is the y-intercept?

ANSWER decay; (0, 1)

3. You buy a savings bond for $25 that pays a yearly interest rate of 4.2%. What will the savings bond be worth after fifteen years?

ANSWER $46.34

4. The initial value of a car is $30,000. After one year, the value of the car is $20,000. Estimate the value of the car after five years.

ANSWER $3950.62

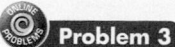 **Problem 3** Modeling Exponential Growth

You invested $1000 in a savings account at the end of 6th grade. The account pays 5% annual interest. How much money will be in the account after six years?

Step 1 Determine if an exponential function is a reasonable model.

The money grows at a fixed rate of 5% per year. An exponential model is appropriate.

Step 2 Define the variables and determine the model.

Let t = the number of years since the money was invested.
Let $A(t)$ = the amount in the account after each year.

A reasonable model is $A(t) = a(1 + r)^t$.

Think

What is the growth rate r?
It is the annual interest rate, written as a decimal: 5% = 0.05.

Step 3 Use the model to solve the problem.

Write the model.	$A(t) = A(1 + r)^t$
Substitute $a = 1000$, $r = 0.05$, and $t = 6$.	$A(6) = 1000(1 + 0.05)^6$
Simplify inside the parentheses.	$= 1000(1.05)^6$
Simplify. Round to two decimal places.	≈ 1340.10

Check Use a graphing calculator to check your answer.

Graph **Y1 = 1000(1.05)^X** and find y when x is 6.

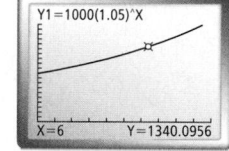

The account contains $1340.10 after six years.

Got It? **3. a.** Suppose you invest $500 in a savings account that pays 3.5% annual interest. How much will be in the account after five years?

b. Reasoning In Problem 3, would there ever be *exactly* $1300 in the account? Explain your reasoning.

Hint
For part (b), check whether the function is continuous.

To model a discrete situation using an exponential function of the form $y = ab^x$, you need to find the growth or decay factor b. If you know y-values for two consecutive x-values, you can find the rate of change r using $r = \frac{y_2 - y_1}{y_1}$ and then find b using $b = 1 + r$.

Problem 3

Q When is an exponential function an appropriate model? **[If finding the solution would require iterative multiplication, an exponential model is appropriate.]**

Q Why would you advise a friend who wants to make his savings account grow as much as possible not to withdraw the interest at the end of each year? **[If you leave the interest in the account, the savings account will pay interest on the interest, but if you withdraw the interest, the account will only pay interest on the original principal.]**

ERROR PREVENTION

Even advanced students may occasionally write a 5% growth rate as 1.5 or a growth rate of 4.5% as 1.45. Making students aware of the error may help prevent it.

EXTENSION

Q How much money would you have if you invested the money at the end of first grade? **[$1710.34]**

Got It?
EXTENSION

Q What model will you use? **[$A(t) = a(1 + r)^t$, where t is the number of years since the money was invested and $A(t)$ is the amount in the account after each year]**

Answers

Got It? (continued)

2. a. exponential growth; 3

b. exponential decay; 11

c. exponential growth; 2000

3. a. $593.84

b. Because interest is paid annually, the function is not continuous. The account contains $1276.28 after 5 years, and $1340.10 after 6 years. The account will never contain any value in between.

Problem 4

> Q Is this problem exponential growth or decay? How do you know? **[decay; answers may vary; sample: The population is decreasing; therefore it must be decay.]**
>
> Q In Step 3, what does the value of 0.8 represent? **[Each year, the population is 80% of what it was the year before.]**
>
> Q The Iberian lynx was placed on the Endangered Species list in 1970. If this trend has been occurring since then, how many Iberian lynx were there when it was placed on the list? Do you think this is reasonable? Explain. **[about 236,658; sample: yes; $236,658(0.8)^{33} \approx 150.$]**

Got It?

> Q If there are fewer than two Iberian lynx in the wild, would there be any hope for a wild population recovery? Explain. **[No; if there are fewer than two animals, mating in the wild is not possible.]**
>
> Q If the trend continues, in what year will there be no hope of a wild Iberian lynx population recovery (excluding captive animals)? **[In 2023, there will be fewer than two wild Iberian lynx, so there will be no possibility of a wild Iberian lynx mating pair.]**

 Problem 4 Writing an Exponential Function

Endangered Species The table shows the world population of the Iberian lynx in 2003 and 2004. If this trend continues and the population is decreasing exponentially, how many Iberian lynx will there be in 2014?

Use the general form of the exponential equation, $y = ab^x = a(1 + r)^x$.

Step 1 Define the variables.

Let x = the number of years since 2003.
Let y = the population of the Iberian lynx.

Step 2 Determine r.

Use the populations for 2003 and 2004.

Write the equation for r.	$r = \dfrac{y_2 - y_1}{y_1}$
Substitute $y_1 = 150$ and $y_2 = 120$.	$= \dfrac{120 - 150}{150}$
Simplify.	$= -0.2$

World Population of Iberian Lynx

Year	2003	2004
Population	150	120

Think

How can you find the value of r?
You can use the populations for two consecutive years to find r.

Step 3 Use r to determine b.

Write the equation for b.	$b = 1 + r$
Substitute $r = -0.2$.	$= 1 + (-0.2)$
Simplify.	$= 0.8$

Step 4 Write the model.

Write the general form of an exponential function.	$y = ab^x$
Substitute. Use the initial values $x = 0$ and $y = 150$.	$150 = a(0.8)^0$
Solve for a.	$150 = a$

The model is $y = 150(0.8)^x$.

Think

How do you find the x-value corresponding to 2014?
The initial x-value corresponds to 2003, so find the difference.

Step 5 Use the model to find the population in 2014.

For the year 2014, $x = 2014 - 2003 = 11$.

Write the model.	$y = 150(0.8)^x$
Substitute 11 for x and simplify.	$= 150(0.8)^{11} \approx 13$

If the 2003–2004 trend continues, there will be approximately 13 Iberian lynx in the wild in 2014.

 Got It? 4. a. For the model in Problem 4, what will be the world population of Iberian lynx in 2020?

      b. Reasoning If you graphed the model in Problem 4, would it ever cross the x-axis? Explain.

Answers

Got It? (continued)

4. a. ≈ 3

   b. No; the function is asymptotic to the x-axis.

Lesson Check

1. decay; 10   **2.** growth; 0.75

3. growth; 1   **4.** decay; 1

5.

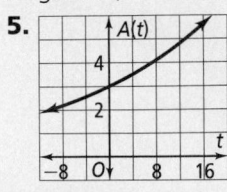

6.

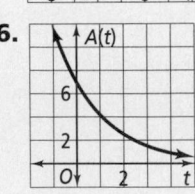

7. If $a > 0$ and $b > 1$, then the function represents exponential growth; if $a > 0$ and $0 < b < 1$, then the function represents exponential decay.

8. a. quadratic; degree 2 with $3x^2$ as the leading term

   b. exponential; the equation is of the form $y = ab^x$.

   c. linear; degree 1 with $2x$ as the leading term

   d. exponential; the equation is of the form $y = ab^x$

9. $0.3 < 1$, so 0.3 is the decay factor

Focus Question What is an exponential function?

Answer An exponential function is a function in which the independent variable is the exponent. The general form is $y = ab^x$, where $a \neq 0$, $b > 0$, and $b \neq 1$. The graph of an exponential function has a horizontal asymptote. Use an exponential function to model exponential growth or decay.

Lesson Check

Do you know HOW?

Without graphing, determine whether the function represents exponential growth or exponential decay. Then find the y-intercept.

1. $y = 10(0.45)^x$
2. $y = 0.75(4)^x$
3. $y = 3^x$
4. $y = 0.95^x$

Graph each function.

5. $A(t) = 3(1.04)^t$
6. $A(t) = 7(0.6)^t$

Do you UNDERSTAND?

7. Vocabulary Explain how you can tell if $y = ab^x$ represents exponential growth or exponential decay.

8. Reasoning Identify each function as *linear*, *quadratic*, or *exponential*. Explain your reasoning.
  a. $y = 3(x + 1)^2$
  b. $y = 4(3)^x$
  c. $y = 2x + 5$
  d. $y = 4(0.2)^x + 1$

9. Error Analysis A classmate says that the growth factor of the exponential function $y = 15(0.3)^x$ is 0.3. What is the student's mistake?

Practice and Problem-Solving Exercises

 **Practice**

Graph each function. ◀ See Problem 1.

10. $y = 6^x$
11. $y = 1000(2)^x$
12. $y = 9(3)^x$
13. $f(x) = 2(3)^x$
14. $s(t) = 1.5^t$
15. $y = 2^{2x}$

Without graphing, determine whether the function represents exponential growth or exponential decay. Then find the y-intercept. ◀ See Problem 2.

16. $y = 129(1.63)^x$
17. $f(x) = 2(0.65)^x$
18. $y = 12\left(\frac{17}{10}\right)^x$
19. $y = 0.8\left(\frac{1}{8}\right)^x$
20. $y = 0.45(3)^x$
21. $y = \frac{1}{100}\left(\frac{4}{3}\right)^x$

22. Population The world population in 2000 was approximately 6.08 billion. The annual rate of increase was about 1.26%. If this rate of increase continues, what will be the approximate world population in 2050? ◀ See Problem 3.

23. Interest Suppose you deposit $2000 in a savings account that pays interest at an annual rate of 4%. If no money is added or withdrawn from the account, answer the following questions.
  a. How much will be in the account after 3 years?
  b. How much will be in the account after 18 years?
  c. How many years will it take for the account to contain $2500?
  d. How many years will it take for the account to contain $3000?

3 Lesson Check

Do you know HOW? ERROR INTERVENTION

- For Exercises 1–4, students may need to be reminded that if there is no stated value of a, then $a = 1$.
- If the students are having difficulty seeing the graph on a calculator screen for Exercises 5 and 6, remind them that they may need to reset the window on their calculators to a standard viewing window from the window they likely used in Problem 5.

Do you UNDERSTAND? ERROR INTERVENTION

- If students have trouble with the vocabulary in Exercise 7, remind them that the value of b is the factor determining growth or decay; r is the rate of growth or decay.
- If students have trouble identifying the function types for Exercise 8, have them determine whether x is an exponent or a base. If x is a base, have them determine the exponent.

Close

Q How can you determine the growth rate or decay rate for an exponential function given two consecutive y-values? **[Find the percentage increase or decrease.]**

Q Why does a rate of decay of 23% correspond to a b value of 0.77? **[Since 23% decays, 77% remains.]**

Practice and Problem-Solving Exercises

10. 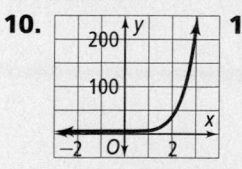
11.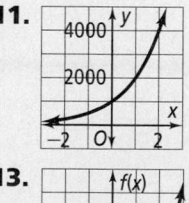

12. 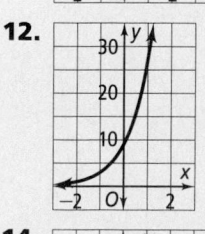
13.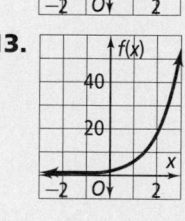

14. 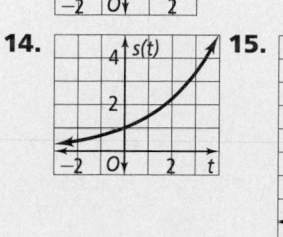
15.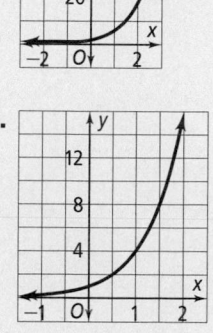

16. exponential growth; 129
17. exponential decay; 2
18. exponential growth; 12
19. exponential decay; 0.8
20. exponential growth; 0.45
21. exponential growth; $\frac{1}{100}$
22. 11.37 billion
23. a. $2249.73
  b. $4051.63
  c. 6 yrs
  d. 11 yrs

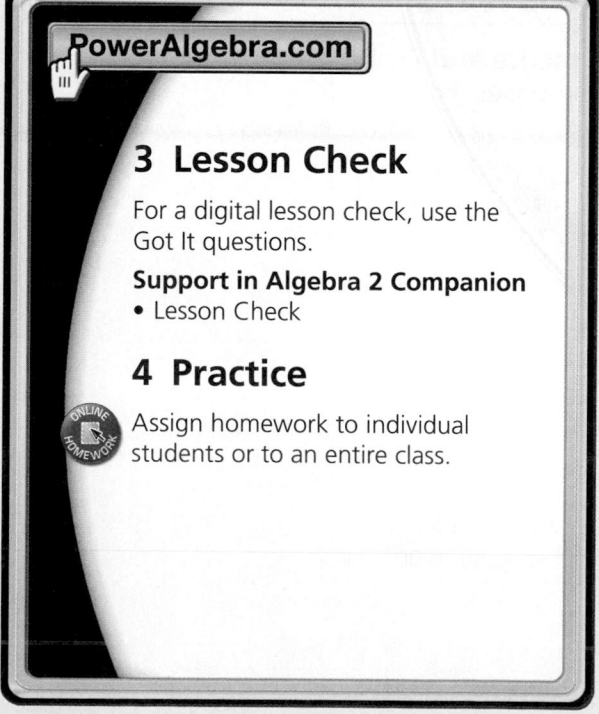

PowerAlgebra.com

3 Lesson Check

For a digital lesson check, use the Got It questions.

Support in Algebra 2 Companion
- Lesson Check

4 Practice

Assign homework to individual students or to an entire class.

4 Practice

Basic: 10–19, 22–27, 35

Average: 10–32, 35, 36

Standardized Test Prep: 37–41

Mixed Review: 42–53

Reasoning exercises have blue headings.

Applications exercises have red headings.

EXERCISE 35: Use the Think About a Plan worksheet in the **Student Companion** (also available in the Teaching Resources in print and online) to further support students' development in becoming independent learners.

HOMEWORK QUICK CHECK

To check students' understanding of key skills and concepts, go over Exercises 16, 22, 25, 27, and 35.

Write an exponential function to model each situation. Find each amount after the specified time.

 See Problem 4.

 Guided Practice

24. A population of 120,000 grows 1.2% per year for 15 years.

To start, record what you know.	Initial amount: 120,000
	Growth rate: 1.2%
	Number of time periods: 15

Then write the growth rate as a decimal.   1.2% = 0.012

25. A population of 1,860,000 decreases 1.5% each year for 12 years.

26. a. Sports Before a basketball game, a referee noticed that the ball seemed under-inflated. She dropped it from 6 feet and measured the first bounce as 36 inches and the second bounce as 18 inches. Write an exponential function to model the height of the ball.
   b. How high was the ball on its fifth bounce?

B Apply

27. Think About a Plan Your friend invested $1000 in an account that pays 6% annual interest. How much interest will your friend have after her college graduation in 4 years?
   • Is an exponential model reasonable for this situation?
   • What equation should you use to model this situation?
   • Is the solution of the equation the final answer to the problem?

For each annual rate of change, find the corresponding growth or decay factor.

28. $+70\%$ **29.** -75% **30.** -55%

31. -0.1% **32.** $+0.1\%$ **33.** $+100\%$

34. Oceanography The function $y = 20(0.975)^x$ models the intensity of sunlight beneath the surface of the ocean. The output y represents the percent of surface sunlight intensity that reaches a depth of x feet. The model is accurate from about 20 feet to about 600 feet beneath the surface.
   a. Find the percent of sunlight 50 feet beneath the surface of the ocean.
   b. Find the percent of sunlight at a depth of 370 feet.

35. Population The population of a certain animal species decreases at a rate of 3.5% per year. You have counted 80 of the animals in the habitat you are studying.
   a. Write a function that models the change in the animal population.
   b. Graph the function. Estimate the number of years until the population first drops below 15 animals.

36. Business A computer valued at $6500 depreciates at the rate of 14.3% per year.
   a. Write a function that models the value of the computer.
   b. Find the value of the computer after three years.

Answers

Practice and Problem-Solving Exercises (continued)

24. $y = 120{,}000(1.012)^x$; 143,512

25. $y = 1{,}860{,}000(0.985)^x$; 1,551,485

26. a. $y = 72\left(\frac{1}{2}\right)^x$
   b. 2.25 in.

27. $262.48

28. 1.70

29. 0.25

30. 0.45

31. 0.999

32. 1.001

33. 2

34. a. about 5.6%
   b. about 0.0017%

35. a. $y = 80(0.965)^x$
   b.
   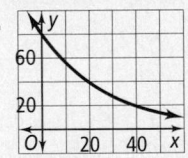
   about 47 yrs

36. a. $y = 6500(0.857)^x$
   b. $4091.25

SAT/ACT

37. Which function represents the value after x years of a new delivery van that costs $25,000 and depreciates 15% each year?

Ⓐ $y = -15(25,000)^x$ Ⓒ $y = 25,000(0.85)^x$
Ⓑ $y = 25,000(0.15)^x$ Ⓓ $y = 25,000(1.15)^x$

38. What is $f(x) = 3x^{\frac{1}{3}}$ for $x = \frac{1}{125}$?

Ⓕ 15   Ⓖ $\frac{3}{5}$ Ⓗ $\frac{\sqrt[3]{3}}{5}$ Ⓘ $5\sqrt[3]{3}$

39. What is the simplified form of $\frac{2+i}{2-i}$?

Ⓐ -1 Ⓑ $\frac{3+4i}{3}$ Ⓒ $\frac{5+4i}{5}$ Ⓓ $\frac{3+4i}{5}$

40. Which graph represents the equation $y = x^2 - x - 2$?

Ⓕ 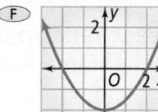 Ⓖ 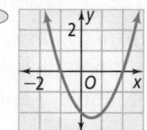 Ⓗ 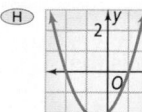 Ⓘ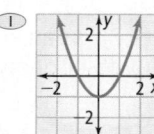

Extended Response

41. You are driving a car when a deer suddenly darts across the road in front of you. Your brain registers the emergency and sends a signal to your foot to hit the brake. The car travels a reaction distance D, in feet, during this time, where D is a function of the speed r, in miles per hour, that the car is traveling when you see the deer, given by $D(r) = \frac{11r + 5}{10}$. Find the inverse and explain what it represents. Is the inverse a function?

Mixed Review

Graph each function.   ◆ **See Lesson 6-8.**

42. $y = 3 - 2\sqrt{x} + 2$ **43.** $y = 3\sqrt[3]{2x - 1}$ **44.** $y = -2 + \sqrt{x}$

Factor the expression.   ◆ **See Lesson 4-4.**

45. $8 + 27x^3$ **46.** $3x^2 + 11x - 4$ **47.** $25 - 40x + 16x^2$

Solve the system of equations using a matrix.   ◆ **See Lesson 3-6.**

48. $\begin{cases} x + 5y = -4 \\ x + 6y = -5 \end{cases}$ **49.** $\begin{cases} 3a + 5b = 0 \\ a + b = 0 \end{cases}$ **50.** $\begin{cases} -x + 2y = 0 \\ y = -2x + 3 \end{cases}$

Get Ready!   To prepare for Lesson 7-2, do Exercises 51–53.

Graph each function.   ◆ **See Lesson 7-1.**

51. $y = 3^x$ **52.** $y = 0.75^x$ **53.** $y = 0.5(4)^x$

---

45. $(2 + 3x)(4 - 6x + 9x^2)$
46. $(3x - 1)(x + 4)$
47. $(4x - 5)(4x - 5)$
48. $(1, -1)$
49. $(0, 0)$
50. $(1.2, 0.6)$
51.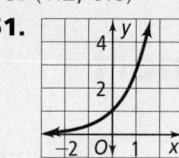
52.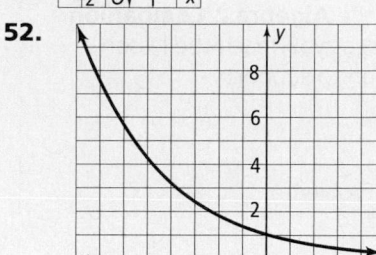
53.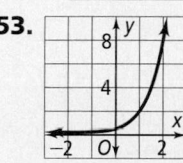

Standardized Test Prep

37. C
38. G
39. D
40. G
41. [4] $r = \frac{11D^{-1}(r) + 5}{10}$

$10r - 5 = 11D^{-1}(r)$

$\frac{10r - 5}{11} = D^{-1}(r)$; this function tells you the speed the car is traveling when you see the deer, given the number of ft the car travels during your reaction time. $D^{-1}(r)$ is a function.

[3] appropriate method and explanation, but with one computational error

[2] incomplete explanation OR inverse and explanation are correct, but inverse is not labeled a function

[1] correct inverse function, but without explanation of what the inverse represents

Mixed Review

42.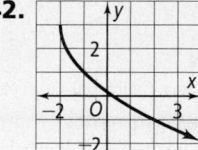

43.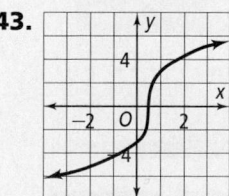

44.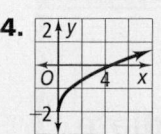

Additional Instructional Support

Algebra 2 Companion

Students can use the **Algebra 2 Companion** worktext (4 pages) as you teach the lesson. Use the Companion to support

- New Vocabulary
- Key Concepts
- Got It for each Problem
- Lesson Check

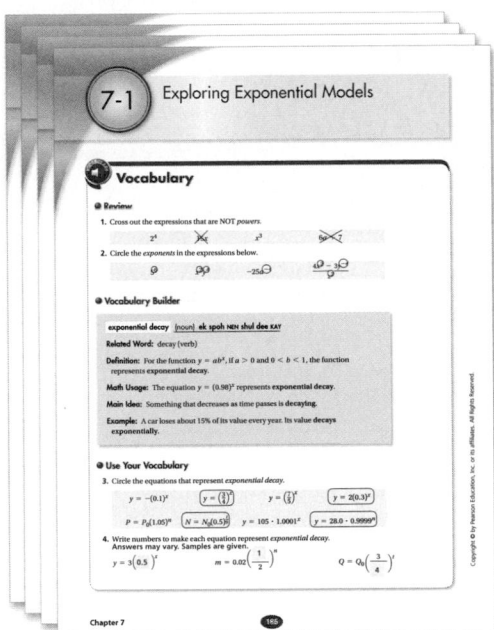

ELL Support

Use Graphic Organizers Have students make a two-column chart. Label the first column *growth* and the second column *decay*. In pairs, have students discuss and decide what words and symbols will help them decode the word problems. Have each pair exchange lists with another pair of students and review their classmates' work. If they disagree on a word in the list, ask them to explain why it should be changed or eliminated. Check the lists when they are finished, and make sure that they have at least the following terms and symbols for growth: *interest*, *appreciation*, *increase*, +, *returns*. For decay, they should have *depreciation*, *decrease*, −, *decline*. Then at the bottom of each column, have students sketch a basic shape of the corresponding graph with *a* labeled and a description of valid values for *b*.

5 Assess & Remediate

Lesson Quiz

1. What is the graph of $y = \left(\frac{1}{3}\right)^x$?
2. Identify $y = 3(1.2)^x$ as an example of exponential growth or decay. What is the *y*-intercept?
3. You deposit $3000 in an account that pays 5% annual interest. What is the balance after 2 years?
4. You invest $75 in a savings account that pays 2% annual interest. If you make no additional deposits or withdrawals, how many years will it take for the account to grow to at least $100?
5. **Do you UNDERSTAND?** There were 50,000 bacteria in a petri dish yesterday at noon, and 40,000 bacteria at noon today. If the trend continues, on what day at noon can you expect to find less than 5,000 bacteria?

ANSWERS TO LESSON QUIZ

1.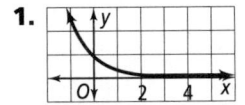

2. growth; (0, 3)
3. $3307.50
4. 15 years
5. on the eleventh day

PRESCRIPTION FOR REMEDIATION

Use the student work on the Lesson Quiz to prescribe a differentiated review assignment:

Points	Differentiated Remediation
0–2	Intervention
3	On-level
4	Extension

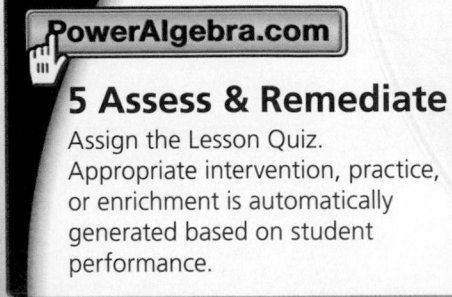

PowerAlgebra.com

5 Assess & Remediate

Assign the Lesson Quiz. Appropriate intervention, practice, or enrichment is automatically generated based on student performance.

Intervention

- **Reteaching** (2 pages) Provides reteaching and practice exercises for the key lesson concepts. Use with struggling students or absent students.
- **English Language Learner Support** Helps students develop and reinforce mathematical vocabulary and key concepts.

All-in-One Resources/Online
Reteaching

7-1 Reteaching
Exploring Exponential Models

- The general form of an exponential function is $y = ab^x$, where *a* is the initial amount and *b* is the growth or decay factor.
- To find *b*, use the formula $b = 1 + r$, where *r* is the constant rate of growth or decay. If *r* is a rate of growth, it will be positive. If *r* is a rate of decay, it will be negative. Therefore, if *b* is greater than 1, the function models growth. If *b* is between zero and 1, the function models decay. When you see words like *increase* or *appreciation*, think growth. When you see words like *decrease* or *depreciation*, think decay.
- For an exponential function, the *y*-intercept is always equal to the value of *a*.

Problem

Carl's weight at 12 yr is 82 lb. Assume that his weight increases at a rate of 16% each year. Write an exponential function to model the increase. What is his weight after 5 years?

Step 1 Find *a* and *b*.

$a = 82$ *a* is the original amount.

$b = 1 + 0.16$ *b* is the growth or decay factor. Since this problem models growth, *r* will be positive. Make sure to rewrite the rate, *r*, as a decimal.

$= 1.16$

Step 2 Write the exponential function.

$y = ab^x$ Use the formula.

$y = 82(1.16)^x$ Substitute.

Step 3 Calculate.

$y = 82(1.16)^5$ Substitute 5 for *x*.

$y \approx 172.228$ Use a calculator.

Carl will weigh about 172 lb in 5 years.

Exercises

Determine whether the function represents exponential growth or exponential decay. Then find the *y*-intercept.

1. $y = 8000(1.15)^x$ growth; 8000
2. $y = 20(0.75)^x$ decay; 20
3. $y = 15\left(\frac{1}{3}\right)^x$ decay; 15
4. $f(x) = 6\left(\frac{3}{2}\right)^x$ growth; 6

All-in-One Resources/Online
English Language Learner Support

7-1 ELL Support
Exploring Exponential Models

Choose the word or phrase from the list that best completes each sentence.

exponential function	exponential growth	exponential decay
asymptote	growth factor	decay factor

1. In the function $y = 12(2.3)^x$, the value 2.3 is the growth factor.
2. An asymptote is a line that a graph approaches as *x* or *y* increases in absolute value.
3. For exponential decay, as the value of *x* increases, the value of *y* decreases.
4. A function in the general form $y = ab^x$ is called an exponential function.
5. For exponential growth, as the value of *x* increases, the value of *y* increases.
6. In the function $y = 4(0.3)^x$, the value 0.3 is the decay factor.

Identify whether each function represents exponential growth or exponential decay.

7. $y = 0.75(4)^x$ exponential growth
8. $y = 0.63(0.5)^x$ exponential decay
9. $y = 9(0.83)^x$ exponential decay
10. $y = 12(7)^x$ exponential growth

Identify the *y*-intercept for each function.

11. $y = 4.5(7)^x$ 4.5
12. $y = 5(3.2)^x$ 5

Differentiated Remediation *continued*

On-Level

- **Practice** (2 pages) Provides extra practice for each lesson. For more challenging practice exercises, use the Form G Practice pages found in the All-in-One Teaching Resources and online.

- **Think About a Plan** Helps students develop specific problem-solving skills and strategies by providing scaffolded guiding questions.

- **Standardized Test Prep** Focuses on all major exercises, all major question types, and helps students prepare for the high-stakes assessments.

Extension

- **Enrichment** Provides students with interesting problems and activities that extend the concepts of the lesson.

- **Activities, Games, and Puzzles** Worksheets that can be used for concepts development, enrichment, and for fun!

Student Companion/All-in-One Resources/Online
Practice page 1

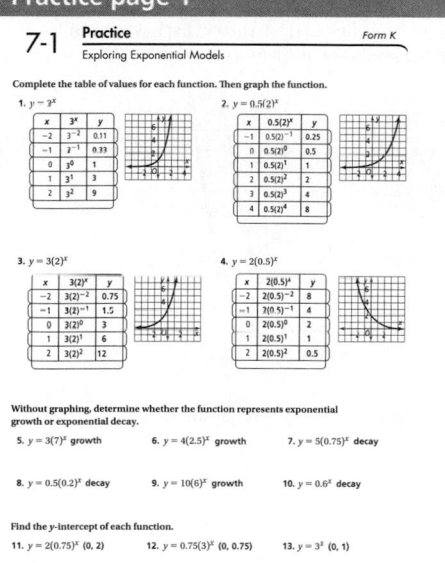

7-1 Practice — Form K
Exploring Exponential Models

Complete the table of values for each function. Then graph the function.

1. $y = 3^x$ 2. $y = 0.5(2)^x$

3. $y = 3(2)^x$ 4. $y = 2(0.5)^x$

Without graphing, determine whether the function represents exponential growth or exponential decay.

5. $y = 3(7)^x$ growth   6. $y = 4(2.5)^x$ growth   7. $y = 5(0.75)^x$ decay

8. $y = 0.5(0.2)^x$ decay   9. $y = 10(6)^x$ growth   10. $y = 0.6^x$ decay

Find the y-intercept of each function.

11. $y = 2(0.75)^x$ (0, 2)   12. $y = 0.75(3)^x$ (0, 0.75)   13. $y = 3^x$ (0, 1)

Student Companion/All-in-One Resources/Online
Think About a Plan

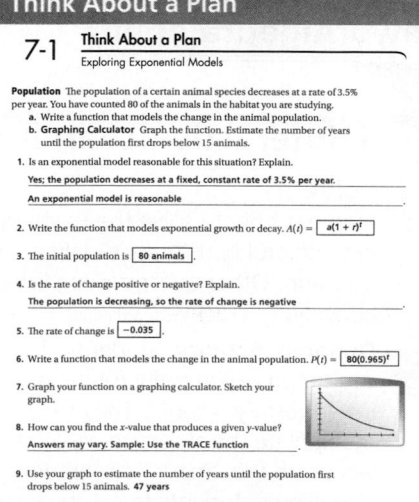

7-1 Think About a Plan
Exploring Exponential Models

Population The population of a certain animal species decreases at a rate of 3.5% per year. You have counted 80 of the animals in the habitat you are studying.
a. Write a function that models the change in the animal population.
b. Graphing Calculator Graph the function. Estimate the number of years until the population first drops below 15 animals.

1. Is an exponential model reasonable for this situation? Explain.
   Yes; the population decreases at a fixed, constant rate of 3.5% per year.
   An exponential model is reasonable.

2. Write the function that models exponential growth or decay. $A(t) = a(1 + r)^t$

3. The initial population is 80 animals .

4. Is the rate of change positive or negative? Explain.
   The population is decreasing, so the rate of change is negative

5. The rate of change is −0.035 .

6. Write a function that models the change in the animal population. $P(t) =$ 80(0.965)^t

7. Graph your function on a graphing calculator. Sketch your graph.

8. How can you find the x-value that produces a given y-value?
   Answers may vary. Sample: Use the TRACE function

9. Use your graph to estimate the number of years until the population first drops below 15 animals. 47 years

---

Student Companion/All-in-One Resources/Online
Practice page 2

7-1 Practice (continued) — Form K
Exploring Exponential Models

For each annual rate of change, find the corresponding growth or decay factor.

14. 35% 1.35   15. −20% 0.8   16. 62% 1.62

17. Identify the meaning of the variables in the exponential growth or decay function.
$$A(t) = a(1 + r)^t$$
a. $a =$ the initial amount
b. $r =$ the rate of growth or decay
c. $t =$ the number of time periods

18. The population of Bainsville is 2000. The population is supposed to grow by 10% each year for the next 5 years. How many people will live in Bainsville in 5 years? 3221

19. **Writing** Describe a situation that could be modeled by the function $A(t) = 200(1.05)^x$.
Answers may vary. Sample: Someone deposits $200 into a bank account that earns 5% interest each year.

20. A music store sold 200 guitars in 2007. The store sold 180 guitars in 2008. The number of guitars that the store sells is decreasing exponentially. If this trend continues, how many guitars will the store sell in 2012?

$r = \frac{y_2 - y_1}{y_1}$ $A(t) = a(1 + r)^t$

$r = \frac{180 - 200}{200}$ $A(5) = 200(1 - 0.1)^5 \approx 118$ guitars

$r = -0.1$

Student Companion/All-in-One Resources/Online
Standardized Test Prep

7-1 Standardized Test Prep
Exploring Exponential Models

Multiple Choice

For Exercises 1 and 2, choose the correct letter.

1. Which of the following functions represents exponential decay and has a y-intercept of 2? D
   Ⓐ $y = 2\left(\frac{4}{3}\right)^x$ Ⓒ $y = \frac{1}{2}(2)^x$
   Ⓑ $y = \frac{1}{2}(0.95)^x$ Ⓓ $y = 2\left(\frac{2}{3}\right)^x$

2. Suppose you deposit $3000 in a savings account that pays interest at an annual rate of 4%. If no other money is added or withdrawn from the account, how much will be in the account after 10 years? H
   Ⓕ $3122.18   Ⓗ $4440.73
   Ⓖ $4994.50   Ⓘ $86,776.40

Extended Response

3. In 2009 there was an endangered population of 270 cranes in a western state. Due to wildlife efforts, the population is increasing at a rate of 5% per year.
   a. What exponential function would be a good model for this population of cranes? Explain in words or show work for how you determined the exponential function.
   b. If this trend continues, how many cranes will there be in this population in 2020? Show your work.
   [4] a. The general form of an exponential function is $y = a(b)^x$. x represents time in years, y represents the population of cranes, and a is the initial value of 270 cranes. Because the crane population is increasing by 5%, $b = 1 + r = 1 + 0.05 = 1.05$. The exponential function that models the crane population is $y = 270(1.05)^x$ OR equivalent explanation.
   b. $y = 270(1.05)^{11} = 461.79$; almost 462 cranes
   [3] appropriate methods and correct function, but with one computational error in evaluating the function
   [2] incorrect function or multiple computational errors in evaluating the function
   [1] correct function, without work shown
   [0] incorrect answers and no work shown OR no answers given

---

All-in-One Resources/Online
Enrichment

7-1 Enrichment
Exploring Exponential Models

Determining Relationships Between Variables

On the basis of data, scientists sometimes hypothesize that a quantity z depends on two quantities x and y such that
$$z = Cx^r y^s$$
where C is a constant and r and s are integers. By doing experiments in which the values of x and y are varied, they determine the values of integers r and s.

For instance, suppose the momentum M of a moving object seems to be related to the mass m and velocity v by the equation $M = Cm^r v^s$. Later, scientists find that doubling the mass and keeping the velocity constant doubles the momentum, so
$$2M = C(2m)^r v^s.$$
Using substitution and simplifying, $2(Cm^r v^s) = C2^r m^r v^s$
Dividing each by $Cm^r v^s$: $2 = 2^r$
                                                $1 = r$

1. Suppose that doubling the velocity while holding the mass constant also doubles the momentum. Express this relationship in an equation. $2M = Cm^r(2v)^s$

2. Solve your equation for s. $s = 1$

3. Use the values of r and s to write an expression for momentum in terms of mass m, velocity v, and the constant C. $M = Cmv$

Use a similar method to solve the following problems.

4. The price P of a diamond is related to both the weight W of the diamond and its brilliance B. If both the weight and brilliance are simultaneously doubled, the price of the diamond increases by a factor of 32. If the weight is doubled and, at the same time, the brilliance is halved, the price increases by a factor of 2. Write a formula for P in terms of W, B, and the constant C. $P = CW^3B^2$

5. The price of wheat depends upon the weight and the water content. A particular wheat trader pays according to this pattern: the price P increases by a factor of 2 when the weight is doubled and the water content is constant. If the weight is doubled and the water content is halved, the price is constant. Write a formula for P in terms of weight W, water content h, and the constant C. $P = Cwh$

Online Teacher Resource Center
Activities, Games, and Puzzles

7-1 Activity: Financial Considerations
Exploring Exponential Models

You can work on your own or with a partner.

Suppose you received a gift of $10,000 and want to invest it. You visit two banks to see what they have to offer. Bank A is near your home and pays 5% interest compounded annually. Bank B is farther from your home and pays 6% interest compounded annually. You do not think a 1% difference in rates is that significant, but you want to check.

Calculate the amount of interest each plan will earn after one year. Record your answers on the lines provided.

Bank A: $10,000(1.05) − $10,000 = $500   Bank B: $10,000(1.06) − $10,000 = $600

You decide to calculate how long it will take each bank to pay $5000 interest.

Complete the table below. Round your answers to the nearest dollar.
Then record the number of years below the table.

Years	1	2	3	4	5	6	7	8	9
Bank A($)	500	1025	1576	2155	2763	3401	4071	4775	5513
Bank B($)	600	1236	1910	2625	3382	4185	5036	5938	6895

Bank A: about 9 years

Bank B: about 7 years

Complete the bar graph to show the amount by which Bank B will outperform Bank A over nine years. Use estimation to determine the heights of the bars.

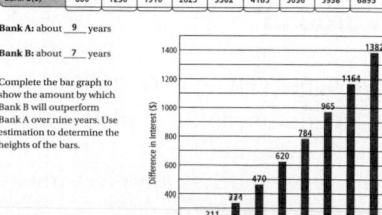

1 Interactive Learning

Solve It!

PURPOSE To identify transformations of exponential functions

PROCESS Students may

- trace one function by hand and place the tracing on top of the other function to determine how it was transformed.
- make a table of plotted points for each function and compare values.

FACILITATE

Q What are the definitions of a compression, reflection, and translation? **[Answers may vary. Sample: compression: shrink; reflection: flip; translation: slide]**

Q Which transformation(s) can be eliminated? Why? **[Reflection. The orientation of the functions has not changed.]**

Q Could the transformation be a compression? A translation? Explain. **[The transformation could be either a compression or a translation. You can divide the function _f_ by 4 to get _g_, or translate _f_ 2 units to the right to get _g_.]**

ANSWER See Solve It in Answers on next page.

CONNECT THE MATH To complete the Solve It, students must identify compressions, reflections, and translations given the graphs of two exponential functions. In the lesson they will identify transformations of the families of exponential functions.

7-2 PART 1 — Properties of Exponential Functions

Objective To explore the properties of functions of the form $y = ab^x$

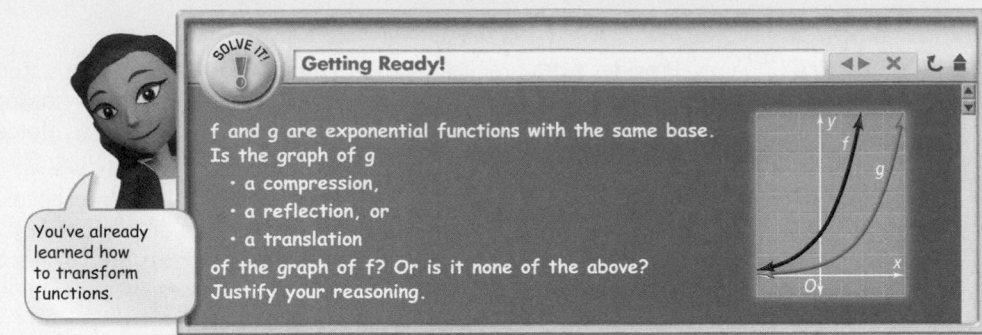

Getting Ready!

f and g are exponential functions with the same base. Is the graph of g
- a compression,
- a reflection, or
- a translation

of the graph of f? Or is it none of the above? Justify your reasoning.

You've already learned how to transform functions.

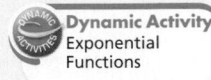

Dynamic Activity
Exponential Functions

You can apply the four types of transformations—stretches, compressions, reflections, and translations—to exponential functions.

Focus Question What are the transformations on exponential functions?

The graphs of $y = 2^x$ (in red) and $y = 3 \cdot 2^x$ (in blue) are shown. Each y-value of $y = 3 \cdot 2^x$ is 3 times the corresponding y-value of the parent function $y = 2^x$.

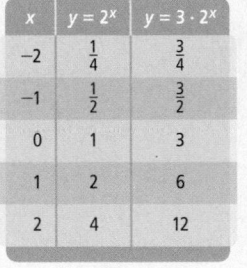

x	$y = 2^x$	$y = 3 \cdot 2^x$
−2	$\frac{1}{4}$	$\frac{3}{4}$
−1	$\frac{1}{2}$	$\frac{3}{2}$
0	1	3
1	2	6
2	4	12

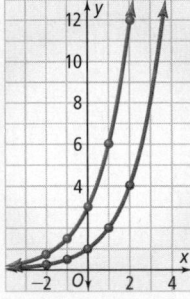

$y = 3 \cdot 2^x$ stretches the graph of the parent function $y = 2^x$ by the factor 3.

7-2 Preparing to Teach

PART 1

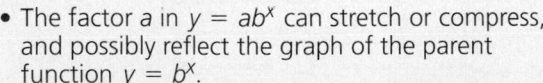

BIG idea **Function**   **UbD**

ESSENTIAL UNDERSTANDINGS

- The factor _a_ in $y = ab^x$ can stretch or compress, and possibly reflect the graph of the parent function $y = b^x$.
- The function $y = ab^x$, $a > 0$, $b > 1$, models exponential growth. $y = ab^x$ models exponential decay if $0 < b < 1$.

Math Background

Like the other functions seen so far, the graphs of exponential functions can be transformed.

The graph of parent function $y = b^x$ for $b \geq 1$ is a smooth curve through (0, 1) and (1, b). It approaches but never touches the x-axis toward the left and rises rapidly toward the right. For a parent function $y = b^x$ and its "offspring," the value b is constant. A different value of b implies a different parent function.

Whether the graph of the parent function is stretched, compressed, or reflected depends on the factor _a_.
- $a > 1$: stretch
- $a < -1$: stretch and reflection in x-axis
- $0 < a < 1$: compression
- $0 > a > -1$: compression and reflection in x-axis

The graph of parent function $y = b^x$ can also be translated. The general form is $y = ab^{(x-h)} + k$, where h is a horizontal translation and k is a vertical translation. Using the laws of exponents, the general form can also be written as $y = (ab^{-h})b^x + k$.

If a factor of _a_ is the constant b^{-h}, then _a_ also translates the parent function horizontally and stretches or compresses it by $\frac{a}{b^h}$.

Support Student Learning

Use the **Algebra 2 Companion** to engage and support students during instruction. See Lesson Resources at the end of this lesson for details.

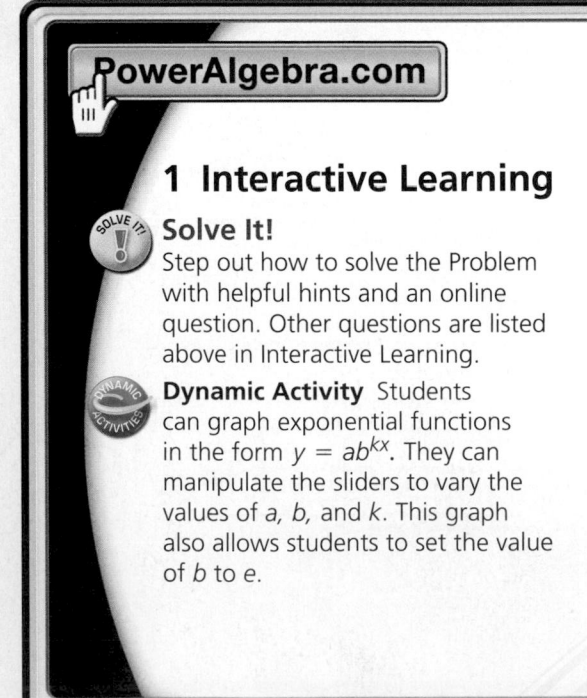

PowerAlgebra.com

1 Interactive Learning

Solve It!
Step out how to solve the Problem with helpful hints and an online question. Other questions are listed above in Interactive Learning.

Dynamic Activity Students can graph exponential functions in the form $y = ab^{kx}$. They can manipulate the sliders to vary the values of a, b, and k. This graph also allows students to set the value of b to e.

 **Problem 1** Graphing $y = ab^x$

How does the graph of each function compare to the graph of the parent function?

A $y = 0.5 \cdot 2^x$

Think

Which *x*-values should you use to make a table?
Use $x = 0$ and then choose both positive and negative values.

Step 1 Make a table of values.

x	$y = 2^x$	$y = 0.5 \cdot 2^x$
−2	0.25	0.125
−1	0.5	0.25
0	1	0.5
1	2	1
2	4	2

Each value is 0.5 times the corresponding value of the parent function.

Step 2 Graph the function.

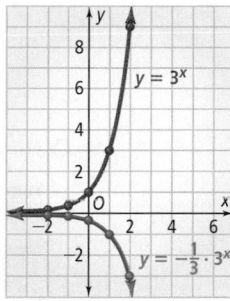

The "0.5" in $y = 0.5 \cdot 2^x$ compresses the graph of the parent function $y = 2^x$ by the factor 0.5. The domain, range, and asymptote remain unchanged. The y-intercept becomes 0.5.

B $y = -\frac{1}{3} \cdot 3^x$

Step 1 Make a table of values.

x	$y = 3^x$	$y = -\frac{1}{3} \cdot 3^x$
−2	$\frac{1}{9}$	$-\frac{1}{27}$
−1	$\frac{1}{3}$	$-\frac{1}{9}$
0	1	$-\frac{1}{3}$
1	3	−1
2	9	−3

Each value is $-\frac{1}{3}$ times the corresponding value of the parent function.

Step 2 Graph the function.

The "$-\frac{1}{3}$" in $y = -\frac{1}{3} \cdot 3^x$ reflects the graph of the parent function $y = 3^x$ across the x-axis and compresses it by the factor $\frac{1}{3}$. The domain and asymptote remain unchanged. The y-intercept becomes $-\frac{1}{3}$ and the range becomes $y < 0$.

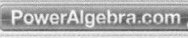 **Got It? 1.** How does the graph of each function compare to the graph of the parent function?

a. $y = 2 \cdot 4^x$ **b.** $y = -0.5 \cdot 5^x$

Hint

You can add the exponents if the bases are the same.
$a\left(b^{-h} \cdot b^x\right) = a\left(b^{(-h+x)}\right)$
$= ab^{(x-h)}$

A horizontal shift $y = ab^{(x-h)}$ is the same as the vertical stretch or compression $y = (ab^{-h})b^x$. A vertical shift $y = ab^x + k$ also shifts the horizontal asymptote from $y = 0$ to $y = k$.

PowerAlgebra.com | Lesson 7-2 Properties of Exponential Functions | 471

---

2 Guided Instruction

Each Problem is worked out and supported online.

Problem 1
Graphing $y = ab^x$
Animated

Alternative Problem 1
Graphing $y = ab^x$

Problem 2
Translating the Parent Function $y = b^x$
Animated

Problem 3
Using an Exponential Model

Support in Algebra 2 Companion
• Vocabulary
• Key Concepts
• Got It?

---

2 Guided Instruction

Problem 1 SYNTHESIZING

Students compare the transformation of an exponential function to its parent function. The transformation consists of a reflection and compression.

Q How does multiplying a parent function by a number between 0 and 1 affect the graph of the function? **[The graph is compressed.]**

Q In 1B, how does multiplying the parent function by −1 affect the graph of the parent function? **[The y-coordinates are the opposite of those of the parent function, so the graph is reflected in the x-axis.]**

Q Is it necessary to use the parent function when graphing these problems? Explain. **[Answers may vary. Sample: No, but constructing a table and graph of the parent function allows you to use transformations to graph the new function.]**

Got It? ERROR PREVENTION

Q In 1b, how is this function a transformation of the parent function $y = 5^x$? **[The graph of the parent function is reflected in the x-axis and compressed by a factor of 0.5.]**

Answers

Solve It!

compression or translation; for each x, $g(x) = f(x - 2)$ and $g(x) = \frac{f(x)}{4}$

Got It?

1. a. Stretches by a factor of 2

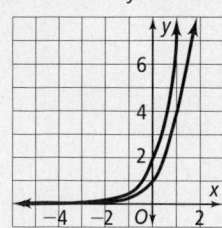

b. Reflects in the x-axis, compresses by a factor of 0.5;

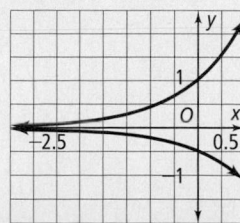

Lesson 7-2 **471**

Problem 2

SYNTHESIZING

> **Q** Will a horizontal shift ever change a horizontal asymptote? Explain. **[No; the x-coordinates are changed, but the y-coordinates stay the same.]**

Students graph a vertical shift of a given parent function.

> **Q** What is the parent function? What are the transformations of the parent function? **[y = ($\frac{1}{2}$)ˣ; to obtain the new function, stretch the parent by a factor of 20, and move it up 10 units.]**

Got It?

ERROR PREVENTION

> **Q** What indicates a horizontal shift in a given exponential equation? **[A value is added to or subtracted from the exponent.]**

> **Q** What indicates a vertical shift in a given exponential equation? **[A value is added to or subtracted from the function.]**

> **Q** What indicates a stretch or compression in a given exponential equation? **[A value is multiplied by the function.]**

How does the graph of each function compare to the graph of the parent function?

A $y = 2^{(x-4)}$

Think

How is the graph of $y = 2^{(x-4)}$ different from the graph of $y = 2^x$?
The graph of $y = 2^{(x-4)}$ is a horizontal translation of $y = 2^x$ to the right 4 units.

Step 1
Make a table of values for $y = 2^x$.

x	y = 2ˣ
−2	0.25
−1	0.5
0	1
1	2
2	4

Step 2
Graph $y = 2^x$, and translate to the right 4 units.

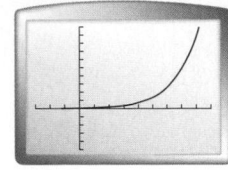

The "$(x − 4)$" in $y = 2^{(x-4)}$ translates the graph of $y = 2^x$ to the right 4 units. The asymptote remains $y = 0$. The y-intercept becomes $\frac{1}{16}$.

Check Use a graphing calculator to graph $y = 2^{(x-4)}$. Find the y-intercept.

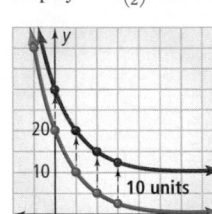

$0.0625 = \frac{1}{16}$

B $y = 20(\frac{1}{2})^x + 10$

Step 1
Make a table of values for $y = 20(\frac{1}{2})^x$.

x	y = 20 · ($\frac{1}{2}$)ˣ
−1	40
0	20
1	10
2	5
3	2.5

Think

Where have you seen this situation before?
The graph of a function like $y = 20(\frac{1}{2})^x + 10$ is both a stretch and a vertical translation of its parent function.

Step 2
Graph $y = 20(\frac{1}{2})^x$ and translate up 10 units.

The "$+ 10$" in $y = 20(\frac{1}{2})^x + 10$ translates the graph of $y = 20(\frac{1}{2})^x$ up 10 units. The asymptote becomes $y = 10$, the y-intercept becomes 30, and the range becomes $y > 10$. The domain is unchanged.

✓ **Got It? 2.** How does the graph of each function compare to the graph of the parent function?
  a. $y = 4^{(x+2)}$ **b.** $y = 5 \cdot 0.25^x + 5$

Additional Problems

1. How does the graph of $y = -\frac{1}{5} \cdot 4^x$ compare to the graph of the parent function?

ANSWER it compresses the parent graph $y = 4^x$ by a factor of $\frac{1}{5}$ and reflects the graph in the x-axis.

2. How does the graph of $y = 3^{(x+1)}$ compare to the graph of the parent function?

ANSWER It shifts the parent graph $y = 3^x$ one unit to the left.

3. Some insects reproduce exponentially. The chart shows the population of roaches in a colony at 36-day intervals. On what day will the colony reach 50,000,000 roaches?

Day	Number of Roaches
1	50
37	1125
73	25,290
109	569,025
145	12,803,040

ANSWER The colony will reach 50,000,000 during the 161ˢᵗ day.

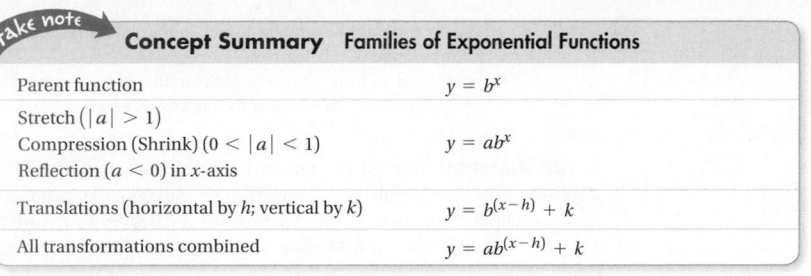

Concept Summary Families of Exponential Functions

Parent function	$y = b^x$
Stretch ($|a| > 1$) Compression (Shrink) ($0 < |a| < 1$) Reflection ($a < 0$) in x-axis	$y = ab^x$
Translations (horizontal by h; vertical by k)	$y = b^{(x-h)} + k$
All transformations combined	$y = ab^{(x-h)} + k$

take note

Problem 3 Using an Exponential Model

Physics The best temperature to brew coffee is between 195°F and 205°F. Coffee is cool enough to drink at 185°F. The table shows temperature readings from a sample cup of coffee. How long does it take for a cup of coffee to be cool enough to drink? Use an exponential model.

Time (min)	Temp (°F)
0	203
5	177
10	153
15	137
20	121
25	111
30	104

Think

Why does it make sense that a graph of this data would have an asymptote?
The temperature of the hot coffee will get closer and closer to room temperature as it cools, but it cannot cool below room temperature.

Know
- Set of values
- Best serving temperature

Need
Time it takes for a cup of coffee to become cool enough to drink

Plan
Use an exponential model to find the time it takes for coffee to reach 185°F.

Step 1
Plot the data to determine if an exponential model is realistic.

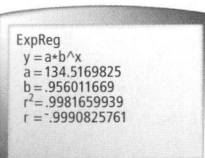

Step 2
Since room temperature is about 68°F, define **L3 = L2 − 68**.

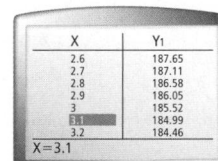

The graphing calculator exponential model assumes the asymptote is $y = 0$.

Hint

Similar to linear and quadratic regressions, an r^2 value close to 1 indicates a strong correlation.

Step 3
Use **ExpReg L1, L3** to find an exponential model.

```
ExpReg
y = a*b^x
a = 134.5169825
b = .956011669
r² = .9981659939
r = ˉ.9990825761
```

Step 4
Shift $y = 134.5(0.956)^x$ up 68 units. Model the original data: $y = 134.5 \cdot 0.956^x + 68$.

X	Y1
2.6	187.65
2.7	187.11
2.8	186.58
2.9	186.05
3	185.52
3.1	184.99
3.2	184.46

X=3.1

The coffee takes about 3.1 min to cool to 185°F.

Take Note VISUAL LEARNERS

Write the equations for Problems 1 and 2 under each equation form. Identify a, b, h, and k, and discuss each transformation. For example, $y = -\frac{1}{3} \cdot 3^x$ is in the form $y = ab^x$ where $a = -\frac{1}{3}$ and $b = 3$. Since $a < 0$, this is a reflection in the x-axis.

Problem 3 SYNTHESIZING

Q What transformation does the calculator include in the exponential model? Explain. [In $y = ab^x$, a suggests a stretch. Other transformations will have to be adjusted by you.]

Q What information does the calculator give you to indicate that the exponential model is the best fit? Explain. [$r^2 = 0.998$; since r^2 is close to 1, the exponential model is the best fit.]

Q What is the horizontal asymptote of your model? Why? [$y = 68$; 68° represents room temperature. In this model, as the coffee cools, its temperature approaches 68° but never equals 68°.]

Answers

Got It? (continued)

2. a. Translate 2 units to the left; the y-intercept becomes 16.

b. Stretch the graph of $y = (0.25)^x$ by a factor of 5 and translate the graph of $y = 5 \cdot 0.25^x$ up 5 units.

Got It?

**ERROR PREVENTION**

Q What is an approximation for your answer? Explain. **[Sample: Longer than 3.1 minutes; since it takes coffee about 3 minutes to cool to 185°, it takes even longer to reach 100°.]**

Q If the function was not translated by 68, would the calculated time to cool the coffee be less than or greater than 3.1 min? Would the result make sense? **[The time would be less than 3.1 (2.7 min) because room temperature would not be a factor. The answer would not make sense, since the original data are for a room-temperature environment, not one of 0°F.]**

3 Lesson Check

Do you know HOW?

• For Exercises 1–4, students may get confused when identifying the transformations. Suggest they write the parent function and then identify which value represents the transformation.

Do you UNDERSTAND?

• For Exercise 5, have students identify the value of each variable in the standard form of the equation. Encourage them to use these values in their explanation.

Close

Q In the equation $y = ab^{(x-h)} + k$, what are the roles of a, h, and k? Consider both positive and negative values. **[If $|a| > 1$, the function is stretched by a factor of a. If $0 < |a| < 1$, the function is compressed by a factor of a. If $a < 0$, the function is reflected in the x-axis. Positive h moves the function to the right h units and negative h moves the function to the left h units. Positive k moves the function up k units and negative k moves the function down k units.]**

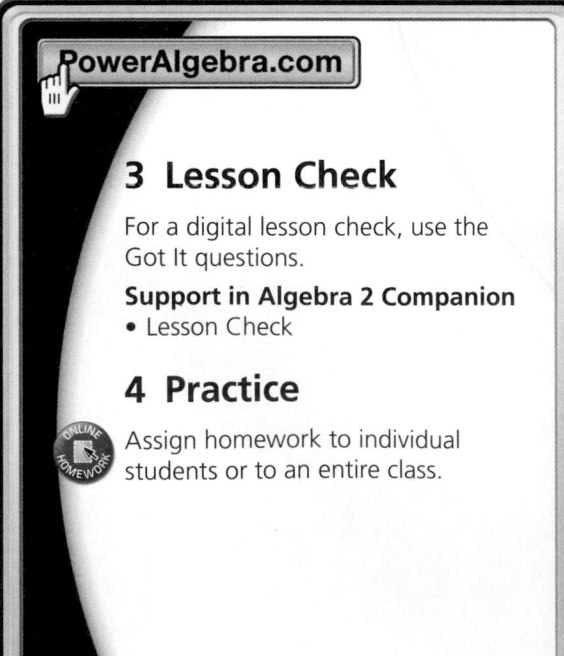

PowerAlgebra.com

3 Lesson Check

For a digital lesson check, use the Got It questions.

Support in Algebra 2 Companion
• Lesson Check

4 Practice

Assign homework to individual students or to an entire class.

**Got It?** **3. a.** Use the exponential model. How long does it take for the coffee to reach a temperature of 100 degrees?
b. Reasoning In Problem 3, would the model of the exponential data be useful if you did not translate the data by 68 units? Explain.

Focus Question What are the transformations on exponential functions?
Answer Every exponential function can be described as a transformation of the parent exponential function, $y = b^x$. The general form is given by $y = ab^{(x-h)} + k$. The values of h and k represent translation. The factor a performs stretches, compressions, and reflections.

Lesson Check

Do you know HOW?

For each function, identify the transformation from the parent function $y = b^x$.

1. $y = -2 \cdot 3^x$

2. $y = \frac{1}{2}(9)^x$

3. $y = 7^{(x-5)}$

4. $y = 5^x + 3$

Do you UNDERSTAND?

5. Error Analysis A student says that the graph of $f(x) = \left(\frac{1}{3}\right)^{x+2} + 1$ is a shift of the parent function 2 units up and 1 unit to the left. Describe and correct the student's error.

Practice and Problem-Solving Exercises

A Practice **Graph each function.**

See Problem 1.

Guided Practice

6. $y = 2(4)^x$

To start, make a table of values.

x	$y = 4^x$	$y = 2(4)^x$
-2	$\frac{1}{16}$	$\frac{1}{8}$
-1	$\frac{1}{4}$	$\frac{1}{2}$
0	1	2
1	4	8
2	16	32

7. $y = -5^x$

8. $y = \left(\frac{1}{2}\right)^x$

9. $y = -9(3)^x$

10. $y = 3(2)^x$

11. $y = 24\left(\frac{1}{2}\right)^x$

12. $y = -\left(\frac{1}{3}\right)^x$

Graph each function as a transformation of its parent function.

See Problem 2.

13. $y = 2^x + 5$

14. $y = 5\left(\frac{1}{3}\right)^x - 8$

15. $y = -(0.3)^{x-2}$

16. $y = -2(5)^{x+3}$

17. $y = 3(2)^{x-1} + 4$

18. $y = -2(3)^{x+1} - 5$

Answers

Got It? (continued)

3. a. about 31.9 min
b. No; a cup of hot coffee cannot cool below room temperature. So, to use exponential data, it is important to translate the data by 68 units.

Lesson Check

1. stretch by a factor of 2 and reflection across the x-axis
2. compress by a factor of $\frac{1}{2}$
3. translate 5 units to the right
4. translate 3 units up
5. The graph is a shift of the parent function 2 units to the left and 1 unit up.

Practice and Problem-Solving Exercises

6.
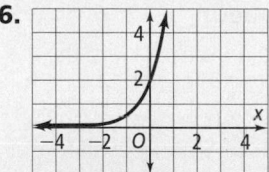

7.
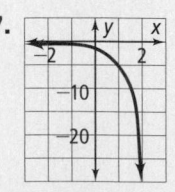

8.
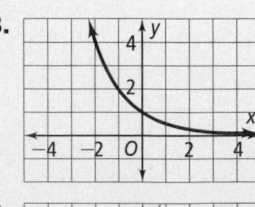

9.
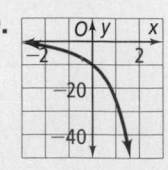

10.
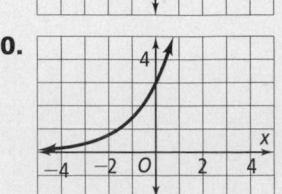

19. Baking A cake recipe says to bake the cake until the center is 180°F, then let the cake cool to 120°F. The table shows temperature readings for the cake.

a. Given a room temperature of 70°F, what is an exponential model for this data set?

b. How long does it take the cake to cool to the desired temperature?

Time (min)	Temp (°F)
0	180
5	126
10	94
15	80
20	73

◀ See Problem 3.

 Apply

20. Assume that a is positive and $b \geq 1$. Describe the effects of $c > 0$, $c = 0$, and $c < 0$ on the graph of the function $y = ab^{cx}$.

21. Graphing Calculator Using a graphing calculator, graph each of the functions below on the same coordinate grid. What do you notice? Explain why the definition of exponential functions has the constraint that $b \neq 1$.

$$y = \left(\tfrac{1}{2}\right)^x \qquad y = \left(\tfrac{8}{10}\right)^x \qquad y = \left(\tfrac{9}{10}\right)^x \qquad y = \left(\tfrac{99}{100}\right)^x$$

The parent function for each graph below is of the form $y = ab^x$. Write the parent function. Then write a function for the translation indicated.

22.
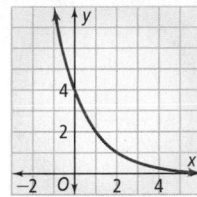
translation: left 4 units, up 3 units

23.
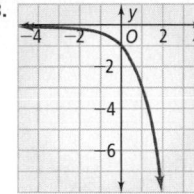
translation: right 8 units, up 2 units

24.
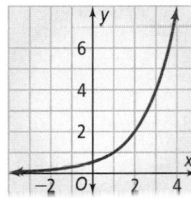
translation: right 6 units, down 7 units

25.
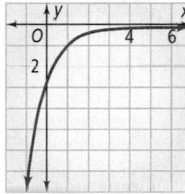
translation: left 15 units, down 1 unit

11.
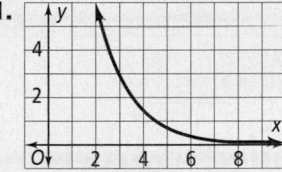

12.
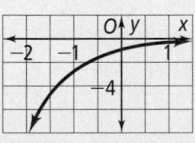

13.
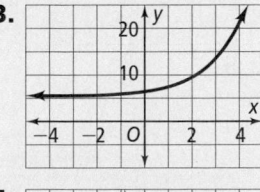

14.
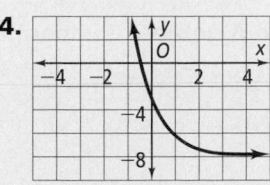

15. **16.**
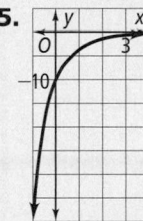

17.
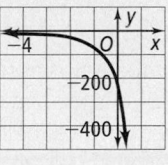

18.
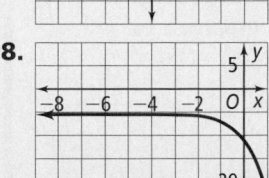

19. a. $y = 127.27(0.836)^x + 70$

b. about 5.2 min

20. If $c < 0$, the graph models exponential decay. If $c = 0$, the graph is a horizontal line. If $c > 0$, the graph models exponential growth.

21.
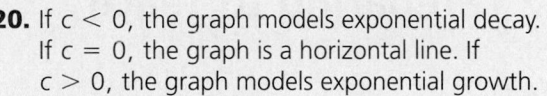
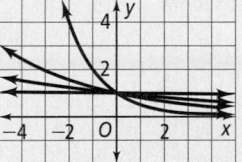

As the value of b approaches 1, the graph comes closer to being a straight line.

22. $y = 4\left(\tfrac{1}{2}\right)^x$; $y = 4\left(\tfrac{1}{2}\right)^{x+4} + 3$

23. $y = -3^x$; $y = -3^{x-8} + 2$

24. $y = \tfrac{1}{2}(2)^x$; $y = \tfrac{1}{2}(2)^{x-6} - 7$

25. $y = -3\left(\tfrac{1}{3}\right)^x$; $y = -3\left(\tfrac{1}{3}\right)^{x+15} - 1$

4 Practice

ASSIGNMENT GUIDE
Basic: 6–11, 13–19, 21, 22
Average: 6–19, 21–24

Reasoning exercises have blue headings.

Applications exercises have red headings.

HOMEWORK QUICK CHECK
To check students' understanding of key skills and concepts, go over Exercises 7, 13, 19, 21, and 22.

1 Launch

CONNECT THE MATH In Part 1, students identified transformations of exponential functions using the standard form of the equation $y = ab^{(x-h)} + k$. In each equation, the base was a rational number. In Part 2, students will explore equations where the base is not a rational value and investigate the irrational base of e.

FOCUS QUESTION

Consider the exponential functions $y = -3(5)^x$ and $y = \left(\frac{1}{2}\right)^{(x+2)}$.

Q What are the values of the bases for each equation? **[5 and $\frac{1}{2}$]**

Q Are the bases rational or irrational? **[rational]**

---

2 Guided Instruction

Problem 4   VISUAL LEARNERS

Q What is the approximate value of e? **[2.7182]**

Q What are the two methods to evaluate a power of e? **[Evaluate the function $y = e^x$ at the given value of x by using the e^x key on a graphing calculator or by finding the value on a graph or table.]**

Q Consider the graph of $y = e^x$. Why does the graphing calculator give an error message when x is sufficiently large? **[The overflow error occurs because the calculator does not have enough memory to store sufficiently large values. $y = e^x$ does not have an upper bound.]**

Objective To graph exponential functions that have base e

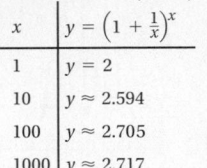
In Part 1 of the lesson, you learned how to transform exponential functions with base b.

Connect to What You Know

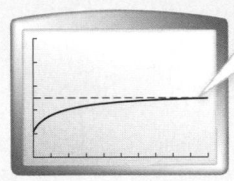
Here you will use what you learned to evaluate exponential functions with the natural base e.

Focus Question What is a natural base exponential function?

So far, you have worked with rational bases. Exponential functions can have irrational bases as well. One important irrational base is the number e.

The graph of $y = \left(1 + \frac{1}{x}\right)^x$ has an asymptote at $y = e$ or $y \approx 2.71828$.

Lesson Vocabulary
• natural base exponential function
• continuously compounded interest

x	$y = \left(1 + \frac{1}{x}\right)^x$
1	$y = 2$
10	$y \approx 2.594$
100	$y \approx 2.705$
1000	$y \approx 2.717$

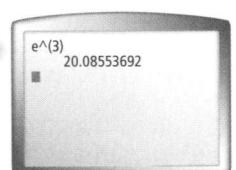
As x approaches infinity the graph approaches the value of e.

Hint
Exponential functions with base e have the same properties as other exponential functions.

Natural base exponential functions are exponential functions with base e. These functions are useful for describing *continuous* growth or decay.

Problem 4 Evaluating e^x

How can you use a graphing calculator to evaluate e^3?

Think
After you press the e^x key, what keys should you press?

Press **3**, **)**, and **enter**.

Method 1 Use the e^x key.

```
e^(3)
        20.08553692
```

Method 2 Use the graph of $y = e^x$.

```
Y1=e^(X)


X=3        Y=20.085537
```

$e^3 \approx 20.086$.

7-2 Preparing to Teach

PART 2

BIG idea Function   **UbD**

ESSENTIAL UNDERSTANDINGS

• The factor a in $y = ab^x$ can stretch or compress and possibly reflect the graph of the parent function $y = b^x$.

• The function $y = ab^x$, $a > 0$, $b > 1$, models exponential growth. $y = ab^x$ models exponential decay if $0 < b < 1$.

Math Background

The number e, commonly defined as the base of the natural logarithm, is an irrational number. This means that the decimal representation of e never terminates or becomes periodic. Euler studied e and proved it irrational, which is why it is sometimes called "Euler's number."

The number e is approximated to 2.71828. It is used in growth and decay models, statistical bell curves, and probability, as well as calculus and other mathematical applications.

During one weekend in May 1994, Robert Nemiroff of the NASA Goddard Space Flight Center computed the first 2 million digits of the number e.

Support Student Learning

Use the **Algebra 2 Companion** to engage and support students during instruction. See Lesson Resources at the end of this lesson for details.

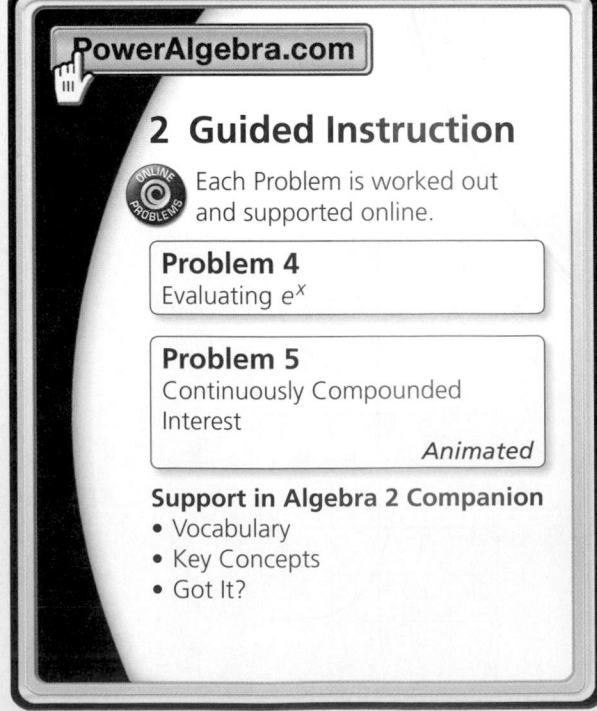

PowerAlgebra.com

2 Guided Instruction

Each Problem is worked out and supported online.

Problem 4
Evaluating e^x

Problem 5
Continuously Compounded Interest
Animated

Support in Algebra 2 Companion
• Vocabulary
• Key Concepts
• Got It?

 **Got It?** 4. How can you use a graphing calculator to calculate e^8?

Hint
In Lesson 7-1 you studied interest that was compounded annually.

The formula for **continuously compounded interest** uses the number e.

 take note

Key Concept Continuously Compounded Interest

amount in account at time t | interest rate (annual)

$$A(t) = P \cdot e^{rt}$$

Principal | time in years

 Problem 5 Continuously Compounded Interest **GRIDDED RESPONSE**

Scholarships Suppose you won a contest at the start of 5th grade that deposited $3000 in an account that pays 5% interest compounded continuously. How much will you have in the account when you enter high school 4 years later? Express the answer to the nearest dollar.

Plan
What is the unknown?
The amount A in the account after 4 years.

Write the equation for continuously compounded interest.	$A = P \cdot e^{rt}$
Substitute values for P, r, and t.	$= 3000e^{(0.05)(4)}$
Simplify.	$= 3000e^{0.2}$
Use a calculator. Round to the nearest dollar.	≈ 3664

The amount in the account, to the nearest dollar, is $3664. Write 3664 in the grid.

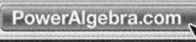 **Got It?** 5. About how much will be in the account after 4 years of high school?

Focus Question What is a natural base exponential function?

Answer A natural base exponential function is an exponential function with the irrational base $e \approx 2.71828$. Use a natural base exponential function to describe continuous growth or decay.

Lesson Check

Do you know HOW?

Use a graphing calculator to evaluate each expression to four decimal places.

1. e^6 2. e^{-1} 3. e^{10}

Do you UNDERSTAND?

4. **Reasoning** Is investing $2000 in an account that pays 5% annual interest compounded continuously the same as investing $1000 at 4% and $1000 at 6%, each compounded continuously? Explain.

Got It? **EXTENSION**

Q How does the graph $y = 3e^x + 1$ compare to the graph of the parent function? **[The graph of the parent function is stretched by a factor of 3 and moved up 1 unit.]**

Take Note **SYNTHESIZING**

Q What does it mean to have interest compounding continuously? **[The principal increases every instant, and the interest earns interest.]**

Problem 5 **SYNTHESIZING**

Q Is compounding continuously or annually better? **[Sample: Continuously; compounding annually pays interest only once a year.]**

Got It? **ERROR PREVENTION**

Q What variable do you want to find? What variable do you know the value of? **[amount A; time t]**

3 Lesson Check

Do you know HOW?
• For Exercises 1–3, encourage students to use both methods to solve the problem.

Do you UNDERSTAND?
• For Exercise 4, if students have difficulty, have them make a chart to organize the information.

Close

Q For $A(t) = Pe^{(rt)}$, what does each variable represent? **[$A(t)$: money in the account after time t; P: principal amount; r: annual interest rate, t: time in years]**

Additional Problems

4. What is the value of $2e^6$? (Use a graphing calculator.)

   ANSWER about 806.86

5. You have $1500 in a bank account that pays 4.5% annual interest compounded continuously. How much will you have in the account after 15 years? Round the answer to the nearest dollar.

   ANSWER $2946

Answers

Got It?
4. $e^8 \approx 2980.957987$; two methods: use the e^x key and let $x = 8$; graph $y = e^x$ and trace to $x = 8$.
5. about $4475

Lesson Check
1. 403.4288
2. 0.3679
3. 22,026.4658
4. no; $2000e^{0.05t} \neq 1000(e^{0.04t} + e^{0.06t})$

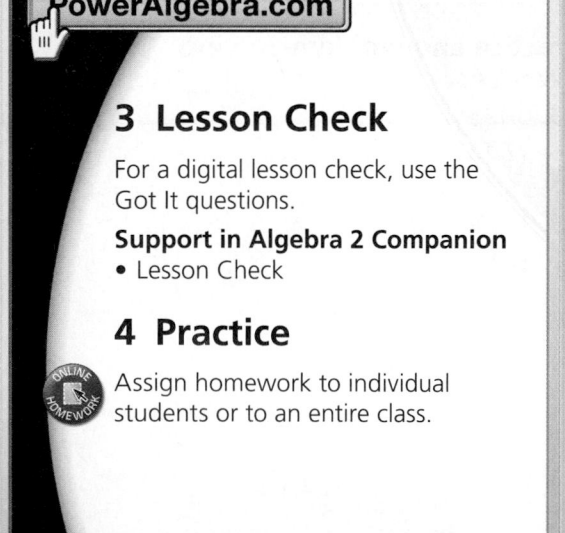

PowerAlgebra.com

3 Lesson Check

For a digital lesson check, use the Got It questions.

Support in Algebra 2 Companion
• Lesson Check

4 Practice

Assign homework to individual students or to an entire class.

4 Practice

ASSIGNMENT GUIDE

Basic: 5–12, 15

Average: 5–15

Standardized Test Prep: 16–21

Mixed Review: 22–33

Reasoning exercises have blue headings.

Applications exercises have red headings.

EXERCISE 12: Use the Think About a Plan worksheet in the **Student Companion** (also available in the Teaching Resources in print and online) to further support students' development in becoming independent learners.

HOMEWORK QUICK CHECK

To check students' understanding of key skills and concepts, go over Exercises 5, 9, 11, 12, and 15.

Practice and Problem Solving Exercises

A Practice   **Graphing Calculator** Use the graph of $y = e^x$ to evaluate each expression to four decimal places.   ◀ See Problem 4.

5. e^{-2} **6.** $e^{\frac{5}{2}}$ **7.** e^e

Find the amount in a continuously compounded account for the given conditions.   ◀ See Problem 5.

Guided Practice

8. principal: $2000
annual interest rate: 5.1%
time: 3 years

$A = P \cdot e^{rt}$

To start, write the equation for continuously compounded interest.

9. principal: $400
annual interest rate: 7.6%
time: 1.5 years

10. principal: $950
annual interest rate: 6.5%
time: 10 years

B Apply

11. Think About a Plan A student wants to save $8000 for college in five years. How much should be put into an account that pays 5.2% annual interest compounded continuously?
• What formula should you use?
• What information do you know?
• What do you need to find?

12. Investment How long would it take to double your principal in an account that pays 6.5% annual interest compounded continuously?

13. Botany The half-life of a radioactive substance is the time it takes for half of the material to decay. Phosphorus-32 is used to study a plant's use of fertilizer. It has a half-life of 14.3 days. Write the exponential decay function for a 50-mg sample. Find the amount of phosphorus-32 remaining after 84 days.

14. Archaeology Archaeologists use carbon-14, which has a half-life of 5730 years, to determine the age of artifacts in carbon dating. Write the exponential decay function for a 24-mg sample. How much carbon-14 remains after 30 millennia?

> **Hint** A millennium is 1000 years.

15. Physics At a constant temperature, the atmospheric pressure p in pascals is given by the formula $p = 101.3e^{-0.001h}$, where h is the altitude in meters. What is p at an altitude of 500 m?

Answers

Practice and Problem-Solving Exercises

5. 0.1353

6. 12.1825

7. 15.1543

8. $2330.65

9. $448.30

10. $1819.76

11. $6168.41

12. about 10.7 yrs

13. $y = 50\left(\frac{1}{2}\right)^{\frac{1}{14.3}x}$; 0.85 mg

14. $y = 24\left(\frac{1}{2}\right)^{\frac{1}{5730}x}$; 0.64 mg

15. ≈ 61.4 pascals

SAT/ACT

16. A savings account earns 4.62% annual interest, compounded continuously. After approximately how many years will a principal of $500 double?

    (A) 2 years   (B) 10 years   (C) 15 years   (D) 44 years

17. What is the inverse of the function $f(x) = \sqrt{x - 4}$?

    (F) $f^{-1}(x) = x^2 - 4, x \geq 0$ (H) $f^{-1}(x) = \sqrt{x + 4}$

    (G) $f^{-1}(x) = x^2 + 4, x \geq 0$ (I) $f^{-1}(x) = \frac{\sqrt{x - 4}}{x - 4}$

In Exercises 18 and 19, let $f(x) = x^2 - 4$ and $g(x) = \frac{1}{x + 4}$.

18. What is $(g \circ f)(x)$?

    (A) $\frac{1}{x^2}$ (B) $\frac{1}{x^2 - 8x + 16} - 4$ (C) $\frac{x^2 - 4}{x + 4}$ (D) $x - 4$

19. What is $(f \circ f)(3)$?

    (F) 1   (G) 5   (H) 21   (I) 77

20. What is the equation of the line shown at the right?

    (A) $y = -\frac{4}{5}x + 2$ (C) $-4x + 5y = 7$

    (B) $y = \frac{5}{4}x - 2$ (D) $4x - 5y = 15$

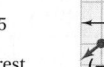

Short Response

21. How much should you invest in an account that pays 6% annual interest compounded continuously if you want exactly $8000 after four years? Show your work.

Mixed Review

Without graphing, determine whether the function represents exponential growth or exponential decay. Then find the y-intercept.   ◄ See Lesson 7-1.

22. $y = 23(3.03)^x$ **23.** $f(x) = 3(5)^x$ **24.** $y = 2\left(\frac{3}{4}\right)^x$

Simplify.   ◄ See Lesson 6-3.

25. $5\sqrt{5} + \sqrt{5}$ **26.** $\sqrt[3]{4} - 2\sqrt[3]{4}$ **27.** $\sqrt{75} + \sqrt{125}$

28. $\sqrt[4]{32} + \sqrt[4]{128}$ **29.** $5\sqrt{3} - 2\sqrt{12}$ **30.** $3\sqrt{63} + \sqrt{28}$

Get Ready!   To prepare for Lesson 7-3, do Exercises 31–33.

Find the inverse of each function. Is the inverse a function?   ◄ See Lesson 6-7.

31. $f(x) = 4x - 1$ **32.** $f(x) = x^7$ **33.** $f(x) = 5x^3 + 1$

Standardized Test Prep
16. C
17. G
18. A
19. H
20. C
21. [2] $A(t) = Pe^{rt}$
    $8000 = Pe^{(0.06)(4)}$
    $P = \frac{8000}{e^{(0.06)(4)}}$
    $P = \$6293.02$

[1] correct amount, but without work shown

Mixed Review
22. exponential growth; 23
23. exponential growth; 3
24. exponential decay; 2
25. $6\sqrt{5}$
26. $-\sqrt[3]{4}$
27. $5(\sqrt{3} + \sqrt{5})$
28. $2(\sqrt[4]{2} + \sqrt[4]{8})$
29. $\sqrt{3}$
30. $11\sqrt{7}$
31. $f^{-1}(x) = \frac{x + 1}{4}$; yes
32. $f^{-1}(x) = x^{\frac{1}{7}}$; yes
33. $f^{-1}(x) = \left(\frac{x - 1}{5}\right)^{\frac{1}{3}}$; yes

Additional Instructional Support

Algebra 2 Companion

Students can use the **Algebra 2 Companion** worktext (4 pages) as you teach the lesson. Use the Companion to support

- New Vocabulary
- Key Concepts
- Got It for each Problem
- Lesson Check

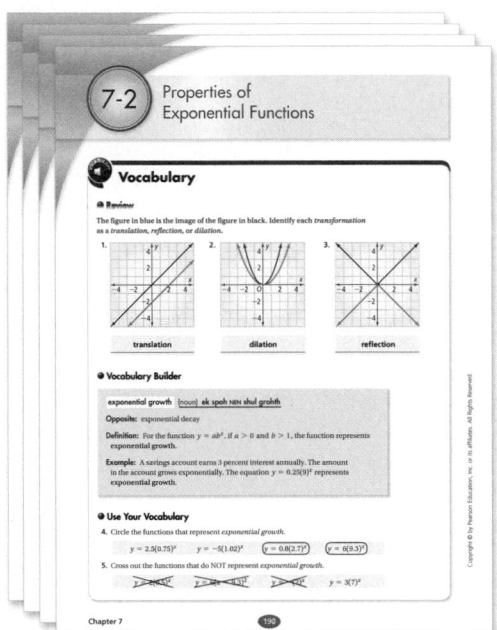

ELL Support

Use Graphic Organizers Instruct students to make a six-column organizer titled "Families of Exponential Functions" with the following column heads: Stretch, Compression, Reflection, Horizontal Translation, Vertical Translation, and All.

Divide students in pairs. Assign Exercises 1–21. Each pair is required to place each exercise in one or more of the five columns. For each exercise, the pair should discuss what the parent function is and what transformation or transformations the problem represents. The pair should be ready to justify each decision. At the end of the activity, the pair of students should have an example for each column.

Each pair should present one exercise to the class explaining their conclusion and justification. They should field questions from the class if necessary.

5 Assess & Remediate

Lesson Quiz

1. How does the graph of $y = 2 \cdot 2^x$ compare to the graph of the parent function?

2. How does the graph of $y = 4^{(x-6)}$ compare to the graph of the parent function?

3. Do you UNDERSTAND? A pot of water is heated to $200°$F. The table shows typical temperature readings for the pot. The room temperature is $70°$F. How long will it take the water to cool to $150°$F?

Time (min)	Temp (°F)
0	200
5	164
10	140
15	124
20	108
25	98

4. You have $10,000. You place it in an account that pays 6.1% annual interest compounded continuously. How much will you have in 20 years? Round the answer to the nearest dollar.

ANSWERS TO LESSON QUIZ

1. $y = 2 \cdot 2^x$ stretches the parent graph $y = 2^x$ by a factor of 2.

2. $y = 4^{(x-6)}$ shifts the parent graph $y = 4^x$ six units to the right.

3. The water will reach $150°$F in about 7.9 min.

4. $33,872

PRESCRIPTION FOR REMEDIATION

Use the student work on the Lesson Quiz to prescribe a differentiated review assignment:

Points	Differentiated Remediation
0–2	Intervention
3	On-level
4	Extension

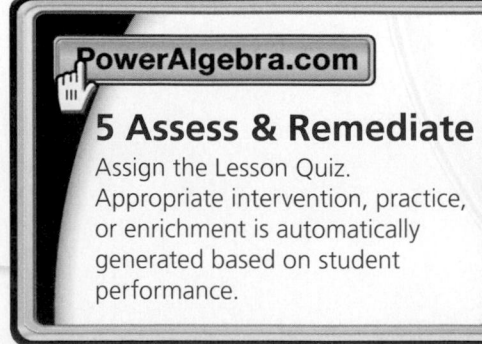

PowerAlgebra.com

5 Assess & Remediate

Assign the Lesson Quiz. Appropriate intervention, practice, or enrichment is automatically generated based on student performance.

Intervention

- **Reteaching** (2 pages) Provides reteaching and practice exercises for the key lesson concepts. Use with struggling students or absent students.

- **English Language Learner Support** Helps students develop and reinforce mathematical vocabulary and key concepts.

All-in-One Resources/Online
Reteaching

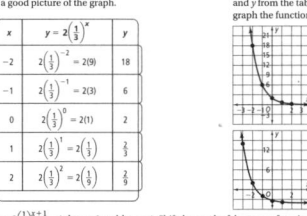

All-in-One Resources/Online
English Language Learner Support

Differentiated Remediation *continued*

On-Level

- **Practice** (2 pages) Provides extra practice for each lesson. For more challenging practice exercises, use the Form G Practice pages found in the All-in-One Teaching Resources and online.

- **Think About a Plan** Helps students develop specific problem-solving skills and strategies by providing scaffolded guiding questions.

- **Standardized Test Prep** Focuses on all major exercises, all major question types, and helps students prepare for the high-stakes assessments.

Extension

- **Enrichment** Provides students with interesting problems and activities that extend the concepts of the lesson.

- **Activities, Games, and Puzzles** Worksheets that can be used for concepts development, enrichment, and for fun!

Student Companion/All-in-One Resources/Online
Practice page 1

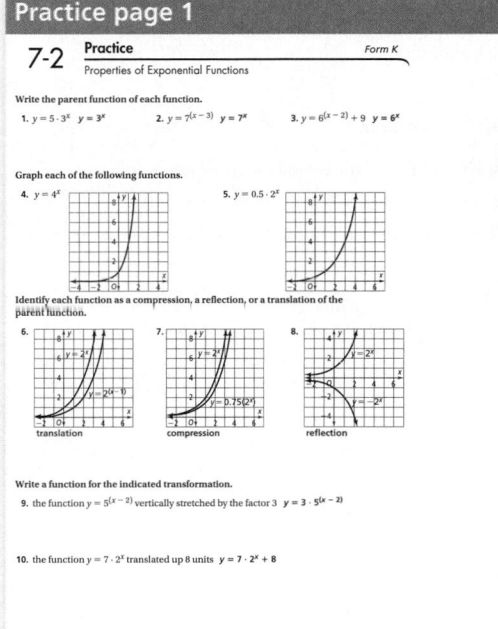

7-2 Practice — Form K
Properties of Exponential Functions

Write the parent function of each function.

1. $y = 5 \cdot 3^x$ $y = 3^x$
2. $y = 7^{(x-3)}$ $y = 7^x$
3. $y = 6^{(x-2)} + 9$ $y = 6^x$

Graph each of the following functions.

4. $y = 4^x$
5. $y = 0.5 \cdot 2^x$

Identify each function as a compression, a reflection, or a translation of the parent function.

6. translation
7. compression
8. reflection

Write a function for the indicated transformation.

9. the function $y = 5^{(x-2)}$ vertically stretched by the factor 3 $y = 3 \cdot 5^{(x-2)}$

10. the function $y = 7 \cdot 2^x$ translated up 8 units $y = 7 \cdot 2^x + 8$

Student Companion/All-in-One Resources/Online
Practice page 2

7-2 Practice (continued) — Form K
Properties of Exponential Functions

Use the graph of $y = e^x$ to evaluate each expression to four decimal places.

11. e^3 20.0855
12. $e^{0.5}$ 1.6487
13. e^{-4} 0.0183

Identify the meaning of the following variables in the formula for continuously compounded interest.

$$A(t) = P \cdot e^{rt}$$

14. P the principal
15. r annual interest rate
16. t time in years

Find the amount in a continuously compounded account for the given conditions.

17. principal: $300
annual interest rate: 5%
time: 4 yr

$A(t) = P \cdot e^{rt}$
$A(4) = \$300 \cdot e^{(0.05)(4)}$
$A(4) = \$366.42$

18. principal: $650
annual interest rate: 6.5%
time: 20 yr

$A(t) = P \cdot e^{rt}$
$A(t) = \$2385.04$

19. Sarah received a paycheck for $1200. She deposited $\frac{1}{4}$ of the money into a bank account. The account has an interest rate of 6% compounded continuously. This is the first and last deposit that Sarah makes into this account. How much money will be in the account in 15 years? $737.88

All-in-One Resources/Online
Enrichment

7-2 Enrichment
Properties of Exponential Functions

A Closer Look at Compounding

The formula for finding the amount of money accumulated in an account is

$A = P\left(1 + \frac{r}{n}\right)^{nt}$.

The variable P represents the **principal**, or amount initially invested.
The variable r represents the interest **rate** as a decimal.
The variable n represents the number of times per year the interest is **compounded**.
The variable t represents the **time**, or number of years for which the money is invested.

1. $750 is invested at 11% compounded quarterly. How much is in the account after 10 yr? $2219.9

2. Write the new formula for $P = \$1$, $r = 1.0$, and $t = 1$ yr. $A = 1\left(1 + \frac{1}{n}\right)^n$

3. Remember that n is the number of times the interest is compounded. What happens as n grows? In other words, what is the effect of compounding more often? Fill in the following table. Round answers to eight decimal places.

n	$\left(1 + \frac{1}{n}\right)^n$
	2.00000000
10	2.59374246
100	2.70481383
1,000	2.71692393
10,000	2.71814593
100,000	2.71826824
1,000,000	2.71828047
10,000,000	2.71828169
100,000,000	2.71828181
1,000,000,000	2.71828183

4. The table suggests that as n increases, the value of $\left(1 + \frac{1}{n}\right)^n$ gets closer to _____. If the value of n is increased further, the decimal approximation in the table will get very close to the value of a number known as e. This number is used in many growth and decay applications. 2.71828183

5. As n grows, you get closer to compounding continuously. This is why the formula used for compounding continuously is $A = Pe^{rt}$. Rework Exercise 1 assuming that compounding is continuous. $2253.12

Student Companion/All-in-One Resources/Online
Think About a Plan

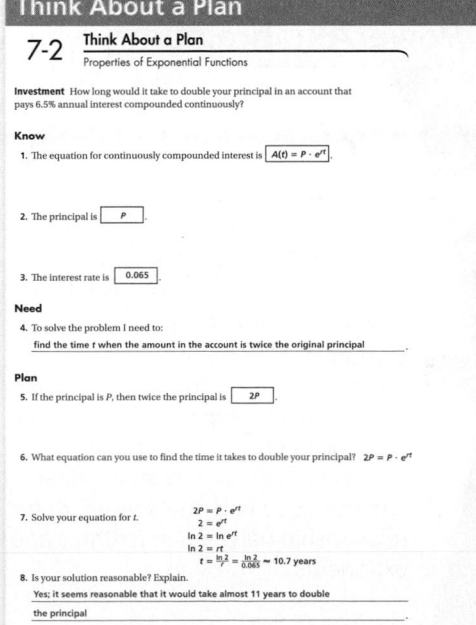

7-2 Think About a Plan
Properties of Exponential Functions

Investment How long would it take to double your principal in an account that pays 6.5% annual interest compounded continuously?

Know

1. The equation for continuously compounded interest is $A(t) = P \cdot e^{rt}$

2. The principal is P

3. The interest rate is 0.065

Need

4. To solve the problem I need to:
find the time t when the amount in the account is twice the original principal

Plan

5. If the principal is P, then twice the principal is $2P$

6. What equation can you use to find the time it takes to double your principal? $2P = P \cdot e^{rt}$

7. Solve your equation for t.
$2P = P \cdot e^{rt}$
$2 = e^{rt}$
$\ln 2 = \ln e^{rt}$
$\ln 2 = rt$
$t = \frac{\ln 2}{r} = \frac{\ln 2}{0.065} \approx 10.7$ years

8. Is your solution reasonable? Explain.
Yes; it seems reasonable that it would take almost 11 years to double the principal

Student Companion/All-in-One Resources/Online
Standardized Test Prep

7-2 Standardized Test Prep
Properties of Exponential Functions

Gridded Response

Solve each exercise and enter your answer in the grid provided.

1. Suppose you deposit $6000 in a savings account that pays interest at an annual rate of 4% compounded continuously. How many years will it take for the balance in your savings account to reach $8000? Round your answer up to the nearest number of years.

2. Suppose you make $1500 at your summer job and you decide to invest this money in a savings account that pays interest at an annual rate of 5.5% compounded continuously. How many dollars will be in the account after 5 years? Express the answer to the nearest whole dollar.

3. The half-life of a radioactive substance is the time it takes for half of the material to decay. Phosphorus-32 is used to study a plant's use of fertilizer. It has a half-life of 14.3 days. How many milligrams of phosphorus-32 remain after 92 days from a 100-mg sample? Express the answer to the nearest whole milligram.

4. A scientist notes the bacteria count in a petrie dish is 40. Three hours later, she notes the count has increased to 75. Using an exponential model, how many hours will it take for the bacteria count to grow from 75 to 120? Express the answer to the nearest tenth of an hour.

Answers

1. 8
2. 1975
3.
4. 2.2

Online Teacher Resource Center
Activities, Games, and Puzzles

7-2 Game: Transforming Graphs
Properties of Exponential Functions

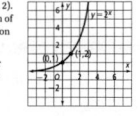

The graph of $y = 2^x$ crosses the y-axis at $(0, 1)$ and contains $(1, 2)$. If you know the images of these points under a transformation of the parent function, then you know an equation for the function you have.

In this game, you are given the image of $(0, 1)$ and $(1, 2)$ under one or more transformations of the graph of $y = 2^x$. If you can write the correct equation, you earn 5 points.

Option 1

Your teacher can play host and all students can be contestants. Play until all the game items have been answered. The highest score wins.

Option 2

Challenge another student to play the game. Players must agree on the correct answers. Play until all the game items have been answered. The highest score wins.

For each item below, write an equation of the form $y = a(2^{x-h}) + k$.

1. $(0, 1) \rightarrow (0, 0.5)$ and $(1, 2) \rightarrow (1, 1)$
$y = 2^{x-1}$

2. $(0, 1) \rightarrow (0, 2)$ and $(1, 2) \rightarrow (1, 3)$
$y = 2^x + 1$

3. $(0, 1) \rightarrow (0, 2)$ and $(1, 2) \rightarrow (1, 4)$
$y = 2^{x+1}$

4. $(0, 1) \rightarrow (0, 0)$ and $(1, 2) \rightarrow (1, 1)$
$y = 2^x - 1$

5. $(0, 1) \rightarrow (0, 3)$ and $(1, 2) \rightarrow (1, 6)$
$y = 3(2^x)$

6. $(0, 1) \rightarrow (0, 0.4)$ and $(1, 2) \rightarrow (1, 0.8)$
$y = 0.4(2^x)$

7. $(0, 1) \rightarrow (1, 2)$ and $(1, 2) \rightarrow (2, 3)$
$y = 2^{x-1} + 1$

8. $(0, 1) \rightarrow (-1, 0)$ and $(1, 2) \rightarrow (0, 1)$
$y = 2^{x+1} - 1$

9. $(0, 1) \rightarrow (2, 3)$ and $(1, 2) \rightarrow (3, 4)$
$y = 2^{x-2} + 2$

10. $(0, 1) \rightarrow (-2, -2)$ and $(1, 2) \rightarrow (-1, -1)$
$y = 2^{x+2} - 3$

11. $(0, 1) \rightarrow (0, 0.75)$ and $(1, 2) \rightarrow (1, 1.5)$
$y = 3(2^{x-2})$

12. $(0, 1) \rightarrow (1, 5)$ and $(1, 2) \rightarrow (2, 11)$
$y = 3(2^x - 1)$

My Total Score: ☐

1 Interactive Learning

Solve It!

PURPOSE To find multiple ways to represent numbers as powers of other numbers

PROCESS Students may
- try to write 2^5 as powers of other numbers and realize the power cannot be a prime such as 5.
- notice that $4^2 = 16$ and write $16^2 = 256$ as powers of numbers.

FACILITATE

Q What operation can you do to 4 to get 16? **[Answers may vary. Samples: You can multiply 4 by 4; you can square 4.]**

Q What is the pattern of smallest numbers? **[Each number must be a power of 2 whose exponent can be factored in the required number of ways. For example, $2^6 = (2^6)^1 = (2^3)^2 = (2^2)^3 = (2^1)^6$.]**

Q What must be the smallest base of each of the smallest numbers? Explain. **[Sample: 2; if the smallest base was 3, the first smallest number would be $9 = 9^1 = 3^2$, and the second smallest would be $81 = 81^1 = 9^2 = 3^4$; 9 and 81 are larger than 4 and 16.]**

ANSWER See Solve It in Answers on next page.

CONNECT THE MATH Students find numbers that can be written as a power function of base 2 to solve this problem. In the lesson they will express numbers as powers of a common base.

2 Guided Instruction

Take Note

Each different base b defines a different logarithmic parent function $y = \log_b x$, just as each base b defines a different exponential parent function $y = b^x$.

7-3 Logarithmic Functions as Inverses

Objectives To write and evaluate logarithmic expressions
To graph logarithmic functions

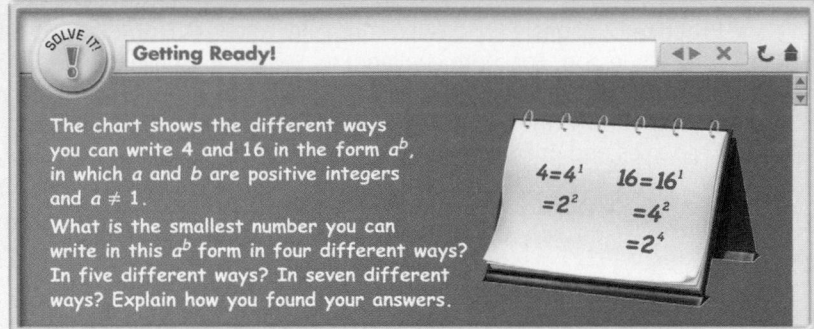

Getting Ready!

The chart shows the different ways you can write 4 and 16 in the form a^b, in which a and b are positive integers and $a \neq 1$.
What is the smallest number you can write in this a^b form in four different ways? In five different ways? In seven different ways? Explain how you found your answers.

$4 = 4^1 = 2^2$ $16 = 16^1 = 4^2 = 2^4$

 **Dynamic Activity** Logarithmic Functions

Lesson Vocabulary
- logarithm
- common logarithm
- logarithmic scale
- logarithmic function

Many even numbers can be written as power functions with base 2. In this lesson you will find ways to express all numbers as powers of a common base.

Focus Question What is a logarithm?

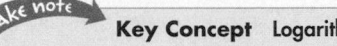

Key Concept   Logarithm

A **logarithm** base b of a positive number x satisfies the following definition.

For $b > 0$, $b \neq 1$, $\log_b x = y$ if and only if $b^y = x$.

You can read $\log_b x$ as "log base b of x." In other words, the logarithm y is the exponent to which b must be raised to get x.

The exponent y in the expression b^y is the logarithm in the equation $\log_b x = y$. The base b in b^y and the base b in $\log_b x$ are the same. In both uses, $b \neq 1$ and $b > 0$.

Since $b \neq 1$ and $b > 0$, it follows that $b^y > 0$. Since $b^y = x$ then $x > 0$, so $\log_b x$ is defined only for $x > 0$.

7-3 Preparing to Teach

BIG idea Function **UbD**

ESSENTIAL UNDERSTANDINGS

- The exponential function $y = b^x$ is one-to-one, so its inverse $x = b^y$ is a function. To express "y as a function of x" for the inverse, write $y = \log_b x$.
- An exponential function is a function with the general form $y = ab^x$, $a \neq 0$, with $b > 0$, and $b \neq 1$. In an exponential function, the base b is a constant. The exponent x is the independent variable with a domain of all real numbers.
- Logarithms are exponents. In fact, $\log_b a = c$ if and only if $b^c = a$.

Math Background

The inverse of the exponential function is the logarithmic function. By definition, $y = b^x$ is equivalent to $\log_b y = x$.

Converting between exponential and logarithmic functions is useful for
- finding the value of a logarithm using properties of exponents,
- making a table of values when graphing a logarithmic function,
- solving exponential and logarithmic equations, as shown in Lesson 7-5.

As inverse functions, the domain of $y = \log_b x$ is the range of $y = b^x$, and the range of $y = \log_b x$ is the domain of $y = b^x$. Logarithms exist only for positive real numbers, which makes sense when you consider that the range of exponential functions is always positive.

Support Student Learning

Use the **Algebra 2 Companion** to engage and support students during instruction. See Lesson Resources at the end of this lesson for details.

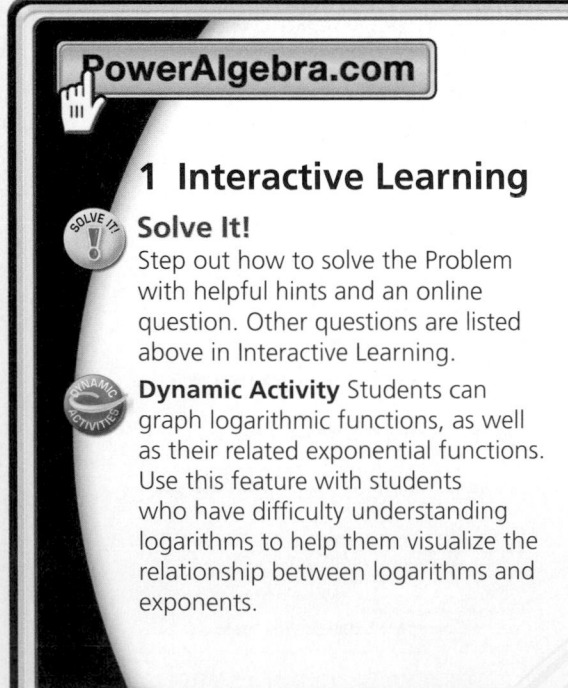

PowerAlgebra.com

1 Interactive Learning

Solve It!

Step out how to solve the Problem with helpful hints and an online question. Other questions are listed above in Interactive Learning.

Dynamic Activity Students can graph logarithmic functions, as well as their related exponential functions. Use this feature with students who have difficulty understanding logarithms to help them visualize the relationship between logarithms and exponents.

You can use the definition of a logarithm to write exponential equations in logarithmic form.

Problem 1 **Writing Exponential Equations in Logarithmic Form**

What is the logarithmic form of each equation?

Think
To what power do you raise 10 to get 100?
10 raised to the 2nd power equals 100.

A $100 = 10^2$

Use the definition of logarithm.

If $x = b^y$ then $\log_b x = y$.

If $100 = 10^2$ then $\log_{10} 100 = 2$.

B $81 = 3^4$

Use the definition of logarithm.

If $x = b^y$ then $\log_b x = y$.

If $81 = 3^4$ then $\log_3 81 = 4$.

✓ **Got It?** 1. What is the logarithmic form of each equation?

a. $36 = 6^2$ b. $1 = 3^0$ c. $\frac{8}{27} = \left(\frac{2}{3}\right)^3$

You can use the exponential form to help you evaluate logarithms.

Problem 2 **Evaluating a Logarithm**

Multiple Choice What is the value of $\log_8 32$?

Ⓐ $\frac{3}{5}$ Ⓑ $\frac{5}{3}$ Ⓒ 3   Ⓓ 5

Plan
How can you use the definition of logarithm to help you find the value of $\log_8$???
If $\log_b x = y$ then $x = b^y$, so to what power must you raise 8 to get 32?

Use the definition of logarithm.	$\log_b x = y$
Write a logarithmic equation.	$\log_8 32 = y$
Use the definition of a logarithm to write an exponential equation.	$32 = 8^y$
Write each side using base 2.	$2^5 = (2^3)^y$
Use the Power Property of Exponents.	$2^5 = 2^{3y}$
Since the bases are the same, the exponents must be equal.	$5 = 3y$
Solve for y.	$\frac{5}{3} = y$

Since $8^{\frac{5}{3}} = 32$, then $\log_8 32 = \frac{5}{3}$.
The correct answer is B.

✓ **Got It?** 2. What is the value of each logarithm?

a. $\log_5 125$ b. $\log_4 32$ c. $\log_{64} \frac{1}{32}$

PowerAlgebra.com   Lesson 7-3   Logarithmic Functions as Inverses   **481**

Problem 1

Q How does the logarithmic form of an exponential equation compare to the original equation? **[The logarithm equals the value of the exponent.]**

ERROR PREVENTION

Use these examples as a model for how students should solve this kind of problem. Make sure they write out the definition each time: If $x = b^y$, then $\log_b x = y$. This will help reduce errors when applying the definition.

Got It?

Q For any $b > 0$, what is $\log_b 1$? Explain. **[$\log_b 1 = 0$, because $b^0 = 1$ for any $b > 0$.]**

Problem 2   **ERROR PREVENTION**

Students can check the reasonableness of their answer when evaluating a logarithm equal to a fraction by checking the value of the integer powers the fraction falls between.

Q Between which two integers is $\frac{5}{3}$? **[1 and 2]**
Q What are 8^1 and 8^2? **[8 and 64]**
Q Is your answer reasonable? Explain. **[Yes; the function is increasing, so $8^{\frac{5}{3}}$ should be greater than 8^1 and less than 8^2, and $8 < 32 < 64$.]**

Got It?   **ERROR PREVENTION**

To evaluate logarithms by the method shown in Problem 2, it is essential that both sides of the equation be expressed in exponential terms with a common base.

---

2 Guided Instruction

 Each Problem is worked out and supported online.

Problem 1
Writing Exponential Equations in Logarithmic Form
Animated

Problem 2
Evaluating a Logarithm
Animated

Problem 3
Using a Logarithmic Scale

Problem 4
Graphing a Logarithmic Function

Problem 5
Translating $y = \log_b x$
Animated

Alternative Problem 5
Translating $y = \log_b x$

Support in Algebra 2 Companion
• Vocabulary
• Key Concepts
• Got It?

Answers

Solve It!

64; 4096; $16,777,216$; $64 = 2^6 = (2^2)^3 = (2^6)^1$;
$4096 = 2^{12} = (2^2)^6 = (2^3)^4 = (2^4)^3 = (2^6)^2$;
$16,777,216 = 2^{24} = (2^2)^{12} = (2^3)^8 = (2^4)^6 = (2^6)^4 = (2^8)^3 = (2^{12})^2$

Got It?

1. a. $\log_6 36 = 2$
    b. $\log_3 1 = 0$
    c. $\log_{\frac{2}{3}} \frac{8}{27} = 3$

2. a. 3
    b. $\frac{5}{2}$
    c. $-\frac{5}{6}$

Problem 3

For an increase of 1 on the Richter scale, the amplitude of the ground motion recorded by a seismograph increases by a factor of ten.

Q What does $\log \frac{I_1}{I_2}$ represent? **[The difference in intensity level determined by a seismograph of two earthquakes]**

Got It?

Q How does the difference in magnitude on the Richter scale of the earthquakes in Problem 3 compare to the difference in magnitude of the earthquakes in the Got It? **[The difference in magnitude is twice as great in the Got It.]**

Q How will the difference in intensities of the earthquakes in the Problem and Got It compare to the magnitude difference on the Richter scale? **[Answers may vary. Sample: The difference in intensity will be much greater than the difference in magnitude on the Richter scale.]**

A **common logarithm** is a logarithm with base 10. You can write a common logarithm $\log_{10} x$ simply as $\log x$, without showing the 10.

Many measurements of physical phenomena have such a wide range of values that the reported measurements are logarithms (exponents) of the values, not the values themselves. When you use the logarithm of a quantity instead of the quantity, you are using a **logarithmic scale**. The Richter scale is a logarithmic scale. It gives logarithmic measurements of earthquake magnitude.

The Richter Scale

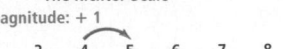

energy released: × 30

Problem 3 Using a Logarithmic Scale

In December 2004, an earthquake with magnitude 9.3 on the Richter scale hit off the northwest coast of Sumatra. The diagram shows the magnitude of an earthquake that hit Sumatra in March 2005. The formula $\log \frac{I_1}{I_2} = M_1 - M_2$ compares the intensity levels of earthquakes where I is the intensity level determined by a seismograph, and M is the magnitude on a Richter scale. How many times more intense was the December earthquake than the March earthquake?

Write the formula.　　　　$\log \frac{I_1}{I_2} = M_1 - M_2$

Substitute $M_1 = 9.3$ and $M_2 = 8.7$.　$\log \frac{I_1}{I_2} = 9.3 - 8.7$

Simplify.　　　　$\log \frac{I_1}{I_2} = 0.6$

Apply the definition of common logarithm.　$\frac{I_1}{I_2} = 10^{0.6}$

Use a calculator.　　　≈ 4

The December earthquake was about 4 times as strong as the one in March.

Think
What is the base of this logarithm?
This is the common logarithm. It has base 10.

✓ **Got It? 3.** In 1995, an earthquake in Mexico registered 8.0 on the Richter scale. In 2001, an earthquake of magnitude 6.8 shook Washington state. How many times more intense was the 1995 earthquake than the 2001 earthquake?

THAILAND
Magnitude 8.7
MALAYSIA
Epicenter, March 2005
Sumatra
INDONESIA

Additional Problems

1. What is the logarithmic form of each equation?
　a. $8^0 = 1$
　b. $4^3 = 64$
　ANSWER
　a. $\log_8 1 = 0$　**b.** $\log_4 64 = 3$

2. What is the value of $\log_{16} 64$?
　ANSWER $\frac{3}{2}$

3. The loudness of a sound in decibels, dB, is defined as $10 \log \frac{I}{10^{-12}}$, where I is the intensity of the sound. How loud is a whisper with an intensity of 10^{-10}?
　ANSWER 20 dB

4. What is the graph of $y = \log_6 x$? Describe the domain and range, and identify the y-intercept and the asymptote.
　ANSWER

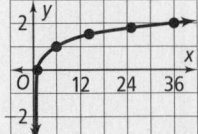

domain: all nonnegative real numbers; range: all real numbers; y-intercept: does not exist; asymptote: $x = 0$

5. How does the graph of $y = \frac{3}{4} \log x - 2$ compare to the graph of the parent function?
　ANSWER The graph is compressed by a factor of $\frac{3}{4}$ and translated down 2 units.

Focus Question What is the relationship between exponential functions and logarithmic functions?

A **logarithmic function** is the inverse of an exponential function. The graph shows $y = 10^x$ and its inverse $y = \log x$. Note that $(0, 1)$ and $(1, 10)$ are on the graph of $y = 10^x$, and that $(1, 0)$ and $(10, 1)$ are on the graph of $y = \log x$.

You can graph $y = \log_b x$ as the inverse of $y = b^x$. Because $y = b^x$ and $y = \log_b x$ are inverse functions, their compositions map a number a to itself. In other words, $b^{\log_b a} = a$ for $a > 0$ and $\log_b b^a = a$ for all a.

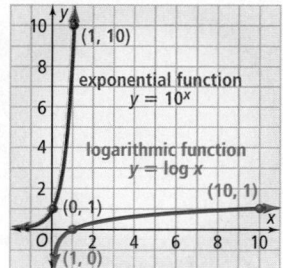

Problem 4 Graphing a Logarithmic Function

What is the graph of $y = \log_3 x$? Describe the domain and range and identify the y-intercept and the asymptote.

$y = \log_3 x$ is the inverse of $y = 3^x$.

Step 1 Graph $y = 3^x$.

Step 2 Reflecting across the line $y = x$ produces the inverse of $y = 3^x$.

Step 3 Choose a few points on $y = 3^x$ and reverse their coordinates. Plot these new points and graph $y = \log_3 x$.

The domain is $x > 0$. The range is all real numbers. There is no y-intercept. The vertical asymptote is $x = 0$.

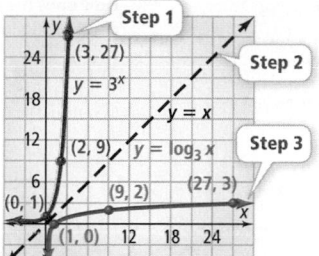

Got It? 4. a. What is the graph of $y = \log_4 x$? Describe the domain, range, y-intercept, and asymptotes.

b. Reasoning Suppose you use the table shown to help you graph $y = \log_2 x$. (Recall that if $y = \log_2 x$, then $2^y = x$.) Copy and complete the table. Explain your answers.

x	$2^y = x$	y
−1	$2^y = -1$	
0	$2^y = 0$	
1	$2^y = 1$	
2	$2^y = 2$	

Q If $y = \log_b x$ and $y = a^x$ are inverse functions, what must be true about a and b? **[$a = b$; the bases must be the same.]**

Q How do the coordinates of the points on the graph of a function compare to the coordinates of the corresponding points on the graph of its inverse? **[The x-coordinates and y-coordinates are reversed.]**

Problem 4

Q Does the graph of $y = \log_3 x$ have a horizontal asymptote? Explain. **[No; the graph increases as x increases in the same way that the exponent decreases as x decreases.]**

Got It?

Q In 4a, how does the graph of $y = \log_3 x$ compare to the graph of $y = \log_4 x$? **[The domain, range, y-intercept and asymptotes are the same. The graph of $y = \log_4 x$ is steeper and above the graph of $y = \log_3 x$ for $x < 1$, and $y = \log_3 x$ is steeper and above the graph of $y = \log_4 x$ for $x > 1$.]**

Q To make a table of values to graph $y = \log_4 x$ in 4b, what are the best x-values to choose to make calculations easy? **[powers of 4, for example, $\frac{1}{16}$, $\frac{1}{4}$, 1, 4, 16]**

Answers

Got It? (continued)

3. ≈ 16 times

4. a. domain: $x > 0$; range: all real numbers; no y-intercept; vertical asymptote: $x = 0$

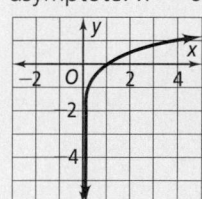

b.

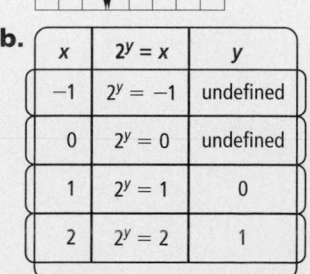

x	$2^y = x$	y
−1	$2^y = -1$	undefined
0	$2^y = 0$	undefined
1	$2^y = 1$	0
2	$2^y = 2$	1

Take Note

ERROR PREVENTION

Note that the base of the logarithm is one parameter that does not change within a family of logarithmic functions. Each base of a logarithm is formally a separate family of functions.

Problem 5

Q How does the shape of the graph of the transformed function compare to the graph of the parent function? **[Answers may vary. Sample: There is no stretch or compression, so the shape is the same.]**

Q How does a horizontal translation by h units affect the domain? **[It translates the domain by h units.]**

Q Could you use the definition of logarithms to make a table of values for the given function and then graph it directly? Explain. **[No; the definition of logarithms only considers the base, x, and y and does not allow for the translations.]**

Got It?

Q What is the parent function of the logarithmic functions in 5a and 5b? **[$y = \log_2 x$]**

Q Does the stretch factor change the intercept or asymptote? Explain. **[No; multiplying the function by a stretch factor does not change the x-value for which $y = 0$, nor does it change the domain of the function.]**

The function $y = \log_b x$ is the parent for a function family. You can graph $y = \log_b(x - h) + k$ by translating the graph of the parent function, $y = \log_b x$, horizontally by h units and vertically by k units. The value of a in $y = a \log_b x$ indicates a stretch, a compression, and possibly a reflection.

Concept Summary Families of Logarithmic Functions

Parent function	$y = \log_b x, b > 0, b \neq 1$
Stretch $(\lvert a \rvert > 1)$ Compression (Shrink) $(0 < \lvert a \rvert < 1)$ Reflection $(a < 0)$ in x-axis	$y = a \log_b x$
Translations (horizontal by h; vertical by k)	$y = \log_b(x - h) + k$
All transformations combined	$y = a \log_b(x - h) + k$

Problem 5 Translating $y = \log_b x$

How does the graph of $y = \log_4(x - 2) + 6$ compare to the graph of the parent function?

Think

How is the function $y = \log_4(x - 2) + 6$ similar to other functions you have seen?
Recall that the graph of $y = f(x - h) + k$ is a vertical and horizontal translation of the parent function, $y = f(x)$.

Step 1
Make a table of values for the parent function. Use the definition of logarithm.

x	$\log_4 x = y \rightarrow 4^y = x$	y
$\frac{1}{16}$	$4^{-2} = \frac{1}{16}$	-2
$\frac{1}{4}$	$4^{-1} = \frac{1}{4}$	-1
1	$4^0 = 1$	0
4	$4^1 = 4$	1
16	$4^2 = 16$	2

Step 2
Graph the parent function. Shift the graph to the right 2 units and up 6 units to graph $y = \log_4(x - 2) + 6$.

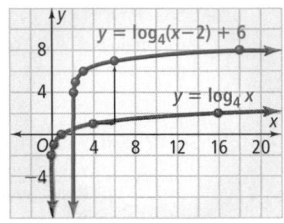

Because $y = \log_4(x - 2) + 6$ translates the graph of the parent function to the right 2 units, the asymptote changes from $x = 0$ to $x = 2$. The domain changes from $x > 0$ to $x > 2$. The range remains all real numbers.

Got It? 5. How does the graph of each function compare to the graph of the parent function?
   a. $y = \log_2(x - 3) + 4$ **b.** $y = 5 \log_2 x$

Answers

Got It? (continued)

5. a. translates the graph of the parent function 3 units to the right and 4 units up; The asymptote changes from $x = 0$ to $x = 3$. The domain changes from $x > 0$ to $x > 3$. The range remains all real numbers.

b. stretches the graph of the parent function by a factor of 5; The asymptote, domain, and the range remain the same.

Focus Question What is a logarithm?

Answer A logarithm y is the exponent to which base b must be raised to get a number x. So, $\log_b x = y$ if and only if $b^y = x$.

Focus Question What is the relationship between exponential functions and logarithmic functions?

Answer Because the exponential function $y = b^x$ is one-to-one, its inverse is a function. The logarithmic function $y = \log_b x$ is the inverse of the exponential function $y = b^x$. The graphs of these functions are reflections of each other in the line $y = x$.

Lesson Check

Do you know HOW?

Write each equation in logarithmic form.

1. $25 = 5^2$ **2.** $64 = 4^3$

3. $243 = 3^5$ **4.** $25 = 5^2$

Evaluate each logarithm.

5. $\log_2 8$ **6.** $\log_9 9$

7. $\log_7 49$ **8.** $\log_2 \frac{1}{4}$

Do you UNDERSTAND?

9. Vocabulary Determine whether each logarithm is a common logarithm.

   a. $\log_2 4$ **b.** $\log 64$ **c.** $\log_{10} 100$ **d.** $\log_5 5$

10. Reasoning Explain how you could use an inverse function to graph the logarithmic function $y = \log_6 x$.

11. Compare and Contrast Compare the graph of $y = \log_2 (x + 4)$ to the graph of $y = \log_2 x$. How are the graphs alike? How are they different?

Practice and Problem-Solving Exercises

Practice   Write each equation in logarithmic form.   **See Problem 1.**

Guided Practice

To start, write the definition of logarithm.   **12.** $49 = 7^2$

   If $x = b^y$, then $\log_b x = y$.

13. $10^3 = 1000$ **14.** $625 = 5^4$ **15.** $\frac{1}{10} = 10^{-1}$

16. $4 = \left(\frac{1}{2}\right)^{-2}$ **17.** $\left(\frac{1}{3}\right)^3 = \frac{1}{27}$ **18.** $10^{-2} = 0.01$

Evaluate each logarithm.   **See Problem 2.**

Guided Practice

To start, write the logarithmic equation.   **19.** $\log_2 16$

 $\log_2 16 = x$

20. $\log_4 2$ **21.** $\log_8 8$ **22.** $\log_4 8$

23. $\log_2 8$ **24.** $\log_{49} 7$ **25.** $\log_5 (-25)$

26. $\log_2 2^5$ **27.** $\log 10{,}000$ **28.** $\log_5 125$

3 Lesson Check

Do you know HOW?

- For Exercises 1–8, if students have trouble converting between logarithmic form and exponential form, remind them to write out the definition of logarithms before beginning.

- For Exercises 5–8, if students have trouble relating the logarithmic *expressions* to the definition for logarithms, which is in the form of an *equation*, then remind them to set the logarithm equal to x before proceeding to evaluate it.

Do you UNDERSTAND?

- If students have difficulty with Exercise 10, remind them that $y = \log_b x$ and $y = b^x$ are inverses. Then remind them that inverses are reflections across the line $y = x$.

Close

Q How can you use the properties of exponents to evaluate a logarithm? **[Answers may vary. Sample: Rewrite the logarithm as a logarithmic function equal to x, convert it to an exponential function, and use the properties of exponents to solve for x.]**

Q How can you use the graph of an exponential function to graph its inverse? **[Answers may vary. Samples: Reflect the graph over the line $y = x$. Choose several points on the graph, reverse the x- and y-coordinates, and plot them.]**

Lesson Check

1. $\log_5 25 = 2$ **2.** $\log_4 64 = 3$

3. $\log_3 243 = 5$ **4.** $\log_5 25 = 2$

5. 3   **6.** 1

7. 2   **8.** −2

9. a. no
   b. yes
   c. yes
   d. no

10. Choose a few points on the graph of $y = 6^x$, reverse their coordinates, and plot them. Then draw a smooth curve through the points.

11. $y = \log_2 (x + 4)$ translates the graph of $y = \log_2 x$ left 4 units. The graphs have the same shape. Asymptote changes from $x = 0$ to $x = -4$. Domain changes from $x > 0$ to $x > -4$. Range remains the same.

Practice and Problem-Solving Exercises

12. $\log_7 49 = 2$

13. $\log 1000 = 3$

14. $\log_5 625 = 4$

15. $\log \frac{1}{10} = -1$

16. $\log_{\frac{1}{2}} 4 = -2$

17. $\log_{\frac{1}{3}} \frac{1}{27} = 3$

18. $\log 0.01 = -2$

19. 4

20. $\frac{1}{2}$

21. 1

22. $\frac{3}{2}$

23. 3

24. $\frac{1}{2}$

25. undefined

26. 5

27. 4

28. 3

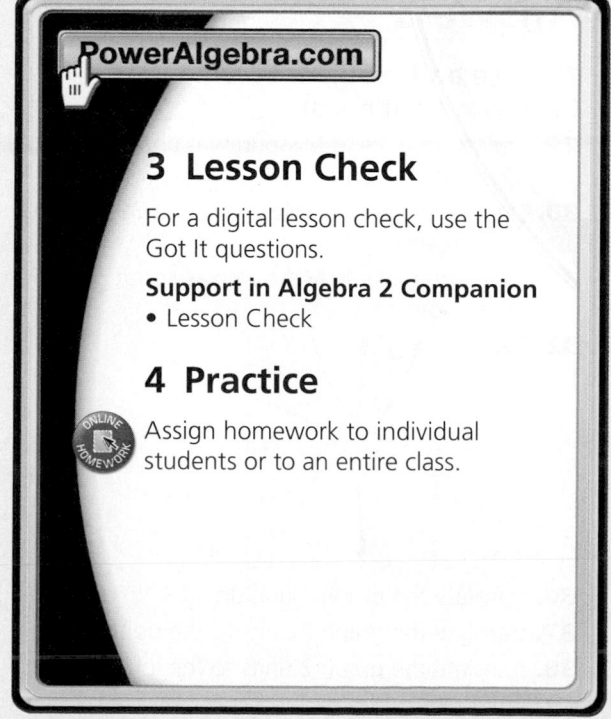

PowerAlgebra.com

3 Lesson Check

For a digital lesson check, use the Got It questions.

Support in Algebra 2 Companion
- Lesson Check

4 Practice

Assign homework to individual students or to an entire class.

4 Practice

ASSIGNMENT GUIDE

Basic: 12–17, 19–25, 29–33, 36–40, 50

Average: 12–45, 48, 50, 51

Standardized Test Prep: 65–68

Mixed Review: 69–77

Reasoning exercises have blue headings.

Applications exercises have red headings.

EXERCISE 40: Use the Think About a Plan worksheet in the **Student Companion** (also available in the Teaching Resources in print and online) to further support students' development in becoming independent learners.

HOMEWORK QUICK CHECK

To check students' understanding of key skills and concepts, go over Exercises 13, 20, 39, 40, and 50.

Seismology In 1812, an earthquake of magnitude 7.9 shook New Madrid, Missouri. Compare the intensity level of that earthquake to the intensity level of each earthquake below.

◀ See Problem 3.

29. magnitude 7.7 in San Francisco, California, in 1906

30. magnitude 9.5 in Valdivia, Chile, in 1960

31. magnitude 3.2 in Charlottesville, Virginia, in 2001

Graph each function on the same set of axes.

◀ See Problem 4.

32. $y = \log_2 x$ **33.** $y = 2^x$ **34.** $y = \log_{\frac{1}{2}} x$ **35.** $y = \left(\frac{1}{2}\right)^x$

Describe how the graph of each function compares with the graph of the parent function, $y = \log_b x$.

◀ See Problem 5.

36. $y = \log_5 x + 1$ **37.** $y = \log_7 (x - 2)$ **38.** $y = \log_4 (x + 2) - 1$

 Apply

39. Think About a Plan The pH of a substance equals $-\log[H^+]$, where $[H^+]$ is the concentration of hydrogen ions, and it ranges from 0 to 14. A pH level of 7 is neutral. A level greater than 7 is basic, and a level less than 7 is acidic. The table shows the hydrogen ion concentration $[H^+]$ for selected foods. Is each food basic or acidic?
- How can you find the pH value of each food?
- What rule can you use to determine if the food is basic or acidic?

Approximate [H⁺] of Foods

Food	[H⁺]
Apple juice	3.2×10^{-4}
Buttermilk	2.5×10^{-5}
Cream	2.5×10^{-7}
Ketchup	1.3×10^{-4}
Shrimp sauce	7.9×10^{-8}
Strained peas	1.0×10^{-6}

40. Chemistry Find the concentration of hydrogen ions in seawater, if the pH level of seawater is 8.5.

Write each equation in exponential form.

41. $\log_2 128 = 7$ **42.** $\log 0.0001 = -4$ **43.** $\log_6 6 = 1$

44. $\log_4 1 = 0$ **45.** $\log_2 \frac{1}{2} = -1$ **46.** $\log_3 \frac{1}{9} = -2$

📱 Find the greatest integer that is less than the value of the logarithm. Use your calculator to check your answers.

47. $\log 5$ **48.** $\log 0.08$ **49.** $\log 17.52$

50. Error Analysis Find the error in the following evaluation of $\log_{27} 3$. Then evaluate the logarithm correctly.

51. Writing Explain why the base b in $y = \log_b x$ cannot equal 1.

52. Open-Ended Write a logarithmic function of the form $y = \log_b x$. Find its inverse function. Graph both functions on one set of axes.

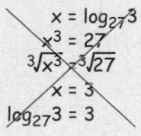

Answers

Practice and Problem-Solving Exercises (continued)

29. The earthquake in Missouri was about 1.58 times more intense.

30. The earthquake in Chile was about 39.81 times more intense.

31. The earthquake in Missouri was about 50,119 times more intense.

32–35.

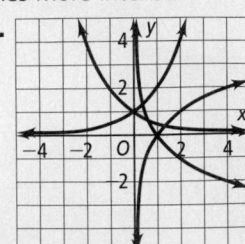

36. translate the graph 1 unit up

37. translate the graph 2 units to the right

38. translate the graph 2 units to the left and 1 unit down

39. apple juice: acidic; buttermilk: acidic; cream: acidic; ketchup: acidic; shrimp sauce: basic; strained peas: acidic

40. $\approx 3.16 \times 10^{-9}$

41. $2^7 = 128$

42. $10^{-4} = 0.0001$

43. $6^1 = 6$

44. $4^0 = 1$

45. $2^{-1} = \frac{1}{2}$

46. $3^{-2} = \frac{1}{9}$

47. 0

48. −2

49. 1

50. error in the second line. It should read $27^x = 3$; the correct answer is $\frac{1}{3}$.

51. First rewrite $y = \log_1 x$ as $1^y = x$. For any real number y, $x = 1$.

52. Answers may vary. Sample: $y = \log_3 x$; $y = 3^x$

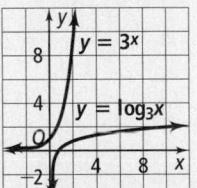

Find the inverse of each function.

53. $y = \log_4 x$ **54.** $y = \log_{10} x$ **55.** $y = \log_2 2x$

56. $y = \log(x + 1)$ **57.** $y = \log 10x$ **58.** $y = \log(x - 6)$

Graph each logarithmic function.

59. $y = \log 2x$ **60.** $y = 2\log_2 x$ **61.** $y = \log_4(2x + 3)$

Find the domain and the range of each function.

62. $y = \log_5 x$ **63.** $y = 3\log x$ **64.** $y = 2\log(x - 2)$

Standardized Test Prep

SAT/ACT

65. Which is the logarithmic form of the exponential equation $2^3 = 8$?

Ⓐ $\log_8 2 = 3$ Ⓑ $\log_8 3 = 2$ Ⓒ $\log_3 8 = 2$ Ⓓ $\log_2 8 = 3$

66. Dan will begin advertising his video production business online pay-per-click method, which charges \$30 as an initial fee, plus a fixed amount each time the ad is clicked. Dan estimates that with the cost of 8 cents per click, his ad will be clicked about 150 times per day. Which expression represents Dan's total estimated cost of advertising, in dollars, after x days?

Ⓕ $(30 + 0.08x)150$ Ⓖ $360x$ Ⓗ $30 + 1200x$ Ⓘ $30 + 12x$

67. Which translation takes $y = |x|$ to $y = |x + 3| - 1$?

Ⓐ 3 units right, 1 unit down Ⓒ 3 units left, 1 unit down

Ⓑ 3 units right, 1 unit up Ⓓ 3 units left, 1 unit up

Short Response

68. What is the expression $\sqrt[3]{(\sqrt{a})^7}$ written as a variable raised to a single rational exponent?

Mixed Review

Graph each function. ◀ See Lesson 7-2.

69. $y = 5^x - 100$ **70.** $y = -10(4)^{x+2}$ **71.** $y = -27(3)^{x-1} + 9$

Factor each expression. ◀ See Lesson 4-4.

72. $4x^2 - 8x + 3$ **73.** $4b^2 - 100$ **74.** $5x^2 + 13x - 6$

Get Ready! To prepare for Lesson 7-4, do Exercises 75–77.

Evaluate each expression for the given value of the variable. ◀ See Lesson 1-3.

75. $x^2 - x$; $x = 2$ **76.** $x^3 \cdot x^5$; $x = 2$ **77.** $\frac{x^8}{x^{10}}$; $x = 2$

71.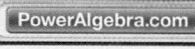

72. $(2x - 3)(2x - 1)$

73. $4(b - 5)(b + 5)$

74. $(5x - 2)(x + 3)$

75. 2

76. 256

77. $\frac{1}{4}$

53. $y = 4^x$

54. $y = 10^x$

55. $y = 2^{x-1}$

56. $y = 10^x - 1$

57. $y = 10^{x-1}$

58. $y = 10^x + 6$

59.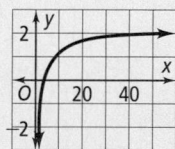

60.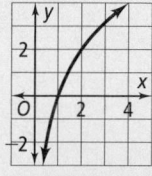

61.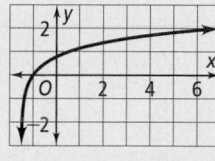

62. domain: $x > 0$, range: all real numbers

63. domain: $x > 0$, range: all real numbers

64. domain: $x > 2$, range: all real numbers

Standardized Test Prep

65. D **66.** I **67.** C

68. [2] $\sqrt[3]{(\sqrt{a})^7} = \left(\left(a^{\frac{1}{2}}\right)^7\right)^{\frac{1}{3}} = a^{\frac{7}{6}}$

[1] correct answer, without work shown

Mixed Review

69.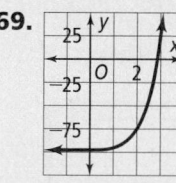

70.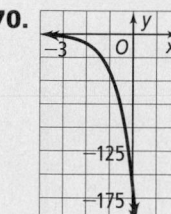

Additional Instructional Support

Algebra 2 Companion

Students can use the **Algebra 2 Companion** worktext (4 pages) as you teach the lesson. Use the Companion to support

- New Vocabulary
- Key Concepts
- Got It for each Problem
- Lesson Check

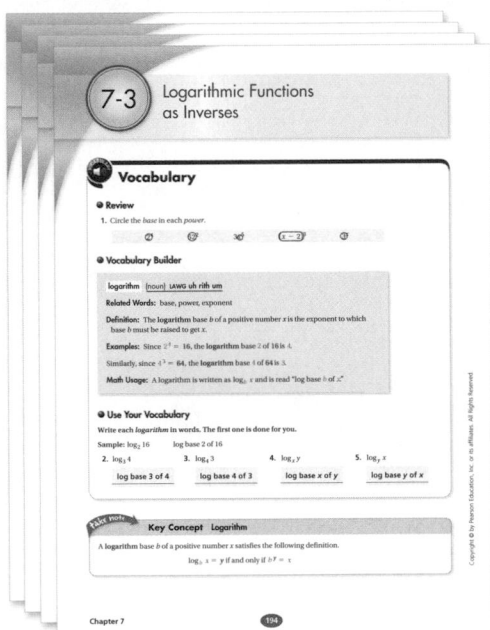

ELL Support

Connect to Prior Knowledge Have a volunteer graph the exponential function $y = 5^x$ on the board. Have students name points that appear on the exponential graph to help the volunteer graph its inverse, $y = \log_5 x$. Have the class explain how each property of the graph of $y = \log_5 x$ is related to the graph of $y = 5^x$, including the domain, range, intercepts, and asymptotes.

Have another volunteer graph the exponential function $y = 4^x$ and this time reflect the graph over the line $y = x$ to find the graph of $y = \log_4 x$. Ask how the graph of $y = \log_4 x$ compares to the graph of $y = \log_5 x$. Ask students to specifically identify why the graphs have the same intercepts and asymptotes and why $\log_4 x < \log_5 x$ when $x < 1$.

5 Assess & Remediate

Lesson Quiz

1. What is the logarithmic form of $144 = 12^2$?

2. What is the value of $\log_9 27$?

3. **Do you UNDERSTAND?** The pH of a substance equals $-\log [H^+]$, where $[H^+]$ is the concentration of hydrogen ions. $[H^+]$ for tomato juice is 10^{-4}. What is the pH of tomato juice?

4. What is the graph of $y = \log_5 x$? Describe the domain and range, and identify the y-intercept and the asymptote.

5. How does the graph of $y = 2\log (x + 5)$ compare to the graph of the parent function?

ANSWERS TO LESSON QUIZ

1. $\log_{12} 144 = 2$

2. $\frac{3}{2}$

3. 4

4. 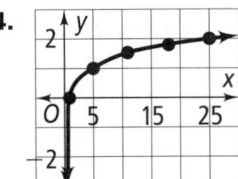 domain: all positive real numbers; range: all real numbers; y-intercept: does not exist; asymptote: $x = 0$

5. The graph is stretched by a factor of 2 and translated to the left 5 units.

PRESCRIPTION FOR REMEDIATION

Use the student work on the Lesson Quiz to prescribe a differentiated review assignment:

Points	Differentiated Remediation
0–2	Intervention
3–4	On-level
5	Extension

PowerAlgebra.com

5 Assess & Remediate

Assign the Lesson Quiz. Appropriate intervention, practice, or enrichment is automatically generated based on student performance.

Intervention

- **Reteaching** (2 pages) Provides reteaching and practice exercises for the key lesson concepts. Use with struggling students or absent students.

- **English Language Learner Support** Helps students develop and reinforce mathematical vocabulary and key concepts.

All-in-One Resources/Online
Reteaching

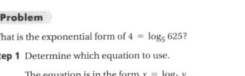

All-in-One Resources/Online
English Language Learner Support

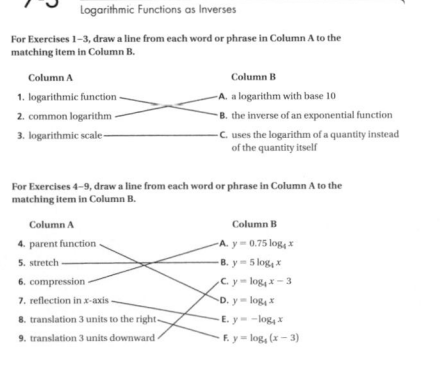

Differentiated Remediation *continued*

On-Level

- **Practice** (2 pages) Provides extra practice for each lesson. For more challenging practice exercises, use the Form G Practice pages found in the All-in-One Teaching Resources and online.

- **Think About a Plan** Helps students develop specific problem-solving skills and strategies by providing scaffolded guiding questions.

- **Standardized Test Prep** Focuses on all major exercises, all major question types, and helps students prepare for the high-stakes assessments.

Extension

- **Enrichment** Provides students with interesting problems and activities that extend the concepts of the lesson.

- **Activities, Games, and Puzzles** Worksheets that can be used for concepts development, enrichment, and for fun!

Student Companion/ All-in-One Resources/Online
Practice page 1

7-3 Practice Form K
Logarithmic Functions as Inverses

Write each equation in logarithmic form.

1. $32 = 2^5$ $\log_2 32 = 5$
2. $243 = 3^5$ $\log_3 243 = 5$
3. $625 = 5^4$ $\log_5 625 = 4$

Write each equation in exponential form.

4. $\log_3 9 = 2$ $9 = 3^2$
5. $\log_5 125 = 3$ $125 = 5^3$
6. $\log_8 512 = 3$ $512 = 8^3$

Evaluate each logarithm.

7. $\log_3 27$
8. $\log_8 256 \ \frac{8}{3}$
9. $\log_{125} \frac{1}{25} \ -\frac{2}{3}$

$\log_3 27 = x$
$27 = 3^x$
$3^3 = (3^2)^x$
$3^3 = 3^{2x}$
$3 = 2x$
$x = \frac{3}{2}$

$\log_8 256 = x$
$256 = 8^x$

The formula $\log \frac{I_1}{I_2} = M_1 - M_2$ is used to compare the intensity levels of earthquakes. The variable I is the intensity measured by a seismograph. The variable M is the measurement on the Richter scale. Use the formula to answer the following problem.

10. In 1906, an earthquake of magnitude 8.25 hit San Francisco, California. Indonesia was hit by an earthquake of magnitude 8.5 in 1938. Compare the intensity of the two earthquakes. **The earthquake in Indonesia was approximately 1.78 times more intense than the earthquake in San Francisco.**

Student Companion/ All-in-One Resources/Online
Practice page 2

7-3 Practice (continued) Form K
Logarithmic Functions as Inverses

11. **Error Analysis** A student drew the graph below to represent the function $y = \log_4 x$. What mistake did the student make when she drew her graph? **She did not reflect the graph across the line $y = x$.**

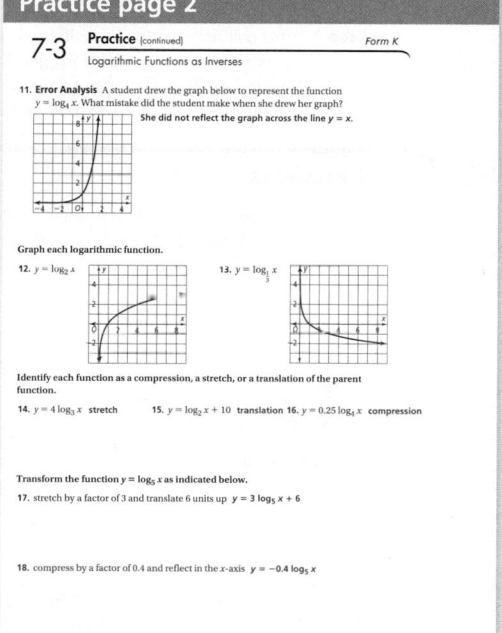

Graph each logarithmic function.

12. $y = \log_2 x$
13. $y = \log_{\frac{1}{3}} x$

Identify each function as a compression, a stretch, or a translation of the parent function.

14. $y = 4 \log_3 x$ stretch
15. $y = \log_2 x + 10$ translation
16. $y = 0.25 \log_4 x$ compression

Transform the function $y = \log_5 x$ as indicated below.

17. stretch by a factor of 3 and translate 6 units up $y = 3 \log_5 x + 6$

18. compress by a factor of 0.4 and reflect in the x-axis $y = -0.4 \log_5 x$

All-in-One Resources/Online
Enrichment

7-3 Enrichment
Logarithmic Functions as Inverses

Log Jams

The logarithm is a tool originally developed and used to aid in calculations, yet this viewpoint of logarithms is not the only one of interest. Logarithms are also useful when thought of as real-valued functions, or as inverse functions of the corresponding exponential functions. The idea of a logarithm as an inverse function of an exponential function means that $\log_2 x$ is a question to be answered. For example, you can read the expression $\log_2 8$ as "what exponent on base 2 gives 8?" The answer is 3, because $2^3 = 8$.

Thinking of a logarithm as an exponent helps to order some logarithms without evaluating them. For example, the logarithms $\log_7 8$, $\log_7 7$, and $\log_7 6$ are in descending order since the exponent needed on base 7 that gives 8 would be greater than 1, and 1 is in turn greater than the exponent needed on base 7 that gives 6.

You can also compose logarithms as you would compose other functions, where their domain and ranges agree. Thus, you evaluate $\log_4 (\log_5 25)$ by evaluating $\log_5 25 = 2$, then evaluating $\log_4 2 = \frac{1}{2}$.

Rewrite each equation in exponential form to solve the equation.

1. Solve for x: $\log_x 81 = 4$ 3
2. Solve for x: $\log_x 2 = 2$ $\sqrt{2}$
3. Which is greater, $\log_2 3$ or $\log_3 2$? $\log_2 3$ is greater
4. Solve for x: $\log_x x = \log_x 3$ 3
5. Which is greater, $\frac{1}{3}$ of $\log_2 2$ or $\frac{1}{2}$ of $\log 10$? $\frac{1}{2} \log 10$ is greater
6. Solve for x: $\log_2 (\log_2 x) = 2$ 16
7. Which is greater, $\frac{1}{2} \log_2 (\log_3 8.5)$ or $\frac{1}{3} \log_3 (\log_2 8.5)$? $\frac{1}{3} \log_3 (\log_2 8.5)$ is greater
8. Which of the following are equal? $\log \frac{1}{2}$ and $\log 1 - \log 2$ are equal

$\log \frac{1}{2}$ $\frac{\log 1}{\log 2}$ $\log 1 - \log 2$

Rewrite in exponential form and solve for x.

9. $\log_5 1 = x$ 0
10. $\log_2 (2x^2 - 7) = 0$ -2, 2
11. $\log_3 7 = 1$ 7
12. $\log_x x^2 = 2$ ± 2
13. $\log 1 = x$ 0
14. $\log_{17} 17 = x$ 1
15. $\log_x 3^4 = 1$ 81
16. $\log_3 x = 0$ 1
17. $\log_3 3^2 = x$ 2
18. $\log_4 (x + 1) = 0$ 0
19. $1 + \log_6 (x - 1) = 1$ 2
20. $-1 + \log x = -1$ 1

Student Companion/ All-in-One Resources/Online
Think About a Plan

7-3 Think About a Plan
Logarithmic Functions as Inverses

Chemistry Find the concentration of hydrogen ions in seawater, if the pH level of seawater is 8.5.

Understanding the Problem

1. What is the pH of seawater? 8.5

2. How do you represent the concentration of hydrogen ions? H^+

3. What is the problem asking you to determine?
the concentration of hydrogen ions in seawater

Planning the Solution

4. Write the formula for the pH of a substance. $pH = -\log[H^+]$

5. Write an equation relating the pH of seawater to the concentration of hydrogen ions in seawater. $8.5 = -\log[H^+]$

Getting an Answer

6. Solve your equation to find the concentration of hydrogen ions in seawater.
$8.5 = -\log[H^+]$
$-8.5 = \log[H^+]$
$10^{-8.5} = 10^{\log[H^+]}$
$10^{-8.5} = [H^+]$
$[H^+] = 10^{-8.5}$ or 3.16×10^{-9}

Student Companion/ All-in-One Resources/Online
Standardized Test Prep

7-3 Standardized Test Prep
Logarithmic Functions as Inverses

Multiple Choice

For Exercises 1–4, choose the correct letter.

1. Which of the following is the logarithmic form of the equation $4^{-3} = \frac{1}{64}$? C
   - Ⓐ $\log_{-3} \left(\frac{1}{64}\right) = 4$
   - Ⓑ $\log_{-3} 4 = \frac{1}{64}$
   - Ⓒ $\log_4 \left(\frac{1}{64}\right) = -3$
   - Ⓓ $\log_{\frac{1}{64}} 4 = -3$

2. What is the value of $\log_2 8$? I
   - Ⓕ 64
   - Ⓖ 8
   - Ⓗ 16
   - Ⓘ 3

3. How does the graph of $y = \log_6 (x - 3)$ compare with the graph of the parent function, $y = \log_6 x$? C
   - Ⓐ translated 3 units to the left
   - Ⓑ translated 3 units down
   - Ⓒ translated 3 units to the right
   - Ⓓ translated 3 units up

4. In 2009, an earthquake of magnitude 6.7 shook the Kermadec Islands off the coast of New Zealand. Also in 2009, an earthquake of magnitude 5.1 occurred in the Alaska Peninsula. How many times stronger was the Kermadec earthquake than the Alaska earthquake? F
   - Ⓕ 39.811
   - Ⓖ 20.593
   - Ⓗ 5.77
   - Ⓘ 0.025

Short Response

5. A single-celled bacterium divides every hour. The number N of bacteria after t hours is given by the formula $\log_2 N = t$.
   a. After how many hours will there be 64 bacteria?
   b. Explain in words or show work for how you determined the number of hours.

[2] a. 6 hours
b. $\log_2 N = t$ can be written in the exponential form $2^t = N$. Substituting 64 for N, the equation becomes $2^t = 64$. Rewriting 64 with base 2, the equation becomes $2^t = 2^6$. Since the bases are equal, $t = 6$.
[1] incorrect exponential form OR incorrect explanation
[0] incorrect answers and no explanation OR no answers given

Online Teacher Resource Center
Activities, Games, and Puzzles

7-3 Puzzle: Evaluating Logs
Logarithmic Functions as Inverses

The puzzle at the bottom of the page has been separated into twelve sections. Each section contains three squares. In each section, there is a number in a circle. This tells you the sum of the two numbers in the section's empty squares. All missing numbers are natural numbers: 1, 2, 3, . . . Additional instructions (A–L) are given for each section of missing numbers.

For example, look at the section marked by Ⓐ. The sum of the two missing numbers in the empty squares is 11. Complete each equation with numbers that meet the requirements for each given section, and then place them in the puzzle.

A. $\log_2 \underline{\ 8\ } = \underline{\ 3\ }$
B. $\log \underline{\ 5\ } 25 = \underline{\ 2\ }$
C. $\log_3 \underline{\ 27\ } = \underline{\ 3\ }$
D. $\log_5 \underline{\ 125\ } = \underline{\ 3\ }$
E. $\log \underline{\ 10\ } 10 = \underline{\ 1\ }$
F. $\log \underline{\ 2\ } 32 = \underline{\ 5\ }$
G. $\log_7 \underline{\ 49\ } = \underline{\ 2\ }$
H. $\log \underline{\ 2\ } 16 = \underline{\ 4\ }$
I. $\log_4 \underline{\ 64\ } = \underline{\ 3\ }$
J. $\log \underline{\ 3\ } \underline{\ 81\ } = 4$
K. $\log \underline{\ 2\ } 32 = 5$
L. $\log \underline{\ 5\ } 25 = 2$

Final Question: Use four letters from the puzzle to find the value of $\log_2 \sqrt{2}$.
"ONE - $\underline{H}\ \underline{A}\ \underline{L}\ \underline{F}$"

Guided Instruction

PURPOSE To fit data to a curve and extrapolate to find a new point that fits the data

PROCESS Students will

• connect data points to determine the type of function that models the data.

• use the **STAT PLOT** feature on a calculator to graph a table of data, and use regression features to find the best-fitting function.

• use the model to extrapolate a new point that fits the data.

DISCUSS The purpose of fitting a curve to data is to *approximate* a function that has the points on its graph. Sometimes not all of the points will lie exactly on the curve. Not all data will have a reasonable model of linear, quadratic, logarithmic, or exponential type.

> **Q** If a set of data is always increasing, could the best-fitting curve be a parabola? Explain. **[Yes; the curve that fits the data could be the increasing portion of an upward-facing parabola.]**

Example 1

> **Q** Why is a linear function not a reasonable model? **[Answers may vary. Sample: The slope of the model is not constant, because the ratio of the change in *x*-values to the change in *y*-values is not constant.]**

Example 2   **VISUAL LEARNERS**

> **Q** How can you tell by looking at the table that the function that models the graph is not logarithmic? **[The *y*-values decrease and then increase. A logarithmic function is always increasing or always decreasing.]**

Concept Byte   Fitting Curves to Data
For Use With Lesson 7-3
TECHNOLOGY

Example 1

Which type of function models the data best—linear, logarithmic, or exponential?

Connect the points with a smooth curve. Since the points do not fall along a line, the function is not linear. The graph appears to approach a horizontal asymptote, so an exponential function models the data best.

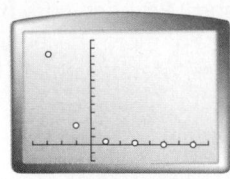 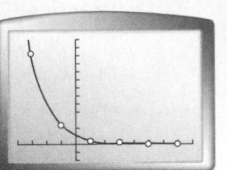

Example 2

Which type of function models the data best—quadratic, logarithmic, or cubic?

Step 1 Press (stat) (enter) to enter the data in lists.

Step 2 Use the (stat plot) feature to draw a scatter plot.

Step 3 If you connect the points with a smooth curve, the end behavior of the graph is up and up. The graph is not cubic or logarithmic, so the quadratic function best models the data.

x	y
0	14
1	7.5
2	4
3	1.8
4	1.8
5	3.9

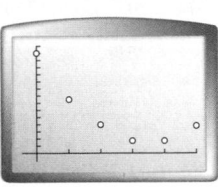

Exercises

1. Which type of function best models the data shown in the graphing-calculator screen—*linear, quadratic, logarithmic, cubic,* or *exponential*?

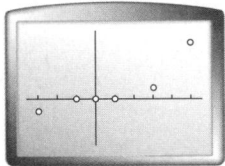

2. Which type of function best models the data in the table—*linear, quadratic, logarithmic, cubic,* or *exponential*?

3. Reasoning Could you use a different model for the data in Exercises 1 and 2? Explain.

x	y
−1	0
1	1.4
3	2.09
5	2.53
7	2.81
9	3.12

Answers

Exercises

1. cubic

2. quadratic

3. Yes; the data in Exercise 1 could also be linear with outliers; the data in Exercise 2 could also be linear or cubic. They cannot be logarithmic due to negative values.

Example 3

The table shows the number of bacteria in a culture after the given number of hours. Find a good model for the data. Based on the model, how many bacteria will be in the culture after an additional ten hours?

Hour	Bacteria
1	2205
2	2270
3	2350
4	2653
5	3052
6	3417
7	3890
8	4522
9	5107
10	5724

Step 1 Press `stat` `enter` to enter the data in lists. Use the `stat plot` feature to draw a scatter plot.

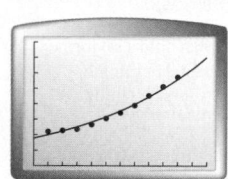

Step 2 Notice from the scatter plot that the data appears exponential. Find the equations for the best-fitting exponential function. Press `stat` ▷ 0 to use the **ExpReg** feature.

$$y = 1779.404(1.121)^x$$

Step 3 Graph the function. Press `y=` `clear` `vars` 5 ▷ ▷ `enter` to enter the ExpReg results. Press `graph` to display the function and the scatter plot together. Press `zoom` 9 to automatically adjust the window.

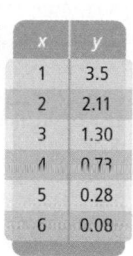

Step 4 In 10 more hours, there will be approximately $y = 1779.404(1.121)^{20} \approx 17{,}474$ bacteria in the culture.

Exercises

Use a graphing calculator to find the exponential or quadratic function that best fits each set of data. Graph each function.

4.

x	y
−1	4.9
0	3.8
1	5.0
2	9.1
3	13.3
4	70.2

5.

x	y
−3	0.1
−1	0.4
1	1.6
3	6.4
5	25.6
7	102.4

6.

x	y
1	3.5
2	2.11
3	1.30
4	0.73
5	0.28
6	0.08

7. Writing In Exercise 6, the function appears to level off. Explain why.

8. Find a quadratic model for the data in Exercise 6. Compare the graphs of the quadratic and exponential models for this data. Predict the y-values for both models when $x = -2$. Discuss the differences if any between the predictions.

Example 3

When the ExpReg feature on the calculator is used, the function that models the data is not given in explicit form. The feature reads the data listed in the table and returns the constants a and b that define the function $y = ab^x$.

Q Do you think you can make a reasonable prediction about the bacteria population 10 days from now? Explain. **[No; the data only covers the population growth over 10 hours. The model may not continue to be reasonable for the much larger time period of 10 days.]**

Exercises   SYNTHESIS

For Exercises 4–6, either a quadratic or an exponential function could be used to model the graph. The exponential model would consist of only half of the parabola. Choose which function to use based on which models the graph of the points most closely.

Q Why is the scale of the axes in the graph important? How can you choose an appropriate scale? **[To see the shape of the curve, the scale must be adjusted so that the points are not clustered too closely on the x- or y-axis. The range of each axis should be slightly larger than the range of the x- and y-values of the data points.]**

Q In Exercise 5, do you think that the quadratic or exponential function would predict a larger y-value for the model when $x = 9$? Why? **[The exponential model, because exponential functions increase more rapidly than quadratic functions.]**

4. $y = 5.46x^2 - 6.16x - 1.44$

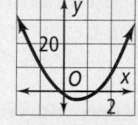

5. $y = 0.8(2)^x$

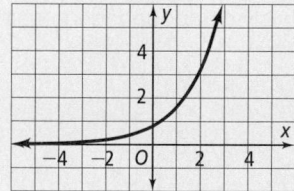

6. $y = 0.13x^2 - 1.59x + 4.88$

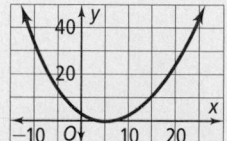

7. $x = 0$ is an asymptote.

8. quadratic model: $y \approx 2.03x^2 + 0.34x - 9.72; f(-2) = -2.28$; exponential model: $y = 0.8(2)^x; f(-2) = 0.2$; The exponential model is the best fit.

Answers

Mid-Chapter Quiz

1. exponential decay; 100

2. exponential growth; $\frac{7}{8}$

3. domain: all real numbers; range: $y < 0$; y-intercept: $(0, -4)$

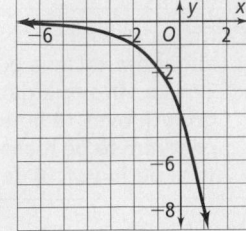

4. domain: all real numbers; range: $y > 0$; y-intercept: $(0, 8)$

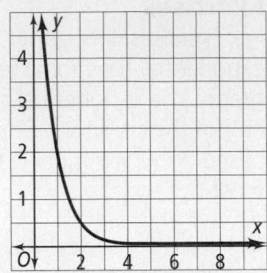

5. $672.97

6. $y = 25,000(0.85)^x$; $11,093

7. $y = 3^x - 2$

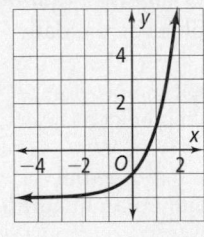

8. $y = 5^x$

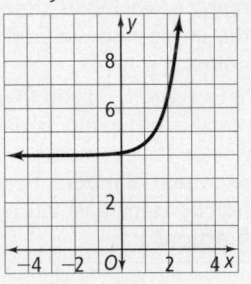

9. $y = (0.5)^x$

10. $y = \left(\frac{3}{4}\right)^x$

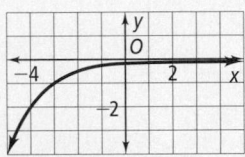
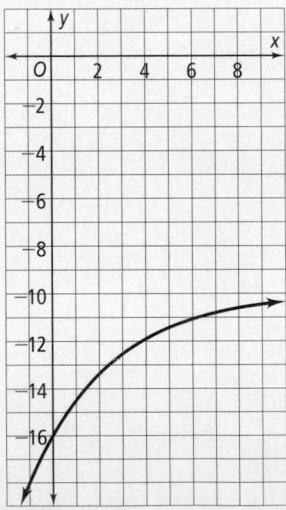

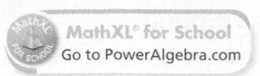

---

7 **Mid-Chapter Quiz**

MathXL® for School
Go to PowerAlgebra.com

Do you know HOW?

Determine whether each function is an example of exponential growth or decay. Then find the y-intercept.

1. $y = 100(0.25)^x$ **2.** $y = \frac{7}{8}(18)^x$

Graph each function. Then find the domain, range, and y-intercept.

3. $y = -4(2)^x$ **4.** $y = 8(0.25)^x$

5. Investment Suppose you deposit $600 into a savings account that pays 3.9% annual interest. How much will you have in the account after 3 years if no money is added or withdrawn?

6. Depreciation The initial value of a car is $25,000. After one year, the value of the car is $21,250. Write an exponential function to model the expected value of the car. Estimate the value of the car after 5 years.

Graph each function as a transformation of its parent function. Write the parent function.

7. $y = 3^x - 2$ **8.** $y = \frac{1}{2}(5)^{x-1} + 4$

9. $y = -(0.5)^{x+3}$ **10.** $y = -6\left(\frac{3}{4}\right)^x - 10$

Evaluate each expression to four decimal places.

11. e^5 **12.** $e^{\frac{3}{2}}$

Find the amount in a continuously compounded account for the given conditions.

13. principal: $500; annual interest rate: 4.9%; time: 2.5 years

14. principal: $6000; annual interest rate: 6.8%; time: 10 years

Write each equation in logarithmic form.

15. $10^4 = 10,000$ **16.** $8 = \left(\frac{1}{2}\right)^{-3}$

Evaluate each logarithm.

17. $\log_8 64$ **18.** $\log_{\frac{1}{5}} 625$

Graph each logarithmic function. Find the domain and range.

19. $y = \log_5 (x - 1)$ **20.** $y = 4 \log x + 5$

21. Crafts For glass to be shaped, its temperature must stay above 1200°F. The temperature of a piece of glass is 2200°F when it comes out of the furnace. The table shows temperature readings for the glass. Write an exponential model for this data set and then find how long it takes for the piece of glass to cool to 1200°F.

Time (min)	Temp (°F)
0	2200
5	1700
10	1275
15	1000
20	850
25	650

Do you UNDERSTAND?

22. Error Analysis A student claims the y-intercept of the graph of the function $y = ab^x$ is the point $(0, b)$. What is the student's mistake? What is the actual y-intercept?

23. Writing Without graphing, how can you tell whether an exponential function represents exponential growth or exponential decay?

24. Compare and Contrast Compare the graph of $y = \log_3 (x + 1)$ to the graph of its inverse $y = 3^x - 1$. How are the graphs alike? How are they different?

25. Vocabulary Explain how the continuously compounded interest formula differs from the annually compounded interest formula.

490 Chapter 7 Mid-Chapter Quiz

---

11. ≈ 148.4132 **12.** ≈ 4.4817

13. $565.16   **14.** $11,843.27

15. $\log 10,000 = 4$ **16.** $\log_{\frac{1}{2}} 8 = -3$

17. 2   **18.** -4

19. domain: $x > 1$, range: all real numbers

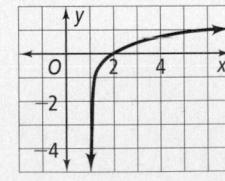

20. domain: $x > 0$, range: all real numbers

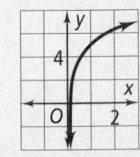

21. $y = 2144.23(0.95)^x$; about 12 minutes

22. The y-intercept is when $x = 0$ i.e. $(0, a)$.

23. If $a > 0$ and $b > 1$, the function represents exponential growth; if $a > 0$ and $0 < b < 1$, the function represents exponential decay.

24. The graphs are a reflection of each other over the line $y = x$. The domain of one is the range of the other, and vice-versa. They both share a common y-intercept, $(0, 0)$.

25. The annually compounded interest formula is $A = P(1 + r)^t$. The continuously compounded interest formula is $A = Pe^{rt}$.

PowerAlgebra.com

MathXL for School

Prepare students for the Mid-Chapter Quiz and Chapter Test with online practice and review.

490 Chapter 7

Focus Question Why is the Change of Base Formula useful?

Hint

You can evaluate any logarithm using your calculator.

The  key on a calculator finds $\log_{10}$ of a number. To evaluate a logarithm with any base, use the **Change of Base Formula**.

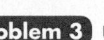

Property   Change of Base Formula

For any positive numbers m, b, and c, with $b \neq 1$ and $c \neq 1$,

$$\log_b m = \frac{\log_c m}{\log_c b}.$$

Here's Why It Works

Multiply $\log_b m$ by $\dfrac{\log_c b}{\log_c b} = 1$.

$\log_b m = \dfrac{(\log_b m)(\log_c b)}{(\log_c b)}$

Use the Power Property of Logarithms.

$= \dfrac{\log_c b^{\log_b m}}{\log_c b}$

Use $b^{\log_b m} = m$.

$= \dfrac{\log_c m}{\log_c b}$

 Problem 3   Using the Change of Base Formula

What is the value of each expression?

Think

What common base has powers that equal 27 and 81?
3 is a common base.
$3^3 = 27$ and $3^4 = 81$.

Ⓐ $\log_{81} 27$

Method 1 Use a common base.

Use the Change of Base Formula. $\log_{81} 27 = \dfrac{\log_3 27}{\log_3 81}$

Simplify. $= \dfrac{3}{4}$

Method 2 Use a calculator and base 10.

Use the Change of Base Formula. $\log_{81} 27 = \dfrac{\log 27}{\log 81}$

Use a calculator. $= 0.75$

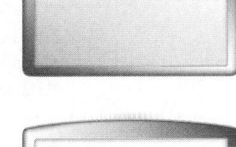

Ⓑ $\log_5 36$

Write the original expression. $\log_5 36$

> There is no common base for 36 and 5.

Think

What would be a reasonable result?
$5^2 = 25$ and $5^3 = 125$, so $\log_5 36$ should be between 2 and 3.

Use the Change of Base Formula and base 10. $= \dfrac{\log 36}{\log 5}$

Use a calculator to evaluate. ≈ 2.23

✓ **Got It?** **3.** Use the Change of Base Formula. What is the value of each expression?

a. $\log_8 32$ **b.** $\log_4 18$

 PowerAlgebra.com | Lesson 7-4   Properties of Logarithms | **493**

Take Note

Q How is this formula useful when you calculate a log with a calculator that only has keys for the common and natural logarithms? **[You can convert a logarithm with any base to a quotient of common or natural logarithms.]**

Here's Why It Works

The Change of Base Formula can also be derived by setting $\log_b m = x$.

$m = b^x$ Definition of Logarithm

$\log_c m = \log_c b^x$ Take logarithm base c of both sides.

$\log_c m = x\log_c b$ Power Property of Logarithms

$x = \dfrac{\log_c m}{\log_c b}$ Solve for x.

$\log_b m = \dfrac{\log_c m}{\log_c b}$ Substitute $\log_b m$ for x.

Problem 3

Q Is 0.75 a reasonable answer for 3A? Explain. **[Yes; because $81^0 = 1$ and $81^1 = 81$, the answer should be between 0 and 1.]**

Q In 3B, how do you know that 36 and 5 have no common base? **[They have no common factor other than 1.]**

Got It?

Q You can check 3a by rewriting the problem as an exponential equation and writing each side with a common base. What base would you choose? Explain. Why did you choose that base? **[Answers may vary. Sample: base 2 because both 32 and 8 are powers of 2]**

Additional Problems

1. What is each expression written as a single logarithm? If possible, simplify the single logarithm.

a. $\log_3 x - 2 \log_3 7$

b. $\log_8 48 + \log_8 \frac{4}{3}$

ANSWER

a. $\log_3 \frac{x}{49}$ **b.** 2

2. What is each logarithm expanded? Simplify your answer, if possible.

a. $\log_5 \frac{125}{xy}$

b. $\log x^2 y^2 z^{-1}$

ANSWER

a. $3 - \log_5 x - \log_5 y$

b. $2 \log x + 2 \log y - \log z$

3. What is the value of each expression?

a. $\log_9 111$ **b.** $\log_{216} 36$

ANSWER

a. about 2.14   **b.** $\frac{2}{3}$

4. The speed s (in mi/h) of the wind near the center of a tornado is related to the distance d (in miles) the tornado travels by $s = 93 \log d + 65$. What was the difference in speed between a tornado that traveled 16 mi and one that traveled 8 mi?

ANSWER about 28 mi/h

Answers

Got It? (continued)

3. a. $\frac{5}{3}$

   b. ≈ 2.085

Problem 4

> **Q** What does the 8.8 difference mean in terms of $[H^+]$ concentration? Why? **[Answers may vary. Sample: The 8.8 pH difference is on a logarithmic scale with base 10, so the concentration of $[H^+]$ in vinegar is $10^{8.8}$ (or 630,000,000) times that of the concentration of $[H^+]$ in ammonia.]**
>
> **Q** The pH level of pure water is 7. What is the concentration of $[H^+]$ in pure water? Explain your method. **[Answers may vary. Sample: Write the formula: $pH = -\log [H^+]$; Substitute: $7 = -\log [H^+]$; Solve for $[H^+]$: $10^{-7} = [H^+]$.]**

Got It?

Because the pH scale is a negative logarithmic scale, a smaller concentration of $[H^+]$ has a greater pH value than a larger concentration.

Problem 4 Using a Logarithmic Scale

Chemistry The pH of a substance equals $-\log [H^+]$, where $[H^+]$ is the concentration of hydrogen ions. $[H^+_a]$ for household ammonia is 10^{-11}. $[H^+_v]$ for vinegar is 6.3×10^{-3}. What is the difference of the pH levels of ammonia and vinegar?

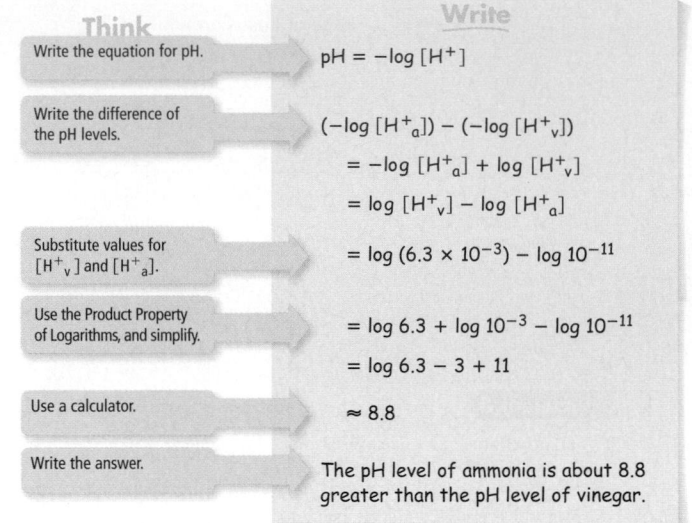

Think

	Write
Write the equation for pH.	$pH = -\log [H^+]$
Write the difference of the pH levels.	$(-\log [H^+_a]) - (-\log [H^+_v])$ $= -\log [H^+_a] + \log [H^+_v]$ $= \log [H^+_v] - \log [H^+_a]$
Substitute values for $[H^+_v]$ and $[H^+_a]$.	$= \log (6.3 \times 10^{-3}) - \log 10^{-11}$
Use the Product Property of Logarithms, and simplify.	$= \log 6.3 + \log 10^{-3} - \log 10^{-11}$ $= \log 6.3 - 3 + 11$
Use a calculator.	≈ 8.8
Write the answer.	The pH level of ammonia is about 8.8 greater than the pH level of vinegar.

Hint

$\log 10^x = x$ for all values of x because a common logarithm has a base of 10.

✓ **Got It?** **4. Reasoning** Suppose the hydrogen ion concentration for Substance A is twice that for Substance B. Which substance has the greater pH level? What is the greater pH level minus the lesser pH level? Explain.

Focus Question How are the properties of logarithms similar to the properties of exponents?

Answer The properties of logarithms are derived from the properties of exponents. Use the Product, Quotient, and Power Properties to simplify or expand logarithms.

Focus Question Why is the Change of Base Formula useful?

Answer The Change of Base Formula allows you to write a logarithmic expression in one base as an equivalent logarithmic expression in another base (usually base 10). Use the Change of Base Formula to evaluate logarithmic expressions with a calculator.

Answers

Got It? (continued)

4. Substance B; $\log 2$; $-\log[H^+_B] + \log[H^+_B]$
$= \log 2$

Lesson Check

Do you know HOW?

Write each expression as a single logarithm.

1. $\log_4 2 + \log_4 8$ **2.** $\log_6 24 - \log_6 4$

Expand each logarithm.

3. $\log_3 \frac{x}{y}$ **4.** $\log m^2 n^5$ **5.** $\log_2 \sqrt{x}$

Do you UNDERSTAND?

6. State which property or properties need to be used to write each expression as a single logarithm.
  a. $\log_4 5 + \log_4 5$ **b.** $\log_5 4 - \log_5 6$

7. Reasoning If $\log x = 5$, what is the value of $\frac{1}{x}$?

8. Open-Ended Write $\log 150$ as a sum or difference of two logarithms. Simplify if possible.

Practice and Problem-Solving Exercises

A Practice

Write each expression as a single logarithm.   ◀ See Problem 1.

Guided Practice

9. $\log_2 9 - \log_2 3$

To start, use the Quotient Property of Logarithms.

$\log_2 9 - \log_2 3 = \log_2 \frac{9}{3}$

10. $\log 7 + \log 2$ **11.** $5 \log 3 + \log 4$ **12.** $\log 8 - 2 \log 6 + \log 3$

Expand each logarithm.   ◀ See Problem 2.

Guided Practice

13. $\log x^3 y^5$

To start, use the Product Property of Logarithms.

$\log x^3 y^5 = \log x^3 + \log y^5$

14. $\log_3 (2x)^2$ **15.** $\log_3 7(2x - 3)^2$ **16.** $\log 10 m^4 n^{-2}$

Use the Change of Base Formula to evaluate each expression.   ◀ See Problem 3.

17. $\log_2 9$ **18.** $\log_{12} 20$ **19.** $\log_7 30$

20. $\log_5 10$ **21.** $\log_3 54$ **22.** $\log_3 33$

23. Science The concentration of hydrogen ions in household dish detergent is 10^{-12}. What is the pH level of household dish detergent?   ◀ See Problem 4.

B Apply

24. Think About a Plan The loudness in decibels (dB) of a sound is defined as $10 \log \frac{I}{I_0}$, where I is the intensity of the sound in watts per square meter (W/m^2). I_0, the intensity of a barely audible sound, is equal to $10^{-12} \, W/m^2$. Town regulations require the loudness of construction work not to exceed 100 dB. Suppose a construction team is blasting rock for a roadway. One explosion has an intensity of $1.65 \times 10^{-2} \, W/m^2$. Is this explosion in violation of town regulations?
  • Which physical value do you need to calculate to answer the question?
  • What values should you use for I and I_0?

Lesson Check

1. $\log_4 16$

2. $\log_6 6$

3. $\log_3 x - \log_3 y$

4. $2 \log m + 5 \log n$

5. $\frac{1}{2} \log_2 x$

6. a. Product Prop. and Power Prop.
  b. Quotient Prop.

7. 0.00001

8. Answers may vary. Sample:
  $\log 150 = \log 25 + \log 6$

Practice and Problem-Solving Exercises

9. $\log_2 3$

10. $\log 14$

11. $\log 972$

12. $\log \frac{2}{3}$

13. $3 \log x + 5 \log y$

14. $2 \log_3 2 + 2 \log_3 x$

15. $\log_3 7 + 2 \log_3 (2x - 3)$

16. $1 + 4 \log m - 2 \log n$

17. ≈ 3.17

18. ≈ 1.21

19. ≈ 1.75

20. ≈ 1.43

21. ≈ 3.63

22. ≈ 3.18

23. 12

24. Yes, because the loudness of the sound is 102 dB.

---

3 Lesson Check

Do you know HOW?

• If students do not know how to proceed with Exercise 5, then remind them that $\sqrt{x} = x^{\frac{1}{2}}$.

Do you UNDERSTAND?

• In Exercise 8, be sure that students separate out factors of 150 and not addends.

Close

Q How can you derive the Power Property of Logarithms using the Power Property of Exponents? [**Sample: Let** $x = \log_b m$;
$m = b^x$ (Definition of Logarithm);
$m^n = (b^x)^n$ (Raise each side to the n power.);
$m^n = b^{nx}$ (Power Property of Exponents);
$\log_b m^n = nx$ (Definition of Logarithm);
$\log_b m^n = n \log_b m$ (Substitute for x.)]

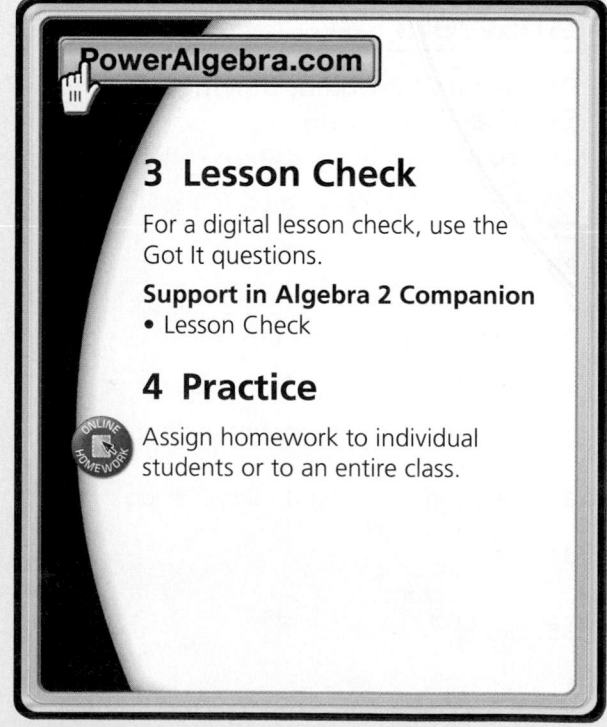

PowerAlgebra.com

3 Lesson Check

For a digital lesson check, use the Got It questions.

Support in Algebra 2 Companion
• Lesson Check

4 Practice

Assign homework to individual students or to an entire class.

4 Practice

ASSIGNMENT GUIDE

Basic: 9–19, 23–25, 36

Average: 9–28, 30–33, 36–42, 46, 48, 49

Standardized Test Prep: 50–53

Mixed Review: 54–65

Reasoning exercises have blue headings.

Applications exercises have red headings.

EXERCISE 25: Use the Think About a Plan worksheet in the **Student Companion** (also available in the Teaching Resources in print and online) to further support students' development in becoming independent learners.

HOMEWORK QUICK CHECK

To check students' understanding of key skills and concepts, go over Exercises 10, 14, 24, 25, and 36.

---

25. Construction The foreman of a construction team puts up a sound barrier that reduces the intensity of their noise by 50%. By how many decibels is the noise reduced? Use the formula $L = 10 \log \frac{I}{I_0}$ to measure loudness. (*Hint:* Find the difference between the expression for loudness for intensity I and the expression for loudness for intensity $0.5I$.)

Use the properties of logarithms to evaluate each expression.

26. $\log_2 4 - \log_2 16$

27. $\log_3 27 - 2\log_3 3$

28. $\log_6 12 + \log_6 3$

29. $\log_4 48 - \frac{1}{2}\log_4 9$

Determine if each statment is *true* or *false*. Justify your answer.

30. $\log_2 4 + \log_2 8 = 5$

31. $\log_3 \frac{3}{2} = \frac{1}{2}\log_3 3$

32. $\log(x - 2) = \frac{\log x}{\log 2}$

33. $(\log x)^2 = \log x^2$

Write each logarithmic expression as a single logarithm.

34. $\frac{1}{2}(\log_x 4 + \log_x y) - 3\log_x z$

35. $x\log_4 m + \frac{1}{y}\log_4 n - \log_4 p$

36. **Error Analysis** Explain why the expansion at the right of $\log_4 \sqrt{\frac{t}{s}}$ is incorrect. Then do the expansion correctly.

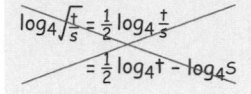

37. **Reasoning** Can you expand $\log_3 (2x + 1)$? Explain.

38. **Writing** Explain why $\log(5 \cdot 2) \neq \log 5 \cdot \log 2$.

Expand each logarithm.

39. $\log \sqrt{\frac{2x}{y}}$

40. $\log \frac{s\sqrt{7}}{t^2}$

41. $\log \left(\frac{2\sqrt{x}}{5}\right)^3$

42. $\log \frac{m^3}{n^4 p^{-2}}$

43. $\log 4\sqrt{\frac{4r}{s^2}}$

44. $\log_4 \frac{\sqrt{x^5 y^7}}{zw^4}$

Write each logarithm as the quotient of two common logarithms. Do not simplify the quotient.

45. $\log_7 2$

46. $\log_5 140$

47. $\log_4 3x$

Astronomy The apparent brightness of stars is measured on a logarithmic scale called magnitude, in which lower numbers mean brighter stars. The relationship between the ratio of apparent brightness of two objects and the difference in their magnitudes is given by the formula $m_2 - m_1 = -2.5 \log\frac{b_2}{b_1}$, where m is the magnitude and b is the apparent brightness.

48. How many times brighter is a magnitude 1.0 star than a magnitude 2.0 star?

49. The star Rigel has a magnitude of 0.12. How many times brighter is Capella than Rigel?

Capella ◯
m = 0.1

Answers

Practice and Problem-Solving Exercises (continued)

25. about 3 dB

26. −2

27. 1

28. 2

29. 2

30. true; $\log_2 4 = 2$ and $\log_2 8 = 3$; $2 + 3 = 5$

31. false; $\frac{1}{2}\log_3 3 = \log_3 3^{\frac{1}{2}}$, not $\log_3 \frac{3}{2}$

32. False; this is not an example of the Quotient Prop: $\log(x - 2) \neq \log x - \log 2$

33. false; $(\log x)^2 = (\log x) \cdot (\log x) \neq \log x^2$

34. $\log_x \frac{2\sqrt{y}}{z^3}$

35. $\log_4 \frac{m^x n^{\frac{1}{y}}}{p}$

36. The coefficient $\frac{1}{2}$ is missing in $\log_4 s$;

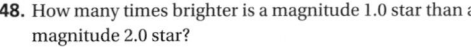

$$\log_4 \sqrt{\frac{t}{s}} = \frac{1}{2}\log_4 \frac{t}{s}$$

$$= \frac{1}{2}(\log_4 t - \log_4 s)$$

$$= \frac{1}{2}\log_4 t - \frac{1}{2}\log_4 s$$

37. No; the expression $(2x + 1)$ is a sum, so it is not covered by the Product, Quotient, or Power Props.

38. The log of a product is equal to the sum of the logs. $\log(MN) = \log M + \log N$.

39. $\frac{1}{2}\log 2 + \frac{1}{2}\log x - \frac{1}{2}\log y$

40. $\log s + \frac{1}{2}\log 7 - 2\log t$

41. $3\log 2 + \frac{3}{2}\log x - 3\log 5$

42. $3\log m - 4\log n + 2\log p$

43. $3\log 2 + \frac{1}{2}\log r - \log s$

44. $\frac{5}{2}\log_4 x + \frac{7}{2}\log_4 y - \log_4 z - 4\log_4 w$

45. $\frac{\log 2}{\log 7}$

46. $\frac{\log 140}{\log 5}$

47. $\frac{\log 3x}{\log 4}$

48. A 1.0 magnitude star is about 2.5 times brighter than a 2.0 magnitude star.

49. Capella is about 1.02 times brighter than Rigel.

Standardized Test Prep

SAT/ACT

50. Which expression is NOT equivalent to $\sqrt[6]{16r^2}$?

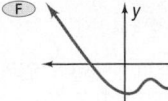

Ⓐ $(16r^2)^{\frac{1}{6}}$ Ⓑ $4r^{\frac{1}{3}}$ Ⓒ $(4r)^{\frac{1}{3}}$ Ⓓ $\sqrt[3]{4r}$

51. Assume that there are no more turning points beyond those shown. Which graph CANNOT be the graph of a fourth degree polynomial?

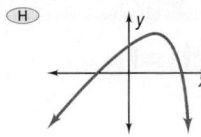

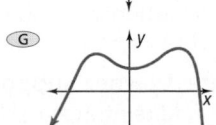
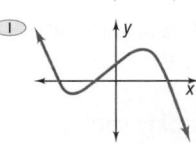

52. A florist is arranging a bouquet of daisies and tulips. He wants twice as many daisies as tulips in the bouquet. If the bouquet contains 24 flowers, how many daisies are in the bouquet?

Ⓐ 8 daisies   Ⓑ 12 daisies   Ⓒ 16 daisies   Ⓓ 24 daisies

Short Response

53. Use the properties of logarithms to write log 18 in four different ways. Name each property you use.

Mixed Review

Write each equation in logarithmic form.   ◆ See Lesson 7-3.

54. $49 = 7^2$ **55.** $\frac{1}{4} = 8^{-\frac{2}{3}}$ **56.** $5^{-3} = \frac{1}{125}$

Solve. Check for extraneous solutions.   ◆ See Lesson 6-5.

57. $\sqrt[3]{y^4} = 16$ **58.** $\sqrt[3]{7x} - 4 = 0$ **59.** $2\sqrt{w-1} = \sqrt{w+2}$

Write a polynomial function with rational coefficients and the given roots.   ◆ See Lesson 5-5.

60. $\sqrt{3}, -5$ **61.** $-i, 4i$ **62.** $-\sqrt{7}, 1 + 2i$

Get Ready!   To prepare for Lesson 7-5, do Exercises 63–65.

Evaluate each logarithm.   ◆ See Lesson 7-3.

63. $\log_{12} 144$ **64.** $\log_4 64$ **65.** $\log_{64} 4$

Standardized Test Prep

50. B

51. I

52. C

53. [2] $\log 18 = \log \frac{36}{2} = \log 36 - \log 2$; Quotient Prop.

$= \log 2 \cdot 9 = \log 2 + \log 9$; Product Prop.

$= \log 324^{\frac{1}{2}} = \frac{1}{2} \log 324$; Power Prop.

$= \log 2 \cdot 3^2 = \log 2 + 2 \log 3$; Product and Power Prop.

[1] log 18 is written in only 2 ways with the properties named OR properties are not named

Mixed Review

54. $\log_7 49 = 2$

55. $\log_8 \frac{1}{4} = -\frac{2}{3}$

56. $-3 = \log_5 \frac{1}{125}$

57. ± 8

58. $\frac{64}{7}$

59. 2

60. $f(x) = x^3 + 5x^2 - 3x - 15$

61. $f(x) = x^4 + 17x^2 + 16$

62. $f(x) = x^4 - 2x^3 - 2x^2 + 14x - 35$

63. 2

64. 3

65. $\frac{1}{3}$

Additional Instructional Support

Algebra 2 Companion
Students can use the **Algebra 2 Companion** worktext (4 pages) as you teach the lesson. Use the Companion to support

- New Vocabulary
- Key Concepts
- Got It for each Problem
- Lesson Check

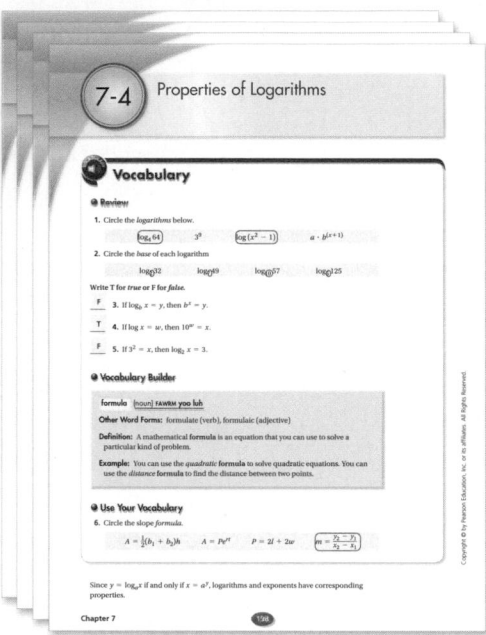

ELL Support
Connect to Prior Knowledge Write the expressions "$m \cdot n$," "$m \times n$," and "mn." Have students work in pairs to brainstorm any words associated with the expression. Expected responses include times, multiply, factor, product, of, variable, etc.

After brainstorming has slowed down, have the group list responses as a whole. If a response does not apply (e.g., addend), ask the pair to describe their reasoning. Write "product" above the expressions.

Ask for a volunteer to say the Product Property of Exponents. (Students may use their textbooks.) Have students write the property and circle the multiplication, mn. Now ask for a volunteer to say the Product Property of Logarithms. Have students write the property and circle the multiplication.

Repeat this exercise for the Quotient and Power Properties of Exponents and Logarithms.

5 Assess & Remediate

Lesson Quiz
1. What is $\log_5 4 + \log_5 3$ written as a single logarithm? If possible, simplify the single logarithm.
2. What is $\log \frac{10}{x^2}$ expanded? Simplify your answer, if possible.
3. What is the value of $\log_7 25$? Use the Change of Base Formula.
4. **Do you UNDERSTAND?** The magnitude of a city can be defined as the common logarithm of the population, p. In 2007, Tallahassee had a population of about 1.7×10^5 people. The town of Bascom, FL, had a population of about 1.1×10^2 people. What is the difference in magnitude between Tallahassee and Bascom?

ANSWERS TO LESSON QUIZ
1. $\log_5 12$
2. $1 - 2 \log x$
3. about 1.65
4. about 3.19

PRESCRIPTION FOR REMEDIATION
Use the student work on the Lesson Quiz to prescribe a differentiated review assignment:

Points	Differentiated Remediation
0–1	Intervention
2–3	On-level
4	Extension

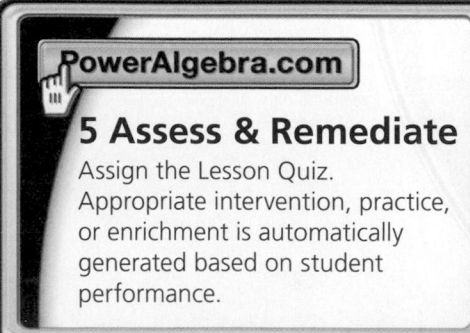

PowerAlgebra.com

5 Assess & Remediate
Assign the Lesson Quiz. Appropriate intervention, practice, or enrichment is automatically generated based on student performance.

Intervention
- **Reteaching** (2 pages) Provides reteaching and practice exercises for the key lesson concepts. Use with struggling students or absent students.
- **English Language Learner Support** Helps students develop and reinforce mathematical vocabulary and key concepts.

All-in-One Resources/Online
Reteaching

7-4 Reteaching
Properties of Logarithms

You can write a logarithmic expression containing more than one logarithm as a single logarithm as long as the bases are equal. You can write a logarithm that contains a number raised to a power as a logarithm with the power as a coefficient. To understand the following properties, remember that logarithms are powers.

Name	Formula	Why?
Product Property	$\log_b mn = \log_b m + \log_b n$	When you multiply two powers, you add the exponents. Example: $2^6 \cdot 2^2 = 2^{(6+2)} = 2^8$
Quotient Property	$\log_b \frac{m}{n} = \log_b m + \log_b n$	When you divide two powers, you subtract the exponents. Example: $\frac{2^6}{2^2} = 2^{(6-2)} = 2^4$
Power Property	$\log_b m^n = n\log_b m$	When you raise a power to a power, you multiply the exponents. Example: $(2^6)^2 = 2^{(6 \cdot 2)} = 2^{12}$

Problem
What is $2\log_2 6 - \log_2 9 + \frac{1}{3}\log_2 27$ written as a single logarithm?

$2\log_2 6 - \log_2 9 + \frac{1}{3}\log_2 27 = \log_2 6^2 - \log_2 9 + \log_2 27^{\frac{1}{3}}$ Use the Power Property twice.

$= \log_2 36 - \log_2 9 + \log_2 3$ $6^2 = 36$, $27^{\frac{1}{3}} = \sqrt[3]{27} = 3$

$= (\log_2 36 - \log_2 9) + \log_2 3$ Group two of the logarithms. Use order of operations.

$= \log_2 \frac{36}{9} + \log_2 3$ Quotient Property

$= \log_2 \left(\frac{36}{9} \cdot 3\right)$ Product Property

$= \log_2 12$ Simplify.

As a single logarithm, $2\log_2 6 - \log_2 9 + \frac{1}{3}\log_2 27 = \log_2 12$.

All-in-One Resources/Online
English Language Learner Support

7-4 ELL Support
Properties of Logarithms

Product Property	Quotient Property	Power Property
$\log_b mn = \log_b m + \log_b n$	$\log_b \frac{m}{n} = \log_b m - \log_b n$	$\log_b m^n = n\log_b m$
Example:	**Example:**	**Example:**
$\log_4(4 \cdot 3) = \log_4 4 + \log_4 3$	$\log_3 \frac{12}{3} = \log_3 12 - \log_3 3$	$\log_5 7^3 = 3\log_5 7$

Identify the property that is demonstrated by each equation.

1. $\log_4 \frac{3}{7} = \log_4 7 - \log_4 3$ quotient property
2. $\log_3 6^5 = 5\log_3 6$ power property
3. $\log_7 \frac{15}{4} = \log_7 15 - \log_7 4$ quotient property
4. $\log_6(6 \cdot 4) = \log_6 6 + \log_6 4$ product property
5. $\log_4 12^5 = 5\log_4 12$ power property

Identify the values of the symbols in the equations below.

6. $\log_4 \left(8 \cdot \square\right) = \log_4 \diamond + \log_4 6$ $\square = $ _6_ $\diamond = $ _8_
7. $\log_3 \frac{15}{\square} = \log_3 \diamond - \log_3 2$ $\square = $ _2_ $\diamond = $ _15_
8. $\log_6 \square = \diamond\log_6 6$ $\square = $ _6_ $\diamond = $ _3_

Write each expression as a single logarithm.

9. $\log_4 6 - \log_4 2 = $ _$\log_4 \frac{6}{2}$_
10. $\log_6 5 + \log_6 3 = $ _$\log_6 (5 \cdot 3)$_

Differentiated Remediation *continued*

On-Level

- **Practice** (2 pages) Provides extra practice for each lesson. For more challenging practice exercises, use the Form G Practice pages found in the All-in-One Teaching Resources and online.

- **Think About a Plan** Helps students develop specific problem-solving skills and strategies by providing scaffolded guiding questions.

- **Standardized Test Prep** Focuses on all major exercises, all major question types, and helps students prepare for the high-stakes assessments.

Extension

- **Enrichment** Provides students with interesting problems and activities that extend the concepts of the lesson.

- **Activities, Games, and Puzzles** Worksheets that can be used for concepts development, enrichment, and for fun!

Student Companion/All-in-One Resources/Online
Practice page 1

7-4 Practice   Form K
Properties of Logarithms

Properties of Logarithms		
Product Property	**Quotient Property**	**Power Property**
$\log_b mn = \log_b m + \log_b n$	$\log_b \frac{m}{n} = \log_b m - \log_b n$	$\log_b m^n = n \log_b m$

Write each expression as a single logarithm.

1. $\log_3 9 + \log_3 24$ $\log_3 216$
2. $\log_4 16^3$ $3 \log_4 16$
3. $\log_2 7 - \log_2 9$ $\log_2 \frac{7}{9}$

4. $\log_3 8^5$ $5 \log_3 8$
5. $\log_4 x - \log_4 y$ $\log_4 \frac{x}{y}$
6. $\log 5 + \log 7$ $\log 35$

Expand each logarithm. Simplify if possible.

7. $\log_3 27x$ $\log_3 27 + \log_3 x$
8. $\log \frac{3}{x}$ $\log 3 - \log 7$
9. $\log_4 y^2 z^3$ $2 \log_4 y + 3 \log_4 z$

10. $\log_3 \frac{3^2}{x}$ $2 \log_3 3 - \log_3 x$
11. $\log_3 15xy$ $1 + \log_3 5 + \log_3 x + \log_3 y$
12. $\log 8xz^4$ $3 \log 2 + \log x + 4 \log z$

13. **Open-Ended** Write three different logarithms. You should be able to expand each logarithm by one of the properties of logarithms. *Answers may vary.*
Sample: $\log_5 6x$, $\log \frac{3}{8}$, $\log_7 2$

Student Companion/All-in-One Resources/Online
Think About a Plan

7-4 Think About a Plan
Properties of Logarithms

Construction The foreman of a construction team puts up a sound barrier that reduces the intensity of the noise by 50%. By how many decibels is the noise reduced? Use the formula $L = 10 \log \frac{I}{I_0}$ to measure loudness. (*Hint:* Find the difference between the expression for loudness for intensity I and the expression for loudness for intensity $0.5I$.)

Know

1. You can represent the intensity of the original noise by I .

2. You can represent the intensity of the reduced noise by $0.5I$.

3. The formula for loudness is $L = 10 \log \frac{I}{I_0}$.

Need

4. To solve the problem I need to find:
the difference between the expression for the original noise intensity and the
expression for the reduced noise intensity

Plan

5. What is an expression for the loudness of the original construction noise? $10 \log \frac{I}{I_0}$

6. What is an expression for the loudness of the reduced construction noise? $10 \log \frac{0.5I}{I_0}$

7. Use your expressions to find the difference between the loudness of the original construction noise and the loudness of the reduced construction noise.
$10 \log \frac{I}{I_0} - 10 \log \frac{0.5I}{I_0} = 10 \left(\log \frac{I}{I_0} - \log \frac{0.5I}{I_0} \right) = 10 \log \frac{I/I_0}{0.5I/I_0} = 10 \log \frac{I}{0.5I} = 10 \log 2 \approx 3$

8. The sound barrier reduced the loudness by 3 dB .

Student Companion/All-in-One Resources/Online
Practice page 2

7-4 Practice (continued)   Form K
Properties of Logarithms

Change of Base Formula

For any positive numbers m, b, and c, with $b \neq 1$ and $c \neq 1$,
$$\log_b m = \frac{\log_c m}{\log_c b}.$$

Use the Change of Base Formula to evaluate each expression.

14. $\log_{32} 4$
$\frac{\log_2 4}{\log_2 32} = \frac{2}{5} = 0.4$
15. $\log_3 27$ 1.5
16. $\log_4 12$ about 1.792

17. **Error Analysis** Your friend used the Change of Base Formula to evaluate the expression $\log_4 8$. Her answer was $\frac{4}{3}$. What error did your friend make? What is the correct answer?
Sample answer: Your friend confused the numerator and the denominator in the
formula. The correct answer is $\frac{3}{2}$.

Use the following formula to solve Exercise 18.

Formula for Loudness of a Sound (decibels)
$$L = 10 \log \frac{I}{I_0}$$
• I is the intensity of a sound in watts per square meter (W/m²).
• I_0 is the intensity of a sound that can barely be heard.
• $I_0 = 10^{-12}$ W/m²

18. Your classmate went to a rock concert. At the loudest point during the concert, the sound had an intensity of 2.35×10^{-3} W/m². What was the loudness of this sound in decibels?
about 93.71 decibels

Student Companion/All-in-One Resources/Online
Standardized Test Prep

7-4 Standardized Test Prep
Properties of Logarithms

Multiple Choice

For Exercises 1–4, choose the correct letter.

1. Which statement correctly demonstrates the Power Property of Logarithms? D
Ⓐ $\frac{1}{2} \log_5 9 = \log_5 81$
Ⓒ $\frac{1}{2} \log_5 9 = \log_5 18$
Ⓑ $\frac{1}{2} \log_5 9 = \log_5 \frac{9}{2}$
Ⓓ $\frac{1}{2} \log_5 9 = \log_5 3$

2. Which expression is the correct expansion of $\log_4 (3x)^2$? G
Ⓕ $\frac{1}{2} (\log_4 3 - \log_4 x)$
Ⓗ $2 (\log_4 3 - \log_4 x)$
Ⓖ $2 (\log_4 3 + \log_4 x)$
Ⓘ $2 \log_4 3 + \log_4 x$

3. Which expression is equivalent to $\log_7 16$? C
Ⓐ $\frac{\log 16}{\log 10}$
Ⓒ $\frac{\log 16}{\log 7}$
Ⓑ $\frac{\log_{16} 10}{\log_7 10}$
Ⓓ $\frac{\log 7}{\log 16}$

4. Which statement correctly expresses $4 \log_3 x + 7 \log_3 y$ as a single logarithm? F
Ⓕ $\log_3 x^4 y^7$
Ⓗ $\log_3 (x^4 + y^7)$
Ⓖ $\log_3 (4x + 7y)$
Ⓘ $\log_3 (4x - 7y)$

Short Response

5. The pH of a substance equals $-\log[H^+]$, where $[H^+]$ is the concentration of hydrogen ions. The concentration of hydrogen ions in pure water is 10^{-7} and the concentration of hydrogen ions in a sodium hydroxide solution is 10^{-14}.
a. Without using a calculator, what is the difference of the pH levels of pure water and the sodium hydroxide solution?
b. Explain in words or show work for how you determined the difference of the pH levels.
[2] a. −7
b. $pH = -\log[H^+]$, $\Delta pH = -\log[H^+_{sw}] - (-\log[H^+_{w}]) = \log[H^+_{w}] - \log[H^+_{sw}]$;
$\log[10^{-14}] - \log[10^{-7}] = -14 \log 10 - (-7 \log 10) = -14(1) + 7(1) = -7$
The pH of pure water is 7 less than the pH of the sodium hydroxide solution.
[1] incorrect equation form OR incorrect explanation
[0] incorrect answers and no work shown OR no answers given

All-in-One Resources/Online
Enrichment

7-4 Enrichment
Properties of Logarithms

Scotsman John Napier and Joost Bürgi from Switzerland are credited for being the first to introduce the concept of a logarithm. While the logarithm they described is quite different than the one we use today, both men used logarithms to simplify mathematical calculations. Arithmetic operations of addition and subtraction are relatively easy to compute, but without the modern calculator, multiplication and division of powers and roots can be time-consuming. Before calculators, logarithms were used to simplify an expression to an addition or subtraction problem. The logarithm values could be found in extensive tables and the calculations were more easily computed.

1. Consider the relation $y = \frac{x^3 \sqrt{x^3}}{(3x+2)^5}$ as an example. Without using a calculator, determine the value for y when $x = 16$. $\frac{512}{312,500,000} = \frac{16}{9,765,625}$

2. While the calculations in Exercise 1 are not impossible, they are certainly time-consuming and, with roots involved, are inaccurate. If you take the log base 10 of both sides, the equation becomes $y = \log \frac{x^3 \sqrt{x^3}}{(3x+2)^5}$. Rewrite the right side of the equation using the log properties.
$\log y = \frac{9}{2} \log x + \frac{3}{2} \log x - 5 \log (3x + 2)$

To evaluate a logarithmic equation like the one above, the values were found in a table and the arithmetic calculations were completed. To get a sense of how this was done, assume you have a table of values for logarithms using base a. In this table you find that $\log_a 2 = 0.301$, $\log_a 3 = 0.477$, and $\log_a 5 = 0.699$.

3. Use logarithm properties to rewrite $\log_a 30$ using the three log values given. Then evaluate your expression. $\log_a 30 = \log_a (2)(3)(5) = \log_a 2 + \log_a 3 + \log_a 5; 1.477$

4. Use logarithm properties to rewrite $\log_a 50$ and evaluate your expression.
$\log_a 50 = \log_a (2)(5^2) = \log_a 2 + 2 \log_a 5; 1.699$

5. Use logarithm properties to rewrite $\log_a 12.5$ and evaluate your expression.
$\log_a (12.5) = \log_a \left(\frac{5^2}{2} \right) = 2 \log_a 5 - \log_a 2; 1.097$

Online Teacher Resource Center
Activities, Games, and Puzzles

7-4 Puzzle: Letter Scramble
Properties of Logarithms

Next to each expression in the left column, write the letter of the expression in the right column whose value is equivalent to it. Some letters will be used more than once. Unscramble the letters to find the four-word phrase that answers the question at the bottom of the page.

1. $\log_2 75$ N   A $\log_2 a + 5 \log_2 b$
2. $\log_2 36$ I   B $4 \log_2 a - 3 \log_2 b$
3. $\log_2 (75 \times 2^a)$ − a N   C 1
4. $\log_2 ab^5$ A   D $\log_5 (5a) - 9$
5. $\log_2 (36 \times 2^5)$ − 5   I   E $5 \log_2 2 + \log_2 2^{20}$
6. $\log_2 108$ P   F $\log_2 (3b)$
7. $\log_2 2^8$ L   G $\log_2 (3a) + 9$
8. $\log_2 (a \times 2^8)$ O   I $2(\log_2 2 + \log_2 3)$
9. $\log_2 (3a \times 2^9)$ G   K 20
10. $\log_2 2^{16}$ − 8   L   L 8
11. $\log_2 \left(\frac{6^2}{2a} \right) + \log_2 (2a)$ I   M $3a$
12. $\log_2 (a^4 b^5)$ S   N $2 \log_2 5 + \log_2 3$
13. $(\log_3 75)(\log_2 (2^{a+1}) - a)$ N   O $\log_5 a + 8$
14. $(\log_2 2)(\log_2 ab^5)$ A   P $3 \log_2 3 + \log_2 4$
15. $\log_2 \left(\frac{a^4}{b^3} \right)$ B   R $a + b$
16. $\log_2 16$ − 5   C   S $4 \log_2 a + 3 \log_2 b$

Where do simple exponents live?   I N   P L A I N   L O G   C A B I N S

1 Interactive Learning

Solve It!

PURPOSE To use equations with variable exponents to make a decision

PROCESS Students may
- estimate the total amount of money for either prize and draw a conclusion when the amount of one prize exceeds the other.
- calculate the total amount of money received in prize B by adding exponential terms.

FACILITATE

Q How can you find an expression to represent each day for Prize B? **[List the amounts for each day to determine a pattern. 1, 2, 4, 8, 16…; the pattern is exponential since numbers are doubled, so Prize B = 2^{n-1} cents, where n is the number of days.]**

Q How much money would you receive from prize B on day 10? 20? **[$5.12; $5,242.88]**

ANSWER See Solve It in Answers on next page.

CONNECT THE MATH Students use their knowledge of exponential growth to make a decision in the Solve It. In this lesson, students will write and solve exponential equations.

2 Guided Instruction

Problem 1

Q How can you check your answer? **[If $x = \frac{1}{4}$, then $16^{\frac{3}{4}} = 8$. So $\sqrt[4]{16} = 2$ and $2^3 = 8$]**

Got It?

Q What common base do you recognize? **[Both 27 and 81 are powers of 3.]**

Objective To solve exponential equations

Lesson Vocabulary
- exponential equation

Any equation that contains an expression of the form b^{cx}, such as $a = b^{cx}$, where the exponent includes a variable is an **exponential equation**.

Focus Question How can you solve exponential equations?

Problem 1 Solving an Exponential Equation—Common Base

Multiple Choice What is the solution of $16^{3x} = 8$?

Ⓐ $x = \frac{1}{4}$ Ⓑ $x = \frac{3}{7}$ Ⓒ $x = 1$ Ⓓ $x = 4$

Plan
What common base is appropriate?
2 because 16 and 8 are both powers of 2.

Write the original equation.	$16^{3x} = 8$
Rewrite each side with a common base.	$(2^4)^{3x} = 2^3$
Use the Power Property of Exponents.	$2^{12x} = 2^3$
Since the bases are the same, their exponents are equal.	$12x = 3$
Solve for x and simplify.	$x = \frac{1}{4}$

The correct answer is A.

Hint
Remember to check your answer using substitution.

✓ **Got It?** 1. What is the solution of $27^{3x} = 81$?

498   Chapter 7   Exponential and Logarithmic Functions

PART 1

BIG ideas Equivalence
          Function   UbD

ESSENTIAL UNDERSTANDINGS
- Logarithms can be used to solve exponential equations. Exponents can be used to solve logarithmic equations.
- An exponential function is a function with the general form $y = ab^x$, $a \neq 0$, with $b > 0$, and $b \neq 1$. In an exponential function, the base b is a constant. The exponent x is the independent variable with a domain of all real numbers.
- The exponential function $y = b^x$ and the logarithmic function $y = \log_b x$ are inverse functions.

Math Background

Exponential and logarithmic functions are inverse functions. This relationship allows you to use logarithms to simplify exponential equations.

- To solve an exponential equation that cannot be rewritten with a common base, take the logarithm of both sides, and use the properties of logarithms to simplify.

The common log or $\log_{10}$ is most often used due to the ease of calculations. Any other base could be used, but the Change of Base formula from Lesson 7-4 would need to be applied in order to find the log using a calculator.

Support Student Learning

Use the **Algebra 2 Companion** to engage and support students during instruction. See Lesson Resources at the end of this lesson for details.

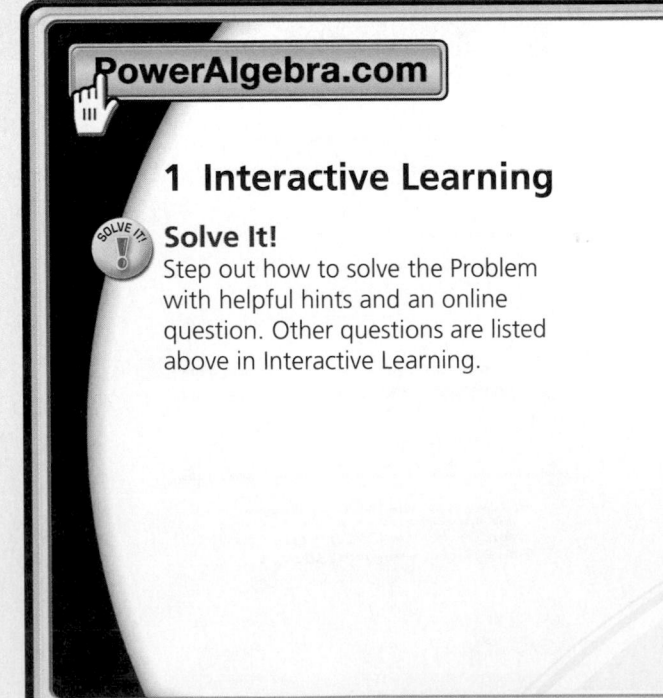

PowerAlgebra.com

1 Interactive Learning

Solve It!

Step out how to solve the Problem with helpful hints and an online question. Other questions are listed above in Interactive Learning.

When the bases are not the same, you can solve an exponential equation by taking the logarithm of each side of the equation. If m and n are positive numbers and $m = n$, then log m = log n.

 Problem 2 Solving an Exponential Equation—Different Bases

What is the solution of $15^{3x} = 285$?

Think

Which property of logarithms will help isolate x?
The rule log $a^x = x$ log a moves x out of the exponent position.

Write the original equation.	$15^{3x} = 285$
Take the logarithm base 10 of each side.	$\log 15^{3x} = \log 285$
Use the Power Property of Logarithms.	$3x \log 15 = \log 285$
Divide each side by 3 log 15 to isolate x.	$x = \dfrac{\log 285}{3 \log 15}$
Use a calculator to evaluate.	$x \approx 0.6958$

Check $15^{3x} = 285$

$15^{3(0.6958)} \approx 285.0840331 \approx 285$ ✓

 Got It? **2. a.** What is the solution of $5^{2x} = 130$?
  b. Reasoning Why can't you use the same method you used in Problem 1 to solve Problem 2?

 **Problem 3** Solving an Exponential Equation With a Graph or Table

What is the solution of $4^{3x} = 6000$?

Method 1 Solve using a graph.

Use a graphing calculator. Graph the equations $Y_1 = 4^{3x}$ and $Y_2 = 6000$.

Adjust the window to find the point of intersection. The solution is $x \approx 2.09$.

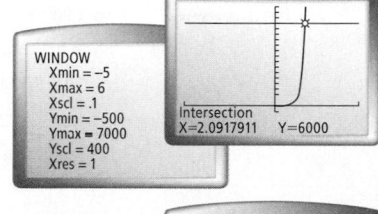

WINDOW
Xmin = −5
Xmax = 6
Xscl = .1
Ymin = −500
Ymax = 7000
Yscl = 400
Xres = 1

Intersection
X=2.0917911   Y=6000

Think

How do you choose TblStart and ΔTbl values?
Start with 0 and 1, respectively. Adjust both values as you close in on the solution.

Method 2 Solve using a table.

Use the table feature of a graphing calculator. Enter $Y_1 = 4^{3x}$.

Use the **TABLE SETUP** and **ΔTbl** features to locate the x-value that gives the y-value closest to 6000. The solution is $x \approx 2.09$.

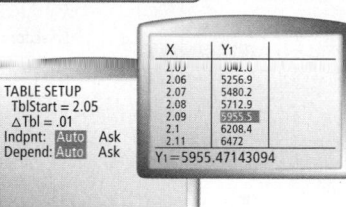

TABLE SETUP
TblStart = 2.05
ΔTbl = .01
Indpnt: Auto Ask
Depend: Auto Ask

X	Y₁
2.05	5041.0
2.06	5256.9
2.07	5480.2
2.08	5712.9
2.09	5955.5
2.1	6208.4
2.11	6472

Y₁=5955.47143094

 Got It? **3.** What is the solution of each exponential equation? Check your answer.
  a. $7^{4x} = 800$ **b.** $5.2^{3x} = 400$

---

2 Guided Instruction

Each Problem is worked out and supported online.

Problem 1
Solving an Exponential Equation—Common Base

Problem 2
Solving an Exponential Equation—Different Bases
Animated

Problem 3
Solving an Exponential Equation With a Graph or Table

Problem 4
Modeling With an Exponential Equation
Animated

Support in Algebra 2 Companion
• Vocabulary
• Key Concepts
• Got It?

Problem 2

Q What logarithmic base is being used to solve this equation? Explain. **[When no base is shown, it is assumed that the logarithm is base 10. This is easier to calculate, because the log button on a calculator is $\log_{10}$.]**

Q Can the method used in this problem be used to solve exponential equations with common bases? Give an example. **[Yes; by taking the log of each side of the equation in Problem 1, you get $3x = \dfrac{\log 8}{\log 16}$, so $x = 0.25$]**

Got It?   EXTENSION

Q How can you use the log of any base to solve an exponential equation with a calculator? **[Use the Change of Base Formula to convert to $\log_{10}$, and then solve the equation.]**

Problem 3
An estimate of the solution is helpful to determine window or table parameters when solving by graphing or using a table.

Q If no parentheses are used to enter $y = 4^{3x}$, how does the calculator interpret what is entered? **[If no parentheses are used, $y = 4^{3x}$ is interpreted as $y = 4^3 x$ (or 64x), which is a linear equation.]**

Got It?

Q How can you determine whether your solution is reasonable? **[For 3a, $7^3 = 343$ and $7^4 = 2401$. Because the exponent is $4x$, x will be between 0.75 and 1.]**

Answers

Solve It!
Prize B; compare the prizes over a year:
$2^{365} > 520,000$

Got It?

1. $\dfrac{4}{9}$

2. a. ≈ 1.5122
  b. because the terms cannot be written with a common base

3. a. ≈ 0.8588
  b. ≈ 1.2114

Problem 4

Suggest students look for key words in the situation to determine if the model represents an increase or decrease, and define the variable accordingly.

Q What does b represent in $y = ab^x$? What does r represent in $T(n) = a(1 + r)^n$? **[The variable b represents the growth factor if $b > 1$, and it represents the decay factor if $b < 1$. The variable r represents the rate of increase if $r > 0$, and it represents the rate of decrease if $r < 0$.]**

Q How can either model be used when writing this equation? Explain. **[The 7% harvest can be used to find the decay factor, or it can represent the rate of decrease. Because 93% of the harvest will remain after each year, a decay factor of $b = 0.93$ can be used. Using the 7% harvest as a rate of decrease, $r = -0.07$.]**

Got It?

VISUAL LEARNERS

Students can use a recursive routine with a graphing calculator to check the reasonableness of their answer. Input the following:

1,200,000   press Enter
Ans * 0.95   press Enter

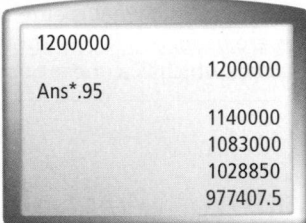

Count the number of times Enter is pressed to find the total number of years.

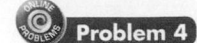 **Problem 4**   Modeling With an Exponential Equation

Resource Management Wood is a sustainable, renewable, natural resource when you manage forests properly. Your lumber company has 1,200,000 trees. You plan to harvest 7% of the trees each year. How many years will it take to harvest half of the trees?

Know	Need	Plan
• Number of trees • Rate of decay	Number of years it takes to harvest 600,000 trees	• Write an exponential equation. • Use logarithms to solve the equation.

Think

What equation should you use to model this situation? Since you are planning to harvest 7% of the trees each year, you should use $y = ab^x$, where b is the decay factor.

Step 1   Is an exponential model reasonable for this situation?

Yes, you are harvesting a fixed percentage each year.

Step 2   Define the variables and determine the model.

Let $n =$ the number of years it takes to harvest half of the trees.

Let $T(n) =$ the number of trees remaining after n years.

A reasonable model is $T(n) = ab^n$.

Step 3   Use the model to write an exponential equation.

a is the initial number of trees.	$a = 1{,}200{,}000$
$T(n)$ is half of the initial number of trees, or $\frac{1}{2}a$.	$T(n) = 600{,}000$
r is the rate of decay.	$r = -7\% = -0.07$
b is the decay factor.	$b = 1 + r = 1 + (-0.07) = 0.93$

So, $1{,}200{,}000(0.93)^n = 600{,}000$.

Step 4   Solve the equation. Use logarithms.

Write the original equation.	$1{,}200{,}000(0.93)^n = 600{,}000$
Isolate the term with n.	$0.93^n = \dfrac{600{,}000}{1{,}200{,}000}$
Take the logarithm of each side.	$\log 0.93^n = \log 0.5$
Use the Power Property of Logarithms.	$n \log 0.93 = \log 0.5$
Solve for n.	$n = \dfrac{\log 0.5}{\log 0.93}$
Use a calculator to evaluate.	$n \approx 9.55$

It will take about 9.55 years to harvest half of the original trees.

 Got It?   **4.** How many years will it take to harvest half of the trees if you harvest 5% instead of 7% each year?

Focus Question   How can you solve exponential equations?
Answer   Use logarithms, a graph, or a table to solve exponential equations.

500   Chapter 7   Exponential and Logarithmic Functions

Additional Problems

1. What is the solution of $256^{2x} = 64$?

ANSWER $\frac{3}{8}$

2. What is the solution of $6^{4x} = 512$?

ANSWER 0.8704

3. What is the solution of $5^{2x} = 3500$?

ANSWER 2.54

4. Your MP3 player has about 126,000,000 bytes of memory. Each month you plan to use 5% of the memory remaining. How many months will it take you to use $\frac{1}{4}$ of the memory?

ANSWER 5.61 months

Answers

Got It? (continued)
4. ≈ 13.51 yrs

500   Chapter 7

Lesson Check

Do you know HOW?

Solve each equation.

1. $3^x = 9$

2. $2^x = 8$

3. $2^{y+1} = 25$

Do you UNDERSTAND?

4. **Reasoning** Is it possible for an exponential equation to have no solutions? If so, give an example. If not, explain why.

Practice and Problem-Solving Exercises

Ⓐ Practice   Solve each equation.   ◆ See Problem 1.

Guided Practice   To start, rewrite each side with a common base.

$$5.\ 3^{2x} = 27$$
$$3^{2x} = 3^3$$

6. $4^{3x} = 64$ 7. $5^{3x} = \frac{1}{125}$ 8. $2^{5x+1} = 32$

9. $3^{-2x+2} = 81$ 10. $2^{3x} = 4^{x+1}$ 11. $3^{x+2} = 27^{2x}$

Solve each equation. Round to the nearest ten-thousandth.   ◆ See Problem 2.
Check your answers.

Guided Practice   To start, take the logarithm of each side.

$$12.\quad 2^x = 3$$
$$\log 2^x = \log 3$$

13. $4^x = 19$ 14. $8 + 10^x = 1008$ 15. $5 - 3^x = -40$

16. $9^{2y} = 66$ 17. $25^{2x+1} = 144$ 18. $2^{3x-4} = 5$

📊 **Graphing Calculator**   Solve by graphing. Round to the nearest ten-thousandth.   ◆ See Problem 3.

19. $4^{7x} = 250$ 20. $5^{3x} = 500$ 21. $6^x = 4565$

Use a table to solve each equation. Round to the nearest hundredth.

22. $2^{x+3} = 512$ 23. $3^{x-1} = 72$ 24. $5^{2x} = 56$

25. The equation $y = 6.72(1.014)^x$ models the world population y, in billions of people, x years after the year 2000. Find the year in which the world population is about 8 billion.   ◆ See Problem 4.

3 Lesson Check

Do you know HOW?   ERROR INTERVENTION

- If students have difficulty with Exercises 1–3, remind them they can either search for a common base or take the logarithm of each side. Taking the logarithm of each side will work for both types of equations, while finding a common base may not be possible.
- For Exercise 3, students might mistakenly believe they can use a common base. Point out that the right side of the equation would have base 5.

Do you UNDERSTAND?

- For Exercise 4, if students cannot find an exponential equation that has no solutions, refer to Problem 6 as an example. The logarithm of a negative number does not have a real solution.

Close

Q How is the relationship between exponents and logarithms used to solve exponential equations? Explain. **[Exponential and logarithmic functions are inverse functions. You can solve an exponential equation by taking logarithms of both sides.]**

Q What methods can be used to solve an exponential equation? **[Rewrite the terms with a common base, or take a logarithm of each side. You can also use a graphing calculator to graph or find a solution using a table.]**

Answers

Lesson Check

1. 2
2. 3
3. ≈ 3.6439
4. Yes; $5^x = 0$ has no solution.

Practice and Problem-Solving Exercises

5. $\frac{3}{2}$
6. 1
7. -1
8. $\frac{4}{5}$
9. -1
10. 2
11. $\frac{2}{5}$
12. 1.5850
13. 2.1240
14. 3
15. 3.4650
16. 0.9534
17. 0.2720
18. 2.1073
19. 0.5690
20. 1.2871
21. 4.7027
22. 6
23. 4.89
24. 1.25
25. about the yr 2012

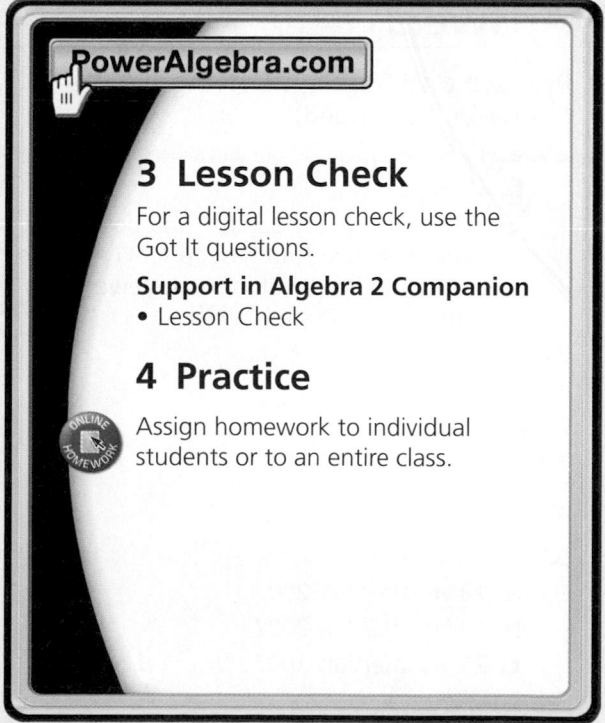

4 Practice

ASSIGNMENT GUIDE

Basic: 5–16, 19–23, 25, 29

Average: 6–25

Reasoning exercises have blue headings.

Applications exercises have red headings.

HOMEWORK QUICK CHECK

To check students' understanding of key skills and concepts, go over Exercises 6, 13, 19, 22, and 25.

 Apply

26. Consider the equation $2^{\frac{x}{3}} = 80$.

   a. Solve the equation by taking the logarithm base 10 of each side.

   b. Solve the equation by taking the logarithm base 2 of each side.

   c. **Writing** Compare your result in parts (a) and (b). What are the advantages of each method? Explain.

27. As a town gets smaller, the population of its high school decreases by 6% each year. The senior class has 160 students now. In how many years will it have about 100 students? Write an equation. Then solve the equation without graphing.

Mental Math Solve each equation.

28. $2^x = \frac{1}{2}$ **29.** $3^x = 27$ **30.** $10^x = \frac{1}{100}$ **31.** $25^x = \frac{1}{5}$

32. **Reasoning** The graphs of $y = 2^{3x}$ and $y = 3^{x+1}$ intersect at approximately $(1.1201, 10.2692)$. What is the solution of $2^{3x} = 3^{x+1}$?

33. **Demography** The table below lists the states with the highest and lowest population growth rates. Determine in how many years each event can occur. Use the model $P = P_0(1 + r)^x$, where P_0 is population from the table, as of July, 2007; x is the number of years after July, 2007, P is the projected population and r is the growth rate.

   a. Population of Idaho exceeds 2 million.

   b. Population of Michigan decreases by 1 million.

   c. Population of Nevada doubles.

State	Growth rate (%)	Population (in thousands)	State	Growth rate (%)	Population (in thousands)
1. Nevada	2.93	2,565	46. New York	0.08	19,298
2. Arizona	2.81	6,339	47. Vermont	0.08	621
3. Utah	2.55	2,645	48. Ohio	0.03	11,467
4. Idaho	2.43	1,499	49. Michigan	−0.30	10,072
5. Georgia	2.17	9,545	50. Rhode Island	−0.36	1,058

Source: U.S. Census Bureau

Solve each equation. If necessary, round to the nearest ten-thousandth.

34. $8^x = 444$ **35.** $9^{2x} = 42$ **36.** $12^{4-x} = 20$

37. $5^{3x} = 125$ **38.** $4^{3x} = 77.2$ **39.** $7^x - 1 = 371$

Answers

Practice and Problem-Solving Exercises (continued)

26. a. 18.9658

   b. 18.9658

   c. Answers may vary. Sample: You don't have to use the change of base formula with the base-10 method, but there are fewer steps with the base-2 method.

27. $y = 160(0.94)^x$; ≈7.6 yrs

28. −1

29. 3

30. −2

31. $-\frac{1}{2}$

32. ≈1.1201

33. a. 13 yrs after July 2007

   b. 35 yrs after July 2007

   c. 25 yrs after July 2007

34. 2.9315

35. 0.8505

36. 2.7944

37. 1

38. 1.0451

39. 3.0417

Objective To solve logarithmic equations

In Part 1 of the lesson, you learned how to solve exponential equations using logarithms.

Connect to What You Know

Here you will learn to solve logarithmic equations using exponents.

Lesson Vocabulary
• logarithmic equation

Focus Question How can you solve logarithmic equations?

A **logarithmic equation** is an equation that includes one or more logarithms involving a variable.

Plan

How do you convert between log form and exponential form?
Use the rule: $\log a = b$ if and only if $a = 10^b$.

Hint

You can also solve using a table. First, let $Y_1 = \text{LOG}(4x - 3)$. Then use TABLE SETUP to find the x-value that corresponds to a y-value of 2.

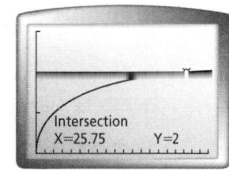

Problem 5 Solving a Logarithmic Equation

What is the solution of $\log(4x - 3) = 2$?

Method 1 Solve using exponents.

Write the original equation.	$\log(4x - 3) = 2$
Write in exponential form.	$4x - 3 = 10^2$
Simplify.	$4x = 103$
Solve for x.	$x = \frac{103}{4} = 25.75$

Method 2 Solve using a graph.

Graph the equations $Y_1 = \text{LOG}(4x - 3)$ and $Y_2 = 2$. Find the point of intersection. The solution is $x = 25.75$.

Intersection
X=25.75   Y=2

 Got It? **5.** What is the solution of $\log(3 - 2x) = -1$? Solve using both exponents and a graph.

---

1 Launch

CONNECT THE MATH In Part 1, students used the inverse relationship between logarithms and exponential functions to solve exponential functions. In Part 2, they use this relationship to solve logarithmic functions using exponents.

FOCUS QUESTION

Q How can you rewrite $3 = \log(25x)$ using exponents? **[$10^3 = 25x$]**

Q What is the solution to the equation you wrote? **[$x = 40$]**

2 Guided Instruction

Problem 5

Converting a logarithmic equation to exponential form can be thought of as raising both sides to the power of 10. Note that $\log(4x - 3) = 2$ is the same as $10^{\log(4x-3)} = 10^2$.

Q What are the advantages and disadvantages of using a graph to solve a logarithmic equation? **[An advantage is that you can see how the exponential equation changes for values of x. A disadvantage is that you must zoom in at the intersection to find more precise answers.]**

Got It?

Q Which method would you choose to solve this problem? Explain. **[Sample: You would choose exponents, because it is simpler to rewrite the equation as $3 - 2x = 10^{-1}$ and solve for x. You need an estimate to set the window in a calculator. Since you have to rewrite the equation in exponential form to estimate, it is easier to just solve for x.]**

7-5 Preparing to Teach

PART 2

BIG ideas Equivalence
Function **UbD**

ESSENTIAL UNDERSTANDINGS
• Logarithms can be used to solve exponential equations. Exponents can be used to solve logarithmic equations.
• An exponential function is a function with the general form $y = ab^x$, $a \neq 0$, with $b > 0$, and $b \neq 1$. In an exponential function, the base b is a constant. The exponent x is the independent variable with a domain of all real numbers.
• The exponential function $y = b^x$ and the logarithmic function $y = \log_b x$ are inverse functions.

Math Background
Exponential and logarithmic functions are inverse functions. This relationship allows

you to use exponents to simplify logarithmic equations.
• To solve a logarithmic equation, rewrite both sides in exponential form to remove the log, and use the properties of exponents to simplify.

Remember the common log or $\log_{10}$ is most often used due to the ease of calculations. Any other base could be used, but the Change of Base formula from Lesson 7-4 would need to be applied in order to find the log using a calculator.

Support Student Learning
Use the **Algebra 2 Companion** to engage and support students during instruction. See Lesson Resources at the end of this lesson for details.

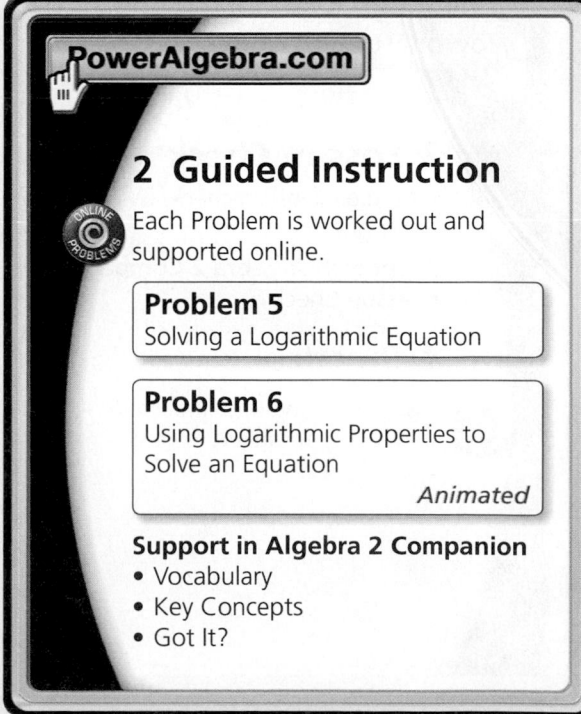

PowerAlgebra.com

2 Guided Instruction

Each Problem is worked out and supported online.

Problem 5
Solving a Logarithmic Equation

Problem 6
Using Logarithmic Properties to Solve an Equation
Animated

Support in Algebra 2 Companion
• Vocabulary
• Key Concepts
• Got It?

Problem 6

> **Q** Why is it not possible to find $\log(-2)$?
> [$\log(-2) = x$ means $10^x = -2$. Raising a positive base to any number, either positive or negative, will never result in a negative number.]

Got It?

> **Q** How can you determine which property of logarithms to use when solving the equation? [**If logarithms are added, use the Product Property. If they are subtracted, use the Quotient Property. If a number is multiplied by a logarithm, use the Power Property.**]

3 Lesson Check

Do you know HOW?   ERROR INTERVENTION

- If students have difficulty with Exercise 2, tell them to use one of the properties of logarithms first to combine the two logarithmic expressions.

Do you UNDERSTAND?

- For Exercise 4, if students cannot find an error, have them look at the properties the student used. Have them determine what must be true of the equations to use those properties.

Close

> **Q** How is the relationship between exponents and logarithms used to solve logarithmic equations? Explain. [**Exponential and logarithmic functions are inverse functions. You can solve a logarithmic equation by rewriting it in exponential form.**]
>
> **Q** What methods can be used to solve a logarithmic equation? [**Rewrite the problem using exponents, use a graph, use a table, or use logarithmic properties.**]

Sometimes you need to use the properties of logarithms before you can rewrite a logarithmic equation in exponential form.

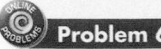 **Problem 6** Using Logarithmic Properties to Solve an Equation

What is the solution of $\log(x - 3) + \log x = 1$?

Write the original equation.	$\log(x - 3) + \log x = 1$
Use the Product Property of Logarithms.	$\log((x - 3)x) = 1$
Write in exponential form.	$(x - 3)x = 10^1$
Use the Distributive Property.	$x^2 - 3x = 10$
Write as a quadratic equation in standard form.	$x^2 - 3x - 10 = 0$
Factor the trinomial.	$(x - 5)(x + 2) = 0$
Solve for x.	$x = 5 \ \text{ or } \ x = -2$

 Think

What is the domain of the logarithm function?
Logs are defined only for positive numbers. The log of a negative number is undefined.

Check

Write the equation.	$\log(x - 3) + \log(x) = 1$	$\log(x - 3) + \log x = 1$
Substitute.	$\log(5 - 3) + \log 5 = 1$	$\log(-2 - 3) + \log(-2) = 1$
Simplify.	$\log 2 + \log 5 = 1$	$\log(-5) + \log(-2) = 1$ ✗
Use a calculator.	$0.3101 + 0.6990 = 1$ ✔	

The solution is $x = 5$.

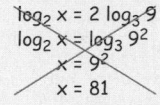 undefined

Got It? 6. What is the solution of $\log 6 - \log 3x = -2$?

Focus Question How can you solve logarithmic equations?

Answer Use exponents to solve logarithmic equations. Solve a logarithmic equation by rewriting it in exponential form and using the properties of logarithms and exponents. You can also use a graph or table.

Lesson Check

Do you know HOW?

Solve each equation.

1. $\log 4x = 2$

2. $\log x - \log 2 = 3$

3. $2 \log x = -1$

Do you UNDERSTAND?

4. Error Analysis Describe and correct the error made in solving the equation.

$\log_2 x = 2 \log_3 9$
$\log_2 x = \log_3 9^2$
$x = 9^2$
$x = 81$

 PowerAlgebra.com

3 Lesson Check

For a digital lesson check, use the Got It questions.

Support in Algebra 2 Companion
- Lesson Check

4 Practice

Assign homework to individual students or to an entire class.

Additional Problems

5. What is the solution of $\log(5x + 2) = 2$?

   ANSWER 19.6

6. What is the solution of $\log 2x^2 - \log 5 = 1$?

   ANSWER 5, -5

Practice and Problem-Solving Exercises

A Practice

Solve each equation. Check your answers.

◆ See Problem 5.

Guided Practice

5. $\log 2x = -1$

To start, write the equation in exponential form.

$2x = 10^{-1}$

6. $\log(3x + 1) = 2$ **7.** $\log x + 4 = 8$ **8.** $\log 6x - 3 = -4$

9. $3 \log x = 1.5$ **10.** $2 \log(x + 1) = 5$ **11.** $\log(5 - 2x) = 0$

Solve each equation.

◆ See Problem 6.

Guided Practice

12. $\log x - \log 3 = 8$

To start, use the Quotient Property of Logarithms.

$\log \frac{x}{3} = 8$

13. $\log x + \log 5 = 2$ **14.** $\log 2x + \log x = 11$ **15.** $2 \log x + \log 4 = 2$

16. $\log 5 - \log 2x = 1$ **17.** $3 \log x - \log 6 + \log 2.4 = 9$ **18.** $\log(7x + 1) = \log(x - 2) + 1$

B Apply

19. Think About a Plan An earthquake of magnitude 9.1 occurred in 2004 in the Indian Ocean near Indonesia. It was about 74,900 times as strong as the greatest earthquake ever to hit Texas. Find the magnitude of the Texas earthquake. (Remember that an increase of 1.0 on the Richter scale means an earthquake is 30 times stronger.)
- Can you write an exponential or logarithmic equation?
- How does the solution of your equation help you find the magnitude?

20. Seismology An earthquake of magnitude 7.7 occurred in 2001 in Gujarat, India. It was 4900 times as strong as the greatest earthquake ever to hit Pennsylvania. What is the magnitude of the Pennsylvania earthquake? (*Hint:* Refer to the Richter scale on page 482.)

Acoustics In Exercises 21 and 22, the loudness measured in decibels (dB) is defined by loudness $= 10 \log\frac{I}{I_0}$, where I is the intensity and $I_0 = 10^{-12}$ W/m^2.

21. The human threshold for pain is 120 dB. Instant perforation of the eardrum occurs at 160 dB.
- **a.** Find the intensity of each sound.
- **b.** How many times as intense is the noise that will perforate an eardrum as the noise that causes pain?

22. The noise level inside a convertible driving along the freeway with its top up is 70 dB. With the top down, the noise level is 95 dB.
- **a.** Find the intensity of the sound with the top up and with the top down.
- **b.** By what percent does leaving the top up reduce the intensity of the sound?

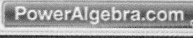
---

4 Practice

ASSIGNMENT GUIDE

Basic: 5–10, 12–17, 19–21, 29–31

Average: 5–32

Standardized Test Prep: 35–39

Mixed Review: 40–50

Reasoning exercises have blue headings.

Applications exercises have red headings.

EXERCISE 20: Use the Think About a Plan worksheet in the **Student Companion** (also available in the Teaching Resources in print and online) to further support students' development in becoming independent learners.

HOMEWORK QUICK CHECK

To check students' understanding of key skills and concepts, go over Exercises 6, 13, 19, 20, and 30.

Answers

Got It? (continued)

5. 1.45

6. 200

Lesson Check

1. 25

2. 2000

3. $\frac{\sqrt{10}}{10}$ or about ≈ 0.3162

4. The log bases are not equal.

$\log_2 x = 2 \log_3 9$

$\log_2 x = \log_3 9^2$

$\log_2 x = 4$

$x = 2^4$

$x = 16$

Practice and Problem-Solving Exercises

5. 0.05

6. 33

7. 10,000

8. $\frac{1}{60}$ or ≈ 0.0167

9. $\sqrt{10}$ or ≈ 3.1623

10. $100\sqrt{10} - 1$ or ≈ 315.2

11. 2

12. 3×10^8

13. 20

14. $100,000\sqrt{5}$ or $\approx 223,606.8$

15. 5

16. $\frac{1}{4}$

17. ≈ 1357.2

18. 7

19. 5.8

20. about 5.2

21. a. 1 W/m^2; 10^4 W/m^2
    b. 10,000 times as intense

22. a. top up: 10^{-5} W/m^2 top down: $10^{-2.5}$ W/m^2
    b. 99.68%

Answers

Practice and Problem-Solving
Exercises (continued)

23. 625

24. 2.3094

25. 1.5

26. 200.8

27. 500

28. $114.\overline{3}$

29. $\frac{1}{2}$

30. 3

31. $\frac{1}{3}$

32. 3

33. Answers may vary. Sample: $\log x = 1.6$; $x \approx 39.81$

34. 143.6

Standardized Test Prep

35. 4

36. 333

37. 25

38. 4

39. 18

Mixed Review

40. $\log 2 + 3 \log x - 2 \log y$

41. $\log_3 x - \log_3 y$

42. $1 + \frac{1}{2}\log_3 x$

43. $x^2 - 3x - 1$

44. $3x^2 - 3$

45. $9x^2 - 1$

46. $1, \pm i$

47. $\pm 2, \pm 2i$

48. $\pm\sqrt{3}, \pm\sqrt{2}$

49. 10

50. 15

Solve each equation. If necessary, round to the nearest ten-thousandth.

23. $\frac{1}{2}\log x + \log 4 = 2$

24. $4 \log_3 2 - 2 \log_3 x = 1$

25. $\log_8(2x - 1) = \frac{1}{3}$

26. $\log(5x - 4) = 3$

27. $\log 4 + 2 \log x = 6$

28. $\log_7 3x = 3$

Mental Math Solve each equation.

29. $\log_9 3 = x$

30. $\log_4 64 = x$

31. $\log_8 2 = x$

32. $\log_7 343 = x$

33. Open-Ended Write and solve a logarithmic equation.

34. Reasoning If $\log 12^{0.5x} = \log 143.6$, then $12^{0.5x} = \underline{\ ?\ }$.

Standardized Test Prep

GRIDDED RESPONSE

SAT/ACT

35. The graph at the right shows the translation of the graph of the parent function $y = |x|$ down 2 units and 3 units to the right. What is the area of the shaded triangle in square units?

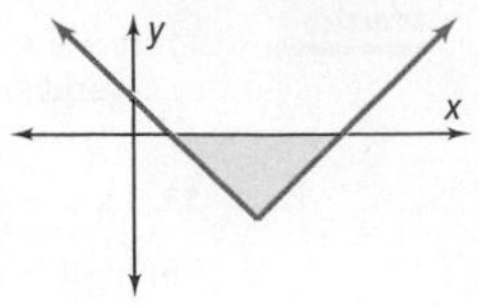

36. What does x equal if $\log(1 + 3x) = 3$?

37. Using the change of base formula, what is the value of x for which $\log_9 x = \log_3 5$?

38. The polynomial $x^4 + 3x^3 + 16x^2 - 19x + 8$ is divided by the binomial $x - 1$. What is the coefficient of x^2 in the quotient?

39. What positive value of b makes $x^2 + bx + 81$ a perfect square trinomial?

Mixed Review

Expand each logarithm.   ◀ See Lesson 7-4.

40. $\log 2x^3 y^{-2}$

41. $\log_3 \frac{x}{y}$

42. $\log_3 \sqrt{9x}$

Let $f(x) = 3x$ and $g(x) = x^2 - 1$. Perform each function operation.   ◀ See Lesson 6-6.

43. $(g - f)(x)$

44. $(f \circ g)(x)$

45. $(g \circ f)(x)$

Find all the zeros of each function.   ◀ See Lesson 5-6.

46. $y = x^3 - x^2 + x - 1$

47. $f(x) = x^4 - 16$

48. $f(x) = x^4 - 5x^2 + 6$

Get Ready!   To prepare for Lesson 8-1, do Exercises 49 and 50.

For Exercises 49 and 50, y varies directly with x.   ◀ See Lesson 2-2.

49. If $y = 4$ when $x = 2$, find y when $x = 5$.

50. If $y = 5$ when $x = 1$, find y when $x = 3$.

Additional Instructional Support

Algebra 2 Companion

Students can use the **Algebra 2 Companion** worktext (4 pages) as you teach the lesson. Use the Companion to support

- New Vocabulary
- Key Concepts
- Got It for each Problem
- Lesson Check

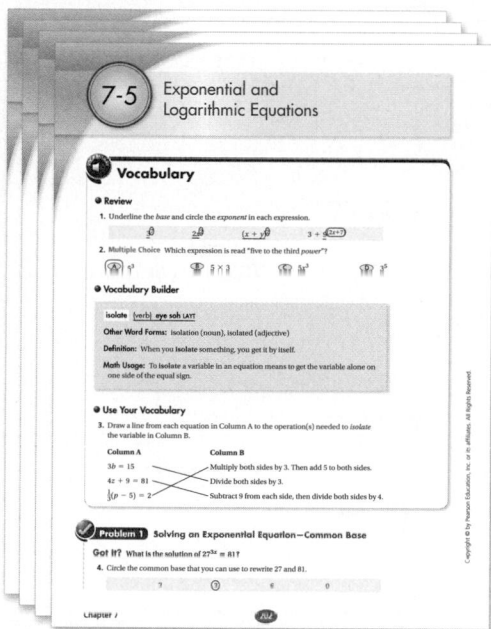

ELL Support

Focus on Communication Have students write exponential or logarithmic properties used to solve equations on index cards, with an example of the property on the back. For example, students can write the Power Property of Exponents, Power Property of Logarithms, Product Property of Logarithms, and Quotient Property of Logarithms. Divide students into pairs, and have one person solve the problem while the other asks a question. Have students ask, "How did you complete that step?" A student might respond by stating, "I used the Power Property of Logarithms," or the student may show the index card with the correct property. If the student uses the index card, encourage the student to read the words of the property to practice using the academic language. Next, have the students switch roles so that each has practice solving the problem and answering questions.

5 Assess & Remediate

Lesson Quiz

1. What is the solution of $16^{-3n+2} = 64$?
2. What is the solution of $12^{4x} = 256$?
3. What is the solution of $36^{-3x} = 1500$?
4. **Do you UNDERSTAND?** A population of 12,000 fish has a growth rate of 4% each year. Write a model for the situation. How many years will it take for the population to reach 20,000?
5. What is the solution of $\log 5x - 3 = 2$?
6. Solve $\log 2x - \log 8 = 3$.

ANSWERS TO LESSON QUIZ

1. $\frac{1}{6}$
2. 0.5579
3. −0.68
4. $12,000(1.04)^n = 20,000$; 13.02 years
5. 20,000
6. 4000

PRESCRIPTION FOR REMEDIATION
Use the student work on the Lesson Quiz to prescribe a differentiated review assignment:

Points	Differentiated Remediation
0–3	Intervention
4–5	On-level
6	Extension

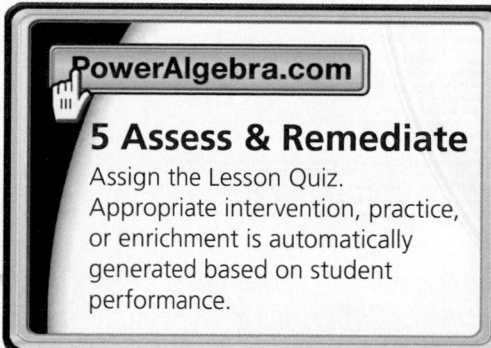

PowerAlgebra.com

5 Assess & Remediate

Assign the Lesson Quiz. Appropriate intervention, practice, or enrichment is automatically generated based on student performance.

Intervention

- **Reteaching** (2 pages) Provides reteaching and practice exercises for the key lesson concepts. Use with struggling students or absent students.
- **English Language Learner Support** Helps students develop and reinforce mathematical vocabulary and key concepts.

All-in-One Resources/Online
Reteaching

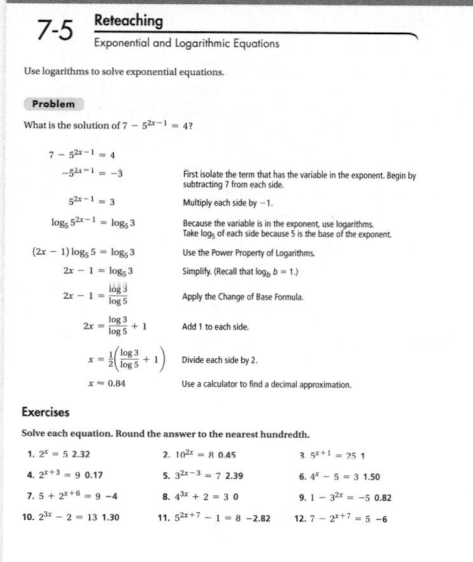

All-in-One Resources/Online
English Language Learner Support

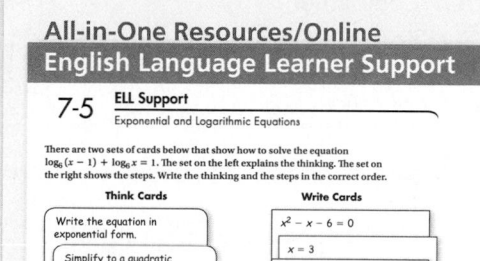

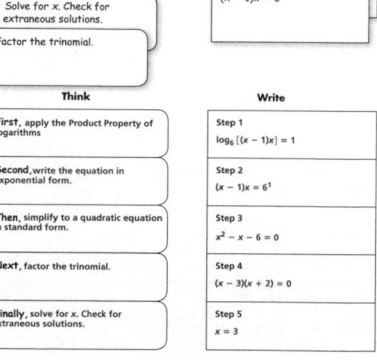

Differentiated Remediation continued

On-Level

- **Practice** (2 pages) Provides extra practice for each lesson. For more challenging practice exercises, use the Form G Practice pages found in the All-in-One Teaching Resources and online.

- **Think About a Plan** Helps students develop specific problem-solving skills and strategies by providing scaffolded guiding questions.
- **Standardized Test Prep** Focuses on all major exercises, all major question types, and helps students prepare for the high-stakes assessments.

Extension

- **Enrichment** Provides students with interesting problems and activities that extend the concepts of the lesson.
- **Activities, Games, and Puzzles** Worksheets that can be used for concepts development, enrichment, and for fun!

Student Companion/All-in-One Resources/Online
Practice page 1

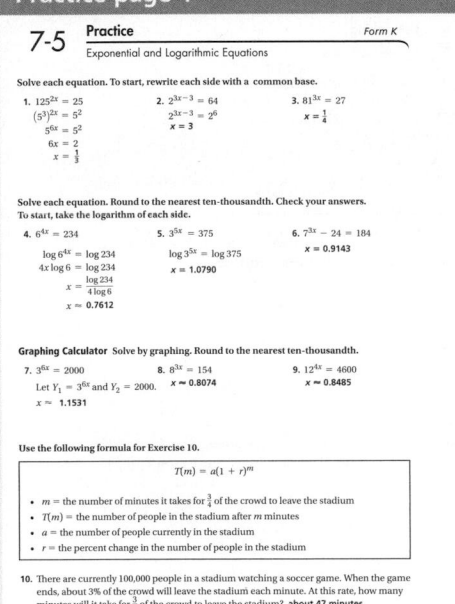

Student Companion/All-in-One Resources/Online
Practice page 2

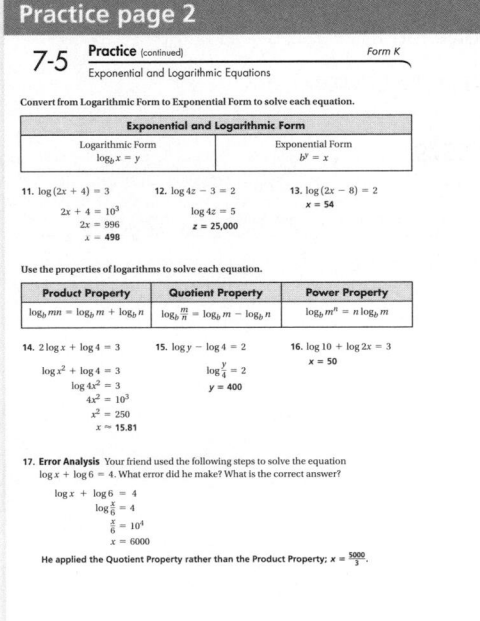

All-in-One Resources/Online
Enrichment

7-5 Enrichment
Exponential and Logarithmic Equations

When solving logarithm equations, you primarily use the Product Property, Quotient Property, and Power Property to simplify the equation. Here is an interesting, lesser-known property of logarithms to explore.

1. Determine the value of each pair of expressions.

   $\log_2 4$, $\log_4 2$ **2, $\frac{1}{2}$**

   $\log_3 81$, $\log_{81} 3$ **4, $\frac{1}{4}$**

   $\log_{10} 1000$, $\log_{1000} 10$ **3, $\frac{1}{3}$**

2. How are the values of each pair of expressions related?
   Answers may vary. Sample: When the base and argument are switched, the expressions are reciprocals.

3. This reciprocal property states that $\log_a b = \frac{1}{\log_b a}$. To prove this property, assume $r = \log_a b$ and $s = \log_b a$. Rewrite each of these equations in exponential form. $a^r = b$, $b^s = a$

4. Next, use one equation to substitute an equivalent expression in for a. What is your new equation? $(b^s)^r = b$

5. Use the laws of exponents to simplify. $b^{sr} = b$

6. Because the bases are the same, what equation can you write for the exponents? $sr = 1$

7. What must be true about s and r if the product equals 1? s and r must be reciprocals.

8. Use this new property to solve the equation $\log_5 x + \frac{1}{\log_x 5} = 4$. **25**

Student Companion/All-in-One Resources/Online
Think About a Plan

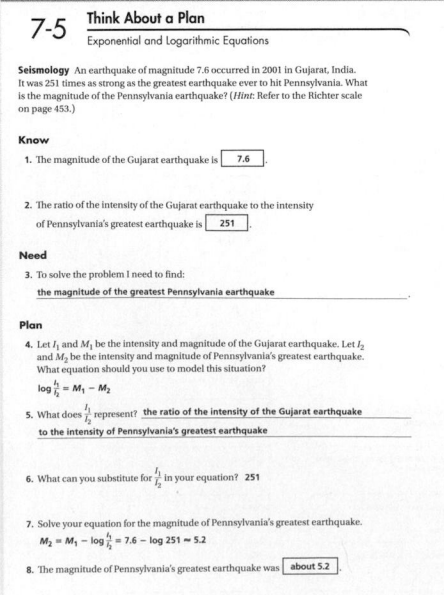

Student Companion/All-in-One Resources/Online
Standardized Test Prep

7-5 Standardized Test Prep
Exponential and Logarithmic Equations

Multiple Choice

For Exercises 1–5, choose the correct letter.

1. If $9^x = 243$, what is the value of x? **C**
   Ⓐ 2   Ⓑ 5   Ⓒ 2.5   Ⓓ 10

2. If $2^{3x+2} = 64$, what is the value of x? **G**
   Ⓕ $\frac{8}{3}$ Ⓖ $\frac{4}{3}$ Ⓗ 2   Ⓘ $\frac{3}{4}$

3. If $\log(3x + 25) = 2$, what is the value of x? **A**
   Ⓐ 25   Ⓑ 75   Ⓒ $41\frac{2}{3}$ Ⓓ 100

4. Which best approximates the solution of $16^{2x} = 124$? **F**
   Ⓕ 0.869   Ⓖ 1.150   Ⓗ 1.739   Ⓘ 3.477

5. Which equation represents the solution of $2^{3x+1} = 7$? **D**
   Ⓐ $x = 3\left(\frac{\log 7}{\log 2} - 1\right)$ Ⓒ $x = \frac{1}{3}\left(\frac{\log 7}{\log 2} - 1\right)$
   Ⓑ $x = \frac{\log 7}{3\log 2} - 1$ Ⓓ $x = \frac{1}{3}\left(\frac{\log 7}{\log 2} - 1\right)$

Short Response

6. In 2007, the population of Tallahassee, Florida was 168,979. Some researchers believe that the population of Tallahassee will increase at a rate of 1% each year for the 10 years following this.
   a. If the researchers are correct, how many years will it take for the population of Tallahassee to reach 180,000?
   b. Explain in words or show your work for how you determined the number of years found in part (a).

   [2] a. **about 7 years**
   b. Because the population grows at a constant rate each year, an exponential model of the situation is $y = 168,979(1.01)^x$. $180,000 = 168,979(1.01)^x \rightarrow \frac{180,000}{168,979} = 1.01^x \rightarrow \log 1.0652 = x \log 1.01 \rightarrow x = \frac{\log 1.0652}{\log 1.01} = 6.348$.
   [1] incorrect number of years OR incorrect explanation
   [0] incorrect answers and no work shown OR no answers given

Online Teacher Resource Center
Activities, Games, and Puzzles

7-5 Game: Analyzing Equations
Exponential and Logarithmic Equations

This is a game for the entire class. You will work in teams of three students. Your teacher can serve as the host. Your teacher will decide the order in which the questions are chosen and he or she may also decide on a time limit for each question. No calculators allowed!

- Write your answer next to each question. A correct response is worth three points.
- **Category 1:** Answer *none*, *one*, or *two*.
- **Category 2:** Give two consecutive numbers such as *5 and 6*.
- **Category 3:** Write *A* or *B*.

	Category 1: How Many Solutions?	Score
1.	$2^x = x + 3$ **two**	
2.	$\log_2 x = x + 2$ **none**	
3.	$2^x = 5$ **one**	
4.	$\log_2 x = 2$ **one**	
5.	$2^x = -5$ **none**	
6.	$\log_2 x = x - 2$ **two**	
7.	$2^x + 2 = 0$ **none**	
8.	$\log_2 (x - 2) = 4x$ **none**	

	Category 2: Between Which Two Whole Numbers is x?	Score
1.	$3 \times 2^x = 75$ **4 and 5**	
2.	$2 \times 2^x = 20$ **3 and 4**	
3.	$\log_2 x = 3.1$ **8 and 9**	
4.	$\log_2 x = 0.1$ **1 and 2**	
5.	$5 \times 2^x = 60$ **3 and 4**	
6.	$-3 \times 2^x = -9$ **1 and 2**	

	Category 3: Which Equation Has the Greater Solution?			Score
1.	A. $2^x = 64$	or	B. $3^x = 81$ **A**	
2.	A. $10^x = 1000$	or	B. $5^x = 25$ **A**	
3.	A. $4^x = 1$	or	B. $5^x = 125$ **B**	
4.	A. $3^x = 27$	or	B. $2^x = 32$ **B**	

Using Logarithms for Exponential Models

You can transform an exponential function into a linear function by taking the logarithm of each side. Since linear models are easy to recognize, you can then determine whether an exponential function is a good model for a set of values.

Write the general form of an exponential function.	$y = ab^x$
Take the logarithm of each side.	$\log y = \log ab^x$
Use the Product Property and the Power Property.	$\log y = \log a + x(\log b)$

If $\log b$ and $\log a$ are constants, then $\log y = (\log b)x + \log a$ is a linear equation in slope-intercept form when you plot the points as $(x, \log y)$.

Activity

Determine whether an exponential function is a good model for the values in the table.

x	0	2	4	6	8	10
y	0.5	2	7.8	32	127.9	511.7

Step 1 Enter the values into stat lists **L₁** and **L₂**. To enter the values of log y, place the cursor in the heading of **L₃** and press log **L₂** enter.

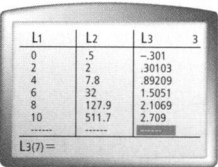

Step 2 To graph log y, access the stat plot feature and press **1**. Then enter **L₃** next to **Ylist:**. Then press zoom **9**.

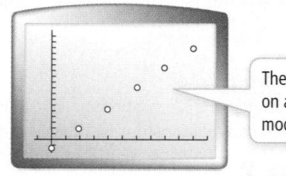

The points $(x, \log y)$ lie on a line, so an exponential model is appropriate.

Step 3 Press stat ▷ 0 enter to find the exponential function $y = 0.5(2)^x$.

Exercises

For each set of values, determine whether an exponential function is a good model. If so, find the exponential function.

1.

x	1	3	5	7	9
y	6	22	54	102	145

2.

x	−1	0	1	2	3
y	40.2	19.8	9.9	5.1	2.5

3. Writing Explain how you could determine whether a logarithmic function is a good model for a set of data.

Guided Instruction

PURPOSE To use logarithms to determine the appropriateness of an exponential model

PROCESS Students will
- take the logarithms of the y-values in a table.
- graph the new points $(x, \log y)$ to see if the new data is linear.

DISCUSS The Product Property of Logarithms is used to write an exponential equation in linear form.
- A linear function in slope-intercept form is $y = mx + b$.
- Visual inspection or a line of best fit can be used to determine if data are linear.

Activity

An exponential model of the original data is appropriate if the points $(x, \log y)$ are linear.

Q What is the difference between using logarithms to solve an exponential equation and using logarithms to determine whether an exponential model is appropriate? **[When solving equations, logarithms of both sides must be taken. When determining appropriateness of an exponential model, use $(x, \log y)$ to see whether the data appears linear.]**

Q What happens if you try to find the logs of the values in a list that contains 0? Explain. **[The calculator gives the message ERR: DOMAIN because the domain contains 0 and log 0 is not defined.]**

Answers

Exercises

1. $y = 5.58(1.48)^x$

2. $y = 20.0(0.50)^x$

3. Answers may vary. Sample: Use the Change of Base Formula to get $\log x = \frac{\log b}{a}y$. Let $L_1 = x$, $L_2 = y$, and $L_3 = \log x$. Graph L_2 and L_3. If it is linear, then the equation is logarithmic.

Performance Task

Pull It All Together

The following questions are designed to:
- Help support students as they do the Tasks.
- Gauge the amount of support students need as they become independent problem solvers.

Task 1

Solve problems involving exponential equations through algebraic, graphic, and numeric methods.
- For what variable in $A(t) = a(1 + r)^t$ will you substitute the expression $e^r - 1$ to answer part a?
- What portion of the graph of the exponential function would you look at to answer part b, remembering that r is expressed as a decimal?
- To which equation should you add 1 so that the equations will have equal value and can be set equal to each other?

Task 2

Model and solve a problem as a system of equations in two unknowns.
- How can you rewrite b^{x-h} as b^x times a constant value in terms of b to answer part a?
- How can you write the inverse of $f_1(x) = b^{x-h}$?
- Is it easier to compare $h(x)$ to $g(x)$ in terms of common logarithms?

> To solve these problems, you will pull together concepts and skills related to exponential functions and logarithms.

BIG idea Modeling

You can represent many real-world mathematical problems algebraically. An algebraic model can lead to an algebraic solution.

Task 1

Suppose you invest a dollars to earn an annual interest rate of r percent (as a decimal). After t years, the value of the investment with interest compounded yearly is $A(t) = a(1 + r)^t$. The value with interest compounded continuously is $A(t) = a \cdot e^{rt}$.

a. Explain why you can call $e^r - 1$ the effective annual interest rate for the continuous compounding.

b. Suppose you can earn interest at some rate between 0% and 5%. Use your knowledge of the exponential function to explain why continuous compounding does not give you much of an investment advantage.

c. For each situation find the unknown quantity, such that continuous compounding gives you a $1 advantage over annually compounded interest.
- How much must you invest for 1 year at 2%?
- At what interest rate must you invest $1000 for 1 year?
- For how long must you invest $1000 at 2%?

BIG idea Function

You can use transformations such as translations, reflections, and dilations to understand relationships within a family of functions.

Task 2

$f(x) = b^x$ and $g(x) = \log_b x$ are inverse functions. Explain why each of the following is true.

a. The translation $f_1(x) = b^{x-h}$ of f is equivalent to a vertical stretch or compression of f.

b. The inverse of $f_1(x) = b^{x-h}$ is equivalent to a translation of g.

c. The inverse of $f_1(x) = b^{x-h}$ is not equivalent to a vertical stretch or compression of g.

d. The function $h(x) = \log_c x$ is a vertical stretch or compression of g or of its reflection $-g$.

Assess
Performance

Pull It All Together

See p. 53 for a holistic scoring rubric to gauge a student's progress on Understanding the Problem, Planning a Solution, Getting an Answer, and Assessing Autonomy.

SOLUTION OUTLINES

1. a. Possible Plan: Set $a(1 + r)^t$ equal to $a \cdot e^{rt}$ and solve for r. (You will find that $r = e^r - 1$. Since r is the annual interest rate, you can call $e^r - 1$ the effective annual interest rate for continuous compounding.)

b. Possible Plan: Calculate the interest earned for $1000 at 1%, 2%, 3%, 4%, and 5% interest compounded yearly for 1 year. Then calculate the interest earned for $1000 at 1%, 2%, 3%, 4%, and 5% interest compounded continuously for 1 year.

Compare the interest earned for each rate.

(You will see that the differences really don't give you that big an advantage. The differences are: 5 cents at 1%; 20 cents at 2%; 45 cents at 3%; 81 cents at 4%, and $1.27 at 5%.)

c. Possible Plan: Use the differences you found in part (b) to answer each question. For example, if the difference for 1 year at 2% is 20 cents then you would need 5 times that or 5 years worth of interest to make a $1 difference. ($5000; 5%; 5 years)

2. a. First step: Use the quotient of powers property to rewrite b^{x-h} as $\frac{b^x}{b^h}$. (So, f_1 is now in the format $y = ab^x$. Thus, f_1 is a vertical stretch or compression of f.)

b. First step: Find the inverse of f_1. ($x = b^{y-h}$)

Second step: Write your result from Step 1 in logarithmic form to show that the inverse of f_1 is a translation of g. ($y = \log_b x + h$)

c. First step: Find the inverse of f_1. ($x = b^{y-h}$)

Second step: Write your result from Step 1 in logarithmic form. (A vertical stretch or compression of g would be in the form $y = a \log_b x + h$ not $y = \log_b x + h$)

d. First step: Use the change of base formula to rewrite $\log_c x$ as $\frac{\log_b x}{\log_b c}$, or $\frac{1}{\log_b c} \cdot \log_b x$. ($h$ is now in the format $y = a \log_b x$. Therefore, h is a vertical stretch or compression of g.)

7 Chapter Review

Connecting BIG ideas and Answering the Essential Questions

1 Modeling
The function
$y = ab^x$, $a > 0$, $b > 1$,
models exponential growth.
$y = ab^x$ models exponential
decay if $0 < b < 1$.

→

Exponential Models (Lesson 7-1)
The population P is
1000 at the start.
In each time period,

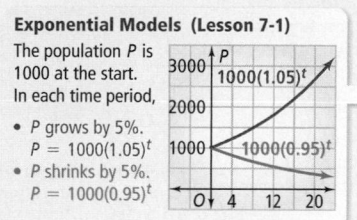

• P grows by 5%.
  $P = 1000(1.05)^t$
• P shrinks by 5%.
  $P = 1000(0.95)^t$

→

Properties of Logarithms (Lesson 7-4)
$$b^a b^c = b^{a+c}$$
$$\log_b mn = \log_b m + \log_b n$$
$$\frac{b^a}{b^c} = b^{a-c}$$
$$\log_b \frac{m}{n} = \log_b m - \log_b n$$
$$\log_b m^n = n \log_b m$$
$$\log_n m = \frac{\log_b m}{\log_b n}$$

2 Equivalence
Logarithms are exponents. In fact, $\log_b a = c$ if and only if $b^c = a$.

3 Function
The exponential function
$y = b^x$ and the logarithmic
function $y = \log_b x$ are
inverse functions.

→

Logarithmic Functions as Inverses (Lesson 7-3)
• $y = 2^x$
• $y = \log_2 x$
• $y = 2^{x-1}$
• $y = (\log_2 x)$
  $+1$

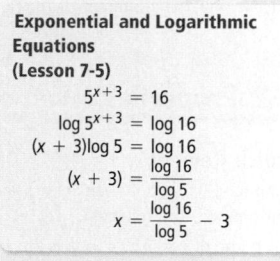

→

Exponential and Logarithmic Equations (Lesson 7-5)
$$5^{x+3} = 16$$
$$\log 5^{x+3} = \log 16$$
$$(x+3)\log 5 = \log 16$$
$$(x+3) = \frac{\log 16}{\log 5}$$
$$x = \frac{\log 16}{\log 5} - 3$$

Chapter Vocabulary

• asymptote (p. 463)
• Change of Base Formula (p. 493)
• common logarithm (p. 482)
• continuously compounded interest (p. 477)
• decay factor (p. 464)

• exponential decay (p. 463)
• exponential equation (p. 498)
• exponential function (p. 462)
• exponential growth (p. 463)
• growth factor (p. 464)
• logarithm (p. 480)

• logarithmic equation (p. 503)
• logarithmic function (p. 483)
• logarithmic scale (p. 482)
• natural base exponential function (p. 476)

Fill in the blanks.

1. There are two types of exponential functions. For __?__ , as the value of x increases, the value of y decreases, approaching zero. For __?__ , as the value of x increases, the value of y increases.

2. As x or y increases in absolute value, the graph may approach a(n) __?__ .

3. A(n) __?__ with a base e is a(n) __?__ .

4. $A = Pe^{rt}$ is known as the __?__ formula.

5. A __?__ uses base 10.

Answers

Chapter Review

1. exponential decay; exponential growth

2. asymptote

3. exponential function; natural base exponential function

4. continuously compounded interest

5. common logarithm

BIG idea Modeling
ESSENTIAL QUESTION How do you model a quantity that changes regularly over time by the same percentage?
ANSWER The function $y = ab^x$, $a > 0$, $b > 1$, models exponential growth. $y = ab^x$ models exponential decay if $0 < b < 1$.

BIG idea Equivalence
ESSENTIAL QUESTION How are exponents and logarithms related?
ANSWER Logarithms are exponents. In fact, $\log_b a = c$ if and only if $b^c = a$.

BIG idea Function
ESSENTIAL QUESTION How are exponential functions and logarithmic functions related?
ANSWER The exponential function $y = b^x$ and the logarithmic function $y = \log_b x$ are inverse functions.

Summative Questions UbD

Use the following prompts as you review this chapter with your students. The prompts are designed to help you assess your students' understanding of the BIG ideas they have studied.

• How could you find the value of $\log_{16} 8$ without using a calculator?

• Compare continuously compounded interest to annual interest. Which method of compounding gives the most interest?

• How can you use exponents to solve a logarithmic equation? How can you use logarithms to solve an exponential equation?

Answers

Chapter Review (continued)

6. exponential growth; $(0, 1)$
7. exponential growth; $(0, 2)$
8. exponential growth; $(0, 0.2)$
9. exponential decay; $(0, 3)$
10. exponential growth; $\left(0, \frac{25}{7}\right)$
11. exponential growth; $(0, 0.0015)$
12. exponential decay; $(0, 2.25)$
13. exponential decay; $(0, 0.5)$
14. $y = 12{,}500(0.91)^x$; \$7800
15. $y = 50(1.03)^x$; \$58
16. The parent graph $y = 2^x$ is stretched by a factor of 5, translated 1 unit to the left, and 3 units up.
17. The parent graph $y = \left(\frac{1}{3}\right)^x$ is reflected across the x-axis, stretched by a factor of 2, and translated 2 units to the right.
18. \$1100.76
19. \$291.91
20. 0.0498
21. 0.3679
22. 148.4132
23. 0.6065

7-1 Exploring Exponential Models

Quick Review

The general form of an **exponential function** is $y = ab^x$, where x is a real number, $a \neq 0$, $b > 0$, and $b \neq 1$. When $b > 1$, the function models **exponential growth**, and b is the **growth factor**. When $0 < b < 1$, the function models **exponential decay**, and b is the **decay factor**. The y-intercept is $(0, a)$.

Example

Determine whether $y = 2(1.4)^x$ is an example of exponential growth or decay. Then, find the y-intercept.

Since $b = 1.4 > 1$, the function represents exponential growth.

Since $a = 2$, the y-intercept is $(0, 2)$.

Exercises

Determine whether each function is an example of exponential growth or decay. Then, find the y-intercept.

6. $y = 5^x$
7. $y = 2(4)^x$
8. $y = 0.2(3.8)^x$
9. $y = 3(0.25)^x$
10. $y = \frac{25}{7}\left(\frac{7}{5}\right)^x$
11. $y = 0.0015(10)^x$
12. $y = 2.25\left(\frac{1}{3}\right)^x$
13. $y = 0.5\left(\frac{1}{4}\right)^x$

Write a function for each situation. Then find the value of each function after five years. Round to the nearest dollar.

14. A \$12,500 car depreciates 9% each year.
15. A baseball card bought for \$50 increases 3% in value each year.

7-2 Properties of Exponential Functions

Quick Review

Exponential functions can be translated, stretched, compressed, and reflected.

The graph of $y = ab^{x-h} + k$ is the graph of the parent function $y = b^x$ stretched or compressed by a factor $|a|$, reflected across the x-axis if $a < 0$, and then translated h units horizontally and k units vertically.

The **continuously compounded interest formula** is $A = Pe^{rt}$, where P is the principal, r is the annual interest rate, and t is time in years.

Example

How does the graph of $y = -3^x + 1$ compare to the graph of the parent function?

The parent function is $y = 3^x$.

Since $a = -1$, the graph is reflected across the x-axis.

Since $k = 1$, it is then translated up 1 unit.

Exercises

How does the graph of each function compare to the graph of the parent function?

16. $y = 5(2)^{x+1} + 3$
17. $y = -2\left(\frac{1}{3}\right)^{x-2}$

Find the amount in a continuously compounded account for the given conditions.

18. principal: \$1000
    annual interest rate: 4.8%
    time: 2 years

19. principal: \$250
    annual interest rate: 6.2%
    time: 2.5 years

Evaluate each expression to four decimal places.

20. e^{-3}
21. e^{-1}
22. e^5
23. $e^{-\frac{1}{2}}$

7-3 Logarithmic Functions as Inverses

Quick Review

If $x = b^y$, then $\log_b x = y$. The **logarithmic function** is the inverse of the exponential function, so the graphs of the functions are reflections of each other in the line $y = x$. Logarithmic functions can be translated, stretched, compressed, and reflected, as represented by $y = a \log_b(x - h) + k$, similarly to exponential functions.

When $b = 10$, the logarithm is called a **common logarithm**, which you can write as $\log x$.

Example

Write $5^{-2} = 0.04$ in logarithmic form.

If $y = b^x$, then $\log_b y = x$.

$y = 0.04$, $b = 5$ and $x = -2$.

So, $\log_5 0.04 = -2$.

Exercises

Write each equation in logarithmic form.

24. $6^2 = 36$ **25.** $2^{-3} = 0.125$

26. $3^3 = 27$ **27.** $10^{-3} = 0.001$

Evaluate each logarithm.

28. $\log_2 64$ **29.** $\log_3 \frac{1}{9}$

30. $\log 0.00001$ **31.** $\log_2 1$

Graph each logarithmic function.

32. $y = \log_3 x$ **33.** $y = \log x + 2$

34. $y = 3 \log_2(x)$ **35.** $y = \log_5(x + 1)$

How does the graph of each function compare to the graph of the parent function?

36. $y = 3 \log_4(x + 1)$ **37.** $y = \log_3(x - 5) + 3$

7-4 Properties of Logarithms

Quick Review

For any positive numbers, m, n, and b where $b \neq 1$, each of the following statements is true. Each can be used to rewrite a logarithmic expression.

- $\log_b mn = \log_b m + \log_b n$ \quad Product Property
- $\log_b \frac{m}{n} = \log_b m - \log_b n$ \quad Quotient Property
- $\log_b m^n = n \log_b m$ \quad Power Property

Example

Write $2 \log_2 y + \log_2 x$ as a single logarithm. Identify any properties used.

Write the expression.	$2 \log_2 y + \log_2 x$
Use the Power Property.	$\log_2 y^2 + \log_2 x$
Use the Product Property.	$\log_2 xy^2$

Exercises

Write each expression as a single logarithm. Identify any properties used.

38. $\log 8 + \log 3$ **39.** $\log_2 5 - \log_2 3$

40. $4 \log_3 x + \log_3 7$ **41.** $\log x - \log y$

42. $\log 5 - 2 \log x$ **43.** $3 \log_4 x + 2 \log_4 x$

Expand each logarithm. State the properties of logarithms used.

44. $\log_4 x^2 y^3$ **45.** $\log 4s^4 t$

46. $\log_3 \frac{2}{x}$ **47.** $\log(x + 3)^2$

48. $\log_2(2y - 4)^3$ **49.** $\log \frac{z^2}{5}$

Use the Change of Base Formula to evaluate each expression.

50. $\log_2 7$ **51.** $\log_3 10$

39. $\log_2 \frac{5}{3}$; Quotient Prop.

40. $\log_3 7x^4$; Power and Product Prop.

41. $\log \frac{x}{y}$; Quotient Prop.

42. $\log \frac{5}{x^2}$; Power and Quotient Prop.

43. $\log_4 x^5$; Power and Product Prop.

44. $2 \log_4 x + 3 \log_4 y$; Product and Power Prop.

45. $\log 4 + 4 \log s + \log t$; Product and Power Prop.

46. $\log_3 2 - \log_3 x$; Quotient Prop.

47. $2 \log(x + 3)$; Power Prop.

48. $3 \log_2 2 + 3 \log_2(y - 2)$; Power and Product Prop.

49. $2 \log z - \log 5$; Power and Quotient Prop.

50. ≈ 2.8

51. ≈ 2.1

24. $2 = \log_6 36$

25. $-3 = \log_2 0.125$

26. $3 = \log_3 27$

27. $-3 = \log 0.001$

28. 6

29. -2

30. -5

31. 0

32.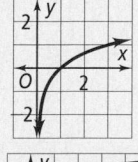

33.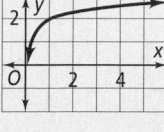

34.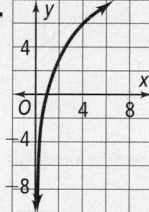

35.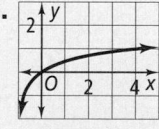

36. The parent graph $y = \log_4 x$ is stretched by a factor of 3 and translated 1 unit to the left.

37. The parent graph $y = \log_3 x$ is translated 5 units to the right and 3 units up.

38. $\log 24$; Product Prop.

Answers

52. 0.75

53. 3.2619

54. 4.6542

55. 1.3652

56. 3.3333

57. 8

58. 50

59. 15.5885

60. 0.9307

61. 0.6599

62. 0.6658

63. 3.0589

64. ≈18.2 h

7-5 Exponential and Logarithmic Equations

Quick Review

An equation in the form $b^{cx} = a$, where the exponent includes a variable, is called an **exponential equation**. You can solve exponential equations by taking the logarithm of each side of the equation. An equation that includes one or more logarithms involving a variable is called a **logarithmic equation**.

Example

Solve $6^{2x} = 75$. Round your answer to the nearest ten-thousandth.

Write the original equation.	$6^{2x} = 75$
Take the logarithm of each side.	$\log 6^{2x} = \log 75$
Use the Power Property.	$2x \log 6 = \log 75$
Divide each side by 2 log 6.	$x = \dfrac{\log 75}{2 \log 6}$
Use a calculator to evaluate.	$x \approx 1.2048$

Exercises

Solve each equation. Round to the nearest ten-thousandth.

52. $25^{2x} = 125$

53. $3^x = 36$

54. $7^{x-3} = 25$

55. $5^x + 3 = 12$

56. $\log 3x = 1$

57. $\log_2 4x = 5$

58. $\log x = \log 2x^2 - 2$

59. $2 \log_3 x = 5$

Solve by graphing. Round to the nearest ten-thousandth.

60. $5^{2x} = 20$

61. $3^{7x} = 160$

62. $6^{3x+1} = 215$

63. $0.5^x = 0.12$

64. A culture of 10 bacteria is started, and the number of bacteria will double every hour. In about how many hours will there be 3,000,000 bacteria?

Do you know HOW?

Determine whether each function is an example of exponential growth or decay. Then find the y-intercept.

1. $y = 3(0.25)^x$

2. $y = 2(6)^{-x}$

3. $y = 0.1(10)^x$

4. $y = 3e^x$

Describe how the graph of each function is related to the graph of its parent function. Then find the domain, range, and asymptotes.

5. $y = 3^x + 2$

6. $y = \left(\frac{1}{2}\right)^{x+1}$

7. $y = -(2)^{x+2}$

Write each equation in logarithmic form.

8. $5^4 = 625$ **9.** $e^0 = 1$

Evaluate each logarithm.

10. $\log_2 8$ **11.** $\log_7 7$

12. $\log_5 \frac{1}{125}$ **13.** $\log_{11} 1$

Graph each logarithmic function. Compare each graph to the graph of its parent function. List each function's domain, range, y-intercept, and asymptotes.

14. $y = \log_3(x-1)$

15. $y = \frac{1}{2}\log_3(x+2)$

16. $y = 1 - \log_2 x$

Write each logarithmic expression as a single logarithm.

17. $\log_2 4 + 3\log_2 9$

18. $3\log a - 2\log b$

Expand each logarithm.

19. $\log_7 \frac{a}{b}$

20. $\log 3x^3 y^2$

Use the properties of logarithms to evaluate each expression.

21. $\log_9 27 - \log_9 9$

22. $2\log 5 + \log 40$

Solve each equation.

23. $(27)^{3x} = 81$

24. $3^{x-1} = 24$

25. $\log(x-2) = 1$

26. $2\log x = -4$

Use the Change of Base Formula to rewrite each expression using common logarithms.

27. $\log_3 16$

28. $\log_2 10$

29. $\log_7 8$

30. $\log_4 9$

Do you UNDERSTAND?

31. Writing Show that solving the equation $3^{2x} = 4$ by taking the common logarithm of each side is equivalent to solving it by taking the logarithm with base 3 of each side.

32. Open-Ended Give an example of an exponential function that models exponential growth and an example of an exponential function that models exponential decay.

33. Investment You put $1500 into an account that pays 7% annual interest compounded continuously. How long will it be before you have $2000 in your account?

The parent graph $y = \log_2 x$ is reflected across the x-axis and translated 1 unit up; domain: $x > 0$, range: all real numbers; no y-intercept; asymptote: $x = 0$

17. $\log_2 2916$

18. $\log \frac{a^3}{b^2}$

19. $\log_7 a - \log_7 b$

20. $\log 3 + 3\log x + 2\log y$

21. $\frac{1}{2}$

22. 3

23. $\frac{4}{9}$

24. ≈ 3.89

25. 12

26. 0.01

27. $\frac{\log 16}{\log 3}$

28. $\frac{1}{\log 2}$

29. $\frac{\log 8}{\log 7}$

30. $\frac{\log 9}{\log 4}$

31.
$$3^{2x} = 4$$
$$\log 3^{2x} = \log 4$$
$$2x\log 3 = \log 4$$
$$x = \frac{\log 4}{2\log 3}$$
$$x \approx 0.6309$$

and

$$3^{2x} = 4$$
$$\log_3 3^{2x} = \log_3 4$$
$$2x = \log_3 4$$
$$x = \frac{1}{2}\log_3 4$$
$$x \approx 0.6309$$

32. Answers may vary. Sample: exponential growth: $y = \frac{1}{3}(2)^x$; exponential decay: $y = 7\left(\frac{1}{5}\right)^x$

33. 4.11 yrs

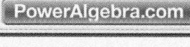
Answers

Chapter Test

1. exponential decay, (0, 3)

2. exponential decay, (0, 2)

3. exponential growth, (0, 0.1)

4. exponential growth, (0, 3)

5. The parent graph $y = 3^x$ is translated 2 units up; domain: all real numbers, range: $y > 2$; asymptote: $y = 2$

6. The parent graph $y = \left(\frac{1}{2}\right)^x$ is translated 1 unit to the left; domain: all real numbers, range $y < 0$; asymptote: $y = 0$

7. The parent graph $y = 2^x$ is translated 2 units to the left and reflected across the x-axis; domain: all real numbers, range: $y > 0$; asymptote: $y = 0$

8. $\log_5 625 = 4$

9. $\log_e 1 = 0$

10. 3

11. 1

12. -3

13. 0

14.
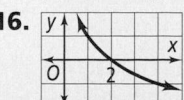

The parent graph $y = \log_3 x$ is translated 1 unit to the right; domain: $x > 1$, range: all real numbers; no y-intercept; asymptote: $x = 1$

15.

The parent graph $y = \frac{1}{2}\log_3 x$ is compressed by the factor $\frac{1}{2}$, then translated 2 units to the left; domain: $x > -2$, range: all real numbers; y-intercept: $\left(0, \frac{1}{2}\log_3 2\right) \approx (0, 0.3155)$; asymptote: $x = -2$

16.

Item Number	Lesson
1	7-1
2	4-8
3	7-4
4	5-3
5	7-5b
6	7-6
7	6-4
8	1-4
9	5-4
10	3-2
11	5-2
12	5-3
13	6-3
14	5-2
15	6-8
16	5-1
17	7-5
18	7-1
19	5-5
20	7-4
21	7-5
22	4-7
23	5-6
24	2-2
25	2-4
26	6-5
27	6-4
28	5-3
29	4-1
30	3-3
31	4-6
32	5-5
33	7-2
34	2-7

7 Cumulative Test Prep

TIPS FOR SUCCESS

Some problems ask you to find lengths of arcs or areas of sectors. Read the question at the right. Then follow the tips to answer the sample question.

TIP 1

Draw a diagram

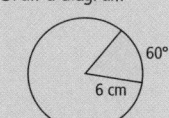

Let $f(x) = \pi x^2$ represent the area of a circle with radius x. Let $g(x) = \frac{60x}{360}$ represent the area of a 60° sector of a circle with area x. A circle with radius 6 centimeters has a sector measuring 60°. What is the area of this sector $(g \circ f)(x)$?

Ⓐ 6π cm^2
Ⓑ 12π cm^2
Ⓒ 24π cm^2
Ⓓ 36π cm^2

TIP 2

Find $f(x)$ first.
$f(x) = \pi x^2$
$\quad = \pi \cdot 6^2$
$\quad = 36\pi$

Think It Through

$g(x) = \frac{60x}{360}$

$(g \circ f)(x) = \frac{60(36\pi)}{360}$

$\quad = \frac{36\pi}{6}$

$\quad = 6\pi$

The correct answer is A.

Vocabulary Builder

As you solve problems, you must understand the meanings of mathematical terms. Match each term with its mathematical meaning.

A. growth factor
B. asymptote
C. logarithmic function
D. exponential equation

I. the inverse of an exponential function

II. a line that a graph approaches as x or y increases in absolute value

III. the value of b in $y = ab^x$, when $b > 1$

IV. an equation of the form $b^{cx} = a$, where the exponent includes a variable

Multiple Choice

Read each question. Then write the letter of the correct answer on your page.

1. The population of a town is modeled by the equation $P = 16{,}581e^{0.02t}$ where P represents the population t years after 2000. According to the model, what will the population of the town be in 2020?

Ⓐ 16,916   Ⓒ 20,252
Ⓑ 17,258   Ⓓ 24,736

2. If $i = \sqrt{-1}$, then which expression is equal to $9i(13i)$?

Ⓕ -117 Ⓗ 117
Ⓖ $117i$ Ⓘ $-117i$

3. Which expression is equivalent to $\log_5 32$?

Ⓐ $\log 5 + \log 32$
Ⓑ $\log 5 - \log 32$
Ⓒ $(\log 5)(\log 32)$
Ⓓ $\dfrac{\log 32}{\log 5}$

Answers

Cumulative Test Prep

A. III
B. II
C. I
D. IV
1. D
2. F
3. D

4. The table shows the height of a ball that was tossed into the air. Which equation best models the relationship between time t and the height of the ball h?

Time (seconds)	0	0.25	0.5	0.75
Height (feet)	4	10.5	15	17.5

   Ⓕ $h = 26t + 4$

   Ⓖ $h = -16t^2 + 30t + 4$

   Ⓗ $h = 4t^2$

   Ⓘ $h = -16t^2 + 4$

5. Which is the graph of $y = 3^x$?

Ⓐ 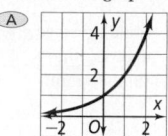   Ⓒ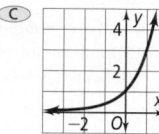

Ⓑ 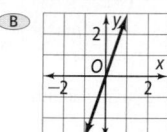   Ⓓ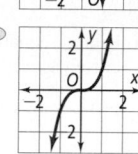

6. Which exponential function is equivalent to $y = \log_3 x$?

   Ⓕ $y = 3^x$ Ⓗ $y = x^3$

   Ⓖ $y = \frac{x}{3}$ Ⓘ $x = 3^y$

7. Simplify $\left(\dfrac{3x^2y^4}{x^2y^3}\right)^2$.

   Ⓐ $\frac{3y^2}{x^3}$ Ⓒ $\frac{9y^2}{x^3}$

   Ⓑ $3x^3y^2$ Ⓓ $9x^0y^2$

8. Solve the mass energy equivalence formula $e = mc^2$ for c.

   Ⓕ $c = e^2m$ Ⓗ $c = \sqrt{\left(\frac{e}{m}\right)}$

   Ⓖ $c = \sqrt{\left(\frac{m}{e}\right)}$ Ⓘ $c = \sqrt{(e - m)}$

9. What is the quotient of $(x^3 + 2x^2 - x + 6) \div (x + 3)$?

   Ⓐ $x^2 + 5x + 14$, R 42   Ⓒ $x^3 + 5x^2 + 14x + 42$

   Ⓑ $x^2 - x + 2$ Ⓓ $x^2 + x - 2$

10. On a certain night, a restaurant employs x servers at \$25 per hour and y bus persons at \$8 per hour. The total hourly cost for the restaurant's 12 employees that night is \$249. The following system of equations can be used to find the number of servers and the number of bus persons at work.

$$\begin{cases} 25x + 8y = 249 \\ \;\;\,x + \;\,y = \;\,12 \end{cases}$$

Based on the solution of the system of equations, which of the following can you conclude?

   Ⓕ Fewer than 2 bus persons were working.

   Ⓖ More than ten servers were working.

   Ⓗ 50% of the people working were bus persons.

   Ⓘ 75% of the people working were servers.

11. Which polynomial equation has the real roots of -3, 1, 1, and $\frac{3}{2}$?

   Ⓐ $x^4 - \frac{1}{2}x^3 - \frac{13}{2}x^2 + \frac{21}{2}x - \frac{9}{2} = 0$

   Ⓑ $x^4 - \frac{1}{2}x^3 - \frac{17}{2}x^2 - 10x - \frac{9}{2} = 0$

   Ⓒ $x^4 + x^3 - 5x^2 + 3x - \frac{3}{2} = 0$

   Ⓓ $(x - 3)(x + 1)(x + 1)\left(x + \frac{3}{2}\right) = 0$

12. What is the factored form of $2x^3 + 5x^2 - 12x$?

   Ⓕ $x(2x - 3)(x + 4)$

   Ⓖ $(2x^2 - 3)(x + 4)$

   Ⓗ $x(2x + 4)(x - 3)$

   Ⓘ $(2x - 4)(x + 3)$

13. Simplify $5\sqrt[3]{x^2} + 3\sqrt[3]{x^2}$.

   Ⓐ $8\sqrt[3]{x^2}$ Ⓑ $8\sqrt[6]{x^2}$ Ⓒ $8\sqrt[3]{x^4}$ Ⓓ $8\sqrt[6]{x^4}$

14. What is the equation of the function graphed below?

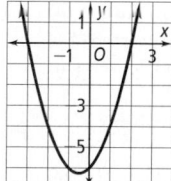

   Ⓕ $y = (x + 2)(x - 3)$ Ⓗ $y = (x + 3)(x - 2)$

   Ⓖ $y = (x - 6)^2$ Ⓘ $y = (x - 1)(x + 5)$

4. G

5. C

6. I

7. C

8. H

9. B

10. I

11. A

12. F

13. A

14. H

Answers

Cumulative Test Prep (continued)

15. D

16. H

17. 1

18. 15

19. 3

20. $\frac{3}{2}$

21. 1.25

22. 0

23. 7

24. 52.5

25. 13

26. 2

27. 243

28. −0.75

29. **[2]** domain: all real numbers, range: $y \le 5$

[1] incorrect domain or range

30. **[2]** let x = a child's weight, then $15 \le x \le 35$

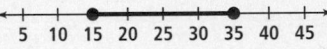

[1] graph drawn with open circles

31. **[2]**
$$x^2 + 3x = 1$$
$$x^2 + 3x + 2.25 = 3.25$$
$$(x + 1.5)^2 = 3.25$$
$$x + 1.5 = \pm\sqrt{3.25}$$
$$x = -1.5 \pm \sqrt{3.25}$$

[1] one computational error

32. **[2]** No, complex roots occur in conjugate pairs. If $a + bi$ is a root, then $a - bi$ is also a root.

[1] incomplete explanation

33. **[2]**

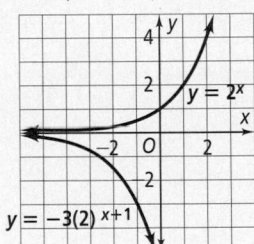

[1] graph is not labeled correctly

34. **[4]** **a.** The graph of $y = -|x - 3| + 2$ is the graph of $y = |x|$ reflected in the x-axis and translated 3 units to the right and 2 units up.

b. $y = -|x + 3| - 2$

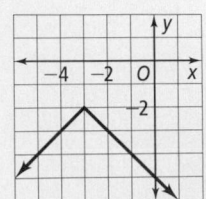

[3] graph is not labeled correctly

[2] only part (a) is correct OR only part (b) is correct

---

15. Which graph shows $y = -\sqrt{x + 3} + 2$, a transformation of the radical parent function $y = \sqrt{x}$?

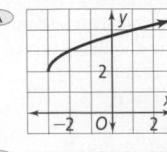

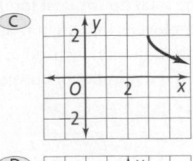

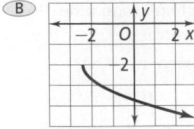

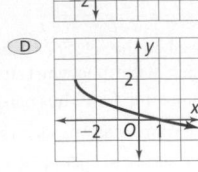

16. Which function would have a graph whose end behavior is up and up?

Ⓕ $f(x) = x^3 + 1$ Ⓗ $f(x) = 5x^2 - 7$

Ⓖ $f(x) = -2x^4$ Ⓘ $f(x) = -3x$

GRIDDED RESPONSE

17. What is the solution of the equation $\log_9 x = \log_6 x$?

18. A savings account pays 4.62% annual interest, compounded continuously. After approximately how many years will a principal of $500 double?

19. The graph of a polynomial has x-intercepts at $(-3, 0)$, $(-1, 0)$, and $(1, 0)$. What is the least possible degree of the polynomial?

20. Evaluate $\log_4 8$.

21. Solve $4^{2x} = 32$.

22. How many different real solutions are there for the equation $4x^2 = -4x - 4$?

23. Use the Fundamental Theorem of Algebra to determine the total number of complex zeros of $f(x) = x^2 - 3x^5 + 4x - x^7 - 44$.

24. y varies directly with x and $y = 30$ when $x = 4$. What is y when $x = 7$?

25. What is the y-intercept of the line that passes through the point $(-2, 7)$ and is parallel to $y = 3x + 5$?

26. What is the solution of $\sqrt{x + 2} = x$?

27. Simplify $9^{\frac{5}{2}}$.

28. What is the x-intercept of $f(x) = x^3 - x^2 + 1$? Round the answer to the nearest hundredth.

Short Response

29. What are the domain and range of the parabola?

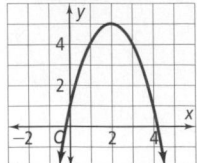

30. To use an outdoor toddler swing, a child must weigh at least 15 pounds, and can weigh no more than 35 pounds. Draw a graph to model this situation.

31. Solve the equation $0 = x^2 + 3x - 1$ by completing the square.

32. Can a quadratic equation with real coefficients have exactly one imaginary root? Explain your answer.

33. Graph the function $y = -3(2)^{x+1}$ as a translation of its parent function.

Extended Response

34. A transformation of the parent absolute value function is shown in the graph.

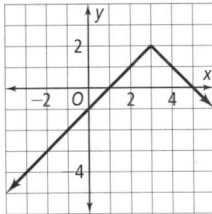

a. What is the transformation from the parent function $y = |x|$?

b. Draw the graph of the transformed function after reflecting it across the y-axis and translating it 4 units down.

[1] part (a) is incorrect and the graph is not labeled correctly

Get Ready!

Lesson 2-2

Using Direct Variation

For each direct variation, find the constant of variation. Then find the value of y when $x = -3$.

1. $y = 4$ when $x = 3$ **2.** $y = 1$ when $x = -1.5$

3. $y = -5$ when $x = \frac{3}{2}$ **4.** $y = -16$ when $x = 7$

Lesson 4-4

Factoring Quadratic Expressions

Factor each expression.

5. $x^2 + x - 6$ **6.** $4x^2 + 17x + 15$

7. $9x^2 - 25$ **8.** $x^2 - 12x + 36$

9. $3x^2 + 10x + 8$ **10.** $x^2 - 5x + 6$

Lesson 4-5

Solving Quadratic Equations

Solve each equation.

11. $x^2 + 7x - 8 = 0$ **12.** $\frac{1}{4}x^2 + \frac{7}{2}x = -12$

13. $3x^2 = 18x - 24$ **14.** $9x^2 + 6x = 0$

15. $4x^2 + 16 = 34x$ **16.** $x^2 - 13x - 30 = 0$

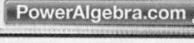

Looking Ahead Vocabulary

17. If you need to drive 30 miles, you have many options. For instance, you can drive 15 miles per hour for 2 hours, 30 miles per hour for 1 hour, or 60 miles per hour for half an hour. Notice that when you double your speed, it takes half as much time to get to your destination. Mathematicians describe this kind of relationship as an *inverse variation*. Why do you suppose they use the word *inverse* to describe it?

18. Suppose you are hiking on a trail and find that the bridge over the river has been washed out, making a gap or *discontinuity* in the trail. Graphs can have gaps too. Sketch what you think a graph with a discontinuity might look like.

Get Ready!

Assign this diagnostic assessment to determine if students have the prerequisite skills for Chapter 8.

Lesson	Skill
2-2	Use Direct Variation
4-4	Factor Quadratic Equations
4-5	Solve Quadratic Equations

To remediate students, select from these resources (available for every lesson).
- Online Problems (PowerAlgebra.com)
- Reteaching (All-in-One Teaching Resources)
- Practice (All-in-One Teaching Resources)

Why Students Need These Skills

USING DIRECT VARIATION
Understanding direct variation is essential to identifying and understanding inverse variation.

FACTORING QUADRATIC EXPRESSIONS
Students will need to be able to factor quadratic expressions in order to determine the domain and the range of rational functions.

SOLVING QUADRATIC EQUATIONS
Students will need to solve the resulting quadratic equations in order to solve rational equations.

Looking Ahead Vocabulary

INVERSE VARIATION Ask students what other meanings they know for the word *inverse*, both in daily life and in math.

DISCONTINUITY Suggest students graph the path a washed-out bridge takes to see what the discontinuity might look like.

Answers

Get Ready!

1. $\frac{4}{3}$; -4

2. $-\frac{2}{3}$; 2

3. $-\frac{10}{3}$; 10

4. $-\frac{16}{7}$; $\frac{48}{7}$

5. $(x + 3)(x - 2)$

6. $(4x + 5)(x + 3)$

7. $(3x - 5)(3x + 5)$

8. $(x - 6)^2$

9. $(3x + 4)(x + 2)$

10. $(x - 3)(x - 2)$

11. $1, -8$

12. $-6, -8$

13. $4, 2$

14. $0, -\frac{2}{3}$

15. $8, \frac{1}{2}$

16. $15, -2$

17. Answers may vary. Inverse is used when one quantity increases as the other quantity decreases.

18. Answers may vary. Sample:

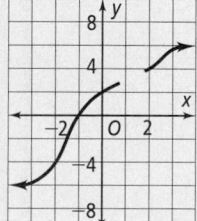

Chapter 8 Overview

UbD Understanding by Design

Chapter 8 expands on students' understandings and skills related to functions, equations, and graphs. In this chapter, students will develop the answers to the Essential Questions posed on the student page as they learn the concepts and skills bulleted below.

BIG idea Proportionality

ESSENTIAL QUESTION Are two quantities inversely proportional if an increase in one corresponds to a decrease in the other?
• Students will identify and describe inverse and direct variation functions.

BIG idea Function

ESSENTIAL QUESTION What kinds of asymptotes are possible for a rational function?
• Students will graph asymptotes of rational functions.
• Students will identify whether a rational function has an asymptote.
• Students will differentiate between vertical, horizontal, and oblique asymptotes.

BIG idea Equivalence

ESSENTIAL QUESTION Are a rational expression and its simplified form equivalent?
• Students will define the domains of simplified rational expressions to make them equivalent to the original expressions.

CHAPTER 8

Rational Functions

PowerAlgebra.com

Your place to get all things digital

VIDEO Download videos connecting math to your world.

VOCABULARY Math definitions in English and Spanish

SOLVE IT! The online Solve It will get you in gear for each lesson.

DYNAMIC ACTIVITIES Interactive! Vary numbers, graphs, and figures to explore math concepts.

ONLINE PROBLEMS Download Step-by-Step Problems with Instant Replay.

ONLINE HOMEWORK Get and view your assignments online.

MathXL FOR SCHOOL Extra practice and review online

Rational functions help explain how surface tension allows some animals to tread across a pond's surface.

How can you graph rational functions and solve rational equations? You will learn how in this chapter.

Vocabulary

English/Spanish Vocabulary Audio Online:

English	Spanish
combined variation, *p. 523*	variación combinada
complex fraction, *p. 559*	fracción compleja
continuous graph, *p. 539*	gráfica continua
discontinuous graph, *p. 539*	gráfica discontinua
inverse variation, *p. 520*	variación inversa
joint variation, *p. 523*	variación conjunta
point of discontinuity, *p. 539*	punto de discontinuidad
rational equation, *p. 565*	ecuación racional
rational expression, *p. 548*	expresión racional
rational function, *p. 538*	función racional
reciprocal function, *p. 530*	función recíproca

PowerAlgebra.com

Chapter 8 Overview

Use these online assets to engage your students. These include support for the Solve It and step-by-step solutions for Problems.

 Show the student-produced video demonstrating relevant and engaging applications of the new concepts in the chapter.

 Find online definitions for new terms in English and Spanish.

 Start each lesson with an attention-getting Problem. View the Problem online with helpful hints.

My Math Video

My Math Video

Use this photo to introduce the concept of inverse variation.

Q What do you see in the photo? **[a lizard walking on its hind legs across some water]**

Q The lizard has webbed feet. How might these help it cross the water? **[The webs can catch air bubbles underneath their feet, displacing water and so helping the lizard float.]**

Q Do you think the lizard could keep walking on the water indefinitely? Why or why not? **[No; samples: the lizard will eventually get tired; the lizard has to maintain a very fast pace in order to stay above the water and will eventually slow too much.]**

EXTENSION

Suggest students research the use of snowshoes. Have them find out how the snowshoe distributes the pressure a person exerts on a surface of snow, allowing a person to walk on top of snow. Have them determine how the size of the snowshoe affects the pressure on the snow.

BIG ideas

1 Proportionality

Essential Question Are two quantities inversely proportional if an increase in one corresponds to a decrease in the other?

2 Function

Essential Question What kinds of asymptotes are possible for a rational function?

3 Equivalence

Essential Question Are a rational expression and its simplified form equivalent?

Chapter Preview

PowerAlgebra.com | Chapter 8 Rational Functions | 519

 Increase students' depth of knowledge with interactive online activities.

 Show Problems from each lesson solved step by step. Instant replay allows students to go at their own pace when studying online.

 Assign homework to individual students or to an entire class.

 Prepare students for the Mid-Chapter Quiz and Chapter Test with online practice and review.

UbD

Proportionality

BIG idea Two quantities are *proportional* if they have the same ratio in each instance where they are measured together. Two quantities are *inversely proportional* if they have the same product in each instance where they are measured together.

ESSENTIAL UNDERSTANDINGS

8-1   In a direct variation, two positive quantities either increase together or decrease together. In an inverse variation, as one quantity increases the other decreases.

8-2   Transformations of the parent reciprocal function include stretches, compressions (or shrinks), reflections, and horizontal and vertical translations.

Function

BIG idea A function is a relationship between variables in which each value of the input variable is associated with a unique value of the output variable. Functions can be represented in a variety of ways, such as graphs, tables, equations, or words. Each representation is particularly useful in certain situations. Some important families of functions are developed through transformations of the simplest form of the function.

ESSENTIAL UNDERSTANDINGS

8-2   See above.

8-3   A rational function is a ratio of polynomial functions. If a rational function is in simplified form and the polynomial in the denominator is not constant, the graph of the rational function features asymptotic behavior. It looks quite different from the graphs of either of its polynomial components.

Equivalence

BIG idea A single quantity may be represented by many different expressions. The facts about a quantity may be expressed by many different equations (or inequalities).

ESSENTIAL UNDERSTANDINGS

8-4   You can use much of what you know about multiplying and dividing fractions to multiply and divide rational expressions.

8-5   To operate with rational expressions, you can use much of what you know about operating with fractions. To add or subtract rational expressions, you first find a common denominator—preferably the least common multiple (LCM) of the denominators.

8-6   To solve an equation containing rational expressions, first multiply each side by the least common denominator of the rational expressions. Doing this, however, can introduce extraneous solutions.

Inverse Variation and Graphing

Inverse variation occurs when one quantity increases as another decreases proportionally. It can be represented in the following forms:

$$xy = k \qquad y = \frac{k}{x} \qquad x = \frac{k}{y}$$

where $k \neq 0$ and k is the constant of variation.

Combined variation occurs when one quantity varies with respect to two or more quantities. **Joint variation** occurs when one quantity varies directly with two or more quantities. The following equations represent combined variations.

$$z = kxy \qquad z = \frac{kxy}{w} \qquad z = \frac{kx}{wy}$$

Graphing Reciprocal Functions

Functions that model inverse variations belong to a family whose parent is the reciprocal function $f(x) = \frac{1}{x}$. The branches of the parent function $y = \frac{1}{x}$ are in Quadrants I and III.

Stretches and compressions of the parent function remain in the same quadrants. **Reflections** are in Quadrants II and IV.

For $y = \frac{a}{x}$, where $x \neq 0$:
* stretch: ($|a| > 1$)
* shrink: ($0 < |a| < 1$)
* reflection ($a < 0$) in the y-axis

Reciprocal functions can also be **translated** horizontally or vertically.

$$y = \frac{a}{x - h} + k, x \neq h;$$

translated vertically by k and horizontally by h.

Example: Compare the graph of $g(x) = \frac{5}{x - 2} + 3$ with $f(x) = \frac{1}{x}$. Sketch the graphs.

Solution: The graph of $g(x)$ has been stretched by a factor of 5 and shifted 3 units vertically and 2 units horizontally.

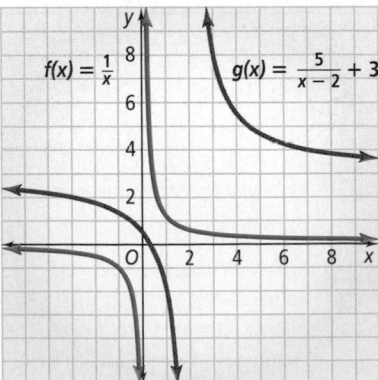

Common Errors with Inverse Variation and Graphing

Errors occur when students write models for combined variations. Remind students that "varies jointly" indicates the variable must be in the numerator. The phrase "varies inversely" indicates a variable must be in the denominator.

Graphs of Rational Functions

The graph of a rational function is **continuous** if it has no jumps, breaks, or holes.

- $\frac{x}{x^2 + 3}$ is continuous because there is no real value of x that makes the denominator 0.

Rational functions are **discontinuous** at the points where the function is undefined. A **removable discontinuity** occurs when the function can be redefined. A **non-removable discontinuity** occurs when there is no way to redefine the function at the point to make it continuous.

- $\frac{(x - 5)(x + 1)}{(x + 1)}$ has removable discontinuity at $x = -1$.
- $\frac{(x - 5)}{(x + 1)}$ has a non-removable discontinuity at $x = -1$.

Asymptotes

An asymptote is a line that the graph approaches as x or y increases in absolute value. A **vertical asymptote** occurs at $x = a$ if this is a non-removable discontinuity. The graph of a rational function can have any number of vertical asymptotes.

The graph of a rational function can have no more than one **horizontal asymptote**. If the degree of the numerator is m and the degree of the denominator is n, then:

- if $m < n$, the graph has a horizontal asymptote $y = 0$.
- if $m > n$, the graph has no horizontal asymptote.
- if $m = n$, the graph has a horizontal asymptote $y = \frac{a}{b}$, where a is the numerator's leading coefficient and b is the denominator's leading coefficient.

Graphing

The graph of a rational function will never touch a vertical asymptote. The graph may touch a horizontal asymptote for other than large absolute values of x.

Example: Graph $y = \frac{-3x + 6}{x - 4}$.

Asymptotes:

vertical: $x = 4$

horizontal: $y = \frac{-3}{1} = -3$

x-intercept: $(2, 0)$

y-intercept: $\left(0, -\frac{3}{2}\right)$

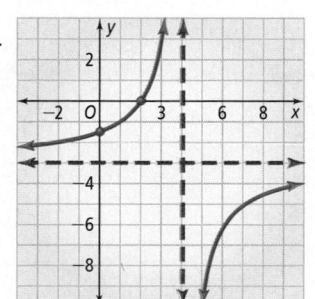

Common Errors When Graphing Rational Functions

Students are often confused by a **removable point of discontinuity** because a graphing calculator makes the graph appear continuous. Have students use the **TRACE** key or **TABLE** function to verify a removable discontinuity point. Emphasize again the importance of using the equation to describe characteristics of any graph before using a graphing calculator.

Solving Rational Equations

Rational Expressions

A rational expression is the quotient of two polynomials. It is in simplest form when its numerator and denominator have no common divisors. Rational expressions may contain restrictions to prevent the denominator of the original expression from being zero.

Operations with Rational Expressions

Example: Find the product of $\frac{5}{x + 3} \cdot \frac{x^2 + 7x + 12}{x + 2}$. State any restrictions.

Solution: Factor and simplify.

$$\frac{5}{x + 3} \cdot \frac{(x + 3)(x + 4)}{x + 2} = \frac{5(x + 4)}{x + 2}.$$

The domain of the original expression does not include -3 and -2. Therefore, -3 and -2 are restricted values.

Use the **Least Common Denominator (LCD)** when needed to add or subtract.

Example: What is $\frac{5}{2x + 6} + \frac{x - 1}{2}$? State any restrictions.

Solution: Factor and find LCD.

$$\frac{5}{2(x + 3)} + \frac{x - 1}{2} \text{ and LCD is } 2(x + 3)$$

$$\frac{5}{2(x + 3)} + \frac{x - 1}{2}\left(\frac{x + 3}{x + 3}\right) - \frac{5 + (x - 1)(x + 3)}{2(x + 3)}$$

$$= \frac{x^2 + 2x + 2}{2(x + 3)}$$

The restricted value is -3.

Solving Rational Equations

A rational equation contains at least one rational expression. Multiply the equation by the LCD to clear the denominators and solve. Check all solutions to determine if solutions are extraneous.

Example: Solve $\frac{3}{x^2 + 4x} + \frac{1}{x + 4} = \frac{1}{x^2 + 4x}$.

Solution: The LCD is $x^2 + 4x$.

$$(x^2 + 4x)\left[\frac{3}{x^2 + 4x} + \frac{1}{x + 4}\right] = (x^2 + 4x)\frac{1}{x^2 + 4x}$$

$3 + x = 1$, so $x = -2$.

Check $\frac{3}{(-2)^2 + 4(-2)} + \frac{1}{(-2) + 4} = \frac{1}{(-2)^2 + 4(-2)}$.

The solution checks.

Common Errors When Solving Rational Expressions and Equations

Students might be confused as to how to use the LCD. Point out the LCD is used to find common denominators when adding or subtracting *expressions*. The LCD is used to clear the denominators when *solving an equation*.

RATIONAL FUNCTIONS
Pacing and Assignment Guide

| Lesson | Teaching Day(s) | TRADITIONAL | | BLOCK |
		Basic	Average	Block
8-1	1	Problems 1–3 Exs. 6–12, 16, 41–55	Problems 1–3 Exs. 6–12, 16, 41–55	**Day 1** Problems 1–5 Exs. 6–12, 16–22, 25–35 odd, 36–55
	2	Problems 4–5 Exs. 17–20, 22, 36–40	Problems 4–5 Exs. 17–22, 25–35 odd, 36–40	
8-2	1	Problems 1–3 Exs. 8–22 even, 38–54	Problems 1–5 Exs. 8–22 even, 23–31, 33–35, 37–54	**Day 2** Problems 1–5 Exs. 8–22 even, 23–31, 33–35, 37–54
	2	Problems 4–5 Exs. 23, 25–27, 29, 37		
8-3	1	Problems 1–3 Exs. 13–18, 20–23, 42–46	Problems 1–3 Exs. 13–23, 42–46	**Day 3** Problems 1–5 Exs. 13–23, 24–30 even, 31–35, 38–40, 42–58
	2	Problems 4–5 Exs. 24–30 even, 34, 35, 38, 47–58	Problems 4–5 Exs. 24–30 even, 31–35, 38–40, 47–58	
8-4	1	Problems 1–2 Exs. 8–18 even, 42–57	Problems 1–4 Exs. 8–18 even, 19–24, 28–35, 38, 40, 42–57	Problems 1–4 Exs. 8–18 even, 19–24, 28–35, 38, 40, 42–57
	2	Problems 3–4 Exs. 19–21, 24, 32, 38		
8-5	1	Problems 1–3 Exs. 7–14, 17, 18, 23	Problems 1–3 Exs. 7–20, 23	**Day 4** Part 1 Problems 1–3 Exs. 7–20, 23 Part 2 Problems 4–5 Exs. 4–18, 21, 22, 24–41
	2	Problems 4–5 Exs. 4–10, 14–16, 25–41	Problems 4–5 Exs. 4–18, 21, 22, 24–41	
8-6	1	Problems 1–3 Exs. 8–14 even, 15, 16–22 even, 28, 29, 32, 44–62	Problems 1–3 Exs. 8–28 even, 29, 32, 33, 34–42 even, 44–62	**Day 5** Problems 1–3 Exs. 8–28 even, 29, 32, 33, 34–42 even, 44–62
Review	1	Chapter 8 Review	Chapter 8 Review	**Day 6** Chapter 8 Review Chapter 8 Test
Assess	1	Chapter 8 Test	Chapter 8 Test	
Total		**13 Days**	**11 Days**	**6 Days**

Note: Pacing does not include Concept Bytes and other feature pages.

Resources

	For the Chapter	8-1	8-2	8-3	8-4	8-5	8-6
Planning							
Teacher Center Online Planner & Grade Book	I	I	I	I	I	I	I
Interactive Learning & Guided Instruction							
My Math Video	I						
Solve It!		I TM	I TM	I TM	I TM	I TM	I TM
Student Companion (SP)*		P M	P M	P M	P M	P M	
Vocabulary Support		I P M	I P M	I P M	I P M	I P M	I P M
Got It? Support		I P	I P	I P	I P	I P	I P
Dynamic Activity	I	I	I				
Online Problems	I	I	I		I	I	I
Additional Problems		M	M	M	M	M	M
English Language Learner Support (TR)		E P M	E P M	E P M	E P M	E P M	E P M
Activities, Games, and Puzzles		E M	E M	E M	E M	E M	E M
Teaching With TI Technology With CD-ROM		✓ P	✓ P				✓ P
TI-Nspire™ Support CD-ROM		✓	✓	✓	✓	✓	✓
Lesson Check & Practice							
Student Companion (SP)*		P M	P M	P M	P M	P M	P M
Lesson Check Support		I P	I P	I P	I P	I P	I P
Think About a Plan (TR)*		E P M	E P M	E P M	E P M	E P M	E P M
Practice Form K (TR)*		E P M	E P M	E P M	E P M	E P M	E P M
Standardized Test Prep (TR)*		P M	P M	P M	P M	P M	P M
Practice Form G (TR)*		E P M	E P M	E P M	E P M	E P M	E P M
Extra Practice	E M						
Find the Errors!	M						
Enrichment (TR)		E P M	E P M	E P M	E P M	E P M	E P M
Answers and Solutions CD-ROM	✓	✓	✓	✓	✓	✓	✓
Assess & Remediate							
ExamView CD-ROM	✓	✓	✓	✓	✓	✓	✓
Lesson Quiz		I TM	I TM	I TM	I TM	I TM	I TM
Quizzes and Tests Form K (TR)*	E P M			E P M			E P M
Quizzes and Tests Form G (TR)*	E P M			E P M			E P M
Reteaching (TR)		E P M	E P M	E P M	E P M	E P M	E P M
Performance Tasks (TR)*	P M						
Cumulative Review (TR)*	P M						
Progress Monitoring Assessments	I P M						

(TR) Available in All-In-One Teaching Resources   * Spanish available

1 Interactive Learning

Solve It!

PURPOSE To use an inverse variation equation to solve an area problem

PROCESS Students may

- express cubic measurement as $\ell \times w \times h$ with the height being $\frac{1}{4}$ ft. Thus 1 bag covers $8 \times 1 \times \frac{1}{4}$ ft. The area covered by one bag is 8 ft^2, thus 20 bags cover 160 ft^2.
- express cubic feet as height × area. In this case, 2 ft^3 = 0.25 ft × area, or $(2)(4)$ ft^2 = area covered by one bag.

FACILITATE

Q What whole number dimensions would give 2 ft^3? Give all dimensions in feet. **[2 × 1 × 1]**

Q What is 3 in. measured in ft? **[$\frac{1}{4}$ ft]**

ANSWER See Solve It in Answers on next page.

CONNECT THE MATH In the Solve It, students used an inverse variation equation to solve an area problem. In the lesson, they will define, identify, and model inverse and combined variations.

2 Guided Instruction

Problem 1   SYNTHESIZING

Q What is the constant of variation in 1A? **[30]**

Q How do you find the equation $y = \frac{30}{x}$? **[Answers may vary. Sample: You can use the inverse variation equation $y = \frac{k}{x}$ and substitute $k = 30$ or use $xy = 30$ and divide both sides by x.]**

Q Why does a quick look at the table and graph show that it *might* be an inverse relationship? **[Not all tables where an increase in x correlates to a decrease in y actually show an inverse relationship. You have to make sure that the product of x and y is constant.]**

8-1 Inverse Variation

Objectives To recognize and use inverse variation
To use joint and other variations

Getting Ready!

You have 20 bags of mulch. You plan to spread the mulch from all the bags to make a rectangular layer that is 3-in. thick. How many square feet can you cover? If ℓ and w represent the length and width of the rectangle in feet, what equation relates ℓ and w? Justify your reasoning.

Mulch is a ground cover that helps keep moisture in the soil.

Lesson Vocabulary
- inverse variation
- combined variation
- joint variation

Among all rectangles with a given area, the longer the length of one side, the shorter the length of an adjacent side.

Focus Question What is inverse variation?

Recall that direct variation has the form $y = kx$, where $k \neq 0$. **Inverse variation** can have the form $xy = k$, $y = \frac{k}{x}$, or $x = \frac{k}{y}$, where $k \neq 0$. When two quantities vary inversely, as one quantity increases, the other decreases proportionally. For both inverse and direct variation, k is the constant of variation.

Think
How can you tell if the quantities vary directly or inversely? If the product of corresponding x- and y-values is constant, they vary inversely. If the ratio of corresponding x- and y-values is constant, they vary directly.

Problem 1 Identifying Direct and Inverse Variations

Is the relationship between the variables a *direct variation*, an *inverse variation*, or *neither*? Write function models for the direct and inverse variations.

A

x	y
2	15
4	7.5
10	3
15	2

As x increases, y decreases. This might be an inverse relationship. A plot confirms that an inverse relationship is possible. Test to see whether xy is constant.

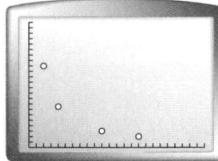

$2 \cdot 15 = 30$ $4 \cdot 7.5 = 30$
$10 \cdot 3 = 30$ $15 \cdot 2 = 30$

The product of each pair is 30, so $xy = 30$ and y varies inversely with x. The constant of variation is 30. The function model is $y = \frac{30}{x}$.

8-1 Preparing to Teach

BIG idea **Proportionality**   **UbD**

ESSENTIAL UNDERSTANDINGS

- If a product is constant, a decrease in the value of one factor must accompany an increase in the value of the other factor.
- In a direct variation, two positive quantities either increase together or decrease together. In an inverse variation, as one quantity increases the other decreases.
- Quantities x and y are inversely proportional only if increasing x by the factor $k(k \neq 0)$ means shrinking y by the factor $\frac{1}{k}$.

Math Background

Direct and inverse variations show a relationship between two quantities.

For direct variation,

- $y = kx$ for nonzero constant k.
- the absolute values of both quantities increase together.
- the graph is a line.

- the quotient of the y-values and the corresponding x-values is constant.

For inverse variation,

- $y = \frac{k}{x}$ for nonzero constant k.
- the absolute value of one quantity increases as the absolute value of the other quantity decreases.
- the product of the y-values and the corresponding x-values is constant.

In a combined variation, one quantity varies with respect to two or more other quantities.

- z varies jointly with x and y: $z = kxy$.
- z varies jointly with x and y and inversely with w: $z = \frac{kxy}{w}$.
- z varies jointly with x and inversely with the product wy: $z = \frac{kx}{wy}$.

Support Student Learning

Use the **Algebra 2 Companion** to engage and support students during instruction. See Lesson Resources at the end of this lesson for details.

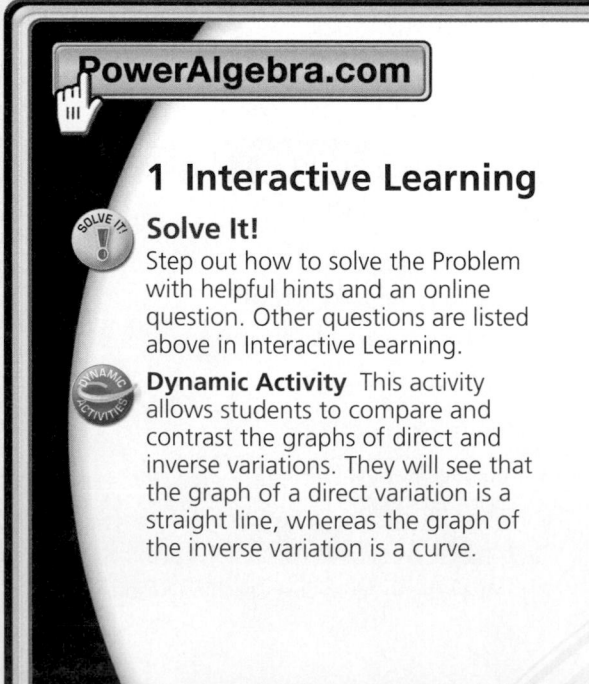

PowerAlgebra.com

1 Interactive Learning

Solve It!
Step out how to solve the Problem with helpful hints and an online question. Other questions are listed above in Interactive Learning.

Dynamic Activity This activity allows students to compare and contrast the graphs of direct and inverse variations. They will see that the graph of a direct variation is a straight line, whereas the graph of the inverse variation is a curve.

Think

Could you model this data with a direct variation?
No. The ratio of corresponding x- and y-values are not constant.

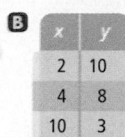

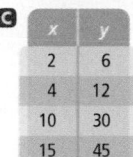

Dynamic Activity
Direct and Inverse Variation

B

x	y
2	10
4	8
10	3
15	1.5

The table and graph suggest that an inverse relationship is possible. Test to see whether the products of x and y are constant.

$2 \cdot 10 = 20, 4 \cdot 8 = 32, 10 \cdot 3 = 30,$ and
$15 \cdot 1.5 = 22.5$

Since the products are not constant, the relationship is not an inverse variation.

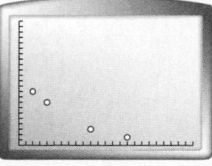

C

x	y
2	6
4	12
10	30
15	45

As x increases, y increases. A quick plot confirms a direct variation is possible. Each y-value is 3 times the corresponding x-value. y varies directly with x. The constant of variation is 3. The function is $y = 3x$.

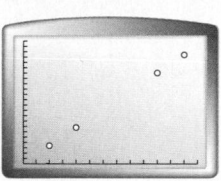

✓ **Got It?** 1. Is the relationship between the variables a *direct variation*, an *inverse variation*, or *neither*? Write function models for the direct and inverse variations.

a.

x	y
0.2	8
0.5	20
1.0	40
1.5	60

b.

x	y
0.2	40
0.5	16
1.0	8.0
2.0	4.0

c.

x	y
0.5	40
1.2	12
2	10
2.5	6

Problem 2 Determining an Inverse Variation

Suppose x and y vary inversely, and $x = 4$ when $y = 12$. Graph the inverse variation. What is the value of y when $x = 10$?

Step 1
Write a function model.

Write the general form for inverse variation. $y = \frac{k}{x}$

Substitute for x and y. $12 = \frac{k}{4}$

Solve for k. $k = 48$

The function is $y = \frac{48}{x}$.

Step 3
Find y when $x = 10$.

Substitute 10 for x and simplify. $y = \frac{48}{10} = 4.8$

$y = 4.8$ when $x = 10$.

Step 2
Make a table of values. Sketch a graph.

x	y
3	16
4	12
6	8
8	6
12	4
16	3

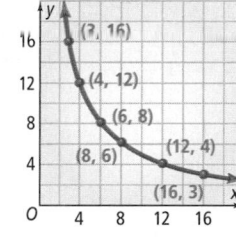

Plan

What x-values should you use to make a table?
Choose x-values that give whole numbers for y-values.

2 Guided Instruction

Each Problem is worked out and supported online.

Problem 1
Identifying Direct and Inverse Variations

Problem 2
Determining an Inverse Variation

Problem 3
Modeling an Inverse Variation
Animated

Problem 4
Using Combined Variation
Animated

Problem 5
Applying Combined Variation
Animated

Support in Algebra 2 Companion
• Vocabulary
• Key Concepts
• Got It?

Got It?   ERROR PREVENTION

Q How do you write the inverse function model?
[$y = \frac{k}{x}$ or $k = xy$.]

Q A graph is a good way to start identifying the type of variation in a table, but why is it not enough by itself? **[A graph shows the rough relationship but does not prove the presence of direct or inverse variations.]**

Problem 2   SYNTHESIZING

It is helpful to write the general form of the inverse variation as a first step when completing a modeling problem.

Q What are the three steps for determining an inverse variation model? **[Write the general form for inverse variation. Substitute values for x and y into the general equation. Solve for the constant of variation.]**

Q What values should you use to determine the table for the graph? **[Any values can be used for x except $x = 0$. It is easiest to use x-values that divide evenly into 48.]**

Q Why can't you use $x = 0$ in an inverse relationship? **[$\frac{k}{x}$ would be undefined.]**

Q Graph $y = \frac{48}{x}$ on a graphing calculator. Why do you see two curves? **[The graphing calculator is considering both positive and negative values for x. The curve in Quadrant I contains pairs of positive x- and y-values. The curve in Quadrant III contains pairs of negative x- and y-values.]**

Answers

Solve It!
160 ft^2; $\ell w = 160$

Got It?
1. **a.** direct; $y = 40x$

   b. inverse; $y = \frac{8}{x}$

   c. neither

Got It?

Q What is different about the given *x*- and *y*-values? **[One of the values is negative.]**

Q What will happen to *k* if one value of *x* or *y* is negative? **[k will be negative.]**

Q What do you need to graph the inverse variation? **[Sample: the function rule]**

Q How does the graph in the Got It appear different than in Problem 2? **[In Problem 2 the branches of the graph are in Quadrants I and III. In the Got It the branches are in Quadrants II and IV.]**

Problem 3

Q Which of the functions, $nt = 255$ and $t = \frac{255}{n}$, is written in function form? Explain. **[$t = \frac{255}{n}$; in function form, one variable must be isolated on one side of the equation.]**

Q Does it matter which equation you use in 3B? Explain. **[No; both give the same answer. The only difference is that $d = \frac{255}{n}$ is in function form.]**

Q Would you use a different model if L3 contained 256, 255, 252, and 258? Explain. **[Not necessarily; all are approximately 255; their average is 255.25.]**

Got It?

Q Which variable determines the domain for the equation that models this situation? **[n, the number of students needed]**

Q What value did you use for *k*? Explain. **[225; all but one of the products was 225.]**

Q What would you conclude if the products of the number of students and the time were 250, 200, 350, and 175? **[no inverse relationship]**

Q What are the two different interpretations of the situation where $n = 3.5$? **[Clearing the debris would take 4 students the assigned amount of time or 3 students working full time and one working half time.]**

 Got It? 2. Suppose *x* and *y* vary inversely, and $x = 8$ when $y = -7$. Graph the inverse variation. What is the value of *y* when $x = 2$?

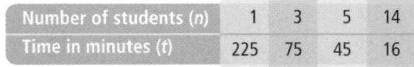 **Problem 3** Modeling an Inverse Variation

Your math class has decided to pick up litter each weekend in a local park. Each week there is approximately the same amount of litter. The table shows the number of students who worked each of the first four weeks of the project and the time needed for the pickup.

Park Cleanup Project

Number of students (*n*)	3	5	12	17
Time in minutes (*t*)	85	51	21	15

Think

Can you still use inverse variation to model the data if $12 \times 21 = 252$? Often, you cannot describe real-world data exactly with a function rule. But 252 is close enough to 255 for inverse variation to still be a good model.

A What function models the data?

Step 1 Investigate the data. The more students who help, the less time the cleanup takes. An inverse variation seems appropriate.

If this is an inverse variation, then $nt = k$. From the table, *nt* (or **L1•L2**) is almost always 255.

L1	L2	L3	3
3	85	255	
5	51	255	
12	21	252	
17	15	255	
-----	-----	-----	
		L3=L1 L2	

Step 2 Determine the model.

$$t = \frac{255}{n}$$

B How many students should there be to complete the project in at most 30 minutes each week?

Use the model from part A.	$nt = 255$
Substitute 30 for *t*.	$n(30) = 255$
Solve for *n* and simplify.	$n = \frac{255}{30} = 8.5$

There should be at least 9 students to do the job in at most 30 minutes.

Hint

If *n* and *t* vary inversely, their product is a constant.

 Got It? 3. After a major storm, your math class volunteers to remove debris from yards. The table shows the time *t* in minutes that it takes a group of *n* students to remove the debris from an average-sized yard.

Number of students (*n*)	1	3	5	14
Time in minutes (*t*)	225	75	45	16

a. What function models the time needed to clear the debris from an average-sized yard relative to the number of students who do the work?

b. How many students should there be to clear debris from an average-sized yard in at most 25 minutes?

Additional Problems

1. Is the relationship between the variables a *direct variation*, an *inverse variation*, or *neither*?

a.

x	y
1	52
2	34
5	4
6	2

b.

x	y
0.2	0.80
0.4	0.40
0.5	0.32
1.0	0.16

ANSWERS

a. neither **b.** inverse

2. Suppose *x* and *y* vary inversely, and $x = 2$ when $y = 8$.

a. What is the function of the inverse variation?

b. What is the graph of this function?

c. What is *y* when $x = 4$?

ANSWERS

a. $y = \frac{16}{x}$

b.

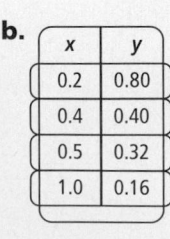

c. 4

3. Your employer decides to hire extra help to deliver papers during the holidays. The table shows the number of employees who delivered papers each week and the time needed for delivery.

Number of employees	2	4	10	20
Time in minutes	100	50	20	10

a. What function models this problem?

b. How many employees should there be to deliver newspapers in at most 40 minutes each week?

ANSWERS

a. $y = \frac{200}{x}$ **b.** at least 5

4. Multiple Choice The volume of a cone varies jointly with its height and the square of its base radius. A cone has base radius 4 ft, height 6 ft, and volume 100.48 ft³. What is the volume of a cone with height 3 ft and base radius 3 ft?

A. 14.13 ft³

B. 28.27 ft³

C. 33.56 ft³

D. 50.25 ft³

ANSWER B

5. The volume of gas varies directly with its temperature and inversely with its pressure. Volume is 100 m³ when temperature is 150 K and pressure is 15 lb/cm². What is the volume when the temperature is 250 K and the pressure is 20 lb/cm²?

ANSWER 125 m³

Focus Question What is combined variation?

You have seen many variation formulas in geometry. Some, like the formula for the perimeter of a square, are simple direct variations. Others, like the volume of a cone, relate three or more variables.

When one quantity varies with respect to two or more quantities, you have a **combined variation**. When one quantity varies directly with two or more quantities, you have **joint variation**.

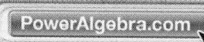

Key Concept   Combined Variations

Combined Variation	Equation Form
z varies jointly with x and y.	$z = kxy$
z varies jointly with x and y and inversely with w.	$z = \dfrac{kxy}{w}$
z varies directly with x and inversely with the product wy.	$z = \dfrac{kx}{wy}$

Plan

How can you write the model?
Write the constant of variation and direct variation variable in the numerator. Write the inverse variation variable in the denominator.

Problem 4 Using Combined Variation

Multiple Choice The number of bags of grass seed n needed to reseed a yard varies directly with the area a to be seeded and inversely with the weight w of a bag of seed. If it takes two 3-lb bags to seed an area of 3600 ft², how many 3-lb bags will seed 9000 ft²?

Ⓐ 3 bags   Ⓑ 4 bags   Ⓒ 5 bags   Ⓓ 6 bags

Step 1
Use the given information to write the variation equation.

n varies directly with a and inversely with w.	$n = \dfrac{ka}{w}$
Substitute for n, a, and w.	$2 = \dfrac{3600k}{3}$
Solve for k.	$\dfrac{(2)(3)}{3600} = k$
Multiply and simplify.	$k = \dfrac{6}{3600} = \dfrac{1}{600}$

The variation equation is $n = \dfrac{a}{600w}$.

Step 2
Use the equation to find the number of bags for 9000 ft².

Use the combined variation equation.	$n = \dfrac{a}{600w}$
Substitute for a and w.	$n = \dfrac{9000}{600 \cdot 3}$
Multiply.	$= \dfrac{9000}{1800}$
Simplify.	$= 5$

You need five 3-lb bags to seed 9000 ft². The correct answer is C.

Hint
The general form for a joint variation is z = kxy.

✔ **Got It?** **4.** The number of bags of mulch you need to cover a planting area varies jointly with the area to be mulched a in square feet and the depth of the mulch d in feet. If you need 10 bags to mulch 120 ft² to a depth of 3 in., how many bags do you need to mulch 200 ft² to a depth of 4 in.?

PowerAlgebra.com   Lesson 8-1 Inverse Variation   523

Take Note   SYNTHESIZING

Q Solve each equation for k. How can the formulas be expressed in terms of direct and inverse variations? **[$\frac{z}{xy} = k$: z varies directly with the product xy; $\frac{zw}{xy} = k$: z varies directly with the product xy and inversely with w; $\frac{zwy}{x} = k$: z varies directly with x and inversely with the product wy.]**

Problem 4
There are three variables in this situation. The number of bags needed depends on the weight of a bag of seed and the area to be reseeded.

Q In the equation $n = \frac{a}{600w}$, why is 600 in the denominator when k is usually in the numerator? **[$k = \frac{1}{600}$, so the 600 is in the denominator.]**

Q If two three-pound bags will reseed 3600 ft², how much area can be reseeded by one pound of grass seed? **[600 ft²]**

Q How many pounds of seed would be needed to reseed 9000 ft²? **[15 lb]**

Got It?   EXTENSION

Q What variation does "joint" imply? **[direct variation]**

Q What are you trying to find? **[the number of bags needed to mulch 200 ft² to a depth of 4 in.]**

Q What is k? **[$\frac{1}{36}$]**

Q What is the joint variation equation? **[$n = \frac{ad}{36}$]**

Answers

Got It? (continued)

2.

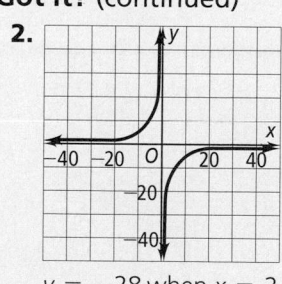

$y = -28$ when $x = 2$.

3. a. $t = \dfrac{225}{n}$

   b. 9 students

4. 23 bags

Problem 5

Joules are the SI units of energy. One joule equals $1 \text{ kg} \cdot \frac{m^2}{\sec^2}$. The units for the gravitational constant g are m/sec^2.

> **Q** What sentence helps you write the formula? **[first sentence]**
>
> **Q** What part of the first sentence shows you that this is a combined variation problem? **[PE varies directly with 2 quantities.]**

Got It?   ERROR PREVENTION

> **Q** Do you have to develop a formula to solve problem 5a? Explain. **[No, use the formula in Problem 5.]**
>
> **Q** What information are you given for 5a? **[m = 41 kg, h = 10 m]**
>
> **Q** In 5b, you want the potential energy of each diver to be the same. Would you expect the diver with less mass would have to dive from higher or lower to achieve the same potential energy? Explain. **[Higher; the diver with less mass needs a great height so the gmh of the first diver is equal to the gmh of the second diver.]**

Problem 5 Applying Combined Variation

Physics Gravitational potential energy *PE* is a measure of energy. *PE* varies directly with an object's mass *m* in kg and its height *h* in meters above the ground. Physicists use *g* to represent the constant of variation, which is gravity.

The skateboarder in the photo has a mass of 58 kg and a potential energy of 2273.6 joules. What is the gravitational potential energy of a 65-kg skateboarder on the halfpipe shown?

HEIGHT 4 M

Know	Need	Plan
• The mass of each skateboarder • The height of each skateboarder • The potential energy of the first skateboarder	The potential energy of the second skateboarder	• Write the variation for potential energy. • Use the known information to find *g*. • Then find the potential energy of the second skateboarder.

Step 1 Write the formula for potential energy. Potential energy varies directly with mass and height. $PE = gmh$

Plan

Can you use the same value of *g* for different situations? The value of *g* is constant on Earth. Potential energy calculations for situations on the moon would use a different value of *g*.

Step 2 Use the given data to find *g*.

Use the potential energy formula.	$PE = gmh$
Substitute 2273.6 for *PE*, 58 for *m*, and 4 for *h*.	$2273.6 = g(58)(4)$
Solve for *g*.	$9.8 = g$

Step 3 Use the formula to find the potential energy of the second skateboarder.

Use the potential energy formula.	$PE = 9.8mh$
Evaluate for $m = 65$ and $h = 4$.	$= 9.8(65)(4)$
Simplify.	$= 2548$

The second skateboarder has 2548 joules of potential energy.

Hint

Refer to the formula for potential energy from Problem 5.

Got It? **5. a.** How much potential energy would a 41-kg diver have standing on a 10-m diving platform?

b. Reasoning An 80-kg diver stands on a 6-m diving platform. At what height should a 40-kg diver stand to have equal potential energy? Do you need to find the potential energy of either diver to solve this? Explain your reasoning.

Answers

Got It? (continued)

5. a. 4018 joules

b. 12 m; No, you need not calculate *PE* to find the height. Substitute the mass and height of the first diver, and the mass of the second diver in $PE = gmh$ and set the two quantities equal to calculate the height of the second diver.

Focus Question What is inverse variation?

Answer Inverse variation relates quantities whose product is constant. Use an inverse variation function when one quantity increases and the other decreases proportionally.

Focus Question What is combined variation?

Answer Combined variation occurs when one quantity varies with respect to two or more quantities. Use combined variation when you want to relate three or more variables. The variables can vary directly and/or inversely.

Lesson Check

Do you know HOW?

Is the relationship between the variables in each table a *direct variation,* an *inverse variation,* or *neither*? Write equations to model the direct and inverse variations.

1.

x	y
1	6
3	2
12	0.5
15	0.4

2.

u	v
−3	−15
5	25
6	30
16	80

Do you UNDERSTAND?

3. Compare and Contrast Describe the difference between direct variation and inverse variation.

4. Writing Describe how the variables in the given equation are related.

$$p = \frac{kqrt}{s}$$

5. Error Analysis A student described the relationship between the variables in the equation below as *d* varies directly with *r* and inversely with *t.* Correct the error in relating the variables.

$$d = \frac{k\sqrt[3]{r}}{t^2}$$

Practice and Problem-Solving Exercises

Ⓐ Practice

Is the relationship between the values in each table a *direct variation,* an *inverse variation,* or *neither*? Write equations to model the direct and inverse variations.

◀ See Problem 1.

6.

x	y
3	15
8	40
10	50
22	110

7.

x	y
3	14
5	8.4
7	6
10.5	4

8.

x	y
0.5	1
2.1	4.2
3.5	7
11	22

Lesson Check

1. inverse; $y = \frac{6}{x}$

2. direct; $y = 5x$

3. In direct variation, two positive quantities either increase together or decrease together. In an inverse variation, as one quantity increases, the other quantity decreases and vice versa.

4. *p* varies directly with *q*, *r*, and *t* and inversely with *s*.

5. *d* varies directly with the cube root of *r* and inversely with the square of *t*.

Practice and Problem-Solving Exercises

6. direct; $y = 5x$

7. neither

8. neither

3 Lesson Check

Do you know HOW?
- For Exercises 1 and 2, remind students that a graph can suggest a possible relationship.

Do you UNDERSTAND? ERROR INTERVENTION
- Instruct students to break down the equations in Exercises 4 and 5 into products and quotients. Then refer students to the Combined Variations Take Note box.

Close

Q How can you tell whether two sets of data show direct variation or inverse variation? **[Answers may vary. Sample: If the quotient of the *y*-values and corresponding *x*-values is constant, the data show direct variation. If the product of the *y*-values and corresponding *x*-values is constant, the data show inverse variation.]**

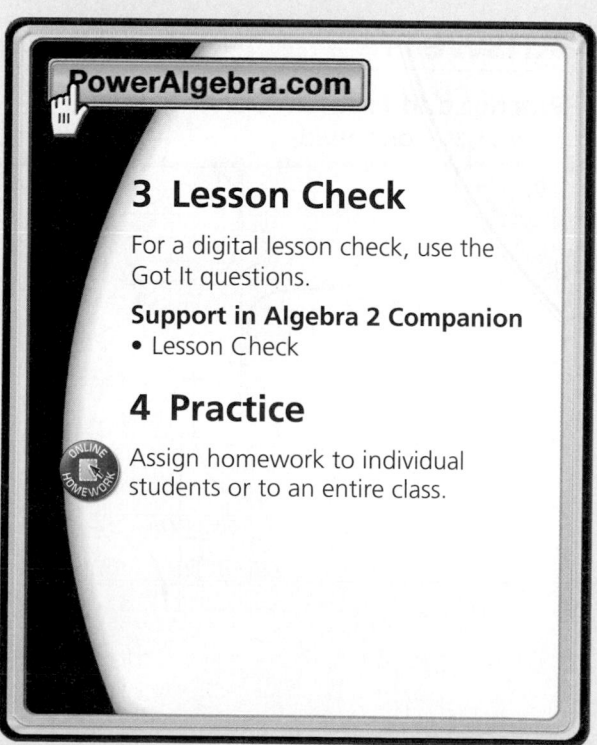

PowerAlgebra.com

3 Lesson Check

For a digital lesson check, use the Got It questions.

Support in Algebra 2 Companion
- Lesson Check

4 Practice

Assign homework to individual students or to an entire class.

4 Practice

ASSIGNMENT GUIDE

Basic: 6–12, 16–20, 22

Average: 6–12, 16–22, 25–35 odd

Standardized Test Prep: 36–40

Mixed Review: 41–55

Reasoning exercises have blue headings.

Applications exercises have red headings.

EXERCISE 22: Use the Think About a Plan worksheet in the **Student Companion** (also available in the Teaching Resources in print and online) to further support students' development in becoming independent learners.

HOMEWORK QUICK CHECK

To check students' understanding of key skills and concepts, go over Exercises 6, 10, 18, 20, and 22.

Suppose that x and y vary inversely. Write a function that models each inverse variation. Graph the function and find y when $x = 10$.

◆ **See Problem 2.**

Guided Practice →

9. $x = 1$ when $y = 11$

To start, write the general form for inverse variation.

$$y = \frac{k}{x}$$

10. $x = -13$ when $y = 100$ **11.** $x = 1$ when $y = 1$ **12.** $x = 1$ when $y = 5$

13. $x = 1.2$ when $y = 3$ **14.** $x = 20$ when $y = -4$ **15.** $x = 5$ when $y = -\frac{1}{3}$

16. Fundraising In a bake sale, you recorded the number of muffins sold and the amount of sales in a table as shown.

◆ **See Problem 3.**

Number of muffins (m)	Sales (s)
5	$12.50
8	$20.00
13	$32.50
20	$50.00

   a. What is a function that relates the sales and the number of muffins?
   b. How many muffins would you have to sell to make at least $250.00 in sales?

Use combined variation to solve each problem.

◆ **See Problem 4.**

17. Painting The number of buckets of paint n needed to paint a fence varies directly with the total area a of the fence and inversely with the amount of paint p in a bucket. It takes three 1-gallon buckets of paint to paint 72 square feet of fence. How many 1-gallon buckets will be needed to paint 90 square feet of fence?

Guided Practice →

To start, record what you know. n varies directly with a and inversely with p.

Then write the combined variation. $n = \frac{ka}{p}$

18. Health A person's body mass index (BMI) varies directly with his or her weight in pounds and inversely with the square of his or her height in inches. A student with a height of 68 in. and a weight of 150 lb has a BMI of 22.8. What is the BMI of a student with a height of 61 in. and a weight of 115 lb?

19. Potential Energy On Earth with a gravitational acceleration g, the potential energy stored in an object varies directly with its mass m and its vertical height h. What is the equation of the potential energy of a 2-kg skateboard that is sliding down a ramp?

◆ **See Problem 5.**

Ⓑ Apply

20. Think About a Plan The table shows data about how the life span s of a mammal relates to its heart rate r. The data can be modeled by an equation of the form $rs = k$. Estimate the life span of a cat with a heart rate of 126 beats/min.
   • How can you estimate a constant of the inverse variation?
   • What expression would you use to find the life span?

Heart Rate and Life Span

Mammal	Heart rate (beats/min)	Life span (min)
Mouse	634	1,576,800
Rabbit	158	6,307,200
Lion	76	13,140,000

Source: *The Handy Science Answer Book*

Answers

Practice and Problem-Solving Exercises (continued)

9. $y = \frac{11}{x}$; 1.1;

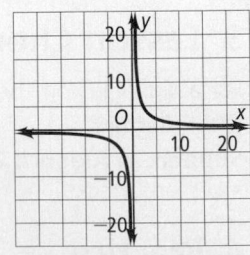

10. $y = -\frac{1300}{x}$; -130;

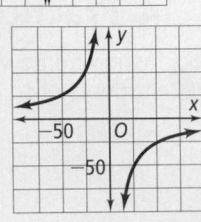

11. $y = \frac{1}{x}$; $\frac{1}{10}$;

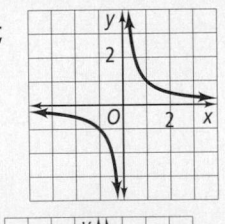

12. $y = \frac{5}{x}$; $\frac{1}{2}$;

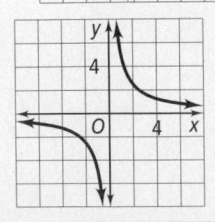

13. $y = \frac{3.6}{x}$; 0.36;

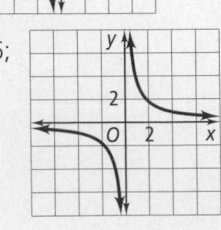

14. $y = -\frac{80}{x}$; -8;

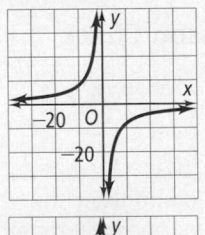

15. $y = -\frac{5}{3x}$; $-\frac{1}{6}$;

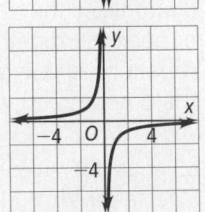

16. a. $s = 2.5m$
   b. 100 muffins

17. ≈4 buckets

18. 21.7

19. $PE = 2gh$

20. about 7,900,000 min, or 15 yrs

21. **Physics** The force F of gravity on a rocket varies directly with its mass m and inversely with the square of its distance d from Earth. Write a model for this combined variation.

22. The spreadsheet shows data that can be modeled by an equation of the form $PV = k$. Estimate P when $V = 62$.

23. **Chemistry** The formula for Ideal Gas Law is $PV = nRT$, where P is the pressure in kilopascals (kPA), V is the volume in liters (L), T is the temperature in Kelvin (K), n is the number of moles of gas, and $R = 8.314$ is the universal gas constant.
 a. What volume is needed to store 5 moles of helium gas at 350 K under the pressure 190 kPA?
 b. A 10-L cylinder is filled with hydrogen gas to a pressure of 5,000 kPA. The temperature of the gas is 300 K. How many moles of hydrogen gas are in the cylinder?

	A	B
	P	V
1	P	V
2	140.00	100
3	147.30	95
4	155.60	90
5	164.70	85
6	175.00	80
7	186.70	75

Write the function that models each variation. Find z when $x = 4$ and $y = 9$.

24. z varies directly with x and inversely with y. When $x = 6$ and $y = 2$, $z = 15$.

25. z varies jointly with x and y. When $x = 2$ and $y = 3$, $z = 60$.

26. z varies inversely with the product of x and y. When $x = 2$ and $y = 4$, $z = 0.5$.

Each pair of values is from a direct variation. Find the missing value.

27. $(2, 5), (4, y)$ 28. $(4, 6), (x, 3)$ 29. $(3, 7), (8, y)$

Each ordered pair is from an inverse variation. Find the constant of variation.

30. $(6, 3)$ 31. $(0.9, 4)$ 32. $\left(\frac{3}{8}, \frac{2}{3}\right)$

Each pair of values is from an inverse variation. Find the missing value.

33. $(2, 5), (4, y)$ 34. $(4, 6), (x, 3)$ 35. $(3, 7), (8, y)$

21. $F = \dfrac{km}{d^2}$

22. 226

23. a. ≈ 76.58 L
   b. ≈ 20 moles

24. $z = \dfrac{5x}{y}$; $\dfrac{20}{9}$

25. $z = 10xy$; 360

26. $z = \dfrac{4}{xy}$; $\dfrac{1}{9}$

27. 10

28. 2

29. $18\frac{2}{3}$

30. 18

31. 3.6

32. $\dfrac{1}{4}$

33. 2.5

34. 8

35. 2.625

Answers

Standardized Test Prep

36. B

37. G

38. C

39. H

40. [2]
$$x = 4y^2 + 5$$
$$x - 5 = 4y^2$$
$$\frac{x-5}{4} = y^2$$
$$\frac{\pm\sqrt{x-5}}{2} = f^{-1}(x), x \geq 5;$$

No, the inv. is not a function.

[1] appropriate methods, with one computational error OR correct inv., without work shown OR inv. incorrectly called a function

Mixed Review

41. 4

42. 2.846

43. $3333.\overline{3}$

44. $-90x^2$

45. $84x^2$

46. $10x^2y^3\sqrt{2y}$

47. $|x^5|y^{50}$

48. $-4ab^2$

49. $2m^2|n|\sqrt[4]{4}$

50. $y = |x|$ translated 2 units up;

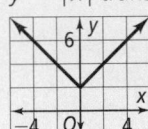

51. $y = |x|$ translated 2 units to the left;

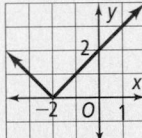

52. $y = |x|$ translated 3 units down;

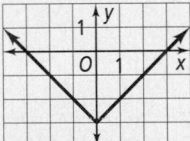

53. $y = |x|$ translated 3 units to the rt.;

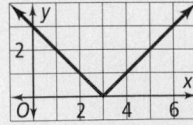

54. $y = |x|$ translated 4 units to the left and 5 units down;

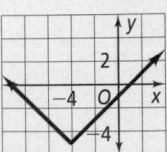

55. $y = |x|$ translated 10 units to the rt. and 7 units up;

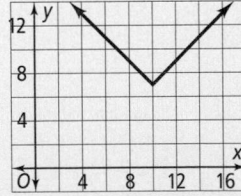

SAT/ACT

36. Which equation represents inverse variation between x and y?

Ⓐ $x = \frac{y}{z}$

Ⓒ $z = -\frac{15y}{x}$

Ⓑ $x = -\frac{15z}{y}$

Ⓓ $xz = 5y$

37. How can you rewrite the expression $(8 - 5i)^2$ in the form $a + bi$?

Ⓕ $39 + 80i$

Ⓗ $89 + 80i$

Ⓖ $39 - 80i$

Ⓘ $89 - 80i$

38. The height of a ball thrown straight up from the ground with a velocity of 96 ft/s is given by the quadratic function $h(t) = -16t^2 + 96t$. What is the maximum height the ball reaches?

Ⓐ 6 ft

Ⓒ 144 ft

Ⓑ 128 ft

Ⓓ 160 ft

39. Which expression is NOT equivalent to $\sqrt[6]{81x^4y^8}$?

Ⓕ $(3xy^2)^{\frac{2}{3}}$

Ⓗ $(3x^2y^2)^{\frac{1}{3}}$

Ⓖ $(3x)^{\frac{2}{3}}y^{\frac{4}{3}}$

Ⓘ $\sqrt[3]{9x^2y^4}$

Short Response

40. What is the inverse of $y = 4x^2 + 5$? Is the inverse a function?

Mixed Review

Solve each equation.

◆ See Lesson 7-5.

41. $3^{2x} = 6561$

42. $7^x - 2 = 252$

43. $\log 3x = 4$

Multiply and simplify.

◆ See Lesson 6-2.

44. $-5\sqrt{6x} \cdot 3\sqrt{6x^3}$

45. $3\sqrt[3]{2x^2} \cdot 7\sqrt[3]{32x^4}$

46. $\sqrt{5x^3} \cdot \sqrt{40xy^7}$

Simplify each radical expression. Use absolute value bars where they are needed.

◆ See Lesson 6-1.

47. $\sqrt{x^{10}y^{100}}$

48. $\sqrt[3]{-64a^3b^6}$

49. $\sqrt[4]{64m^8n^4}$

Get Ready! To prepare for Lesson 8-2, do Exercises 50–55.

Graph each equation. Then describe the transformation of the parent function $f(x) = |x|$.

◆ See Lesson 2-7.

50. $y = |x| + 2$

51. $y = |x + 2|$

52. $y = |x| - 3$

53. $y = |x - 3|$

54. $y = |x + 4| - 5$

55. $y = |x - 10| + 7$

Additional Instructional Support

Algebra 2 Companion

Students can use the **Algebra 2 Companion** worktext (4 pages) as you teach the lesson. Use the Companion to support

- New Vocabulary
- Key Concepts
- Got It for each Problem
- Lesson Check

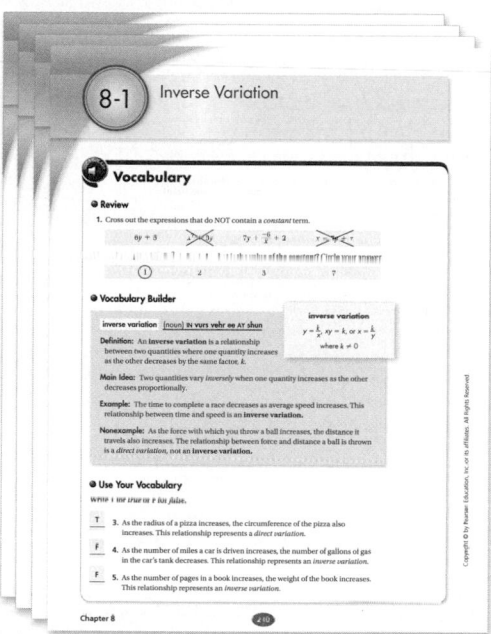

ELL Support

Focus on Language Write the equation forms on the board for all of the variations. The activity steps are as follows:

1. Choose an equation form, and state the rule. (Example: x and y vary inversely.)
2. Substitute values for x and y, and compute k.
3. Write the function rule with the k value.
4. Choose values for all variables except one, and determine its missing value.
5. Repeat.

Ask for one volunteer to complete step 1. This volunteer is responsible for choosing another student for step 2. The process is repeated until all students have participated and all formulas have been used.

5 Assess & Remediate

Lesson Quiz

1. Is the relationship between the variables a *direct variation*, an *inverse variation*, or *neither*? If the relation is a variation, write the function rule.

x	y
2	9
3	6
4	4.5
5	3.6

2. Suppose x and y vary inversely, and $x = 5$ when $y = 10$.
   a. What is the function of the inverse variation?
   b. What is the graph of this function?
   c. What is y when $x = 2$?

3. **Do you UNDERSTAND?** The electrical resistance r of a wire varies directly with its length ℓ and inversely with the square of its diameter d. If 100 m of wire with diameter 3 mm has a resistance of 8 ohms, what is the resistance of 150 m of wire with a diameter of 4 mm?

ANSWERS TO LESSON QUIZ

1. Inverse variation; $y = \dfrac{18}{x}$
2. a. $y = \dfrac{50}{x}$
   b.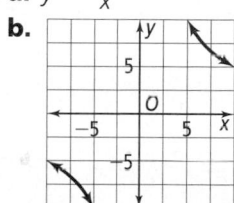
   c. 25
3. 6.75 ohms

PRESCRIPTION FOR REMEDIATION

Use the student work on the Lesson Quiz to prescribe a differentiated review assignment:

Points	Differentiated Remediation
0–1	Intervention
2	On-level
3	Extension

PowerAlgebra.com

5 Assess & Remediate

Assign the Lesson Quiz. Appropriate intervention, practice, or enrichment is automatically generated based on student performance.

Intervention

- **Reteaching** (2 pages) Provides reteaching and practice exercises for the key lesson concepts. Use with struggling students or absent students.
- **English Language Learner Support** Helps students develop and reinforce mathematical vocabulary and key concepts.

All-in-One Resources/Online
Reteaching

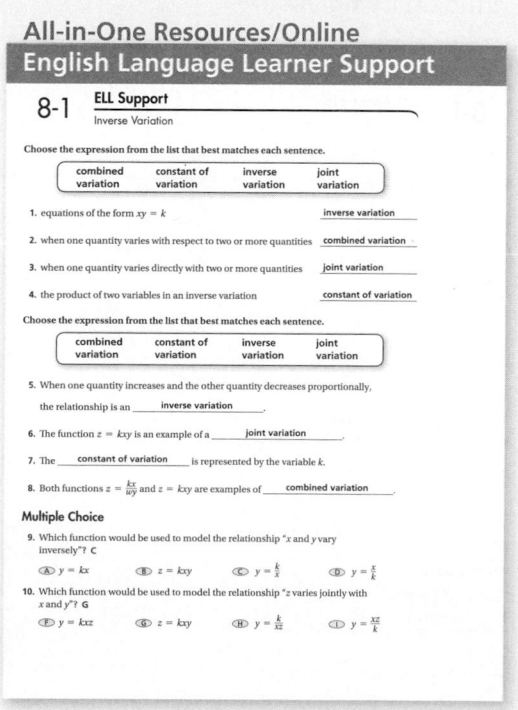

All-in-One Resources/Online
English Language Learner Support

Differentiated Remediation *continued*

On-Level

- **Practice** (2 pages) Provides extra practice for each lesson. For more challenging practice exercises, use the Form G Practice pages found in the All-in-One Teaching Resources and online.

- **Think About a Plan** Helps students develop specific problem-solving skills and strategies by providing scaffolded guiding questions.

- **Standardized Test Prep** Focuses on all major exercises, all major question types, and helps students prepare for the high-stakes assessments.

Extension

- **Enrichment** Provides students with interesting problems and activities that extend the concepts of the lesson.

- **Activities, Games, and Puzzles** Worksheets that can be used for concepts development, enrichment, and for fun!

Student Companion/All-in-One Resources/Online
Practice page 1

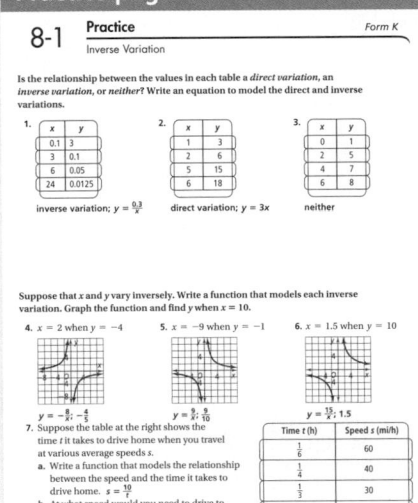

Student Companion/All-in-One Resources/Online
Practice page 2

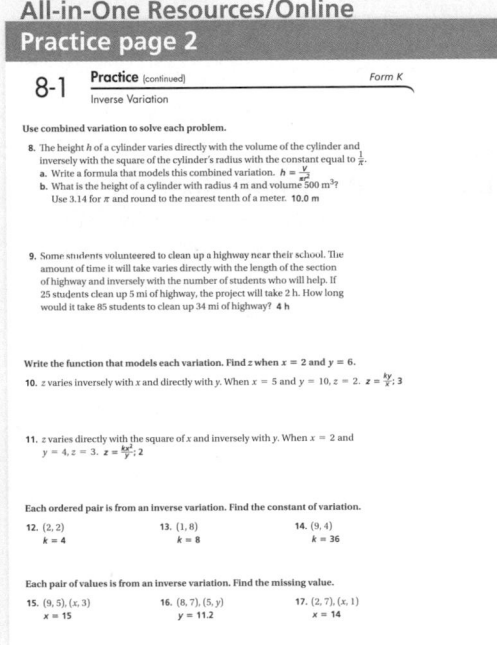

All-in-One Resources/Online
Enrichment

Student Companion/All-in-One Resources/Online
Think About a Plan

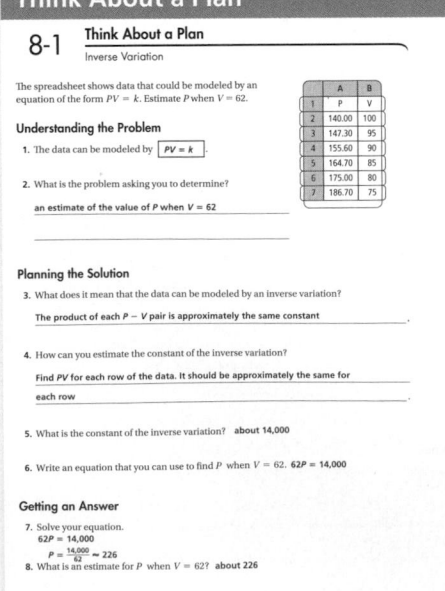

Student Companion/All-in-One Resources/Online
Standardized Test Prep

Online Teacher Resource Center
Activities, Games, and Puzzles

Graphing Rational Functions

You can use your graphing calculator to graph *rational functions* and other members of the reciprocal function family. It is sometimes preferable to use the **DOT** plotting mode rather than **CONNECTED** plotting mode. The **CONNECTED** mode can join branches of a graph that should be separated. Try both modes to get the best graph.

Example

Graph $y = \frac{4}{x - 3} - 1.5$.

Step 1 Press the `mode` key. Scroll down to highlight the word **DOT**. Then press `enter`.

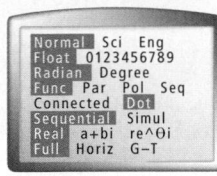

Step 2 Enter the function. Use parentheses to enter the denominator accurately.

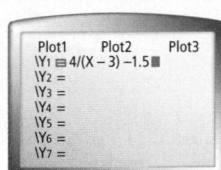

Step 3 Graph the function.

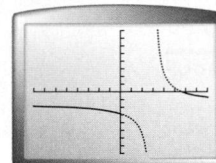

Exercises

1. a. Graph the parent reciprocal function $y = \frac{1}{x}$.
 b. Examine both negative and positive values of x. Describe what happens to the y-values as x approaches zero.
 c. What happens to the y-values as x increases? As x decreases?

2. a. Change the mode on your calculator to **CONNECTED**. Graph the function from the example.
 b. Press `trace` and trace the function. What happens between $x \approx 2.8$ and $x \approx 3.2$?
 c. **Reasoning** How does your graph differ from the graph in the example? Explain the differences.

Use a graphing calculator to graph each function. Then sketch the graph.

3. $y = \frac{7}{x}$

4. $y = \frac{3}{x + 4} - 2$

5. $y = \frac{x + 2}{(x + 1)(x + 3)}$

6. $y = \frac{4x + 1}{x - 3}$

7. $y = \frac{2}{x - 2}$

8. $y = \frac{1}{x + 2} + 3$

9. $y = \frac{2x}{x + 3}$

10. $y = \frac{x^2}{x^2 - 5}$

11. $y = \frac{20}{x^2 + 5}$

Guided Instruction

PURPOSE To graph rational functions
PROCESS Students will
• use the dot-and-connected mode on a graphing calculator to graph rational functions.
• describe the behavior of the graph.

DISCUSS This Concept Byte introduces graphs of rational functions, a topic examined in detail in Lesson 8-3. Draw five columns on the board with the titles *function, sketch, increases, decreases,* and *approaches.* Ask students to copy and complete the columns as they work through the Example.

Example

Q At what value is the graph undefined? **[3]**
Q What happens to the y-values as x approaches 3 from the right? **[They increase.]**
Q What happens to the y-values as x approaches 3 from the left? **[They decrease.]**
Q Where is the graph increasing? **[nowhere]**
Q Where is the graph decreasing? **[throughout its domain]**
Q What is the domain of this function? **[all real numbers except $x = 3$]**

Exercises

Q How does the calculator table show where the function is undefined? **[Error]**
Q For Exercise 5, at how many values is the function undefined? **[two]**
Q For Exercise 5, how many parts make up the graph? **[three]**

Answers

Concept Byte

1. a.

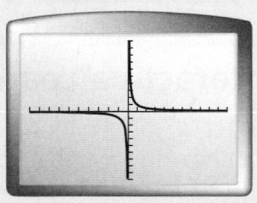

 b. If x is negative and approaches 0, the y-values approach $-\infty$. If x is positive and approaches 0, the y-values approach $+\infty$.

 c. If x is positive, as x increases, the y-values approach 0. If x is negative, as x decreases, the y-values approach 0.

2. a.

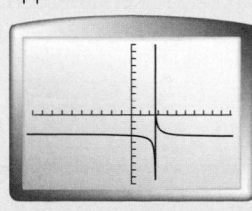

 b. Answers may vary. Sample: The y-values change from very large negative values to very large positive values.

 c. In connected mode, the calculator will try to connect the values for $x \approx 2.8$ and $x \approx 3.2$.

3.

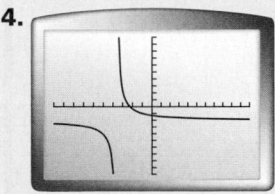

4.

5–11. See back of book.

1 Interactive Learning

Solve It!

PURPOSE To apply a translation of a reciprocal function graphically and algebraically

PROCESS Students may

- sketch points or a new graph with the new y-values plotted eight units higher than the original.
- write an algebraic function for the graph and add eight as a constant value.

FACILITATE

Q What is the value of the product of the x-coordinate and y-coordinate? What is its real world meaning? **[240; the total cost of renting the hall before the food fee is added]**

Q What equation expresses the cost per student as a function of students if the cost is C and the number of students is x? **[$f(x) = \frac{C}{x}$]**

Q How can you modify the function to include the additional eight dollars each class member must pay? What effect does this have on the graph? **[Add eight to the function; $f(x) = \frac{C}{x} + 8$; it translates the graph up 8 units.]**

ANSWER See Solve It in Answers on next page.
CONNECT THE MATH The Solve It is solved by translating a reciprocal function. In the lesson students will graph transformations of reciprocal functions.

2 Guided Instruction

Take Note

Q What happens to the graph as x gets close to 0? **[The absolute values of the y-values increase very quickly.]**

Q What happens as the absolute value of x increases? **[The value of y approaches 0.]**

8-2 The Reciprocal Function Family

Objectives To graph reciprocal functions
To graph translations of reciprocal functions

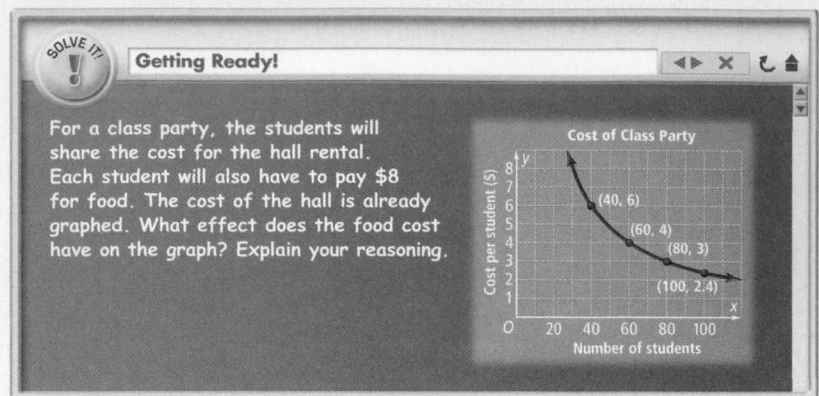

Getting Ready!

For a class party, the students will share the cost for the hall rental. Each student will also have to pay $8 for food. The cost of the hall is already graphed. What effect does the food cost have on the graph? Explain your reasoning.

Cost of Class Party

(40, 6)
(60, 4)
(80, 3)
(100, 2.4)

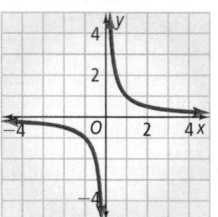

Dynamic Activity
Graphing Translations of Inverse Variations

Lesson Vocabulary
- reciprocal function
- branch

Functions that model inverse variation have the form $f(x) = \frac{a}{x}$, where $x \neq 0$. They belong to a family whose parent is the **reciprocal function** $f(x) = \frac{1}{x}$, where $x \neq 0$.

Focus Question What are reciprocal functions?

> **take note**
>
> ### Key Concept General Form of the Reciprocal Function Family
>
> The general form of a member of the reciprocal function family is $y = \frac{a}{x - h} + k$, where $x \neq h$.
>
> The inverse variation functions, $y = \frac{a}{x}$, are stretches, shrinks, and reflections of the parent reciprocal function, depending on the value of a.
>
> The graph of the parent reciprocal function, $y = \frac{1}{x}$, is shown at the right.

530 **Chapter 8** Rational Functions

8-2 Preparing to Teach

BIG ideas Function
Proportionality **UbD**

ESSENTIAL UNDERSTANDINGS

- Transformations of the parent reciprocal function include stretches, compressions (or shrinks), reflections, and horizontal and vertical translations.
- A rational function may have zero or one horizontal asymptote and zero or more vertical asymptotes.
- Quantities x and y are inversely proportional only if increasing x by the factor $k(k \neq 0)$ means shrinking y by the factor $\frac{1}{k}$.

Math Background

The function $y = \frac{1}{x}$ is the parent function of all reciprocal functions, including the inverse variation function, $y = \frac{a}{x}$, and the functions expressing transformations of the parent function, given in general form as $y = \frac{a}{x - h} + k$. Transformations work the

same way with rational functions as they did with linear, absolute value, quadratic, and exponential functions.

- a indicates a stretch when $|a| > 1$ and a shrink when $0 < |a| < 1$, each by a factor of a.
- If a is negative, the transformation involves a reflection in the x-axis.
- h indicates a horizontal translation.
- k indicates a vertical translation.
- $x = h$ is a vertical asymptote.
- $y = k$ is a horizontal asymptote.

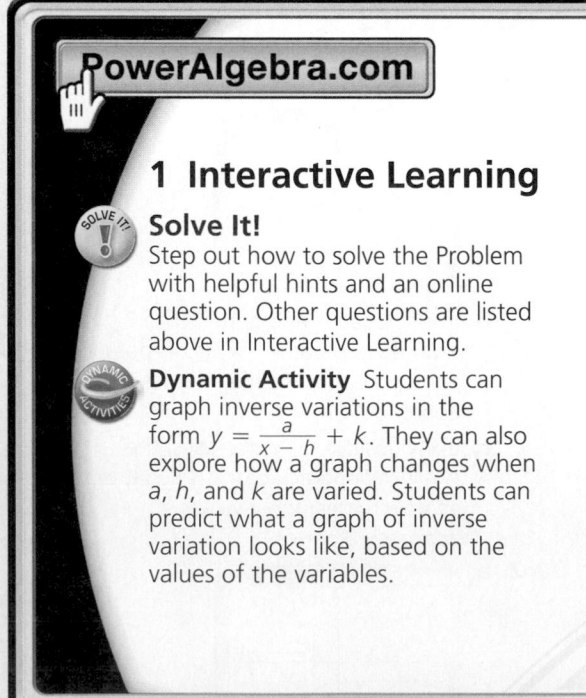

PowerAlgebra.com

1 Interactive Learning

Solve It!

Step out how to solve the Problem with helpful hints and an online question. Other questions are listed above in Interactive Learning.

Dynamic Activity Students can graph inverse variations in the form $y = \frac{a}{x - h} + k$. They can also explore how a graph changes when a, h, and k are varied. Students can predict what a graph of inverse variation looks like, based on the values of the variables.

 **Problem 1** Graphing an Inverse Variation Function

What is the graph of $y = \frac{8}{x}, x \neq 0$? Identify the x- and y-intercepts and the asymptotes of the graph. Also, state the domain and range of the function.

Think

What values should you choose for x?
Choose values of x that divide nicely into 8. Make a table of points that are easy to graph.

Step 1
Make a table of values that includes positive and negative values of x.

x	y	x	y
−16	$-\frac{1}{2}$	$\frac{1}{2}$	16
−8	−1	1	8
−4	−2	2	4
−2	−4	4	2
−1	−8	8	1
$-\frac{1}{2}$	−16	16	$\frac{1}{2}$

Step 2
Graph the points from the table.

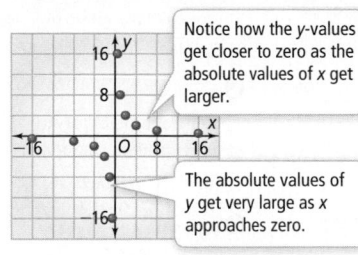

Notice how the y-values get closer to zero as the absolute values of x get larger.

The absolute values of y get very large as x approaches zero.

Step 3
Connect the points with a smooth curve.

x cannot be zero, so there is no y-intercept.
The numerator is never zero, so y is never 0.
There is no x-intercept.

The x-axis is a horizontal asymptote.
The y-axis is a vertical asymptote.
Knowing the asymptotes provides you with the basic shape of the graph.

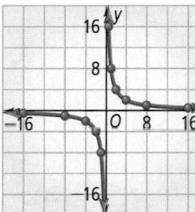

The domain is the set of all real numbers except $x = 0$.
The range is the set of all real numbers except $y = 0$.

 Got It? **1. a.** What is the graph of $y = \frac{12}{x}$? Identify the x- and y-intercepts and the asymptotes of the graph. Also, state the domain and range of the function.
b. Reasoning Would the function $y = \frac{6}{x}$ have the same domain and range as $y = \frac{8}{x}$ or $y = \frac{12}{x}$? Explain.

Hint

The graph of the function in Problem 1 might look like two separate graphs, but it is defined by a single function.

Each part of the graph of a reciprocal function is called a **branch**. The branches of the parent function $y = \frac{1}{x}$ are in Quadrants I and III. Stretches and compressions of the parent function remain in the same quadrants. Reflections are in Quadrants II and IV.

PowerAlgebra.com | Lesson 8-2 The Reciprocal Function Family | 531

Problem 1

Q Why is it important to include a fractional value for x? **[The function may change very significantly close to where it is undefined, in this case where x is 0.]**

Q Why is it necessary to include so many values in the table? **[While it may only take two points to determine a line, you need to look at many points when you are graphing curves by plotting points.]**

Q Why are the points $\left(\frac{1}{2}, 16\right)$ and $\left(-\frac{1}{2}, -16\right)$ not connected? **[They are not connected because the function is not defined at zero. Also, the function is going in different vertical directions on either side of zero.]**

Q In what way do the asymptotes help you graph a reciprocal function? **[The asymptotes provide boundaries for the branches of the graph to approach when you sketch the graph. This helps provide the curve's shape.]**

EXTENSION

Q How would you describe the symmetry of the graph? **[The graph is symmetric about the lines $y = -x$ and $y = x$, and about the origin.]**

Got It?

Q How can you tell there will be an asymptote at $x = 0$? **[x is in the denominator, so $x \neq 0$.]**

Q How can you tell there will be asymptote at $y = 0$? **[The fraction has a nonzero numerator, so the fraction can never equal 0.]**

---

2 Guided Instruction

Each Problem is worked out and supported online.

Problem 1
Graphing an Inverse Variation Function

Problem 2
Identifying a Reciprocal Function Transformation
Animated

Problem 3
Graphing a Translation

Alternative Problem 3
Graphing a Translation

Problem 4
Writing the Equation of a Transformation
Animated

Problem 5
Using a Reciprocal Function
Animated

Support in Algebra 2 Companion
• Vocabulary
• Key Concepts
• Got It?

Answers

Solve It!

It will raise the graph 8 units up. The cost with food is $8 more.

Got It?

1. a.

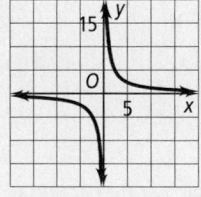

no x- or y-intercept; horizontal asymptote: $y = 0$, vert. asymptote: $x = 0$; domain: all real numbers except $x = 0$, range: all real numbers except $y = 0$

b. Yes; because they have similar graphs

Lesson 8-2 **531**

Problem 2

> Q How can you mathematically show that $y = \frac{6}{x}$ is a stretch of $y = \frac{1}{x}$ by a factor of 6? **[Sample: Express the y-values as a ratio: $\frac{6}{x} \div \frac{1}{x} = 6$.]**

EXTENSION

> Q How does the effect of a on the reciprocal function compare to previous functions you have studied? **[Sample: a has the same effect on the graph of the quadratic ($y = ax^2$) and absolute value ($y = a|x|$) functions.]**
>
> Q In the reciprocal function $y = \frac{a}{x}$, what does the sign of a tell you? **[If a is positive, the branches will be in Quadrants I and III. If a is negative, the branches will be in Quadrants II and IV.]**

Got It?

> Q How can you tell whether the transformation will be a shrink or a stretch? **[Sample: When $|a|$ is between 0 and 1, the transformation will be a shrink. When $|a|$ is greater than 1, the transformation will be a stretch.]**

Take Note   **ERROR PREVENTION**

If students translate the graph of a reciprocal function vertically before they reflect it in the x-axis, they will likely end up with the wrong graph. Point out the difference between $-a(\frac{1}{x}) + k$ and $-a(\frac{1}{x} + k)$. Ask which form corresponds to a reflection followed by a translation and which corresponds to a translation followed by a reflection.

 **Problem 2** Identifying Reciprocal Function Transformations

For each given value of a, how do the graphs of $y = \frac{1}{x}$ and $y = \frac{a}{x}$ compare? What is the effect of a on the graph?

Hint
For each x-value, the y-value for $y = \frac{6}{x}$ is stretched 6 times as far from the x-axis as the y-value for $y = \frac{1}{x}$.

A $a = 6$

The graph (in red) of $y = \frac{6}{x}$ is a stretch of the graph of $y = \frac{1}{x}$ (in black) by the factor 6.

B $a = 0.25$

The graph (in blue) of $y = \frac{0.25}{x}$ is a shrink of the graph of $y = \frac{1}{x}$ (in black) by the factor $\frac{1}{4}$.

Think
How does the negative sign affect the graph?
The y-values have signs that are opposite those in part A. The graph in A reflects across the x-axis.

C $a = -6$

The graph of $y = \frac{-6}{x}$ is the stretch by the factor 6 in part A followed by a reflection across the x-axis.

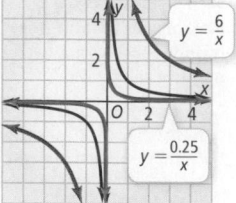
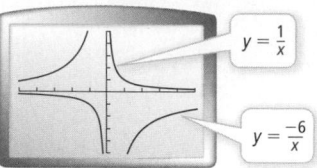

✓ **Got It? 2.** For each given value of a, how do the graphs of $y = \frac{1}{x}$ and $y = \frac{a}{x}$ compare? What is the effect of a on the graph?

  a. $a = \frac{1}{2}$ **b.** $a = 2$ **c.** $a = -\frac{1}{2}$

You can translate a reciprocal function horizontally or vertically just as you can other functions.

take note

Key Concept The Reciprocal Function Family	
Parent function	$y = \frac{1}{x}, x \neq 0$
Stretch ($|a| > 1$) Compression (Shrink) ($0 < |a| < 1$) Reflection ($a < 0$) in x-axis	$y = \frac{a}{x}, x \neq 0$
Translation (horizontal by h; vertical by k) with vertical asymptote $x = h$; horizontal asymptote $y = k$	$y = \frac{1}{x - h} + k; x \neq h$
All transformations combined	$y = \frac{a}{x - h} + k; x \neq h$

Additional Problems

1. What is the graph of $y = \frac{128}{x}, x \neq 0$? Identify the x- and y-intercepts and the asymptotes of the graph. Also, state the domain and the range of the function.

ANSWER

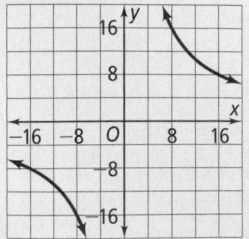

no x- or y-intercepts; asymptotes: $x = 0$ and $y = 0$; domain: all real numbers except $x = 0$; range: all real numbers except $y = 0$

2. How does the graph of $y = \frac{-1.5}{x}$ compare to the graph of $y = \frac{1}{x}$?

ANSWER The graph is reflected across the x-axis and stretched by a factor of 1.5.

3. What is the graph of $y = \frac{1}{x - 2} + 3$? Identify the domain and range.

ANSWER

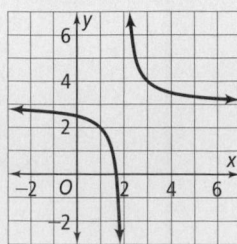

domain: all real numbers except $x = 2$; range: all real numbers except $y = 3$

4. This graph of a function is a translation of the graph of $y = \frac{1}{x}$. What is an equation for the function?

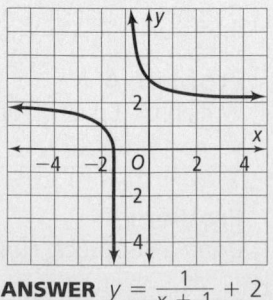

ANSWER $y = \frac{1}{x + 1} + 2$

5. A mystery society is renting a Victorian mansion for a murder mystery party. The owner is charging the group, which has 75 members, $650 for the weekend rental but does not want more than 30 people in the house. All of the members attending the party will split the cost of the rental equally except that the member playing the dead body does not have to pay. Model the cost per member C as a function of the number of members attending n. How many members have to attend for the cost to be less than $25 per person?

ANSWER $C = \frac{650}{n - 1}$; between 28 and 30, inclusive

When you graph a translated reciprocal function, a good first step is to draw the asymptotes.

PROBLEM **Problem 3** Graphing a Translation

Think

How do you find the asymptotes?
Translate the asymptotes of $y = \frac{1}{x}$ (the axes) 4 units left and 6 units down.

What is the graph of $y = \frac{1}{x + 4} - 6$? Identify the domain and range.

Step 1 Draw the asymptotes (red).

For, $y = \frac{1}{x + 4} - 6$, $h = -4$ and $k = -6$.
The vertical asymptote is $x = -4$.
The horizontal asymptote is $y = -6$.

Step 2 Translate the graph of $y = \frac{1}{x}$.

The graph of $y = \frac{1}{x}$ contains the points $(1, 1)$ and $(-1, -1)$.
Translate these points 4 units to the left and 6 units down to $(-3, -5)$ and $(-5, -7)$, respectively. Draw the branches through these points (blue).

The domain is the set of all real numbers except $x = -4$. The range is the set of all real numbers except $y = -6$.

✓ **Got It? 3.** What is the graph of $y = \frac{1}{x - 2} + 4$? Identify the domain and range.

If you know the asymptotes of the graph of a reciprocal function and the value of a, you can write the equation of the function.

PROBLEM **Problem 4** Writing the Equation of a Transformation

Multiple Choice This graph is a translation of the graph of $y = \frac{2}{x}$. What is an equation for the function?

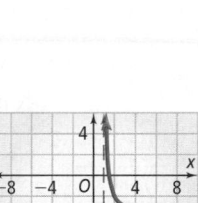

A) $y = \frac{2}{x + 3} + 4$ C) $y = \frac{2}{x - 3} + 4$

B) $y = \frac{2}{x + 3} - 4$ D) $y = \frac{2}{x - 3} - 4$

Plan

How can you get started?
Identify the asymptotes of the graph.

The asymptotes are $x = -3$ and $y = 4$. Thus, $h = -3$ and $k = 4$.

Write the general form. $y = \frac{a}{x - h} + k$

Substitute for a, h, and k. $y = \frac{2}{x - (-3)} + 4$

Simplify. $y = \frac{2}{x + 3} + 4$

Hint

Use a graphing calculator to check. Remember to use parentheses around the denominator.

The correct choice is A.

✓ **Got It? 4.** This graph is a translation of the graph of $y = \frac{2}{x}$. What is an equation for the function?

Problem 3

Q In Step 1, why does $h = -1$ instead of 1? **[Sample: Rewrite $x + 1$ as $x - (-1)$, since the expression is $x - h$.]**

Q Algebraically, why is -1 not included in the domain? **[-1 leads to division by zero.]**

Q Algebraically, why can y never equal -2? **[For y to equal -2, the expression $\frac{1}{x + 1}$ would have to equal zero. A rational expression only equals zero if the numerator equals zero. The numerator is never zero, so y can never equal -2.]**

Got It?

Q How are the domain and range related to the asymptotes? **[The x-value of the vertical asymptote is excluded from the domain, and the y-value of the horizontal asymptote is excluded from the range.]**

Problem 4

Q Where does the value for a come from? **[from the original function, which is a transformation of the parent function]**

Q Why are $x = h$ and $y = k$ asymptotes? **[Answers may vary. Sample: The value of h will make the fraction undefined, and y cannot be the value of k because the fraction cannot equal 0.]**

Got It?

Q What are the domain and range of the function? **[The domain is all real numbers except $x = 1$; the range is all real numbers except $y = -4$.]**

Answers

4. $y = \frac{2}{x - 1} - 4$

Got It? (continued)

2. a. $y = \frac{1}{2x}$ is a shrink of the graph of $y = \frac{1}{x}$ by a factor of $\frac{1}{2}$.

b. $y = \frac{2}{x}$ is a stretch of the graph of $y = \frac{1}{x}$ by a factor of 2.

c. $y = -\frac{1}{2x}$ is a reflection across the x-axis and a shrink of the graph of $y = \frac{1}{x}$ by a factor of $\frac{1}{2}$.

3.

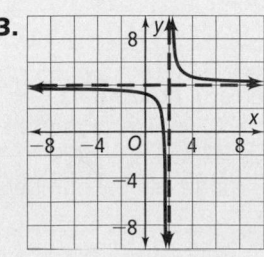

domain: all real numbers except $x = 2$, range: all real numbers except $y = 4$

Problem 5

Q How would you describe the range of the function? **[Sample: The range consists of all possible money values between and including the least amount a student would have to pay ($750 ÷ 52), about $14.42, and the most a student would have to pay, $750.]**

Q What is a function that models the cost per student with respect to the number of people on the bus? **[$c = \frac{750}{n-5}$]**

Q Why can you ignore the other branch of the graph of the function altogether? **[No x-values from the other branch of the graph are included in the domain.]**

Q What is a good window in which to view the relevant portion of the graph to answer the final question? Explain. **[x-values from 0 to 52 and y-values from 0 to 25; the domain is a good set of values for x, and a portion of the range that includes the $20 limit is a good set of values for y; in addition, include zero in both the domain and range in order to see the x- and y-axes on the graph.]**

Got It?

Q What inequality will you write to model the situation in 5a? **[$\frac{1200}{n} \le 7.5$]**

Q In 5b, why is the domain of students 1 to 312 instead of 1 to 325? **[There must be 13 adult chaperones, and the facility holds a maximum of 325 people. 325 − 13 = 312]**

Q How will your inequality change for 5b? **[$\frac{1200}{n-30} \le 7.5$]**

 **Problem 5** Using a Reciprocal Function

Clubs The rowing club is renting a 57-passenger bus for a day trip. The cost of the bus is $750. Five passengers will be chaperones. If the students who attend share the bus cost equally, what function models the cost per student C with respect to the number of students n who attend? What is the domain of the function? How many students must ride the bus to make the cost per student no more than $20?

Know	Need	Plan
• The bus holds 57 passengers. • The bus costs $750. • Five riders are chaperones who pay nothing for the bus.	• A function for the cost per student • The number of students needed so that the cost does not exceed $20 per student	• Write a reciprocal function for the situation. • Graph the function and solve an inequality using the $20 limit.

Step 1 Write a function.

To share the cost equally, divide by the number of students who attend. $\qquad C = \frac{750}{n}$

The function that models the cost per student is $C(n) = \frac{750}{n}$.

Step 2 Identify the domain.

Think
Is the domain $n \le 52$? No. The domain is the possible numbers of students, so only positive integers make sense.

The bus has a capacity of 57 passengers and there will be 5 chaperones. The maximum number of students is $57 - 5 = 52$.

The domain is the set of integers from 1 to 52.

Step 3 Use a graphing calculator to solve the inequality $\frac{750}{n} \le 20$.

Let **Y1** $= \frac{750}{x}$ and **Y2** $= 20$.

Adjust the window dimensions to get a closer look at the graph. Use the **intersect** feature.

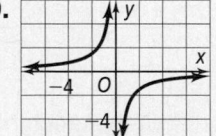
For all values greater than or equal to 38, the cost is less than $20.

If $x = 37$, the cost will be more than $20.

Intersection X = 37.5   Y = 20

The number of people must be a whole number.

At least 38 students must ride the bus.

Hint
For part (c), let **Y1** be the function you wrote for part (a) and let **Y2** be 7.50.

✓ **Got It?** **5.** The junior class is renting a laser tag facility with a capacity of 325 people. The cost for the facility is $1200. The party must have 13 adult chaperones.
  a. If the students who attend share the facility cost equally, what function models the cost per student C with respect to the number of students n who attend?
  b. What is the domain of the function?
  c. How many students must attend to make the cost per student no more than $7.50?

Answers

Got It? (continued)

5. a. $C = \frac{1200}{n}$;

  b. domain: whole numbers from 1 to 312;

  c. 160 students

Lesson Check

1.

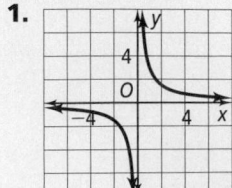

2. $y = \frac{1}{x}$ translated 5 units up

3. $y = \frac{1}{x}$ reflected across the x-axis and stretched by a factor of 4

4. horizontal asymptote: $y = -7$, vertical asymptote: $x = -2$

5. shrink of the graph of $y = \frac{1}{x}$ by a factor of $\frac{1}{2}$

6. $y = -\frac{1}{x}$

7. for $y = \frac{a}{x}$: stretch if $|a| > 1$ and compression if $0 < |a| < 1$

Practice and Problem-Solving Exercises

8.

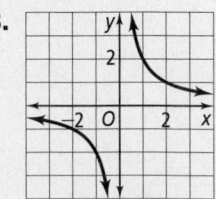

no x- or y-intercept; horizontal asymptote: $y = 0$, vertical asymptote: $x = 0$; domain: all real numbers except $x = 0$, range: all real numbers except $y = 0$

9.

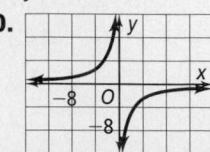

no x- or y-intercept; horizontal asymptote: $y = 0$, vertical asymptote: $x = 0$; domain: all real numbers except $x = 0$, range: all real numbers except $y = 0$

10.

no x- or y-intercept; horizontal asymptote: $y = 0$, vertical asymptote: $x = 0$; domain: all real numbers except $x = 0$, range: all real numbers except $y = 0$

Focus Question What are reciprocal functions?

Answer A reciprocal function is a function with the independent variable in the denominator of a fraction. All reciprocal functions can be written in the form $y = \frac{a}{x-h} + k$ as transformations of the parent function, $y = \frac{1}{x}$. Use a reciprocal function to model inverse variation.

Lesson Check

Do you know HOW?

1. Graph the equation $y = \frac{3}{x}$.

Describe the transformation from the graph of $y = \frac{1}{x}$ to the graph of the given function.

2. $y = \frac{1}{x} + 5$

3. $y = \frac{-4}{x}$

4. What are the asymptotes of the graph of $y = \frac{5}{x+2} - 7$?

Do you UNDERSTAND?

5. **Vocabulary** What transformation changes the graph of $y = \frac{1}{x}$ into the graph of $y = \frac{1}{2x}$?

6. Write an equation of the reflection of the graph $y = \frac{1}{x}$ in the x-axis.

7. **Writing** Explain how you can tell if a function $y = \frac{a}{x}$ is a stretch or compression of the parent function $y = \frac{1}{x}$.

Practice and Problem-Solving Exercises

Ⓐ Practice

Graph each function. Identify the x- and y-intercepts and the asymptotes of the graph. Also, state the domain and the range of the function.
◀ **See Problem 1.**

8. $y = \frac{2}{x}$

9. $y = \frac{-3}{x}$

10. $y = -\frac{10}{x}$

11. $y = \frac{10}{x}$

📱 **Graphing Calculator** Graph the equations $y = \frac{1}{x}$ and $y = \frac{a}{x}$ using the given value of a. Then identify the effect of a on the graph.
◀ **See Problem 2.**

12. $a = 2$

13. $a = -4$

14. $a = 0.5$

15. $a = 0.75$

Sketch the asymptotes and the graph of each function. Identify the domain and range.
◀ **See Problem 3.**

Guided Practice

To start, compare the equation to general form to identify h and k.

16. $y = \frac{1}{x} - 3$

$y = \frac{a}{x-h} + k$

$y = \frac{1}{x-0} + (-3)$

17. $y = \frac{-2}{x} - 3$

18. $y = \frac{1}{x-2} + 5$

19. $y = \frac{1}{x-3} + 4$

20. $y = \frac{2}{x+6} - 1$

21. $y = \frac{1}{x} - 2$

22. $y = \frac{-8}{x+5} - 6$

Write an equation for the translation of $y = \frac{2}{x}$ that has the given asymptotes.
◀ **See Problem 4.**

23. $x = 0$ and $y = 4$

24. $x = -2$ and $y = 3$

25. $x = 4$ and $y = -8$

11.

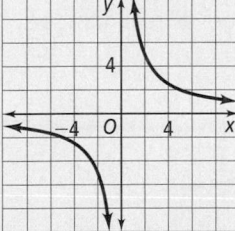

no x- or y-intercept; horizontal asymptote: $y = 0$, vertical asymptote: $x = 0$; domain: all real numbers except $x = 0$, range: all real numbers except $y = 0$

12.

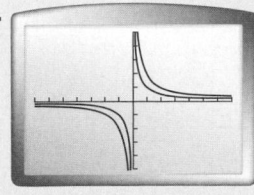

13.

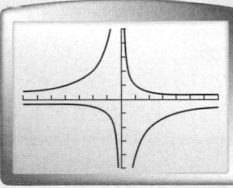

reflection across the x-axis and a stretch by a factor of 4

14.

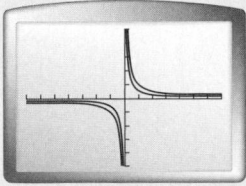

compression by a factor of 0.5

15.

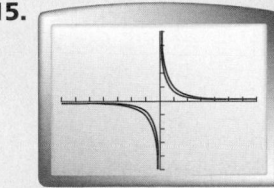

compression by a factor of 0.75

16–25. See next page.

---

3 Lesson Check

Do you know HOW?
• For Exercise 1, students struggling with graphing may need to make a table of values and plot points to check their graphs.
• For Exercises 2 and 3, if students are having difficulty describing the transformations, have them graph both the given function and the parent function on the same set of axes.
• For Exercise 4, if students are having difficulty identifying the asymptotes from the equation, have them rewrite the equation as $y = \frac{5}{x - (-2)} - 7$.

Do you UNDERSTAND?
• For Exercise 5, if students cannot identify the transformation, ask, "Is dividing by two the same as multiplying by $\frac{1}{2}$?"
• For Exercise 7, if students are unsure whether the function $y = \frac{a}{x}$ is a stretch or a compression, suggest they compare $y = \frac{a}{x}$ to a quadratic function with the same value for a and determine the effect by comparison. Then experiment with various values for a on a graphing calculator.

Close

Q How are functions of the form $y = \frac{a}{x-h} + k$ related to the parent function $y = \frac{1}{x}$? **[The functions are stretched or compressed by a factor of a, reflected in the x-axis if the value of a is negative, translated h units horizontally, and translated k units vertically.]**

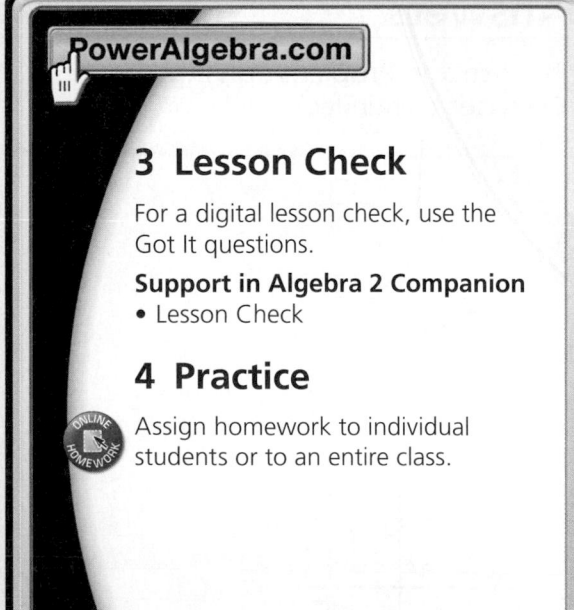

PowerAlgebra.com

3 Lesson Check

For a digital lesson check, use the Got It questions.

Support in Algebra 2 Companion
• Lesson Check

4 Practice

Assign homework to individual students or to an entire class.

4 Practice

ASSIGNMENT GUIDE

Basic: 8–22 even, 23, 25–27, 29, 37

Average: 8–22 even, 23–31, 33–35, 37

Stndardized Test Prep: 38–42

Mixed Review: 43–54

Reasoning exercises have blue headings.

Applications exercises have red headings.

EXERCISE 37: Use the Think About a Plan worksheet in the **Student Companion** (also available in the Teaching Resources in print and online) to further support students' development in becoming independent learners.

HOMEWORK QUICK CHECK

To check students' understanding of key skills and concepts, go over Exercises 8, 12, 17, 27, and 37.

---

26. Construction The weight P in pounds that a beam can safely carry is inversely proportional to the distance D in feet between the supports of the beam. For a certain type of wooden beam, $P = \frac{9200}{D}$. What distance between supports is needed to carry 1200 lb?

◀ See Problem 5.

 Apply

27. Think About a Plan A high school decided to spend \$750 on student academic achievement awards. At least 5 awards will be given, they should be equal in value, and each award should not be less than \$50. Write and sketch a function that models the relationship between the number a of awards and the cost c of each award. What are the domain and range of the function?
- Which equation describes the relationship between a and c?
- What information can you use to determine the domain and range?

28. Open-Ended Write an equation for a horizontal translation of $y = \frac{2}{x}$. Then write an equation for a vertical translation of $y = \frac{2}{x}$. Identify the horizontal and vertical asymptotes of the graph of each function.

Sketch the graph of each function.

29. $xy = 3$ **30.** $xy + 5 = 0$ **31.** $5xy = 2$ **32.** $10xy = -4$

33. The formula $p = \frac{69.1}{a + 2.3}$ models the relationship between atmospheric pressure p in inches of mercury and altitude a in miles.

Use the data shown with the photo. At which location does the model predict the pressure to be about 23.93 in. of mercury? (*Hint:* 1 mi = 5280 ft.)

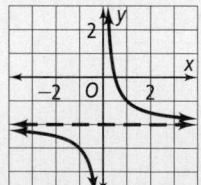

Sahara Desert average alt. 1500 ft

Kalahari Desert average alt. 3100 ft

Mt. Kilimanjaro alt. 19,340 ft

Vinson Massif alt. 16,680 ft

Ⓐ Sahara Desert
Ⓑ Kalahari Desert
Ⓒ Mt. Kilimanjaro
Ⓓ Vinson Massif

📟 **Graphing Calculator** Graph each pair of functions. Find the approximate point(s) of intersection.

34. $y = \frac{6}{x - 2}, y = 6$ **35.** $y = -\frac{1}{x - 3} - 6, y = 6.2$ **36.** $y = \frac{3}{x + 1}, y = -4$

37. a. Gasoline Mileage Suppose you drive an average of 10,000 miles each year. Your gasoline mileage (mi/gal) varies inversely with the number of gallons of gasoline you use each year. Write and graph a model for your average mileage m in terms of the gallons g of gasoline used.
b. After you begin driving on the highway more often, you use 50 gal less per year. Write and graph a new model to include this information.
c. Calculate your old and new mileage assuming that you originally used 400 gal of gasoline per year.

Answers

Practice and Problem-Solving Exercises (continued)

16.

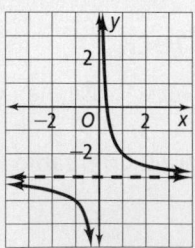

domain: all real numbers except $x = 0$, range: all real numbers except $y = -3$

17.

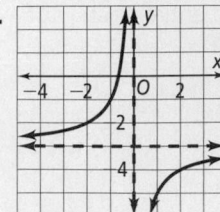

domain: all real numbers except $x = 0$, range: all real numbers except $y = -3$

18.

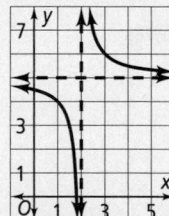

domain: all real numbers except $x = 2$, range: all real numbers except $y = 5$

19.

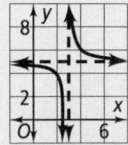

domain: all real numbers except $x = 3$, range: all real numbers except $y = 4$

20.

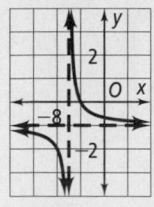

domain: all real numbers except $x = -6$, range: all real numbers except $y = -1$

21.

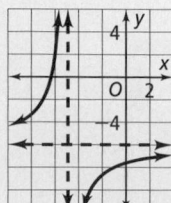

domain: all real numbers except $x = 0$, range: all real numbers except $y = -2$

22.

domain: all real numbers except $x = -5$, range: all real numbers except $y = -6$

SAT/ACT

38. What is an equation for the translation of $y = \frac{2}{x}$ that has asymptotes at $x = 3$ and $y = -5$?

Ⓐ $y = \frac{2}{x-3} - 5$ Ⓑ $y = \frac{2}{x+3} + 5$ Ⓒ $y = \frac{2}{x+5} - 3$ Ⓓ $y = \frac{2}{x-5} + 3$

39. The graph at the right shows which inequality?

Ⓕ $y < -2.5x + 5$ Ⓗ $-2.5x + y < 5$

Ⓖ $2.5x + y \geq 5$ Ⓘ $5x + y \leq 5$

40. If p and q vary inversely, and $p = 10$ when $q = -4$, what is q when $p = -2$?

Ⓐ 20 Ⓒ $-\frac{4}{5}$

Ⓑ $\frac{4}{5}$ Ⓓ -20

41. Which equation represents the inverse of the graph at the right?

Ⓕ $y = \log_3 x$ Ⓗ $y = \log_x 3$

Ⓖ $x = \log_3 y$ Ⓘ $x = \log_y 3$

Short Response

42. What is b if the graph of $y = 27b^x$ includes the point $(-1, 81)$?

Mixed Review

Suppose that x and y vary inversely. Write a function that models each inverse variation and find y when $x = -5$. ◀ See Lesson 8-1.

43. $x = 2$ when $y = 12$ **44.** $x = 25$ when $y = 2$ **45.** $x = 12$ when $y = 4$

Without graphing, determine whether the function represents exponential growth or exponential decay. Then find the y-intercept. ◀ See Lesson 7-1.

46. $y = 3(4)^x$ **47.** $y = 0.1(2)^x$ **48.** $y = 5(0.8)^x$

Multiply. ◀ See Lesson 6-3.

49. $(5\sqrt{3} - 2)^2$ **50.** $(4 + 2\sqrt{3})(6 - 3\sqrt{3})$ **51.** $(\sqrt{3} + \sqrt{5})(\sqrt{3} - \sqrt{5})$

Get Ready! To prepare for Lesson 8-3, do Exercises 52–54.

Factor each expression. ◀ See Lesson 4-4.

52. $x^2 + 6x - 27$ **53.** $2x^2 + x - 28$ **54.** $2x^2 - 19x + 24$

23. $y = \frac{2}{x} + 4$ **24.** $y = \frac{2}{x+2} + 3$

25. $y = \frac{2}{x-4} - 8$

26. 7.67 ft

27.
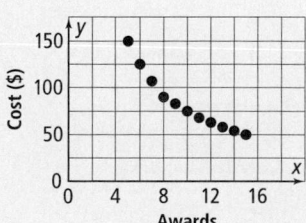

$c = \frac{750}{a}$; domain: whole numbers from 5 to 15, range: $50 \leq c \leq 750$

28. Check students' work.

29. 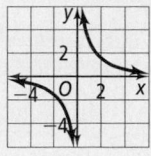 **30.**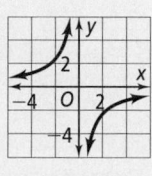

31. 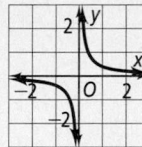 **32.**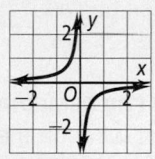

33. B

34. 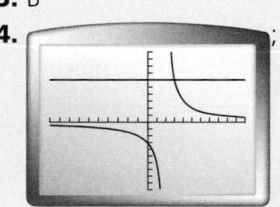 ; (3, 6)

35. 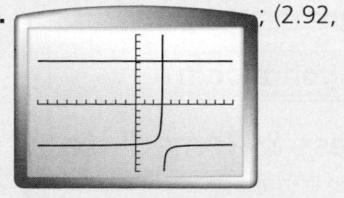 ; (2.92, 6.2)

36. 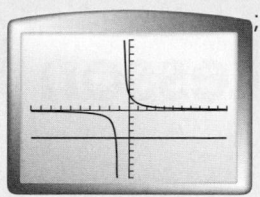 ; (−1.75, −4)

37. a. $m = \frac{10,000}{g}$

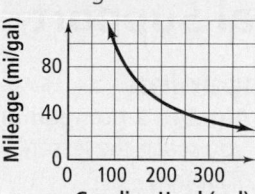

b. $m = \frac{10,000}{g - 50}$

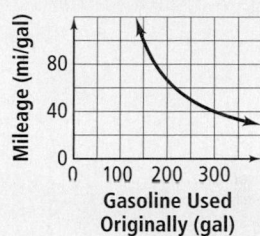

c. 25 mi/gal; 28.57 mi/gal

Standardized Test Prep

38. A **39.** F

40. A **41.** F

42. [2] $81 = 27b^{-1}$

$81 = \frac{27}{b}$

$b = \frac{27}{81}$

$b = \frac{1}{3}$

[1] correct answer, without work shown

Mixed Review

43. $y = \frac{24}{x}$; $-\frac{24}{5}$

44. $y = \frac{50}{x}$; -10

45. $y = \frac{48}{x}$; $-\frac{48}{5}$

46. exponential growth; 3

47. exponential growth; 0.1

48. exponential decay; 5

49. $79 - 20\sqrt{3}$

50. 6

51. -2

52. $(x + 9)(x - 3)$

53. $(2x - 7)(x + 4)$

54. $(2x - 3)(x - 8)$

Differentiated Remediation

Additional Instructional Support

Algebra 2 Companion

Students can use the **Algebra 2 Companion** worktext (4 pages) as you teach the lesson. Use the Companion to support

- New Vocabulary
- Key Concepts
- Got It for each Problem
- Lesson Check

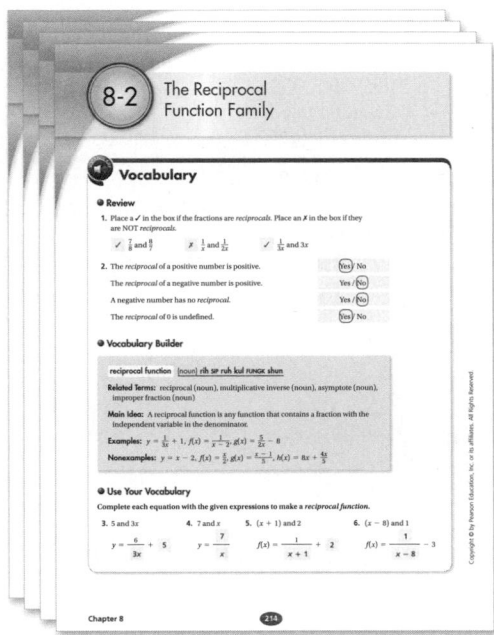

ELL Support

Assess Understanding To check that students understand the roles of a, h, and k in the general form of the reciprocal function, have them graph $y = \frac{3}{x}$, $y = \frac{-3}{x}$, $y = \frac{1}{x} + 3$, and $y = \frac{1}{x - 3}$ using a graphing calculator. Have students copy each graph and explain each transformation in words. Check the students' explanations for correctness. Then have the students work in pairs and explain their transformations to each other aloud, using the algebraic terms listed in the Essential Understanding on page 507. If students did not use those terms in their written explanations, help them rewrite their explanations of the transformations using the algebraic terms.

5 Assess & Remediate

Lesson Quiz

1. What transformation changes the graph of $y = \frac{1}{x}$ into the graph of $y = \frac{-2}{x}$?
2. What is the graph of $y = \frac{1}{x + 3} + 1$? Identify the domain and range, the x- and y-intercepts, and the asymptotes of the graph.
3. **Do you UNDERSTAND?** A local theater will hold an after-prom movie. The theater seats 300 people, and the total cost is $400. If ten parents go as chaperones, model the cost per student C as a function of the number of attendees n. How many students must attend the movie for the cost to be no more than $3.25 per student? Assume the chaperones do not pay.

ANSWERS TO LESSON QUIZ

1. The graph is reflected in the x-axis and stretched by a factor of 2.

2.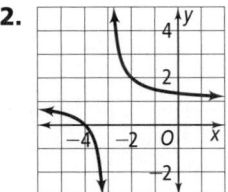

   domain: all real numbers except $x = -3$; range: all real numbers except $y = 1$; x-intercept: $(-4, 0)$; y-intercept: $(0, \frac{4}{3})$; vertical asymptote: $x = -3$, horizontal asymptote: $y = 1$

3. $C = \frac{400}{n - 10}$; at least 124 students

PRESCRIPTION FOR REMEDIATION

Use the student work on the Lesson Quiz to prescribe a differentiated review assignment:

Points	Differentiated Remediation
0–1	Intervention
2	On-level
3	Extension

PowerAlgebra.com

5 Assess & Remediate

Assign the Lesson Quiz. Appropriate intervention, practice, or enrichment is automatically generated based on student performance.

Intervention

- **Reteaching** (2 pages) Provides reteaching and practice exercises for the key lesson concepts. Use with struggling students or absent students.
- **English Language Learner Support** Helps students develop and reinforce mathematical vocabulary and key concepts.

All-in-One Resources/Online
Reteaching

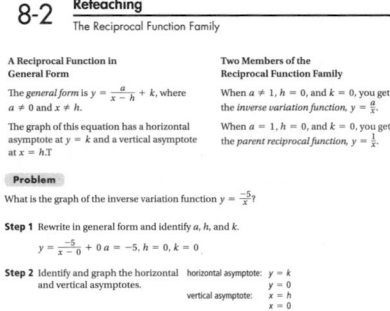

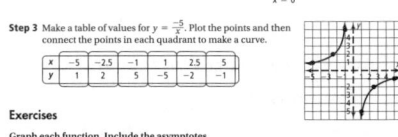

All-in-One Resources/Online
English Language Learner Support

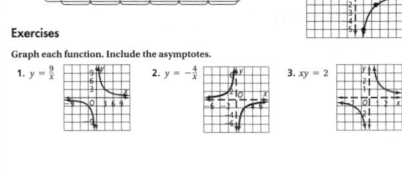

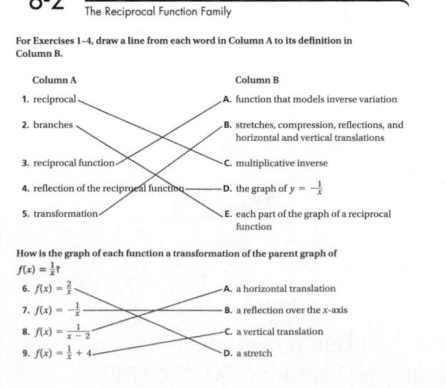

Differentiated Remediation *continued*

On-Level

- **Practice** (2 pages) Provides extra practice for each lesson. For more challenging practice exercises, use the Form G Practice pages found in the All-in-One Teaching Resources and online.

- **Think About a Plan** Helps students develop specific problem-solving skills and strategies by providing scaffolded guiding questions.

- **Standardized Test Prep** Focuses on all major exercises, all major question types, and helps students prepare for the high-stakes assessments.

Extension

- **Enrichment** Provides students with interesting problems and activities that extend the concepts of the lesson.

- **Activities, Games, and Puzzles** Worksheets that can be used for concepts development, enrichment, and for fun!

Student Companion/ All-in-One Resources/Online
Practice page 1

8-2 Practice — Form K
The Reciprocal Function Family

Graph each function. Identify the *x*- and *y*-intercepts and asymptotes of the graph. Also, state the domain and range of the function.

1. $y = -\frac{2}{x}$ 2. $y = \frac{4}{x}$ 3. $y = -\frac{5}{x}$

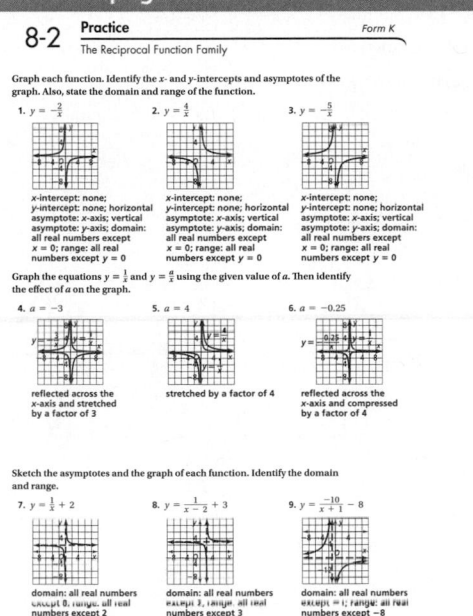

x-intercept: none; *y*-intercept: none; horizontal asymptote: *x*-axis; vertical asymptote: *y*-axis; domain: all real numbers except *x* = 0; range: all real numbers except *y* = 0

(repeated for each)

Graph the equations $y = \frac{1}{x}$ and $y = \frac{a}{x}$ using the given value of *a*. Then identify the effect of *a* on the graph.

4. $a = -3$ 5. $a = 4$ 6. $a = -0.25$

reflected across the *x*-axis and stretched by a factor of 3 / stretched by a factor of 4 / reflected across the *x*-axis and compressed by a factor of 4

Sketch the asymptotes and the graph of each function. Identify the domain and range.

7. $y = \frac{1}{x} + 2$ 8. $y = \frac{1}{x-2} + 3$ 9. $y = \frac{-10}{x+1} - 8$

domain: all real numbers except 0; range: all real numbers except 2 / domain: all real numbers except 2; range: all real numbers except 3 / domain: all real numbers except −1; range: all real numbers except −8

Student Companion/ All-in-One Resources/Online
Practice page 2

8-2 Practice (continued) — Form K
The Reciprocal Function Family

Write an equation for the translation of $y = \frac{3}{x}$ that has the given asymptotes.

10. $x = 0$ and $y = 2$ 11. $x = -2$ and $y = 4$ 12. $x = 5$ and $y = -3$
$y = \frac{3}{x} + 2$ $y = \frac{3}{x+2} + 4$ $y = \frac{3}{x-5} - 3$

Sketch the graph of each function.

13. $3xy = 1$ 14. $xy - 8 = 0$ 15. $2xy = -6$

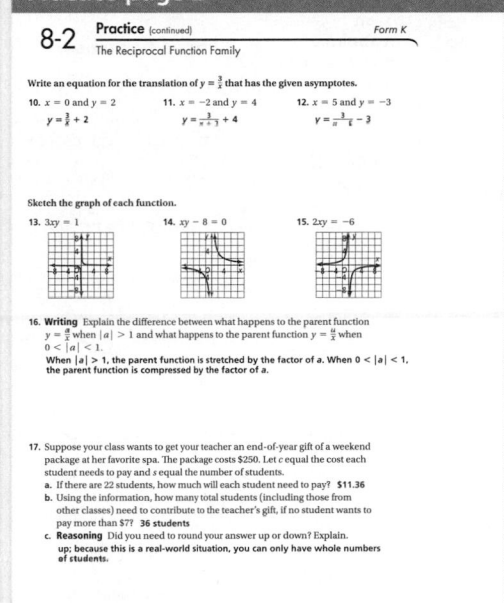

16. **Writing** Explain the difference between what happens to the parent function $y = \frac{a}{x}$ when $|a| > 1$ and what happens to the parent function $y = \frac{a}{x}$ when $0 < |a| < 1$.
When $|a| > 1$, the parent function is stretched by the factor of *a*. When $0 < |a| < 1$, the parent function is compressed by the factor of *a*.

17. Suppose your class wants to get your teacher an end-of-year gift of a weekend package at her favorite spa. The package costs $250. Let *c* equal the cost each student needs to pay and *s* equal the number of students.
 a. If there are 22 students, how much will each student need to pay? **$11.36**
 b. Using the information, how many total students (including those from other classes) need to contribute to the teacher's gift, if no student wants to pay more than $7? **36 students**
 c. **Reasoning** Did you need to round your answer up or down? Explain.
 up; because this is a real-world situation, you can only have whole numbers of students.

All-in-One Resources/Online
Enrichment

8-2 Enrichment
The Reciprocal Function Family

Understanding Horizontal Asymptotes

The line $y = \frac{3}{4}$ is a horizontal asymptote for the graph of the function $y = \frac{3x + 5}{4x - 8}$. By using long division, you can rewrite this function in the form quotient + remainder divided by the divisor: $y = \frac{3}{4} + \frac{11}{4x - 8}$.

Examine what happens to the remainder divided by the divisor and the value of *y* as the value of *x* gets larger. Fill in the following table to four decimal places.

	x	$\frac{11}{4x-8}$	$y = \frac{3}{4} + \frac{11}{4x-8}$
1.	3	2.7500	3.5000
2.	10	0.3438	1.0938
3.	100	0.0281	0.7781

Note that as *x* gets larger, both the remainder and the value of *y* get smaller. Although the value of *y* is always greater than $\frac{3}{4}$, it gets closer to $\frac{3}{4}$ as *x* gets larger. As *x* gets infinitely large, *y* approaches $\frac{3}{4}$ from above. Write this as:
As $x \to +\infty$, $y \to \frac{3}{4}$ from above.

Examine what happens as *x* gets smaller. Fill in the following table to four decimal places.

	x	$\frac{11}{4x-8}$	$y = \frac{3}{4} + \frac{11}{4x-8}$
4.	−3	−0.5500	0.2000
5.	−10	−0.2292	0.5208
6.	−100	−0.0270	0.7230

Here the value of *y* is always less than $\frac{3}{4}$, but it gets closer to $\frac{3}{4}$ as *x* gets smaller (more negative). Write this as: As $x \to -\infty$, $y \to \frac{3}{4}$ from below.
In both cases, *y* approaches $\frac{3}{4}$, the horizontal asymptote.

Student Companion/ All-in-One Resources/Online
Think About a Plan

8-2 Think About a Plan
The Reciprocal Function Family

a. **Gasoline Mileage** Suppose you drive an average of 10,000 miles each year. Your gasoline mileage (mi/gal) varies inversely with the number of gallons of gasoline you use each year. Write and graph a model for your average mileage *m* in terms of the gallons *g* of gasoline used.

b. After you begin driving on the highway more often, you use 50 gal less per year. Write and graph a new model to include this information.

c. Calculate your old and new mileage assuming that you originally used 400 gal of gasoline per year.

1. Write a formula for gasoline mileage in words.

The mileage is equal to the number of miles divided by the number of gallons.

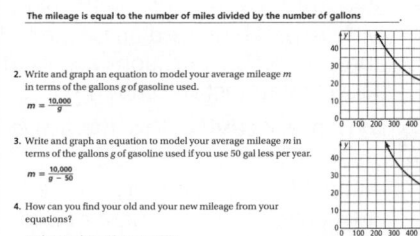

2. Write and graph an equation to model your average mileage *m* in terms of the gallons *g* of gasoline used.
$m = \frac{10,000}{g}$

3. Write and graph an equation to model your average mileage *m* in terms of the gallons *g* of gasoline used if you use 50 gal less per year.
$m = \frac{10,000}{g - 50}$

4. How can you find your old and your new mileage from your equations?
Evaluate each equation at $g = 400$

5. What is your old mileage? **25 mi/gal**

6. What is your new mileage? **about 28.6 mi/gal**

Student Companion/ All-in-One Resources/Online
Standardized Test Prep

8-2 Standardized Test Prep
The Reciprocal Function Family

Multiple Choice

For Exercises 1–3, choose the correct letter.

1. What is an equation for the translation of $y = -\frac{4.5}{x}$ that has asymptotes at $x = 3$ and $y = -5$? **A**
 A. $y = -\frac{4.5}{x-3} - 5$ C. $y = -\frac{4.5}{x-3} + 3$
 B. $y = -\frac{4.5}{x+3} - 5$ D. $y = -\frac{4.5}{x+3} + 3$

2. What is the equation of the vertical asymptote of $y = \frac{2}{x-5}$? **I**
 F. $x = -5$ G. $x = 0$ H. $x = 2$ I. $x = 5$

3. Which is the graph of $y = \frac{1}{x+1} - 2$? **D**
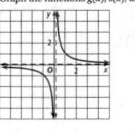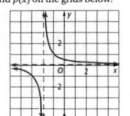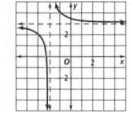

Extended Response

4. A race pilot's average rate of speed over a 720-mi course is inversely proportional to the time in minutes *t* the pilot takes to fly a complete race course. The pilot's final score *s* is the average speed minus any penalty points *p* earned.
 a. Write a function to model the pilot's score for a given *t* and *p*. (*Hint: d = rt*)
 b. Graph the function for a pilot who has 2 penalty points.
 c. What is the maximum time a pilot with 2 penalty points can take to finish the course and still earn a score of at least 3?

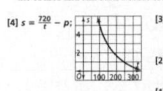
[4] $s = \frac{720}{t} - p$;
144 min

[3] correct answer with most of work shown and appropriate strategies used OR incorrect answer with all work shown and appropriate strategies used
[2] correct answer with little work shown OR incorrect answer but work shown reflects some understanding of problem
[1] answer is incomplete or incorrect and no work is shown
[0] no answer given

Online Teacher Resource Center
Activities, Puzzles, and Games

8-2 Activity: Family First
The Reciprocal Function Family

Complete this activity on your own.

A Function Fable

Given: $g(x) = \frac{1}{x}$, $s(x) = \frac{1}{x+2}$, $d(x) = \frac{1}{x-5}$, $m(x) = \frac{1}{x-5} + 6$, $p(x) = \frac{1}{x-5} + 3$, and $j(x) = \frac{-1}{x+2} - 3$

Grandma function $g(x)$ had two children. Her son Steve $s(x)$ was left-handed and her daughter Diana $d(x)$ was right-handed. Diana had one very tall child Michel $m(x)$, who towered above her. Steve had two children as well. Pat $p(x)$ and Jo $j(x)$ were twins, but opposites of one another.

Graph the functions $g(x)$, $s(x)$, and $p(x)$ on the grids below.

Activity
Make a reciprocal function family with at least 3 "generations" and 6 individual functions. Explain the transformations that yield each family member. Have at least one member in the third generation be a driving, graduate-athlete given:
- A horizontal translation corresponds to being a driver.
- A vertical translation corresponds to being an athlete.
- A reflection corresponds to being a high-school graduate.

Note: In the fable above, Jo was the only driving, graduate-athlete.

Then sketch a graph of one function from each generation (including the driving, graduate-athlete), showing all asymptotes.

Check student's work.
Optional Extension: Have students come up with their own creative story about a family, as in the fable. It should also have details based in mathematics.

1 Interactive Learning

Solve It!

PURPOSE To model a real-world situation using a rational function

PROCESS Students may
- guess and check to find the answer using integer values for *x*.
- input the rational function into a graphing calculator, and use the Table function to find the least integer *x*-value that returns $y \geq 0.4$.
- solve $0.4 = \frac{x + 3}{x + 16}$.

FACILITATE

Q What is your percentage if you make your next shot? your next two? **[0.24, 0.28]**

Q What function gives your percentage if you make your next *x* shots? $\left[\frac{3 + x}{16 + x}\right]$

Q Can you reach 100%? 99%? Explain your answers. **[No; yes; since you already missed some shots you can never reach 100%. You will reach 99% if you make your next 1284 shots without a miss.]**

ANSWER See Solve It in Answers on next page.

CONNECT THE MATH In the Solve It students write two linear functions—one for shots made and one for shots attempted—and form a rational function as the quotient of the two linear functions to find the answer. In the lesson, students analyze and graph rational functions and use them to solve concentration problems.

8-3 Rational Functions and Their Graphs

Objectives To identify properties of rational functions
To graph rational functions

For sure, 100% is out of reach!

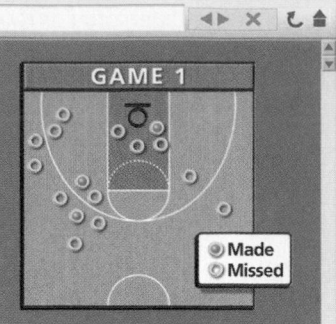

Dynamic Activity Rational Functions

Lesson Vocabulary
- rational function
- continuous graph
- discontinuous graph
- point of discontinuity
- removable discontinuity
- non-removable discontinuity

You use a ratio of polynomial functions to form a *rational function*, like $y = \frac{x + 3}{x + 16}$.

Focus Question What is a rational function?

A **rational function** is a function that you can write in the form $f(x) = \frac{P(x)}{Q(x)}$ where $P(x)$ and $Q(x)$ are polynomial functions. The domain of $f(x)$ is all real numbers except those values for which $Q(x) = 0$.

Here are graphs of three rational functions:

$$y = \frac{x^2}{x^2 + 1}$$

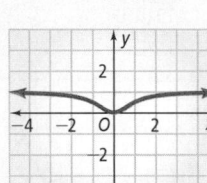

$$y = \frac{(x + 3)(x + 2)}{(x + 2)}$$

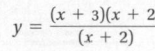
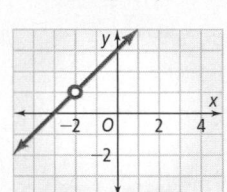

$$y = \frac{x + 4}{x - 2}$$

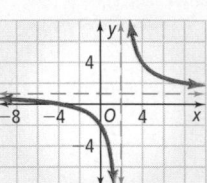

538   Chapter 8   Rational Functions

8-3 Preparing to Teach

BIG ideas   Equivalence
Function

UbD

ESSENTIAL UNDERSTANDINGS
- A rational function is a ratio of polynomial functions.
- If a function has a polynomial in its denominator, its graph has a gap at each zero of the polynomial. The gap could be a one-point hole in the graph, or it could be the location of a vertical asymptote for the graph.
- A rational function may have no asymptotes, one horizontal or oblique asymptote, and any number of vertical asymptotes.
- A reasonable graph for a rational function can be sketched by finding all intercepts and asymptotes. Sometimes a few extra points should be plotted to get a good sense of the shape of the graph.

Math Background

A rational function is a ratio of polynomial functions $\frac{P(x)}{Q(x)}$. The domain is all real numbers except *x*-values where $Q(x) = 0$. Near these *x*-values, the graph may increase or decrease without bound. The zeros of $Q(x)$ can signify discontinuities, holes, and vertical asymptotes. The zeros of $P(x)$ signify *x*-intercepts.

To graph the function, plot intercepts and asymptotes, plot a few points between and beyond each intercept and vertical asymptote, then sketch a smooth curve to complete the graph.

Support Student Learning

Use the **Algebra 2 Companion** to engage and support students during instruction. See Lesson Resources at the end of this lesson for details.

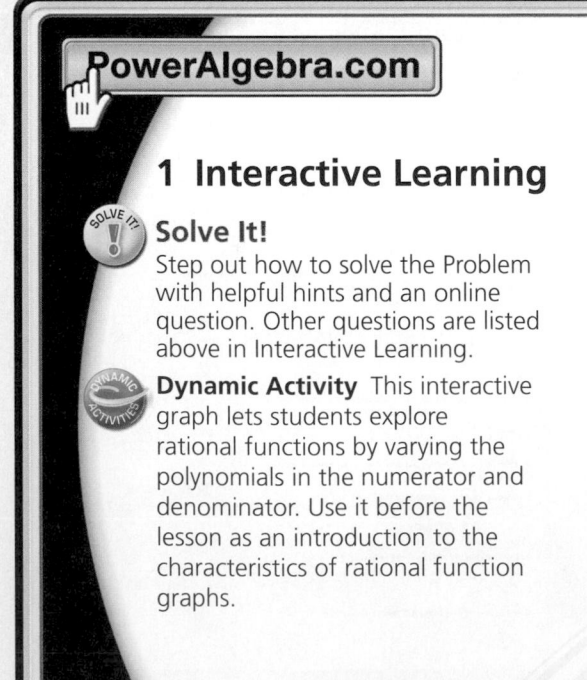

PowerAlgebra.com

1 Interactive Learning

Solve It!
Step out how to solve the Problem with helpful hints and an online question. Other questions are listed above in Interactive Learning.

Dynamic Activity This interactive graph lets students explore rational functions by varying the polynomials in the numerator and denominator. Use it before the lesson as an introduction to the characteristics of rational function graphs.

For the first rational function, $y = \frac{x^2}{x^2 + 1}$, there is no value of x that makes the denominator 0. The graph is a **continuous graph** because it has no jumps, breaks, or holes. You can draw the graph and your pencil never leaves the paper.

For $y = \frac{(x + 3)(x + 2)}{x + 2}$, $x \neq -2$ For $y = \frac{x + 4}{x - 2}$, $x \neq 2$. The second and third graphs are **discontinuous graphs**.

take note

Key Concept   Point of Discontinuity

If a is a real number for which the denominator of a rational function $f(x)$ is zero, then a is not in the domain of $f(x)$. The graph of $f(x)$ is not continuous at $x = a$ and the function has a **point of discontinuity** at $x = a$.

The graph of $y = \frac{(x + 3)(x + 2)}{x + 2}$ has a **removable discontinuity** at $x = -2$. The hole in the graph is called a removable discontinuity because you could make the function continuous by redefining it at $x = -2$ so that $f(-2) = 1$.

The graph of $y = \frac{x + 4}{x - 2}$ has a **non-removable discontinuity** at $x = 2$. There is no way to redefine the function at 2 to make the function continuous.

The discontinuity caused by $(x - a)$ in the denominator is removable if the numerator also has $(x - a)$ as a factor.

Hint

When you look for discontinuities, it is helpful to factor the numerator and denominator as a first step. The factors of the denominator will reveal the points of discontinuity.

Problem 1   Finding Points of Discontinuity

What are the domain and points of discontinuity of each rational function? Are the points of discontinuity *removable* or *non-removable*? What are the x- and y-intercepts?

A $y = \frac{x + 3}{x^2 - 4x + 3}$

Step 1 Factor (if possible) to identify the domain.

$$y = \frac{x + 3}{x^2 - 4x + 3} = \frac{x + 3}{(x - 1)(x - 3)}$$

The function is undefined where $x - 1 = 0$ and where $x - 3 = 0$, at $x = 1$ and $x = 3$. The domain of the function is the set of all real numbers except $x = 1$ and $x = 3$.

Step 2 Identify the points of discontinuity.

There are non-removable points of discontinuity at $x = 1$ and $x = 3$.

Think

Are the discontinuities removable?
There are no common factors in the numerator and denominator. Any discontinuity is non-removable.

Step 3 Identify the x- and y-intercepts.

The x-intercept occurs where y equals 0, at $x = -3$.

To find the y-intercept, let $x = 0$ and simplify.

$y = 0$ when the numerator of y equals zero.

$$y = \frac{0 + 3}{(0 - 1)(0 - 3)} = \frac{3}{(-1)(-3)} = \frac{3}{3} = 1$$

---

2 Guided Instruction

Q Which of the functions you have studied were continuous for all values of x? **[linear, quadratic, absolute value, polynomial, exponential]**

Take Note

Q Input $y = ((x + 3)(x + 2))/(x + 2)$ into your graphing calculator. Set ΔTbl = 0.1. What happens to y as x approaches -2 from lesser x-values? as x approaches -2 from greater x-values? **[As x approaches -2 from the left, y increases at a constant rate towards 1. As x approaches -2 from the right, y decreases at a constant rate towards 1.]**

Q Input $y = (x + 4)/(x - 2)$ into your graphing calculator. What happens to y as x approaches 2 from lesser x-values? greater x-values? **[As x approaches 2 from the left, y decreases at an increasing rate towards $-\infty$. As x approaches 2 from the right, y increases at an increasing rate towards $+\infty$.]**

Problem 1

Q Why is the function undefined if $x - 3 = 0$ or if $x - 1 = 0$? **[The Zero-Product Property states that if the product of two expressions is zero, then one of the expressions must be zero, making the function undefined.]**

Q Why do you find the x-intercept by setting only the numerator equal to zero? **[When the numerator of the function is 0, $y = 0$. The x-intercept is defined as the x-value at $y = 0$.]**

Q Why do you find the y-intercept by evaluating the function at $f(0)$? **[The y-intercept is defined as the y-value at $x = 0$.]**

Q How many discontinuities would you expect to find and why? **[You would expect two because the denominator is a factorable quadratic.]**

---

2 Guided Instruction

Each Problem is worked out and supported online.

Problem 1
Finding Points of Discontinuity
Animated

Problem 2
Finding Vertical Asymptotes

Problem 3
Finding Horizontal Asymptotes
Animated

Problem 4
Graphing Rational Functions
Animated

Problem 5
Using a Rational Function

Support in Algebra 2 Companion
• Vocabulary
• Key Concepts
• Got It?

Answers

Solve It!
6 consecutive shots; the more shots you take, the closer your percentage will get to 100. You can never reach 100% because that would mean that you never missed a shot (and you already missed 13).

Q In 1B, is the graph symmetrical across the *y*-axis? How do you know? **[No; the only *x*-intercept is at *x* = 5, so the graph cannot be symmetrical across the *y*-axis.]**

ERROR PREVENTION

Q In 1C, why does the function not have an *x*-intercept at (4, 0)? **[The function has a removable discontinuity at *x* = 4. Because the (*x* − 4) factor in the numerator can be factored out, the point (4, 0) does not count as an *x*-intercept.]**

Got It?

Q Which denominators can be factored? **[a, c]**

Q In 1a, what is the *x*-intercept? **[The function has no *x*-intercept because the numerator cannot be zero.]**

Q In 1b, why are there two *x*-intercepts? **[as the numerator, $x^2 - 1$, can be factored as (*x* + 1)(*x* − 1). Neither factor is also present in the denominator.]**

Q In 1b, why are there no discontinuities? **[because there are no real solutions to $x^2 + 3 = 0$]**

Q In 1c, how would you redefine *f*(−1)? Why? **[*f*(−1) = 1; *x* = −1 is a removable discontinuity. Factoring the equation gives $f(x) = \frac{1}{x + 2}$. $f(-1) = \frac{1}{-1 + 2} = 1$.]**

Take Note

Q What is an example of a rational function that fits the first sentence? **[Sample: $\frac{x + 3}{x - 4}$.]**

Q What is an example of a rational function that fits the second sentence? **[Sample: $\frac{(x - 4)^2}{(x - 4)^3}$.]**

B $y = \frac{x - 5}{x^2 + 1}$

Step 1 Factor (if possible) to identify the domain.

You cannot factor the numerator or the denominator. Also, no values of *x* make the denominator 0. The domain is all real numbers, so there are no discontinuities.

Step 2 Identify the *x*- and *y*-intercepts.

The *x*-intercept occurs where the numerator equals 0, at *x* = 5.

To find the *y*-intercept, let *x* = 0 and simplify: $y = \frac{0 - 5}{0^2 + 1} = \frac{-5}{1} = -5$

C $y = \frac{x^2 - 3x - 4}{x - 4}$

Step 1 Factor (if possible) to identify the domain. $y = \frac{x^2 - 3x - 4}{x - 4} = \frac{(x - 4)(x + 1)}{(x - 4)}$

The function is undefined where *x* − 4 = 0, at *x* = 4. The domain is all real numbers except *x* = 4.

Step 2 Identify the points of discontinuity.

Notice that the graph is identical to the graph of *y* = *x* + 1, except at *x* = 4, where there is a removable discontinuity.

You can "remove" this discontinuity by redefining a piecewise function using the domain and the *x*-value of the discontinuity. At *x* = 4, *y* = *x* + 1 = 4 + 1 = 5. Remove the discontinuity by redefining the function as shown at the right: $y = \begin{cases} \frac{x^2 - 3x - 4}{x - 4}, & \text{if } x \neq 4 \\ 5, & \text{if } x = 4 \end{cases}$

Graph contains a hole at *x* = 4.

Step 3 Identify the *x*- and *y*-intercepts.

The *x*-intercept occurs where the numerator factor *x* + 1 = 0, at *x* = −1.

To find the *y*-intercept, let *x* = 0 and simplify.

$$y = \frac{0^2 - 3 \cdot 0 - 4}{0 - 4} = \frac{0 - 0 - 4}{-4} = \frac{-4}{-4} = 1$$

Think

When is the denominator zero? x^2 is at least 0, so $x^2 + 1$ is always greater than 0.

Think

Is there also an *x*-intercept at *x* = 4? No; although *x* = 4 is a zero of the numerator, it is not in the domain.

✓ **Got It?** 1. What are the domain and points of discontinuity of the rational function? Are the points of discontinuity *removable* or *non-removable*? What are the *x*- and *y*-intercepts of the rational function?

    a. $y = \frac{1}{x^2 - 16}$ **b.** $y = \frac{x^2 - 1}{x^2 + 3}$ **c.** $y = \frac{x + 1}{x^2 + 3x + 2}$

Hint

An <u>asymptote</u> is a line that a graph approaches as *x* or *y* increases in absolute value.

If a rational function has a non-removable discontinuity at *x* = *a*, the graph has a vertical asymptote at *x* = *a*.

take note

Key Concept   **Vertical Asymptotes of Rational Functions**

The graph of the rational function $f(x) = \frac{P(x)}{Q(x)}$ has a vertical asymptote at each real zero of *Q*(*x*) if *P*(*x*) and *Q*(*x*) have no common zeros. If *P*(*x*) and *Q*(*x*) have $(x - a)^m$ and $(x - a)^n$ as factors, respectively and *m* < *n*, then *f*(*x*) also has a vertical asymptote at *x* = *a*.

540   Chapter 8   Rational Functions

Additional Problems

1. What are the domain and points of discontinuity of $y = \frac{x^2 + 4x + 4}{x + 2}$? Are the points of discontinuity removable or non-removable? What are the *x*- and *y*-intercepts?

ANSWER Domain: all real numbers except *x* = −2; removable discontinuity: *x* = −2; *y*-intercept: (0, 2); no *x*-intercept

2. What are the vertical asymptotes for the graph of $y = \frac{x - 3}{(x^2 - 3x + 2)}$?

ANSWER *x* = 1, 2

3. What is the horizontal asymptote for the graph of $y = \frac{x^2 + 1}{-3x + 6}$?

ANSWER The graph has no horizontal asymptote.

4. What is the graph of the rational function $y = \frac{x^2 + 1}{-3x + 6}$?

ANSWER

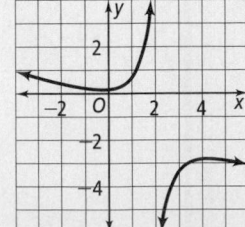

5. Whole milk contains 3.7% fat. You want to add 2%-fat milk to 5 fl oz of whole milk to make 3%-fat milk. The function

$y = \frac{(5)(0.037) + x(0.02)}{5 + x}$ gives the percentage of fat in a new concentration after you add *x* fluid ounces of the 2% milk. How many fluid ounces of 2% milk must you add?

ANSWER 3.5 fl oz

 **Problem 2** Finding Vertical Asymptotes

What are the vertical asymptotes for the graph of $y = \dfrac{(x + 1)}{(x - 2)(x - 3)}$?

Since 2 and 3 are roots of the denominator and neither is a root of the numerator, the lines $x = 2$ and $x = 3$ are vertical asymptotes.

Got It? 2. What are the vertical asymptotes for the graph of $y = \dfrac{x - 2}{(x - 1)(x + 3)}$?

While the graph of a rational function can have any number of vertical asymptotes, it can have no more than one horizontal asymptote.

 take note

Key Concept Horizontal Asymptote of a Rational Function

To find the horizontal asymptote of the graph of a rational function, compare the degree of the numerator m to the degree of the denominator n.

If $m < n$, the graph has horizontal asymptote $y = 0$ (the x-axis).

If $m > n$, the graph has no horizontal asymptote.

If $m = n$, the graph has horizontal asymptote $y = \dfrac{a}{b}$ where a is the coefficient of the term of greatest degree in the numerator and b is the coefficient of the term of greatest degree in the denominator.

Problem 3 Finding Horizontal Asymptotes

What is the horizontal asymptote for the graph of each rational function?

A $y = \dfrac{2x}{x - 3}$

The degree of the numerator and denominator are the same.

$y = \dfrac{2x}{x - 3}$ ← degree: 1
← degree: 1

The horizontal asymptote is $y = \dfrac{2}{1}$, or $y = 2$.

B $y = \dfrac{x - 2}{x^2 - 2x - 3}$

The degree of the numerator is less than the degree of the denominator.

$y = \dfrac{x - 2}{x^2 - 2x - 3}$ ← degree: 1
← degree: 2

The horizontal asymptote is $y = 0$.

C $y = \dfrac{x^2}{2x - 5}$

The degree of the numerator is greater than the degree of the denominator.

$y = \dfrac{x^2}{2x - 5}$ ← degree: 2
← degree: 1

There is no horizontal asymptote.

Got It? 3. What is the horizontal asymptote for each rational function?

a. $y = \dfrac{-2x + 6}{x - 5}$ **b.** $y = \dfrac{x - 1}{x^2 + 4x + 4}$ **c.** $y = \dfrac{x^2 + 2x - 3}{x - 2}$

PowerAlgebra.com | Lesson 8-3 Rational Functions and Their Graphs | 541

Problem 2

Q What if there was a factor $x - 2$ in the numerator? How would this change the vertical asymptotes? **[$x = 3$ would be the only vertical asymptote.]**

Got It?

Q Why is the vertical asymptote $x = -3$ instead of $x = 3$? **[The asymptote is where the value of x makes the denominator undefined, or equal to 0, so $x + 3 = 0$ or $x = -3$.]**

Take Note

Q Why does a function with a denominator of greater degree than the numerator have a horizontal asymptote at $y = 0$? **[As $|x|$ increases, the absolute value of the denominator grows much faster than the absolute value of the numerator, so their quotient gets closer to 0.]**

Problem 3

Q In 3B, do you have to factor the denominator to find the horizontal asymptote? Explain. **[No. The horizontal asymptote is dependent only on the degrees of the numerator and denominator.]**

Got It?

Q In 3a, why does the graph approach $y = -2$ for large $|x|$? **[As $|x|$ increases, the constant coefficients $+6$ and -5 have less influence on the shape of the graph. The graph comes to resemble $y = \dfrac{-2x}{x} = -2$.]**

Answers

Got It?

1. a. domain: all real numbers except $x = 4$ and $x = -4$ pts. of discontinuity: non-removable at $x = 4$ and $x = -4$; no x-intercept, y-intercept: $\left(0, -\dfrac{1}{16}\right)$

b. domain: all real numbers; no pts. of discontinuity; x-intercepts: $(1, 0)$ and $(-1, 0)$, y-intercept: $\left(0, -\dfrac{1}{3}\right)$

c. domain: all real numbers except $x = -2$ and $x = -1$; points of discontinuity: non-removable at $x = -2$, removable at $x = -1$; no x-intercept, y-intercept: $\left(0, \dfrac{1}{2}\right)$

2. $x = 1$ and $x = -3$

3. a. $y = -2$
b. $y = 0$
c. no horizontal asymptote

Problem 4

Q How do you know that the graph goes toward $-\infty$ as x approaches -2 from the left? **[The points $(-4, 0)$ and $(-3, -\frac{6}{5})$ show that the graph is decreasing. There is no other x-intercept between -3 and -2, so the graph continues decreasing, approaching the asymptote at $x = -2$.]**

Q The graph goes toward $+\infty$ as x approaches -2 from the right. How do the x-intercepts tell you that the graph also goes toward $+\infty$ as x approaches $+2$? **[Because there is no x-intercept from -2 to $+2$, the graph cannot cross the x-axis over that range. The graph must curve back up toward $+\infty$.]**

Got It?   ERROR PREVENTION

Students may not realize that a graph can cross its horizontal asymptote. A graph will never cross a vertical asymptote.

Q What is the horizontal asymptote of this graph? What is the x-intercept? What can you say about the behavior of the graph before and after the x-intercept? **[The horizontal asymptote is $y = 0$. The x-intercept is $(-3, 0)$. The graph has a turning point at $(-3, 0)$, so the function changes sign.]**

Problem 4 Graphing Rational Functions

What is the graph of the rational function $y = \frac{x^2 + x - 12}{x^2 - 4}$?

Plan

How can you graph this function?
Find the horizontal and vertical asymptotes and the x- and y-intercepts. Look for holes and find additional points to help get a better sense of the graph.

Think

Identify the degrees of the numerator and denominator.

Factor the numerator and the denominator. Identify holes or vertical asymptotes.

Find the x- and y-intercepts. The x-intercepts occur where $y = 0$. The y-intercepts occur where $x = 0$.

Find a few more points on the graph.

Graph the asymptotes. Then plot the intercepts and additional points. Use the points to sketch the graph.

Write

$y = \frac{x^2 + x - 12}{x^2 - 4}$ ← degree: 2
  ← degree: 2

The degrees are the same.

horizontal asymptote: $y = \frac{1}{1} = 1$

$y = \frac{(x + 4)(x - 3)}{(x + 2)(x - 2)}$

There are no common factors, so there are no holes. There are vertical asymptotes at the zeros of the denominator.

vertical asymptotes: $x = -2$ and $x = 2$

$y = 0$ when the numerator equals zero.

x-intercepts: $(-4, 0)$ and $(3, 0)$

Substitute $x = 0$.

$y = \frac{(0 + 4)(0 - 3)}{(0 + 2)(0 - 2)} = \frac{(4)(-3)}{(2)(-2)} = \frac{-12}{-4} = 3$

y-intercept: $(0, 3)$

More points on the graph:

$(-3, -\frac{6}{5}), (-1, 4), (1, \frac{10}{3})$ and $(4, \frac{2}{3})$

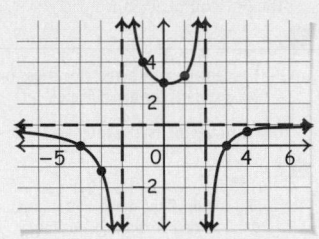

Got It? **4.** What is the graph of the rational function $y = \frac{x + 3}{x^2 - 6x + 5}$?

Answers

Got It? (continued)

4.

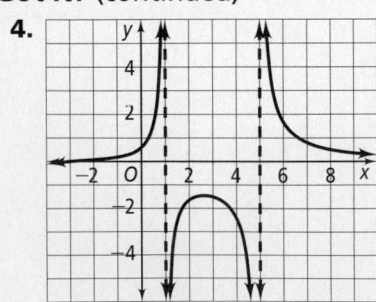

Problem 5 Using a Rational Function   GRIDDED RESPONSE

Chemistry You work in a pharmacy that mixes different concentrations of saline solutions for its customers. The pharmacy has a supply of two concentrations, 0.5% and 2%. The function $y = \frac{(100)(0.02) + x(0.005)}{100 + x}$ gives the concentration of the saline solution after adding x milliliters of the 0.5% solution to 100 milliliters of the 2% solution. How many milliliters of the 0.5% solution must you add for the combined solution to have a concentration of 0.9%?

Plan

How can you use a calculator to solve the problem?
Graph
$y = \frac{(100)(0.02) + x(0.005)}{100 + x}$
and $y = 0.009$ in the calculator and find the point of intersection.

Step 1 Use a graphing calculator to graph **Y1** $= \frac{(100)(0.02) + x(0.005)}{100 + x}$ and **Y2** $= 0.009$.

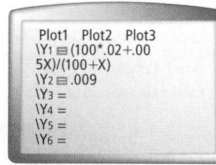 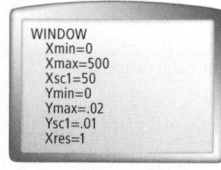 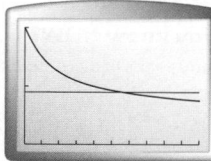

Step 2 Find the point of intersection of the two functions.

Graphic Solution   Table Solution

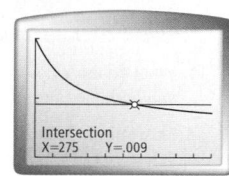 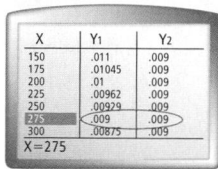   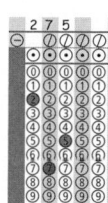

You should add 275 mL of the 0.5% solution to get a 0.9% solution.
Write 275 in the grid.

Check Write the original function. $y = \frac{(100)(0.02) + x(0.005)}{100 + x}$

Substitute 275 for x. $y \stackrel{?}{=} \frac{(100)(0.02) + (275)(0.005)}{100 + 275}$

Simplify. $y \stackrel{?}{=} \frac{2 + 1.375}{375}$

Use a calculator. $y = 0.009$ ✔

Hint

For part (a), convert 40% to a decimal, 0.4. Define **Y2** = 0.4.

✓ **Got It?** **5. a.** You want to mix a 10% orange juice drink with 100% pure orange juice to make a 40% orange juice drink. The function $y = \frac{(2)(1.0) + x(0.1)}{2 + x}$ gives the concentration y of orange juice in the drink after you add x gallons of the 10% drink to 2 gallons of pure juice. How much of the 10% drink must you add to get a drink that is 40% juice?

   b. Reasoning If you wanted a drink that is 80% juice, would you need to add half as much as your answer in part (a)? Explain.

Problem 5

Q Your textbook shows how to solve this problem by using a graphing calculator. This problem can also be solved algebraically. How would you do that? Describe the steps. **[You want to solve for $y = 0.009$, so you can set the given formula equal to 0.009: $0.009 = \frac{(100)(0.02) + x(0.005)}{100 + x}$. Multiply both sides by $(100 + x)$ and simplify: $0.9 + 0.009x = 2 + 0.005x$. Isolate the x-terms: $0.004x = 1.1$. Divide both sides by 0.004: $x = 275$.]**

Q How many mL of 0.9% solution do you end up with? **[375 mL (100 mL of 2% solution and 275 mL of 0.5% solution)]**

Q Where is the vertical asymptote of the graph of this function? Do you have to think about the behavior of the graph at that point? Why or why not? **[The function has a vertical asymptote at $x = -100$. In this problem, x represents an amount of solution added. Adding a negative amount does not make sense for this problem, so the vertical asymptote does not matter.]**

Got It?

Q What are three different ways to solve this problem? **[Answers may vary. Samples: Graph the formula with $y = 0.4$; use a table on a graphing calculator; solve an equation.]**

Q What is the domain of the function that makes sense for this problem? **[$x \geq 0$]**

Q What does y represent? **[the concentration of the mixed juice]**

Q What is the maximum possible value of y? Explain. **[The juice cannot have a concentration greater than 100%, or 1.]**

Q What is the range of this function for the domain you just defined? **[$0.1 < y \leq 1$]**

PowerAlgebra.com   Lesson 8-3 Rational Functions and Their Graphs   **543**

---

5. a. 4 gal
   b. No, because the graph changes when $y_1 = 0.8$ and intersects the graph of $y_2 = \frac{2 + (0.1)x}{2 + x}$ at $x \approx 0.6$. So, to have 80% orange juice, about 0.6 gal should be added.

3 Lesson Check

Do you know HOW?
- In Exercises 1–8, the first step should be to factor the numerator and denominator, when possible.
- In Exercises 1 and 2, make sure students understand the question: find all discontinuities and not just vertical asymptotes.
- In Exercises 2, 4, and 7, make sure students factor the numerator.
- In Exercise 8, the discriminant shows that the numerator does not have any real roots. Thus there are no *x*-intercepts and no common factors in the denominator and numerator. Thus there is no need to factor the numerator.

Do you UNDERSTAND?
- In Exercise 11, students have no way of knowing from the **Y1** values on the calculator whether the error is caused by a removable discontinuity or an asymptote.

Close

> **Q** What causes discontinuities in a graph? What is the first step in finding them? **[A denominator that can equal 0; factor the denominator, and set each factor to zero.]**
>
> **Q** How does the graph of a function behave as it approaches removable and non-removable discontinuities? **[A function tends toward a single specific value near a removable discontinuity. A function tends towards ±∞ near a nonremovable discontinuity.]**

Focus Question What is a rational function?

Answer A rational function is a function whose numerator and denominator are both polynomials. If a function has a polynomial in its denominator, its graph has a gap at each zero of the polynomial. The gap could be a one-point hole, or it could be the location of a vertical asymptote.

Focus Question What information is useful for graphing a rational function?

Answer Find the asymptotes and intercepts of a rational function to make a reasonable graph.

Lesson Check

Do you know HOW?

Find any points of discontinuity for each rational function.

1. $y = \frac{x + 5}{x^2 + 9x + 20}$ 2. $y = \frac{x^2 + 2x}{x^2 - 7x - 18}$

3. $y = \frac{x - 1}{(x + 1)^2}$ 4. $y = \frac{x^2 - x - 2}{3x^2 - 7x + 2}$

Find the vertical asymptotes of the graph of each rational function.

5. $y = \frac{x - 3}{x + 5}$ 6. $y = \frac{x - 3}{x^2 + 5x + 6}$

7. $y = \frac{2x + 2}{x^2 - 1}$ 8. $y = \frac{x^2 + 2x + 3}{x^2 + 2x - 3}$

Sketch the graph of each rational function.

9. $y = \frac{3x}{x - 4}$ 10. $y = \frac{x + 3}{(x - 1)(x - 6)}$

Do you UNDERSTAND?

For Exercises 11 and 12, use the following table. The table shows data for a rational function.

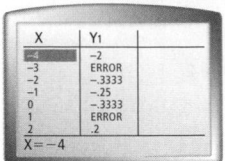

X	Y1
-4	-2
-3	ERROR
-2	-.3333
-1	-.25
0	-.3333
1	ERROR
2	.2

X= -4

11. What do the **Y1** entries for **X = −3** and **X = 1** tell you about the rational function?

12. **Reasoning** Assume that there are no more **ERROR** values in the **Y1** column. What is the lowest possible degree of the denominator? Explain how you know.

Practice and Problem-Solving Exercises

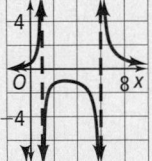

A Practice   Find the domain, points of discontinuity, and *x*- and *y*- intercepts of each rational function. Determine whether the discontinuities are removable or non-removable.   **See Problem 1.**

Guided Practice   To start, factor the numerator and denominator if possible.

13. $y = \frac{2x^2 + 5}{x^2 - 2x}$

$y = \frac{2x^2 + 5}{x(x - 2)}$

14. $y = \frac{x^2 + 2x}{x^2 + 2}$ 15. $y = \frac{3x - 3}{x^2 - 1}$ 16. $y = \frac{6 - 3x}{x^2 - 5x + 6}$

Find the vertical asymptotes and holes for the graph of each rational function.   **See Problem 2.**

17. $y = \frac{x + 5}{x + 5}$ 18. $y = \frac{x + 3}{(2x + 3)(x - 1)}$ 19. $y = \frac{(x + 3)(x - 2)}{(x - 2)(x + 1)}$

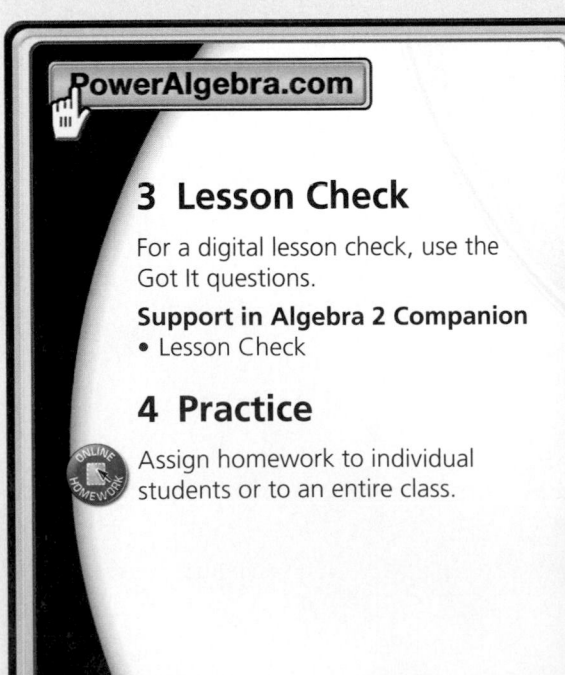

3 Lesson Check

For a digital lesson check, use the Got It questions.

Support in Algebra 2 Companion
- Lesson Check

4 Practice

Assign homework to individual students or to an entire class.

Answers

Lesson Check
1. at $x = -5$ and $x = -4$
2. at $x = 9$ and $x = -2$
3. at $x = -1$
4. at $x = \frac{1}{3}$ and $x = 2$
5. $x = -5$
6. $x = -2$ and $x = -3$
7. $x = 1$
8. $x = 1$ and $x = -3$
9.

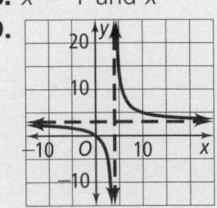

10.

11. at $x = 1$ and $x = -3$; The function is undefined.

12. degree 2; function is discontinuous at 2 values of x

Practice and Problem-Solving Exercises

13. domain: all real numbers except $x = 0$ and $x = 2$; pts. of discontinuity: non-removable at $x = 0$ and $x = 2$; no *x*- or *y*-intercept

14. domain: all real numbers; no pts. of discontinuity; *x*-intercepts: (0, 0) and (−2, 0), *y*-intercept: (0, 0)

15–19. See next page.

Find the horizontal asymptote of the graph of each rational function. ◀ **See Problem 3.**

◀ See Problem 3.

Guided Practice

To start, identify the degree of the numerator and denominator.

20. $y = \dfrac{5}{x + 6}$

$y = \dfrac{5}{x + 6}$ ← degree: 0
   ← degree: 1

21. $y = \dfrac{x + 1}{x + 5}$

22. $y = \dfrac{x^2 + 2}{2x^2 - 1}$

23. $y = \dfrac{5x^3 + 2x}{2x^5 - 4x^3}$

Sketch the graph of each rational function. ◀ **See Problem 4.**

24. $y = \dfrac{x^2 - 4}{3x - 6}$

25. $y = \dfrac{4x}{x^3 - 4x}$

26. $y = \dfrac{x + 4}{x - 4}$

27. $y = \dfrac{x(x + 1)}{x + 1}$

28. $y = \dfrac{x + 6}{(x - 2)(x + 3)}$

29. $y = \dfrac{3x}{(x + 2)^2}$

30. Pharmacology Use the rational function given in Problem 5. How many milliliters of the 0.5% solution must be added to the 2% solution to get a 0.65% solution? ◀ **See Problem 5.**

B Apply

Find the vertical and horizontal asymptotes, if any, of the graph of each rational function.

31.
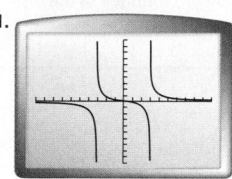

32.
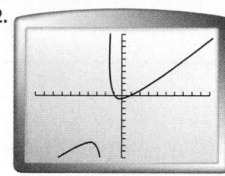

33.
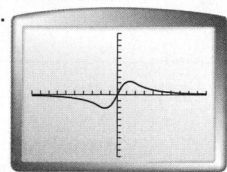

34. Think About a Plan A basketball player has made 21 of her last 30 free throws—a percentage of 70%. How many more consecutive free throws does she need to raise her free throw percentage to 75%?
 • How can you model the player's free throw percentage as a rational function?
 • How can a graph help you answer this question?

Hint Let x = the number of additional free throws needed.

35. Grades A student earns an 82% on her first test. How many consecutive 100% test scores does she need to bring her average up to 95%? Assume that each test has equal impact on the average grade.

36. Business CDs can be manufactured for $.19 each. The development cost is $210,000. The first 500 discs are samples and will not be sold.
 a. Write a function for the average cost of a disc that is not a sample. Graph the function.
 b. What is the average cost if 5000 discs are produced? If 15,000 discs are produced?
 c. How many discs must be produced to bring the average cost under $10?
 d. What are the vertical and horizontal asymptotes of the graph of the function?

37. Writing Describe the conditions that will produce a rational function with a graph that has no vertical asymptotes.

ASSIGNMENT GUIDE

Basic: 13–18, 20–23, 24–30 even, 34, 35, 38

Average: 13–19 odd, 20–30 even, 31–35, 38, 39

Standardized Test Prep: 42–46

Mixed Review: 47–58

Reasoning exercises have blue headings.

Applications exercises have red headings.

EXERCISE 35: Use the Think About a Plan worksheet in the **Student Companion** (also available in the Teaching Resources in print and online) to further support students' development in becoming independent learners.

HOMEWORK QUICK CHECK

To check students' understanding of key skills and concepts, go over Exercises 15, 22, 34, 35, and 38.

---

15. domain: all real numbers except $x = \pm 1$; pts. of discontinuity: non-removable at $x = -1$, removable at $x = 1$; no x-intercept, y-intercept: (0, 3)

16. domain: all real numbers except $x = 2$ and $x = 3$; pts. of discontinuity: non-removable at $x = 3$, removable at $x = 2$; no x-intercept, y-intercept: (0, 1)

17. hole at $x = -5$

18. vert. asymptotes at $x = -\frac{3}{2}$ and $x = 1$

19. vert. asymptote at $x = -1$, hole at $x = 2$

20. $y = 0$

21. $y = 1$

22. $y = \frac{1}{2}$

23. $y = 0$

24.
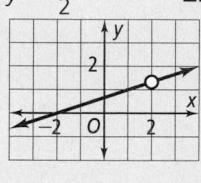

25.
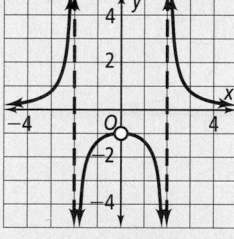

26.
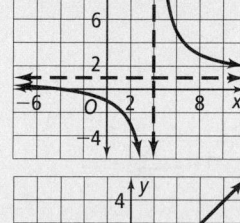

27.
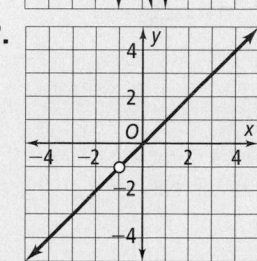

28.
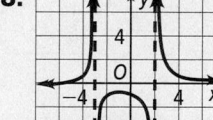

29.
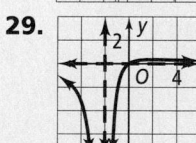

30. 900 mL

31. vert. asymptotes at $x = -3$ and $x = 3$, horizontal asymptote at $y = 0$

32. vert. asymptote at $x = -2$

33. horizontal asymptote at $y = 0$

34–37. See next page.

Answers

Practice and Problem-Solving Exercises (continued)

34. 6 free throws; $y = \frac{21 + x}{30 + x}$

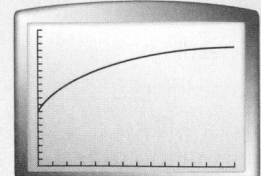

WINDOW FORMAT
Xmin=0
Xmax=100
Xscl=10
Ymin=.5
Ymax=1
Yscl=.1

35. 3 test scores

36. a. $y = \frac{0.19x + 210,000}{x - 500}$

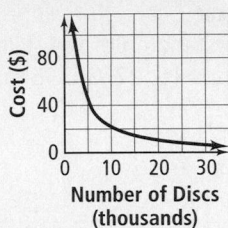

b. $46.88; $14.68

c. at least 21,917 discs

d. $x = 500$, $y = 0.19$

37. Answers may vary. Sample: There is no value of x for which the denominator equals 0.

38. correct answer: vertical asymptotes: $x = -5$ and $x = -1$, horizontal asymptote: $y = 1$

39.

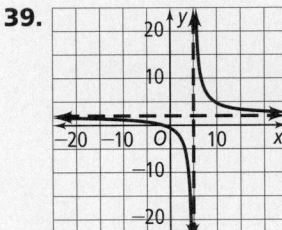

40.

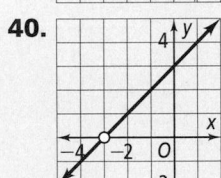

41.

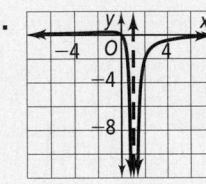

Standardized Test Prep

42. 4   **43.** 8

44. 5   **45.** $\frac{2}{3}$

46. 1.39

Mixed Review

47.

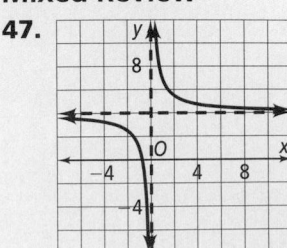

domain: all real numbers except $x = 0$, range: all real numbers except $y = 4$

---

38. **Error Analysis** A student listed the asymptotes of the function $y = \frac{x^2 - 3x + 2}{x^2 + 6x + 5}$ as shown at the right. Explain the student's error. What are the correct asymptotes?

vertical asymptotes:
~~$x = 1$, $x = 2$~~
horizontal asymptotes:
~~$y = -1$, $y = -5$~~

Sketch the graph of each rational function.

39. $y = \frac{2x + 3}{x - 5}$ **40.** $y = \frac{x^2 + 6x + 9}{x + 3}$ **41.** $y = -\frac{x}{(x - 1)^2}$

Standardized Test Prep

GRIDDED RESPONSE

SAT/ACT

42. What is $\log 33,000 - \log 99 + \log 30$?

43. Suppose z varies directly with x and inversely with y. If z is 1.5 when x is 9 and y is 4, what is z when x is 6 and y is 0.5?

44. What is the y-coordinate of the vertex of the parabola $y = -3(x - 4)^2 + 5$?

45. What is the real solution of $54x^3 - 16 = 0$ written as a fraction?

46. Using the Change of Base Formula, what is the value of $\log_7 15$ rounded to the nearest hundredth?

Mixed Review

Sketch the asymptotes and the graph of each equation. Identify the domain and range.

◀ See Lesson 8-2.

47. $y = \frac{3}{x} + 4$ **48.** $y = \frac{2}{x + 3}$ **49.** $y = \frac{5}{x - 7} - 3$

Find the inverse of each function. Determine if the inverse is a function.

◀ See Lesson 6-7.

50. $y = 2x - 3$ **51.** $y = 2x^2$ **52.** $y = \frac{1}{x + 2}$

Solve each inequality. Graph the solution.

◀ See Lesson 1-5.

53. $6a - 17 < 47$ **54.** $5(x - 11) + 13 \geq 47$ **55.** $6 + y < 3y - 2$

Get Ready! To prepare for Lesson 8-4, do Exercises 56–58.

Factor each expression.

◀ See Lesson 4-4.

56. $2x^2 - 3x + 1$ **57.** $4x^2 - 9$ **58.** $5x^2 + 6x + 1$

48.

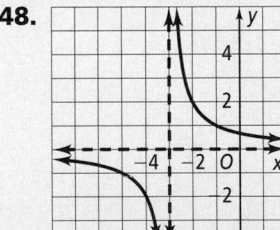

domain: all real numbers except $x = -3$, range: all real numbers except $y = 0$

49.

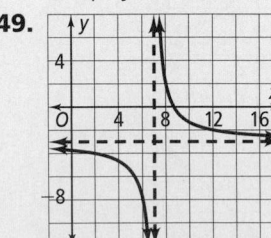

domain: all real numbers except $x = 7$, range: all real numbers except $y = -3$

50. $y = \frac{x + 3}{2}$; yes   **51.** $y = \pm\sqrt{\frac{x}{2}}$; no

52. $y = \frac{1}{x} - 2$; yes

53. $a < 10\frac{2}{3}$

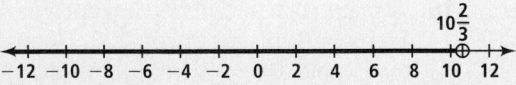

54. $x \geq 17\frac{4}{5}$

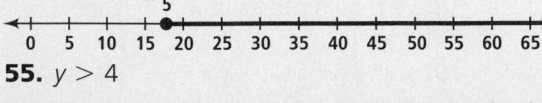

55. $y > 4$

56. $(2x - 1)(x - 1)$

57. $(2x - 3)(2x + 3)$

58. $(5x + 1)(x + 1)$

Additional Instructional Support

Algebra 2 Companion

Students can use the **Algebra 2 Companion** worktext (4 pages) as you teach the lesson. Use the Companion to support

- New Vocabulary
- Key Concepts
- Got It for each Problem
- Lesson Check

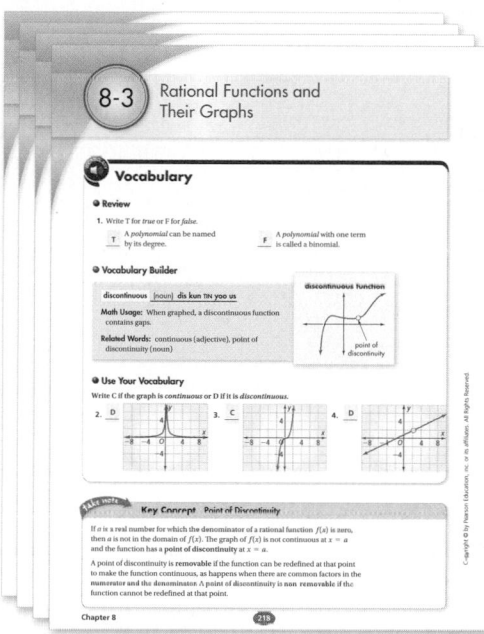

ELL Support

Focus on Language Discuss the meaning of the words *nation* and *national*. Ask how adding -al to the end of a word changes the meaning. Ask students for other words, like *person*, that form an adjective by adding -al. Explain that a function that is a *ratio* of functions is a *rational* function.

Discuss the meaning of the words *agree* and *disagree*. Ask how adding *dis-* to a word changes its meaning. Ask students for other examples, such as *disorient* or *disregard*. Explain that a *discontinuous* function has a point where it does *not* go on as usual.

5 Assess & Remediate

Lesson Quiz

1. What are the domain and points of discontinuity of $y = \dfrac{x - 4}{x^2 + 8x - 20}$? What are the x- and y-intercepts?

2. What are the vertical and horizontal asymptotes for the graph of $y = \dfrac{x^2 + 3x}{x(x^2 + 4)}$?

3. What is the graph of the rational function $y = \dfrac{x^2}{x^2 + 4x + 3}$?

4. **Do you UNDERSTAND?** You are making iced tea for a friend who prefers it at 80% strength. The function $y = \dfrac{(6)(1.0) + x(.5)}{6 + x}$ gives the concentration of the tea after adding x fluid ounces of a 50% tea solution to 6 fluid ounces of 100% strength tea. How many fluid ounces of 50% strength tea should you add to 6 fl oz of 100% strength tea?

ANSWERS TO LESSON QUIZ

1. domain: all real numbers except $x = 2$ and $x = -10$; nonremovable discontinuities at $x = 2$ and $x = -10$; x-intercept $(4, 0)$; y-intercept $\left(0, \frac{1}{5}\right)$

2. no vertical asymptote; horizontal asymptote at $y = 0$

3.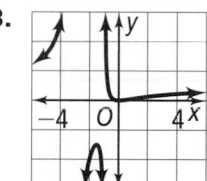

4. 4 fl oz

PRESCRIPTION FOR REMEDIATION

Use the student work on the Lesson Quiz to prescribe a differentiated review assignment:

Points	Differentiated Remediation
0–2	Intervention
3	On-level
4	Extension

PowerAlgebra.com

5 Assess & Remediate

Assign the Lesson Quiz. Appropriate intervention, practice, or enrichment is automatically generated based on student performance.

Intervention

- **Reteaching** (2 pages) Provides reteaching and practice exercises for the key lesson concepts. Use with struggling students or absent students.

- **English Language Learner Support** Helps students develop and reinforce mathematical vocabulary and key concepts.

All-in-One Resources/Online
Reteaching

8-3 Reteaching
Rational Functions and Their Graphs

A rational function may have one or more types of discontinuities: holes (removable points of discontinuity), vertical asymptotes (non-removable points of discontinuity), or a horizontal asymptote.

If	Then	Example
a is a zero with multiplicity m in the numerator and multiplicity n in the denominator, and $m \geq n$	hole at $x = a$	$f(x) = \dfrac{(x - 5)(x + 6)}{(x - 5)}$ hole at $x = 5$
a is a zero of the denominator only, or a is a zero with multiplicity m in the numerator and multiplicity n in the denominator, and $m < n$	vertical asymptote at $x = a$	$f(x) = \dfrac{x^2}{x - 3}$ vertical asymptote at $x = 3$

Let m = degree of numerator.
Let n = degree of denominator.

• $m < n$	horizontal asymptote at $y = 0$	$f(x) = \dfrac{4x^2}{7x^2 + 2}$
• $m > n$	no horizontal asymptote exists	horizontal asymptote at $y = \frac{4}{7}$
• $m = n$	horizontal asymptote at $y = \frac{a}{b}$ where a and b are coefficients of highest degree terms in numerator and denominator	

Problem

What are the points of discontinuity of $y = \dfrac{x^2 + x - 6}{3x^2 - 12}$, if any?

Step 1 Factor the numerator and denominator completely. $y = \dfrac{(x - 2)(x + 3)}{3(x - 2)(x + 2)}$

Step 2 Look for values that are zeros of both the numerator and the denominator. The function has a hole at $x = 2$.

Step 3 Look for values that are zeros of the denominator only. The function has a vertical asymptote at $x = -2$.

Step 4 Compare the degrees of the numerator and denominator. They have the same degree. The function has a horizontal asymptote at $y = \frac{1}{3}$.

Exercises

Identify any points of discontinuity of each rational function.

1. $y = \dfrac{x}{x^2 - 9}$ vertical asymptote: $x = 3, -3$; horizontal asymptote: $y = 0$
2. $y = \dfrac{6x^2 - 6}{x - 1}$ hole: $x = 1$
3. $y = \dfrac{4x + 5}{3x + 2}$ vertical asymptote: $x = -\frac{2}{3}$; horizontal asymptote: $y = \frac{4}{3}$

All-in-One Resources/Online
English Language Learner Support

8-3 ELL Support
Rational Functions and Their Graphs

Concept List

continuous	discontinuous	factors
horizontal asymptote	non-removable discontinuity	point of discontinuity
rational function	removable discontinuity	vertical asymptote

Choose the concept from the list above that best represents the item in each box.

1. the line that a graph approaches as y increases in absolute value **vertical asymptote**	2. In the denominator, these reveal the points of discontinuity. **factors**	3. This type of discontinuity appears as a hole in the graph. **removable discontinuity**
4. This type of graph has no jumps, breaks, or holes. **continuous**	5. a function that you can write in the form $f(x) = \dfrac{P(x)}{Q(x)}$ where $P(x)$ and $Q(x)$ are polynomial functions **rational function**	6. a graph that has a one-point hole or a vertical asymptote **discontinuous**
7. This type of discontinuity appears as a vertical asymptote on the graph. **non-removable discontinuity**	8. The graph of $f(x)$ is not continuous at this point. **point of discontinuity**	9. the line that a graph approaches as x increases in absolute value **horizontal asymptote**

Differentiated Remediation *continued*

On-Level

- **Practice** (2 pages) Provides extra practice for each lesson. For more challenging practice exercises, use the Form G Practice pages found in the All-in-One Teaching Resources and online.

- **Think About a Plan** Helps students develop specific problem-solving skills and strategies by providing scaffolded guiding questions.

- **Standardized Test Prep** Focuses on all major exercises, all major question types, and helps students prepare for the high-stakes assessments.

Extension

- **Enrichment** Provides students with interesting problems and activities that extend the concepts of the lesson.

- **Activities, Games, and Puzzles** Worksheets that can be used for concepts development, enrichment, and for fun!

Student Companion/ All-in-One Resources/Online
Practice page 1

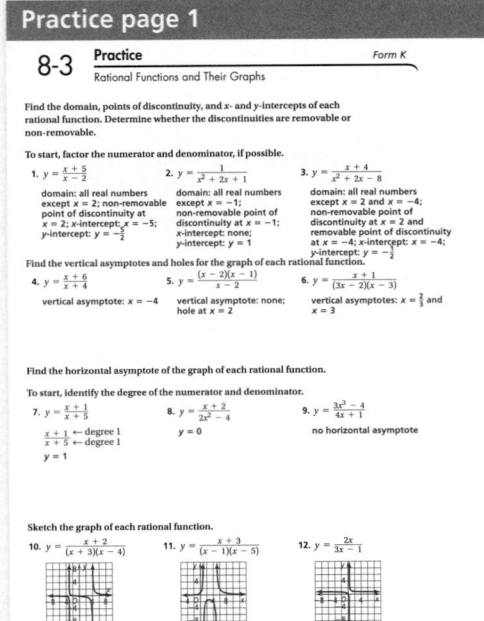

Student Companion/ All-in-One Resources/Online
Practice page 2

All-in-One Resources/Online
Enrichment

Student Companion/ All-in-One Resources/Online
Think About a Plan

Student Companion/ All-in-One Resources/Online
Standardized Test Prep

Online Teacher Resource Center
Activities, Games, and Puzzles

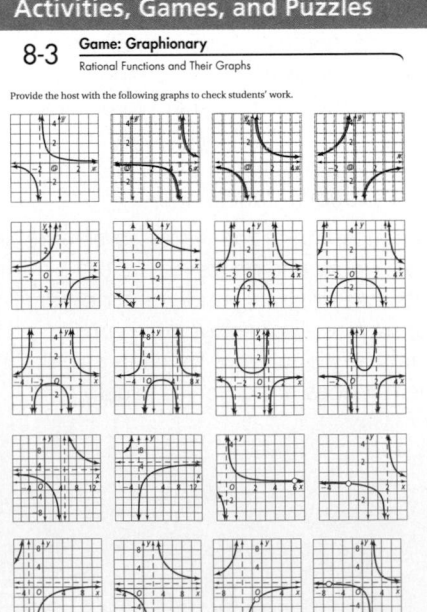

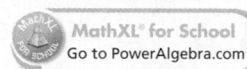
MathXL® for School
Go to PowerAlgebra.com

Do you know HOW?

If $z = 30$ when $x = 3$ and $y = 2$, write the function that models the relationship.

1. z varies jointly with x and y.

2. z varies directly with x and inversely with y.

3. z varies inversely with the product of x and y.

Is the relationship between the values in the table a *direct variation*, an *inverse variation*, or *neither*?

4.

x	y
22	104
35	174
48	239
54	269

5.

x	y
15	2.4
18	2
20	1.8
45	0.8

Suppose that x and y vary inversely. Write a function that models the inverse variation.

6. $x = 13$ when $y = 17$

7. $x = -12$ when $y = 4$

8. $x = 52$ when $y = \frac{1}{4}$

Explain how the graph of y_2 is related to the graph of y_1.

9. $y_1 = \frac{4}{x}$ and $y_2 = \frac{9}{x}$

10. $y_1 = \frac{1}{x}$ and $y_2 = \frac{1}{x} + 5$

11. $y_1 = \frac{1}{x-1} + 2$ and $y_2 = \frac{1}{x+1} - 2$

Find any holes and vertical or horizontal asymptotes for the graph of each rational function.

12. $y = \frac{1}{x^2 + 3x - 10}$

13. $y = \frac{x+2}{(x+2)(x-3)}$

14. $y = \frac{x-1}{x^2 - 2x + 1}$

15. $y = \frac{5x-2}{x+2}$

Sketch the graph of each rational function. Then identify the domain and range.

16. $y = \frac{-2}{x}$

17. $y = \frac{5}{x+3} - 4$

18. $y = \frac{x^2 - 9}{2x + 6}$

19. $y = \frac{3x}{x^3 - x}$

20. $y = \frac{x+3}{x-3}$

21. $y = \frac{x^2 - 2x}{x - 2}$

Do you UNDERSTAND?

Open-Ended Write a rational function with the given characteristics.

22. a vertical asymptote at $x = 8$ and a horizontal asymptote at $y = 0$

23. a vertical asymptote at $x = -4$ and a horizontal asymptote at $y = 3$

24. a hole at $x = -5$ and a vertical asymptote at $x = 2$

25. Reasoning How many inverse variation functions have (2, 3) as a solution?

26. Reasoning The graph of an inverse variation function contains the point (a, b). Using a and b, identify 3 other points on the graph.

27. Reasoning Graph the equations $y = \frac{x^2 + x - 6}{x^2 - 5x + 6}$ and $y = \frac{x+3}{x-3}$. Are they equivalent? Explain.

17. 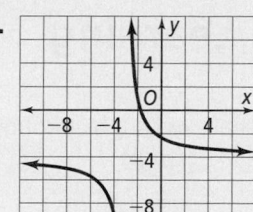 domain: all real numbers except $x = -3$; range: all real numbers except $y = -4$

18. 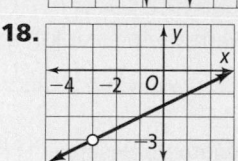 domain: all real numbers except $x = -3$; range: all real numbers except $y = -3$

19. 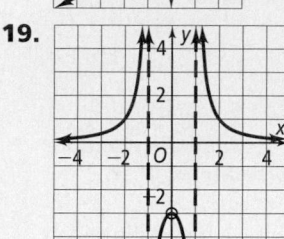 domain: all real numbers except $x = -1$, $x = 0$, and $x = 1$; range: $y < -3$ or $y > 0$

20. 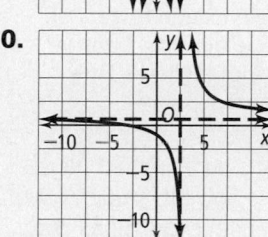 domain: all real numbers except $x = 3$; range: all real numbers except $y = 1$

21. 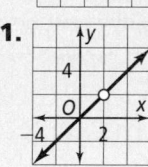 domain: all real numbers except $x = 2$; range: all real numbers except $y = 2$

22. Answers may vary. Sample: $y = \frac{1}{x - 8}$

23. Answers may vary. Sample: $y = \frac{3x}{x + 4}$

24. Answers may vary. Sample: $y = \frac{(x + 5)}{(x - 2)(x + 5)}$

25. one

26. Answers may vary. Sample answer:
$\left(-a, -b\right), \left(2a, \frac{b}{2}\right), \left(3a, \frac{b}{3}\right)$

27.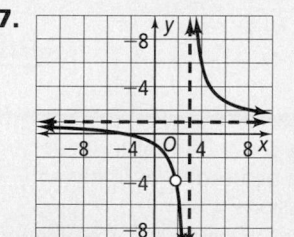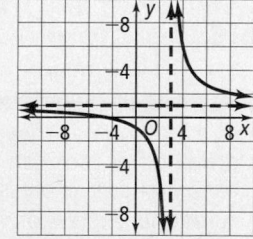

They are not equivalent functions. The first function has a hole at $x = 2$.

Answers

Mid-Chapter Quiz

1. $z = 5xy$

2. $z = \frac{20x}{y}$

3. $z = \frac{180}{xy}$

4. neither

5. inverse

6. $y = \frac{221}{x}$

7. $y = \frac{-48}{x}$

8. $y = \frac{-13}{x}$

9. The graph of y_2 is a stretch of the graph of y_1 by a factor of $\frac{9}{4}$.

10. The graph of y_2 is the graph of y_1 translated 5 units up.

11. The graph of y_2 is the graph of y_1 translated 4 units down and 2 units to the rt.

12. vert. asymptotes at $x = -5$ and $x = 2$, horizontal asymptote at $y = 0$

13. hole at $x = -2$, vert. asymptote at $x = 3$, horizontal asymptote at $y = 0$

14. vert. asymptote at $x = 1$, horizontal asymptote at $y = 0$

15. vert. asymptote at $x = -2$, horizontal asymptote at $y = 5$

16.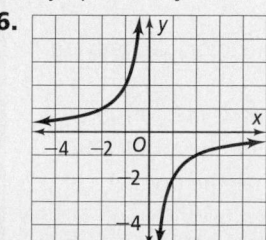

domain: all real numbers except $x = 0$; range: all real numbers except $y = 0$.

1 Interactive Learning

Solve It!
PURPOSE To explore rational expressions through examination of the Golden Rectangle

PROCESS Students may
- write and compare ratios of $\frac{length}{width}$ for the small and large non-square rectangles.
- repeatedly substitute for a variable to establish an infinite expression.

FACILITATE

Q If you define $x + 1$ as the length of the large rectangle, what is the ratio of the length of the large rectangle to the length of the similar smaller rectangle? $[\frac{x+1}{x}]$

Q Can you rewrite the ratio $\frac{x+1}{x}$ as $1 + \frac{1}{x}$? If so, how? **[Yes; rewrite the ratio as two ratios with the common denominator x. Then $\frac{x}{x}$ simplifies to 1.]**

Q How many times do you have to substitute for x on the right side of the equation to get "an expression with no x"? Explain. **[An infinite number of times. As x approaches ∞, the fraction $\frac{1}{x}$ approaches zero.]**

ANSWER See Solve It in Answers on next page.
CONNECT THE MATH In the Solve It, students write an equation using two rational expressions and then rewrite the expression and simplify it. Students will simplify rational expressions in this lesson.

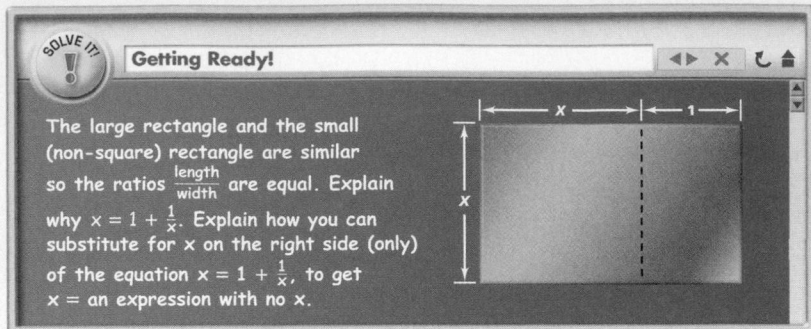

8-4 Rational Expressions

Objectives To simplify rational expressions
To multiply and divide rational expressions

Getting Ready!

The large rectangle and the small (non-square) rectangle are similar so the ratios $\frac{length}{width}$ are equal. Explain why $x = 1 + \frac{1}{x}$. Explain how you can substitute for x on the right side (only) of the equation $x = 1 + \frac{1}{x}$, to get x = an expression with no x.

Lesson Vocabulary
- rational expression
- simplest form

The expression $1 + \frac{1}{x}$ in the Solve It is equivalent to the *rational expression* $\frac{x+1}{x}$. A **rational expression** is the quotient of two polynomials. You will find that, at different times, it is helpful to think of rational expressions as ratios, as fractions, or as quotients.

Focus Question How is multiplying and dividing rational expressions similar to multiplying and dividing fractions?

A rational expression is in **simplest form** when its numerator and denominator are polynomials that have no common factors.

In simplest form	Not in simplest form
$\frac{x+1}{x-1}$, $\frac{x^2+3x+2}{x+3}$	$\frac{x}{x^2}$, $\frac{3(x-3)}{x-3}$, $\frac{x^2-x-6}{x^2+x-2}$

Hint
You used the same method to simplify numerical fractions.
$\frac{12}{80} = \frac{3 \cdot 4}{4 \cdot 20} = \frac{3}{20}$

You simplify a rational expression by dividing out the common factors in the numerator and the denominator. Factoring the numerator and denominator will help you identify the common factors.

A rational expression and any simplified form must have the same domain in order to be equivalent.

$\frac{x^2-x-6}{x^2+x-2} = \frac{(x-3)(x+2)}{(x-1)(x+2)}$ and $\frac{x-3}{x-1}$, $x \neq -2$, are equivalent.

In the example above, you must exclude -2 from the domain of $\frac{x-3}{x-1}$ because -2 is not in the domain of $\frac{x^2-x-6}{x^2+x-2}$. Note that this restriction is not clear from the simplified expression $\frac{x-3}{x-1}$.

8-4 Preparing to Teach

BIG ideas Equivalence
Function

UbD

ESSENTIAL UNDERSTANDINGS
- Much of what is true about multiplying and dividing fractions can be used to multiply and divide rational expressions.
- A rational expression is in simplest form when its numerator and denominator are polynomials that have no common divisors.
- A rational function may have zero or one horizontal asymptote and zero or more vertical asymptotes.
- Functions such as $f(x) = \frac{x+a}{x^2-a^2}$ and $g(x) = \frac{1}{x-a}$, $x \neq \pm a$, are equivalent.

Math Background
Operations with rational expressions are like operations with fractions. However, in order for the simplified rational expression to be equivalent to the original rational expression, domain restrictions must be defined. To simplify a rational expression:
- factor each polynomial in the numerator and denominator;
- identify the domain restrictions by setting each polynomial in the denominator equal to 0 and solving for x; and
- divide out common factors, identifying excluded values.

Sometimes the domain restrictions are not evident in the simplified expression. For example, $\frac{x^2-1}{x-1}$ has the domain restriction $x \neq 1$. The simplified expression is $x + 1$; the restriction $x \neq 1$ is not evident but must be included for the expressions to be equivalent. The simplified expression is $x + 1$, $x \neq 1$.

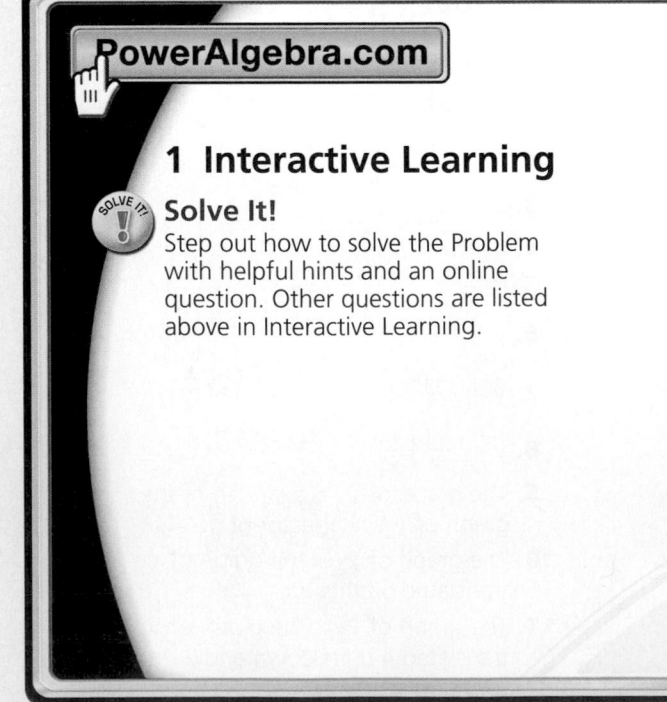

PowerAlgebra.com

1 Interactive Learning

Solve It!
Step out how to solve the Problem with helpful hints and an online question. Other questions are listed above in Interactive Learning.

Problem 1 Simplifying a Rational Expression

What is $\frac{x^2 + 7x + 10}{x^2 - 3x - 10}$ in simplest form? State any restrictions on the variable.

Factor the numerator and denominator.
$$\frac{x^2 + 7x + 10}{x^2 - 3x - 10} = \frac{(x + 2)(x + 5)}{(x + 2)(x - 5)}$$

Divide out common factors.
$$= \frac{(x + 2)(x + 5)}{(x + 2)(x - 5)}$$

Simplify.
$$= \frac{x + 5}{x - 5}$$

The simplified form is $\frac{x + 5}{x - 5}$ for $x \neq 5$ and $x \neq -2$. The restriction $x \neq -2$ is not clear from the simplified form, but is needed to prevent the denominator of the original expression from being zero.

 Got It? 1. What is the rational expression in simplest form? State any restrictions on the variables.

a. $\frac{24x^3y^2}{-6x^2y^3}$ b. $\frac{x^2 + 2x - 8}{x^2 - 5x + 6}$ c. $\frac{12 - 4x}{x^2 - 9}$

You can use what you know about simplifying rational expressions when you multiply and divide them.

 Problem 2 Multiplying Rational Expressions

What is the product $\frac{x^2 + x - 6}{x - 5} \cdot \frac{x^2 - 25}{x^2 + 4x + 3}$ in simplest form? State any restrictions on the variable.

Write the original expression.
$$\frac{x^2 + x - 6}{x - 5} \cdot \frac{x^2 - 25}{x^2 + 4x + 3}$$

Factor all polynomials.
$$= \frac{(x + 3)(x - 2)}{x - 5} \cdot \frac{(x + 5)(x - 5)}{(x + 3)(x + 1)}$$

Divide out common factors.
$$= \frac{(x + 3)(x - 2)}{x - 5} \cdot \frac{(x + 5)(x - 5)}{(x + 3)(x + 1)}$$

Simplify.
$$= \frac{(x - 2)(x + 5)}{x + 1}$$

The product is $\frac{(x - 2)(x + 5)}{x + 1}$ for $x \neq -3, x \neq -1$, and $x \neq 5$. The restrictions $x \neq -3$ and $x \neq 5$ are not clear from the simplified form, but are needed to prevent the denominators in the original product from being zero.

 Got It? 2. What is the product $\frac{2x - 8}{x^2 - 16} \cdot \frac{x^2 + 5x + 4}{x^2 + 8x + 16}$ in simplest form? State any restrictions on the variable.

Think

Is there more than one restriction?
Yes, before you divided the common factors out, $(x + 2)$ was one of the factors of the denominator so $x \neq -2$.

Plan

How is multiplying rational expressions like multiplying fractions?
To multiply rational expressions, you multiply the numerators and multiply the denominators.

2 Guided Instruction

Problem 1

Q Why is -5 not excluded from the domain? **[because $(x + 5)$ is not a factor of the denominator]**

Q Which step do you need to use to identify if there are restrictions on the domain? **[after factoring the denominator and before the common factors are divided out]**

Got It?

Q The rational expression in 1c factors as $\frac{4(3 - x)}{(x + 3)(x - 3)}$. How can you cancel the factors $(x - 3)$ and $(3 - x)$? **[Factor out -1 from one factor so that the factors are the same.]**

Problem 2

Q Why can you divide out a factor from the numerator of the first rational expression and a factor from the denominator of the second rational expression, and vice versa? **[When you multiply fractions or rational expressions, all the numerators become one numerator and all the denominators become one denominator. This does not happen when the terms are in a sum.]**

Got It?

Q What should your first step be? **[Factor the numerator and denominator.]**

Q The denominator of the expression of the product has four factors. Why are there not four exclusions from the domain? **[There are repeated factors.]**

2 Guided Instruction

 Each Problem is worked out and supported online.

Problem 1
Simplifying a Rational Expression

Problem 2
Multiplying Rational Expressions
Animated

Problem 3
Dividing Rational Expressions
Animated

Problem 4
Using Rational Expressions to Solve a Problem
Animated

Support in Algebra 2 Companion
• Vocabulary
• Key Concepts
• Got It?

Answers

Solve It!
Take the ratios of both the rectangles and set them equal: $\frac{x + 1}{x} = \frac{x}{1}$. Simplify the equation to get $x = 1 + \frac{1}{x}$. Replace x on the right side with $1 + \frac{1}{x}$ to get $x = 1 + \cfrac{1}{1 + \frac{1}{x}}$. Replace x with $1 + \frac{1}{x}$ again on the right side to get $x = 1 + \cfrac{1}{1 + \cfrac{1}{1 + \frac{1}{x}}}$.

Continue in this way to get the continued fraction

$$x = 1 + \cfrac{1}{1 + \cfrac{1}{1 + \cfrac{1}{1 + \frac{1}{\ddots}}}}$$

Got It?
1. a. $-\frac{4x}{y}; x \neq 0, y \neq 0$ b. $\frac{x + 4}{x - 3}; x \neq 2$ or 3

   c. $-\frac{4}{x + 3}; x \neq \pm 3$

2. $\frac{2(x + 1)}{(x + 4)^2}; x \neq \pm 4$

Lesson 8-4   549

Problem 3

Q Which polynomials in the original problem may restrict the possible values of the variable? Explain. **[$x^2 + 2x + 1$, $x^2 - 1$ and $x^2 + 3x - 10$ may restrict the possible values of x; any values for x that make one of the expressions 0 will cause division by zero.]**

Q The $x^2 + 3x - 10$ is in the numerator, so why is it involved in the restrictions? **[Because division is the same as multiplication by the reciprocal, this expression becomes a denominator.]**

Got It?

Q Suppose a student accidentally inverts the first rational expression and multiplies. How will the student's answer be different from the correct answer? **[The student's simplified expression will be inverted, and the restrictions on the variable will be incorrect.]**

Q How can you count up the maximum number of restrictions on the domain? **[The degree of each expression tells you the maximum number of roots. Add the degrees of the expressions that would create restrictions on the domain.]**

EXTENSION

Q For 3b, would the number of possible restrictions be the same if the question were a product instead of a quotient? Explain. **[No; only restrictions from the original denominators would need to be considered. The maximum number of restrictions would be only four.]**

Plan

How do you start?
Think of division as multiplying by the reciprocal.

To divide rational expressions, you multiply by the reciprocal of the divisor, just as you do when you divide rational numbers.

Problem 3 Dividing Rational Expressions

What is the quotient $\frac{2 - x}{x^2 + 2x + 1} \div \frac{x^2 + 3x - 10}{x^2 - 1}$ in simplest form? State any restrictions on the variable.

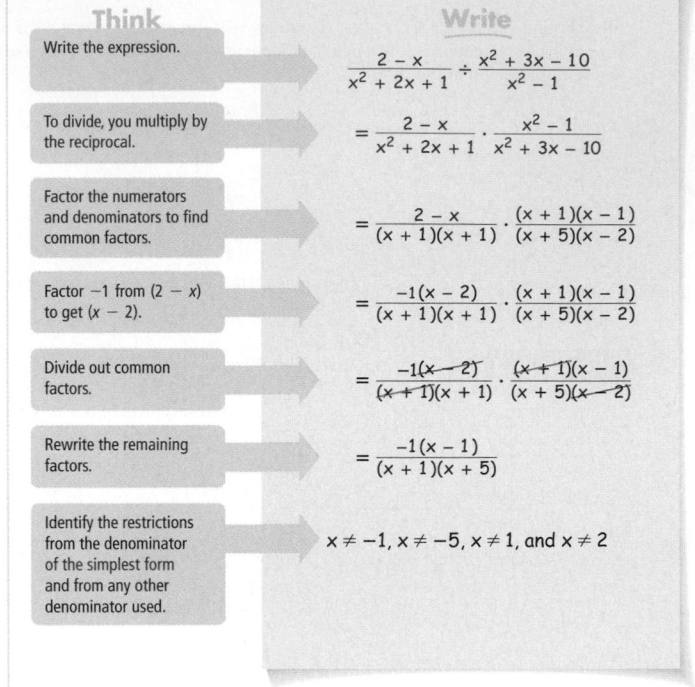

Think	Write
Write the expression.	$\frac{2 - x}{x^2 + 2x + 1} \div \frac{x^2 + 3x - 10}{x^2 - 1}$
To divide, you multiply by the reciprocal.	$= \frac{2 - x}{x^2 + 2x + 1} \cdot \frac{x^2 - 1}{x^2 + 3x - 10}$
Factor the numerators and denominators to find common factors.	$= \frac{2 - x}{(x + 1)(x + 1)} \cdot \frac{(x + 1)(x - 1)}{(x + 5)(x - 2)}$
Factor -1 from $(2 - x)$ to get $(x - 2)$.	$= \frac{-1(x - 2)}{(x + 1)(x + 1)} \cdot \frac{(x + 1)(x - 1)}{(x + 5)(x - 2)}$
Divide out common factors.	$= \frac{-1\cancel{(x - 2)}}{\cancel{(x + 1)}(x + 1)} \cdot \frac{\cancel{(x + 1)}(x - 1)}{(x + 5)\cancel{(x - 2)}}$
Rewrite the remaining factors.	$= \frac{-1(x - 1)}{(x + 1)(x + 5)}$
Identify the restrictions from the denominator of the simplest form and from any other denominator used.	$x \neq -1, x \neq -5, x \neq 1,$ and $x \neq 2$

✓ **Got It?** **3. a.** What is the quotient $\frac{x^2 + 5x + 4}{x^2 + x - 12} \div \frac{x^2 - 1}{2x^2 - 6x}$ in simplest form? State any restrictions on the variable.

b. Reasoning Without doing the calculation, what is greatest number of restrictions the quotient $\frac{x^2 + 8x + 7}{x^2 - x - 12} \div \frac{x^2 + 2x - 8}{x^2 + 13x + 24}$ could have? Explain.

Hint
For part (b), recall that the greatest possible number of zeros of a quadratic function is 2.

Additional Problems

1. What is $\frac{9x^2 + 6x}{36x + 24}$ in simplest form? State any restrictions on the variable.
ANSWER $\frac{x}{4}$; $x \neq -\frac{2}{3}$

2. What is the product $\frac{x^2 - 3x + 2}{x + 2} \cdot \frac{x^2 - 36}{x^2 + 5x - 6}$ in simplest form? State any restrictions on the variable.
ANSWER $\frac{(x - 2)(x - 6)}{x + 2}$; $x \neq 1, x \neq -2, x \neq -6$

3. What is the quotient $\frac{6x - 3x^2}{36 - x^2} \div \frac{x^3 - x^2 - 2x}{x^2 - 5x - 6}$ in simplest form? State any restrictions on the variable.
ANSWER $\frac{3}{6 + x}$; $x \neq -1, x \neq 0, x \neq 2, x \neq 6, x \neq -6$

4. Which jewelry box uses less material for the bottom and for the lid if the perimeters of the boxes are the same: a jewelry box shaped like a circle or a jewelry box shaped like a regular hexagon?
ANSWER circle

 **Problem 4** Using Rational Expressions to Solve a Problem

Construction Your community is building a park. It wants to fence in a play space for toddlers. It wants the maximum area for a given amount of fencing. Which shape, a square or a circle, provides a more efficient use of fencing?

Step 1 One measure of efficiency is the ratio $\frac{\text{area fenced}}{\text{fencing used}}$, or $\frac{\text{area}}{\text{perimeter}}$.

Find this ratio for both shapes.

	Square	Circle
Define area A and perimeter P.	Area $\rightarrow A = s^2$ Perimeter $\rightarrow P = 4s$	Area $\rightarrow A = \pi r^2$ Perimeter $\rightarrow P = 2\pi r$
Express s and r in terms of a common variable, P.	$s = \frac{P}{4}$	$r = \frac{P}{2\pi}$
Write the ratios.	$\frac{\text{Area}}{\text{Perimeter}} = \frac{s^2}{P}$	$\frac{\text{Area}}{\text{Perimeter}} = \frac{\pi r^2}{P}$
Substitute for s and r.	$= \frac{\left(\frac{P}{4}\right)^2}{P}$	$= \frac{\pi\left(\frac{P}{2\pi}\right)^2}{P}$
Simplify.	$= \frac{P^2}{16} \cdot \frac{1}{P} = \frac{P}{16}$	$= \frac{\pi P^2}{4\pi^2} \cdot \frac{1}{P} = \frac{P}{4\pi}$

Step 2 Compare the ratios. Which has the greater ratio?

Since $\frac{P}{4\pi} > \frac{P}{16}$, a circle provides a more efficient use of fencing.

Got It? 4. Which shape of play space provides for a more efficient use of fencing, a square or an equilateral triangle?

Think

How can you compare $\frac{P}{16}$ and $\frac{P}{4\pi}$ without evaluating P? Since the numerators are the same, the fraction with the smaller denominator is the greater fraction.

Hint

The area of an equilateral triangle with sides is $\frac{1}{2}(s)\left(\frac{\sqrt{3}}{2}s\right)$. The perimeter is $3s$.

Focus Question How is multiplying and dividing rational expressions similar to multiplying and dividing fractions?

Answer Multiply and divide rational expressions as you would multiply and divide fractions. Restrict the domain to ensure the original expression is never undefined.

Lesson Check

Do you know HOW?

Simplify each rational expression. State any restrictions on the variables.

1. $\frac{4z - 12}{8z + 24}$
2. $\frac{3x - 3}{x^2 - x}$

Multiply or divide. State any restrictions on the variables.

3. $\frac{x^2 + 3x - 10}{x^2 + 4x - 12} \cdot \frac{3x + 18}{x + 3}$

4. $\frac{x^2 - 7x + 10}{x^2 - 8x + 15} \div \frac{4 - x^2}{x^2 + 3x - 18}$

Do you UNDERSTAND?

5. **Vocabulary** Is the equation $y = \frac{x + 1}{x^2 + 1}$ in simplest form? Explain how you can tell.

6. **Error Analysis** A student claims that $x = 2$ is the only solution of the equation $\frac{x}{x - 2} = \frac{2}{x - 2}$. Is the student correct? Explain.

7. **Reasoning** The width of the rectangle is $\frac{a + 10}{3a + 24}$. Write an expression for the length of the rectangle in simplest form.

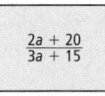
$\frac{2a + 20}{3a + 15}$, w, ℓ

Problem 4

Q Why express the ratio of $\frac{\text{Area}}{\text{Perimeter}}$ in terms of P? **[The perimeter is a shared parameter value. Expressing the ratio in terms of P allows you to compare the ratios.]**

Q Are there values for P so $\frac{P}{4\pi}$ is not greater than $\frac{P}{16}$? What are they? Are these values important in the context of the problem? **[Yes. If $P = 0$, then $\frac{P}{4\pi} = \frac{P}{16}$. If $P < 0$, then $\frac{P}{4\pi} < \frac{P}{16}$. These values are not possible because you cannot have zero or negative fencing.]**

Got It?

Q If you use s to represent the length of a side of an equilateral triangle with given perimeter P, can you also use s to represent the length of the side of the square? Explain. **[No; the square's perimeter would be greater than the perimeter of the equilateral triangle.]**

3 Lesson Check

Do you know HOW?   ERROR INTERVENTION
- If students do not get the correct answers for Exercises 1–4, have them check their factoring by multiplying.

Do you UNDERSTAND?
- If students have trouble with Exercise 5, ask "What are the factors of $x^2 + 1$?"

Close

Q Why is it important to examine the factors of the original problem to determine variable restrictions? **[Some restrictions may not be obvious after factors are divided out and multiplication and division have been performed.]**

Answers

Got It? (continued)

3. **a.** $\frac{2x}{x - 1}$; $x \neq 1, -1, -4,$ or 3

    b. Six restrictions; two in each of the original denominators, and two in the reciprocal of the second rational expression.

4. a square

Lesson Check

1. $\frac{z - 3}{2(z + 3)}$; $z \neq -3$

2. $\frac{3}{x}$; $x \neq 0$ or 1

3. $\frac{3(x + 5)}{x + 3}$; $x \neq -3, -6,$ or 2

4. $-\frac{x + 6}{x + 2}$; $x \neq -6, -2, 2, 3,$ or 5

5. Yes; the numerator and denominator are polynomials with no common factor.

6. No; $x = 2$ will make the denominator of $\frac{x}{x - 2}$ equal to 0, so $x = 2$ is not a solution. There is no solution to the eq.

7. Length $= \frac{2(a + 8)}{a + 5}$; $-10 < a < -5$, $a \neq -8$

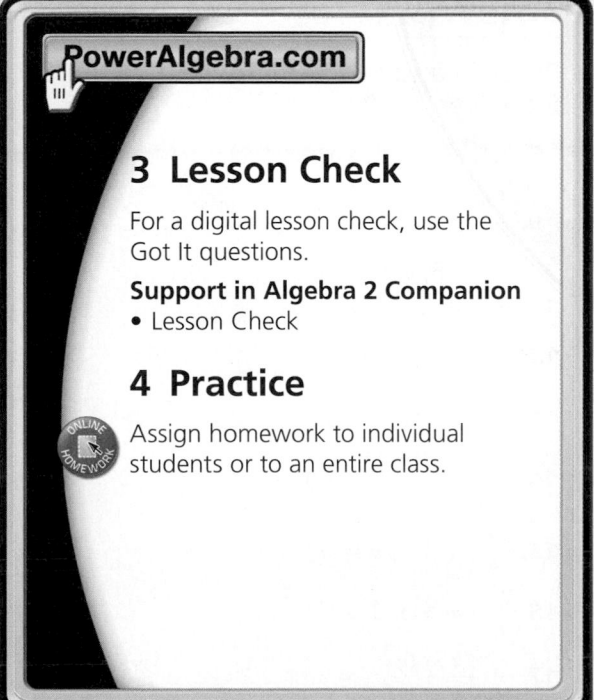

PowerAlgebra.com

3 Lesson Check

For a digital lesson check, use the Got It questions.

Support in Algebra 2 Companion
- Lesson Check

4 Practice

Assign homework to individual students or to an entire class.

4 Practice

ASSIGNMENT GUIDE

Basic: 8–18 even, 19–21, 24, 32, 38

Average: 8–18 even, 19–24, 28–35, 38, 40

Standardized Test Prep: 42–45

Mixed Review: 46–57

Reasoning exercises have blue headings.

Applications exercises have red headings.

EXERCISE 38: Use the Think About a Plan worksheet in the **Student Companion** (also available in the Teaching Resources in print and online) to further support students' development in becoming independent learners.

HOMEWORK QUICK CHECK

To check students' understanding of key skills and concepts, go over Exercises 16, 21, 24, 32, and 38.

Practice and Problem-Solving Exercises

 Practice

Simplify each rational expression. State any restrictions on the variables.

◆ See Problem 1.

8. $\dfrac{5x^3y}{15xy^3}$

9. $\dfrac{2x}{4x^2 - 2x}$

10. $\dfrac{6c^2 + 9c}{3c}$

11. $\dfrac{49 - z^2}{z + 7}$

12. $\dfrac{x^2 + 8x + 16}{x^2 - 2x - 24}$

13. $\dfrac{12 - x - x^2}{x^2 - 8x + 15}$

Multiply. State any restrictions on the variables.

◆ See Problem 2.

Guided Practice

To start, factor all polynomials.

14. $\dfrac{x^2 - 4}{x^2 - 1} \cdot \dfrac{x + 1}{x^2 + 2x}$

$\dfrac{(x - 2)(x + 2)}{(x - 1)(x + 1)} \cdot \dfrac{x + 1}{x(x + 2)}$

15. $\dfrac{2x^4}{10y^{-2}} \cdot \dfrac{5y^3}{4x^3}$

16. $\dfrac{8y - 4}{10y - 5} \cdot \dfrac{5y - 15}{3y - 9}$

17. $\dfrac{2x + 12}{3x - 9} \cdot \dfrac{6 - 2x}{3x + 8}$

18. $\dfrac{x^2 - 5x + 6}{x^2 - 4} \cdot \dfrac{x^2 + 3x + 2}{x^2 - 2x - 3}$

Divide. State any restrictions on the variables.

◆ See Problem 3.

Guided Practice

To start, rewrite the division as multiplication by the reciprocal.

19. $\dfrac{7x}{4y^3} \div \dfrac{21x^3}{8y}$

$\dfrac{7x}{4y^3} \cdot \dfrac{8y}{21x^3}$

20. $\dfrac{3x^3}{5y^2} \div \dfrac{6y^{-3}}{5x^{-5}}$

21. $\dfrac{6x + 6y}{y - x} \div \dfrac{18}{5x - 5y}$

22. $\dfrac{x^2}{x^2 + 2x + 1} \div \dfrac{3x}{x^2 - 1}$

23. $\dfrac{y^2 - 5y + 6}{y^3} \div \dfrac{y^2 + 3y - 10}{4y^2}$

24. Industrial Design A storage tank will have a circular base of radius r and a height of r. The tank can be either cylindrical or hemispherical (half a sphere).

◆ See Problem 4.

a. Write and simplify an expression for the ratio of the volume of the hemispherical tank to its surface area (including the base). For a sphere, $V = \frac{4}{3}\pi r^3$ and $SA = 4\pi r^2$.

b. Write and simplify an expression for the ratio of the volume of the cylindrical tank to its surface area (including the bases). For a cylinder, $V = \pi r^2 h$ and $SA = 2\pi r^2 + 2\pi rh$.

c. Compare the ratios of volume to surface area for the two tanks.

d. Compare the volumes of the two tanks.

Answers

Practice and Problem-Solving Exercises

8. $-\dfrac{x^2}{3y^2}$; $x \neq 0, y \neq 0$

9. $\dfrac{1}{2x - 1}$; $x \neq 0$ or $\frac{1}{2}$

10. $2c + 3$; $c \neq 0$

11. $7 - z$; $z \neq -7$

12. $\dfrac{x + 4}{x - 6}$; $x \neq 6$ or -4

13. $-\dfrac{x + 4}{x - 5}$; $x \neq 5$ or 3

14. $\dfrac{7}{15x^2}$; $x \neq 0, y \neq 0$

15. $\dfrac{xy^5}{4}$; $x \neq 0, y \neq 0$

16. $\dfrac{4}{3}$; $y \neq \frac{1}{2}$ or 3

17. $-\dfrac{4(x + 6)}{3(3x + 8)}$; $x \neq 3$ or $-\frac{8}{3}$

18. 1; $x \neq -2, -1, 2,$ or 3

19. $\dfrac{2}{3x^2y^2}$; $x \neq 0, y \neq 0$

20. $\dfrac{y}{2x^2}$; $x \neq 0, y \neq 0$

21. $\dfrac{-5(x + y)}{3}$; $x \neq y$

22. $\dfrac{x(x - 1)}{3(x + 1)}$; $x \neq -1, 1,$ or 0

23. $\dfrac{4(y - 3)}{y(y + 5)}$; $y \neq 2, -5,$ or 0

24. a. $\dfrac{\frac{2}{3}\pi r^3}{2\pi r^2 + \pi r^2} = \dfrac{2r}{9}$

b. $\dfrac{\pi r^2(r)}{2\pi r^2 + 2\pi r(r)} = \dfrac{r}{4}$

c. The ratio for the cylindrical tank is always larger.

d. For a given value of r, the cylindrical tank will have a larger volume.

25. Architecture An architecture firm is designing a new office building in the shape of a cylinder. The company wants the maximum volume for a given surface area. The cylinder will either have a circular base with radius r and a height $2r$, or a circular base with radius $2r$ and a height r.
  a. Write and simplify an expression for the ratio of the volume to the surface area for a building with a circular base of radius r and height $2r$.
  b. Write and simplify an expression for the ratio of the volume to the surface area for a building with a circular base of radius $2r$ and height r.
  c. Compare the ratios of volume to surface area for the two buildings. Which building will be more efficient?

 Apply

Simplify each rational expression. State any restrictions on the variables.

26. $\dfrac{x^2 - 5x - 24}{x^2 - 7x - 30}$

27. $\dfrac{2y^2 + 8y - 24}{2y^2 - 8y + 8}$

28. $\dfrac{xy^3 - 9xy}{12xy^2 + 12xy - 144x}$

29. $\dfrac{(x^2 - x)^2}{x(x - 1)^{-2}(x^2 + 3x - 4)}$

30. $\dfrac{2x + 6}{(x - 1)^{-1}(x^2 + 2x - 3)}$

31. $\dfrac{54x^3y^{-1}}{3x^{-2}y}$

32. Think About a Plan A cereal company wants to use the most efficient packaging for their new product. They are considering a cylindrical-shaped box and a cube-shaped box. Compare the ratios of the volume to the surface area of the containers to determine which packaging will be more efficient.
  • How can you measure the cereal box's efficiency?
  • What formulas will you need to use to solve this problem?

Multiply or divide. State any restrictions on the variables.

33. $\dfrac{6x^3 - 6x^2}{x^4 + 5x^3} \div \dfrac{3x^2 - 15x + 12}{2x^2 + 2x - 40}$

34. $\dfrac{2x^2 - 6x}{x^2 + 18x + 81} \cdot \dfrac{9x + 81}{x^2 - 9}$

35. $\dfrac{x^2 - x - 2}{2x^2 - 5x + 2} \div \dfrac{x^2 - x - 12}{2x^2 + 5x - 3}$

36. $\dfrac{2x^2 + 5x + 2}{4x^2 - 1} \cdot \dfrac{2x^2 + x - 1}{x^2 + x - 2}$

37. Reasoning Write a simplified expression for the area of the rectangle at the right. State all restrictions on a.

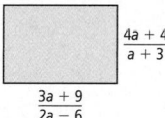

38. Manufacturing A toy company is considering a cube or sphere-shaped container for packaging a new product. The height of the cube would equal the diameter of the sphere. Compare the volume-to-surface area ratios of the containers. Which packaging will be more efficient? (*Hint:* For a sphere, $SA = 4\pi r^2$.)

39. Open-Ended Write three rational expressions that simplify to $\dfrac{x}{x + 1}$.

Decide whether the given statement is *always*, *sometimes*, or *never* true.

40. Rational expressions are undefined for values of the variables that make the denominator 0.

41. Restrictions on variables change when a rational expression is simplified.

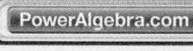

25. a. $\dfrac{\pi r^2(2r)}{2\pi r^2 + 2\pi r(2r)} = \dfrac{r}{3}$

  b. $\dfrac{\pi(2r)^2(r)}{2\pi(2r)^2 + 2\pi(2r)(r)} = \dfrac{r}{3}$

  c. The ratios are equal. The buildings are equally efficient.

26. $\dfrac{x - 8}{x - 10}$; $x \neq -3$ or 10

27. $\dfrac{y + 6}{y - 2}$; $y \neq 2$

28. $\dfrac{y(y + 3)}{12(y + 4)}$; $x \neq 0$, $y \neq -4$ or 3

29. $\dfrac{x(x - 1)^3}{x + 4}$; $x \neq -4, 0,$ or 1

30. 2; $x \neq -3$ or 1

31. $\dfrac{18x^5}{y^2}$; $x \neq 0$, $y \neq 0$

32. $R_{cylinder} = \dfrac{V_{cylinder}}{SA_{cylinder}} = \dfrac{rh}{2(r + h)}$;

  $R_{cube} = \dfrac{V_{cube}}{SA_{cube}} = \dfrac{s}{6}$;

if $r = h = s$, then $R_{cylinder} = \dfrac{r}{4}$ and $R_{cube} = \dfrac{r}{6}$. $R_{cylinder} > R_{cube}$. The cylindrical shaped box is more efficient. If $s = h = 2r$ (diameter), then $R_{cylindrical} = R_{cube}$. The boxes are equally efficient.

33. $\dfrac{4}{x}$; $x \neq 0, -5, 4,$ or 1

34. $\dfrac{18x}{(x + 9)(x + 3)}$; $x \neq -9, -3,$ or 3

35. $\dfrac{x + 1}{x - 4}$; $x \neq -3, \dfrac{1}{2}, 2,$ or 4

36. $\dfrac{x + 1}{x - 1}$; $x \neq -\dfrac{1}{2}, \dfrac{1}{2}, 1,$ or -2

37. $\dfrac{6(a + 1)}{a - 3}$; $|a| > 3$

38. They are equally efficient.

39. Check students' work.

40. always

41. never

Answers

Standardized Test Prep

42. D

43. H

44. C

45. [2] $-x \log 3 = \log \frac{1}{243}$

$$-x = \frac{\log \frac{1}{243}}{\log 3}$$

$$-x = -5$$

$$x = 5$$

[1] correct answer, without work shown

Mixed Review

46. hole at $x = 3$

47. vert. asymptotes at $x = -\frac{2}{3}$ and $x = -1$

48. hole at $x = 4$, vert. asymptote at $x = -3$

49. 3

50. -5

51. $\frac{3}{4}$

52. 49

53. 168

54. 2

55. $\frac{17}{38}$

56. $\frac{11}{72}$

57. $\frac{137}{180}$

Standardized Test Prep

42. Which function is graphed at the right?

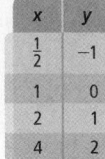

  Ⓐ $y = (x + 4)(x - 1)(x + 2)$

  Ⓑ $y = (x - 4)(x - 1)(x + 2)$

  Ⓒ $y = (x - 4)(x + 1)(x - 2)$

  Ⓓ $y = (x + 4)(x + 1)(x - 2)$

43. Which function generates the table of values at the right?

  Ⓕ $y = \log_{\frac{1}{2}} x$

  Ⓖ $y = -\log_2 x$

  Ⓗ $y = \log_2 x$

  Ⓘ $y = \left(\frac{1}{2}\right)^x$

x	y
$\frac{1}{2}$	-1
1	0
2	1
4	2

44. Which expression equals $\frac{x}{x^2 - 2x - 3} \cdot \frac{2x - 6}{x^2 - 4x + 3}$?

  Ⓐ $\frac{2x - 1}{(x - 1)(x + 3)(x + 1)}$ Ⓒ $\frac{2x}{(x - 1)(x + 1)(x - 3)}$

  Ⓑ $\frac{2x + 1}{(x - 1)(x + 1)(x - 3)}$ Ⓓ $\frac{2x}{(x + 3)(x - 1)(x + 1)}$

45. What is the solution of the equation $3^{-x} = \frac{1}{243}$?

Mixed Review

Find the vertical asymptotes and holes for the graph of each rational function.   ◀ See Lesson 8-3.

46. $y = \frac{x - 3}{x - 3}$ **47.** $y = \frac{x - 1}{(3x + 2)(x + 1)}$ **48.** $y = \frac{(x - 4)(x + 5)}{(x + 3)(x - 4)}$

Evaluate each logarithm.   ◀ See Lesson 7-3.

49. $\log_4 64$ **50.** $\log_2 \frac{1}{32}$ **51.** $\log_{16} 8$

Solve. Check for extraneous solutions.   ◀ See Lesson 6-5.

52. $\sqrt{x} - 3 = 4$ **53.** $\sqrt{x + 1} - 5 = 8$ **54.** $\sqrt{5x - 3} = \sqrt{2x + 3}$

Get Ready!   To prepare for Lesson 8-5, do Exercises 55–57.

Add or subtract.   ◀ See p. 866.

55. $\frac{5}{19} + \frac{7}{38}$ **56.** $\frac{7}{24} - \frac{5}{36}$ **57.** $\frac{11}{12} - \frac{7}{45}$

Additional Instructional Support

Algebra 2 Companion

Students can use the **Algebra 2 Companion** worktext (4 pages) as you teach the lesson. Use the Companion to support

- New Vocabulary
- Key Concepts
- Got It for each Problem
- Lesson Check

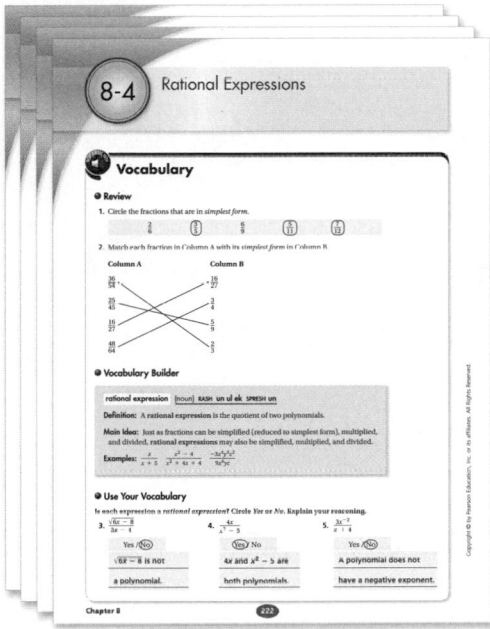

ELL Support

Focus on Communication Have students write out instructions as a list of steps to solve Lesson Check Exercise 3 or 4. Pair students with different problems, and have them trade instruction steps. Students should then solve the other exercise following the exact instruction steps. Student pairs should then orally help each other revise their instructions as necessary to be complete and accurate.

5 Assess & Remediate

Lesson Quiz

1. What is $\dfrac{x^2 + x - 12}{x^2 + 2x - 8}$ in simplest form? State any restrictions on the variable.

2. What is the product $\dfrac{x + 3}{x^2 - 9} \cdot \dfrac{x^2 + 2x - 15}{x^2 - 2x + 1}$ in simplest form? State any restrictions on the variable.

3. What is the quotient $\dfrac{16 - x^2}{x^2 + 2x - 3} \div \dfrac{x - 4}{x^2 + 4x + 3}$ in simplest form? State any restrictions on the variable.

4. **Do you UNDERSTAND?** A friend gives you a puppy for your birthday and offers to buy fencing for a dog run. For a given amount of fencing, what shape gives your puppy more area to run: a rectangle whose length is twice the width or a regular hexagon?

ANSWERS TO LESSON QUIZ

1. $\dfrac{x - 3}{x - 2}$; $x \neq -4, x \neq 2$

2. $\dfrac{x + 5}{(x - 1)^2}$; $x \neq 3, x \neq -3, x \neq 1$

3. $-\dfrac{(x + 4)(x + 1)}{x - 1}$, $x \neq 1, x \neq -3, x \neq 4$ $x \neq -1$

4. regular hexagon

PRESCRIPTION FOR REMEDIATION

Use the student work on the Lesson Quiz to prescribe a differentiated review assignment:

Points	Differentiated Remediation
0–2	Intervention
3	On-level
4	Extension

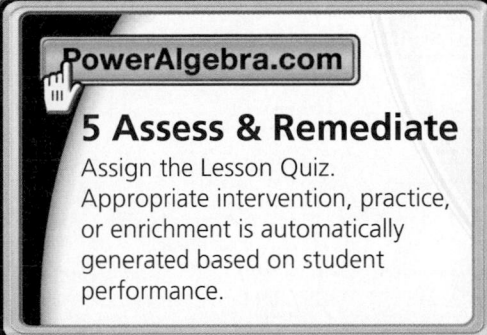

PowerAlgebra.com

5 Assess & Remediate

Assign the Lesson Quiz. Appropriate intervention, practice, or enrichment is automatically generated based on student performance.

Intervention

- **Reteaching** (2 pages) Provides reteaching and practice exercises for the key lesson concepts. Use with struggling students or absent students.

- **English Language Learner Support** Helps students develop and reinforce mathematical vocabulary and key concepts.

All-in-One Resources/Online

Reteaching

All-in-One Resources/Online

English Language Learner Support

Differentiated Remediation *continued*

On-Level

- **Practice** (2 pages) Provides extra practice for each lesson. For more challenging practice exercises, use the Form G Practice pages found in the All-in-One Teaching Resources and online.

- **Think About a Plan** Helps students develop specific problem-solving skills and strategies by providing scaffolded guiding questions.

- **Standardized Test Prep** Focuses on all major exercises, all major question types, and helps students prepare for the high-stakes assessments.

Extension

- **Enrichment** Provides students with interesting problems and activities that extend the concepts of the lesson.

- **Activities, Games, and Puzzles** Worksheets that can be used for concepts development, enrichment, and for fun!

Student Companion/ All-in-One Resources/Online
Practice page 1

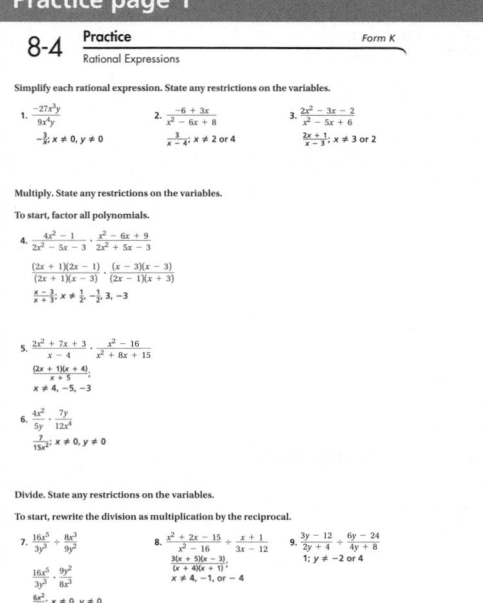

Student Companion/ All-in-One Resources/Online
Practice page 2

All-in-One Resources/Online
Enrichment

Student Companion/ All-in-One Resources/Online
Think About a Plan

Student Companion/ All-in-One Resources/Online
Standardized Test Prep

Online Teacher Resource Center
Activities, Puzzles, and Games

8-5 PART 1 Adding and Subtracting Rational Expressions

Objective To add and subtract rational expressions

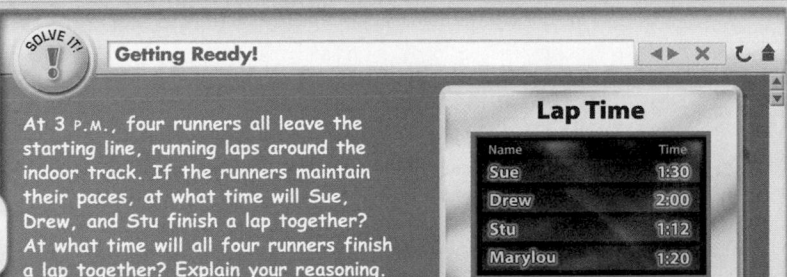

SOLVE IT!

Getting Ready!

At 3 P.M., four runners all leave the starting line, running laps around the indoor track. If the runners maintain their paces, at what time will Sue, Drew, and Stu finish a lap together? At what time will all four runners finish a lap together? Explain your reasoning.

Lap Time

Name	Time
Sue	1:30
Drew	2:00
Stu	1:12
Marylou	1:20

The runners finish a lap together in a common time.

You use common multiples of polynomials to add and subtract rational expressions, just as you use common multiples of numbers to add and subtract fractions.

Hint
You can use any common denominator, but it is often easiest to use the LCM of the denominators.

Focus Question How do you add and subtract rational expressions?

To add or subtract rational expressions, first find the least common multiple (LCM) of the denominators. To find the LCM of several expressions, factor the expressions (numbers or polynomials) completely. The LCM is the product of the prime factors, each raised to the greatest power that occurs in any of the expressions.

Plan
How do you determine the exponent of each factor for the LCM?
Use the exponent from the expression that has that factor to the greatest power.

Problem 1 Finding the Least Common Multiple

What is the LCM of $12x^2y(x^2 + 2x + 1)$ and $18xy^3(x^2 + 5x + 4)$?

Step 1 Find the prime factors of each expression.

Write the expression.	$12x^2y(x^2 + 2x + 1)$	$18xy^3(x^2 + 5x + 4)$
Factor the trinomial.	$= 12x^2y(x + 1)(x + 1)$	$= 18xy^3(x + 1)(x + 4)$
Factor completely.	$= 2^2 \cdot 3x^2y(x + 1)^2$	$= 2 \cdot 3^2xy^3(x + 1)(x + 4)$

Step 2 Identify the greatest power of each factor that occurs in either expression.

$$12x^2y(x^2 + 2x + 1) = 2^2 \cdot 3 \cdot x^2 \cdot y \cdot (x + 1)^2$$
$$18xy^3(x^2 + 5x + 4) = 2 \cdot 3^2 \cdot x \cdot y^3 \cdot (x + 1) \cdot (x + 4)$$

Step 3 Write the product of the factors you identified above.

$$2^2 \cdot 3^2 \cdot x^2 \cdot y^3 \cdot (x + 1)^2 \cdot (x + 4)$$

The LCM is $2^2 \cdot 3^2x^2y^3(x + 1)^2(x + 4)$, or $36x^2y^3(x + 1)^2(x + 4)$.

PowerAlgebra.com | Lesson 8-5 Adding and Subtracting Rational Expressions | **555**

---

1 Interactive Learning

Solve It!
PURPOSE To review finding the least common multiple (LCM)
PROCESS Students may
- make a table of minutes with a row for each runner and columns for numbers of laps.
- guess and check using multiples of 2 minutes.
- write each rate as a decimal fraction and find the LCM of the rates.

FACILITATE

Q How long will it take each runner to go 3 laps? **[Sue 4:30, Drew 6:00, Stu 3:36, Marylou 4:00]**

Q Where on the track are Sue, Drew, and Stu after 6 minutes? **[All at the same spot, just on different laps.]**

Q How do you know that the solution will be a multiple of 2 minutes? **[Drew has the slowest rate—one lap every 2 minutes. The solution must be a multiple of his rate.]**

ANSWER See Solve It in Answers on next page.
CONNECT THE MATH To answer the Solve It, students add or subtract fractions by finding the LCM of the denominators. In the lesson they will use the same method to add and subtract rational expressions.

2 Guided Instruction

Problem 1

Q What is the LCM of 12 and 30, and how can you find it? **[$12 = 2^2 \times 3$, $30 = 2 \times 3 \times 5$, so the LCM = $2^2 \times 3 \times 5 = 60$.]**

Q What does *prime factor* mean? **[Prime factor means a factor that cannot be divided evenly by any factors except 1 and itself.]**

8-5 Preparing to Teach

PART 1

BIG ideas Function
Equivalence **UbD**

ESSENTIAL UNDERSTANDINGS
- Much of what is true about operating with fractions can be used to operate with rational expressions. Rational expressions can be added or subtracted by first finding a common denominator—preferably the least common multiple (LCM) of the denominators.
- The LCM of denominators is the product of their prime factors, each raised to the greatest power that occurs in any of the expressions.

Math Background
Rational expressions can be added and subtracted using the same methods as for adding and subtracting fractions.

- Factor the denominators.
- Find the LCM of the denominators, which will be the LCD, least common denominator.
- Rewrite each expression with the LCD by multiplying by the necessary factors.
- Add or subtract the numerators, combining like terms.
- Factor the numerator.
- Simplify the expression by dividing out any common factors.

In order for the simplified result to be equivalent to the original form, it is necessary to note which values of x must be excluded from the domain to allow for the simplification.

Support Student Learning
Use the **Algebra 2 Companion** to engage and support students during instruction. See Lesson Resources at the end of this lesson for details.

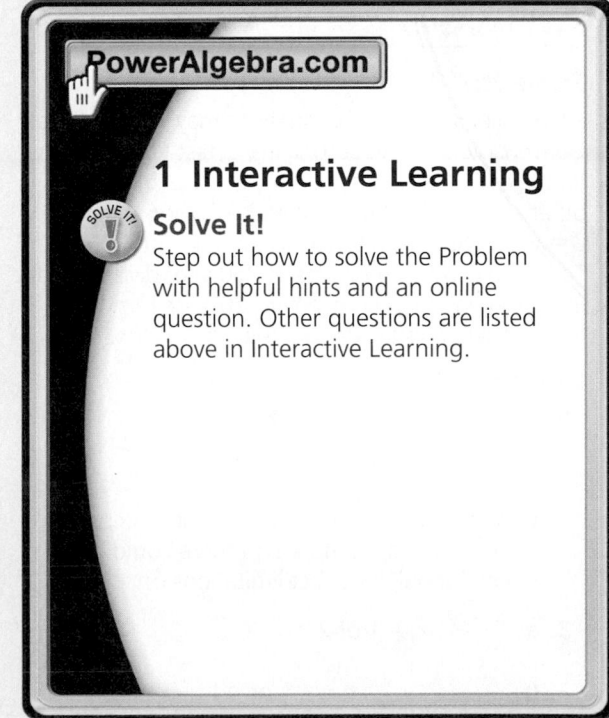

PowerAlgebra.com

1 Interactive Learning

SOLVE IT!

Solve It!
Step out how to solve the Problem with helpful hints and an online question. Other questions are listed above in Interactive Learning.

Got It?

Q In 1a, what prime factor do the two expressions share? **[x + 2]**

Q What are two numbers whose LCM is the product of the numbers? **[Sample: 2, 3]**

Q Under what circumstance would simply multiplying the expressions result in the LCM? **[When the expressions share no common factors, then the product of the expressions is the LCM.]**

Problem 2

Q Why is the LCM $(x - 1)(x - 2)$ and not $(x - 1)^2(x - 2)$? **[Common factors indicate the greatest number of times they appear in either expression, not both.]**

Q What does the second expression need to be multiplied by in order to add the expressions? Explain. **[Nothing; the denominator of the second expression already contains both factors that make up the LCD of the two expressions.]**

Q Once you add the two numerators, why not multiply the factors of the denominator to get a simpler form? **[Once you simplify the numerator you need to factor the numerator and look for common factors in the numerator and denominator.]**

Got It?

Q After finding the LCD in 2a, the sum is $\frac{x^2 + x - 2}{x(x - 1)}$. Is this expression in simplest form? Explain. **[No. $x^2 + x - 2 = (x + 2)(x - 1)$. The $(x - 1)$ factors in the numerator and denominator can be divided out.]**

Q What happens if you don't use the LCD? **[There will be factoring left to do at the end.]**

 Got It? **1.** What is the LCM of each pair of expressions?
  a. $2x + 4$ and $x^2 - x - 6$
  b. $x^2 + 3x - 4$, $x^2 + 2x - 8$, and $x^2 - 4x + 4$

The LCM of the denominators of two rational expressions is also the Least Common Denominator (LCD). You can use the LCD to add or subtract the rational expressions.

Recall how you used the LCD to add fractions.

$$\frac{1}{8} + \frac{1}{10} = \frac{1}{2^3} + \frac{1}{2 \cdot 5} = \frac{1}{2^3}\left(\frac{5}{5}\right) + \frac{1}{2 \cdot 5}\left(\frac{2^2}{2^2}\right) = \frac{5}{40} + \frac{4}{40} = \frac{9}{40}$$

 Problem 2 Adding Rational Expressions

What is the sum of the two rational expressions in simplest form? State any restrictions on the variable. $\frac{x}{x - 1} + \frac{2x - 1}{x^2 - 3x + 2}$

Plan
How does the LCD help you simplify this sum?
The LCD is $(x - 1)(x - 2)$.
Multiply the first expression by $\frac{x - 2}{x - 2}$ to get a common denominator.

Write the original expression.	$\frac{x}{x - 1} + \frac{2x - 1}{x^2 - 3x + 2}$
Factor the denominators.	$= \frac{x}{x - 1} + \frac{2x - 1}{(x - 1)(x - 2)}$
Rewrite each expression with the LCD.	$= \frac{x}{x - 1} \cdot \frac{x - 2}{x - 2} + \frac{2x - 1}{(x - 1)(x - 2)}$
Simplify the first expression.	$= \frac{x^2 - 2x}{(x - 1)(x - 2)} + \frac{2x - 1}{(x - 1)(x - 2)}$
Add the numerators. Combine like terms.	$= \frac{x^2 - 2x + 2x - 1}{(x - 1)(x - 2)}$
Simplify the numerator.	$= \frac{x^2 - 1}{(x - 1)(x - 2)}$
Factor the numerator. Divide out the common factors.	$= \frac{(x - 1)(x + 1)}{(x - 1)(x - 2)}$
Write the equivalent expression in simplest form.	$= \frac{x + 1}{x - 2}, x \neq 1$

The sum of the expressions is $\frac{x + 1}{x - 2}$ for $x \neq 1$ and $x \neq 2$.

Hint
For part (c), think about the different common denominators you could use to find the sum $\frac{5}{12} + \frac{9}{16}$.

 Got It? **2.** What is the sum of the two rational expressions in simplest form? State any restrictions on the variable.

  a. $\frac{x + 1}{x - 1} + \frac{-2}{x^2 - x}$

  b. $\frac{x}{x^2 - 4} + \frac{1}{x + 2}$

  c. Reasoning Is it possible to add the rational expressions in Problem 2 by finding a common denominator, but not the *least* common denominator? Explain.

Answers

Solve It!

−3:06 P.M.; 3:12 P.M.; Explanations may vary. Sample: Convert the times to seconds, and test times that are multiples of 120 s to see if they are divisible by the other runners' lap times. After 360 s, or 6 min, Sue, Drew, and Stu will finish a lap together, at 3:06 P.M. Then you can test multiples of 360 s for divisibility by 80 s, Marylou's lap time. After 720 s, or 12 min, all four runners finish a lap together, at 3:12 P.M.

Got It?

1. a. $2(x + 2)(x - 3)$ **b.** $(x - 1)(x - 2)^2(x + 4)$

2. a. $\frac{x + 2}{x}, x \neq 1$ or 0 **b.** $\frac{2(x - 1)}{x^2 - 4}; x \neq \pm 2$

  c. Yes, however the denominator would have to be factored more and there could be additional, incorrect limitations on x.

3. a. $\frac{x - 2}{x - 1}, x \neq 1$ or 2

  b. $\frac{x^2 - x - 4}{x^2 + 6x + 5}; x \neq -5$ or -1

PowerAlgebra.com

2 Guided Instruction

Each Problem is worked out and supported online.

Problem 1
Finding the Least Common Multiple

Problem 2
Adding Rational Expressions
Animated

Problem 3
Subtracting Rational Expressions

Alternative Problem 3
Subtracting Rational Expressions
Animated

Support in Algebra 2 Companion
• Vocabulary
• Key Concepts
• Got It?

Plan

How is this problem similar to Problem 2? The method is the same except you subtract the rational expressions instead of adding them.

What is the difference of the two rational expressions in simplest form? State any restrictions on the variable. $\dfrac{x+2}{x^2-2x} - \dfrac{x+2}{2x-4}$

Think

Write the original expression. Factor the denominators to find the LCD.

Rewrite each expression with the LCD.

Simplify the numerators and subtract.

Factor the numerator and divide out the common factors.

Hint

Multiplying by $\frac{2}{2}$ did not introduce any restrictions on the variable because $\frac{2}{2}$ is defined for all values of x.

Write the answer. State any restrictions on the domain.

Write

$$\dfrac{x+2}{x^2-2x} - \dfrac{x+2}{2x-4}$$

$$=\dfrac{x+2}{x(x-2)} - \dfrac{x+2}{2(x-2)}$$

The LCD is $2x(x-2)$.

$$=\dfrac{x+2}{x(x-2)}\cdot\dfrac{2}{2} - \dfrac{x+2}{2(x-2)}\cdot\dfrac{x}{x}$$

$$=\dfrac{2(x+2)}{2x(x-2)} - \dfrac{x(x+2)}{2x(x-2)}$$

$$=\dfrac{2x+4}{2x(x-2)} - \dfrac{x^2+2x}{2x(x-2)}$$

$$=\dfrac{2x+4-(x^2+2x)}{2x(x-2)}$$

$$=\dfrac{2x+4-x^2-2x}{2x(x-2)}$$

$$=\dfrac{-x^2+4}{2x(x-2)}$$

$$=\dfrac{-(x^2-4)}{2x(x-2)}$$

$$=\dfrac{-(x-2)(x+2)}{2x(x-2)}$$

$$=\dfrac{-(x+2)}{2x}$$

The difference is $\dfrac{-(x+2)}{2x}$ for $x\neq 2$ and $x\neq 0$.

Got It? **3.** What is the difference of the two rational expressions in simplest form? State any restrictions on the variable.

a. $\dfrac{x+3}{x-2} - \dfrac{6x-7}{x^2-3x+2}$

b. $\dfrac{x-1}{x+5} - \dfrac{x+3}{x^2+6x+5}$

Problem 3

Q What do you need to watch for when you subtract the $\dfrac{x^2+2x}{2x(x-2)}$ term? **[that you distribute the negative sign to both terms in the numerator]**

Q Do you distribute the negative to both the numerator and denominator? Explain. **[No, that would be equivalent to $\dfrac{-1}{-1}=1$]**

Q How does $\dfrac{x+2}{x^2-2x} - \dfrac{x+2}{2x-4}$ differ from $-\dfrac{x+2}{2x}$? **[The first expression has a discontinuity at $x=2$, while $-\dfrac{x+2}{2x}$ is defined at $x=2$.]**

Q If two rational expressions are functions, is the sum or difference of the expressions also a function? Explain. **[Yes. the definition of a funtion states that for each x-value the funtion will return a single y-value. The sum or difference of two y-values at any x will also be a single value at that x, and thus the sum or difference of the two expressions is a function.]**

Got It?   ERROR PREVENTION

When multiplying expressions to create a common denominator, students should multiply out the numerators but leave the denominator factored.

Q Are the restrictions on the problems and on the answers different? **[No difference; both restrictions are the same.]**

Q What is the maximum number of restrictions in each problem? **[3]**

Additional Problems

1. What is the LCM of $x^2+4x-12$ and x^2-6x+8?

ANSWER
$(x-2)(x-4)(x+6)$

2. What is the sum $\dfrac{4}{x^2+3x} + \dfrac{x-2}{x^2+6x+9}$ in simplest form? State any restrictions on the variable.

ANSWER $\dfrac{x^2+2x+12}{x(x+3)^2}$;
$x\neq 0, x\neq -3$

3. What is the difference $\dfrac{x+1}{x^2+2x-8} - \dfrac{x}{4x-8}$ in simplest form? State any restrictions on the variable.

ANSWER $\dfrac{-(x+2)}{4(x+4)}$; $x\neq 2$, $x\neq -4$

Answers

Lesson Check

1. $\dfrac{2a-10}{3a-5}$; $a\neq\dfrac{5}{3}$

2. $\dfrac{6x-11}{x^2-4}$; $x\neq \pm 2$

3. $\dfrac{-11m}{3m+6}$; $m\neq -2$

4. $\dfrac{-4(2b-5)}{(b-4)(b+4)(b-2)}$; $b\neq 2$ or ± 4

5. Answers may vary. Sample:
$\dfrac{x^2-1}{x^2-6x+5}$, $\dfrac{x^2+6x+5}{x^2-25}$

6. Factor the polynomials completely. Then identify the greatest power of each factor that occurs in either expression. The least common multiple is the product of those factors.

3 Lesson Check

Do you know HOW? ERROR INTERVENTION

- If students are unsure how to find restrictions on the variable in Exercises 1–4, have them set the denominator of each rational expression equal to zero. For instance in Exercise 1, solve $3a - 5 = 0$.
- In Exercise 3, be sure that students factor the first denominator before attempting to find the LCD.

Do you UNDERSTAND? ERROR INTERVENTION

- For Exercise 5, remind students that they can multiply a fraction by 1 or any expression that is equivalent to 1.
- If students are struggling with Exercise 6, have them first go back to an example of a numeric fraction.

Close

> **Q** Why should you find the *least* common denominator when adding or subtracting rational expressions? **[Answers may vary. Sample: Any common denominator can be used to add or subtract rational expressions, but using the least common denominator means that fewer factors will be multiplied across or canceled out. This makes the calculation simpler.]**

4 Practice

ASSIGNMENT GUIDE

Basic: 7–14, 17, 18, 23

Average: 7–20, 23

Reasoning exercises have blue headings.

Applications exercises have red headings.

HOMEWORK QUICK CHECK

To check students' understanding of key skills and concepts, go over Exercises 8, 11, 13, 17, and 23.

Focus Question How do you add and subtract rational expressions?

Answer Add and subtract rational expressions just as you would add and subtract fractions. Rewrite the expressions using the LCM of the denominators. Remember to include any restrictions on the variable.

 Lesson Check

Do you know HOW?

Simplify each sum or difference. State any restrictions on the variables.

1. $\frac{a + 11}{3a - 5} + \frac{a - 21}{3a - 5}$

2. $\frac{1}{x^2 - 4} + \frac{6}{x + 2}$

3. $\frac{m}{3m + 6} - \frac{4m}{m + 2}$

4. $\frac{b - 4}{b^2 + 2b - 8} - \frac{b + 2}{b^2 - 16}$

Do you UNDERSTAND?

5. **Open-Ended** Write two rational expressions that simplify to $\frac{x + 1}{x - 5}$.

6. **Writing** Explain how to find the least common multiple of two polynomials.

 Practice and Problem-Solving Exercises

A Practice — Find the least common multiple of each pair of polynomials. ◆ See Problem 1.

> Guided Practice — To start, completely factor each expression.
>
> 7. $9(x + 2)(2x - 1)$ and $3(x + 2)$
>
> $3^2 \cdot (x + 2) \cdot (2x - 1)$ and $3 \cdot (x + 2)$

8. $x^2 - 1$ and $x^2 + 2x + 1$

9. $x^2 - 32x - 10$ and $2x + 10$

Simplify each sum or difference. State any restrictions on the variables. ◆ See Problems 2 and 3.

> Guided Practice — To start, factor the denominators and identify the LCD.
>
> 10. $\frac{5y + 2}{xy^2} + \frac{2x - 4}{4xy}$
>
> $\frac{5y + 2}{x \cdot y^2} + \frac{2x - 4}{4 \cdot x \cdot y}$ The LCD is $4xy^2$.

11. $\frac{d - 3}{2d + 1} + \frac{d - 1}{2d + 1}$

12. $\frac{-2}{x} - \frac{1}{x}$

13. $\frac{-5y}{2y - 1} - \frac{y + 3}{2y - 1}$

14. $\frac{5x}{x^2 - 9} + \frac{2}{x + 4}$

15. $\frac{y}{2y + 4} - \frac{3}{y + 2}$

16. $\frac{x}{3x + 9} - \frac{8}{x^2 + 3x}$

B Apply — Add or subtract. Simplify where possible. State any restrictions on the variables.

17. $\frac{3}{4x} - \frac{2}{x^2}$

18. $\frac{3}{x + 1} + \frac{x}{x - 1}$

19. $\frac{4}{x^2 - 9} + \frac{7}{x + 3}$

20. $\frac{5x}{x^2 - x - 6} - \frac{4}{x^2 + 4x + 4}$

21. $3x + \frac{x^2 + 5x}{x^2 - 2}$

22. $\frac{5y}{y^2 - 7y} - \frac{4}{2y - 14} + \frac{9}{y}$

23. **Writing** Explain how factoring is used when adding or subtracting rational expressions. Include an example in your explanation.

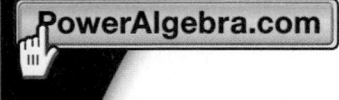

3 Lesson Check

For a digital lesson check, use the Got It questions.

Support in Algebra 2 Companion
- Lesson Check

4 Practice

 Assign homework to individual students or to an entire class.

Answers

1–6. See previous page.

Practice and Problem-Solving Exercises

7. $9(x + 2)(2x - 1)$

8. $(x - 1)(x + 1)^2$

9. $2(x + 5)(x^2 - 32x - 10)$

10. $\frac{xy + 8y + 4}{2xy^2}$; $x \neq 0$, $y \neq 0$

11. $\frac{2(d - 2)}{2d + 1}$; $d \neq -\frac{1}{2}$

12. $\frac{-3}{x}$; $x \neq 0$

13. $\frac{-3(2y + 1)}{2y - 1}$; $y \neq \frac{1}{2}$

14. $\frac{7x^2 + 20x - 18}{(x - 3)(x + 3)(x + 4)}$; $x \neq \pm 3$ or -4

15. $\frac{y - 6}{2(y + 2)}$; $y \neq -2$

16. $\frac{x^2 - 24}{3x(x + 3)}$; $x \neq 0$ or -3

17. $\frac{3x - 8}{4x^2}$; $x \neq 0$

18. $\frac{x^2 + 4x - 3}{(x + 1)(x - 1)}$; $x \neq \pm 1$

19. $\frac{7x - 17}{(x - 3)(x + 3)}$; $x \neq \pm 3$

20. $\frac{5x^2 + 6x + 12}{(x - 3)(x + 2)^2}$; $x \neq 3$ or -2

21. $\frac{x(3x^2 + x - 1)}{x^2 - 2}$; $x \neq \pm \sqrt{2}$

22. $\frac{3(4y - 21)}{y(y - 7)}$; $y \neq 0$ or 7

23. Factoring is used to determine the LCM of the denominators; check students' work.

 **8-5**
PART 2

Adding and Subtracting Rational Expressions

Objective To add and subtract rational expressions

In Part 1 of the lesson, you learned how to add and subtract rational expressions using the LCD.

Connect to What You Know

Here you will use what you learned to simplify complex fractions.

Lesson Vocabulary
• complex fraction

Focus Question What is a complex fraction?

A **complex fraction** is a rational expression that has at least one fraction in its numerator or denominator or both. Here are some examples.

$$\frac{\frac{1}{x} + \frac{1}{y}}{\frac{1}{xy}} \qquad \frac{x+3}{\frac{2}{x-4}} \qquad \frac{\frac{x+3}{x^2-2x+1} + \frac{x}{x^2-3x+2}}{\frac{x}{x^2-4x+4} - \frac{2}{x^2-4}}$$

Sometimes you can simplify a complex fraction by multiplying the numerator and denominator by the LCD of all the rational expressions. Consider a numerical example:

$$\frac{\frac{1}{2} + \frac{2}{3}}{\frac{1}{3}} = \frac{\left(\frac{1}{2} + \frac{2}{3}\right) \cdot 6}{\frac{1}{3} \cdot 6} = \frac{\frac{1}{2} \cdot 6 + \frac{2}{3} \cdot 6}{\frac{1}{3} \cdot 6} = \frac{3+4}{2} = \frac{7}{2}$$

You can also simplify this complex fraction by combining the fractions in the numerator and those in the denominator.

$$\frac{\frac{1}{2} + \frac{2}{3}}{\frac{1}{3}} = \frac{\frac{1}{2} \cdot \frac{3}{3} + \frac{2}{3} \cdot \frac{2}{2}}{\frac{1}{3}} = \frac{\frac{3}{6} + \frac{4}{6}}{\frac{1}{3}} = \frac{\frac{7}{6}}{\frac{1}{3}}$$

Then divide the new numerator by the new denominator.

$$\frac{7}{6} \div \frac{1}{3} = \frac{7}{6} \cdot \frac{3}{1} = \frac{21}{6} = \frac{7}{2}$$

 Hint
To divide a fraction by another fraction, multiply the first fraction by the reciprocal of the second fraction.

1 Launch

CONNECT THE MATH In Part 2, students will simplify complex fractions. They will use the skills they learned in Part 1 to find the LCD and simplify. Two methods will be introduced. One method clears the complex fraction by finding the LCD of all of the rational expressions. The other method simplifies the numerator and denominator separately before multiplying by the reciprocal.

FOCUS QUESTION
How do you simplify $\frac{1}{x} + \frac{x}{y}$?
Q What is the LCD? **[xy]**
Q Rewrite each fraction using the LCD. $\left[\frac{y}{xy} + \frac{x^2}{xy}\right]$
Q What is the simplified form and what are the restrictions? $\left[\frac{x^2 + y}{xy}, x \neq 0, y \neq 0\right]$

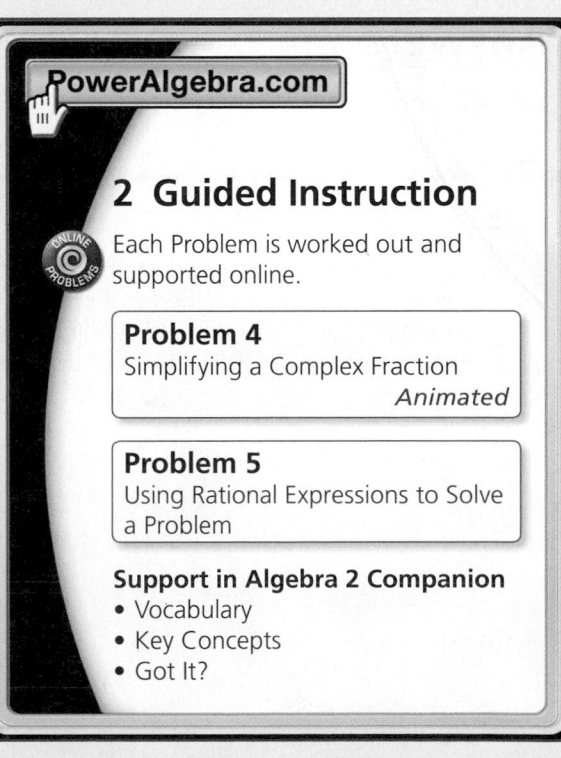

8-5 Preparing to Teach

PART 2

BIG ideas **Function**
        Equivalence   **UbD**

ESSENTIAL UNDERSTANDINGS
• Much of what is true about operating with fractions can be used to operate with rational expressions. Rational expressions can be added or subtracted by first finding a common denominator—preferably the least common multiple (LCM) of the denominators.
• The LCM of denominators is the product of their prime factors, each raised to the greatest power that occurs in any of the expressions.

Math Background
A complex fraction is a rational expression that contains fractions in the numerator and/or denominator. To simplify a complex fraction,
• combine the fractions in the numerator and denominator by finding the common denominator,

• multiply the fraction in the numerator by the reciprocal of the fraction in the denominator, and
• divide out any common factors.

In order for the simplified result to be equivalent to the original form, it is necessary to note which values of x must be excluded from the domain to allow for the simplification.

Support Student Learning
Use the **Algebra 2 Companion** to engage and support students during instruction. See Lesson Resources at the end of this lesson for details.

PowerAlgebra.com

2 Guided Instruction

Each Problem is worked out and supported online.

Problem 4
Simplifying a Complex Fraction
Animated

Problem 5
Using Rational Expressions to Solve a Problem

Support in Algebra 2 Companion
• Vocabulary
• Key Concepts
• Got It?

2 Guided Instruction

Problem 4

Q What is a *reciprocal*? **[Sample: A reciprocal *r* of an expression *a* is defined so that *ra* = 1. Thus, $r = \frac{1}{a}$. You can find the reciprocal of a rational expression by swapping the numerator and denominator.]**

Q Why do you multiply by the reciprocal in Method 2? **[A fraction still represents division. To divide fractions, you multiply the first by the reciprocal of the second.]**

Q Both methods return the same simplified fraction. How are the methods the same? How are they different? **[Answers may vary. Sample: Both methods multiply all the terms by the LCD of all the rational expressions in the complex fraction. The first method does this all at once. The second method does this in separate steps that may allow for simplifying during the multiplication.]**

Q In the second multiplication step of Method 2, do you have to multiply the numerator of the left expression by *y*? Explain. **[No, you do not have to multiply by *y* because it cancels with the *y* in the denominator of the left expression.]**

Got It?

Have students find the answer to each problem using both Method 1 and Method 2.

Q What types of problems do you think Method 1 is better for? Method 2? **[Answers may vary. Sample: Method 1 is better when the LCM has fewer factors; Method 2 is better for more complicated problems.]**

Think

What is the LCD of $\frac{1}{x}$, $\frac{x}{y}$, and $\frac{1}{y}$?

The LCD of the rational expressions is *xy*.

 Problem 4 Simplifying a Complex Fraction

What is the simplest form of the complex fraction? $\dfrac{\frac{1}{x} + \frac{x}{y}}{\frac{1}{y} + 1}$

Method 1 Multiply both the numerator and the denominator by the LCD of all the rational expressions and simplify the result.

Multiply the numerator and the denominator by *xy*.
$$\frac{\frac{1}{x} + \frac{x}{y}}{\frac{1}{y} + 1} = \frac{\left(\frac{1}{x} + \frac{x}{y}\right) \cdot xy}{\left(\frac{1}{y} + 1\right) \cdot xy}$$

Use the Distributive Property.
$$= \frac{\frac{1}{x} \cdot xy + \frac{x}{y} \cdot xy}{\frac{1}{y} \cdot xy + 1 \cdot xy}$$

Simplify.
$$= \frac{y + x^2}{x + xy}$$

Method 2 Combine the expressions in the numerator and those in the denominator. Then multiply the new numerator by the reciprocal of the new denominator.

Write equivalent expressions with common denominators.
$$\frac{\frac{1}{x} + \frac{x}{y}}{\frac{1}{y} + 1} = \frac{\frac{1}{x} \cdot \frac{y}{y} + \frac{x}{y} \cdot \frac{x}{x}}{\frac{1}{y} + 1 \cdot \frac{y}{y}}$$

> The LCD of the fractions in the numerator is *xy*.

Multiply.
$$= \frac{\frac{y}{xy} + \frac{x^2}{xy}}{\frac{1}{y} + \frac{y}{y}}$$

> The LCD of the fractions in the denominator is *y*.

Add.
$$= \frac{\frac{y + x^2}{xy}}{\frac{1 + y}{y}}$$

Divide the numerator fraction by the denominator fraction.
$$= \frac{y + x^2}{xy} \div \frac{1 + y}{y}$$

Multiply by the reciprocal.
$$= \frac{y + x^2}{xy} \cdot \frac{y}{1 + y}$$

Divide out the common factor, *y*.
$$= \frac{\cancel{y}(y + x^2)}{x\cancel{y}(1 + y)}$$

Simplify.
$$= \frac{y + x^2}{x(1 + y)}$$

Use the Distributive Property.
$$= \frac{y + x^2}{x + xy}$$

✓ **Got It?** 4. What is the simplest form of the complex fraction?

a. $\dfrac{x}{\frac{1}{x} + \frac{1}{y}}$

b. $\dfrac{\frac{x-2}{x} + \frac{2}{x+1}}{\frac{3}{x-1} - \frac{1}{x+1}}$

c. **Reasoning** Which method from Problem 4 is easier to use? Explain.

Answers

Got It? (continued)

4. a. $\dfrac{x^2 y}{x + y}$

b. $\dfrac{(x - 1)^2}{2x}$

c. Answers may vary. Samples: Method 1; it requires fewer steps. Method 2; it is easier to simplify the numerator and denominator separately.

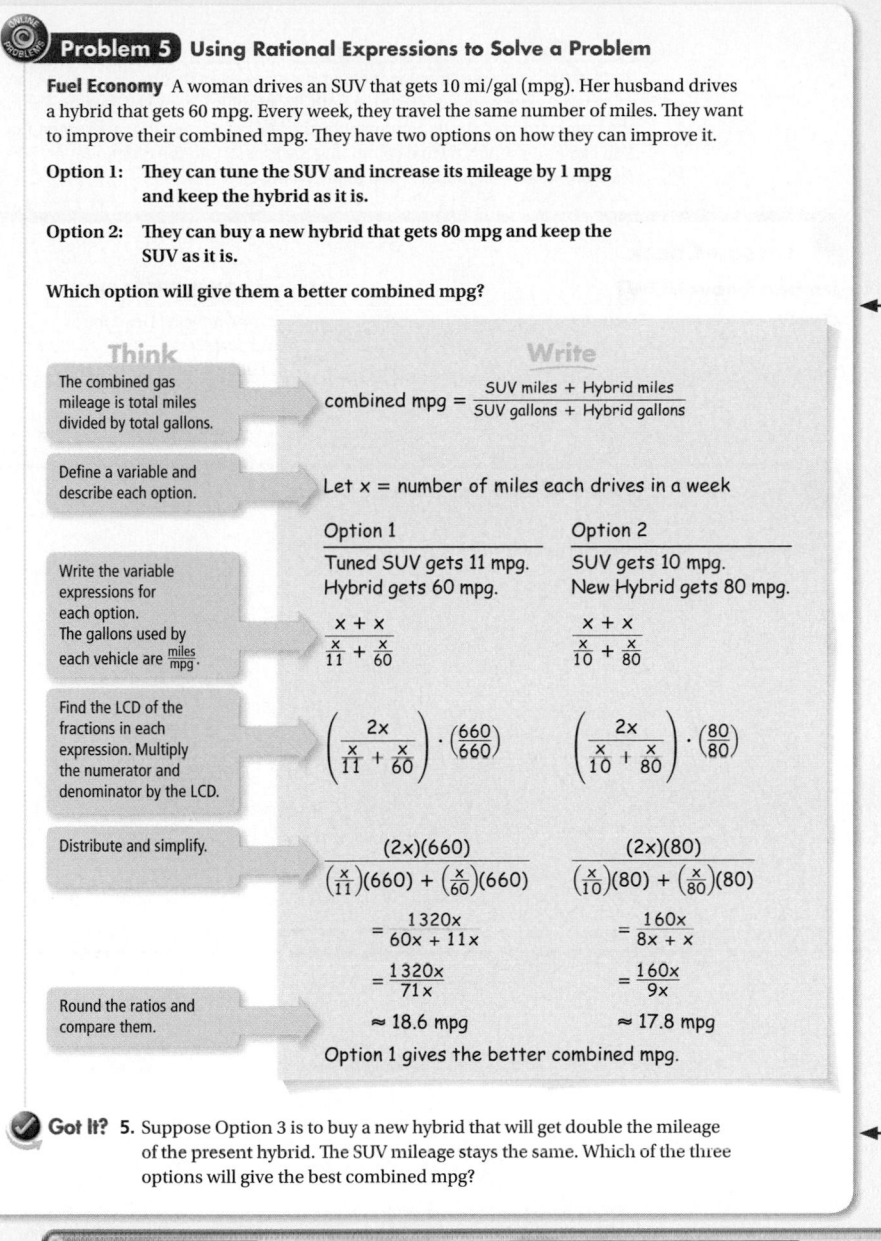

Problem 5 Using Rational Expressions to Solve a Problem

Fuel Economy A woman drives an SUV that gets 10 mi/gal (mpg). Her husband drives a hybrid that gets 60 mpg. Every week, they travel the same number of miles. They want to improve their combined mpg. They have two options on how they can improve it.

Option 1: They can tune the SUV and increase its mileage by 1 mpg and keep the hybrid as it is.

Option 2: They can buy a new hybrid that gets 80 mpg and keep the SUV as it is.

Which option will give them a better combined mpg?

Think

The combined gas mileage is total miles divided by total gallons.

Define a variable and describe each option.

Write the variable expressions for each option. The gallons used by each vehicle are $\frac{miles}{mpg}$.

Find the LCD of the fractions in each expression. Multiply the numerator and denominator by the LCD.

Distribute and simplify.

Round the ratios and compare them.

Write

$$\text{combined mpg} = \frac{\text{SUV miles} + \text{Hybrid miles}}{\text{SUV gallons} + \text{Hybrid gallons}}$$

Let x = number of miles each drives in a week

Option 1	Option 2
Tuned SUV gets 11 mpg. Hybrid gets 60 mpg.	SUV gets 10 mpg. New Hybrid gets 80 mpg.

$$\frac{x + x}{\frac{x}{11} + \frac{x}{60}} \qquad \frac{x + x}{\frac{x}{10} + \frac{x}{80}}$$

$$\left(\frac{2x}{\frac{x}{11} + \frac{x}{60}}\right) \cdot \left(\frac{660}{660}\right) \qquad \left(\frac{2x}{\frac{x}{10} + \frac{x}{80}}\right) \cdot \left(\frac{80}{80}\right)$$

$$\frac{(2x)(660)}{\left(\frac{x}{11}\right)(660) + \left(\frac{x}{60}\right)(660)} \qquad \frac{(2x)(80)}{\left(\frac{x}{10}\right)(80) + \left(\frac{x}{80}\right)(80)}$$

$$= \frac{1320x}{60x + 11x} \qquad = \frac{160x}{8x + x}$$

$$= \frac{1320x}{71x} \qquad = \frac{160x}{9x}$$

$$\approx 18.6 \text{ mpg} \qquad \approx 17.8 \text{ mpg}$$

Option 1 gives the better combined mpg.

✓ **Got It?** 5. Suppose Option 3 is to buy a new hybrid that will get double the mileage of the present hybrid. The SUV mileage stays the same. Which of the three options will give the best combined mpg?

PowerAlgebra.com | Lesson 8-5 Adding and Subtracting Rational Expressions | 561

Problem 5   ERROR PREVENTION

Students often think that averaging the two rates provides the solution. Help students to focus on the ratio of *total* miles to *total* gallons.

Q An increase from 10 mpg to 11 mpg is what percent increase? from 60 mpg to 80 mpg? **[10%; 33%]**

Q For any distance, *x*, that the SUV and hybrid both drive, what fraction of the total gallons goes to the SUV? to the hybrid? **[$\frac{6}{7}$; $\frac{1}{7}$]**

Q Why does Option 1 result in a better combined mpg than Option 2? **[Answers may vary. Sample: The SUV uses so much more gasoline than the hybrid that increasing the efficiency of the hybrid by 33% does not have as great an effect on the combined mpg as increasing the efficiency of the SUV by 10%.]**

                    EXTENSION

Q What is the combined mpg before any change to the vehicles is made? **[17.1 mpg]**

Got It?

Q What rational expression represents Option 3? $\left[\frac{x + x}{\frac{x}{10} + \frac{x}{120}}\right]$

Additional Problems

4. What is a simpler form of $\dfrac{3x - \dfrac{1}{y}}{\dfrac{y^2}{x} + x}$?

ANSWER $\dfrac{3x^2y - x}{x^2y + y^2}$

5. Your Internet connection has a download speed of 1400 kilobytes per second (kb/s) and an upload speed of 350 kb/s. If you download a picture to your computer and then upload the same picture to your blog, what is the combined rate for the entire process?

ANSWER 560 kb/s

Answers

Got It? (continued)

5. Option 1 still gives the better combined mpg since Option 3 gives 18.46 mpg.

3 Lesson Check

Do you know HOW? ERROR INTERVENTION
- For Exercises 2–4, remind students to factor to find the LCD.

Do you UNDERSTAND? ERROR INTERVENTION
- If students have trouble identifying the error in Exercise 3, have them perform the steps in Method 2 of Problem 4 in the lesson.

Close

> **Q** What are two different methods for simplifying complex fractions? **[Method 1: Clear all the fractions in the numerator and denominator by multiplying the numerator and denominator by the LCD of all of the rational expressions. Method 2: Combine expressions in the numerator and denominator separately and then divide by multiplying by the reciprocal of the denominator.]**

Focus Question What is a complex fraction?

Answer A complex fraction is a rational expression that has at least one fraction in its numerator or denominator or both. To simplify a complex fraction, multiply the numerator and the denominator by the LCD of all the rational expressions. You can also simplify by first combining the fractions in the numerator and the fractions in the denominator and then dividing.

Lesson Check

Do you know HOW?

Simplify each complex fraction.

1. $\dfrac{\frac{1}{x}}{\frac{2}{y}}$

2. $\dfrac{\frac{1}{3}}{\frac{3}{b}}$

Do you UNDERSTAND?

3. **Error Analysis** Describe and correct the error made in simplifying the complex fraction.

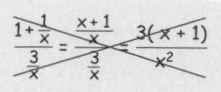

Practice and Problem-Solving Exercises

A Practice   Simplify each complex fraction.   ⬅ See Problem 4.

Guided Practice

To start, multiply the numerator and the denominator by the LCD of all the rational expressions.

4. $\dfrac{1 - \frac{1}{4}}{2 - \frac{3}{5}}$

$\dfrac{\left(1 - \frac{1}{4}\right) \cdot 20}{\left(2 - \frac{3}{5}\right) \cdot 20}$

5. $\dfrac{\frac{2}{x+y}}{3}$

6. $\dfrac{\frac{-2}{x}}{\frac{2}{x}}$

7. $\dfrac{1}{1 + \frac{x}{y}}$

8. $\dfrac{3}{\frac{2}{x} + y}$

9. $\dfrac{\frac{2}{x+y}}{\frac{5}{x+y}}$

10. $\dfrac{12}{\frac{3}{x} + \frac{6}{y}}$

11. $\dfrac{-3}{\frac{5}{x} + y}$

12. $\dfrac{\frac{3}{x-4}}{1 - \frac{2}{x-4}}$

13. $\dfrac{\frac{2}{x+4} + 2}{1 + \frac{3}{x+4}}$

3 Lesson Check

For a digital lesson check, use the Got It questions.

Support in Algebra 2 Companion
- Lesson Check

4 Practice

Assign homework to individual students or to an entire class.

Answers

Lesson Check

1. $\dfrac{y}{2x}$

2. $\dfrac{b}{9}$

3. error in dividing by the common denominator:

$$\dfrac{1 + \frac{1}{x}}{\frac{3}{x}} = \dfrac{\frac{x+1}{x}}{\frac{3}{x}}$$

$$= \dfrac{x+1}{x} \cdot \dfrac{x}{3}$$

$$= \dfrac{x+1}{3}$$

Practice and Problem-Solving Exercises

4. $\dfrac{15}{28}$

5. $\dfrac{2}{3(x+y)}$

6. -1

7. $\dfrac{y}{x+y}$

8. $\dfrac{3x}{2 + xy}$

9. $\dfrac{2}{5}$

10. $\dfrac{4xy}{2x + y}$

11. $\dfrac{-3x}{5 + xy}$

12. $\dfrac{3}{x-6}$

13. $\dfrac{2(x+5)}{x+7}$

14. Your car gets 25 mi/gal around town and 30 mi/gal on the highway.  See Problem 5.

    a. If 50% of the miles you drive are on the highway and 50% are around town, what is your overall average miles per gallon?

    b. If 60% of the miles you drive are on the highway and 40% are around town, what is your overall average miles per gallon?

B Apply

15. Think About a Plan For the image of the overhead projector to be in focus, the distance d_i from the projector lens to the image, the projector lens focal length f, and the distance d_o from the transparency to the projector lens must satisfy the thin-lens equation $\frac{1}{f} = \frac{1}{d_i} + \frac{1}{d_o}$. What is the focal length of the projector lens if the transparency placed 4 in. from the projector lens is in focus on the screen located 8 ft from the projector lens?

- Can you write the equation for the unknown variable?
- What units would you use for the focal length of the lens?

16. Optics To read small font, you use a magnifying lens with the focal length 3 in. How far from the magnifying lens should you place the page if you want to hold the lens at 1 foot from your eyes? Use the thin-lens equation from Exercise 15.

Simplify each sum or difference. State any restrictions on the variables.

17. $\dfrac{-3x}{x^2 - 9} + \dfrac{4}{2x - 6}$

18. $\dfrac{5x}{x^2 - x - 6} + \dfrac{4}{x^2 + 4x + 4}$

19. $\dfrac{2x}{x^2 - x - 2} - \dfrac{4x}{x^2 - 3x + 2}$

20. Open-Ended Write two complex fractions that simplify to $\dfrac{x - 2}{x + 4}$.

Simplify each complex fraction.

21. $\dfrac{\frac{2}{x} + \frac{3}{y}}{\frac{-5}{x} + \frac{7}{y}}$

22. $\dfrac{1 + \frac{2}{x}}{2 + \frac{3}{2x}}$

23. $\dfrac{\frac{1}{xy} - \frac{1}{y^2}}{\frac{1}{x^2 y} - \frac{1}{xy^2}}$

24. Harmony The harmonic mean of two numbers a and b equals $\dfrac{2}{\frac{1}{a} + \frac{1}{b}}$. As you vary the length of a violin or guitar string, its pitch changes. If a full-length string is 1 unit long, then many lengths that are simple fractions produce pitches that harmonize, or sound pleasing together. The harmonic mean relates two lengths that produce harmonious sounds. Find the harmonic mean for each pair of string lengths.

    a. 1 and $\frac{1}{2}$

    b. $\frac{3}{4}$ and $\frac{1}{2}$

    c. $\frac{3}{4}$ and $\frac{3}{5}$

    d. $\frac{1}{2}$ and $\frac{1}{4}$

Hint Remember that for $b \neq 0$, $\frac{1}{b}$ is the reciprocal of b. So, if $b = \frac{3}{4}$, then $\frac{1}{b} = \frac{4}{3}$.

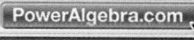
---

14. a. $27.\overline{27}$ mi/gal

    b. $27.\overline{7}$ mi/gal

15. 3.84 in.

16. 4 in.

17. $\dfrac{-x + 6}{(x - 3)(x + 3)}; x \neq \pm 3$

18. $\dfrac{5x^2 + 14x - 12}{(x - 3)(x + 2)^2}; x \neq 3$ or -2

19. $\dfrac{-2x(x + 3)}{(x - 2)(x - 1)(x + 1)}; x \neq \pm 1$ or 2

20. Check students' work.

21. $\dfrac{3x + 2y}{7x - 5y}$

22. $\dfrac{2(x + 2)}{4x + 3}$

23. x

24. a. $\frac{2}{3}$

    b. $\frac{3}{5}$

    c. $\frac{2}{3}$

    d. $\frac{1}{3}$

4 Practice

ASSIGNMENT GUIDE

Basic: 4–10, 14–16

Average: 4–18, 21, 22, 24

Standardized Test Prep: 25–29

Mixed Review: 30–41

Reasoning exercises have blue headings.

Applications exercises have red headings.

EXERCISE 16: Use the Think About a Plan worksheet in the **Student Companion** (also available in the Teaching Resources in print and online) to further support students' development in becoming independent learners.

HOMEWORK QUICK CHECK

To check students' understanding of key skills and concepts, go over Exercises 6, 8, 14, 15, and 16.

Answers

Standardized Test Prep

25. C

26. G

27. A

28. F

29. [2] First factor both denominators:
$$x^2 - 5x - 6 = (x - 6)(x + 1)$$
$$x^2 - 12x + 36 = (x - 6)^2$$
The LCD would have to include the factors $(x - 6)$, $(x + 1)$ and $(x - 6)^2$, so the LCD is $(x - 6)^2(x + 1)$.

[1] correct LCD, without work shown

Mixed Review

30. $\dfrac{12x}{x + 3}$; $x \neq 2$ or ± 3

31. $\dfrac{3(x + 2)}{4(x - 3)}$; $x \neq \pm 2$ or 3

32. $\dfrac{3(x + 1)}{2(x + 3)}$; $x \neq \pm 1$ or -3

33. $\log_3 yt^4$

34. $\log p^7 q^2$

35. $\log_5 \dfrac{x}{\sqrt[5]{y}}$

36. 30

37. 82

38. $\dfrac{15}{4}$

39. $-\dfrac{4}{5}$

40. 21

41. 18

SAT/ACT

25. Which expression equals $\dfrac{5x}{x^2 - 9} - \dfrac{4x}{x^2 + 5x + 6}$?

  Ⓐ $\dfrac{7x}{(x - 3)(x + 3)(x + 2)}$ Ⓒ $\dfrac{x^2 + 22x}{(x - 3)(x + 3)(x + 2)}$

  Ⓑ $\dfrac{x^2 - 2x}{(x - 3)(x + 3)(x + 2)}$ Ⓓ $\dfrac{9x^2 - 2x}{(x - 3)(x + 3)(x + 2)}$

26. Which of the relationships is represented by the graph at the right?

  Ⓕ $y = \log_4(x - 1) + 5$

  Ⓖ $y = \log_4(x - 1) - 2$

  Ⓗ $y = \log_4(x + 2) - 2$

  Ⓘ $y = \log_4(x - 1) - 1$

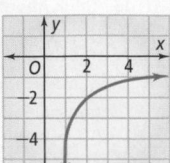

27. What is the simpler form of $\dfrac{\frac{2}{x} - 5}{\frac{6}{x} - 3}$?

  Ⓐ $\dfrac{2 - 5x}{6 - 3x}$ Ⓑ $\dfrac{2 + 5x}{6 - 3x}$ Ⓒ $\dfrac{2x - 5}{6x + 3}$ Ⓓ $\dfrac{6 + 3x}{2 - 5x}$

28. What word makes the statement "The domain and range of a(n) _____ function is the set of all real numbers" *sometimes* true?

  Ⓕ polynomial   Ⓗ exponential

  Ⓖ logarithmic   Ⓘ quadratic

Short Response

29. What is the least common denominator for the rational expressions $\dfrac{1}{x^2 - 5x - 6}$ and $\dfrac{1}{x^2 - 12x + 36}$? Show your work.

Mixed Review

Divide. State any restrictions on the variable.   ◀ See Lesson 8-4.

30. $\dfrac{3x^2 - 9x}{x - 2} \div \dfrac{x^2 - 9}{4x - 8}$ **31.** $\dfrac{3x - 6}{12x - 24} \div \dfrac{x^2 - 5x + 6}{3x^2 - 12}$ **32.** $\dfrac{5x + 15}{10x - 10} \div \dfrac{x^2 + 6x + 9}{3x^2 - 3}$

Write each logarithmic expression as a single logarithm.   ◀ See Lesson 7-4.

33. $\log_3 y + 4 \log_3 t$ **34.** $7 \log p + 2 \log q$ **35.** $\log_5 x - \dfrac{1}{5} \log_5 y$

Let $f(x) = x^2 + 1$ and $g(x) = 3x$. Evaluate each expression.   ◀ See Lesson 6-6.

36. $(g \circ f)(-3)$ **37.** $(f \circ g)(-3)$ **38.** $(g \circ f)\left(\dfrac{1}{2}\right)$

Get Ready!   To prepare for Lesson 8-6, do Exercises 39–41.

Solve each equation. Check your answers.   ◀ See Lesson 1-4.

39. $-3(x - 4) = 2(x + 8)$ **40.** $0.2(x + 8) - 3.4 = 2.4$ **41.** $\dfrac{x}{2} + \dfrac{x}{3} = 15$

Additional Instructional Support

Algebra 2 Companion

Students can use the **Algebra 2 Companion** worktext (4 pages) as you teach the lesson. Use the Companion to support

- New Vocabulary
- Key Concepts
- Got It for each Problem
- Lesson Check

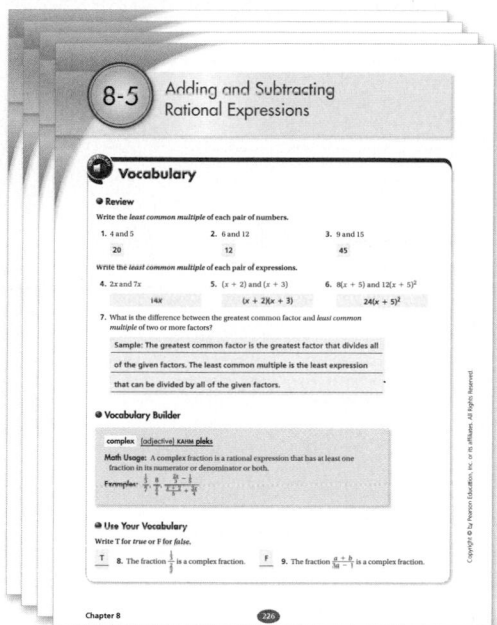

ELL Support

Focus on Language Pick up two common classroom objects, such as a pen and pencil. "What do these objects have *in common*?" Pick another pair of objects and ask the same question. Bring out the idea that two objects have something *in common* because they share something; because there is something both objects have. Have students write two simple quadratic expressions on separate index cards or small pieces of paper. Encourage them to make their quadratics by multiplying factors with ±1, ±2, and ±3. Have them trade one card with a neighbor. "Each of these quadratic expressions is made up of two factors. Examine your expressions. Do they contain any *common* factors? Are there any factors that both expressions have?" Allow students to show their expressions and common factors. Have them write the LCM of the two expressions. Tell them the LCM will have each of its factors in common with at least one expression.

5 Assess & Remediate

Lesson Quiz

1. What is the LCM of $8x - 24$ and $2(x^2 - 6x + 9)$?

2. What is the sum $\frac{x}{x + 3} + \frac{7x + 6}{x^2 + x - 6}$ in simplest form? State any restrictions on the variable.

3. What is the difference $\frac{x + 2}{x^2 + 4x - 5} - \frac{3}{x^2 + 6x + 5}$ in simplest form? State any restrictions on the variable.

4. What is a simpler form of $\dfrac{y}{\frac{1}{xy} + 1}$?

5. **Do you UNDERSTAND?** Your friend flew to Miami in a plane that averaged 600 mi/h. She drove back home, averaging 50 mi/h. What is her average speed in miles per hour for the whole trip? Assume the distances by plane and car are equal.

ANSWERS TO LESSON QUIZ

1. $8(x - 3)^2$
2. $\dfrac{x + 2}{x - 2}$; $x \neq 2$, $x \neq -3$
3. $\dfrac{x^2 + 5}{(x - 1)(x + 1)(x + 5)}$; $x \neq 1$, $x \neq -1$, $x \neq -5$
4. $\dfrac{xy^2}{1 + xy}$
5. about 92 mi/h

PRESCRIPTION FOR REMEDIATION
Use the student work on the Lesson Quiz to prescribe a differentiated review assignment:

Points	Differentiated Remediation
0–2	Intervention
3–4	On-level
5	Extension

PowerAlgebra.com

5 Assess & Remediate

Assign the Lesson Quiz. Appropriate intervention, practice, or enrichment is automatically generated based on student performance.

Intervention

- **Reteaching** (2 pages) Provides reteaching and practice exercises for the key lesson concepts. Use with struggling students or absent students.
- **English Language Learner Support** Helps students develop and reinforce mathematical vocabulary and key concepts.

All-in-One Resources/Online
Reteaching

All-in-One Resources/Online
English Language Learner Support

Differentiated Remediation *continued*

On-Level

- **Practice** (2 pages) Provides extra practice for each lesson. For more challenging practice exercises, use the Form G Practice pages found in the All-in-One Teaching Resources and online.

- **Think About a Plan** Helps students develop specific problem-solving skills and strategies by providing scaffolded guiding questions.

- **Standardized Test Prep** Focuses on all major exercises, all major question types, and helps students prepare for the high-stakes assessments.

Extension

- **Enrichment** Provides students with interesting problems and activities that extend the concepts of the lesson.

- **Activities, Games, and Puzzles** Worksheets that can be used for concepts development, enrichment, and for fun!

Student Companion/ All-in-One Resources/Online
Practice page 1

8-5 **Practice** *Form K*
Adding and Subtracting Rational Expressions

Find the least common multiple of each pair of polynomials.

To start, completely factor each expression.

1. $4x^2 - 36$ and $6x^2 + 36x + 54$ 2. $(x - 2)(x + 3)$ and $10(x + 3)^2$

$(2)(2)(x - 3)(x + 3)$ and $(2)(3)(x + 3)(x + 3)$ $10(x - 2)(x + 3)^2$

$12(x - 3)(x + 3)$

Simplify each sum or difference. State any restrictions on the variables.

To start, factor the denominators and identify the LCD.

3. $\frac{6x - 1}{x^2y} + \frac{3y + 2}{2xy}$ 4. $\frac{1}{x^2 - 4x - 12} - \frac{3x}{4x + 8}$ 5. $\frac{2x}{x^2 + 5x + 4} + \frac{2x}{3x + 3}$

Add or subtract. Simplify where possible. State any restrictions on the variables.

6. $\frac{x + 2}{x - 1} + \frac{x - 3}{2x + 1}$ 7. $\frac{x}{x^2 - x} + \frac{1}{x}$ 8. $4y - \frac{y + 2}{3y}$

9. **Error Analysis** A classmate said that the sum of $\frac{4}{x^2 - 9}$ and $\frac{7}{x + 3}$ is $\frac{7x + 25}{x^2 - 9}$.
What mistake did your classmate make? What is the correct sum?

Student Companion/ All-in-One Resources/Online
Think About a Plan

8-5 **Think About a Plan**
Adding and Subtracting Rational Expressions

Optics To read small font, you use the magnifying lens with the focal length 3 in. How far from the magnifying lens should you place the page if you want to hold the lens at 1 foot from your eyes? Use the thin-lens equation.

Know

1. The focal length of the magnifying lens is ____3 in.____

2. The distance from the lens to your eyes is ____12 in.____

3. The thin-lens equation is $\frac{1}{f} = \frac{1}{d_i} + \frac{1}{d_o}$.

Need

4. To solve the problem I need to find:
the distance from the page to the lens

Plan

5. What are the known variables in the thin-lens equation?
f is the focal length of the lens, or 3 in.; d_i is the distance from the lens to the eyes, or 12 in.

6. Solve the thin-lens equation for the unknown variable. $d_o = \frac{fd_i}{d_i - f}$

7. Substitute the known values into your equation and solve. $d_o = \frac{fd_i}{d_i - f} = \frac{3 \cdot 12}{12 - 3} = \frac{36}{9} = 4$

8. How far from the page should you hold the magnifying lens? 4 in.

Student Companion/ All-in-One Resources/Online
Practice page 2

8-5 **Practice** (continued) *Form K*
Adding and Subtracting Rational Expressions

Simplify each complex fraction.

To start, multiply the numerator and the denominator by the LCD of all the rational expressions.

10.   11.   12.

13. **Reasoning** What real numbers are not in the domain of the function $f(x)$?
Explain.
$x \neq -2, -3, -4$; any of these values of x create an undefined denominator, so they are not in the domain of the function.

14. If you jog 12 mi at an average rate of 4 mi/h and walk the same route back at an average rate of 3 mi/h, you have traveled 24 mi in 7 h and your overall rate is $\frac{24}{7}$ mi/h. What is your overall average rate if you travel d mi at 3 mi/h and d mi at 4 mi/h?

15. **Multiple Choice** Simplify. A

Student Companion/ All-in-One Resources/Online
Standardized Test Prep

8-5 **Standardized Test Prep**
Adding and Subtracting Rational Expressions

Multiple Choice

For Exercises 1–4, choose the correct letter.

1. Which is the least common denominator of fractions that have denominators $5x + 10$ and $25x^2 - 100$? C
   - Ⓐ $5(x - 2)$
   - Ⓒ $25(x^2 - 4)$
   - Ⓑ $5(x^2 - 20)$
   - Ⓓ $75(x + 2)(x^2 - 4)$

2. Which expression equals? G

3. Which expression equals $\frac{4}{x^2 - 3x} + \frac{6}{3x - 9}$? A

4. The harmonic mean of two numbers a and b equals $\frac{2}{\frac{1}{a} + \frac{1}{b}}$. Which expression equals the harmonic mean of x and $x + 1$? I

Short Response

5. Subtract $3 - \frac{1}{x^2 + 5}$. Write your answer in simplest form. State any restrictions on the variable. Show your work.

All-in-One Resources/Online
Enrichment

8-5 **Enrichment**
Adding and Subtracting Rational Expressions

The Superposition Principle

The illumination received from a light source is given by the formula

$$I = S \cdot D^{-2} \text{ or } I = \frac{S}{D^2}$$

where I is the illumination at a certain point, S is the strength of the light source, measured in watts or kilowatts, and D is the distance of the point from the light source. The superposition principle states that the total illumination received at a given point is equal to the sum of the illuminations from each of the sources.

Suppose a plant is positioned at point A. Copy and complete the following to find the total illumination received by the plant when both lights are on.

L1 = 100 W   2 m   A   3 m   L2 = 200 W

$I_{total} = I_{L1} + I_{L2}$
$= \frac{100}{2^2} + \frac{200}{3^2}$
$= 25 + 22.2$
$= 47.2$ Round to the nearest tenth.

1. The amount of illumination received by the plant is ___about 47.2 watts/m²___

Lighthouse A contains a 10-kW light and is located on the shore of the ocean. Lighthouse B contains a 20-kW light and is located 8 km out to sea from a point 6 km down the beach from Lighthouse A.

2. A man is walking down the beach away from lighthouse A and toward point C. When he is x kilometers away from lighthouse A, what illumination does he receive as a function of x before he reaches point C?

3. Now suppose that the man is x kilometers beyond point C as he walks down the beach. What illumination does he receive as a function of x?

Online Teacher Resource Center
Activities, Games, and Puzzles

8-5 **Activity: Graphing Calculator Check**
Adding and Subtracting Rational Expressions

This activity can be done in groups of two or three students. Discuss each group's results once everyone is finished.

Example: Use your graphing calculator to add the following rational expressions.
$\frac{x}{x + 4} + \frac{3}{x - 3}$

Step 1   Enter $Y_1 = \frac{x}{x + 4}$ Turn on the Y_1 function *only*. (You switch a function on or off by moving the cursor over the equals sign and pressing

Step 2   Enter $Y_2 = \frac{3}{x - 3}$ ENTER. A highlighted equals sign means that a function is

Step 3   Enter $Y_3 = Y_1 + Y_2$ turned on.) Graph Y_3 (see Figures 1 and 2).

Step 4   Add $\frac{x}{x + 4} + \frac{3}{x - 3} = \frac{x(x - 3)}{(x + 4)(x - 3)} + \frac{3(x + 4)}{(x - 3)(x + 4)}$
$= \frac{(x^2 - 3x) + (3x + 12)}{(x + 4)(x - 3)}$
$= \frac{x^2 + 12}{(x + 4)(x - 3)}$

Step 5   On another calculator; have a classmate enter $Y_4 = \frac{x^2 + 12}{(x + 4)(x - 3)}$
(see Figures 3 and 4).

Since these graphs coincide, you can conclude the addition was performed correctly.

Figure 1   Figure 2   Figure 3   Figure 4

Repeat this process for the following expressions.

1. $\frac{2}{x + 3} - \frac{2}{x - 3}$ 2. $\frac{2}{x - 2} - \frac{2}{x + 2}$

3. $\frac{1}{x^2 - 4x} + \frac{1}{x^2 - 16}$ 4. $\frac{10}{x^2 - 2x - 10} - \frac{10}{x^2 + 3x - 10}$

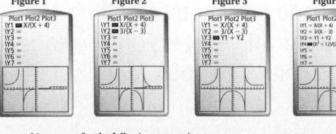

8-6 Solving Rational Equations

Objectives To solve rational equations
To use rational equations to solve problems

A straight path is the shortest distance between two points.

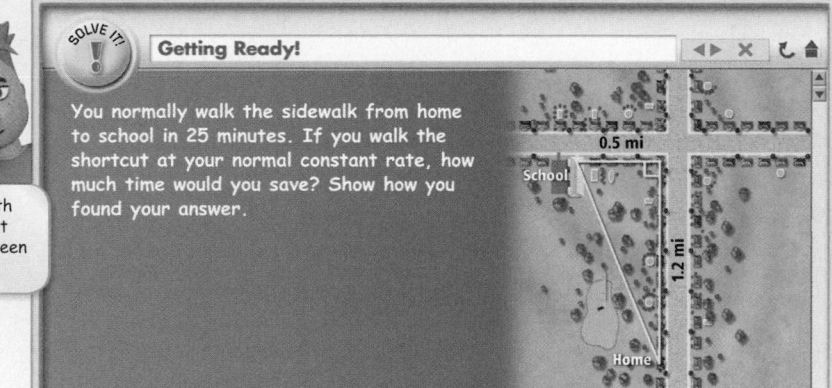

SOLVE IT!

Getting Ready!

You normally walk the sidewalk from home to school in 25 minutes. If you walk the shortcut at your normal constant rate, how much time would you save? Show how you found your answer.

0.5 mi
School
1.2 mi
Home

Lesson Vocabulary
• rational equation

Sometimes you can solve a problem using a proportion—an equation involving two rational expressions set equal to each other.

Focus Question How is solving a rational equation similar to solving a polynomial equation?

A **rational equation** contains at least one rational expression. You can make it easier to solve a rational equation if you first clear the equation of denominators. Multiply each side of the equation by the LCD of the rational expressions in the equation.

Rational Equation	**Not a Rational Equation**
$\dfrac{x}{x+1} + \dfrac{x}{x-1} = \dfrac{2}{x^2-1}$	$x + \dfrac{1}{2} = \dfrac{2}{3}$

Hint

Recall that an extraneous solution is a solution of the derived equation, but not a solution of the original equation.

Any time you multiply each side of an equation by an algebraic expression, it is possible to introduce extraneous solutions. You must check all solutions in the original equation to confirm that they are indeed solutions.

Solve It!

PURPOSE To use proportions to determine an unknown

PROCESS Students may
• use the Pythagorean Theorem to determine the length of the shortcut.
• use a proportion to find the time on the shorter route.

FACILITATE

Q How can you find the new distance? **[Use the Pythagorean Theorem.]**

Q Is it possible to find the constant rate of walking from the information given? Explain. **[Yes; to find a rate you need the number of minutes it takes to go a certain distance. It takes 25 minutes to walk along 1.7 miles, so the rate is $\frac{1.7 \text{ mi}}{25 \text{ min}}$, which is about 0.068 mi/min.]**

Q What information is needed to find the amount of time saved by the shortcut? Explain how to find this information. **[Sample: The length of the shortcut and the rate you walk; divide the length of the shortcut by the rate and subtract the result from 25 min.]**

ANSWER See Solve It in Answers on next page.

CONNECT THE MATH Students use proportions to answer the question in the Solve It. In this lesson students use proportions and the LCD to solve rational equations.

8-6 Preparing to Teach

BIG idea Equivalence   **UbD**

ESSENTIAL UNDERSTANDING
• Solving an equation containing rational expressions begins by multiplying each side by the least common denominator of the rational expressions. Doing this, however, can introduce extraneous solutions.

Math Background

Rational equations contain at least one variable in the denominator, so they cannot always be solved simply by using inverse operations to isolate the variable.

When solving a rational equation algebraically, one method is to eliminate all denominators in order to solve.
• Factor the denominators to find the LCD.
• Multiply both sides of the equation by the LCD eliminates the denominators.
• Simplify and solve.

Rational equations can also be solved with a graphing calculator.
• Graph each side of the equation as a separate function.
• Identify the intersection. This may be done visually on the graph or by looking at the table of values and finding each x-value that makes the functions equal, or by using the intersect feature in the CALC menu of a graphing calculator.

Support Student Learning

Use the **Algebra 2 Companion** to engage and support students during instruction. See Lesson Resources at the end of this lesson for details.

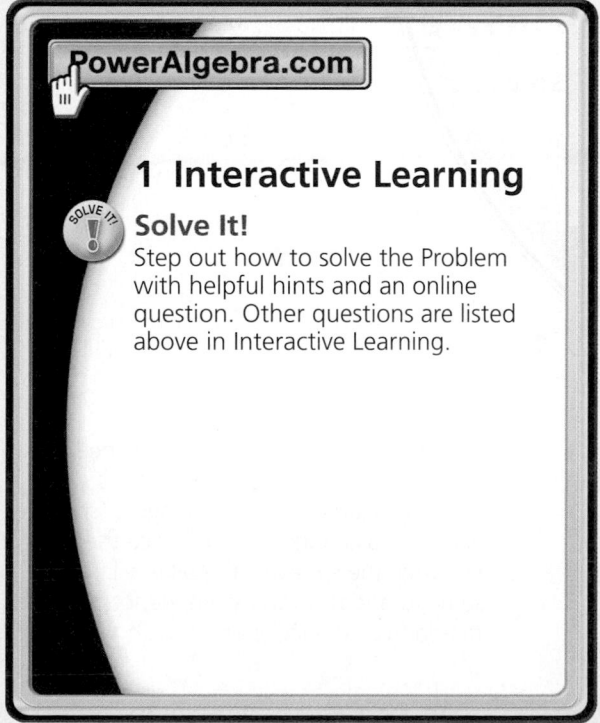

PowerAlgebra.com

1 Interactive Learning

SOLVE IT!

Solve It!

Step out how to solve the Problem with helpful hints and an online question. Other questions are listed above in Interactive Learning.

2 Guided Instruction

Problem 1

> **Q** What are the restrictions on the variable in 1A? 1B? Explain. **[The denominators cannot be 0. For 1A, x cannot be 3 or -3. For 1B, x cannot be -1 or -2.]**
>
> **Q** How is solving a rational equation similar to adding rational expressions? How is it different? **[Both require the use of the LCD. When solving an equation, you use the LCD to remove denominators. When you add rational expressions, you use the LCD to get a common denominator.]**
>
> **Q** How can you use the methods for adding rational expressions to solve 1A? **[Multiply each fraction on the left by a ratio equal to 1, simplify, and combine terms:**
> $$\frac{x}{x-3} \cdot \left(\frac{x+3}{x+3}\right) + \frac{x}{x+3} \cdot \left(\frac{x-3}{x-3}\right) = \frac{2}{x^2-9}$$
> $$\frac{x^2+3x}{x^2-9} + \frac{x^2-3x}{x^2-9} = \frac{2}{x^2-9}$$
> $$\frac{2x^2}{x^2-9} = \frac{2}{x^2-9}$$
> **Cross-multiply, or equate the numerators, and solve.]**

Got It?   SYNTHESIZING

> **Q** What methods can you use to solve 1b? Explain. **[Multiply each side by the LCD of $(x+1)(x+4)$. Or, subtract $\frac{3}{x+4}$ from both sides, forming a proportion after combining terms. Solve the equation by cross-multiplying.]**
>
> **Q** What are the restrictions on the domain? **[For 1a, $x \neq -2$; for 1b, $x \neq -1$, $x \neq -4$.]**
>
> **Q** Are there extraneous solutions? **[In 1a, 2 is extraneous; in 1b, no extraneous solutions.]**

 **Problem 1**   Solving a Rational Equation

What are the solutions of the rational equation?

Ⓐ $\frac{x}{x-3} + \frac{x}{x+3} = \frac{2}{x^2-9}$

Hint

> The factoring pattern for a difference of squares is $a^2 - b^2 = (a-b)(a+b)$.

Think

> Factor the denominators to find the LCD.

Write

$$\frac{x}{x-3} + \frac{x}{x+3} = \frac{2}{x^2-9}$$
$$\frac{x}{x-3} + \frac{x}{x+3} = \frac{2}{(x-3)(x+3)}$$

Think

> Multiply each side by the LCD to clear denominators.

Write

$$(x-3)(x+3)\left[\frac{x}{x-3} + \frac{x}{x+3}\right] = (x-3)(x+3)\frac{2}{(x-3)(x+3)}$$

Think

> Now distribute, simplify, and solve.

Write

$$x(x+3) + x(x-3) = 2$$
$$x^2 + 3x + x^2 - 3x = 2$$
$$x^2 + 3x + x^2 - 3x = 2$$
$$2x^2 = 2$$
$$x^2 = 1, \text{ so } x = \pm 1$$

Think

> Check whether $x = 1$ or $x = -1$ is extraneous. Use the original equation.

Write

$$\frac{1}{1-3} + \frac{1}{1+3} \stackrel{?}{=} \frac{2}{(1)^2-9}$$
$$-\frac{1}{2} + \frac{1}{4} = -\frac{1}{4} \checkmark$$

$$\frac{-1}{-1-3} + \frac{-1}{-1+3} \stackrel{?}{=} \frac{2}{(-1)^2-9}$$
$$\frac{1}{4} + -\frac{1}{2} = -\frac{1}{4} \checkmark$$

Think

> Write the solutions.

Write

The solutions are $x = 1$ and $x = -1$.

Ⓑ $\frac{x-1}{x^2+3x+2} + \frac{2x}{x+2} = \frac{x-1}{x+1}$

Think

> **How is this rational equation related to a quadratic equation?** Multiplying each side of the equation by the LCD of the rational expressions turns it into a quadratic equation.

$$\frac{x-1}{x^2+3x+2} + \frac{2x}{x+2} = \frac{x-1}{x+1} \quad \boxed{\text{The LCD is } (x+2)(x+1).}$$

$$(x+2)(x+1)\left[\frac{x-1}{(x+2)(x+1)} + \frac{2x}{x+2}\right] = (x+2)(x+1)\left(\frac{x-1}{x+1}\right)$$

$$(x-1) + 2x(x+1) = (x+2)(x-1)$$
$$2x^2 + 3x - 1 = x^2 + x - 2$$
$$x^2 + 2x + 1 = 0$$
$$(x+1)(x+1) = 0, \text{ so } x = -1$$

The solution $x = -1$ is extraneous because the original equation restricts x so that $x \neq -2$ and $x \neq -1$. There is no solution to this equation.

 Got It? 1. What are the solutions of the rational equation?

a. $\frac{x-1}{x+2} = \frac{x^2+2x-3}{x+2}$ **b.** $\frac{x}{x+1} + \frac{3}{x+4} = \frac{x+3}{x+4}$

Answers

Solve It!

Your speed on the normal route is $\frac{0.5+1.2}{25} = 0.068$ mi/min, so the time it takes to walk the shortcut is $\frac{\sqrt{(0.5) + (1.2)^2}}{0.068} \approx 19$ min. The time saved is about $25 - 19 = 6$ min.

Got It?

1. a. 1
   b. 0

2. a. ≈ 4.47 mi/h

   b. The direction of wind affects the speed (rate) of the bike. Since the speed is inversely related to time, change in speed will lead to change in time. Since there is no wind, the speed of the bike will remain same to and from the store, hence the time to and from the store will remain the same.

PowerAlgebra.com

2 Guided Instruction

Each Problem is worked out and supported online.

Problem 1
Solving a Rational Equation
Animated

Problem 2
Using Rational Equations
Animated

Problem 3
Using a Graphing Calculator to Solve a Rational Equation
Animated

Support in Algebra 2 Companion
• Vocabulary
• Key Concepts
• Got It?

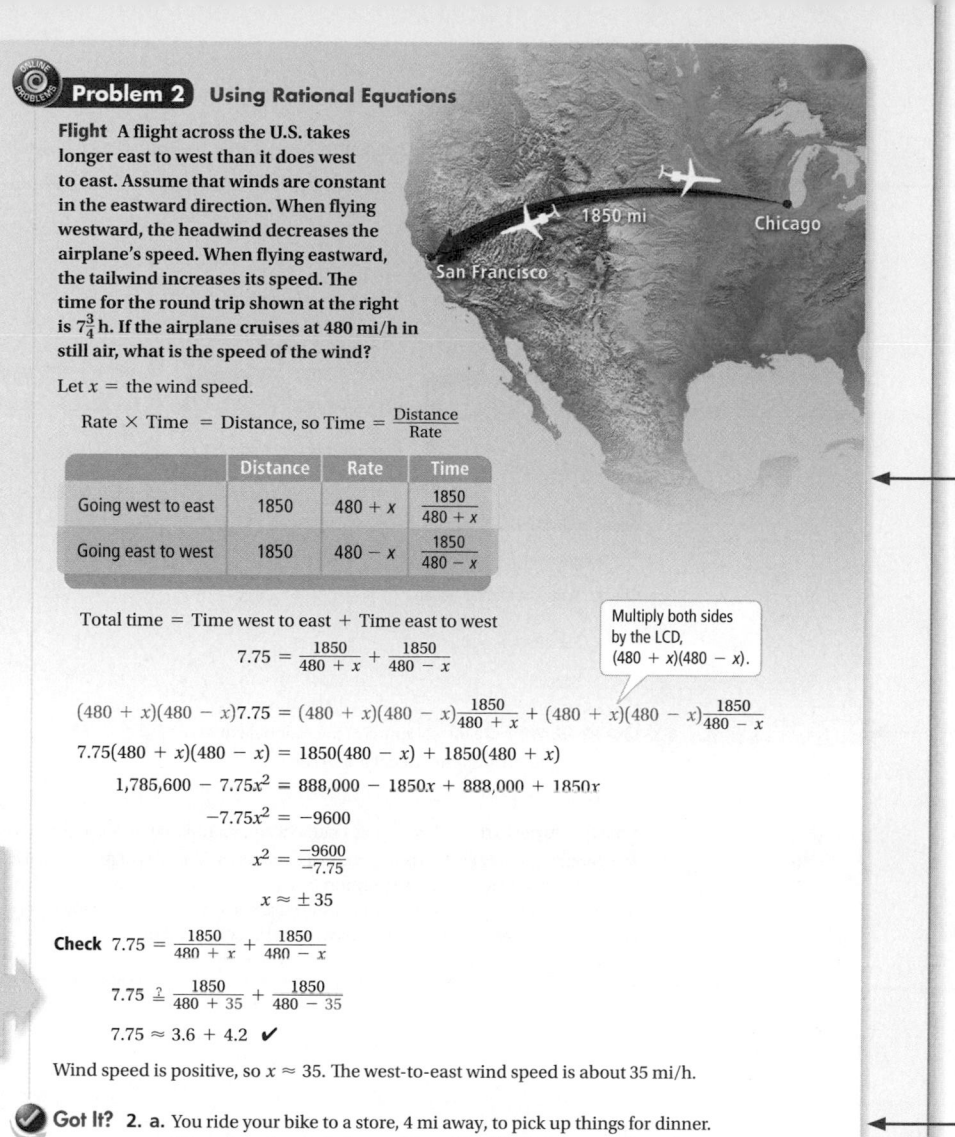

Problem 2 Using Rational Equations

Flight A flight across the U.S. takes longer east to west than it does west to east. Assume that winds are constant in the eastward direction. When flying westward, the headwind decreases the airplane's speed. When flying eastward, the tailwind increases its speed. The time for the round trip shown at the right is $7\frac{3}{4}$ h. If the airplane cruises at 480 mi/h in still air, what is the speed of the wind?

1850 mi   Chicago

San Francisco

Let $x =$ the wind speed.

Rate $\times$ Time $=$ Distance, so Time $= \frac{\text{Distance}}{\text{Rate}}$

	Distance	Rate	Time
Going west to east	1850	$480 + x$	$\frac{1850}{480 + x}$
Going east to west	1850	$480 - x$	$\frac{1850}{480 - x}$

Total time = Time west to east + Time east to west

$$7.75 = \frac{1850}{480 + x} + \frac{1850}{480 - x}$$

> Multiply both sides by the LCD, $(480 + x)(480 - x)$.

$$(480 + x)(480 - x)7.75 = (480 + x)(480 - x)\frac{1850}{480 + x} + (480 + x)(480 - x)\frac{1850}{480 - x}$$

$$7.75(480 + x)(480 - x) = 1850(480 - x) + 1850(480 + x)$$

$$1{,}785{,}600 - 7.75x^2 = 888{,}000 - 1850x + 888{,}000 + 1850x$$

$$-7.75x^2 = -9600$$

$$x^2 = \frac{-9600}{-7.75}$$

$$x \approx \pm 35$$

Think

If you substitute 35 for x will the equation check exactly?

No; since 35 is an approximation, it is likely that the values will be nearly equal, but probably not equal.

Check $7.75 = \frac{1850}{480 + x} + \frac{1850}{480 - x}$

$$7.75 \stackrel{?}{=} \frac{1850}{480 + 35} + \frac{1850}{480 - 35}$$

$$7.75 \approx 3.6 + 4.2 \ ✔$$

Wind speed is positive, so $x \approx 35$. The west-to-east wind speed is about 35 mi/h.

✓ **Got It? 2. a.** You ride your bike to a store, 4 mi away, to pick up things for dinner. When there is no wind, you ride at 10 mi/h. Today your trip to the store and back took 1 hour. What was the speed of the wind today?

     b. Reasoning Explain why there is no difference between the travel time to and from the store when there is no wind.

Problem 2   ERROR PREVENTION

Remind students that when adding rational expressions, it is necessary to multiply each ratio by a form of 1 so as not to change the expression.

Because this problem involves an equation, multiplying both sides of the equation by the same number will not change the equation as long as extraneous roots are excluded.

Q Could this equation be solved using a proportion? Explain. **[Yes; multiply each fraction by the correct ratio to get denominators of $(480 + x)(480 - x)$. Then add the fractions to get one ratio and cross-multiply to solve the proportion.]**

Q What is a reasonable domain for this equation? Explain. **[$0 < x < 480$. Wind speed must be positive, and the rate must also be positive, so the speed cannot be greater than 480. If the speed were 480, the denominator of the rational equation would be zero, so it must be less than 480.]**

Got It?

Q To find the wind speed, do you need to know whether the trip has a headwind or tailwind? Explain. **[No. You know the distance in both directions is 4 mi. The rate you ride will be either $10 + x$ or $10 - x$, depending on headwind or tailwind. Because the numerator will be 4 for each ratio, you do not need to know whether the trip to the store had a headwind or tailwind.]**

Q What equation do you need to solve? $[1 = \frac{4}{10 + x} + \frac{4}{10 - x}]$

Q What is a reasonable domain? **[$0 < x < 10$]**

Additional Problems

1. What are the solutions of the rational equation?

   a. $\frac{4}{x + 2} = \frac{5}{2x + 3}$

   b. $\frac{1}{x^2 - 5x} + \frac{x - 7}{x} = \frac{4}{x^2 - 5x}$

ANSWERS

a. $-\frac{2}{3}$

b. 8 and 4

2. A carpenter can build a desk in 6 h. Another carpenter can build the same desk in 8 h. How long will it take the carpenters working together to build one desk?

ANSWER about 3.43 h

3. What are the solutions of the rational equation?
$\frac{5}{x + 1} + \frac{x}{x - 1} = 5$

ANSWER 0 and 1.5

Problem 3

Q How can the graph be used to determine the restrictions on the variable? **[The vertical asymptotes are at $x = 2$ and -2, so x cannot be 2 or -2.]**

Got It?

Q What keystrokes do you use to enter the left side of the equation in the graphing calculator? **[(x + 2)/(1 − 2x)]**

Q What is an appropriate viewing window? **[Answers may vary, but YMAX must be greater than 5.]**

You can also use a graphing calculator to solve a rational equation.

 Problem 3 Using a Graphing Calculator to Solve a Rational Equation

What are the solutions of the rational equation? Use a graphing calculator to solve.

$$\frac{2}{x+2} + \frac{x}{x-2} = 1$$

Plan
How do the graphs of the two sides of the equation help you find solutions?
The x-values of the points of intersection are the solutions to the equation.

Enter one side of the equation as Y_1. Enter the other side as Y_2.

There appears to be only one intersection point, at $x = 0$.

$Y_1 = Y_2$ when $x = 0$.

```
Plot1  Plot2  Plot3
\Y1 ▤ (2/(X+2))+(X/(X−2))
\Y2 ▤ 1
\Y3 =
\Y4 =
\Y5 =
\Y6 =
\Y7 =
```

X	Y₁	Y₂
−1	2.3333	1
0	1	1
1	−.3333	1
2	ERROR	1
3	3.4	1
4	2.3333	1
5	1.9524	1
X=0		

The solution is $x = 0$.

Check Write the original equation. $\dfrac{2}{x+2} + \dfrac{x}{x-2} = 1$

Substitute $x = 0$. $\dfrac{2}{0+2} + \dfrac{0}{0-2} \stackrel{?}{=} 1$

Simplify. $1 + 0 = 1$ ✔

 Got It? 3. What are the solutions of the rational equation $\frac{x+2}{1-2x} = 5$? Use a graphing calculator to solve.

Focus Question How is solving a rational equation similar to solving a polynomial equation?
Answer Multiply each side of a rational equation by the LCD of the rational expressions in the equation to rewrite it as a polynomial equation. Then use the techniques for solving polynomial equations to find solutions. Because you multiplied each side of an equation by an algebraic expression, you must check for extraneous solutions.

Answers

Got It? (continued)
3. $0.\overline{27}$

Lesson Check

Do you know HOW?

Solve each equation. Check each solution.

1. $\frac{4}{x-2} = \frac{x-1}{x-2}$

2. $\frac{2a+1}{6} + \frac{a}{2} = \frac{a-1}{3}$

3. $\frac{2}{n} + \frac{n+2}{n+1} = \frac{-2}{n^2+n}$

4. **Flight** If the speed of an airplane is 350 mi/h with a tail wind of 40 mi/h, what is the speed of the plane in still air?

Do you UNDERSTAND?

5. **Error Analysis** Describe and correct the error made in solving the equation.

$$\frac{5}{x} + \frac{9}{7} = \frac{28}{x}$$
$$\frac{14}{x+7} = \frac{28}{x}$$
$$14x = 28(x+7)$$
$$14x = 28x + 196$$
$$-196 = 14x$$
$$-14 = x$$

6. **Open-Ended** Write a rational equation using expressions that have $x^2 - 9$ as their LCD.

7. **Reasoning** Describe two methods you can use to check whether a solution is extraneous.

Practice and Problem-Solving Exercises

A Practice

Solve each equation. Check each solution.

◀ See Problem 1.

 Guided Practice

To start, multiply each side by the LCD, 6.

8. $\frac{2x}{3} - \frac{1}{2} = \frac{2x+5}{6}$

$6 \cdot \left(\frac{2x}{3} - \frac{1}{2}\right) = 6 \cdot \frac{2x+5}{6}$

9. $\frac{1}{4} - x = \frac{x}{8}$

10. $\frac{y}{5} + \frac{y}{2} = 7$

11. $\frac{1}{x} + \frac{x}{2} = \frac{x+4}{2x}$

12. $\frac{3}{2x} - \frac{5}{3x} = 2$

13. $\frac{2}{y} + \frac{1}{2} = \frac{5}{2y}$

14. $\frac{1}{4x} - \frac{3}{4} = \frac{7}{x}$

15. **Transportation** The speed s of an airplane is given by $s = \frac{d}{t}$, where d represents the distance and t is the time.

◀ See Problem 2.

   a. A plane flies 700 miles from New York to Chicago at a speed of 360 mi/h. Find the time for the trip.

   b. On the return trip from Chicago to New York, a tail wind helps the plane move faster. The total flying time for the round trip is 3.5 h. Find the speed x of the tail wind.

 Graphing Calculator Solve each equation. Check each solution.

◀ See Problem 3.

16. $\frac{3}{x} = 5$

17. $\frac{2}{x-1} = 4$

18. $\frac{3x-1}{x+2} = 7$

19. $\frac{2}{x} = \frac{x}{2}$

20. $\frac{2}{x+3} = \frac{x-3}{2}$

21. $\frac{2}{x-1} + \frac{3}{x+1} = 4$

B Apply

Solve each equation for the given variable.

22. $m = \frac{2E}{V^2}$ for E

23. $\frac{c}{E} - \frac{1}{mc} = 0$ for E

24. $\frac{m}{F} = \frac{1}{a}$ for F

25. $\frac{1}{c} - \frac{c}{a^2-b^2} = 0$ for c

26. $\frac{\ell}{T^2} = \frac{g}{4\pi^2}$ for T

27. $\frac{q}{m} = \frac{2V}{B^2r^2}$ for B

Lesson Check

1. 5

2. −1

3. −2

4. 310 mi/h

5. LCD was not found; the correct answer is
$$\frac{35+9x}{7x} = \frac{28(7)}{7x}, x \neq 0$$
$$9x = 161$$
$$x = \frac{161}{9} = 17.\overline{8}.$$

6. Answers may vary. Sample:
$$\frac{2}{x-3} + \frac{1}{x+3} = \frac{5x}{x^2-9}$$

7. Answers may vary. Sample: (1) Substitute the solution into the original eq. (2) Check to see if the solution is in the domain of the graph of the original eq.

Practice and Problem-Solving Exercises

8. 4

9. $\frac{2}{9}$

10. 10

11. −1, 2

12. $-\frac{1}{12}$

13. 1

14. −9

15. a. $\frac{35}{18}$ h

   b. 90 mi/h

16. 0.6

17. 1.5

18. −3.75

19. ±2

20. ≈±3.6

21. 1.69, −0.44

22. $E = \frac{mV^2}{2}$

23. $E = mc^2$

24. $F = ma$

25. $c = \pm\sqrt{a^2-b^2}$

26. $T = \pm2\pi\sqrt{\frac{\ell}{g}}$

27. $B = \pm\sqrt{\frac{2Vm}{r^2q}}$

---

3 Lesson Check

Do you know HOW?   ERROR INTERVENTION

- For Exercises 1–3, if students are not sure how to start, remind them to eliminate the denominators by multiplying by the LCD.

Do you UNDERSTAND?

- If students have trouble correcting the error in Exercise 5, remind them that several methods can be used to find a solution. Ask students to identify the method the student was trying to use and what the steps are for that method. Then have them follow the student's problem to see if they can find the error.

Close

Q Which methods can be used to solve a rational equation? [**Multiply through by the LCD, rearrange the equation into a proportion and use cross products, use a table or graph to find a solution, or add the rational expression on each side of the equal sign and then use cross products.**]

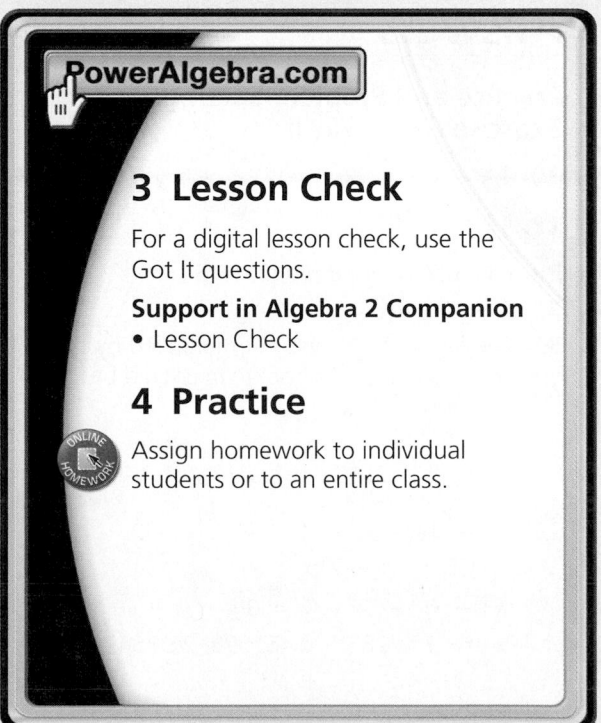

PowerAlgebra.com

3 Lesson Check

For a digital lesson check, use the Got It questions.

Support in Algebra 2 Companion
- Lesson Check

4 Practice

Assign homework to individual students or to an entire class.

4 Practice

ASSIGNMENT GUIDE

Basic: 8–14 even, 15, 16–22 even, 28, 29, 32

Average: 8–28 even, 29, 32, 33, 34–42 even

Standardized Test Prep: 44–47

Mixed Review: 48–62

Reasoning exercises have blue headings.

Applications exercises have red headings.

EXERCISE 29: Use the Think About a Plan worksheet in the **Student Companion** (also available in the Teaching Resources in print and online) to further support students' development in becoming independent learners.

HOMEWORK QUICK CHECK

To check students' understanding of key skills and concepts, go over Exercises 10, 16, 28, 29, and 32.

---

28. **Think About a Plan** You and a classmate have volunteered to contact every member of your class by phone to inform them of an upcoming event. You can complete the calls in six days if you work alone. Your classmate can complete them in four days. How long will it take to complete the calls working together?
   - If N is the total number of calls, what expression represents the number of calls that you can make per day? What expression represents the number of calls your friend can make per day?
   - What is the expression for the number of days needed to make N calls if you are working together?

29. **Storage** One pump can fill a tank with oil in 4 hours. A second pump can fill the same tank in 3 hours. If both pumps are used at the same time, how long will they take to fill the tank?

30. **Teamwork** You can stuff envelopes twice as fast as your friend. Together, you can stuff 6750 envelopes in 4.5 hours. How long would it take each of you working alone to complete the job?

31. **Grades** On the first four tests of the term your average is 84%. You think you can score 96% on each of the remaining tests. How many consecutive test scores of 96% would you need to bring your average up to 90% for the term?

32. **Error Analysis** Describe and correct the error made in solving the equation shown on the right.

33. **Fuel Economy** Suppose you drive an average of 15,000 miles per year, and your car gets 24 miles per gallon. Suppose gasoline costs $3.60 a gallon.
   a. How much money do you spend each year on gasoline?
   b. You plan to trade in your car for one that gets x more miles per gallon. Write an expression to represent the new yearly cost of gasoline.
   c. Write an expression to represent your total savings on gasoline per year.
   d. Suppose you can save $600 a year with the new car. How many miles per gallon does the new car get?

$$x - \frac{2}{x-2} = \frac{x+1}{x+2}$$
$$x - 2(x+2) = (x+1)(x-2)$$
$$x - 2x - 4 = x^2 - x - 2$$
$$0 = x^2 + 2$$
$$-2 = x^2$$

There is no square root of a negative number, so the equation has no solution.

Solve each equation. Check each solution.

34. $\frac{15}{x} + \frac{9x-7}{x+2} = 9$

35. $\frac{2}{x+2} - \frac{1}{x} = \frac{-4}{x(x+2)}$

36. $\frac{1}{b+1} + \frac{1}{b-1} = \frac{2}{b^2-1}$

37. $c - \frac{c}{3} + \frac{c}{5} = 26$

38. $\frac{1}{x-5} = \frac{x}{x^2-25}$

39. $\frac{k}{k+1} + \frac{k}{k-2} = 2$

40. $\frac{5}{x^2-7x+12} - \frac{2}{3-x} = \frac{5}{x-4}$

41. $\frac{2}{x+3} - \frac{3}{4-x} = \frac{2x-2}{x^2-x-12}$

Answers

Practice and Problem-Solving Exercises (continued)

28. 2.4 days

29. $1\frac{5}{7}$ h

30. you: 6.75 h; your friend: 13.5 h

31. 4 test scores

32. The first term, x, was not multiplied by the LCD $(x-2)(x+2)$. The solution should be:

$$x - \frac{2}{x-2} = \frac{x+1}{x+2}$$
$$\frac{x(x-2)(x+2) - 2(x+2)}{(x-2)(x+2)} = \frac{(x+1)(x-2)}{(x-2)(x+2)}$$
$$x^3 - 4x - 2x - 4 = x^2 - x - 2,$$
$$\text{LCD} = (x-2)(x+2)$$
$$x^3 - x^2 - 5x - 2 = 0$$
$$x \approx -1.47283, -0.462598, 2.93543$$

33. a. $2250

b. $\frac{15,000}{24+x}(3.60)$

c. $2250 - \frac{15,000}{24+x}(3.60)$

d. ≈ 32.7 mpg

34. 3

35. no solution

36. no solution

37. 30

38. no solution

39. -4

40. no solution

41. -1

42. Woodworking A tapered cylinder is made by decreasing the radius of a rod continuously as you move from one end to the other. The rate at which it tapers is the taper per foot. You can calculate the taper per foot using the formula $T = \frac{24(R - r)}{L}$. The lengths R, r, and L are measured in inches.

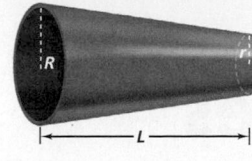

a. Solve this equation for L.

b. What is L for $T = 0.75, 0.85,$ and 0.95, if $R = 4$ in.; $r = 3$ in.?

43. Writing Write and solve a problem that can be modeled by a rational equation.

Standardized Test Prep

44. What is the solution of $x + \frac{1}{x} = -2$?

(A) $1, -1$　　(B) 0 only　　(C) $-\frac{1}{2}$ only　　(D) -1 only

45. Which of the following is equivalent to $\frac{6\sqrt{24}}{2\sqrt{3}}$?

(F) $2\sqrt{2}$　　(G) $3\sqrt{2}$　　(H) $5\sqrt{2}$　　(I) $6\sqrt{2}$

46. An investment of $750 will be worth $1500 after 12 years of continuous compounding at a fixed interest rate. What is that interest rate?

(A) 2.00%　　(B) 5.78%　　(C) 6.93%　　(D) 200%

Extended Response

47. A librarian orders 48 fiction and nonfiction books for the school library. A fiction book costs $15 and a nonfiction book costs $20. The total cost of the order was $900. How many nonfiction books did the librarian order? Show your work.

Mixed Review

Simplify each difference.　　　　　　　　　　　◄ See Lesson 8-5.

48. $\frac{3y + 1}{4y + 4} - \frac{2y + 7}{2y + 2}$　　**49.** $\frac{5x}{2y + 4} - \frac{6}{y^2 + 2y}$　　**50.** $\frac{x + 1}{2x - 2} - \frac{2x}{x^2 + 2x - 3}$

Solve each equation.　　　　　　　　　　　　◄ See Lesson 7-5.

51. $\log_{10} 0.001 = x$　　**52.** $\log_3 27 = 3x + 6$　　**53.** $\log_{0.5}(x + 1) = 3$

Find the inverse of each function. Is the inverse a function?　◄ See Lesson 6-7.

54. $y = 5 - 2x$　　**55.** $y = x^2 + 1$　　**56.** $y = x^3 - 4$

Get Ready! To prepare for Lesson 9-1, do Exercises 57–62.

Identify the pattern and find the next three terms.　　　◄ See Lesson 1-1.

57. $1, 3, 5, 7, \ldots$　　**58.** $-2, -4, -6, -8, \ldots$　　**59.** $0.2, 1, 5, 25, 125, \ldots$

60. $50, 45, 40, 35, \ldots$　　**61.** $16, 32, 64, \ldots$　　**62.** $-3, -7, -11, -15, \ldots$

---

42. a. $L = \frac{24(R - r)}{T}$

b. 32 in.; $\approx$28.24 in.; $\approx$25.26 in.

43. Check students' work.

Standardized Test Prep

44. D

45. I

46. B

47. [4] Write and solve the system of eqs.:
Let n = no. of nonfiction books,
Let f = no. of fiction books,
$\begin{cases} f + n = 48 \\ 15f + 20n = 900 \end{cases}$
solution: $n = 36$.

[3] appropriate methods, but with one computational error

[2] incorrect system solved correctly OR correct system solved incorrectly

[1] correct answer, without work shown

Mixed Review

48. $\frac{-y - 13}{4(y + 1)}$

49. $\frac{5xy - 12}{2y(y + 2)}$

50. $\frac{x^2 + 3}{2(x - 1)(x + 3)}$

51. $x = -3$

52. $x = -1$

53. $x = -0.875$

54. $y = \frac{5 - x}{2}$; yes

55. $y = \pm\sqrt{x - 1}$; no

56. $y = \sqrt[3]{x + 4}$; yes

57. add 2; 9, 11, 13

58. subtract 2; $-10, -12, -14$

59. multiply by 5; 625, 3125, 15625

60. subtract 5; 30, 25, 20

61. multiply by 2; 128, 256, 512

62. subtract 4; $-19, -23, -27$

Additional Instructional Support

Algebra 2 Companion

Students can use the **Algebra 2 Companion** worktext (4 pages) as you teach the lesson. Use the Companion to support

- New Vocabulary
- Key Concepts
- Got It for each Problem
- Lesson Check

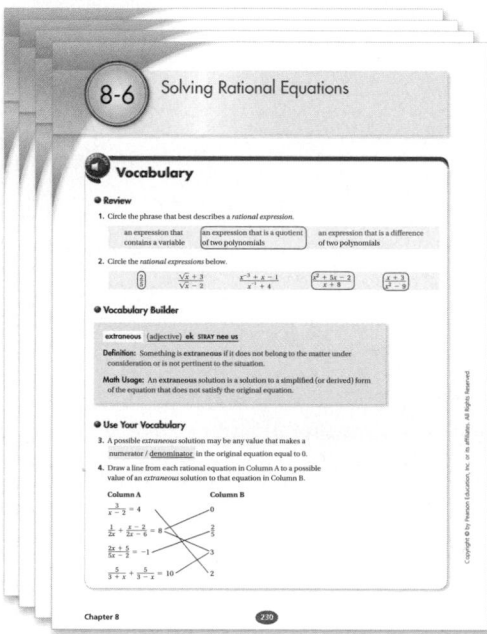

ELL Support

Use Role Playing Have students act out the distance problem from Problem 2 to help them understand the meaning of the terms used. Use a map or two points in the classroom to indicate San Francisco and Chicago. Instruct students to make a sign indicating both locations as well as the distance between them. Next, have students use a picture or make a paper airplane and write the speed or rate on the airplane. Use the words "speed" and "rate" interchangeably, so students are aware that speed is a type of rate. Use a fan or students holding paper fans at either location to represent a headwind and tailwind. Point out that if the airplane is moving towards the fan, the wind is a headwind and the rate of the airplane is slower. Conversely, if the airplane is moving away from the fan, the wind is a tailwind and the rate of the airplane is faster. Have students fill in the table from Problem 2 as they act out each part of the demonstration.

5 Assess & Remediate

Lesson Quiz

1. What are the solutions of the rational equation $\frac{3}{x^2 + 6x + 8} + \frac{x + 1}{x + 2} = \frac{1}{x + 2}$?

2. **Do you UNDERSTAND?** A gardener completes park maintenance in 12 h. Another gardener takes 10 h. How long it will take both gardeners working together to complete the maintenance?

3. What are the solutions of the rational equation $6 = \frac{3a + 6}{a} + \frac{1}{a}$? Use a graphing calculator to solve.

ANSWERS TO LESSON QUIZ

1. -3 and -1
2. about 5.45 h
3. $\frac{7}{3}$

PRESCRIPTION FOR REMEDIATION

Use the student work on the Lesson Quiz to prescribe a differentiated review assignment:

Points	Differentiated Remediation
0–1	Intervention
2	On-level
3	Extension

PowerAlgebra.com

5 Assess & Remediate

Assign the Lesson Quiz. Appropriate intervention, practice, or enrichment is automatically generated based on student performance.

Differentiated Remediation

Intervention

- **Reteaching** (2 pages) Provides reteaching and practice exercises for the key lesson concepts. Use with struggling students or absent students.

- **English Language Learner Support** Helps students develop and reinforce mathematical vocabulary and key concepts.

All-in-One Resources/Online
Reteaching

8-6 Reteaching (continued)
Solving Rational Equations

You often can use rational equations to model and solve problems involving rates.

Problem

Quinn can refinish hardwood floors four times as fast as his apprentice, Jack. They are refinishing 100 ft² of flooring. Working together, Quinn and Jack can finish the job in 3 h. How long would it take each of them working alone to refinish the floor?

Let x be Jack's work rate in ft²/h. Quinn's work rate is four times faster, or $4x$.

square feet refinished per hour by Jack and Quinn together	=	square feet of floor they refinish together	÷	hours worked together
ft²/h	=	ft²	÷	h

$x + 4x = \frac{100}{3}$ Their work rates sum to 100 ft² in 3 h.

$3(x) + 3(4x) = 3\left(\frac{100}{3}\right)$ They work for 3 h. Refinished floor area = rate × time.

$15x = 100$ Simplify.

$x \approx 6.67$ Divide each side by 15.

Jack works at the rate of 6.67 ft²/h. Quinn works at the rate of 26.67 ft²/h.

Let j be the number of hours Jack takes to refinish the floor alone, and let q be the number of hours Quinn takes to refinish the floor alone.

$6.67 = \frac{100}{j}$ $26.67 = \frac{100}{q}$

$j(6.67) = j\left(\frac{100}{j}\right)$ $q(26.67) = q\left(\frac{100}{q}\right)$

$6.67j = 100$ $26.67q = 100$

$j \approx 15$ $q \approx 3.75$

Jack would take 15 h and Quinn would take 3.75 h to refinish the floor alone.

Exercises

13. An airplane flies from its home airport to a city and back in 5 h flying time. The plane travels the 720 mi to the city at 295 mi/h with no wind. How strong is the wind on the return flight? Is the wind a headwind or a tailwind? **about 14 mi/h; headwind**

14. Miguel can complete the decorations for a school dance in 5 days working alone. Nasim can do it alone in 3 days, and Denise can do it alone in 4 days. How long would it take the three students working together to decorate? **about 1.3 days**

All-in-One Resources/Online
English Language Learner Support

8-6 ELL Support
Solving Rational Equations

Problem

What are the solutions of the rational equation? Justify your steps.

$\frac{x}{x - 2} + \frac{1}{x - 4} = \frac{2}{x^2 - 6x + 8}$ Write original equation.

$\frac{x}{x - 2} + \frac{1}{x - 4} = \frac{2}{(x - 2)(x - 4)}$ Factor the denominators to find the LCD.

$(x - 2)(x - 4)\left[\frac{x}{x - 2} + \frac{1}{x - 4}\right]$

$= (x - 2)(x - 4)\left[\frac{2}{(x - 2)(x - 4)}\right]$ Multiply each side by the LCD to clear the denominators.

$x(x - 4) + 1(x - 2) = 2$

$x^2 - 3x - 4 = 0$ Distribute and simplify.

$(x - 4)(x + 1) = 0$ Factor the quadratic.

$x = 4$ or $x = -1$ Solve for x.

$x = 4$ causes division by 0, so $x = 4$ is an extraneous solution. Check for extraneous solutions.

Because $\frac{-1}{-1 - 2} + \frac{1}{-1 - 4} = \frac{2}{(-1)^2 - 6(-1) + 8}$, the solution is $x = -1$.

Exercise

What are the solutions of the rational equation? Justify your steps.

$\frac{5}{x} + \frac{4}{x + 3} = \frac{8}{x^2 + 3x}$ Write the original equation.

$\frac{5}{x} + \frac{4}{x + 3} = \frac{8}{x(x + 3)}$ Factor the denominator to find the LCD

$x(x + 3)\left[\frac{5}{x} + \frac{4}{(x + 3)}\right] = x(x + 3)\frac{8}{x(x + 3)}$ Multiply each side by the LCD

$9x + 15 = 8$ Distribute and simplify.

$x = -\frac{7}{9}$ Solve

Differentiated Remediation *continued*

On-Level

- **Practice** (2 pages) Provides extra practice for each lesson. For more challenging practice exercises, use the Form G Practice pages found in the All-in-One Teaching Resources and online.

- **Think About a Plan** Helps students develop specific problem-solving skills and strategies by providing scaffolded guiding questions.

- **Standardized Test Prep** Focuses on all major exercises, all major question types, and helps students prepare for the high-stakes assessments.

Extension

- **Enrichment** Provides students with interesting problems and activities that extend the concepts of the lesson.

- **Activities, Games, and Puzzles** Worksheets that can be used for concepts development, enrichment, and for fun!

Student Companion/All-in-One Resources/Online
Practice page 1

8-6 Practice *Form K*
Solving Rational Equations

Solve each equation. Check each solution.

To start, multiply each side by the LCD.

1. $\frac{x}{4} - \frac{3}{x} = \frac{1}{4}$

   $4x\left(\frac{x}{4} - \frac{3}{x}\right) = (4x)\left(\frac{1}{4}\right)$

   $x = -3$ or 4

2. $x + \frac{6}{x} = -5$

   $x = -3$ or -2

3. $\frac{5}{2x-2} = \frac{15}{x^2-1}$

   $x = 5$

4. The aerodynamic covering on a bicycle increases a cyclist's average speed by 10 mi/h. The time for a 75-mi trip is reduced by 2 h.
   a. Using t for time, write a rational equation you can use to determine the average speed using the aerodynamic covering. $\frac{75}{t} = \frac{75}{t} + 10$
   b. What is the average speed for the trip using the aerodynamic covering? **25 mi/h**

Using a graphing calculator, solve each equation. Check each solution.

5. $\frac{4}{2x} = \frac{5}{x}$ $x = -2.5$ or 4

6. $x + 5 = \frac{6}{x}$ $x = -6, 1$

7. $\frac{2}{x} = \frac{x}{x^2-49}$ $x = 14$

Solve each equation for the given variable.

8. $\frac{c}{F} = \frac{mv^2}{r}$ for v $v = \sqrt{\frac{Fr}{m}}$

9. $\frac{c}{d} = Qm$ for d $d = \frac{c}{Qm}$

10. $\frac{F}{Gm_1} = \frac{m_2}{r^2}$ for r $r = \sqrt{\frac{Gm_1m_2}{F}}$

Student Companion/All-in-One Resources/Online
Practice page 2

8-6 Practice *(continued)* *Form K*
Solving Rational Equations

11. You can travel 40 mi on your motorbike in the same time it takes your friend to travel 15 mi on his bicycle. If your friend rides his bike 20 mi/h slower than you ride your motorbike, find the speed for each bike.
    rate for motorbike: 32 mi/h; rate for bicycle: 12 mi/h

12. A passenger train travels 392 mi in the same time that it takes a freight train to travel 322 mi. If the passenger train travels 20 mi/h faster than the freight train, find the speed of each train.
    rate for freight train: 92 mi/h; rate for passenger train: 112 mi/h

13. You can paint a fence twice as fast as your sister can. Working together, the two of you can paint a fence in 6 h. How many hours would it take each of you working alone?
    you: 9 h; your sister: 18 h

Solve each equation. Check each solution.

14. $\frac{2}{x-3} - \frac{4}{x+3} = \frac{8}{x^2-9}$ $x = 5$

15. $\frac{5}{x+5} + \frac{2}{5-x} = \frac{-4}{x^2-25}$ $x = 21$

16. $\frac{3}{x^2-1} + \frac{4x}{x+1} = \frac{1.5}{x-1}$ $x = 0.375$

17. You are planning a school field trip to a local theater. It costs $60 to rent the bus. Each theater ticket costs $5.50.
    a. Write a function $c(x)$ to represent the cost per student if x students sign up for the trip. $c(x) = 5.50 + \frac{60}{x}$
    b. How many students must sign up if the cost is to be no more than $10 per student? **14 students**

All-in-One Resources/Online
Enrichment

8-6 Enrichment
Solving Rational Equations

Gravitational Attraction

Many physical phenomena obey inverse-square laws. That is the strength of the quantity is inversely proportional to the square of the distance from the source.

Isaac Newton was the first to discover that gravity obeys an inverse-square law. The gravitational force F between objects of masses M and m separated by a distance D is given by $F = \frac{GMm}{D^2}$, where G is a constant.

Suppose that two stars, Alpha Major and Beta Minor, are separated by a distance of 6 light-years. Alpha Major has four times the mass of Beta Minor. Let M represent the mass of Beta Minor. Suppose that an object of mass m is placed between the two stars at a distance of D light-years from Beta Minor.

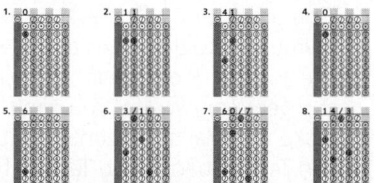

1. Write an expression for the gravitational force between this object and Beta Minor. $\frac{GMm}{D^2}$

2. Write an expression for the gravitational force between this object and Alpha Major. $\frac{4GMm}{(6-D)^2}$

3. What is the distance of a neutral position of the object with mass m from Beta Minor? At neutral position, both Beta Minor and Alpha Major exert equal force on m. **2 light-yr**

A spaceship is stationary between a planet and its moon, experiencing an equal gravitational pull from each. When measurements are taken, it is determined that the craft is 300,000 km from the planet and 100,000 km from the moon.

4. What is the ratio of the mass of the planet to the mass of the moon? **9 : 1**

5. What would be the ratio of their masses if the distance of the spaceship from the planet was R times the distance of the spaceship to the moon? $R^2 : 1$

Once every 277 yr, the two moons of the planet Omega Minus line up in a straight line with the planet. The moons are equal in mass, and the inner moon is equidistant from the outer moon and from the planet. Measurements show that an object two thirds of the distance from the planet to the inner moon, and in the same line as all three, experiences an equal gravitational pull in both directions.

b. What is the ratio of the mass of the planet to the mass of one of its moons? **17 : 4**

Student Companion/All-in-One Resources/Online
Think About a Plan

8-6 Think About a Plan
Solving Rational Equations

Storage One pump can fill a tank with oil in 4 hours. A second pump can fill the same tank in 3 hours. If both pumps are used at the same time, how long will they take to fill the tank?

Understanding the Problem

1. How long does it take the first pump to fill the tank? **4 h**

2. How long does it take the second pump to fill the tank? **3 h**

3. What is the problem asking you to determine?
   the length of time it takes for both pumps to fill the tank when used at the same time

Planning the Solution

4. If V is the volume of the tank, what expressions represent the portion of the tank that each pump can fill in one hour?

   First pump: $\frac{1}{4}V$ Second pump: $\frac{1}{3}V$

5. What expression represents the part of the tank the two pumps can fill in one hour if they are used at the same time?
   $\frac{1}{4}V + \frac{1}{3}V$

6. Let t be the number of hours. Write an equation to find the time it takes for the two pumps to fill one tank.
   $\left(\frac{1}{4}V + \frac{1}{3}V\right)t = V$

Getting an Answer

7. Solve your equation to find how long the pumps will take to fill the tank if both pumps are used at the same time.
   $\left(\frac{1}{4}V + \frac{1}{3}V\right)t = V$ $\frac{7}{12}t = 1$
   $\left(\frac{1}{4} + \frac{1}{3}\right)t = 1$ $t = \frac{12}{7} = 1\frac{5}{7}$ hours

---

Student Companion/All-in-One Resources/Online
Standardized Test Prep

8-6 Standardized Test Prep
Solving Rational Equations

Gridded Response

For Exercises 1–8, what are the solutions of each rational equation? Enter your answer in the grid provided. If necessary, enter your answer as a fraction.

1. $\frac{3-x}{6} = \frac{6-x}{12}$

2. $\frac{2}{6x+2} = \frac{x}{3x^2+11}$

3. $\frac{3}{2x-4} = \frac{5}{3x+7}$

4. $\frac{2}{x+2} + \frac{5}{x-2} = \frac{6}{x^2-4}$

5. $\frac{7}{x^2-5x} + \frac{2}{x} = \frac{3}{2x-10}$

6. $\frac{1}{4-5x} = \frac{3}{x+9}$

7. $\frac{7}{2} = \frac{7x}{8} - 4$

8. $4 + \frac{2y}{y-5} = \frac{8}{y-5}$

Answers

Online Teacher Resource Center
Activities, Games, and Puzzles

8-6 Game: Rational Learning
Solving Rational Equations

Points	Vocabulary: Question	Answer
10	Rational equation?	An equation containing rational expressions
20	Least common denominator?	The smallest integer that can be evenly divided by all the denominators
30	Cross products?	For the equation $\frac{a}{b} = \frac{c}{d}$, ad and bc
40	Solution of rational equation?	A value that, when substituted for the variable, makes the rational equation true
50	Extraneous solution?	A solution of the derived equation, but not of the original equation

Points	Solution: Question	Answer		Points	Solve: Question	Answer
10	$\frac{4}{x} = \frac{x}{9}$; $x = 6$ and $x = -6$	yes; yes		10	$\frac{3x}{4} + \frac{2}{5} = \frac{x}{7} - \frac{1}{6}$	5
20	$\frac{4}{x-3} = \frac{-3}{x+1}$; $x = 3$ and $x = 4$	yes; no		20	$\frac{x}{x+3} = \frac{-5}{x+5}$	$-4, 3$
30	$\frac{8(x-1)}{x-2} = \frac{4}{x-2}$; $x = 4$	no		30	$x + \frac{10}{x-2} = \frac{x^2+3x}{x-2}$	no solution
40	$1 + \frac{x^2}{x-1} = \frac{14}{2x-1}$; $x = 3$	no		40	$\frac{2}{x} + \frac{1}{x+1} = \frac{5}{x+x}$	1
50	$1 + \frac{2}{x-4} = \frac{15}{x^2-4x}$; $x = -3$ and $x = 5$	yes; yes		50	$\frac{x+3}{x^2+3x-4} = \frac{x+2}{x^2-16}$	-5

Points	Review: Question	Answer
10	What is the next number in the pattern 1, 4, 7, 10, . . . ?	13
20	What is the next number in the pattern 1, -3, 9, -27, . . . ?	81
30	Solve $5n + 2 = 37$.	7
40	What is the 4th term of the expansion of $(2x + 3y)^6$?	$4320x^3y^3$
50	Solve $-6144 = -3(2^n)$.	11

Performance Task    UbD

Pull It All Together

The concepts and skills required to solve these problems are from several lessons within this chapter and from earlier chapters. As students solve these problems, they will demonstrate their reasoning strategies and their growth as independent problem solvers.

Task 1

Use a function to model and solve a problem.
- What equation represents the perimeter of rectangle R? For which variable should you solve?
- Describe the graph of the area function.

Task 2

Write a function to model a problem and analyze the function to solve a problem.
- What equation represents the area of rectangle R? For which variable should you solve?
- What happens to $\frac{8}{\ell}$ as ℓ gets very large?

Task 3

Analyze the relationship between a function and its parent function.
- What are the linear factors?
- How will rewriting $x \pm 3$ as $x - 3 \pm 6$ help you describe the transformations on $y = \frac{1}{x}$?

Task 4

Solve an equation by finding an equivalent equation.
- What are the linear factors of the numerator and denominator of the fraction under the radical?
- Does the solution you found check in the original equation?

 **8**

Pull It All Together

> To solve these problems, you will pull together concepts and skills related to rational expressions, functions, and equations.

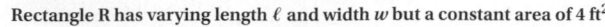

BIG idea Proportionality

Inverse proportionality involves a relationship in which the products of two quantities remain constant as the corresponding values of the quantities change.

Task 1

Rectangle R has varying length ℓ and width w but a constant perimeter of 4 ft.

a. Express the area A as a function of ℓ. What do you know about this function?

b. For what values of ℓ and w will the area of R be greatest? Give an algebraic argument. Give a geometric argument.

Task 2

Rectangle R has varying length ℓ and width w but a constant area of 4 ft^2.

a. Express the perimeter P as a function of ℓ. What kind of function is P? What is its domain?

b. Describe the asymptotic behavior of P. What can you say about R because of this behavior? Could you have made a similar statement about R in Task 1?

c. For what values of ℓ and w will the perimeter of R be least? Give a calculator-based argument. Give a geometric argument.

BIG idea Function

You can represent functions in a variety of ways (such as graphs, tables, equations, or words). Each representation is particularly useful in certain situations.

Task 3

Describe the discontinuities of $f(x) = \frac{x^2 + x - 6}{x^2 - 5x + 6}$. Find an equivalent form for f that shows how the graph of f is related to the graph of $y = \frac{1}{x}$. Describe the relationship. (You do not have to draw the graphs, but you can if you wish.)

BIG idea Equivalence

You can use symbols to represent an equation in an unlimited number of ways, where all equations have the same solution.

Task 4

Solve $x - 1 = \sqrt{\dfrac{x^4 - 2x^3}{x^2 - 4}}$.

Answers

Pull It All Together

See p. 49 for a holistic scoring rubric to gauge a student's progress on Understanding the Problem, Planning a Solution, Getting an Answer, and Assessing Autonomy.

SOLUTION OUTLINES

1. a. Represent the perimeter of rectangle R. ($2 = \ell + w$) Solve for w. ($w = 2 - \ell$) Substitute your result from Step 2 into $A = \ell w$. ($A = 2\ell - \ell^2$; A is a polynomial function of degree 2.)

b. Algebraic argument: Factor -1 from $2\ell - \ell^2$ to get $-(\ell^2 - 2\ell)$. Then complete the square on the binomial to get $-(\ell^2 - 2\ell + 1)$. Factor the trinomial and solve for ℓ. (The greatest area of R will occur when $\ell = 1$ and $w = 1$.)

Geometric argument: Graph your result for part (a) and find the maximum value. (Since $a < 0$, the parabola opens downward and the y-coordinate of the vertex is the maximum value of the function. The y-coordinate of the vertex is 1. So, the greatest area of R will occur when both ℓ and w equal 1.)

2. a. Represent the area of rectangle R. ($4 = \ell \cdot w$) Solve for w. $\left(w = \frac{4}{1}\right)$ Substitute into $P = 2\ell + 2w$. $\left(P = 2\ell + \frac{8}{1}; P\right.$ is a rational function.)

b. Graph your result from part (a). (The graph of $P = 2\ell + \frac{8}{1}$ is asymptotic to the y-axis and the line $y = 2x$. R can be infinitely long and very narrow. No, you can't make a similar statement about R in Task 1, because in Task 1 the perimeter is constant.)

c. Geometric argument:

First step: From the graph in part (b), you can see that R will have the least perimeter when both ℓ and w equal 2. To prove this, consider a rectangle with area 4 and dimensions $(2 - x)$ and $(2 + y)$.

Second step: Represent the area of the new rectangle. ($4 = (2 - x)(2 + y)$ or $-2x + 2y = xy$)

Third step: Represent the perimeter of the new rectangle. ($P = 2(2 - x) + 2(2 + y)$ or $P = 8 - 2x + 2y$)

Fourth step: Use your results to compare the perimeter of the new rectangle to the original.

(Perimeter of original rectangle: $2(2) + 2(2) = 8$;

Perimeter of new rectangle: $8 - 2x + 2y = 8 + xy$; $8 + xy > 8$ so R has the least perimeter when $\ell = w = 2$)

3. Possible Plan: Factor the numerator and denominator. Simplify. Identify any points of discontinuity. Then describe the

 **Chapter Review**

Connecting BIG ideas and Answering the Essential Questions

1 Proportionality
Quantities x and y are inversely proportional only if growing x by the factor k ($k > 1$) means shrinking y by the factor $\frac{1}{k}$.

Inverse Variation (Lesson 8-1)
Are ℓ and w inversely proportional?
$A = \ell w$
$P = 2\ell + 2w$
- for a constant area—yes
- for a constant perimeter—no

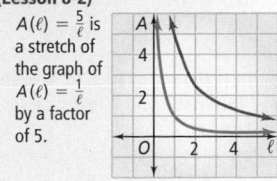

The Reciprocal Function Family (Lesson 8-2)
$A(\ell) = \frac{5}{\ell}$ is a stretch of the graph of $A(\ell) = \frac{1}{\ell}$ by a factor of 5.

2 Function
A rational function may have no asymptotes, one horizontal or oblique asymptote, and any number of vertical asymptotes.

Rational Functions and Their Graphs (Lesson 8-3)
Asymptotes:
For $y = \frac{2x^2}{x^2 - 9}$
horizontal: $y = 2$
vertical: $x = \pm 3$

For $y = \frac{2x^3 + 6x^2}{x^2 + 1}$
oblique: $y = 2x + 6$.
$y = \frac{x^4 + 5}{x^2 + 1}$ has no asymptotes.

Solving Equations Involving Rational Expressions (Lessons 8-4, 8-5, and 8-6)
$\frac{2x^2}{x^2 - 9} = \frac{x - 6}{x - 3} + \frac{18}{x^2 - 9}$
$\frac{2x^2}{x^2 - 9} = \frac{(x - 6)(x + 3)}{(x - 3)(x + 3)} + \frac{18}{x^2 - 9}$
$2x^2 = x^2 - 3x - 18 + 18$
$x^2 + 3x = 0$
$x(x + 3) = 0$
$x = 0$ ✓ or $x = -3$ ✗

3 Equivalence
$f(x) = \frac{x + a}{x^2 - a^2}$, $x \neq \pm a$, and $g(x) = \frac{1}{x - a}$, $x \neq \pm a$, are equivalent.

Chapter Vocabulary

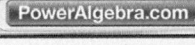

- branch (p. 531)
- combined variation (p. 523)
- complex fraction (p. 559)
- continuous graph (p. 539)
- discontinuous graph (p. 539)
- inverse variation (p. 520)
- joint variation (p. 523)
- non-removable discontinuity (p. 539)
- point of discontinuity (p. 539)
- rational equation (p. 565)
- rational expression (p. 548)
- rational function (p. 538)
- reciprocal function (p. 530)
- removable discontinuity (p. 539)
- simplest form (p. 548)

Choose the correct term to complete each sentence.

1. When the numerator and denominator of a rational expression are polynomials with no common factors, the rational expression is in ___?___ .

2. If a quantity varies directly with one quantity and inversely with another, it is a(n) ___?___ .

3. A(n) ___?___ has a fraction in its numerator, denominator, or both.

4. If a is a zero of the polynomial denominator of a rational function, the function has a(n) ___?___ at $x = a$.

5. A(n) ___?___ of the graph of a rational function is one of the continuous pieces of its graph.

PowerAlgebra.com | Chapter 8 Chapter Review | 573

---

relationship of $f(x)$ to $y = \frac{1}{x}$.
$(f(x) = \frac{x^2 + x - 6}{x^2 - 5x + 6} = \frac{(x - 2)(x + 3)}{(x - 2)(x - 3)}$
$= \frac{(x + 3)}{(x - 3)}$; There are non-removable points of discontinuity at $x = 3$ and $x = -3$. There is a removable discontinuity at $x = 2$. The graph of $f(x)$ is a transformation of $y = \frac{1}{x}$. It has a vertical shift of 3 units and a horizontal shift of 3 units.)

4. First step: Square both sides.

Second step: Factor the numerator and denominator of the expression on the right-hand side of the equation.

Third step: Simplify the expression on the right-hand side of the equation.

Fourth step: Multiply both sides of the equations by $(x + 2)$.

Fifth step: Expand the left-hand side of the equation.

Sixth step: Add $-x^3$ to both sides.
Then solve for x. $\left(x = \frac{2}{3}\right)$

Seventh step: Check $x = \frac{2}{3}$ in the original equation. The solution is extraneous, and the equation has no solution.

Answers

Chapter Review

1. simplest form
2. combined variation
3. complex fraction
4. pt. of discontinuity
5. branch

Essential Questions

BIG idea Proportionality
ESSENTIAL QUESTION Are two quantities inversely proportional if an increase in one corresponds to a decrease in the other?
ANSWER Quantities x and y are inversely proportional only if increasing x by the factor k ($k > 1$) means shrinking y by the factor $\frac{1}{k}$.

BIG idea Function
ESSENTIAL QUESTION What kinds of asymptotes are possible for a rational function?
ANSWER A rational function may have zero or more horizontal and zero or more of vertical asymptotes.

BIG idea Equivalence
ESSENTIAL QUESTION Are a rational expression and its simplified form equivalent?
ANSWER $f(x) = \frac{(x + a)}{(x^2 + a^2)}$, $x \neq \pm a$, and $g(x) = \frac{1}{(x - a)}$, $x \neq \pm a$, are equivalent.

Summative Questions UbD

Use the following prompts as you review this chapter with your students. The prompts are designed to help you assess your students' understanding of the BIG ideas they have studied.

- When one value changes with respect to another, how can you tell whether they show inverse or direct variation?
- When you simplify rational expressions, why must you include any restrictions on the domain of the original expression, even when they are not restrictions on the simplified form?
- How are operations with rational expressions like operations with fractions? How are they different?
- What would be the first step in the solution process of $\frac{x}{x + 2} - \frac{x}{x - 2} = \frac{3}{x^2 - 4}$ if solved algebraically? graphically?

Chapter Review 573

Answers

Chapter Review (continued)

6. 12

7. $y = \frac{72}{x}$

8. $y = 6x$

9. $z = \frac{7}{4}xy$; 56

10. $z = \frac{4x}{y}$; 2

11.

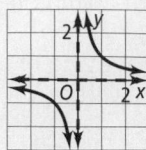

no x- or y-intercept; vert. asymptote: $x = 0$, horizontal asymptote: $y = 0$

12.

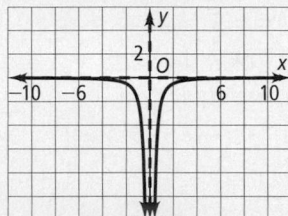

no x- or y-intercept; vert. asymptote: $x = 0$, horizontal asymptote: $y = 0$

13.

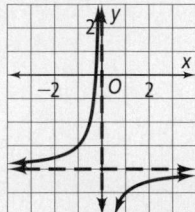

x-intercept: $(-0.25, 0)$, no y-intercept; vert. asymptote: $x = 0$, horizontal asymptote: $y = -4$

14.

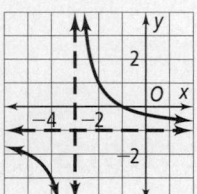

x-intercept: $(-1, 0)$, y-intercept: $(0, -\frac{1}{3})$; vert. asymptote: $x = -3$, horizontal asymptote: $y = -1$

15. $y = \frac{4}{x} + 3$

16. $y = \frac{4}{x - 2} + 2$

17. $y = \frac{4}{x + 3} - 4$

18. $y = \frac{4}{x - 4} - 3$

8-1 Inverse Variation

Quick Review

An equation in two variables of the form $y = \frac{k}{x}$ or $xy = k$, where $k \neq 0$, is an **inverse variation** with a *constant of variation k*. **Joint variation** describes when one quantity varies directly with two or more other quantities.

Example

Suppose that x and y vary inversely, and $x = 10$ when $y = 15$. Write a function that models the inverse variation. Find y when $x = 6$.

$y = \frac{k}{x}$

$15 = \frac{k}{10}$, so $k = 150$.

The inverse variation is $y = \frac{150}{x}$.

When $x = 6$, $y = \frac{150}{6} = 25$.

Exercises

6. Suppose that x and y vary inversely, and $x = 30$ when $y = 2$. Find y when $x = 5$.

Write a direct or inverse variation equation for each relation.

7.

x	y
3	24
4	18
8	9

8.

x	y
5	30
7	42
9	54

Write the function that models each relationship. Find z when $x = 4$ and $y = 8$.

9. z varies jointly with x and y. When $x = 2$ and $y = 2$, $z = 7$.

10. z varies directly with x and inversely with y. When $x = 5$ and $y = 2$, $z = 10$.

8-2 The Reciprocal Function Family

Quick Review

The graph of a **reciprocal function** has two parts called **branches**. The graph of $y = \frac{k}{x - b} + c$ is a translation of $y = \frac{k}{x}$ by b units horizontally and c units vertically. It has a vertical asymptote at $x = b$ and a horizontal asymptote at $y = c$.

Example

Graph the equation $y = \frac{3}{x - 2} + 1$. Identify the x- and y-intercepts and the asymptotes of the graph.

$b = 2$, so the vertical asymptote is $x = 2$.

$c = 1$, so the horizontal asymptote is $y = 1$.

Translate $y = \frac{3}{x}$ two units to the right and one unit up.

When $y = 0$, $x = -1$.
The x-intercept is $(-1, 0)$.

When $x = 0$, $y = -\frac{1}{2}$.
The y-intercept is $(0, -\frac{1}{2})$.

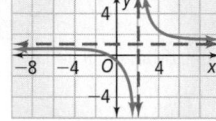

Exercises

Graph each equation. Identify the x- and y-intercepts and the asymptotes of the graph.

11. $y = \frac{1}{x}$

12. $y = \frac{-2}{x^2}$

13. $y = \frac{-1}{x} - 4$

14. $y = \frac{2}{x + 3} - 1$

Write an equation for the translation of $y = \frac{4}{x}$ that has the given asymptotes.

15. $x = 0, y = 3$

16. $x = 2, y = 2$

17. $x = -3, y = -4$

18. $x = 4, y = -3$

8-3 Rational Functions and Their Graphs

Quick Review

The **rational function** $f(x) = \frac{P(x)}{Q(x)}$ has a **point of discontinuity** for each real zero of $Q(x)$.

If $P(x)$ and $Q(x)$ have

- no common factors, then $f(x)$ has a vertical asymptote when $Q(x) = 0$.
- a common real zero a, then there is a hole or a vertical asymptote at $x = a$.
- degree of $P(x) <$ degree of $Q(x)$, then there is a horizontal asymptote at $y = 0$.
- degree of $P(x) =$ degree of $Q(x)$, then there is a horizontal asymptote at $y = \frac{a}{b}$, where a and b are the coefficients of the terms of greatest degree in $P(x)$ and $Q(x)$, respectively.
- degree of $P(x) >$ degree of $Q(x)$, then there is no horizontal asymptote.

Example

Find any points of discontinuity for the graph of the rational function $y = \frac{2.5}{x + 7}$. Describe any vertical or horizontal asymptotes and any holes.

There is a vertical asymptote at $x = -7$ and a horizontal asymptote at $y = 0$.

Exercises

Find any points of discontinuity for each rational function. Sketch the graph. Describe any vertical or horizontal asymptotes and any holes.

19. $y = \frac{x - 1}{(x + 2)(x - 1)}$

20. $y = \frac{x^3 - 1}{x^2 - 1}$

21. $y = \frac{2x^2 + 3}{x^2 + 2}$

22. The start-up cost of a company is \$150,000. It costs \$.17 to manufacture each headset. Graph the function that represents the average cost of a headset. How many must be manufactured to result in a cost of less than \$5 per headset?

8-4 Rational Expressions

Quick Review

A **rational expression** is in **simplest form** when its numerator and denominator are polynomials that have no common factors.

Example

Simplify the rational expression. State any restrictions on the variable.

$$\frac{2x^2 + 7x + 3}{x - 4} \cdot \frac{x^2 - 16}{x^2 + 8x + 15}$$

$$= \frac{(2x + 1)(x + 3)}{x - 4} \cdot \frac{(x - 4)(x + 4)}{(x + 3)(x + 5)}$$

$$= \frac{(2x + 1)(x + 4)}{x + 5}, x \neq -5, x \neq -3, \text{ and } x \neq 4$$

Exercises

Simplify each rational expression. State any restrictions on the variable.

23. $\frac{x^2 + 10x + 25}{x^2 + 9x + 20}$

24. $\frac{x^2 - 2x - 24}{x^2 + 7x + 12} \cdot \frac{x^2 - 1}{x - 6}$

25. $\frac{4x^2 - 2x}{x^2 + 5x + 4} \div \frac{2x}{x^2 + 2x + 1}$

26. What is the ratio of the volume of a sphere to its surface area?

19. pts. of discontinuity: $x = -2, 1$;

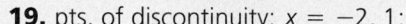
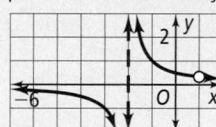

vert. asymptote: $x = -2$, horizontal asymptote: $y = 0$; hole at $x = 1$

20. pts. of discontinuity: $x = 1, -1$

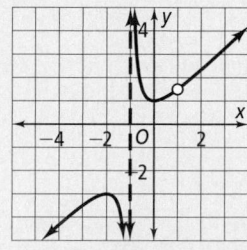

vert. asymptote: $x = -1$; hole at $x = 1$

21. no pts. of discontinuity

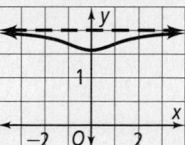

horizontal asymptote: $y = 2$

22.

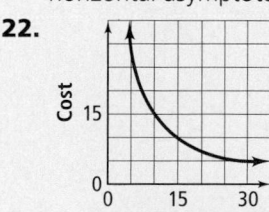

$\approx 31{,}056$ headsets

23. $\frac{x + 5}{x + 4}$; $x \neq -4$ or -5

24. $\frac{(x - 1)(x + 1)}{x + 3}$; $x \neq -4, -3,$ or 6

25. $\frac{(2x - 1)(x + 1)}{x + 4}$; $x \neq -4, -1,$ or 0

26. $\frac{r}{3}$, where r is the radius

Answers

Chapter Review (continued)

27. $\dfrac{3(3x-4)}{(x-2)(x+2)}$; $x \neq \pm 2$

28. $\dfrac{-x^2+3x+2}{x(x+1)(x-1)(x+3)}$; $x \neq \pm 1, 0,$ or -3

29. $\dfrac{2(x-1)}{3x-1}$

30. $\dfrac{1}{4(x+y)}$

31. -1

32. no solution

33. $-12, 9$

34. you: 10 mi/h friend: 8 mi/h

8-5 Adding and Subtracting Rational Expressions

Quick Review

To add or subtract rational expressions with different denominators, rewrite each expression with the LCD. A fraction that has a fraction in its numerator or denominator or in both is called a **complex fraction**. Sometimes you can simplify a complex fraction by multiplying the numerator and denominator by the LCD of all the rational expressions.

Example

Simplify the complex fraction. $\dfrac{\frac{1}{x}+3}{\frac{5}{y}+4}$

$$\frac{\frac{1}{x}+3}{\frac{5}{y}+4} = \frac{\left(\frac{1}{x}+3\right)\cdot xy}{\left(\frac{5}{x}+4\right)\cdot xy}$$

$$= \frac{\frac{1}{x}\cdot xy + 3\cdot xy}{\frac{5}{x}\cdot xy + 4\cdot xy}$$

$$= \frac{y+3xy}{5y+4xy}$$

Exercises

Simplify the sum or difference. State any restrictions on the variable.

27. $\dfrac{3x}{x^2-4} + \dfrac{6}{x+2}$

28. $\dfrac{1}{x^2-1} - \dfrac{2}{x^2+3x}$

Simplify the complex fraction.

29. $\dfrac{2-\frac{2}{x}}{3-\frac{1}{x}}$

30. $\dfrac{\frac{1}{x+y}}{4}$

Lesson 8-6 Solving Rational Equations

Quick Review

Solving a **rational equation** often requires multiplying each side by an algebraic expression. This may introduce extraneous solutions—solutions that solve the derived equation but not the original equation. Check all possible solutions in the original equation.

Example

Solve the equation. Check your solution.

$$\frac{1}{2x} - \frac{2}{5x} = \frac{1}{2}$$

$$10x\left(\frac{1}{2x} - \frac{2}{5x}\right) = 10x\left(\frac{1}{2}\right)$$

$$5 - 4 = 5x$$

$$x = \frac{1}{5}$$

Check $\quad \dfrac{1}{2\left(\frac{1}{5}\right)} - \dfrac{2}{5\left(\frac{1}{5}\right)} = \dfrac{5}{2} - 2 = \dfrac{1}{2}$ ✔

Exercises

Solve each equation. Check your solutions.

31. $\dfrac{1}{x} = \dfrac{5}{x-4}$

32. $\dfrac{2}{x+3} - \dfrac{1}{x} = \dfrac{-6}{x(x+3)}$

33. $\dfrac{1}{2} + \dfrac{x}{6} = \dfrac{18}{x}$

34. You travel 10 mi on your bicycle in the same amount of time it takes your friend to travel 8 mi on his bicycle. If your friend rides his bike 2 mi/h slower than you ride your bike, find the rate at which each of you is traveling.

Chapter Test

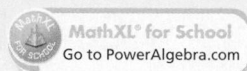

MathXL® for School
Go to PowerAlgebra.com

Do you know HOW?

Write a function that models each variation.

1. $x = 2$ when $y = -8$, and y varies inversely with x.

2. $x = 0.2$ and $y = 3$ when $z = 2$, and z varies jointly with x and y.

3. $x = \frac{1}{3}$, $y = \frac{1}{5}$, and $r = 3$ when $z = \frac{1}{2}$, and z varies directly with x and inversely with the product of r^2 and y.

Is the relationship between the values in each table a *direct variation*, an *inverse variation*, or *neither*? Write equations to model any direct or inverse variations.

4.

x	y
3	6
5	8
7	10
9	12

5.

x	y
4	32
8	16
16	8
32	4

Write and graph an equation of the translation of $y = \frac{7}{x}$ that has the given asymptotes.

6. $x = 1$; $y = 2$ **7.** $x = -3$; $y = -2$

For each rational function, identify any holes or horizontal or vertical asymptotes of the graph.

8. $y = \frac{x+1}{x-1}$ **9.** $y = \frac{x+3}{x+3}$

10. $y = \frac{x-2}{(x+1)(x-2)}$ **11.** $y = \frac{2x^2}{x^2-4x}$

12. $y = \frac{1}{x+2} - 3$ **13.** $y = \frac{x^2+5}{x-5}$

Simplify each complex fraction.

14. $\dfrac{\frac{2}{x}}{1-\frac{1}{y}}$ **15.** $\dfrac{3-\frac{3}{x}}{\frac{1}{2}-\frac{1}{x}}$

Simplify each rational expression. State any restrictions on the variable.

16. $\frac{x^2+7x+12}{x^2-9}$

17. $\frac{(x+3)(2x-1)}{x(x+4)} \div \frac{(-x-3)(2x+1)}{x}$

18. $\frac{x^2-1}{x^2+2x-3} - \frac{x+1}{x+3}$

19. $\frac{x(x+4)}{x-2} + \frac{x-1}{x^2-4}$

Solve each equation. Check your solutions.

20. $\frac{x}{2} = \frac{x+1}{4}$ **21.** $\frac{3}{x-1} = \frac{4}{3x+2}$

22. $\frac{3x}{x+1} = 0$ **23.** $\frac{3}{x+1} = \frac{1}{x^2-1}$

24. $\frac{1}{x} + \frac{1}{3} = \frac{6}{x^2}$ **25.** $\frac{1}{x} + \frac{x}{x+2} = 1$

26. Your neighbor can seal your driveway in 4 hours. Working together, you and your neighbor can seal it in 2.3 hours. How long would it take you to seal it working alone?

Do you UNDERSTAND?

27. Vocabulary Describe a situation that represents an inverse variation.

28. Compare and Contrast How is simplifying rational expressions similar to simplifying fractions? How is it different?

29. Writing When does a discontinuity result in a vertical asymptote? When does it result in a hole in the graph?

30. Open-Ended Write a function whose graph has a hole, a vertical asymptote, and a horizontal asymptote.

31. Reasoning State any restrictions on the variable in the complex fraction. $\dfrac{\frac{x-3}{x+4}}{\frac{x^2-1}{x}}$

20. 1
21. -2
22. 0
23. $\frac{4}{3}$
24. -6 or 3
25. 2
26. ≈ 5.4 h
27. Check students' work.
28. Answers may vary. Sample: In both situations, you find common factors and cancel them. Also, the denominator cannot be zero. Rational expressions may contain variable expressions, whereas fractions may contain only numbers.
29. A discontinuity is a vert. asymptote when the denominator is zero and the numerator and denominator have no common factors. When the numerator and denominator have a common factor a, then the discontinuity is a hole at $x = a$.
30. Check students' work.
31. $x \neq \pm 1$, 0, or -4

Answers

Chapter Test

1. $y = -\frac{16}{x}$

2. $z = \frac{10}{3}xy$

3. $z = \frac{2.7x}{r^2 y}$

4. neither

5. inv. variation; $y = \frac{128}{x}$

6. $y = \frac{7}{x-1} + 2$;

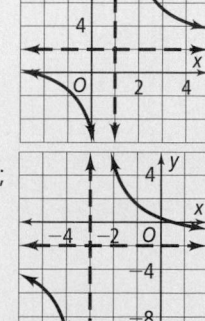

7. $y = \frac{7}{x+3} - 2$;

8. vert. asymptote: $x = 1$, horizontal asymptote: $y = 1$

9. hole at $x = -3$

10. hole at $x = 2$; vert. asymptote: $x = -1$, horizontal asymptote: $y = 0$

11. hole at $x = 0$; vert. asymptote: $x = 4$, horizontal asymptote: $y = 2$

12. vert. asymptote: $x = -2$, horizontal asymptote: $y = -3$

13. vert. asymptote: $x = 5$

14. $\frac{2y}{x(y-1)}$

15. $\frac{6(x-1)}{x-2}$

16. $\frac{x+4}{x-3}$; $x \neq -3$, or 3

17. $-\frac{2x-1}{(x+4)(2x+1)}$; $x \neq -4, -3, -\frac{1}{2}$, or 0

18. 0; $x \neq -3, 1$

19. $\frac{x^3+6x^2+9x-1}{x^2-4}$; $x \neq \pm 2$

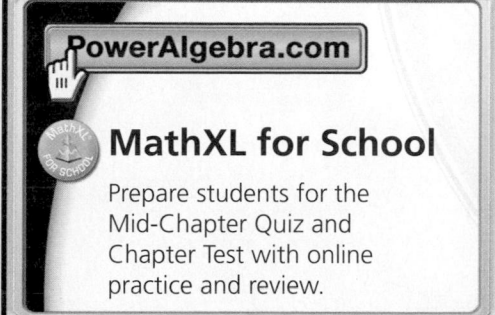

PowerAlgebra.com

MathXL for School

Prepare students for the Mid-Chapter Quiz and Chapter Test with online practice and review.

Item Number	Lesson
1	8-4
2	8-6
3	2-4
4	8-5
5	7-4
6	6-5
7	6-3
8	6-4
9	4-8
10	4-1
11	7-5
12	7-6
13	6-6
14	6-6
15	6-7
16	8-6
17	7-5
18	3-2
19	5-4
20	6-6
21	5-3
22	4-6
23	4-7
24	5-1
25	1-6
26	4-6
27	1-4
28	5-2
29	5-1
30	7-1
31	8-2
32	6-7
33	5-5
34	1-6

TIPS FOR SUCCESS

Some problems ask you to find the lateral area or the (total) surface area of a three-dimensional figure. Read the sample question at the right. Then follow the tips to answer the question.

What is the approximate lateral area of the cone shown below?

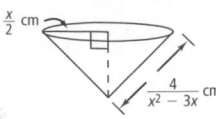

$\frac{x}{2}$ cm

$\frac{4}{x^2 - 3x}$ cm

Ⓐ $\frac{3}{x + 3}$ Ⓒ $\frac{3}{x - 3}$

Ⓑ $\frac{6}{x - 3}$ Ⓓ $\frac{6}{x + 3}$

TIP 1

Use the formula for the lateral area of a cone:
$S = \pi r \ell$.

TIP 2

Use the information from the diagram for the values you need in the formula.

Think It Through

radius: $r = \frac{x}{2}$

slant height: $\ell = \frac{4}{x^2 - 3x}$

$S = \pi r \ell$

$\quad = \pi \left(\frac{x}{2} \right) \left(\frac{4}{x^2 - 3x} \right)$

$\quad = \frac{2\pi}{x - 3}$

Since $\pi \approx 3$, the correct answer is B.

Vocabulary Builder

As you solve test items, you must understand the meanings of mathematical terms. Match each term with its mathematical meaning.

A. joint variation

B. branch

C. point of discontinuity

D. inverse variation

E. reciprocal function

I. a point where the graph of a function breaks into branches

II. each piece of a discontinuous graph

III. a relation represented by an equation of the form $y = \frac{k}{x}$ or $xy = k$, where $k \neq 0$

IV. a function that can be written in the form $f(x) = \frac{a}{x - h} + k$, where $a \neq 0$

V. one variable varies directly with two or more other variables

Multiple Choice

Read each question. Then write the letter of the correct answer on your paper.

1. Which expression equals $\frac{5x}{x^2 - 9} - \frac{4x}{x^2 + 5x + 6}$?

Ⓐ $\frac{7x}{(x - 3)(x + 3)(x + 2)}$

Ⓑ $\frac{x^2 - 2x}{(x - 3)(x + 3)(x + 2)}$

Ⓒ $\frac{x^2 + 22x}{(x - 3)(x + 3)(x + 2)}$

Ⓓ $\frac{9x^2 - 2x}{(x - 3)(x + 3)(x + 2)}$

2. If x is a real number, for what values of x is the equation $\frac{2x - 8}{4x^{-1}} = \frac{x^2 - 4x}{2}$ true?

Ⓕ all values of x

Ⓖ some values of x

Ⓗ no values of x

Ⓘ impossible to determine

Answers

Cumulative Test Prep

A. V

B. II

C. I

D. III

E. IV

1. C

2. F

3. What is the equation of the line that goes through the point $(-3, 2)$ and is parallel to the line shown in the graph below?

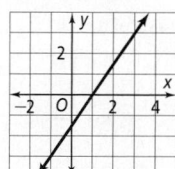

- Ⓐ $y + 3 = 1.5(x - 2)$
- Ⓑ $y + 2 = 1.5(x - 3)$
- Ⓒ $y - 3 = 1.5(x - 2)$
- Ⓓ $y - 2 = 1.5(x + 3)$

4. Which expression is a simpler form of the complex fraction $\dfrac{\frac{1}{x} + \frac{3}{y}}{\frac{2}{xy}}$?

- Ⓕ $\dfrac{3xy}{2}$
- Ⓗ $\dfrac{3}{2}$
- Ⓖ $\dfrac{3x + y}{2xy}$
- Ⓘ $\dfrac{3x + y}{2}$

5. Which is the first *incorrect* step in simplifying $\log_9 243$?

Step 1: $\log_9 243 = x$

Step 2: $\qquad 9^x = 243$

Step 3: $\qquad x = 243 \div 9$

Step 4: $\qquad = 27$

- Ⓐ Step 1
- Ⓒ Step 3
- Ⓑ Step 2
- Ⓓ Step 4

6. Which is/are the solution(s) of the equation $\sqrt{2x + 2} = 2x - 4$?

- Ⓕ $x = 3.5$ and $x = 1$
- Ⓖ $x = 3.5$ and $x = -1$
- Ⓗ $x = 3.5$
- Ⓘ $x = 1$

7. Which is the simplest form of the expression? $4\sqrt{18x^4} - 3\sqrt{72x^4}$

- Ⓐ $-6x^2\sqrt{2}$
- Ⓒ -6
- Ⓑ $-6x^2$
- Ⓓ none of the above

8. Ana and Matthew each worked out the same problem, as shown below. Which statement is true of their solutions?

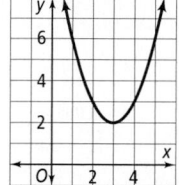

Ana's Work

$\dfrac{a^{\frac{2}{3}} b^{\frac{4}{3}}}{\sqrt[3]{a^5 b}} = \dfrac{a^{\frac{2}{3}} b^{\frac{4}{3}}}{a^{\frac{5}{3}} b}$

$= a^{\frac{2}{3} - \frac{3}{5}} b^{\frac{4}{3} - 1}$

$= a^{\frac{10}{15} - \frac{9}{15}} b^{\frac{4}{3} - \frac{3}{3}}$

$= a^{\frac{1}{15}} b^{\frac{1}{3}}$

Matthew's work

$\dfrac{a^{\frac{2}{3}} b^{\frac{4}{3}}}{\sqrt[3]{a^5 b}} = \dfrac{a^{\frac{2}{3}} b^{\frac{4}{3}}}{a^{\frac{5}{3}} b^{\frac{1}{3}}}$

$= a^{\frac{2}{3} - \frac{5}{3}} b^{\frac{4}{3} - \frac{1}{3}}$

$= a^{-1} b^1$

$= \dfrac{b}{a}$

- Ⓕ Ana is correct.
- Ⓖ Matthew is correct.
- Ⓗ Both answers are incorrect.
- Ⓘ Both answers are correct.

9. If $i = \sqrt{-1}$, what is the value of $-i^4$?

- Ⓐ i
- Ⓒ 1
- Ⓑ $-i$
- Ⓓ -1

10. What is the range of the graph shown below?

- Ⓕ $x \geq 3$
- Ⓗ $x \geq 2$
- Ⓖ $y \geq 3$
- Ⓘ $y \geq 2$

11. Given the equation $y = \log_x n$ where $n > 0$ and $y < 0$, which statement is valid for real values of x?

- Ⓐ $x < 0$
- Ⓒ $x \geq 0$
- Ⓑ $x \leq 0$
- Ⓓ $x > 0$

3. D
4. F
5. C
6. H
7. A
8. G
9. D
10. I
11. D

Answers

Cumulative Test Prep (continued)

12. F   **13.** C

14. I   **15.** 48

16. 5   **17.** 1003

18. 1   **19.** 21

20. −12   **21.** −0.89

22. $\frac{25}{4}$ **23.** 0

24. [2]

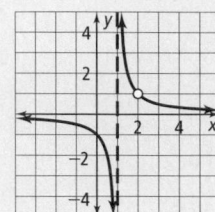

    [1] hole and asymptote are not shown

25. [2] $|2x - 5| < 9$

        $2x - 5 < 9$ or $2x - 5 > -9$

          $2x < 14$ or $2x > -4$

           $x < 7$ or $x > -2$

              $-2 < x < 7$

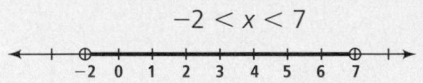

    [1] correct solution, with incorrect graph OR incorrect solution, correct graph given previous results OR correct solution and graph, without work shown

26. [2] substitute $a = 2$, $b = -12$, $c = -11$

        into the Quadratic Formula to find

        $x = \frac{6 \pm \sqrt{58}}{2}$

    [1] correct solution, without work shown

27. [2] $\frac{2g^2}{d} - c = 3x$

          $\frac{2g^2}{d} = 3x + c$

          $2g^2 = d(3x + c)$

           $g^2 = \frac{1}{2}d(3x + c)$

           $g = \pm\sqrt{\frac{d(3x + c)}{2}}$

    [1] appropriate method, with one computational error

28. [2] $x(x^2 - 12x + 35)$

        $x(x - 7)(x - 5)$

    [1] factored correctly, without work shown

29. [2] Since the highest degree of the polynomial is even, the graph does not have up and down end behavior.

    [1] incomplete explanation

30. [2]

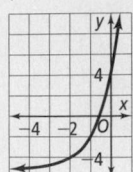

    [1] axes are not labeled

---

12. Which expression represents the solution to $4^x = 13$?

    Ⓕ $\frac{\log 13}{\log 4}$

    Ⓖ $\log_4 + \log_{13}$

    Ⓗ $\frac{\log 4}{\log 13}$

    Ⓘ $\log_{13} 4$

13. If $f(x) = x^2$ and $g(x) = x - 1$, which statement is true?

    Ⓐ $(f \circ g)(x) \geq (g \circ f)(x)$ for all values of x.

    Ⓑ $(f \circ g)(x) \leq (g \circ f)(x)$ for all values of x.

    Ⓒ $(f \circ g)(x) = (g \circ f)(x)$ only for $x = 1$.

    Ⓓ $(f \circ g)(x) \neq (g \circ f)(x)$ for any value of x.

14. If $g(x) = x^2 - 4$ and $h(x) = 4x - 6$, which expression is equal to $\left(\frac{g}{h}\right)(x)$?

    Ⓕ $\frac{4x - 6}{x^2 - 4}$

    Ⓖ $\frac{x^2 - 2}{4x - 3}$

    Ⓗ $x^2 - 4 - (4x - 6)$

    Ⓘ $\frac{(x + 2)(x - 2)}{2(2x - 3)}$

GRIDDED RESPONSE

15. Suppose that x and y vary inversely. What is the constant of variation if $x = 12$ when $y = 4$?

16. Solve for x: $\frac{5}{2x - 2} = \frac{15}{x^2 - 1}$.

17. Solve for x: $\log(x - 3) = 3$.

18. What is the x-coordinate of the solution of the system of equations?
$$\begin{cases} 2x + y = 6 \\ y - 3 = x \end{cases}$$

19. What is the remainder when $x^4 - 3x^2 + 7x + 3$ is divided by $x - 2$?

20. The product of three consecutive even integers is −2688. What is the value of the largest integer?

21. What is the smallest zero of $f(x) = 2x^5 - 4x^2 + 3x + 7$? Round your answer to the nearest hundredth.

22. What number do you add to each side of the equation when you solve $x^2 + 5x = 4$ by completing the square?

23. How many real roots does $y = x^2 - 3x + 7$ have?

Short Response

24. Sketch the graph of $y = \frac{x - 2}{(x - 2)(x - 1)}$.

25. Solve the inequality $|2x - 5| < 9$. Graph the solution.

26. Solve $2x^2 - 11 = 12x$.

27. Solve the equation $\frac{2g^2}{d} - c = 3x$ for g. Show your work.

28. Factor $x^3 - 12x^2 + 35x$ completely.

29. Explain how you know that the graph of $f(x) = -x^4 - 3x + 7$ does not have up and down end behavior.

30. Graph $y = 3^{x+2} - 5$.

Extended Response

31. Explain how to find an equation for the translation of $y = \frac{3}{x}$ that has asymptotes at $x = -13$ and $y = 5$.

32. What is the inverse of $y = x^2 + 15$? Is the inverse a function? Explain.

33. A third-degree polynomial equation with rational coefficients has roots -4 and $-4i$. If the leading coefficient of the equation is $\frac{3}{2}$, what is the equation? Show your work.

34. Graph $y + 2 < |x - 4|$. How did you decide where to shade and whether the boundary was a dashed or a solid line?

---

31. [4] The graph of $y = \frac{3}{x}$ is translated 13 units to the left and 5 units up to get the graph of the eq. $y = \frac{3}{x + 13} + 5$.

    [3] appropriate method, one careless error

    [2] correct eq., incomplete explanation

    [1] correct eq., without explanation

32. [4] $x = y^2 + 15$

        $y = \pm\sqrt{x - 15}$; no; it does not pass the vert. line test.

    [3] one computational error

    [2] incomplete or incorrect explanation

    [1] correct inv., no other questions answered or explained.

33. [4] $y = \frac{3}{2}(x + 4)(x + 4i)(x - 4i)$

        $= \frac{3}{2}(x + 4)(x^2 + 16)$

        $= \frac{3}{2}(x^3 + 4x^2 + 16x + 64)$

        $= \frac{3}{2}x^3 + 6x^2 + 24x + 96$

    [3] one computational error

    [2] leading coefficient was not taken into account

    [1] correct eq., without work shown

34. [4]

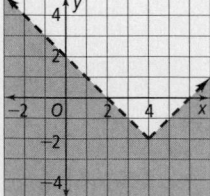

    Substitute a pt. that is not on the boundary into the inequality. If the pt. satisfies the inequality, shade that region. If not, shade the other region. The boundary is a dashed line since the inequality sign is strictly less than.

    [3] careless error in graph, with correct and complete explanation

    [2] incomplete explanation

    [1] correct graph, without any explanation

Get Ready!

Lesson 2-1 **Evaluating Functions**

For each function, find $f(1), f(2), f(3)$, and $f(4)$.

1. $f(x) = 2x + 7$ **2.** $f(x) = 5x - 4$

3. $f(x) = 0.2x + 0.7$ **4.** $f(x) = -5x + 3$

5. $f(x) = 4x - \frac{2}{3}$ **6.** $f(x) = -3x - 9$

Lesson 1-1 **Identifying Mathematical Patterns**

Identify a pattern and find the next three numbers in the pattern.

7. $9, 4, -1, -6, \ldots$ **8.** $1, 2, 4, 8, \ldots$

9. $18, 9, 10, 1, 2, \ldots$ **10.** $7, 10, 13, 16, \ldots$

Lesson 8-5 **Simplifying Complex Fractions**

Simplify each complex fraction.

11. $\dfrac{1 - \frac{1}{3}}{\frac{1}{2}}$ **12.** $\dfrac{\frac{1}{3} + \frac{1}{6}}{\frac{2}{3}}$ **13.** $\dfrac{1}{1 - \frac{2}{5}}$ **14.** $\dfrac{1 - \frac{3}{8}}{2 + \frac{1}{4}}$

Looking Ahead Vocabulary

15. Think of a function and evaluate the function for the input numbers 1, 2, 3, 4, and 5. List the five outputs in order. This list is a *sequence* of numbers. The sequence can be infinitely long.

16. Use a linear function to generate a sequence of five numbers. Beginning with the second number, subtract the number that precedes it. Continue doing this until you have found all four differences. Are the results the same? If so, you have discovered that your sequence has a *common difference*.

17. Now use an exponential function to define your sequence. Instead of subtracting, divide each number by the number that precedes it. Do this until you find all four quotients. Are these four results the same? If so, you have discovered that your sequence has a *common ratio*.

Get Ready!

Assign this diagnostic assessment to determine if students have the prerequisite skills for Chapter 9.

Lesson	Skill
2-1	Evaluate Functions
1-1	Identify Mathematical Patterns
8-5	Simplify Complex Fractions

To remediate students, select from these resources (available for every lesson).
- Online Problems (PowerAlgebra.com)
- Reteaching (All-in-One Teaching Resources)
- Practice (All-in-One Teaching Resources)

Why Students Need These Skills

EVALUATING FUNCTIONS
Students will need to evaluate functions when determining the nth term in a sequence or series.

IDENTIFYING MATHEMATICAL PATTERNS
Students will need to identify mathematical patterns within sequences to write recursive definitions and explicit formulas for the pattern.

SIMPLIFYING COMPLEX FRACTIONS
Students will need to simplify complex fractions when finding the sum of an infinite geometric series.

Looking Ahead Vocabulary

SEQUENCE Ask students what differentiates a sequence from a set of numbers.

COMMON DIFFERENCE Ask students what it means to have something in common. Have them consider what it means to have a difference in common.

COMMON RATIO Ask students how to find the ratio between two numbers. Have them compare common difference to common ratio.

Answers

Get Ready!

1. 9, 11, 13, 15

2. 1, 6, 11, 16

3. 0.9, 1.1, 1.3, 1.5

4. −2, −7, −12, −17

5. $3\frac{1}{3}, 7\frac{1}{3}, 11\frac{1}{3}, 15\frac{1}{3}$

6. −12, −15, −18, −21

7. subtract 5; −11, −16, −21

8. mult. by 2; 16, 32, 64

9. alternate subtract 9 and add 1; −7, −6, −15

10. add 3; 19, 22, 25

11. $\frac{4}{3}$

12. $\frac{3}{4}$

13. $\frac{5}{3}$

14. $\frac{5}{18}$

15. Answers may vary. Sample: $f(x) = 2x - 1$; 1, 3, 5, 7, 9

16. Answers may vary. Sample: $g(x) = 1 - 2x$; −1, −3, −5, −7, −9; yes; common difference: −2

17. Answers may vary. Sample: $h(x) = 5(2)^x$; 10, 20, 40, 80, 160; yes; common ratio: 2

Chapter 9 Overview

Chapter 9 expands on students' understandings and skills related to sequences and series. In this chapter, students will develop the answers to the Essential Questions posed on the student page as they learn the concepts and skills bulleted below.

BIG idea **Variable**

ESSENTIAL QUESTIONS How can you represent the terms of a sequence explicitly? How can you represent them recursively?

- Students will identify mathematical patterns found in a sequence.
- Students will find a rule (or formula) to describe a pattern.

BIG idea **Equivalence**

ESSENTIAL QUESTION What are equivalent explicit and recursive definitions for an arithmetic sequence?

- Students will find the common difference of an arithmetic sequence.

BIG idea **Modeling**

ESSENTIAL QUESTIONS How can you model a geometric sequence? How can you model its sum?

- Students will find the common ratio of a geometric sequence.
- Students will determine whether a geometric series converges.

CHAPTER 9 Sequences and Series

PowerAlgebra.com

Your place to get all things digital

VIDEO Download videos connecting math to your world.

VOCABULARY Math definitions in English and Spanish

SOLVE IT! The online Solve It will get you in gear for each lesson.

DYNAMIC ACTIVITIES Interactive! Vary numbers, graphs, and figures to explore math concepts.

ONLINE PROBLEMS Download Step-by-Step Problems with Instant Replay.

ONLINE HOMEWORK Get and view your assignments online.

MathXL FOR SCHOOL Extra practice and review online

Arithmetic and geometric sequences are types of patterns. What patterns do you see in these terraced rice fields? You will learn about all kinds of sequences in this chapter.

Vocabulary

English/Spanish Vocabulary Audio Online:

English	Spanish
arithmetic sequence, p. 592	progresión aritmética
arithmetic series, p. 607	serie aritmética
common difference, p. 592	diferencia común
common ratio, p. 600	razón común
converge, p. 617	convergir
diverge, p. 617	divergir
explicit formula, p. 585	fórmula explícita
geometric sequence, p. 600	progresión geométrica
geometric series, p. 614	serie geométrica
limits, p. 610	límites
recursive formula, p. 586	formula recursiva

PowerAlgebra.com

Chapter 9 Overview

Use these online assets to engage your students. These include support for the Solve It and step-by-step solutions for Problems.

 Show the student-produced video demonstrating relevant and engaging applications of the new concepts in the chapter.

 Find online definitions for new terms in English and Spanish.

 Start each lesson with an attention-getting Problem. View the Problem online with helpful hints.

My Math Video

My Math Video
Use this photo to introduce students to mathematical patterns.

Q What pattern do you see in the planted rice seedlings? **[Samples: rows and columns are the same distance apart; a pattern of squares with seedlings at the vertices]**

Q What pattern do you see in the differences between the heights of the terraced rice fields? **[The difference between the heights of any two consecutive terraces is about the same.]**

Q If a worker is planting a row of rice seedlings 30 cm. apart, how far will the nth seedling be from the first? **[$30(n - 1)$ cm.]**

EXTENSION
Have students research how and why rice is planted in this pattern. One method of planting in this pattern is to tie strings to evenly spaced sticks on the edges of the fields. Planting rice in this way increases the production.

BIG ideas

1 Variable
Essential Questions How can you represent the terms of a sequence explicitly? How can you represent them recursively?

2 Equivalence
Essential Question What are equivalent explicit and recursive definitions for an arithmetic sequence?

3 Modeling
Essential Questions How can you model a geometric sequence? How can you model its sum?

Chapter Preview

PowerAlgebra.com   Chapter 9 Sequences and Series   583

 Increase students' depth of knowledge with interactive online activities.

 Show problems from each lesson solved step by step. Instant replay allows students to go at their own pace when studying online.

 Prepare students for the Mid-Chapter Quiz and Chapter Test with online practice and review.

SEQUENCES AND SERIES
Math Background

UbD

Variable

BIG idea Quantities are used to form expressions, equations, and inequalities. An expression refers to a quantity but does not make a statement about it. An equation (or an inequality) is a statement about the quantities it mentions. Using variables in place of numbers in equations (or inequalities) allows the statement of relationships among numbers that are unknown or unspecified.

ESSENTIAL UNDERSTANDINGS

9-1 If the numbers in a list follow a pattern, variables may be used to relate each number in the list to its numerical position in the list.

9-2 In an arithmetic sequence, the difference between any two consecutive terms is always the same number. This number can be represented by a variable.

9-4 When two terms and the number of terms in a finite arithmetic sequence are known, they can be substituted for variables in a formula to find the sum of the terms.

Equivalence

BIG idea A single quantity may be represented by many different expressions. The facts about a quantity may be expressed by many different equations (or inequalities).

ESSENTIAL UNDERSTANDINGS

9-1 If the numbers in a list follow a pattern, each number in the list can be related to its numerical position in the list with equivalent formulas.

9-2 In an arithmetic sequence, the difference between any two consecutive terms is always the same number. An arithmetic sequence can be built by adding the same number to each term.

9-4 When two terms and the number of terms in a finite arithmetic sequence are known, one of two equivalent formulas can be used to find the sum of the terms.

Modeling

BIG idea Many real-world mathematical problems can be represented algebraically. These representations can lead to algebraic solutions.

ESSENTIAL UNDERSTANDINGS

9-1 If the numbers in a list follow a pattern, a model can relate each number in the list to its numerical position in the list with a formula.

9-3 In a geometric sequence, the ratio of any term (after the first) to its preceding term is a constant value, no matter what two terms are compared. Each term of a geometric sequence can be built by multiplying the previous term by that constant.

9-5 Just as with finite arithmetic series, the sum of a finite geometric series can be found using a formula. The first term, the number of terms, and the common ratio must be known.

Arithmetic Sequences and Series

A **sequence** is an ordered list of numbers. Each number in a sequence is a *term* of the sequence.

An **arithmetic sequence** is a sequence where the difference between consecutive terms is constant. This difference is the common difference d.

Example: Is the sequence 6, 10, 14, 18, . . . arithmetic?

Using consecutive terms:

$10 - 6 = 4 \qquad 14 - 10 = 4 \qquad 18 - 14 = 4$

The difference between consecutive terms is constant, therefore the sequence is arithmetic.

Explicit Formula

An explicit formula can be used to represent terms or find a certain term. For an arithmetic sequence, the nth term is given by the formula $a_n = a_1 + (n - 1)d$, for $n \geq 1$.

Example: Find the 20th term of the arithmetic sequence 8, 11, 14, 17, . . .

If $d = 11 - 8 = 3$, and $a = 8$, then $n = 20$.

$a_{20} = 8 + (20 - 1)3 = 65$

Arithmetic Series

An arithmetic series is the sum of terms in an arithmetic sequence. The sum of a finite series can be found with the formula $S_n = \frac{n}{2}(a_1 + a_n)$.

Example: Find the sum of $5 + 10 + 15 + \ldots + 150$.

If $a_1 = 5$, and $a_n = 150$, then $n = \frac{150}{5} = 30$.

$S_n = \frac{30}{2}(5 + 150) = 2325$

Summation Notation

Summation notation can be used to represent finite and infinite arithmetic series.

Upper limit →

Lower limit → $\displaystyle\sum_{n=1}^{10} 4n + 1$ ← Explicit formula

The sum is $S_n = \frac{10}{2}(5 + 41) = 230$.

Common Errors With Arithmetic Sequences and Series

Students should not assume that two terms can be used to determine an explicit formula. For example, the sequence 3, 6, . . . could be arithmetic or geometric.

When using **summation notation**, students must remember to count the actual number of terms rather than looking at the upper limit. For example, if the lower limit is 0 and the upper limit is 10, the number of terms is 11.

Geometric Sequences and Series

A **geometric sequence** is a sequence in which the ratio of any term (after the first) to its preceding term is a constant value.

Example: Is the sequence 2, 6, 18, 54 geometric?

Using consecutive terms:

$$\frac{6}{2} = 3 \qquad \frac{18}{6} = 3 \qquad \frac{54}{18} = 3$$

The ratio is constant. This is a geometric sequence in which the common ratio is 3.

Explicit Formula

An explicit formula is used to represent terms or find a term. The nth term of a geometric sequence is given by the formula $a_n = a_1 r^{n-1}$, for $n \geq 1$.

Example: Find the 11th term of the geometric sequence 4, −8, 16, −32, . . .

$$r = \frac{-8}{4} = -2, a_1 = 4, n = 11$$

$$a_{11} = (4)(-2)^{10} = 4096$$

Geometric Series

A geometric series is the sum of terms in a geometric sequence. The sum of a **finite series** can be found by:

$$S_n = \frac{a_1\left(1 - r^n\right)}{1 - r}$$

Example: Find the sum of $1 + 3 + 9 + \ldots + 729$.

Step 1 Use the explicit formula to find the number of terms:

$r = \frac{3}{1} = 3$, $a_1 = 1$, so $729 = (1)(3)^{n-1}$ and $n = 7$.

Step 2 Use the formula for the sum of a finite series:

$$S_7 = \frac{1(1 - 3^7)}{1 - 3} = \frac{-2186}{-2} = 1093$$

Common Errors With Geometric Sequences and Series

Geometric sequence errors can occur when the ratio is negative. Remind students that r^n means that the entire value of r (including the negative) is raised to the power.

Recursive Definitions

A recursive definition specifies the first term of a series plus a recursive formula that generate each successive term.

Recursive Definition for Arithmetic Sequences

$a_n = a_{n-1} + d$, for $n > 1$

Example: Write the next four terms of the sequence given by the recursive formula $a_1 = -6$ and $a_n = a_{n-1} - 2$.

$$a_2 = -6 - 2 = -8, a_3 = -8 - 2 = -10,$$
$$a_4 = -10 - 2 = -12, a_5 = -12 - 2 = -14$$

The sequence is $-6, -8, -10, -12, -14, \ldots$

Recursive Definition for Geometric Sequences

$a_n = a_{n-1}r$, for $n > 1$

Example: Write the first four terms of the sequence given by the recursive formula $a_1 = 3$, $a_n = 2a_{n-1}$.

$a_1 = 3, a_2 = 2(3) = 6, a_3 = 2(6) = 12, a_4 = 2(12) = 24$

The sequence is 3, 6, 12, 24, . . .

Writing Recursive Definitions

To write a recursive definition from a sequence of numbers,
- determine whether the sequence is arithmetic or geometric
- calculate the common ratio or common difference
- identify the first term

Example: Write the recursive definition of 12, 16, 20, 24, . . .

The sequence is arithmetic. The common difference is 4. The first term is 12.

$$a_1 = 12, \quad a_n = a_{n-1} + 4$$

Example: Write the recursive definition of $-8, -16, -32, -64, \ldots$

The sequence is geometric. The common ratio is 2. The first term is -8.

$$a_1 = -8, \quad a_n = a_{n-1} \cdot 2$$

Common Errors When Using Recursive Definitions

Errors can occur as students become familiar with **subscript notation**. Have students write the meanings in words to help them understand the following: a_n means the current term; a_{n-1} means the term before a_n.

SEQUENCES AND SERIES
Pacing and Assignment Guide

		TRADITIONAL		BLOCK
Lesson	Teaching Day(s)	Basic	Average	Block
9-1	1	Problems 1–4 Exs. 7–13 odd, 14–32 even, 33, 38, 49, 54–67	Problems 1–4 Exs. 7–13 odd, 14–32 even, 33–38, 39–51 odd, 54–67	**Day 1** Problems 1–4 Exs. 7–13 odd, 14–32 even, 33–38, 39–51 odd, 54–67
9-2	1	Problems 1–4 Exs. 7–11 odd, 13–27, 34, 41, 50, 60–72	Problems 1–4 Exs. 7–19 odd, 20–32 even, 41–49 odd, 50–58 even, 60–72	Problems 1–4 Exs. 7–19 odd, 20–32 even, 41–49 odd, 50–58 even, 60–72
9-3	1	Problems 1–4 Exs. 7–20, 38, 39, 44–46, 48–65	Problems 1–4 Exs. 7–20, 22–38 even, 39–47 odd, 48–65	**Day 2** Problems 1–4 Exs. 7–20, 22–38 even, 39–47 odd, 48–65
9-4	1	Problems 1–3 Exs. 8–20, 31, 36–49	Problems 1–3 Exs. 8–14 even, 15 –20, 21–33 odd, 36–49	**Day 3** Problems 1–3 Exs. 8–14 even, 15–20, 21–33 odd, 36–49
9-5	1	Problems 1–3 Exs. 8–19, 21–24, 31, 36–41	Problems 1–3 Exs. 8–24, 25–33 odd, 36–41	**Day 4** Problems 1–3 Exs. 8–24, 25–33 odd, 36–41
Review	1	Chapter 9 Review	Chapter 9 Review	**Day 5** Chapter 9 Review Chapter 9 Test
Assess	1	Chapter 9 Test	Chapter 9 Test	
Total		**7 Days**	**7 Days**	**5 Days**

Note: Pacing does not include Concept Bytes and other feature pages.

Resources

	For the Chapter	9-1	9-2	9-3	9-4	9-5
Planning						
Teacher Center Online Planner & Grade Book	I	I	I	I	I	I
Interactive Learning & Guided Instruction						
My Math Video	I					
Solve It!		I T M	I T M	I T M	I T M	I T M
Student Companion (SP)*		P M	P M	P M	P M	P M
Vocabulary Support		I P M	I P M	I P M	I P M	I P M
Got It? Support		I P	I P	I P	I P	I P
Dynamic Activity			I	I		
Online Problems		I	I	I	I	I
Additional Problems		M	M	M	M	M
English Language Learner Support (TR)		E P M	E P M	E P M	E P M	E P M
Activities, Games, and Puzzles		E M	E M	E M	E M	E M
Teaching With TI Technology With CD-ROM						
TI-Nspire™ Support CD-ROM		✓	✓	✓	✓	✓
Lesson Check & Practice						
Student Companion (SP)*		P M	P M	P M	P M	P M
Lesson Check Support		I P	I P	I P	I P	I P
Think About a Plan (TR)*		E P M	E P M	E P M	E P M	E P M
Practice Form K (TR)*		E P M	E P M	E P M	E P M	E P M
Standardized Test Prep (TR)*		P M	P M	P M	P M	P M
Practice Form G (TR)*		E P M	E P M	E P M	E P M	E P M
Extra Practice	E M					
Find the Errors!	M					
Enrichment (TR)		E P M	E P M	E P M	E P M	E P M
Answers and Solutions CD-ROM	✓	✓	✓	✓	✓	✓
Assess & Remediate						
ExamView CD-ROM	✓	✓	✓	✓	✓	✓
Lesson Quiz		I T M	I T M	I T M	I T M	I T M
Quizzes and Tests Form K (TR)*	E P M			E P M		E P M
Quizzes and Tests Form G (TR)*	E P M			E P M		E P M
Reteaching (TR)		E P M	E P M	E P M	E P M	E P M
Performance Tasks (TR)*	P M					
Cumulative Review (TR)*	P M					
Progress Monitoring Assessments	I P M					

(TR) Available in All-In-One Teaching Resources   * Spanish available

1 Interactive Learning

Solve It!

PURPOSE To identify, continue, and describe a pattern mathematically

PROCESS Students may

- continue drawing the pattern of squares and adding the numbers in the squares.
- find and continue the pattern of differences between the number in the central square of each figure (8, 12, 16, . . .).
- analyze the pattern and write a formula using a variable that corresponds to figures 1–4.

FACILITATE

Q In Figure 1, $4 \times 1 = 4$. In Figure 2, $4 \times 1 + 4 \times 2 = 12$. What is another way to write $4 \times 1 + 4 \times 2$? **[$4(1 + 2)$ or 4×3]**

Q How can 24 be obtained from the other numbers shown in Figure 3? **[$4(1 + 2 + 3) = 24$]**

Q For the nth figure, the central number will be equal to 4 times what? Use words to describe the relationship. **[4 times the sum of the integers from 1 to n]**

Q How can you write this relationship using numbers? **[$4(1 + 2 + 3 + \ldots + n)$]**

If students know the formula for adding n integers, have them find the formula for this pattern. **[$4\left(\dfrac{n(n + 1)}{2}\right) = 2n(n + 1)$]**

ANSWER See Solve It in Answers on next page.

CONNECT THE MATH This Solve It introduces a new kind of pattern called a *sequence*. In the lesson, students will generate sequences from formulas and write formulas to describe sequences.

Objectives To identify mathematical patterns found in a sequence
To use a formula to find the nth term of a sequence

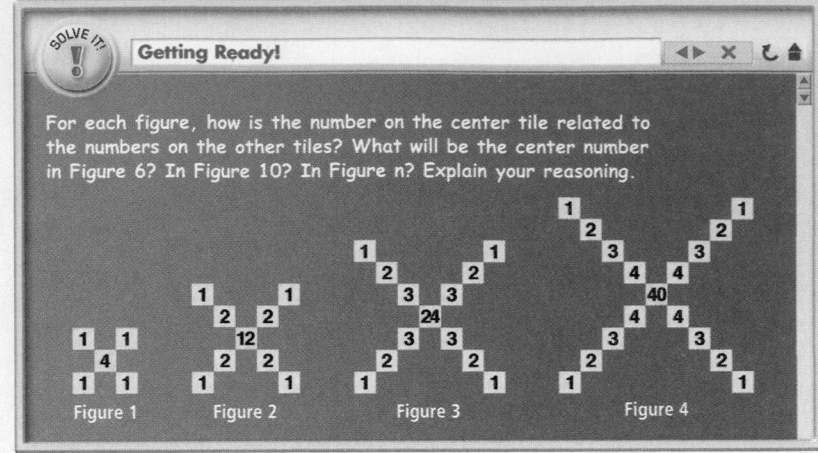

Figure 1   Figure 2   Figure 3   Figure 4

Sometimes you can easily state a rule to describe a pattern. At other times, you have to do a bit of work to find a rule.

Lesson Vocabulary
- sequence
- term
- explicit formula
- recursive formula

Focus Question What is a sequence?

A **sequence** is an ordered list of numbers. Each number in a sequence is a **term** of the sequence. You can represent a term of a sequence by using a variable with a subscript number to indicate its position in the sequence. For example, a_5 is the fifth term in the sequence $a_1, a_2, a_3, a_4, \ldots$.

The subscripts of sequence terms are often positive integers starting with 1. If so, you can generalize a term as a_n, the nth term in the sequence.

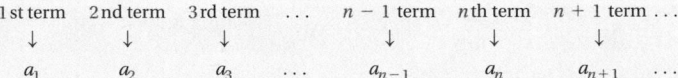

1st term	2nd term	3rd term	. . .	$n − 1$ term	nth term	$n + 1$ term . . .
↓	↓	↓		↓	↓	↓
a_1	a_2	a_3	. . .	$a_{n−1}$	a_n	a_{n+1} . . .

BIG ideas   Equivalence
Modeling
Variable

UbD

ESSENTIAL UNDERSTANDINGS

- If the numbers in a list follow a pattern, it may be possible to relate each number in the list to its numerical position in the list with a rule or formula.
- A sequence can be defined explicitly by describing its nth term with a formula using n or recursively by stating its first term and a formula for its nth term using the $(n − 1)$ term.

Math Background

A sequence can be represented by an explicit formula or by a recursive definition.

An explicit formula

- allows direct computation of any term for a sequence.
- describes the nth term of a sequence using n.
- is easy to evaluate for the nth term.

- works well for finding terms in a sequence that are far apart.
- can be difficult to find since there is no one method.

A recursive definition

- requires an initial condition to compute the next term with a recursive formula.
- defines each term after the first term using the previous term.
- moves from one term to the next and is easy to evaluate for adjacent terms.
- works well for small segments of a sequence.
- is easy to find given an initial condition, rate of change, and any constant value.

Support Student Learning

Use the **Algebra 2 Companion** to engage and support students during instruction. See Lesson Resources at the end of this lesson for details.

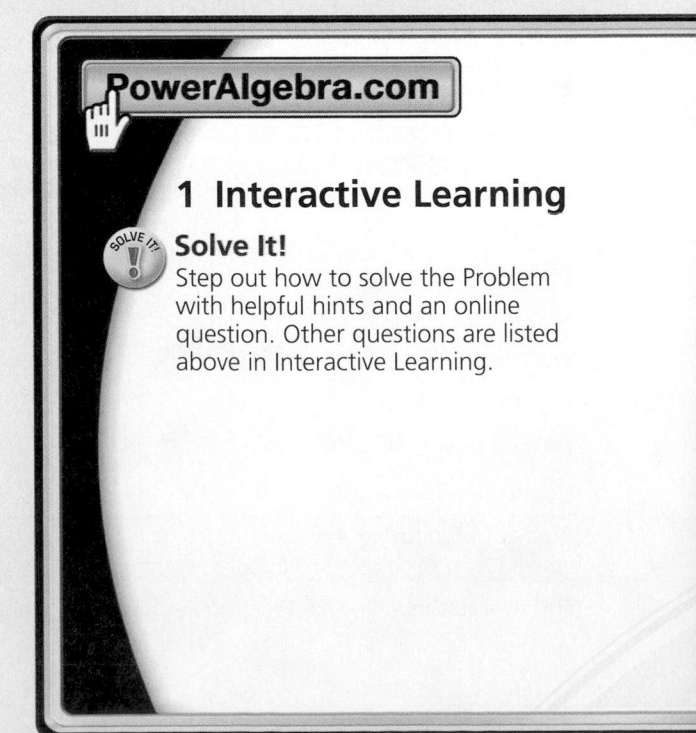

PowerAlgebra.com

1 Interactive Learning

Solve It!
Step out how to solve the Problem with helpful hints and an online question. Other questions are listed above in Interactive Learning.

An **explicit formula** describes the *n*th term of a sequence using the number *n*.

For example, in the sequence 2, 4, 6, 8, 10, . . . , the *n*th term is twice the value of *n*. You write this as $a_n = 2n$. The table shows how to find a_n by substituting the value of *n* into the explicit formula.

n	*n*th term
1	$a_1 = 2(1) = 2$
2	$a_2 = 2(2) = 4$
3	$a_3 = 2(3) = 6$
4	$a_4 = 2(4) = 8$

Problem 1 Generating a Sequence Using an Explicit Formula

Plan

How does the explicit formula help you find the value of a term?
Replace *n* in the formula with the number of the term. Simplify to find the value of the term.

A sequence has an explicit formula $a_n = 3n - 2$. What are the first 10 terms of this sequence?

Write the formula.	$a_n = 3n - 2$
Substitute 1 for *n*.	$a_1 = 3(1) - 2$
Simplify.	$= 1$
Substitute 2 for *n*.	$a_2 = 3(2) - 2$
Simplify.	$= 4$

You can use a table to organize your work for the remaining terms.

n	a_n
3	$a_3 = 3(3) - 2 = 7$
4	$a_4 = 3(4) - 2 = 10$
5	$a_5 = 3(5) - 2 = 13$
6	$a_6 = 3(6) - 2 = 16$
7	$a_7 = 3(7) - 2 = 19$
8	$a_8 = 3(8) - 2 = 22$
9	$a_9 = 3(9) - 2 = 25$
10	$a_{10} = 3(10) - 2 = 28$

Substitute 3 for *n* and simplify.

And so on.

The first ten terms are 1, 4, 7, 10, 13, 16, 19, 22, 25, 28.

Got It? 1. A sequence has an explicit formula $a_n = 12n + 3$. What is term a_{12} in the sequence?

2 Guided Instruction

Problem 1

Terms and variables with subscripts are usually read aloud by saying the variable, then "sub," then the subscripted letter or number: "*a* sub 1," "*a* sub 2," "*a* sub *n*."

Q How can you use a graphing calculator to generate a table with the same values shown in the table on your page? **[Sample: Key the equation $y = 3x - 2$. Then use the Table function with TblStart = 3 and ΔTbl = 1.]**

Q From the formula, would you expect the sequence to have a constant difference of 3? Explain. **[Yes; the variable *n* has a constant coefficient of 3. The sequence will increase by 3 for each increase of 1 in the variable.]**

Q How are the sequence formula $a_n = 3n - 2$ and the linear function $y = 3x - 2$ the same? How are they different? **[Sample: Both increase by 3 for every increase of 1 in the variable. The linear function has a domain of all real numbers, but the sequence formula has a domain of natural numbers.]**

Got It?   EXTENSION

Q If you knew that $a_{10} = 123$, how could you find a_9 without substituting in the formula? Find a_9. **[The constant coefficient on the variable is 12, so a_9 must be 12 less than a_{10}. Thus $a_9 = 111$.]**

Q What is a_{n-1}? What is a_{n+1}? **[$a_{n-1} = 12n - 9$; $a_{n+1} = 12n + 15$.]**

Q What is the difference between a_{37} and a_{41}? **[48]**

2 Guided Instruction

 Each Problem is worked out and supported online.

Problem 1
Generating a Sequence Using an Explicit Formula
Animated

Problem 2
Writing a Recursive Definition for a Sequence
Animated

Problem 3
Writing an Explicit Formula for a Sequence
Animated

Problem 4
Using Formulas to Find Terms of a Sequence

Support in Algebra 2 Companion
• Vocabulary
• Key Concepts
• Got It?

Answers

Solve It!
It is the sum of the numbers on the other tiles; 84; 220; $2n(n + 1)$

Got It?
1. 147

Problem 2

This problem shows how to write a recursive definition for triangular numbers.

> **Q** What is the relationship between the number of the term and the difference from the previous term? **[The number of the term is identical to the difference from the previous term.]**
>
> **Q** Why must you state the initial condition when giving a recursive definition? **[Each term in a recursive definition is defined as an arithmetic operation on the previous term. If a_1 is not given, then no other terms can be found.]**

EXTENSION

> **Q** If the recursive definition of a sequence were $a_1 = 5$ and $a_n = a_{n-1} + n$, what sequence would result? **[5, 7, 10, 14, 19, 25, 32, …]**

Got It?

> **Q** In 2a, is the pattern based on simple addition or on multiplication? Explain. **[Multiplication; there is no pattern in the differences between consecutive terms, but there is a pattern of ratios: $a_2 - a_1 = 1$; $a_3 - a_2 = 4$; $a_4 - a_3 = 18$; $\frac{a_2}{a_1} = 2$; $\frac{a_3}{a_2} = 3$; $\frac{a_4}{a_3} = 4$.]**
>
> **Q** In 2b, what pattern do you see in the differences of successive terms? **[The differences make up the sequence of square numbers greater than 1.]**

Hint
A recursive formula is used to find the next term after a given term in a sequence.

Sometimes you can see the pattern in a sequence by comparing each term after the first term to the one that came before it. For example, in the sequence 133, 130, 127, 124, …, each term is equal to three less than the previous term.

A recursive definition for this sequence contains two parts.
(a) an initial condition (the value of the first term): $a_1 = 133$
(b) a **recursive formula** (relates each term to the one before it): $a_n = a_{n-1} - 3$, for $n > 1$

Problem 2 Writing a Recursive Definition for a Sequence

The number of blocks in a two-dimensional pyramid is a sequence that follows a recursive formula. Look at the picture below. What is a recursive definition for the sequence?

Think	Write
Count the number of blocks in each pyramid.	1, 3, 6, 10, 15, 21
Subtract consecutive terms to find out what happens from one term to the next.	$a_2 - a_1 = 3 - 1 = 2$ $a_3 - a_2 = 6 - 3 = 3$ $a_4 - a_3 = 10 - 6 = 4$ $a_5 - a_4 = 15 - 10 = 5$ $a_6 - a_5 = 21 - 15 = 6$
Use n to express the relationship between successive terms.	$a_n - a_{n-1} = n$
To write a recursive definition, state the initial condition and the recursive formula.	$a_1 = 1$ and $a_n = a_{n-1} + n$.

Hint
Look for simple addition or multiplication patterns to relate consecutive terms.

✓ **Got It?** **2.** What is a recursive definition for each sequence?
  a. 1, 2, 6, 24, 120, 720, …
  b. 1, 5, 14, 30, 55, …

586 Chapter 9 Sequences and Series

Additional Problems

1. A sequence has an explicit formula $a_n = n^2 - 10$. What is the term a_8 in the sequence?

ANSWER $a_8 = 54$

2. What is a recursive definition for the sequence 4, 14, 44, 134, …?

ANSWER $a_1 = 4$ and $a_n = 3a_{n-1} + 2$

3. What is an explicit formula for the sequence 1, −1, 1, −1, 1, …?

ANSWER $a_n = (-1)^{n-1}$ (or $a_n = (-1)^{n+1}$)

4. In a certain kind of online auction, the price for an item begins high and falls over time until someone purchases the item. If an item begins at $100 and decreases by 25% every 5 minutes, what is the price after a half hour? Round to the nearest cent.

ANSWER $17.80

586 Chapter 9

Recursive definitions can be very helpful when you look at a small section of a sequence. However, if you want to know both a_3 and a_{5000} of a sequence, an explicit formula is often more useful.

 Problem 3 Writing an Explicit Formula for a Sequence

What is the 100th term of the pyramid sequence in Problem 2?

Step 1 Find an explicit formula.

Consider different ways of expressing the terms of the pyramid sequence.

a_1	a_2	a_3	a_4	a_5	...	a_n
1	$1 + 2$	$1 + 2 + 3$	$1 + 2 + 3 + 4$	$1 + 2 + 3 + 4 + 5$	...	$1 + 2 + \ldots + n$
1	3	6	10	15	...	■

So, you can write the nth term of the pyramid sequence as the sum of the first n positive integers.

$$a_n = 1 + 2 + 3 + \cdots + (n - 2) + (n - 1) + n$$

You can also write the nth term as follows.

$$a_n = n + (n - 1) + (n - 2) + \cdots + 3 + 2 + 1$$

Now add the two previous equations as shown to get the following result:

$$
\begin{array}{rl}
a_n = & 1 \ + \ 2 \ + \ 3 \ + \cdots + (n - 2) + (n - 1) + \ n \\
a_n = & n \ + (n - 1) + (n - 2) + \cdots + \ 3 \ + \ 2 \ + \ 1 \\
\hline
2a_n = & (n + 1) + (n + 1) + (n + 1) + \cdots + (n + 1) + (n + 1) + (n + 1)
\end{array}
$$

$$2a_n = n \cdot (n + 1)$$ ⟵ There are n terms. Every term is $(n + 1)$.

$$a_n = \tfrac{1}{2}n(n + 1)$$ ⟵ Solve for a_n.

The explicit formula for this sequence is $a_n = \tfrac{1}{2}n(n + 1)$.

Step 2 Use the explicit formula to find the 100th term.

Write the formula. $a_n = \tfrac{1}{2}n(n + 1)$

Substitute 100 for n. $a_{100} = \tfrac{1}{2}(100)(100 + 1)$

Add. $= \tfrac{1}{2}(100)(101)$

Simplify. $= 5050$

The 100th term is 5050.

✔ **Got It? 3. a.** What is an explicit formula for the sequence 0, 3, 8, 15, 24, ... ? What is the 20th term?

  b. Reasoning Why is using an explicit formula often more efficient than using a recursive definition?

Plan

Why do you use the explicit formula to find a_{100}?
Because starting with a_1, it would take 99 iterations of the formula to get a_{100} using the recursive formula.

Hint

Remember that addition is commutative. You can reverse the order of the terms without changing the sum.

Problem 3

There are several strategies for finding an explicit formula for the nth term of a sequence. A good starting strategy is to put the terms of the sequence in line with the counting numbers 1, 2, 3, 4, ... and look for a pattern. The procedure shown in Problem 3 may not work for other sequences.

Q Why was the expanded sum for a_n written forward, then backward, and then added? **[Sample: Writing the expanded sum forward, then backward, and then adding them together, makes each term in the expanded sum equal to $(n + 1)$. Once all the terms are equal to the same number, the sum can be factored to find the explicit formula.]**

Q Does the explicit formula for the triangular numbers remind you of a common geometric formula? If so, which one? **[Yes; the formula for the area of a triangle.]**

Got It?

Q What are the differences between successive terms? Do you know another sequence that has this same pattern of differences? **[The differences are the odd numbers: 3, 5, 7, 9, ...; sample: The sequence of square numbers also has this pattern of differences.]**

Q What are two ways to write the formula? **[$n^2 - 1$ or $(n + 1)(n - 1)$]**

Answers

Got It? (continued)

2. a. $a_1 = 1$ and $a_n = na_{n-1}$

  b. $a_1 = 1$ and $a_n = a_{n-1} + n^2$

3. a. $a_n = n^2 - 1$; 399

  b. To find the nth term using an explicit formula, you simply substitute for n in the formula. To find the nth term using a recursive definition may require many iterations.

Problem 4

Q Why was a recursive definition used rather than an explicit formula? **[Sample: A recursive definition was easier to fit than an explicit formula. Because a calculator makes repeated operations trivial, a recursive definition is close enough.]**

Q What does the "ANS" you keyed into your calculator mean in the recursive definition? **[ANS means the previous answer or a_{n-1}.]**

Got It?

Q Can you find the answer by solving the equation $\$1000 = 1.018x + 29$? Explain. **[No. This is a linear function, and Pierre's debt is not accumulating linearly.]**

3 Lesson Check

Do you know HOW?   ERROR INTERVENTION
• If students have trouble getting started on Exercises 1 and 2, suggest they substitute 1, 2, 3, 4, and 5 for n in each formula.

Do you UNDERSTAND?
• If students say there is no error in Exercise 6, clarify that the first term is a_1, not a_0.

Close

Q What are some advantages and disadvantages of recursive definitions and explicit formulas? **[Samples: Recursive definitions are usually easy to find. Recursive definitions cannot calculate any term directly, while explicit formulas can. Explicit formulas can be used to find the number of a term when a value is given.]**

 **Problem 4** Using Formulas to Find Terms of a Sequence

Finance Pierre began the year with an unpaid balance of $300 on his credit card. Because he had not read the credit card agreement, he did not realize that the company charged 1.8% interest each month on his unpaid balance, in addition to a $29 penalty in any month he might fail to make a minimum payment. Pierre ignored his credit card bill for 4 consecutive months before finally deciding to pay off the balance. What did he owe after 4 months of non-payment?

Step 1   Write a recursive definition.
Initial condition: $a_0 = 300$ (Use a_0 so that a_1 represents the balance after 1 month.)
Recursive formula: $a_n = 1.018 \cdot a_{n-1} + 29$, for $n > 1$

 Think
Why is it helpful to change FLOAT to 2? This problem involves money, so real-world solutions will have only 2 decimal places.

Step 2   Use a calculator. In the **MODE** menu, change the digit display from **FLOAT** to 2.

Step 3   Use a calculator. Enter 300. Then enter the recursive formula **1.018ANS + 29** and press `enter` for the balance after one month.

Step 4   Press `enter` three more times until the calculator shows the balance after 4 months.

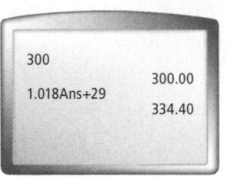

After 4 months, Pierre owes $441.36.

 Got It?   **4.** Suppose the credit card company allowed Pierre to continue making no payments. After how many months would his balance exceed $1000?

Focus Question   What is a sequence?
Answer   A sequence is an ordered list of numbers, called terms. To find the nth term of a sequence, use either an explicit formula or a recursive definition.

Lesson Check

Do you know HOW?
Find the first five terms of each sequence.

1. $a_n = 5n - 3$ **2.** $a_n = n^2 - 2n$

3. What is a recursive definition for the sequence $3, 6, 12, 24, \ldots$?

4. What is an explicit formula for the sequence $5, 8, 11, 14, \ldots$?

Do you UNDERSTAND?

5. Vocabulary Explain the difference between an explicit formula and a recursive definition. Give an example of each.

6. Error Analysis A student writes that $a_n = 3n + 1$ is an explicit formula for the sequence $1, 4, 7, 10, \ldots$. Explain the student's error and write a correct explicit formula for the sequence.

PowerAlgebra.com

3 Lesson Check

For a digital lesson check, use the Got It questions.

Support in Algebra 2 Companion
• Lesson Check

4 Practice

Assign homework to individual students or to an entire class.

Answers

Got It? (continued)
4. 18 months

Lesson Check
1. 2, 7, 12, 17, 22
2. −1, 0, 3, 8, 15
3. $a_1 = 3$ and $a_n = 2a_{n-1}$
4. $a_n = 2 + 3n$
5. A recursive formula defines the terms in a sequence by relating each term after the first term to the one before it and requires that the previous term be known to find a given term. An example of a recursive formula for the sequence $8, 4, 2, 1, \ldots$ is $a_1 = 8$ and $a_n = \frac{1}{2}a_{n-1}$. An explicit formula describes the nth term of a sequence using the variable n and only requires the number of the term to be known. An example of an explicit formula

for the sequence $1, 3, 5, 7, \ldots$ is $a_n = 2n - 1$.

6. The "+1" in $a_n = 3n + 1$ is incorrect for the sequence $1, 4, 7, 10, \ldots$ The correct explicit formula is $a_n = -2 + 3n$.

Practice and Problem-Solving Exercises

 Practice

Find the first six terms of each sequence.

◀ See Problem 1.

Guided Practice

7. $a_n = -5n + 1$
To start, substitute 1 for n. $\qquad$ $a_1 = -5(1) + 1$
Simplify. $\qquad\qquad\qquad$ $= -4$

8. $a_n = \frac{1}{2}n$ $\qquad$ **9.** $a_n = n^2 + 1$ $\qquad$ **10.** $a_n = 3n^2 - n$

11. $a_n = 2^n - 1$ $\qquad$ **12.** $a_n = \frac{1}{2}n^3 - 1$ $\qquad$ **13.** $a_n = (-3)^n$

Write a recursive definition for each sequence.

◀ See Problem 2.

Guided Practice

14. $80, 77, 74, 71, 68, \ldots$
To start, look for simple addition $\qquad$ $77 - 80 = -3$
or multiplication patterns to relate $\qquad$ $74 - 77 = -3$
consecutive terms. $\qquad\qquad\qquad$ $71 - 74 = -3$
$\qquad\qquad\qquad\qquad\qquad\qquad$ $68 - 71 = -3$

15. $4, 8, 16, 32, 64, \ldots$ $\qquad$ **16.** $0, 3, 7, 12, 18, \ldots$ $\qquad$ **17.** $1, 4, 7, 10, 13, \ldots$

18. $100, 10, 1, 0.1, 0.01, \ldots$ $\qquad$ **19.** $\frac{1}{2}, \frac{1}{4}, \frac{1}{8}, \frac{1}{16}, \frac{1}{32}, \ldots$ $\qquad$ **20.** $4, -8, 16, -32, 64, \ldots$

Write an explicit formula for each sequence. Find the tenth term.

◀ See Problem 3.

21. $4, 5, 6, 7, 8, \ldots$ $\qquad$ **22.** $3, 7, 11, 15, 19, \ldots$ $\qquad$ **23.** $-2\frac{1}{2}, -2, -1\frac{1}{2}, -1, \ldots$

24. $1, 4, 9, 16, \ldots$ $\qquad$ **25.** $\frac{1}{2}, \frac{1}{3}, \frac{1}{4}, \frac{1}{5}, \frac{1}{6}, \ldots$ $\qquad$ **26.** $\frac{1}{2}, -\frac{1}{4}, \frac{1}{8}, -\frac{1}{16}, \ldots$

Find the eighth term of each sequence.

27. $-2, -1, 0, 1, 2, \ldots$ $\qquad$ **28.** $43, 41, 39, 37, 35, \ldots$ $\qquad$ **29.** $40, 20, 10, 5, \frac{5}{2}, \ldots$

30. $6, 1, -4, -9, \ldots$ $\qquad$ **31.** $\frac{1}{2}, \frac{1}{4}, \frac{1}{8}, \frac{1}{16}, \frac{1}{32}, \ldots$ $\qquad$ **32.** $\frac{3}{4}, -\frac{3}{2}, 3, -6, \ldots$

33. Exercise You walk 1 mile the first day of your training, 1.2 miles the second day, 1.6 miles the third day, and 2.4 miles the fourth day. If you continue this pattern, how many miles do you walk the seventh day?

◀ See Problem 4.

 **Apply**

Determine whether each formula is *explicit* or *recursive*. Then find the first five terms of each sequence.

34. $a_n = 2a_{n-1} + 3$, where $a_1 = 3$ $\qquad$ **35.** $a_n = (n - 5)(n + 5)$

36. $a_n = -3a_{n-1}$, where $a_1 = -2$ $\qquad$ **37.** $a_n = -4n^2 - 2$

---

4 Practice

ASSIGNMENT GUIDE
Basic: 7–12, 14–19, 21–31, 33, 38, 49

Average: 7–13 odd, 14–32 even, 33–38, 39–51 odd

Standardized Test Prep: 54–58

Mixed Review: 59–67

Reasoning exercises have blue headings.

Applications exercises have red headings.

EXERCISE 49: Use the Think About a Plan worksheet in the **Student Companion** (also available in the Teaching Resources in print and online) to further support students' development in becoming independent learners.

HOMEWORK QUICK CHECK
To check students' understanding of key skills and concepts, go over Exercises 9, 16, 33, 38, and 49.

Practice and Problem-Solving Exercises

7. $-4, -9, -14, -19, -24, -29$

8. $\frac{1}{2}, 1, \frac{3}{2}, 2, \frac{5}{2}, 3$

9. $2, 5, 10, 17, 26, 37$

10. $2, 10, 24, 44, 70, 102$

11. $1, 3, 7, 15, 31, 63$

12. $-\frac{1}{2}, 3, \frac{25}{2}, 31, \frac{123}{2}, 107$

13. $-3, 9, -27, 81, -243, 729$

14. $a_1 = 80$ and $a_n = a_{n-1} - 3$

15. $a_1 = 4$ and $a_n = 2a_{n-1}$

16. $a_1 = 0$ and $a_n = a_{n-1} + (n + 1)$

17. $a_1 = 1$ and $a_n = a_{n-1} + 3$

18. $a_1 = 100$ and $a_n = \frac{1}{10}a_{n-1}$

19. $a_1 = \frac{1}{2}$ and $a_n = \frac{1}{2}a_{n-1}$

20. $a_1 = 4$ and $a_n = -2a_{n-1}$

21. $a_n = n + 3; 13$

22. $a_n = 4n - 1; 39$

23. $a_n = \frac{n - 6}{2}; 2$

24. $a_n = n^2; 100$

25. $a_n = \frac{1}{n + 1}; \frac{1}{11}$

26. $a_n = -\left(-\frac{1}{2}\right)^n$ or $a_n = (-1)^{n+1}\frac{1}{2^n}$ or $a_n = (-1)^{n-1}\frac{1}{2^n}; -\frac{1}{1024}$

27. 5

28. 29

29. $\frac{5}{16}$

30. -29

31. $\frac{1}{256}$

32. -96

33. 13.6 mi

34. recursive; 3, 9, 21, 45, 93

35. explicit; $-24, -21, -16, -9, 0$

36. recursive; $-2, 6, -18, 54, -162$

37. explicit; $-6, -18, -38, -66, -102$

Answers

Practice and Problem-Solving
Exercises (continued)

38. $140

39. 15; 26; 40

40. 20, 23; $a_n = 3n + 2$, explicit OR
$a_n = a_{n-1} + 3$, $a_1 = 5$, recursive

41. 96, 192; $a_n = 3 \cdot 2^{n-1}$, explicit OR
$a_n = 2a_{n-1}$, $a_1 = 3$, recursive

42. 216, 343; $a_n = n^3$, explicit

43. 4096, 16,384; $a_n = 4^n$, explicit OR
$a_n = 4a_{n-1}$, $a_1 = 4$, recursive

44. 144, 169; $a_n = (n + 6)^2$, explicit OR
$a_n = a_{n-1} + 2n + 11$, $a_1 = 49$, recursive

45. −1, 1; $a_n = (-1)^n$, explicit OR $a_n = -1(a_{n-1})$,
$a_1 = -1$, recursive

46. −1, $-\frac{1}{2}$; $a_n = \frac{-32}{2^n}$, explicit OR $a_n = \frac{a_{n-1}}{2}$,
$a_1 = -16$, recursive

47. −47, −40; $a_n = -82 + 7n$, explicit OR
$a_n = a_{n-1} + 7$, $a_1 = -75$, recursive

48. −11, −19; $a_n = 29 - 8n$, explicit OR
$a_n = a_{n-1} - 8$, $a_1 = 21$, recursive

49. a. 25 boxes

  b. 110 boxes

  c. 9 levels

50. 25, 36, 49, 64

51. $\frac{16}{5}, \frac{25}{6}, \frac{36}{7}, \frac{49}{8}$

52. $\frac{5}{6}, \frac{6}{7}, \frac{7}{8}, \frac{8}{9}$

53. Answers may vary. Sample:

  a. 1, −2, 4, −8, . . .

  b. $a_n = -2(a_{n-1})$, and $a_1 = 1$; $a_n = (-2)^{n-1}$

  c. −524,288

---

38. Think About a Plan You invested money in a company and each month you receive a payment for your investment. Over the first four months, you received $50, $52, $56, and $62. If this pattern continues, how much do you receive in the tenth month?
  • What pattern do you see between consecutive terms?
  • Can you write a recursive or explicit formula to describe the pattern?
  • How can you use your formula to find the amount you receive in the tenth month?

39. Entertainment Suppose you are building a tower of cards with levels as displayed below. Copy and complete the table, assuming the pattern continues.

Number of Levels	Cards Needed
1	2
2	7
3	■
4	■
5	■

Find the next two terms in each sequence. Write a formula for the *n*th term. Identify each formula as *explicit* or *recursive*.

40. 5, 8, 11, 14, 17, . . .   **41.** 3, 6, 12, 24, 48, . . .   **42.** 1, 8, 27, 64, 125, . . .

43. 4, 16, 64, 256, 1024, . . .   **44.** 49, 64, 81, 100, 121, . . .   **45.** −1, 1, −1, 1, −1, 1, . . .

46. −16, −8, −4, −2, . . .   **47.** −75, −68, −61, −54, . . .   **48.** 21, 13, 5, −3, . . .

49. Geometry Suppose you are stacking boxes in levels that form squares. The numbers of boxes in successive levels form a sequence. The figure at the right shows the top four levels as viewed from above.
  a. How many boxes of equal size would you need for the next lower level?
  b. How many boxes of equal size would you need to add three levels?
  c. Suppose you are stacking a total of 285 boxes. How many levels will you have?

Use the given rule to write the 4th, 5th, 6th, and 7th terms of each sequence.

50. $a_n = (n + 1)^2$ **51.** $a_n = \frac{n^2}{n + 1}$ **52.** $a_n = \frac{n + 1}{n + 2}$

53. a. Open-Ended Write four terms of a sequence of numbers that you can describe both recursively and explicitly.
  b. Write a recursive definition and an explicit formula for your sequence.
  c. Find the 20th term of the sequence by evaluating one of your formulas. Use the other formula to check your work.

SAT/ACT

54. Scientists determine an object is moving at the rate of $(5 - \sqrt{2})$ ft/s. How many seconds will it take the object to travel 125 ft? Round the answer to the nearest tenth of a second.

55. What is the solution of $\sqrt{4x - 23} - 3 = 2$?

56. Using a calculator, what is the solution of $1080 = 15^{3x-4}$? Round the answer to the nearest hundredth.

57. Using the change of base formula, what is the solution of $\log_5 x = \log_3 20$? Round the answer to the nearest tenth.

58. The battery power available to operate a deep space probe is given by the formula $P = 42e^{-0.005t}$, where P is power in watts and t is time in years. For how many years can the probe run if it requires 35 watts? Round the answer to the nearest tenth of a year.

Mixed Review

Solve each equation. Check the solution. ◀ See Lesson 8-6.

59. $\dfrac{y}{y + 1} = \dfrac{2}{3}$ **60.** $\dfrac{4}{2a} = \dfrac{5}{a + 6}$ **61.** $\dfrac{3}{b + 2} = \dfrac{6}{b - 1}$

Find the slope of the line that passes through the two points. ◀ See Lesson 2-3.

62. $(4, 5)$ and $(1, 8)$ **63.** $(-3, -3)$ and $(2, 2)$ **64.** $(1, 3)$ and $(4, 9)$

Get Ready! To prepare for Lesson 9-2, do Exercises 65–67.

Identify the pattern and find the next three terms. ◀ See Lesson 1-1.

65. $10, 8, 6, 4, 2, 0, \ldots$ **66.** $100, 117, 134, 151, 168, \ldots$ **67.** $\dfrac{5}{7}, \dfrac{8}{7}, \dfrac{11}{7}, 2, \ldots$

Standardized Test Prep
54. 34.9
55. 12
56. 2.19
57. 80.5
58. 36.5

Mixed Review
59. 2
60. 4
61. -5
62. -1
63. 1
64. 2
65. subtract 2; $-2, -4, -6$
66. add 17; 185, 202, 219
67. add $\dfrac{3}{7}$; $\dfrac{17}{7}, \dfrac{20}{7}, \dfrac{23}{7}$

Lesson Resources

Differentiated Remediation

Additional Instructional Support

Algebra 2 Companion

Students can use the **Algebra 2 Companion** worktext (4 pages) as you teach the lesson. Use the Companion to support

- New Vocabulary
- Key Concepts
- Got It for each Problem
- Lesson Check

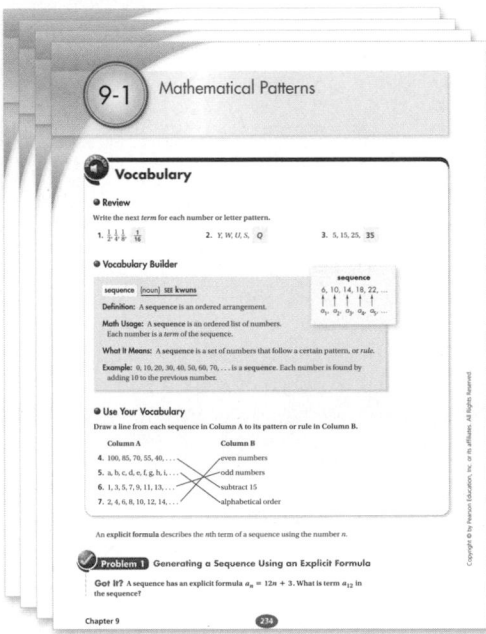

ELL Support

Assess Understanding Divide students into pairs. Have one member of each pair write one recursive definition and one explicit formula. Allow them to consult the textbook. Have the other member of each pair identify which is which and describe how he or she could tell.

"Write your name in cursive." If students do not know cursive script, demonstrate by writing your own name and indicating the letters and how they are connected.

"What are some words that describe cursive writing?" Expected answers include *connected, smooth, curved, looped*.

"In cursive writing, many letters curve or loop back onto themselves. *Recursive* is the same as *cursive* with *re-* added to the front. In English, *re-* added to the front of a verb often means 'going back.' For example, *reset* means 'go back to the original setting.'"

"What do you think *recursive* means? Does this make sense with how a recursive definition works?"

5 Assess & Remediate

Lesson Quiz

1. What are the first five terms of the sequence $a_n = \frac{n}{n+1}$?
2. What is a recursive definition for the sequence $0, -3, -6, -9, \ldots$?
3. What is an explicit formula for the sequence $0, -3, -6, -9, \ldots$?
4. **Do you UNDERSTAND?** Over the last 40 years, the population of a city has increased by roughly 2% each year. If the population was 220,000 at the beginning of this period a_0, what was the population 10 years later?

ANSWERS TO LESSON QUIZ

1. $\frac{1}{2}, \frac{2}{3}, \frac{3}{4}, \frac{4}{5}, \frac{5}{6}$
2. $a_1 = 0$ and $a_n = a_{n-1} - 3$
3. $a_n = -3n + 3$
4. about 268,179

PRESCRIPTION FOR REMEDIATION
Use the student work on the Lesson Quiz to prescribe a differentiated review assignment:

Points	Differentiated Remediation
0–2	Intervention
3	On-level
4	Extension

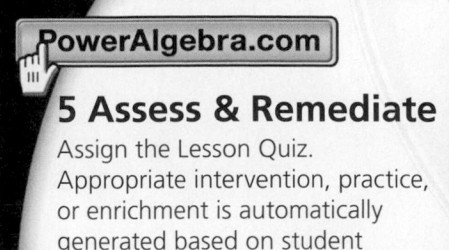

PowerAlgebra.com

5 Assess & Remediate
Assign the Lesson Quiz. Appropriate intervention, practice, or enrichment is automatically generated based on student performance.

Intervention

- **Reteaching** (2 pages) Provides reteaching and practice exercises for the key lesson concepts. Use with struggling students or absent students.
- **English Language Learner Support** Helps students develop and reinforce mathematical vocabulary and key concepts.

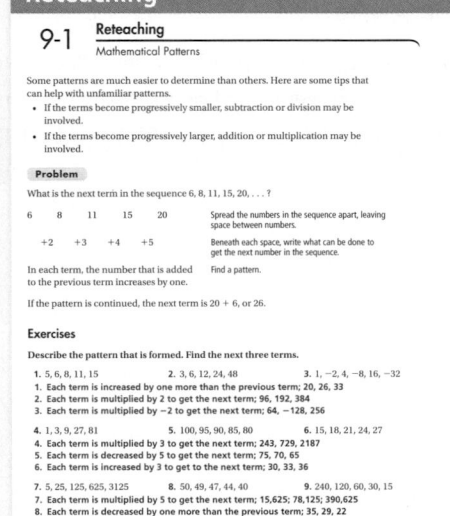

Differentiated Remediation *continued*

On-Level

- **Practice** (2 pages) Provides extra practice for each lesson. For more challenging practice exercises, use the Form G Practice pages found in the All-in-One Teaching Resources and online.
- **Think About a Plan** Helps students develop specific problem-solving skills and strategies by providing scaffolded guiding questions.
- **Standardized Test Prep** Focuses on all major exercises, all major question types, and helps students prepare for the high-stakes assessments.

Extension

- **Enrichment** Provides students with interesting problems and activities that extend the concepts of the lesson.
- **Activities, Games, and Puzzles** Worksheets that can be used for concepts development, enrichment, and for fun!

Student Companion/ All-in-One Resources/Online
Practice page 1

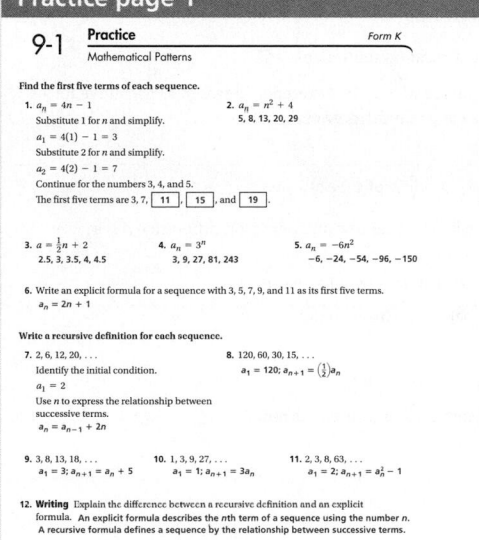

9-1 Practice *Form K*
Mathematical Patterns

Find the first five terms of each sequence.

1. $a_n = 4n - 1$
   Substitute 1 for n and simplify.
   $a_1 = 4(1) - 1 = 3$
   Substitute 2 for n and simplify.
   $a_2 = 4(2) - 1 = 7$
   Continue for the numbers 3, 4, and 5.
   The first five terms are 3, 7, [11], [15], and [19].
2. $a_n = n^2 + 4$
   5, 8, 13, 20, 29
3. $a = \frac{1}{2}n + 2$
   2.5, 3, 3.5, 4, 4.5
4. $a_n = 3^n$
   3, 9, 27, 81, 243
5. $a_n = -6n^2$
   −6, −24, −54, −96, −150
6. Write an explicit formula for a sequence with 3, 5, 7, 9, and 11 as its first five terms.
   $a_n = 2n + 1$

Write a recursive definition for each sequence.

7. 2, 6, 12, 20, . . .
   Identify the initial condition.
   $a_1 = 2$
   Use n to express the relationship between successive terms.
   $a_n = a_{n-1} + 2n$
8. 120, 60, 30, 15, . . .
   $a_1 = 120;\ a_{n+1} = \left(\frac{1}{2}\right)a_n$
9. 3, 8, 13, 18, . . .
   $a_1 = 3;\ a_{n+1} = a_n + 5$
10. 1, 3, 9, 27, . . .
    $a_1 = 1;\ a_{n+1} = 3a_n$
11. 2, 3, 8, 63, . . .
    $a_1 = 2;\ a_{n+1} = a_n^2 - 1$
12. **Writing** Explain the difference between a recursive definition and an explicit formula. **An explicit formula describes the *n*th term of a sequence using the number *n*. A recursive formula defines a sequence by the relationship between successive terms.**

Student Companion/ All-in-One Resources/Online
Practice page 2

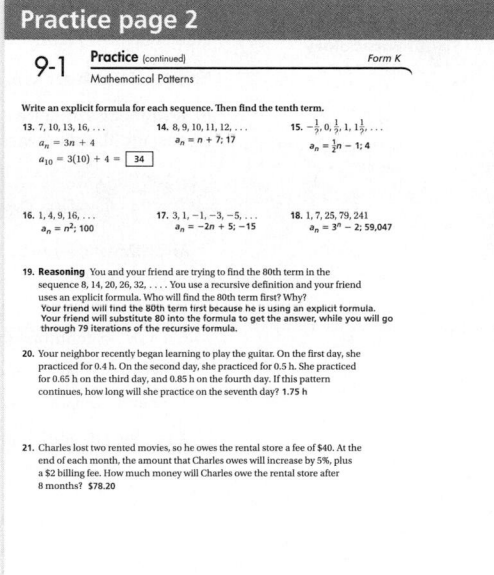

9-1 Practice (continued) *Form K*
Mathematical Patterns

Write an explicit formula for each sequence. Then find the tenth term.

13. 7, 10, 13, 16, . . .
    $a_n = 3n + 4$
    $a_{10} = 3(10) + 4 =$ [34]
14. 8, 9, 10, 11, 12, . . .
    $a_n = n + 7$; 17
15. $-\frac{1}{2}, 0, \frac{1}{2}, 1, 1\frac{1}{2}, \ldots$
    $a_n = \frac{1}{2}n - 1$; 4
16. 1, 4, 9, 16, . . .
    $a_n = n^2$; 100
17. 3, 1, −1, −3, −5, . . .
    $a_n = -2n + 5$; −15
18. 1, 7, 25, 79, 241
    $a_n = 3^n - 2$; 59,047
19. **Reasoning** You and your friend are trying to find the 80th term in the sequence 8, 14, 20, 26, 32, ... You use a recursive definition and your friend uses an explicit formula. Who will find the 80th term first? Why?
    Your friend will find the 80th term first because he is using an explicit formula. Your friend will substitute 80 into the formula to get the answer, while you will go through 79 iterations of the recursive formula.
20. Your neighbor recently began learning to play the guitar. On the first day, she practiced for 0.4 h. On the second day, she practiced for 0.5 h. She practiced for 0.65 h on the third day, and 0.85 h on the fourth day. If this pattern continues, how long will she practice on the seventh day? **1.75 h**
21. Charles lost two rented movies, so he owes the rental store a fee of $40. At the end of each month, the amount that Charles owes will increase by 5%, plus a $2 billing fee. How much money will Charles owe the rental store after 8 months? **$78.20**

All-in-One Resources/Online
Enrichment

9-1 Enrichment
Mathematical Patterns

You can define the terms in a sequence using an explicit formula or a recursive definition. You can use another method, called iteration, to form a sequence. The word *iteration* means to repeat an action. In mathematics, a sequence of numbers is generated through iteration when the same procedure is performed on each output.

1. Consider the function $f(x) = 5x + 1$. Let the first term of a sequence be 0. What is $f(0)$? Let $f(0)$ be the second term of the sequence. Write the sequence. **0, 1**
2. To create more terms of this sequence through iteration, continue to apply $f(x)$ to each output. The third term in this sequence can be described as $f(f(0))$. What is the third term? $f(f(0)) = f(1) = 6$
3. Determine the first 10 terms of this sequence. You already have the first 3 terms.
   0; 1; 6; 31; 156; 781; 3906; 19,531; 97,656; 488,281
4. Determine the first 5 terms of the sequence formed through iterations of $f(x) = \frac{x}{2} + 1$. Begin with $x = 2$. Describe the sequence.
   2, 2, 2, 2, 2; all of the terms in the sequence are 2.
5. Will you get the same type of sequence if you start with a different number? **No; for example, if you start with $x = 0$, the sequence is 0, 1, 1.5, . . .**
6. Iterations have uses other than to form numerical sequences. Consider this iterative process, which forms a sequence of a set of three integers. Make a set of any three integers. Compute the absolute value of the difference between each pair of integers in the set. This produces a new set of three integers. Continue this process on each new set of three integers. Describe what eventually happens. **No matter what three integers you choose to start with, the set will eventually repeat itself in combinations of the set {0, *a*, *a*}, where *a* is a positive integer.**
7. You can form fractals through iterations. Fractals are geometric figures just like circles or rectangles, but fractals have a special property that these geometric figures do not. You make fractals by iterating the figure itself. For example, start by drawing an equilateral triangle on graph paper. Divide each side into three equal parts. Draw another equilateral triangle on one side of the triangle that has the middle section as its base. Repeat this process on the remaining two sides. You have just created the first two iterations of a fractal called the Koch snowflake.

Student Companion/ All-in-One Resources/Online
Think About a Plan

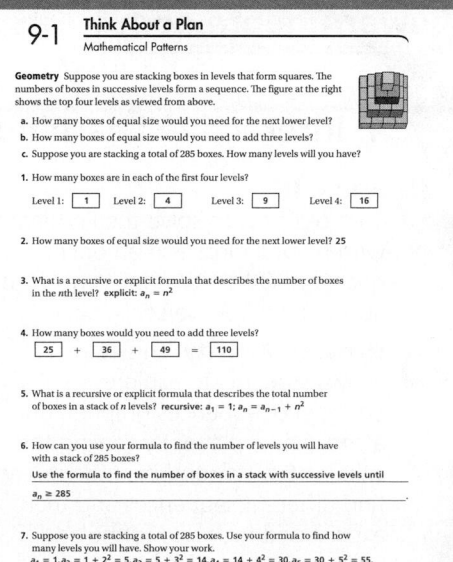

9-1 Think About a Plan
Mathematical Patterns

Geometry Suppose you are stacking boxes in levels that form squares. The numbers of boxes in successive levels form a sequence. The figure at the right shows the top four levels as viewed from above.

a. How many boxes of equal size would you need for the next lower level?
b. How many boxes of equal size would you need to add three levels?
c. Suppose you are stacking a total of 285 boxes. How many levels will you have?

1. How many boxes are in each of the first four levels?
   Level 1: [1] Level 2: [4] Level 3: [9] Level 4: [16]
2. How many boxes of equal size would you need for the next lower level? **25**
3. What is a recursive or explicit formula that describes the number of boxes in the nth level? **explicit: $a_n = n^2$**
4. How many boxes would you need to add three levels?
   [25] + [36] + [49] = [110]
5. What is a recursive or explicit formula that describes the total number of boxes in a stack of n levels? **recursive: $a_1 = 1;\ a_n = a_{n-1} + n^2$**
6. How can you use your formula to find the number of levels you will have with a stack of 285 boxes?
   Use the formula to find the number of boxes in a stack with successive levels until $a_n \geq 285$.
7. Suppose you are stacking a total of 285 boxes. Use your formula to find how many levels you will have. Show your work.
   $a_1 = 1, a_2 = 1 + 2^2 = 5, a_3 = 5 + 3^2 = 14, a_4 = 14 + 4^2 = 30, a_5 = 30 + 5^2 = 55,$
   $a_6 = 55 + 6^2 = 91, a_7 = 91 + 7^2 = 140, a_8 = 140 + 8^2 = 204, a_9 = 204 + 9^2 = 285$
8. You need [9] levels to make a stack of 285 boxes.

Student Companion/ All-in-One Resources/Online
Standardized Test Prep

9-1 Standardized Test Prep
Mathematical Patterns

Multiple Choice

For Exercises 1–6, choose the correct letter.

1. What are the first five terms of the sequence? **C**
   $$a_n = 3^n - 1$$
   (A) 2, 5, 8, 11, 14 (B) 3, 9, 27, 81, 243 (C) 2, 8, 26, 80, 242 (D) 2, 4, 8, 16, 32
2. The formula $a_n = 3n + 2$ best represents which sequence? **G**
   (F) 3, 6, 9, 12, 15 (G) 5, 8, 11, 14, 17 (H) 4, 7, 10, 13, 16 (I) 5, 9, 29, 83, 245
3. Which pattern can be represented by $a_n = n^2 - 3$? **D**
   (A) −1, 0, 5, 12, 21 (B) 4, 7, 12, 19, 28 (C) 1, 4, 9, 16, 25 (D) −2, 1, 6, 13, 22
4. The sequence 4, 16, 36, 64, 100, . . . can best be represented by which formula? **G**
   (F) $a_n = 4n$ (G) $a_n = 4n^2$ (H) $a_n = 4n^3$ (I) $a_n = 2n^4$
5. For the sequence 0, 6, 16, 30, 48, . . . , what is the 40th term? **A**
   (A) 3198 (B) 3200 (C) 4000 (D) 16,000
6. A student sets up a savings plan to transfer money from his checking account to his savings account. The first week $10 is transferred, the second week $12 is transferred, the third week $16 is transferred, and the fourth week $24 is transferred. If this pattern continues and he starts with $100 in his checking account, how many weeks will pass before his balance is zero? **G**
   (F) 4 (G) 5 (H) 6 (I) 7

Short Response

7. After training for and running a marathon, an athlete wants to reduce her daily run by half each day. The marathon is about 26 mi. How many days will it take after the marathon before she runs less than a mile a day? Show your work.
   [2] 5 days; Day 1: 13 mi, Day 2: 6.5 mi, Day 3: 3.25 mi, Day 4: 1.625 mi, Day 5: 0.8125 mi
   [1] correct answer, without work shown OR incorrect answer with correct sequence
   [0] incorrect answers and no work shown OR no answers given

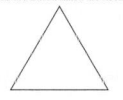

Online Teacher Resource Center
Activities, Games, and Puzzles

9-1 Game: De-"Term"-ining the Answer
Mathematical Patterns

Provide the host with the following list of explicit formulas or recursive formulas with initial term and corresponding terms for twenty sequences.

Formula	Next 10 Terms
$a_n = \frac{1}{n}$	$1, \frac{1}{2}, \frac{1}{3}, \frac{1}{4}, \frac{1}{5}, \frac{1}{6}, \frac{1}{7}, \frac{1}{8}, \frac{1}{9}, \frac{1}{10}$
$a_n = n + 2$	3, 4, 5, 6, 7, 8, 9, 10, 11, 12
$a_n = n - 7$	−6, −5, −4, −3, −2, −1, 0, 1, 2, 3
$a_n = 4n$	4, 8, 12, 16, 20, 24, 28, 32, 36, 40
$a_n = 2n - 1$	1, 3, 5, 7, 9, 11, 13, 15, 17, 19
$a_n = 3n + 5$	8, 11, 14, 17, 20, 23, 26, 29, 32, 35
$a_n = n^3$	1, 8, 27, 64, 125, 216, 343, 512, 729, 1000
$a_n = n^2 + n + 1$	3, 7, 13, 21, 31, 43, 57, 73, 91, 111
$a_{n+1} = a_n + 6;\ a_1 = -1$	5, 11, 17, 23, 29, 35, 41, 47, 53, 59
$a_{n+1} = a_n + n;\ a_1 = 1$	2, 4, 7, 11, 16, 22, 29, 37, 46, 56
$a_{n+1} = a_n + 2n;\ a_1 = 1$	3, 7, 13, 21, 31, 43, 57, 73, 91, 111
$a_{n+1} = a_n + n^2;\ a_1 = 1$	2, 6, 15, 31, 56, 92, 141, 205, 286, 386
$a_{n+1} = a_n + 2^n;\ a_1 = 1$	3, 7, 15, 31, 63, 127, 255, 511, 1023, 2047
$a_{n+1} = a_n + n + 4^n;\ a_1 = 0$	5; 23; 90; 350; 1379; 5481; 21,872; 87,416; 349,569; 1,398,155
$a_{n+1} = a_n + 5(-3)^n;\ a_1 = 0$	−15; 30; −105; 300; −915; 2730; −8205; 24,600; −73,815; 221,430
$a_{n+1} = 3a_n;\ a_1 = 2$	6; 18; 54; 162; 486; 1458; 4374; 13,122; 39,366; 118,098
$a_{n+1} = na_n;\ a_1 = 1$	1; 2; 6; 24; 120; 720; 5040; 40,320; 362,880; 3,628,800
$a_{n+1} = \frac{1}{2}a_n;\ a_1 = 1$	$\frac{1}{2}, \frac{1}{4}, \frac{1}{8}, \frac{1}{16}, \frac{1}{32}, \frac{1}{64}, \frac{1}{128}, \frac{1}{256}, \frac{1}{512}, \frac{1}{1024}$
$a_{n+1} = 3a_n - n;\ a_1 = 1$	2; 4; 9; 23; 64; 186; 551; 1645; 4926; 14,768
$a_{n+1} = 1 + \frac{1}{a_n};\ a_1 = 1$	$2, \frac{3}{2}, \frac{5}{3}, \frac{8}{5}, \frac{13}{8}, \frac{21}{13}, \frac{34}{21}, \frac{55}{34}, \frac{89}{55}, \frac{144}{89}$

1 Interactive Learning

Solve It!

PURPOSE To write an arithmetic sequence
PROCESS Students may
- subtract 4 km from 10 km and divide by 8 to find the constant value.
- use trial-and-error to find the daily running distance between 4 km and 10 km.

FACILITATE
Q What is the least and most you will run in a day during the training? **[4 km; 10 km]**

Q How many training weeks are left after week 1? **[8]**

Q How many km must be divided in the remaining weeks? **[6]**

Q What expression will determine the equal amount of increase? $[\frac{10-4}{8}]$

Q How are the terms of the sequence generated? **[Add 0.75 to 4 and continue adding 0.75 to the next term until the sum is 10.]**

ANSWER See Solve It in Answers on next page.
CONNECT THE MATH In the Solve It, students write an arithmetic sequence. In the lesson, they will define, identify, and analyze arithmetic sequences.

2 Guided Instruction

Take Note   SYNTHESIZING
If the explicit formula for the nth term in summation notation is a *linear* function of n, then the sequence is arithmetic. The slope of the linear function is the common difference between terms of the sequence.

9-2 Arithmetic Sequences

Objective To define, identify, and apply arithmetic sequences

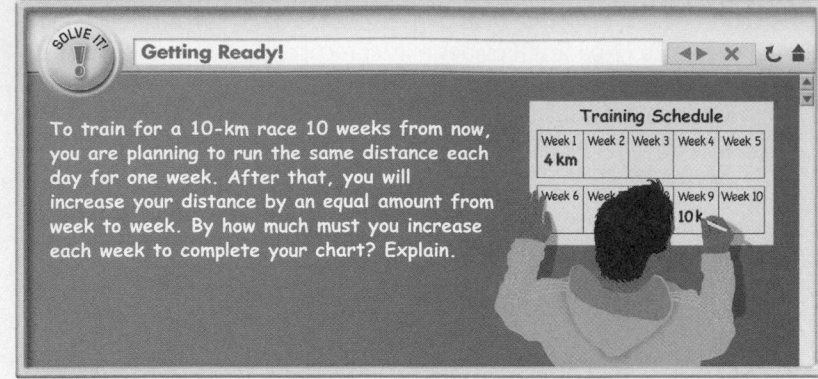

Dynamic Activity
Arithmetic Sequences

Lesson Vocabulary
- arithmetic sequence
- common difference
- arithmetic mean

It sometimes is helpful to represent a situation with a sequence of numbers. There are different types of numerical sequences.

Focus Question What is an arithmetic sequence?

An **arithmetic sequence** is a sequence where the difference between consecutive terms is constant. This difference is the **common difference**.

Key Concept Arithmetic Sequence

An arithmetic sequence with a starting value a and common difference d is a sequence of the form

$$a, a + d, a + 2d, a + 3d, \ldots$$

A recursive definition for this sequence has two parts:

initial condition $a_1 = a$

recursive formula $a_n = a_{n-1} + d$, for $n > 1$

An explicit definition for this sequence is a single formula:

$$a_n = a + (n - 1)d, \text{ for } n \geq 1$$

9-2 Preparing to Teach

BIG ideas Equivalence
                Variable   **UbD**

ESSENTIAL UNDERSTANDINGS
- In an arithmetic sequence, the difference between any two consecutive terms is always the same number. An arithmetic sequence can be built by adding the same number to each term.
- A sequence can be defined explicitly by describing its nth term with a formula using n or recursively by stating its first term and a formula for its nth term using the $(n - 1)$ term.
- $a_n = a + (n - 1)d$ and $a_1 = a$, $a_n = a_{n-1} + d$ for $n > 1$ define the same arithmetic sequence, $a, a + d, a + 2d, \ldots$.

Math Background
An arithmetic sequence has a constant (or common) difference between consecutive terms. An arithmetic sequence is related to a special case of a linear function whose domain is the set of

natural numbers. The slope of the graph of this corresponding linear function is equal to the common difference of the sequence.

Any missing term of an arithmetic sequence can be found if any of the following information is known:
- the first term and the common difference,
- the first term and another term.

Note that an arithmetic sequence can be finite or infinite and can have positive and negative terms.

Support Student Learning
Use the **Algebra 2 Companion** to engage and support students during instruction. See Lesson Resources at the end of this lesson for details.

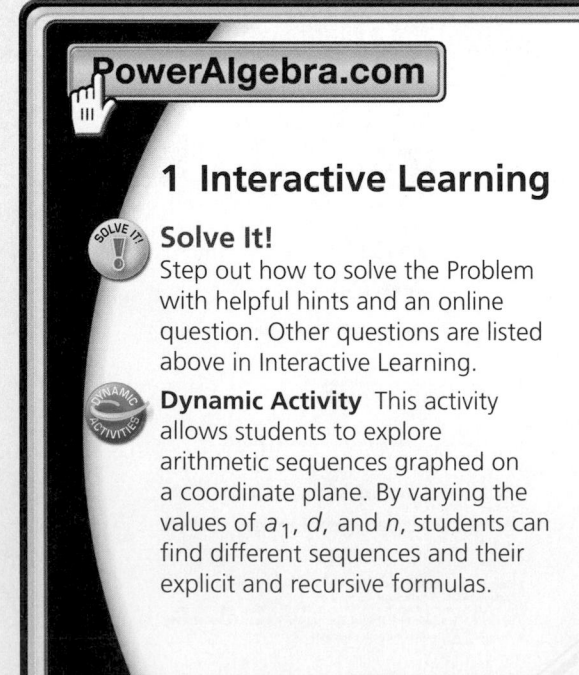

PowerAlgebra.com

1 Interactive Learning

Solve It!
Step out how to solve the Problem with helpful hints and an online question. Other questions are listed above in Interactive Learning.

Dynamic Activity This activity allows students to explore arithmetic sequences graphed on a coordinate plane. By varying the values of a_1, d, and n, students can find different sequences and their explicit and recursive formulas.

How do you know whether a sequence is arithmetic? The differences between consecutive terms in an arithmetic sequence are the same.

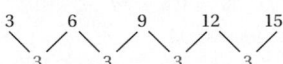 **Problem 1** Identifying Arithmetic Sequences

Is the sequence an arithmetic sequence?

A 3, 6, 9, 12, 15, . . .

Find the differences between consecutive terms.

3   6   9   12   15
   3   3   3   3

The sequence has a common difference of 3. This sequence is an arithmetic sequence.

B 1, 4, 9, 16, 25, . . .

Find the differences between consecutive terms.

1   4   9   16   25
   3   5   7   9

The differences are not the same. This sequence is not an arithmetic sequence.

✓ **Got It?** **1.** Is the sequence an arithmetic sequence?

     a. 2, 4, 8, 16, . . .   **b.** 1, 5, 9, 13, 17, . . .

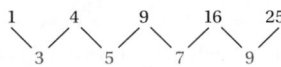 **Problem 2** Analyzing Arithmetic Sequences

A What is the 100th term of the arithmetic sequence that begins 6, 11, . . .?

Step 1   Identify the common difference.

The first term a is 6. The second term is 11.
The common difference d is $11 - 6 = 5$.

Step 2   Identify the 100th term.

Use the explicit formula. $a_n = a + (n - 1)d$

Substitute 100 for n, 6 for a, and 5 for d. $a_{100} = 6 + (100 - 1)5$

Simplify. $a_{100} = 501$

The 100th term is 501.

Problem 1   SYNTHESIZING

Q What is the common difference in 1A? **[3]**

Q What is a description in words of the arithmetic sequence elements in 1A? **[multiples of 3, beginning with 3]**

Q How would you describe the values in the sequence 1B? **[squares of 1, 2, 3, 4, 5 . . .]**

Got It?   ERROR PREVENTION

Q What are the differences between consecutive terms in 1a? **[2, 4, 8]**

Q Is there a common difference in 1b? If so, what is it? **[yes; 4]**

Problem 2   SYNTHESIZING

Q What does n represent in the explicit definition? **[the number of the term]**

Q What equation would you write in 2A if you were asked for the 150th term? **[$a_{150} = 6 + (150 - 1)5$]**

---

2 Guided Instruction

 Each Problem is worked out and supported online.

Problem 1
Identifying Arithmetic Sequences
Animated

Problem 2
Analyzing Arithmetic Sequences
Animated

Problem 3
Using the Arithmetic Mean

Problem 4
Using an Explicit Formula for an Arithmetic Sequence
Animated

Support in Algebra 2 Companion
• Vocabulary
• Key Concepts
• Got It?

Answers

Solve It!
0.75 km; you will increase your daily running distance by 6 km over 8 weeks. So, each week you will increase your distance by $\frac{6}{8} = 0.75$ km.

Got It?
1. a. no
     b. yes

Q If there were 3 terms between 100 and 82 in 2B, what equation would you write to find d?
[82 = 100 + 4d]

Got It?

Q What information do you need to find additional terms of an arithmetic sequence? **[Samples: first term and common difference; at least two terms.]**

Q What equation would you write in 2a?
[$a_{46} = 3 + 2(46 - 1)$]

Q What is the sign of the common difference in 2b? Why? **[Positive, because the terms of the sequence are increasing.]**

Problem 3

Q Can you use the arithmetic mean to find a missing term given any two terms? Explain. **[No; the three terms involved must be consecutive, unless certain other conditions are also true]**

Got It?   ERROR PREVENTION

Q What must be true about the 10th term? **[It must be less than 132, greater than 98, and the average of 132 and 98.]**

Q Is it possible to get a negative term? Explain. **[Yes; since $d = -17$, each term in descending order is reduced by 17; the first and second terms are both negative in this case.]**

Plan

What do you need to find the second term given the first term? You need to know the common difference of the arithmetic sequence.

B What are the second and third terms of the arithmetic sequence 100, ■, ■, 82, …?

Step 1 Identify the common difference.

There are 3 common differences between 100 and 82.

100 ■ ■ 82

| | |
Write an equation. | $82 = 100 + 3d$
Isolate the variable term. | $-18 = 3d$
Solve for d. | $-6 = d$

Step 2 Identify the missing terms.

Find the second term. $100 + (-6) = 94$
Find the third term. $94 + (-6) = 88$

The second and third terms are 94 and 88.

Got It? 2. a. What is the 46th term of the arithmetic sequence that begins 3, 5, 7, …?
b. What are the second and third terms of this arithmetic sequence?
80, ■, ■, 125, …

The **arithmetic mean**, or average, of two numbers x and y is $\frac{x+y}{2}$.

In an arithmetic sequence, the middle term of any three consecutive terms is the arithmetic mean of the other two terms.

Problem 3 Using the Arithmetic Mean   GRIDDED RESPONSE

Think

To use the formula for arithmetic mean, what are x and y? x is 15 and y is 59.

What is the missing term of the arithmetic sequence …, 15, ■, 59, …?

Use the formula for the arithmetic mean to find the missing term.   arithmetic mean $= \frac{x+y}{2}$

Substitute 15 for x and 59 for y. $= \frac{15+59}{2}$

Simplify. $= \frac{74}{2} = 37$

The missing term is 37.

Got It? 3. a. The 9th and 11th terms of an arithmetic sequence are 132 and 98. What is the 10th term?
b. Reasoning If you know the 5th and 6th terms of an arithmetic sequence, how can you find the 7th term using the arithmetic mean?

Additional Problems

1. Is the sequence an arithmetic sequence?
a. 12, 22, 32, 42, 52, …
b. 1, 1, 2, 3, 5, …
ANSWERS a. yes **b.** no

2. What are the indicated terms of the arithmetic sequence?
a. the 110th term of the sequence that begins 5, 9, …
b. the second and third terms of the sequence 90, ■, ■, 12, …
ANSWERS a. 441 **b.** 64, 38

3. What is the missing term of the arithmetic sequence … 35, ■, 53, …?
ANSWER 44

4. Over the last ten years the amount of snow a town received formed an arithmetic sequence. If 21 in. of snow fell 10 years ago and 19 in. fell 9 years ago, how many inches fell 2 years ago?
ANSWER 5 in.

Answers

Got It? (continued)
2. a. 93
b. 95, 110
3. a. 115
b. Use the formula for arithmetic mean and solve for a_7:
$a_7 = 2a_6 - a_5$.

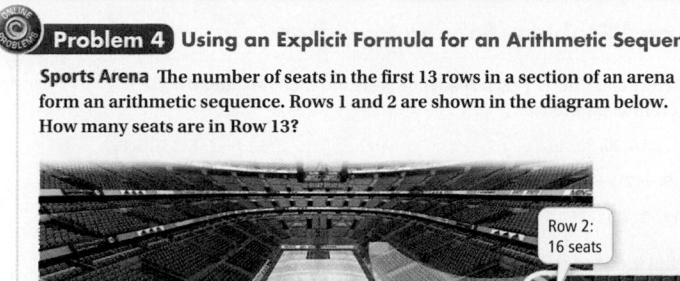

Problem 4 Using an Explicit Formula for an Arithmetic Sequence

Sports Arena The number of seats in the first 13 rows in a section of an arena form an arithmetic sequence. Rows 1 and 2 are shown in the diagram below. How many seats are in Row 13?

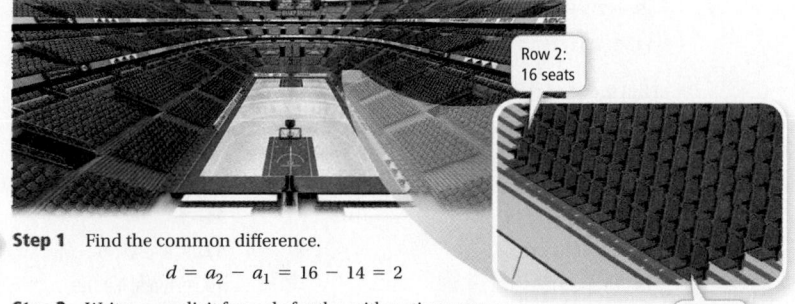

Row 2: 16 seats

Row 1: 14 seats

Plan

 What two terms should you use to find the common difference?
Use the consecutive terms given.

Step 1 Find the common difference.

$$d = a_2 - a_1 = 16 - 14 = 2$$

Step 2 Write an explicit formula for the arithmetic sequence.

Use the explicit formula. $\quad a_n = a + (n - 1)d$

Substitute 13 for n, 14 for a, and 2 for d. $\quad a_{13} = 14 + (13 - 1)2$

Simplify. $\quad = 38$

There are 38 seats in Row 13.

 Got It? 4. The number of seats in the first 16 rows in a curved section of another arena form an arithmetic sequence. If there are 20 seats in Row 1 and 23 seats in Row 2, how many seats are in Row 16?

Focus Question What is an arithmetic sequence?

Answer In an arithmetic sequence, the difference between any two consecutive terms is constant. You can build an arithmetic sequence by adding the same number to each term.

Lesson Check

Do you know HOW?

Find the tenth term of each arithmetic sequence.

1. 2, 8, 14, 20, . . . **2.** 15, 23, 31, . . .

Find the missing term of each arithmetic sequence.

3. . . . 4, ■, 22 . . . **4.** . . . 25, ■, 53 . . .

Do you UNDERSTAND?

5. Vocabulary Explain what it means for a sequence to be an arithmetic sequence.

6. Open-Ended Give an example of a sequence that is not an arithmetic sequence.

Problem 4

Q Could you use the explicit definition to find the number of seats in any of the 13 rows? Explain. **[Yes; you have the first term and the common difference.]**

Got It? EXTENSION

Q What explicit formula gives the number of seats in the third row? **[$a_3 = 20 + (3 - 1)3$]**

3 Lesson Check

Do you know HOW?

• For Exercises 3 and 4, students can use the arithmetic mean to find the term since the missing term is one of three consecutive terms.

Do you UNDERSTAND? ERROR INTERVENTION

• For Exercise 6, review that the difference between terms of a non-arithmetic sequence is not constant.

Close

Q How do you identify an arithmetic sequence and find its missing terms? **[Sample: A sequence is an arithmetic sequence if the difference between the terms is constant. You can use the explicit formula if you have the first term and either another term or the common difference. You can also use the arithmetic mean to find a missing term if certain conditions are true.]**

---

4. 65 seats

Lesson Check

1. 56

2. 87

3. 13

4. 39

5. In an arithmetic sequence, the diff. between any two consecutive terms is always the same number.

6. Answers may vary. Sample: 2, 4, 8, 16, 32, . . .

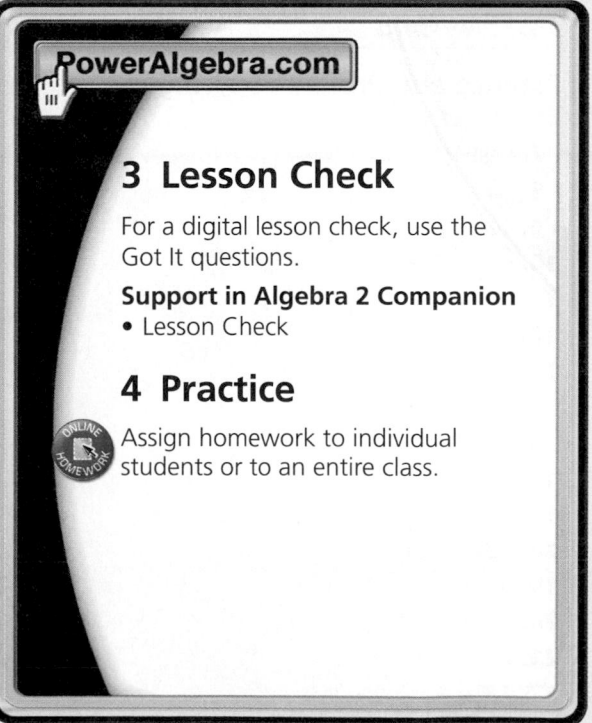

PowerAlgebra.com

3 Lesson Check

For a digital lesson check, use the Got It questions.

Support in Algebra 2 Companion
• Lesson Check

4 Practice

Assign homework to individual students or to an entire class.

4 Practice

ASSIGNMENT GUIDE

Basic: 7–11, 13–17, 20–24, 27, 34, 41, 50

Average: 7–19 odd, 20–27, 28–40 even, 41–49 odd, 50–58 even

Standardized Test Prep: 60–62

Mixed Review: 63–72

Reasoning exercises have blue headings.

Applications exercises have red headings.

EXERCISE 50: Use the Think About a Plan worksheet in the **Student Companion** (also available in the Teaching Resources in print and online) to further support students' development in becoming independent learners.

HOMEWORK QUICK CHECK

To check students' understanding of key skills and concepts, go over Exercises 15, 21, 34, 41, and 50.

Practice and Problem-Solving Exercises

 **Practice**

Determine whether each sequence is arithmetic. If so, identify the common difference.   ◀ See Problem 1.

7. 10, 20, 30, 40, . . .   **8.** 1, 1, 2, 3, 5, 8, . . .

9. −21, −18, −15, −12, . . .   **10.** 97, 86, 75, 64, . . .

11. 3, 7, 11, 15, . . .   **12.** 100, 10, 1, 0.1, . . .

Find the 32nd term of each sequence.   ◀ See Problem 2.

Guided Practice

To start, identify the common difference.

13. 34, 37, 40, 43, . . .
37 − 34 = 3

14. −9, −8.7, −8.4, . . .   **15.** 3, 1, −1, −3, . . .

16. 23, 30, 37, 44, . . .   **17.** 9, 4, −1, −6, −11, . . .

18. 13, 17, 21, 25, . . .   **19.** 0.1, 0.5, 0.9, 1.3, . . .

Find the missing term of each arithmetic sequence.   ◀ See Problem 3.

Guided Practice

To start, use the formula for the arithmetic mean.

20. −15, ■, 1, . . .
arithmetic mean = $\dfrac{x + y}{2}$

21. 14, ■, 28, . . .   **22.** . . . 5, ■, 21, . . .

23. 103, ■, −119, . . .   **24.** . . . 98, ■, 66, . . .

25. 25, ■, −10, . . .   **26.** . . . 65, ■, −60, . . .

27. Savings A student deposits the same amount of money into her bank account each week. At the end of the second week she has $30 in her account. At the end of the third week she has $45 in her account. How much will she have in her bank account at the end of the ninth week?   ◀ See Problem 4.

 Apply

Find the 17th term of each sequence.

28. $a_{16} = 18, d = 5$ **29.** $a_{16} = 21, d = -3$

30. $a_{18} = -5, d = 12$ **31.** $a_{18} = 32, d = -4$

32. $a_{16} = \frac{1}{5}, d = \frac{1}{2}$ **33.** $a_{18} = -9, d = -11$

34. Think About a Plan The arithmetic mean of the monthly salaries of two employees is $3210. One employee earns $3470 per month. What is the monthly salary of the other employee?
- What is the given information and what is the unknown?
- What equation can you use to find the other monthly salary?

Answers

Practice and Problem-Solving Exercises

7. yes; 10

8. no

9. yes; 3

10. yes; −11

11. yes; 4

12. no

13. 127

14. 0.3

15. −59

16. 240

17. −146

18. 137

19. 12.5

20. −7

21. 21

22. 13

23. −8

24. 82

25. 7.5

26. 2.5

27. $135

28. 23

29. 18

30. −17

31. 36

32. $\frac{7}{10}$

33. 2

34. $2950

Find the arithmetic mean a_n of the given terms.

35. $a_{n-1} = 7, a_{n+1} = 1$

36. $a_{n-1} = 21, a_{n+1} = 5$

37. $a_{n-1} = -19, a_{n+1} = -21$

38. $a_{n-1} = 4, a_{n+1} = -3$

39. $a_{n-1} = 0.3, a_{n+1} = 1.9$

40. $a_{n-1} = 9, a_{n+1} = -11$

41. Error Analysis A student claims that the next term of the arithmetic sequence 0, 2, 4, . . . is 8. Explain and correct the student's error.

Write an explicit and a recursive formula for each sequence.

42. 0, 6, 12, 18, 24, . . .

43. $-5, -4, -3, -2, -1, \dots$

44. $-4, -8, -12, -16, -20, \dots$

45. $-5, -3.5, -2, -0.5, 1, \dots$

46. $-32, -20, -8, 4, 16, \dots$

47. 27, 15, 3, $-9, -21, \dots$

48. Reasoning What information do you need to find a term of a sequence using an explicit formula?

49. Writing Describe some advantages and some disadvantages of a recursive formula and an explicit formula. When is it appropriate to use each formula?

50. Transportation Suppose a trolley stops at a certain intersection every 14 min. The first trolley of the day gets to the stop at 6:43 A.M. How long do you have to wait for a trolley if you get to the stop at 8:15 A.M.? At 3:20 P.M.?

Find the missing terms of each arithmetic sequence.

51. 2, $a_2, a_3, a_4, -22, \dots$

52. 10, $a_2, a_3, a_4, -11.6, \dots$

53. 1, $a_2, a_3, a_4, -35, \dots$

54. $\dots \frac{13}{5}, a_6, a_7, a_8, \frac{37}{5}, \dots$

55. 17, $a_2, a_3, a_4, 17, \dots$

56. 660, $a_2, a_3, a_4, 744, \dots$

> **Hint** The arithmetic mean of the first and fifth terms is the third term.

57. Income The arithmetic mean of the monthly salaries of two people is $4475. One person earns $3895 per month. What is the monthly salary of the other person?

58. Reasoning Suppose you turn the water on in an empty bathtub with vertical sides. After 20 s, the water has reached a level of 1.15 in. You then leave the room. You want to turn the water off when the level in the bathtub is 8.5 in. How many minutes later should you return? (*Hint:* Begin by identifying two terms of an arithmetic sequence.)

59. a. Graphing Calculator Use your calculator to generate an arithmetic sequence with a common difference of -7. How could you use a calculator to find the 6th term? The 8th term? The 20th term?

b. Reasoning Explain how your answer to part (a) relates to the explicit formula $a_n = a_1 + (n - 1)d$.

35. 4

36. 13

37. -20

38. $\frac{1}{2}$

39. 1.1

40. -1

41. The student multiplied the third term by 2 instead of adding 2. The correct answer is 6.

42. $a_n = 0 + 6(n - 1)$; $a_n = a_{n-1} + 6, a_1 = 0$

43. $a_n = -5 + 1(n - 1)$; $a_n = a_{n-1} + 1, a_1 = -5$

44. $a_n = -4 - 4(n - 1)$; $a_n = a_{n-1} - 4, a_1 = -4$

45. $a_n = -5 + 1.5(n - 1)$; $a_n = a_{n-1} + 1.5, a_1 = -5$

46. $a_n = -32 + 12(n - 1)$; $a_n = a_{n-1} + 12, a_1 = -32$

47. $a_n = 27 - 12(n - 1)$; $a_n = a_{n-1} - 12, a_1 = 27$

48. All you need is the term number, since you have an explicit formula.

49. Answers may vary. Sample: An advantage of a recursive formula is that only the preceding term must be known to find the next term; a disadvantage is that many calculations may be required to find a term. An advantage of an explicit formula is that it is easy to find any term. Use the recursive formula when the previous term and common diff. are known. Use the explicit formula when the term number and common diff. are known.

50. 6 min; 1 min

51. $-4, -10, -16$

52. 4.6, $-0.8, -6.2$

53. $-8, -17, -26$

54. $\frac{19}{5}, 5, \frac{31}{5}$

55. 17, 17, 17

56. 681, 702, 723

57. $5055

58. 2.13 min, or 2 min 8 s

59. a. Answers may vary. Sample: 25, 18, 11, 4, $-3, -10, \dots$; to find the 6th term, multiply 5 times (-7) and add to a_1; to find the 8th term, multiply 7 times (-7) and add to a_1; to find the 20th term, multiply 19 times (-7) and add to a_1.

b. Answers may vary. Sample: Start with the first term and continue to subtract 7 for each term. For each term, you subtract $7 \cdot$ (term number $- 1$) from the first term.

Answers

Standardized Test Prep

60. C

61. F

62. [4] $\dfrac{3}{(x-1)(x+1)} + \dfrac{4x(x-1)}{(x-1)(x+1)}$

$= \dfrac{1.5(x+1)}{(x-1)(x+1)}, x \ne \pm 1$

$3 + 4x^2 - 4x = 1.5x + 1.5$

$4x^2 - 5.5x + 1.5 = 0$

$x^2 - \dfrac{11}{8}x + \dfrac{3}{8} = 0$

$\left(x - 1\right)\left(x - \dfrac{3}{8}\right) = 0$

$x = \dfrac{3}{8}$

(reject $x = 1$ because 1 is not in the domain)

[3] appropriate methods, but with one computational error

[2] both 1 and $\dfrac{3}{8}$ are given as solutions

[1] correct solution, without work shown

Mixed Review

63. recursive; $-2, -7, -12, -17, -22$

64. explicit; 6, 18, 36, 60, 90

65. explicit; 0, 3, 8, 15, 24

66. $y - 3 = \dfrac{8}{3}x$ or $y - 11 = \dfrac{8}{3}(x - 3)$

67. $y - 6 = 4(x - 4)$ or $y - 30 = 4(x - 10)$

68. $y - 10 = 8(x - 1)$ or $y - 42 = 8(x - 5)$

69. $r = \dfrac{\sqrt[3]{6\pi^2 V}}{2\pi}$

70. 32

71. 625

72. -81

Standardized Test Prep

 SAT/ACT

60. The equation $X(t) = t^4 - 5t^2 + 6$ gives the position of a comet relative to a fixed point, measured in millions of miles, at time t, measured in days. Solve the equation $X(t) = 0$. At what times is the position zero?

    Ⓐ 2, 3   Ⓒ $\sqrt{2}, \sqrt{3}$

    Ⓑ $-2, -3$ Ⓓ $\pm\sqrt{2}, \pm\sqrt{3}$

61. Simplify $\dfrac{3 - \frac{1}{x}}{\frac{1}{2x} - 5}$.

    Ⓕ $\dfrac{6x - 2}{1 - 10x}$ Ⓗ $\dfrac{4}{1 - 10x}$

    Ⓖ $\dfrac{3x - 1}{1 - 10x}$ Ⓘ $\dfrac{3x - 1}{1 - 5x}$

Extended Response

62. What are all the solutions of $\dfrac{3}{x^2 - 1} + \dfrac{4x}{x + 1} = \dfrac{1.5}{x - 1}$? Show your work.

Mixed Review

Determine whether each formula is *explicit* or *recursive*. Then find the first five terms of each sequence.   ◆ **See Lesson 9-1.**

63. $a_1 = -2, a_n = a_{n-1} - 5$ **64.** $a_n = 3n(n + 1)$ **65.** $a_n = n^2 - 1$

Write an equation in point-slope form for each pair of points.   ◆ **See Lesson 2-4.**

66. $(0, 3)$ and $(3, 11)$ **67.** $(4, 6)$ and $(10, 30)$ **68.** $(1, 10)$ and $(5, 42)$

69. Geometry The formula for volume V of a sphere with radius r is $V = \frac{4}{3}\pi r^3$. Find the radius of a sphere as a function of its volume. Rationalize the denominator.   ◆ **See Lesson 6-2.**

Get Ready!   **To prepare for Lesson 9-3, do Exercises 70–72.**

Find the next term in each sequence.   ◆ **See Lesson 9-1.**

70. 2, 4, 8, 16, . . .   **71.** 1, 5, 25, 125, . . .   **72.** $-1, -3, -9, -27, . . .$

Additional Instructional Support

Algebra 2 Companion

Students can use the **Algebra 2 Companion** worktext (4 pages) as you teach the lesson. Use the Companion to support

- New Vocabulary
- Key Concepts
- Got It for each Problem
- Lesson Check

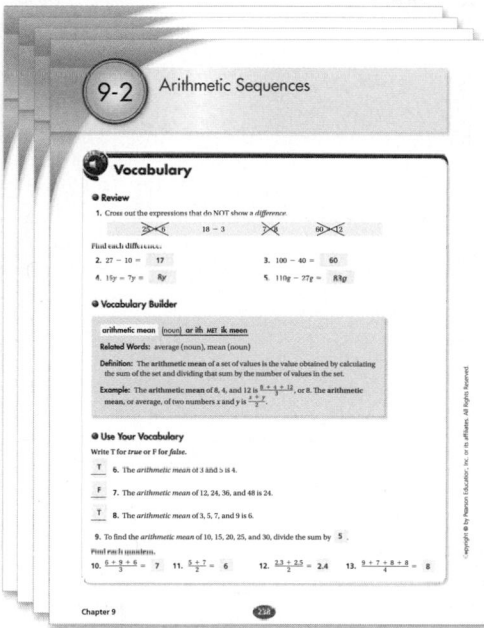

ELL Support

Focus on Language Have one pair of students sit with another pair. Have one pair write an arithmetic sequence and pose questions like the following to the other pair:

- Why is this an arithmetic sequence?
- What is the common difference?
- Give an example of a sequence that is not arithmetic.
- Given the first two terms, how would you find the 50th term?
- Can you explain more than one way to find the missing terms of a sequence?
- What is the arithmetic mean, and how do you use it with a sequence?

Have pairs reverse roles and play again. Travel from group to group and answer questions. Point out that the common *difference* is always the *same* amount.

5 Assess & Remediate

Lesson Quiz

1. Is the sequence an arithmetic sequence? 1, 4, 12, 16, 20, . . .

2. What are the second and third terms of the arithmetic sequence 30, ■, ■, 51, . . . ?

3. What is the missing term of the arithmetic sequence . . . 24, ■, 48, . . . ?

4. Do you UNDERSTAND? The number of toy rockets made by an assembly line for 8 hours forms an arithmetic sequence. If the line produced 40 rockets in hour one and 43 rockets in hour two, how many rockets will be produced in hour seven?

ANSWERS TO LESSON QUIZ

1. no
2. 37, 44
3. 36
4. 58

PRESCRIPTION FOR REMEDIATION
Use the student work on the Lesson Quiz to prescribe a differentiated review assignment:

Points	Differentiated Remediation
0–2	Intervention
3	On-level
4	Extension

PowerAlgebra.com

5 Assess & Remediate

Assign the Lesson Quiz. Appropriate intervention, practice, or enrichment is automatically generated based on student performance.

Intervention

- **Reteaching** (2 pages) Provides reteaching and practice exercises for the key lesson concepts. Use with struggling students or absent students.

- **English Language Learner Support** Helps students develop and reinforce mathematical vocabulary and key concepts.

All-in-One Resources/Online
Reteaching

9-2 Reteaching
Arithmetic Sequences

The explicit formula for the *n*th term of an arithmetic sequence is $a_n = a + (n-1)d$.
- *a* is the starting value and *d* is the common difference.
- *n* is always greater than or equal to 1.
- You can write the sequence as $a, a + d, a + 2d, a + 3d, \ldots$

Problem

Find the 15th term of an arithmetic sequence whose first three terms are 20, 16.5, and 13.

$20 - 16.5 = 3.5$ First, find the common difference. The difference between
$16.5 - 13 = 3.5$ consecutive terms is 3.5. The sequence decreases. The common
difference is -3.5.

$a_n = a + (n-1)d$ Use the explicit formula.
$a_{13} = 20 + (15-1)(-3.5)$ Substitute $a = 20$, $n = 15$, and $d = -3.5$.
$= 20 + (14)(-3.5)$ Subtract within parentheses.
$= 20 + -49$ Multiply.
$= -29$ The 15th term is -29.

Check the answer. Write $a_1, a_2, \ldots, a_{15}$ down the left side of your paper. Start with $a_1 = 20$. Subtract 3.5 and record 16.5 next to a_2. Continue until you find a_{15}.

Exercises

Find the 25th term of each sequence.

1. 20, 18, 16, 14, . . . **−28**   **2.** 0.0057, 0.0060, 0.0063, . . . **0.0129**

3. 4, 0, −4, −8, . . . **−92**   **4.** 0.2, 0.7, 1.2, 1.7, . . . **12.2**

5. −10, −8.8, −7.6, −6.4, . . . **18.8**   **6.** 22, 26, 30, 34, . . . **118**

All-in-One Resources/Online
English Language Learner Support

9-2 ELL Support
Arithmetic Sequences

Arithmetic Sequence

An arithmetic sequence is a sequence where the difference between consecutive terms is constant.

$$a, a + d, a + 2d, a + 3d, \ldots$$

Sample 2, 5, 8, 11, 14, . . .

Determine whether or not each sequence is arithmetic.

1. 1, 4, 7, 9, 11, . . .   not arithmetic

2. 3, 9, 15, 21, 27, . . .   arithmetic

3. 0, 15, 30, 45, 60, . . .   arithmetic

4. 0, 1, 3, 6, 10, . . .   not arithmetic

Use the formula $a_n = a + (n-1)d$ to find the indicated term in each arithmetic sequence.

5. Find the 12th term in the sequence that begins 3, 6, 9, . . .   36

6. Find the 38th term in the sequence that begins 4, 10, 16, . . .   226

7. Find the 104th term in the sequence that begins 5, 9, 13, . . .   417

Arithmetic Mean

The arithmetic mean is the average of a set of numbers. The arithmetic mean of two numbers x and y is found using the formula displayed below.

$$\frac{x+y}{2}$$

Sample The arithmetic mean of 4 and 6 is $\frac{4+6}{2} = \frac{10}{2} = 5$.

Find the missing number in the arithmetic sequence. This number is the arithmetic mean of the two given numbers.

8. . . . , 13, ___, 37, . . .   25

9. . . . , 26, ___, 42, . . .   34

10. . . . , 45, ___, 99, . . .   72

Differentiated Remediation *continued*

On-Level

- **Practice** (2 pages) Provides extra practice for each lesson. For more challenging practice exercises, use the Form G Practice pages found in the All-in-One Teaching Resources and online.

- **Think About a Plan** Helps students develop specific problem-solving skills and strategies by providing scaffolded guiding questions.

- **Standardized Test Prep** Focuses on all major exercises, all major question types, and helps students prepare for the high-stakes assessments.

Extension

- **Enrichment** Provides students with interesting problems and activities that extend the concepts of the lesson.

- **Activities, Games, and Puzzles** Worksheets that can be used for concepts development, enrichment, and for fun!

Student Companion/All-in-One Resources/Online
Practice page 1

9-2 Practice — Form K
Arithmetic Sequences

Determine whether each sequence is arithmetic. If so, identify the common difference.

1. 1, 4, 7, 10, . . .
$4 - 1 = 3$
$7 - 4 = 3$
$10 - 7 = 3$
This sequence is arithmetic.
The common difference is ☐ 3 ☐.

2. 6, 10, 14, 18, 22, . . . arithmetic; 4

3. 3, 1, 3, 6, 10, 15, . . . not arithmetic

4. −16, −13, −9, −4, 2, . . . not arithmetic

5. 2, 9, 16, 23, 30, . . . arithmetic; 7

6. 43, 56, 69, 82, . . . arithmetic; 13

7. Reasoning Is the sequence represented by the formula $a_n = 4n + 8$ arithmetic? Explain.
Yes; the difference between consecutive terms is 4.

Find the 24th term of each arithmetic sequence.

8. 4, 6, 8, 10, 12, . . .
$a_n = a_1 + (n - 1)d$
$a_{24} = 4 + (24 - 1)2$
$a_{24} = 4 + 46$
$a_{24} = $ ☐ 50 ☐

9. 2, 5, 8, 11, 14, . . .
$a_n = a_1 + (n - 1)d$
71

10. 9, 5, 1, −3, −7, . . .
−83

Find the missing terms in the following arithmetic sequences.

11. 2, __, __, 14, . . .
$14 = 2 + 3d$
$12 = 3d$
$d = 4$
$2 + 4 = $ ☐ 6 ☐
$6 + 4 = $ ☐ 10 ☐

12. 3, ☐ 9 ☐, ☐ 15 ☐, 21, . . .

13. 65, ☐ 54 ☐, ☐ 43 ☐, 32, . . .

14. Error Analysis Noah used the formula $a_n = a + (n − 1)d$ to find the 12th term in the sequence 2, 4, 7, 11, 16, ... Did Noah find the correct term? How do you know? No; Noah applied the explicit formula for arithmetic sequences to a sequence that is not arithmetic.

Student Companion/All-in-One Resources/Online
Think About a Plan

9-2 Think About a Plan
Arithmetic Sequences

Transportation Suppose a trolley stops at a certain intersection every 14 min. The first trolley of the day gets to the stop at 6:43 A.M. How long do you have to wait for a trolley if you get to the stop at 8:15 A.M.? At 3:20 P.M.?

Know

1. If you define 12:00 A.M. as minute 0, then 6:43 A.M. is ☐ 403 min ☐ from 0.

2. 8:15 A.M. is ☐ 495 min ☐ from 0 and 3:20 P.M. is ☐ 920 min ☐ from 0.

3. The trolley stops every ☐ 14 min ☐.

Need

4. To solve the problem I need to find:
the closest times that the trolley gets to the stop that are after 8:15 A.M.
and 3:20 P.M.

Plan

5. What is an explicit formula for the number of minutes after 12:00 A.M. that the trolley gets to the stop?
$a_n = 403 + (n - 1)14$

6. Use your formula to find the smallest n that gives the minutes just after 8:15 A.M. that the trolley arrives at the stop. 8

7. Using this n in your formula, when does the trolley stop? at 501 min
How long do you have to wait for this trolley? 6 min

8. Use your formula to find the smallest n that gives the minutes just after 3:20 P.M. that the trolley arrives at the stop. 38

9. Using this n in your formula, when does the trolley stop? at 921 min
How long do you have to wait for this trolley? 1 min

Student Companion/All-in-One Resources/Online
Practice page 2

9-2 Practice (continued) — Form K
Arithmetic Sequences

Find the missing term of each arithmetic sequence.

15. 4, __, 18, . . .
Find the arithmetic mean of the given terms.
$4 + 18 = 22$
$22 ÷ 2 = 11$
The missing term is ☐ 11 ☐.

16. 9, ☐ 23 ☐, 37, . . .

17. 46, ☐ 37 ☐, 28, . . .

18. −12, ☐ −8 ☐, −4, . . .

19. 4, ☐ −20 ☐, −44, . . .

20. Error Analysis Your friend used the arithmetic mean to find the missing term in the following sequence: 3, __, 29, 42, ... His answer was 13. What error did your friend make? What is the correct answer?
He subtracted 3 from 29 when he should have added 3 and 29; 16

21. An architect is designing a building with sides in the shape of a trapezoid. The number of windows on each floor forms an arithmetic sequence. There are 124 windows on the first floor and 116 windows on the second floor.
a. Write an explicit formula to represent the sequence. $a_n = 132 - 8n$
b. How many windows are on the tenth floor? 52 windows

22. Your cousin opened a bank account with a deposit of $256 dollars. After one week, she had $280 in her account. After two weeks, she had $304, and after three weeks she had $328. If this pattern continues, how much money will your cousin have in her account after 18 weeks? $688

23. There is a puddle 1.4 cm deep in your backyard. After one minute of rain, the puddle was 1.45 cm deep. The puddle was 1.5 cm deep after it rained for two minutes. If the pattern continues, how deep will the puddle be after it rains for 45 min? 3.65 cm

---

Student Companion/All-in-One Resources/Online
Standardized Test Prep

9-2 Standardized Test Prep
Arithmetic Sequences

Multiple Choice

For Exercises 1–6, choose the correct letter.

1. Which sequence is an arithmetic sequence? A
Ⓐ 7, 10, 13, 16, 19, . . . Ⓒ 7, 14, 28, 56, 112, . . .
Ⓑ 7, 8, 10, 13, 17, . . . Ⓓ 1, 7, 14, 22, 31, 41, . . .

2. An arithmetic sequence begins 4, 9, ... What is the 20th term? I
Ⓕ 76 Ⓗ 84 Ⓘ 99

3. What are the missing terms of the arithmetic sequence 5, __, __, 62, . . . ? C
Ⓐ 19, 24 Ⓑ 19, 34 Ⓒ 24, 43 Ⓓ 43, 62

4. What is the missing term of the arithmetic sequence 25, __, 45, . . . ? G
Ⓕ 30 Ⓖ 35 Ⓗ 37 Ⓘ 40

5. The seventh and ninth terms of an arithmetic sequence are 197 and 173. What is the eighth term? C
Ⓐ 161 Ⓑ 180 Ⓒ 185 Ⓓ 221

6. An artist is creating a tile mosaic. She uses 4 green tiles in the first row, 11 green tiles in the second row, 18 green tiles in the third row, and 25 green tiles in the fourth row. If she continues this pattern, how many green tiles will she use in the 20th row? I
Ⓕ 32 Ⓖ 58 Ⓗ 134 Ⓘ 137

Extended Response

7. What is the 100th term in the arithmetic sequence beginning with 3, 19, . . . ?
Show your work.
[4] 1587; $a = 3$, $n = 100$, $d = 16$, $a_n = a + (n − 1)d$;
$a_{100} = 3 + (100 − 1)16 = 3 + 1584 = 1587$
[3] appropriate method shown, with one computational error
[2] appropriate method shown, with several computational errors OR correct term found incorrectly with work shown
[1] incorrect term, without work shown
[0] incorrect answers and no work shown OR no answers given

All-in-One Resources/Online
Enrichment

9-2 Enrichment
Arithmetic Sequences

There are many types of sequences. One interesting type of sequence is the *Farey sequence*. The first four Farey sequences are:

$F_1: \left\{ \frac{0}{1}, \frac{1}{1} \right\}$

$F_2: \left\{ \frac{0}{1}, \frac{1}{2}, \frac{1}{1} \right\}$

$F_3: \left\{ \frac{0}{1}, \frac{1}{3}, \frac{1}{2}, \frac{2}{3}, \frac{1}{1} \right\}$

$F_4: \left\{ \frac{0}{1}, \frac{1}{4}, \frac{1}{3}, \frac{1}{2}, \frac{2}{3}, \frac{3}{4}, \frac{1}{1} \right\}$

Each Farey sequence is a list of fractions in increasing order between 0 and 1, written in simplest form with a denominator less than or equal to the integer n. For any n greater than 1, there are an odd number of terms in the sequence and the middle term is $\frac{1}{2}$.

Problem

What are the terms of the Farey sequence for $n = 5$?

The Farey sequence for $n = 5$ contains all the terms of the Farey sequence F_4 plus the fractions between 0 and 1 which have a denominator of 5 when written in simplest form.

The fractions $\frac{0}{5}$ and $\frac{5}{5}$ will not be added because they simplify to $\frac{0}{1}$ and $\frac{1}{1}$. Insert the fractions $\frac{1}{5}, \frac{2}{5}, \frac{3}{5}$, and $\frac{4}{5}$ in the Farey sequence F_4.

$F_5: \left\{ \frac{0}{1}, \frac{1}{5}, \frac{1}{4}, \frac{1}{3}, \frac{2}{5}, \frac{1}{2}, \frac{3}{5}, \frac{2}{3}, \frac{3}{4}, \frac{4}{5}, \frac{1}{1} \right\}$

Exercises

1. How many terms are in each of the first five Farey sequences? 2, 3, 5, 7, 11

2. What are the terms for the Farey sequence F_6? $\left\{ \frac{0}{1}, \frac{1}{6}, \frac{1}{5}, \frac{1}{4}, \frac{1}{3}, \frac{2}{5}, \frac{1}{2}, \frac{3}{5}, \frac{2}{3}, \frac{3}{4}, \frac{4}{5}, \frac{5}{6}, \frac{1}{1} \right\}$

3. What will be the new terms in the Farey sequence F_7? $\frac{1}{7}, \frac{2}{7}, \frac{3}{7}, \frac{4}{7}, \frac{5}{7}$, and $\frac{6}{7}$

4. Since 11 is a prime number, how many more terms will be in the sequence F_{11} compared to the sequence F_{10}? 10

5. Is there any limit to how large n can be? No, n can be any positive integer although the computations become tedious.

6. Can you give examples of any other sequences?
Answers may vary. Sample: arithmetic, geometric, and Fibonacci

---

Online Teacher Resource Center
Activities, Games, and Puzzles

9-2 Game: Four Thought
Arithmetic Sequences

This is a game for two players.

To begin the game, roll a number cube twice. The first roll gives the column of your number on the board, and the second roll gives the row of your number on the board. You get to keep that number by writing it down and crossing it off the board. Then your opponent rolls a number cube twice and keeps another number from the board, but only if that number has not already been taken. Otherwise, the player rolls the number cube twice more. If a player rolls two 1's or two 6's, the player gets a FREE PICK! and may choose any number on the board that has not been taken.

The object of the game is to be the first player to collect four numbers that form an arithmetic sequence. You can recognize arithmetic sequences by looking for a constant difference in any four numbers you have taken from the board.

Example: Four of your numbers are 2, 13, 24, and 35.

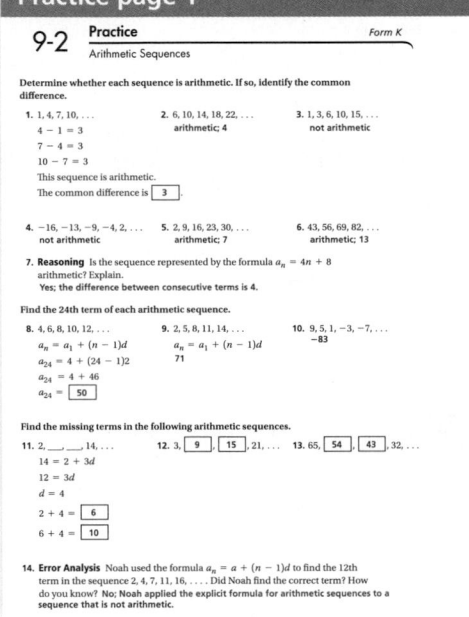

This is an arithmetic sequence because consecutive numbers have a common difference d equal to 11.

The first player to collect an arithmetic sequence of four numbers wins! **Check students' work.**

30 FREE PICK!	5	32	3	16	22
10	28	12	34	27	8
35	17	31	6	15	33
21	1	13	24	18	4
7	20	9	26	2	11
19	36	14	29	23	25 FREE PICK!

Do you know HOW?

Find the first five terms of each sequence.

1. $a_n = 3n + 1$

2. $a_n = -2n - 1$

3. $a_n = n^2 + 2n$

4. $a_n = 3a_{n-1}$, where $a_1 = 2$

5. $a_n = 5 - a_{n-1}$, where $a_1 = 1$

6. $a_n = a_{n-1} + 2n$, where $a_1 = 1$

Write a recursive definition for each sequence.

7. $2, -4, 8, -16, \ldots$

8. $1, 4, 7, 10, \ldots$

9. $4, 2, 5, 1, 6, \ldots$

Write an explicit formula for each sequence.

10. $2, 4, 8, 16, \ldots$

11. $5, 2, -1, -4, \ldots$

12. $2, 5, 10, 17, \ldots$

Find the ninth and tenth terms of each arithmetic sequence.

13. $1, 8, 15, 22, \ldots$

14. $4, 10, 16, 22, \ldots$

15. $6, 3, 0, -3, \ldots$

Determine whether each sequence is arithmetic. If so, identify the common difference.

16. $1, 3, 9, 27, \ldots$

17. $11, 22, 33, 44, \ldots$

18. $1, -1, -3, -5, -7, \ldots$

19. $0, 2, 5, 9, 14, \ldots$

Find the missing term of each arithmetic sequence.

20. $\ldots, 3, \blacksquare, 17, \ldots$

21. $\ldots, 25, \blacksquare, -15, \ldots$

22. $\ldots, -3, \blacksquare, 8, \ldots$

23. $\ldots, 66, \blacksquare, 48, \ldots$

Find the missing terms of each arithmetic sequence.

24. $4, a_2, a_3, a_4, 32, \ldots$

25. $10, a_2, a_3, a_4, -20, \ldots$

26. $5, a_2, a_3, a_4, 35, \ldots$

Do you UNDERSTAND?

27. **Open-Ended** Write the first four terms of an arithmetic sequence with a common difference of 3 and a third term of 10. Then write both a recursive definition and an explicit formula for this sequence.

28. **Investments** You invested money in a fund and each month you receive a payment for your investment. Over the first four months, you received $50, $52, $55, and $59. If this pattern continues, how much will you receive in the tenth month?
    a. Write a formula to describe this sequence.
    b. Identify your formula as explicit or recursive.
    c. **Writing** Explain the difference between an explicit formula and a recursive formula. Use your formula from part (a) as part of your explanation.

29. **Open-Ended** Write the first five terms of a sequence that is not an arithmetic sequence. Then give both an explicit and recursive formula to describe this sequence.

30. **Sports** A tennis club charges players a $20 court fee plus a $10 hourly charge with a 5-hour maximum. A posted list of the total charges for 1, 2, 3, 4, or 5 hours forms an arithmetic sequence. What is the first term and what is the common difference?

formula would have a formula for the nth term involving the initial term, the common difference, and the term number, n. The formula $a_n = a_1 + (n - 1)d$ is an explicit formula.

29. Answers may vary. Sample: 10, 11, 13, 16, 20;
    $a_n = a_{n-1} + (n - 1), a_1 = 10$;
    $a_n = 10 + \dfrac{n(n - 1)}{2}$

30. 30; 10

Answers

Mid-Chapter Quiz

1. 4, 7, 10, 13, 16

2. $-3, -5, -7, -9, -11$

3. 3, 8, 15, 24, 35

4. 2, 6, 18, 54, 162

5. 1, 4, 1, 4, 1

6. 1, 5, 11, 19, 29

7. $a_n = -2a_{n-1}, a_1 = 2$

8. $a_n = a_{n-1} + 3, a_1 = 1$

9. $a_n = a_{n-1} + (-1)^{n-1}n, a_1 = 4$

10. $a_n = 2^n$

11. $a_n = 5 - 3(n - 1)$

12. $a_n = n^2 + 1$

13. 57, 64

14. 52, 58

15. $-18, -21$

16. no

17. yes; 11

18. yes; -2

19. no

20. 10   21. 5   22. 2.5   23. 57

24. 11, 18, 25

25. 2.5, -5, -12.5

26. 12.5, 20, 27.5

27. 4, 7, 10, 13; $a_n = a_{n-1} + 3, a_1 = 4$;
    $a_n = 4 + 3(n - 1)$

28. 104;
    a. recursive: $a_n = a_{n-1} + n$,
       $a_1 = 50$ OR
       explicit:
       $a_n = 49 + \dfrac{n(n + 1)}{2}$
    b. See the answer to part (a).
    c. A recursive formula would have the initial term, a_1, and a formula for the nth term involving the previous term and the common difference, d. The formula $a_n = a_{n-1} + n$ is a recursive formula. An explicit

PowerAlgebra.com

MathXL for School
Prepare students for the Mid-Chapter Quiz and Chapter Test with online practice and review.

1 Interactive Learning

Solve It!
PURPOSE To extend and compare geometric sequences

PROCESS Students may divide successive terms to find the ratio and then multiply the fourth term by that ratio. They may look for and apply formulas that represent the relationship between the first term and each successive term.

FACILITATE

Q How can you express division by 10 and division by -3 as multiplication? **[multiplication by 0.1 and $-\frac{1}{3}$]**

Q What is the mathematical relationship between the consecutive terms of each sequence? **[A: multiply by two; B: multiply by 0.1; C: multiply by $-\frac{1}{3}$]**

ANSWER See Solve It in Answers on next page.

CONNECT THE MATH In the Solve It, students use ratios to find terms in geometric sequences. In the lesson, they find and use common ratios to express geometric sequences recursively and explicitly.

2 Guided Instruction

Take Note
Notice that both sequence definitions use the common ratio r. However, the recursive definition uses the previous term in the sequence, and the explicit definition uses the first term in the sequence.

Problem 1

Q In 1A, how would the common ratio change if all the terms were negative? if every other term was negative? **[It would not change; it would be negative.]**

Objective To define, identify, and apply geometric sequences

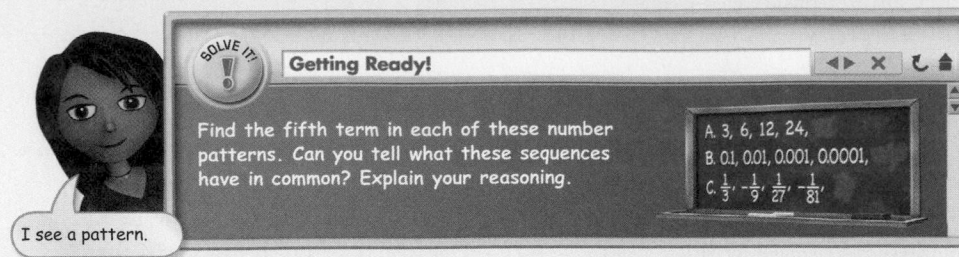

SOLVE IT! Getting Ready!

Find the fifth term in each of these number patterns. Can you tell what these sequences have in common? Explain your reasoning.

A. 3, 6, 12, 24,
B. 0.1, 0.01, 0.001, 0.0001,
C. $\frac{1}{3}, -\frac{1}{9}, \frac{1}{27}, -\frac{1}{81}$

I see a pattern.

Dynamic Activity Geometric Sequences

Lesson Vocabulary
• geometric sequence
• common ratio
• geometric mean

You build a *geometric sequence* by multiplying each term by a constant.

Focus Question What is a geometric sequence?

take note **Key Concept** Geometric Sequence

A **geometric sequence** with a starting value a and a **common ratio** r is a sequence of the form

$$a, ar, ar^2, ar^3, \ldots$$

A recursive definition for the sequence has two parts:

initial condition $\qquad a_1 = a$

recursive formula $\qquad a_n = a_{n-1} \cdot r$, for $n > 1$

An explicit definition for this sequence is a single formula:

$a_n = a_1 \cdot r^{n-1}$, for $n \geq 1$

Think

How do you find the ratios between consecutive terms? Divide the second term by the first term, then the third term by the second term, and so on.

Problem 1 Identifying Geometric Sequences

Is the sequence geometric? If it is, what are a_1 and r?

A 3, 6, 12, 24, 48, ...

Find the ratios between consecutive terms.

3   6   12   24   48

The common ratio is 2. $\frac{6}{3} = \frac{12}{6} = \frac{24}{12} = \frac{48}{24} = 2$

This sequence is geometric with $a_1 = 3$ and $r = 2$.

9-3 Preparing to Teach

BIG idea Modeling   **UbD**

ESSENTIAL UNDERSTANDINGS

• In a geometric sequence, the ratio of any term (after the first) to its preceding term is a constant value, no matter what two terms are compared. Each term of a geometric sequence can be built by multiplying the previous term by that constant.

• A geometric sequence can be modeled explicitly or recursively.

Math Background

• Between consecutive terms, a geometric sequence has a common ratio with each term given by a constant multiple of the previous term; an arithmetic sequence has a common difference.

• A geometric sequence is built by multiplying each term by a constant; an arithmetic sequence is built by adding a constant to each term.

• A geometric sequence is an exponential function with a base equal to the common ratio. An arithmetic sequence is a linear function with a slope equal to the common difference.

• The second of 3 consecutive terms in a geometric sequence is the square root of the product of the proceeding and following terms. The second of 3 consecutive terms in an arithmetic sequence is the mean of the preceding and following terms.

For two terms x and y, $\sqrt{xy}$ is the geometric mean. The geometric mean provides the value of the term between x and y in a geometric sequence and has other mathematical and real-world applications (e.g. calculating average rates of growth).

Support Student Learning
Use the **Algebra 2 Companion** to engage and support students during instruction. See Lesson Resources at the end of this lesson for details.

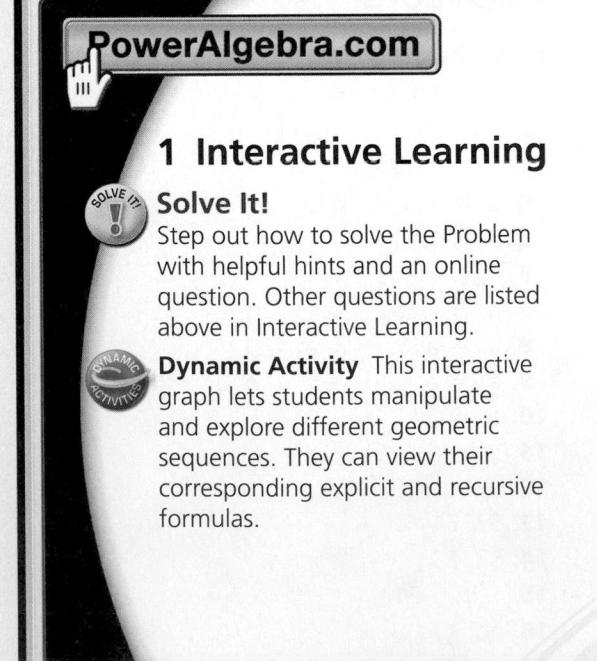

PowerAlgebra.com

1 Interactive Learning

Solve It!
Step out how to solve the Problem with helpful hints and an online question. Other questions are listed above in Interactive Learning.

Dynamic Activity This interactive graph lets students manipulate and explore different geometric sequences. They can view their corresponding explicit and recursive formulas.

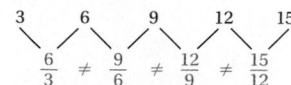 **B** $3, 6, 9, 12, 15, \ldots$

Find the ratios between consecutive terms.

$$3 \quad 6 \quad 9 \quad 12 \quad 15$$

$$\frac{6}{3} \neq \frac{9}{6} \neq \frac{12}{9} \neq \frac{15}{12}$$

The ratios are different. With no common ratio, this sequence is not geometric.

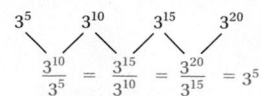 **C** $3^5, 3^{10}, 3^{15}, 3^{20}, \ldots$

Use the properties of exponents to simplify the ratios of consecutive terms.

$$3^5 \quad 3^{10} \quad 3^{15} \quad 3^{20}$$

$$\frac{3^{10}}{3^5} = \frac{3^{15}}{3^{10}} = \frac{3^{20}}{3^{15}} = 3^5$$

The common ratio is 3^5. This sequence is geometric with $a_1 = 3^5$ and $r = 3^5$.

Got It? **1.** Is the sequence geometric? If it is, what are a_1 and r?
  a. $2, 4, 8, 16, \ldots$ **b.** $1, 5, 9, 13, 17, \ldots$ **c.** $2^3, 2^7, 2^{11}, 2^{15}, \ldots$

Problem 2 Analyzing Geometric Sequences

What are the indicated terms of the geometric sequence?

A the 10th term of the geometric sequence $4, 12, 36, \ldots$

The first term a_1 is 4. The common ratio r is $12 \div 4 = 3$.

Use the explicit formula.	$a_n = a_1 r^{n-1}$
Substitute 10 for n, 4 for a_1, and 3 for r.	$a_{10} = 4 \cdot 3^{10-1}$
Simplify.	$a_{10} = 78{,}732$

The 10th term is 78,732.

B the second and third terms of the geometric sequence $2, \blacksquare, \blacksquare, -54, \ldots$

Step 1 Identify the common ratio.

The first term a_1 is 2. The fourth term a_4 is -54.

Use the explicit formula.	$a_n = a_1 r^{n-1}$
Substitute 4 for n and 2 for a_1.	$a_4 = 2r^{4-1}$
Substitute -54 for a_4. Simplify.	$-54 = 2r^3$
Divide each side by 2.	$-27 = r^3$
Solve for r.	$-3 = r$

Step 2 Identify the missing terms.

Find the second term.	$2 \cdot (-3) = -6$
Find the third term.	$-6 \cdot (-3) = 18$

The second and third terms are -6 and 18.

 Got It? **2. a.** What is the 8th term of the geometric sequence that begins $2, 10, \ldots$?
  b. What are the second and third terms of this geometric sequence?
    $120, \blacksquare, \blacksquare, 15, \ldots$

Q In 1C, why might someone mistakenly think that the sequence is arithmetic rather than geometric? **[The exponents form an arithmetic sequence.]**

Got It?

Q How many pairs of successive terms must you divide to determine whether a sequence is geometric? Give an example to show why this is important. **[The ratios between all of the successive pairs of terms must be checked. Samples: 2, 4, 8, 14 ... and 2, 4, 8, 16 ...]**

Problem 2

Q Why is the explicit formula easier to use than the recursive definition for 2A? Is there ever a time that the recursive definition would be more convenient? **[Sample: To find the tenth term, you also have to find terms four through nine when you use the recursive definition. The recursive definition is more convenient when you know terms very close to the term you want to find.]**

Q In 2B, what do you know about the signs of the successive terms of the sequence? Will this always be true when r is negative? Explain. **[The signs alternate. Yes because even powers will be positive and odd powers will be negative.]**

Got It?

Q In 2b, if the fourth term was changed to -15, what would be the common ratio? How does this affect the second and third terms of the sequence? **[$-\frac{1}{2}$; the sign of the ratio will change the value of the second term but not the third term. The third term will have the same sign as the first term regardless of the sign of the common ratio.]**

---

2 Guided Instruction

Each Problem is worked out and supported online.

Problem 1
Identifying Geometric Sequences
Animated

Problem 2
Analyzing Geometric Sequences
Animated

Problem 3
Using a Geometric Sequence

Problem 4
Using the Geometric Mean
Animated

Support in Algebra 2 Companion
• Vocabulary
• Key Concepts
• Got It?

Answers

Solve It!
A. 48
B. 0.00001
C. $\frac{1}{243}$

Each seq. is generated by multiplying the previous term by a common ratio.

Got It?
1. a. yes; $a_1 = 2, r = 2$
  b. no
  c. yes; $a_1 = 2^3, r = 2^4$
2. a. 156,250
  b. 60; 30

Problem 3

Q When you find the common ratio for the sequence of the ball bounce heights, what does the value of the ratio represent in the context of the ball bounce height? **[The value represents the portion of the height of a bounce that the next bounce will reach.]**

EXTENSION

Q Would the sequence that represents the changes in heights from bounce to bounce also form a geometric sequence? What would r be for that sequence? Explain. **[Yes; it would also have a common ratio of 0.7, or $\frac{7}{10}$. To show this, the changes in height are $-30, -21, -14.7 \ldots$]**

Q Is it necessary to start with a to find the heights of the fourth and fifth bounces recursively? Explain. **[No; you can use a recursive definition on any term in a sequence. Beginning with the height of the third bounce creates fewer calculations.]**

Got It?

Q What criteria will you use to determine whether to use an explicit formula or a recursive definition? Is either formula less valid as a method to find terms in a geometric sequence? **[Samples: the known terms, the number of the term to be found, the format of the answer, and the manner of calculation; both formulas are equally valid as methods to find terms in a geometric sequence.]**

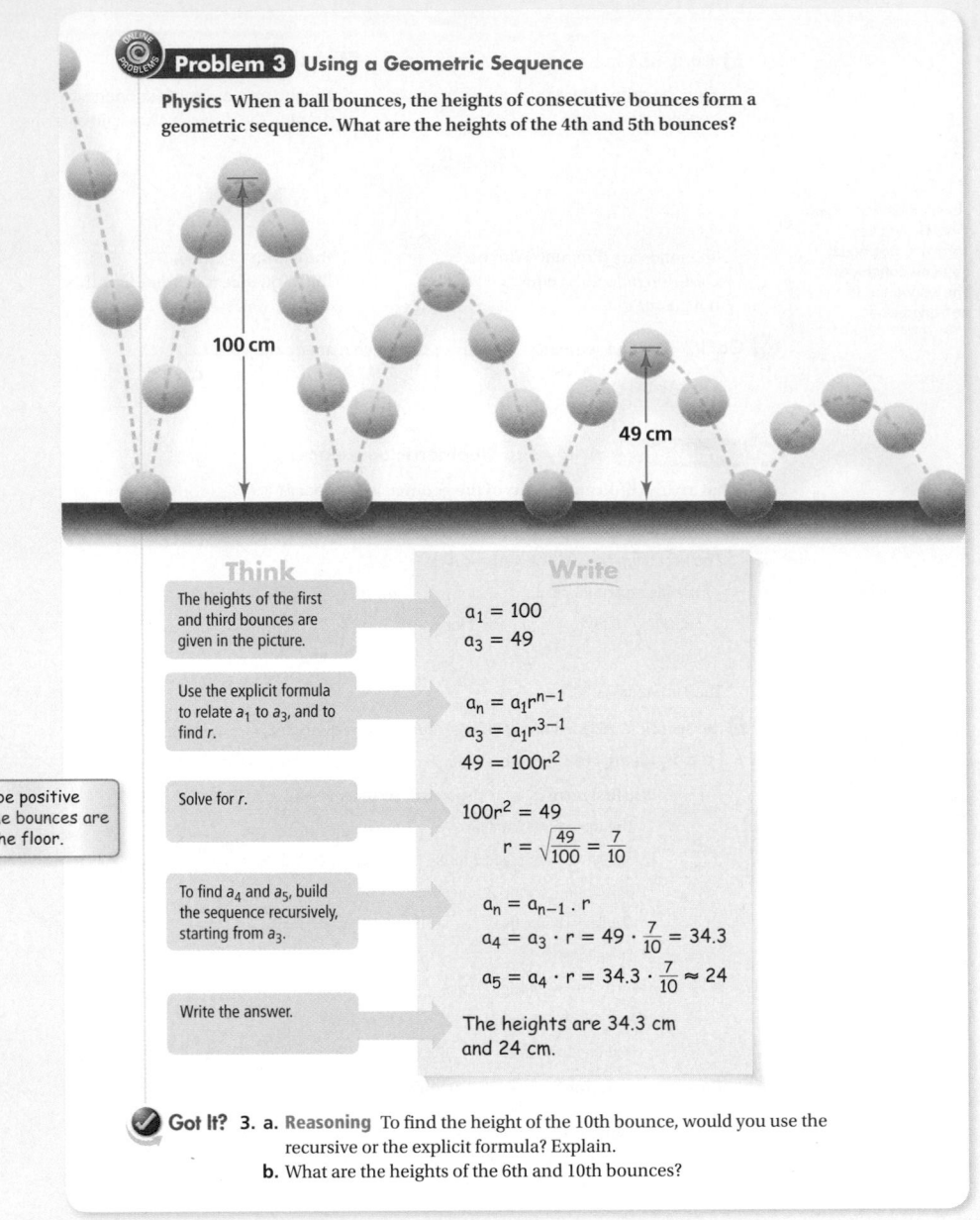

Problem 3 Using a Geometric Sequence

Physics When a ball bounces, the heights of consecutive bounces form a geometric sequence. What are the heights of the 4th and 5th bounces?

100 cm

49 cm

Think	Write
The heights of the first and third bounces are given in the picture.	$a_1 = 100$ $a_3 = 49$
Use the explicit formula to relate a_1 to a_3, and to find r.	$a_n = a_1 r^{n-1}$ $a_3 = a_1 r^{3-1}$ $49 = 100r^2$
Solve for r.	$100r^2 = 49$ $r = \sqrt{\frac{49}{100}} = \frac{7}{10}$
To find a_4 and a_5, build the sequence recursively, starting from a_3.	$a_n = a_{n-1} \cdot r$ $a_4 = a_3 \cdot r = 49 \cdot \frac{7}{10} = 34.3$ $a_5 = a_4 \cdot r = 34.3 \cdot \frac{7}{10} \approx 24$
Write the answer.	The heights are 34.3 cm and 24 cm.

Hint
r must be positive since the bounces are above the floor.

✓ **Got It?** **3. a. Reasoning** To find the height of the 10th bounce, would you use the recursive or the explicit formula? Explain.
b. What are the heights of the 6th and 10th bounces?

Additional Problems

1. Is the sequence geometric? If it is, what are a and r?
  a. 5, 10, 50, . . .
  b. -10, 6, -3.6, . . .
  ANSWERS
  a. no
  b. yes; $a = -10$, $r = -0.6$

2. What are the 2nd and 3rd terms of the geometric sequence 2, ■, ■, 128, . . . ?
  ANSWER 8, 32

3. You work as a store manager and need to clear some inventory. You decide to discount each item by 30% of the previous week's price until the entire inventory is sold. The original price of one item was $60. What will be the cost of the item during the fifth week of the sale?
  ANSWER $10.08

4. What are the possible values of the missing term of the geometric sequence 28, ■, 7?
  ANSWER 14 and -14

Q Does the geometric mean give a possible value for the missing term? Explain. **[Yes; sample: Consider the terms 48, x, 3 ...; $\frac{x}{48}$ and $\frac{3}{x}$ are equal ratios. Solve $\frac{x}{48} = \frac{3}{x}$; $x^2 = 48 \cdot 3$, so $x = \pm\sqrt{144}$.]**

Q If the missing term is 12, what is r? If the missing term is -12, what is r? **[$\frac{1}{4}$; $-\frac{1}{4}$]**

Q Do you need to write perfect square factors when finding the geometric mean? Explain. **[No; you can multiply 48 × 3 = 144. Thus, $\sqrt{144} = \pm12$.]**

Hint
The sequence at the right is an example of why you must consider two possible values for the missing term.

In a geometric sequence, the square of the middle term of any three consecutive terms is equal to the product of the other two terms. For example, examine the sequence 2, −6, 18, −54, . . . , as shown here.

$$(-6)^2 = 2 \cdot 18 = 36$$

$$2, -6, 18, -54, \ldots$$

$$18^2 = (-6)(-54) = 324$$

In an arithmetic sequence, recall that the middle term of any three consecutive terms is the arithmetic mean of the other two terms.

The **geometric mean** of two positive numbers x and y is $\sqrt{xy}$. By definition, the geometric mean is positive.

For a geometric sequence a_1, , a_3, ..., there are two possible values for the missing term. The geometric mean is one possible value. The opposite of the geometric mean is the other.

Problem 4 Using the Geometric Mean

Multiple Choice What are the possible values of the missing term of the geometric sequence?

48, , 3, . . .

A ±4   B ±9   C ±12   D ±20

Find the geometric mean of 48 and 3.

Think
Why would this question ask for "possible values" rather than "the value"?
The geometric mean and its opposite are both possible values.

Use the formula for the geometric mean to find a possible value for the missing term.	geometric mean $= \sqrt{xy}$
Substitute 48 for x and 3 for y.	$= \sqrt{48 \cdot 3}$
Simplify.	$= \sqrt{144}$
	$= 12$

The possible values for the missing term are the geometric mean and its opposite, or ±12. The correct answer is C.

✓ **Got It?** 4. The 9th and 11th terms of a geometric sequence are 45 and 80. What are possible values for the 10th term?

Focus Question What is a geometric sequence?
Answer In a geometric sequence, the ratio of any term (after the first) to its preceding term is a constant value. You can build a geometric sequence by multiplying each term by a constant.

Got It?

Q Is it necessary to find a? Would the solution change if you had to find the eighth term and the seventh and ninth terms were 45 and 80? Explain. **[No; the answers would be the same, because the geometric mean of 45 and 80 remains the same.]**

Q What are the possible values of r? Explain. **[Sample: Divide the last term by the possible missing term: $r = \frac{80}{\pm 60} = \pm\frac{4}{3}$.]**

Answers

Got It? (continued)

3. a. Answers may vary. Sample: explicit; it is easier to use because only one calculation is needed.

  b. about 16.8 cm, about 4 cm

4. ±60

3 Lesson Check

Do you know HOW?
- Students can check their answers for Exercises 3 and 4 by using both a recursive definition and an explicit formula.

Do you UNDERSTAND?
- If students have difficulty explaining the error in Exercise 5, have them review Problem 4. Remind them that the geometric mean is used to find the middle value of three consecutive terms.
- If students have trouble with Exercise 6, suggest that they work out an example of each type and compare the steps.

Close

> **Q** How can you find a specific term of a geometric sequence when you know a term and the common ratio? **[Sample: Use an explicit formula or a recursive formula, depending on the term you have to find.]**
>
> **Q** Is it possible to determine whether a series is geometric using only two terms? Use an example to explain your reasoning. **[No; using the terms 5, 10, … this could be an arithmetic series with a common difference of 5 or a geometric sequence with a common ratio of 2.]**

Lesson Check

Do you know HOW?
Determine whether each sequence is geometric. If so, find the common ratio.

1. 5, 10, 15, . . .

2. 10, 20, 40, . . .

Find the seventh term of each geometric sequence.

3. 1, −3, 9, . . .

4. 100, 20, 4, . . .

Do you UNDERSTAND?

5. Error Analysis To find the third term of the geometric sequence 5, 10, ■, ■, 80, your friend says that there are two possible answers—the geometric mean of 5 and 80, and its opposite. Explain your friend's error.

6. Compare and Contrast How is finding a missing term of a geometric sequence using the geometric mean similar to finding a missing term of an arithmetic sequence using the arithmetic mean? How is it different?

Practice and Problem-Solving Exercises

Ⓐ Practice Determine whether each sequence is geometric. If so, find the common ratio. ◀ **See Problem 1.**

7. 1, 2, 4, 8, . . . **8.** 1, 2, 3, 4, . . . **9.** 1, −2, 4, −8, . . .

10. −1, 1, −1, 1, . . . **11.** 7, 0.7, 0.07, 0.007, . . . **12.** −1, −6, −36, −216, . . .

Find the eighth term of each geometric sequence. ◀ **See Problem 2.**

Guided Practice

> **13.** 3, 9, 27, . . .
> To start, identify the common ratio. $\frac{9}{3} = 3$

14. −3, 6, −12, . . . **15.** 24, −6, $\frac{3}{2}$, . . . **16.** −30, 7.5, −1.875, . . .

17. Science When radioactive substances decay, the amount remaining will form a geometric sequence when measured over constant intervals of time. The table shows the amount of Np-240, a radioactive isotope of Neptunium, initially and after 2 hours. What are the amounts left after 1 hour, 3 hours, and 4 hours? ◀ **See Problem 3.**

Hours Elapsed	0	1	2	3	4
Grams of Np-240	1244	■	346	■	■

Find the missing term of each geometric sequence. It could be the geometric mean or its opposite. ◀ **See Problem 4.**

Guided Practice

> **18.** 5, ■, 911.25, . . .
> To start, use the formula for the geometric mean. geometric mean $= \sqrt{xy}$

19. $\frac{2}{5}$, ■, $\frac{8}{45}$, . . . **20.** 3, ■, 0.75, . . . **21.** 5, ■, 2.8125, . . .

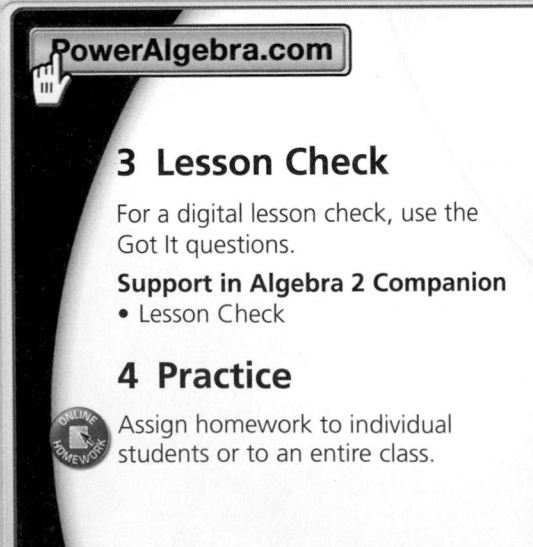

PowerAlgebra.com

3 Lesson Check

For a digital lesson check, use the Got It questions.

Support in Algebra 2 Companion
- Lesson Check

4 Practice

Assign homework to individual students or to an entire class.

Answers

Lesson Check
1. no
2. yes; 2
3. 729
4. 0.0064
5. The third term would be the geometric mean of 5 and 80 which is 20. Since a is pos. and r^2 is always pos., the third term, ar^2, cannot be neg.
6. For both the arithmetic mean and the geometric mean, the middle term of any three consecutive terms can be determined using the first and last of the three terms. The arithmetic mean is the sum of the first and last terms divided by 2, whereas the geometric mean is the square root (or its opposite) of the product of the first and the last terms.

Practice and Problem-Solving Exercises
7. yes; 2
8. no
9. yes; −2
10. yes; −1
11. yes; 0.1
12. yes; 6
13. 6561
14. 384
15. $\frac{-3}{2048}$
16. $\frac{15}{8192}$
17. about 656.1 g; about 182.5 g; about 96.2 g
18. ±67.5
19. ±$\frac{4}{15}$
20. ±1.5
21. ±3.75

 **Apply**

Write an explicit formula for each sequence. Then generate the first five terms.

22. $a_1 = 1, r = 0.5$ **23.** $a_1 = 100, r = -20$ **24.** $a_1 = 7, r = 1$

25. $a_1 = 1024, r = 0.5$ **26.** $a_1 = 4, r = 0.1$ **27.** $a_1 = 10, r = -1$

Identify each sequence as *arithmetic, geometric,* or *neither*. Then find the next two terms.

28. $45, 90, 180, 360, \ldots$ **29.** $25, 50, 75, 100, \ldots$ **30.** $3, -3, 3, -3, \ldots$

31. $-5, 10, -20, 40, \ldots$ **32.** $2, 1, 0.5, 0.25, \ldots$ **33.** $1, 4, 9, 16, \ldots$

Find the missing terms of each geometric sequence.

34. $972, \blacksquare, \blacksquare, \blacksquare, 12, \ldots$ **35.** $2.5, \blacksquare, \blacksquare, \blacksquare, 202.5, \ldots$

36. $12.5, \blacksquare, \blacksquare, \blacksquare, 5.12, \ldots$ **37.** $-4, \blacksquare, \blacksquare, \blacksquare, -30\frac{3}{8}, \ldots$

> **Hint** The geometric mean of the first and fifth terms is the third term. Some terms might be negative.

38. Think About a Plan Suppose a balloon is filled with 5000 cm³ of helium. It then loses one fourth of its helium each day. How much helium will be left in the balloon at the start of the tenth day?
  • How can you write a sequence of numbers to represent this situation?
  • Is the sequence arithmetic, geometric, or neither?
  • How can you write a formula for this sequence?

39. Athletics During your first week of training for a marathon, you run a total of 10 miles. You increase the distance you run each week by twenty percent. How many miles do you run during your twelfth week of training?

40. a. Open-Ended Choose two positive numbers. Find their geometric mean.
  b. Find the common ratio for a geometric sequence that includes the terms from part (a) as its first three terms.
  c. Find the 9th term of the geometric sequence from part (b).
  d. Find the geometric mean of the term from part (c) and the first term of your sequence. What term of the sequence have you just found?

For the geometric sequence 3, 12, 48, 192, ..., find the indicated term.

41. 17th term **42.** 20th term **43.** *n*th term

Find the 10th term of each geometric sequence.

44. $a_9 - 8, r - \frac{1}{2}$ **45.** $a_9 - -5, r - -\frac{1}{2}$ **46.** $a_9 = -\frac{1}{3}, r = \frac{1}{2}$

47. Writing Describe the similarities and differences between a common difference and a common ratio.

---

22. $a_n = 0.5^{n-1}$; 1, 0.5, 0.25, 0.125, 0.0625

23. $a_n = 100(-20)^{n-1}$; 100, -2000, 40,000, -800,000, 16,000,000

24. $a_n = 7$; 7, 7, 7, 7, 7

25. $a_n = 1024(0.5)^{n-1}$; 1024, 512, 256, 128, 64

26. $a_n = 4(0.1)^{n-1}$; 4, 0.4, 0.04, 0.004, 0.0004

27. $a_n = 10(-1)^{n-1}$; 10, -10, 10, -10, 10

28. geometric; 720, 1440

29. arithmetic; 125, 150

30. geometric; 3, -3

31. geometric; -80, 160

32. geometric; 0.125, 0.0625

33. neither; 25, 36

34. 324, 108, 36 or -324, 108, -36

35. 7.5, 22.5, 67.5 or -7.5, 22.5, -67.5

36. 10, 8, 6.4 or -10, 8, -6.4

37. -6.64, -11.02, -18.30 or 6.64, -11.02, 18.30

38. about 375.42 cm³

39. about 74.3 mi

40. Answers may vary. Sample:
  a. 3 and 12; 6
  b. 3, 6, 12; 2
  c. 768
  d. 48; 5th term

41. 3×4^{16}, or 12,884,901,888

42. 3×4^{19}, or 824,633,720,832

43. $3(4)^{n-1}$

44. 4

45. 2.5

46. $-\frac{1}{6}$

47. Both the common diff. and the common ratio are used to find the next term in a sequence, but a common diff. is added and a common ratio is multiplied.

---

4 Practice

ASSIGNMENT GUIDE

Basic: 7–20, 38, 39, 44–46

Average: 7–20, 22–38 even, 39–47 odd

Standardized Test Prep: 48–51

Mixed Review: 52–65

Reasoning exercises have blue headings.

Applications exercises have red headings.

EXERCISE 39: Use the Think About a Plan worksheet in the **Student Companion** (also available in the Teaching Resources in print and online) to further support students' development in becoming independent learners.

HOMEWORK QUICK CHECK

To check students' understanding of key skills and concepts, go over Exercises 14, 17, 19, 38, and 39.

Answers

Standardized Test Prep

48. B
49. H
50. C
51. G

Mixed Review

52. $a_n = -3 + 3(n-1)$; $a_n = a_{n-1} + 3$, $a_1 = -3$

53. $a_n = 17 - 9(n-1)$; $a_n = a_{n-1} - 9$, $a_1 = 17$

54. $a_n = -2 - 11(n-1)$; $a_n = a_{n-1} - 11$, $a_1 = -2$

55. $a^4 + 20a^3 + 150a^2 + 500a + 625$

56. $x^3 - 27x^2 + 243x - 729$

57. $32x^5 + 80x^4y + 80x^3y^2 + 40x^2y^3 + 10xy^4 + y^5$

58. $b^{12} - 18b^{10} + 135b^8 - 540b^6 + 1215b^4 - 1458b^2 + 729$

59. vert. asymptote: $x = -3$

60. vert. asymptote: $x = -1$

61. vert. asymptotes: $x = 0, 1$

62. vert. asymptote: $x = 3$; hole at $x = -3$

63. $a_n = a_{n-1} + n$, $a_1 = 1$

64. $a_n = a_{n-1} + (2n - 1)$, $a_1 = 1$

65. $a_n = a_{n-1} + n^2$, $a_1 = 1$

Standardized Test Prep

SAT/ACT

48. What is the common ratio in the geometric sequence $4, 10, 25, 62.5, \ldots$?

    Ⓐ 0.4   Ⓒ 15
    Ⓑ 2.5   Ⓓ 25

49. The first term of a geometric sequence is 1 and its common ratio is 6. What is the sixth term?

    Ⓕ 31   Ⓗ 7776
    Ⓖ 3176   Ⓘ 46,656

50. Determine by inspection the end behavior of the graph of $y = -2x^3 + 5x - 4$.

    Ⓐ falls to the left, falls to the right: (↙ , ↘)
    Ⓑ falls to the left, rises to the right: (↙, ↗)
    Ⓒ rises to the left, falls to the right: (↖, ↘)
    Ⓓ rises to the left, rises to the right: (↖, ↗)

51. What are the asymptotes of the graph of $y = \frac{10}{x-5}$?

    Ⓕ $x = 0, y = 5$ Ⓗ $x = 5, y = 10$
    Ⓖ $x = 5, y = 0$ Ⓘ $x = 10, y = 5$

Mixed Review

Write an explicit and a recursive formula for each arithmetic sequence.   ◀ See Lesson 9-2.

52. $-3, 0, 3, 6, \ldots$ **53.** $17, 8, -1, \ldots$ **54.** $-2, -13, -24, \ldots$

Expand each binomial.   ◀ See Lesson 5-7.

55. $(a + 5)^4$ **56.** $(x - 9)^3$ **57.** $(2x + y)^5$ **58.** $(b^2 - 3)^6$

Find the vertical asymptotes and holes for the graph of each rational function.   ◀ See Lesson 8-3.

59. $y = \frac{x-3}{x+3}$ **60.** $y = \frac{x-3}{x+1}$

61. $y = \frac{x-3}{x(x-1)}$ **62.** $y = \frac{x(x+3)}{(x-3)(x+3)}$

Get Ready! To prepare for Lesson 9-4, do Exercises 63–65.

Write a recursive formula for each sequence.   ◀ See Lesson 9-1.

63. $1, 3, 6, 10, \ldots$ **64.** $1, 4, 9, 16, \ldots$ **65.** $1, 5, 14, 30, \ldots$

Additional Instructional Support

Algebra 2 Companion

Students can use the **Algebra 2 Companion** worktext (4 pages) as you teach the lesson. Use the Companion to support

- New Vocabulary
- Key Concepts
- Got It for each Problem
- Lesson Check

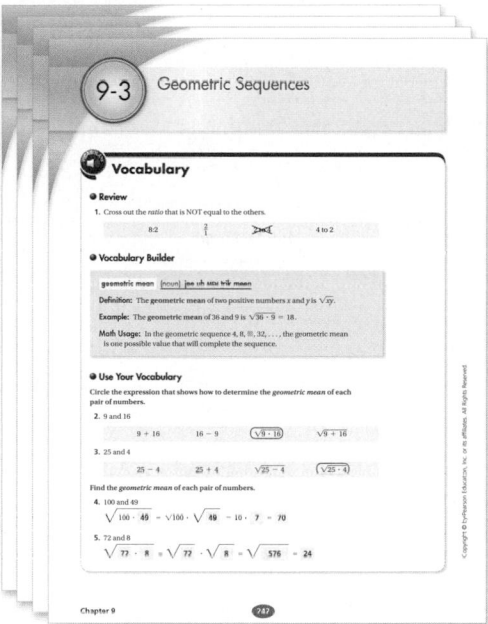

ELL Support

Use Graphic Organizers Have students make a chart summarizing recursive definitions and explicit formulas for both arithmetic and geometric sequences. Students should label the rows of the chart *arithmetic* and *geometric* and should label the columns *recursive*, *explicit*, and *example*. Have students choose a value for *a* and a value to use for both *r* and *d*. In the example column, have students generate the first 5 terms of the arithmetic and geometric sequences. To help students see the difference, have them graph the sequences using the sequence term number for *x* and the sequence term for *y*.

Focus on Language One student in a small group states a recursion or explicit rule for a sequence. Partner(s) identify it as recursive or explicit, arithmetic or geometric.

5 Assess & Remediate

Lesson Quiz

1. Is the sequence geometric? If it is, what are *a* and *r*? 1.5, −4.5, 13.5, …

2. What is the 8th term of the geometric sequence 3, …, …, 81, …?

3. **Do you UNDERSTAND?** You drop a ball from a staircase that is 36 ft high. By the time you get down the stairs to measure the height of the bounce, the ball has bounced four times and has a height of 2.25 ft after its fourth bounce. How high did the ball bounce after it first hit the floor?

4. What are the possible values of the missing term of the geometric sequence 6, …, 13.5?

ANSWERS TO LESSON QUIZ

1. yes; $a = 1.5$, $r = -3$
2. 6561
3. 18 feet
4. 9 and −9

PRESCRIPTION FOR REMEDIATION

Use the student work on the Lesson Quiz to prescribe a differentiated review assignment:

Points	Differentiated Remediation
0–2	Intervention
3	On-level
4	Extension

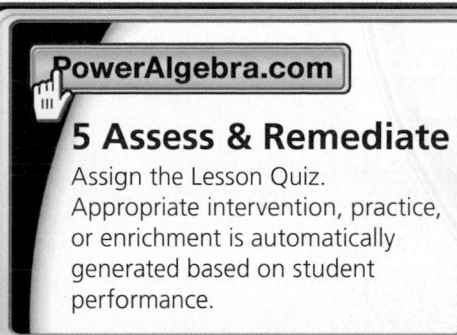

5 Assess & Remediate

Assign the Lesson Quiz. Appropriate intervention, practice, or enrichment is automatically generated based on student performance.

Intervention

- **Reteaching** (2 pages) Provides reteaching and practice exercises for the key lesson concepts. Use with struggling students or absent students.

- **English Language Learner Support** Helps students develop and reinforce mathematical vocabulary and key concepts.

All-in-One Resources/Online
Reteaching

9-3 Reteaching
Geometric Sequences

- A geometric sequence has a constant ratio between consecutive terms. This number is called the common ratio.
- A geometric sequence can be described by a recursive formula. $a_n = a_{n-1} \cdot r$, or as an explicit formula, $a_n = a \cdot r^{n-1}$.

Problem
Find the 12th term of the geometric sequence 5, 15, 45, … .

5, 15, 45, …

$r = \frac{15}{5} = \frac{45}{15} = 3$ Find *r* by calculating the common ratio between consecutive terms. This is a geometric sequence because there is a common ratio between consecutive terms.

$a_n = 5(3)^{n-1}$ Substitute $a = 5$ and $r = 3$ into the explicit formula to find a formula for the *n*th term of the sequence.

$a_{12} = 5(3)^{11}$ Substitute $n = 12$ to find the 12th term of the sequence.

$a_{12} = 885,735$ Remember to first calculate 3^{11}, then multiply by 5.

Exercises
Find the indicated term of the geometric sequence.

1. 4, 2, 1, … Find a_{10}. $\frac{1}{128}$ 2. 5, $\frac{15}{2}$, $\frac{45}{4}$, … Find a_9. $\frac{10,935}{128}$ 3. 6, −2, $\frac{2}{3}$, … Find a_{12}. $\frac{2}{59,049}$

4. 1, $-\frac{2}{3}$, $\frac{4}{9}$, … Find a_7. $\frac{64}{729}$ 5. 100, 200, 400, … Find a_9. 25,600   6. 8, 32, 128, … Find a_4. 512

Write the explicit formula for each sequence. Then generate the first five terms.

7. $a_1 = 1$, $r = \frac{1}{2}$ 8. $a_1 = 2$, $r = 3$ 9. $a_1 = 12$, $r = 3$
$a_n = 1(\frac{1}{2})^{n-1}$; 1, $\frac{1}{2}$, $\frac{1}{4}$, $\frac{1}{8}$, $\frac{1}{16}$ $a_n = 2(3)^{n-1}$; 2, 6, 18, 54, 162 $a_n = 12(3)^{n-1}$; 12, 36, 108, 324, 972

10. $a_1 = 1$, $r = \frac{1}{4}$ 11. $a_1 = 5$, $r = \frac{1}{10}$ 12. $a_1 = 1$, $r = \frac{1}{3}$
$a_n = 1(\frac{1}{4})^{n-1}$; 1, $\frac{1}{4}$, $\frac{1}{16}$, $\frac{1}{64}$, $\frac{1}{256}$ $a_n = 5(\frac{1}{10})^{n-1}$; 5, $\frac{1}{2}$, $\frac{1}{20}$, $\frac{1}{200}$, $\frac{1}{2000}$ $a_n = 1(\frac{1}{3})^{n-1}$; 1, $\frac{1}{3}$, $\frac{1}{9}$, $\frac{1}{27}$, $\frac{1}{81}$

13. $a_1 = 5$, $r = 2$ 14. $a_1 = 1$, $r = 3$ 15. $a_1 = 3$, $r = 6$
$a_n = 5(2)^{n-1}$; 5, 10, 20, 40, 80 $a_n = 1(3)^{n-1}$; 1, 3, 9, 27, 81 $a_n = 3(6)^{n-1}$; 3, 18, 108, 648, 3888

16. $a_1 = 3$, $r = 3$ 17. $a_1 = 2$, $r = 2$ 18. $a_1 = 2$, $r = \frac{1}{2}$
$a_n = 3(3)^{n-1}$; 3, 9, 27, 81, 243 $a_n = 2(2)^{n-1}$; 2, 4, 8, 16, 32 $a_n = 2(\frac{1}{2})^{n-1}$; 2, 1, $\frac{1}{2}$, $\frac{1}{4}$, $\frac{1}{8}$

19. $a_1 = 1$, $r = \frac{1}{5}$ 20. $a_1 = 3$, $r = 4$ 21. $a_1 = 5$, $r = \frac{1}{4}$
$a_n = 1(\frac{1}{5})^{n-1}$; 1, $\frac{1}{5}$, $\frac{1}{25}$, $\frac{1}{125}$, $\frac{1}{625}$ $a_n = 3(4)^{n-1}$; 3, 12, 48, 192, 768 $a_n = 5(\frac{1}{4})^{n-1}$; 5, $\frac{5}{4}$, $\frac{5}{16}$, $\frac{5}{64}$, $\frac{5}{256}$

All-in-One Resources/Online
English Language Learner Support

9-3 ELL Support
Geometric Sequences

Use the chart below to review vocabulary. These vocabulary words will help you complete this page.

Vocabulary Words	Explanations	Examples
Geometric sequence	A sequence in which the ratio of any term (after the first) to its preceding term is a constant value.	The sequence 3, 6, 12, 24, … is geometric because all of the consecutive terms have a ratio of 2.
Common ratio	the ratio of each term to its preceding term in a geometric sequence	The common ratio in the sequence 1, 4, 16, 64, 256, … is 4.
Geometric mean	The geometric mean of two numbers *x* and *y* is $\sqrt{xy}$.	The geometric mean of the numbers 4 and 9 is $\sqrt{4 \cdot 9} = \sqrt{36} = 6$.

1. The terms in the sequence 2, 6, 18, 54, 162, … all share a _common ratio_ with their preceding terms.

2. The numbers 8 and 2 have a _geometric mean_ of 4.

3. The consecutive terms in a _geometric sequence_ all share a common ratio.

Identify each sequence as arithmetic or geometric.

4. 2, 8, 32, 128, …   _geometric_

5. 1, 3, 9, 27, …   _geometric_

6. 1, 4, 7, 10, …   _arithmetic_

Identify the common ratio for each geometric sequence.

7. 3, 12, 48, 192, …   _4_

8. 12, 60, 300, 1500, …   _5_

Find the missing term in the geometric sequence.

9. …, 4, ___, 16, …   _8_

10. …, 9, ___, 25, …   _15_

Differentiated Remediation *continued*

On-Level

- **Practice** (2 pages) Provides extra practice for each lesson. For more challenging practice exercises, use the Form G Practice pages found in the All-in-One Teaching Resources and online.

- **Think About a Plan** Helps students develop specific problem-solving skills and strategies by providing scaffolded guiding questions.

- **Standardized Test Prep** Focuses on all major exercises, all major question types, and helps students prepare for the high-stakes assessments.

Extension

- **Enrichment** Provides students with interesting problems and activities that extend the concepts of the lesson.

- **Activities, Games, and Puzzles** Worksheets that can be used for concepts development, enrichment, and for fun!

Student Companion/All-in-One Resources/Online
Practice page 1

9-3 Practice   Form K
Geometric Sequences

Determine whether each sequence is geometric. If so, find the common ratio.

1. 1, 3, 9, 27, . . .   **2.** 2, 5, 8, 11, 14, . . .
Find the ratios between consecutive terms.   **not geometric**
$\frac{3}{1} = \frac{9}{3} = \frac{27}{9}$
The sequence is geometric.
The common ratio is **3**.

3. −2, −4, −8, −16, . . .   **4.** 500, 50, 5, 0.5, . . .   **5.** 0, 25, 50, 75, 100, . . .
   geometric; 2   geometric; $\frac{1}{10}$ not geometric

6. Open-Ended Write a geometric sequence with a common ratio of $\frac{1}{4}$. Explain how you developed the sequence.
Answers may vary. Sample: 64, 16, 4, 1, ... I divided the first term by 4 to get the second term. Then I divided the second and third terms by 4.

Find the ninth term of each geometric sequence.

7. 3, 12, 48, 192, . . .   **8.** 2, 6, 18, 54, . . .   **9.** 1875, 375, 75, 15, . . .
Use the explicit formula.   13,122   0.0048
$a_n = a_1 \cdot r^{n-1}$
$a_9 = 3(4^8)$
$a_9 = 3(65,536)$
$a_9 =$ **196,608**

Find the missing terms of each geometric sequence.

10. 2, ___, ___, 128, . . .   **11.** 1, **2**, **4**, 8, . . .   **12.** 108, **36**, **12**, 4, . . .
Identify the common ratio.
$a_n = a_1 \cdot r^{n-1}$
$a_4 = 2r^{4-1}$
$128 = 2r^3$
$64 = r^3$
$4 = r$
The second term is **8**.
The third term is **32**.

Student Companion/All-in-One Resources/Online
Think About a Plan

9-3 Think About a Plan
Geometric Sequences

Athletics During your first week of training for a marathon, you run a total of 10 miles. You increase the distance you run each week by twenty percent. How many miles do you run during your twelfth week of training?

Understanding the Problem

1. How can you write a sequence of numbers to represent this situation?
Answers may vary. Sample: Start with 10, and multiply it and each successive term by 120% or 1.2

2. Is the sequence arithmetic, geometric, or neither?   geometric

3. What is the first term of the sequence? **10**

4. What is the common ratio of the sequence? **1.2**

5. What is the problem asking you to determine?
the 12th term of a geometric sequence that represents the number of miles you run each week

Planning the Solution

6. Write a formula for the sequence.
$a_n = 10(1.2)^{n-1}$

Getting an Answer

7. Evaluate your formula to find the number of miles you run during your twelfth week of training.
about 74.3

Student Companion/All-in-One Resources/Online
Practice page 2

9-3 Practice (continued)   Form K
Geometric Sequences

Find the missing term of each geometric sequence. It could be the geometric mean or its opposite.

13. 5, ___, 45, . . .   **14.** 2, **±12**, 72, . . .
Find the geometric mean of 5 and 45.
$\sqrt{xy}$
$\sqrt{45 \cdot 5}$
$\sqrt{225}$
±15

15. $\frac{1}{4}$, **−$\frac{3}{4}$**, 2$\frac{1}{4}$, . . .   **16.** 175, **±35**, 7, . . .   **17.** 1.2, **±7.2**, 43.2, . . .

18. Error Analysis On a recent math test, your classmate was asked to find the missing term in the geometric sequence 4, ___, 256. Her answer was 130. What error did your classmate make? What is the correct answer?
She found the arithmetic mean of 256 and 4 rather than the geometric mean; 32

19. The bacteria population in a petri dish was 14 at the beginning of an experiment. After 30 min, the population was 28, and after an hour the population was 56.
a. Write an explicit definition to represent this sequence. $a_n = 14 \cdot 2^{n-1}$
b. If this pattern continues, what will be the bacteria population after 4 h? **3584**

20. A corporation earned a profit of $420,000 in its first year of operation. Over the next 10 years, the company's CEO hopes to increase the profit by 8% each year. If the CEO reaches her goal, what will be the company's profit in its seventh year, to the nearest dollar? **$666,487**

Student Companion/All-in-One Resources/Online
Standardized Test Prep

9-3 Standardized Test Prep
Geometric Sequences

Multiple Choice

For Exercises 1–6, choose the correct letter.

1. What is the 10th term of the geometric sequence 1, 4, 16, . . .? **C**
  Ⓐ 40   Ⓑ 180,224   Ⓒ 262,144   Ⓓ 2,883,584

2. Which sequence is a geometric sequence? **H**
  Ⓕ 1, 3, 5, 7, 9, . . .   Ⓗ 2, 4, 8, 16, 32, . . .
  Ⓖ 12, 9, 6, 3, 0, . . .   Ⓘ −2, −6, −10, −14, −18, . . .

3. Which could be the missing term of the geometric sequence 5, ___, 125, . . .? **A**
  Ⓐ 25   Ⓑ 50   Ⓒ 75   Ⓓ 100

4. What could be the missing term of the geometric sequence −12, ___, −$\frac{3}{4}$, . . .? **H**
  Ⓕ −4   Ⓖ −6.375   Ⓗ 3   Ⓘ 4

5. In the explicit formula for the 9th term of the geometric sequence 1, 6, 36, . . . what number is *a*? **A**
  Ⓐ 1   Ⓑ 6   Ⓒ 36   Ⓓ 1,679,616

6. In each successive round of a backgammon tournament, the number of players decreases by half. If the tournament starts with 32 players, which rule could predict the number of players in the *n*th round? **I**
  Ⓕ 32 = (0.5)^n Ⓖ 32 = 0.5^{n-1} Ⓗ $a_n = 15^{n-1}$ Ⓘ $a_n = (32)(0.5)^{n-1}$

Short Response

7. What is the 6th term of the geometric sequence 100, 50, . . .? Show your work using the explicit formula.
[2] 3.125; $a_n = ar^{n-1}$; $a_n = 100(\frac{1}{2})^{n-1}$; $a_6 = 100(\frac{1}{2})^5 = 3.125$; correct term with work shown
[1] incorrect term OR correct answer, without work shown
[0] incorrect answers and no work shown OR no answers given

All-in-One Resources/Online
Enrichment

9-3 Enrichment
Geometric Sequences

Doubling Periods in Geometric Sequences

Consider the geometric sequence 3, 4$\frac{1}{2}$, 6$\frac{3}{4}$, 10$\frac{1}{8}$, ...

1. Describe how the terms of the sequence are related. **Each term is 1$\frac{1}{2}$ times the preceding term.**

2. For any term of the sequence, how many terms does it take before the value of the term has at least doubled? **2**

The doubling period of a geometric sequence is the number of terms needed to reach a term at least twice as large as a given term. What is the doubling period for the given sequence? **2 terms**

3. Write the first ten terms of the geometric sequence $a_1 = 3$, $r = 1.1$ to two decimal places. **3, 3.3, 3.63, 3.99, 4.39, 4.83, 5.31, 5.85, 6.43, 7.07**

4. What is the doubling period for $a_1 = 3$? for $a_2 = 3.3$? **8 terms; 8 terms**

Although the doubling period does not depend on which term is given, it does depend on the common ratio. For what value(s) of r is the doubling period of a geometric sequence greater than 1? **1 < |r| < 2**

The idea of a *doubling period* applies to certain everyday situations. For example, under optimum conditions, bacteria reproduce by splitting in two. Their numbers increase geometrically over time. Suppose at noon on a certain day, there are 1000 bacteria in a dish. At 6 P.M. on the same day, there are 8000 bacteria.

5. If a count is taken every hour, how many terms are in the geometric sequence? What is the common ratio? What is the doubling period? **7; $\sqrt{2}$; 2 terms**

6. If a count is taken every 40 min, how many terms are in the sequence? What is the common ratio? What is the doubling period? **10; $\sqrt[3]{2}$; 3 terms**

7. In both cases, how many hours does it take the bacteria to double? **2**

Online Teacher Resource Center
Activities, Games, and Puzzles

9-3 Activity: Finding the Next Term
Geometric Sequences

Work with a partner for this activity.

Select one of the geometric sequences in the top grid and cross it out. Your partner has to locate the next term of that sequence in the bottom grid and cross it out. Take turns selecting the sequence and locating the next term.

The activity ends when all entries in both grids have been crossed out.

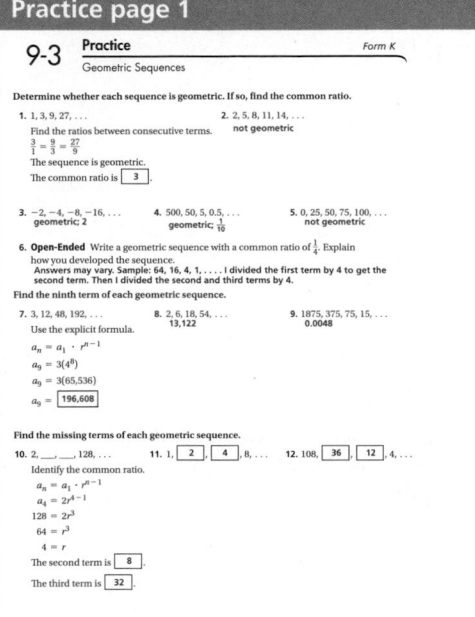

9-4 Arithmetic Series

Objective To define arithmetic series and find their sums

> You will learn an easier way to find the sum in this lesson.

SOLVE IT!

Getting Ready!

The first four rows of chairs are set up for a meeting. The seating pattern is to continue through 20 rows. How many chairs will there be in all 20 rows? Explain your reasoning.

Lesson Vocabulary

- series
- finite series
- infinite series
- arithmetic series
- limits

Just as you found formulas for terms of sequences, you can find formulas for the sums of the terms of sequences.

Focus Question What is an arithmetic series?

A **series** is the indicated sum of the terms of a sequence. A **finite series**, like a finite sequence, has a first term and a last term, while an **infinite series** continues without end.

Finite sequence	Finite series
6, 9, 12, 15, 18	$6 + 9 + 12 + 15 + 18$ (The sum is 60.)
Infinite sequence	**Infinite series**
3, 7, 11, 15, . . .	$3 + 7 + 11 + 15 + . . .$

An **arithmetic series** is a series whose terms form an arithmetic sequence (as shown above). When a series has a finite number of terms, you can use a formula involving the first and last term to evaluate the sum.

Property   Sum of a Finite Arithmetic Series

The sum S_n of a finite arithmetic series $a_1 + a_2 + a_3 + \cdots + a_n$ is

$$S_n = \frac{n}{2}(a_1 + a_n)$$

where a_1 is the first term, a_n is the nth term, and n is the number of terms.

---

1 Interactive Learning

Solve It!
PURPOSE To use a pattern to find a sum
PROCESS Students may
- recognize the number of seats in each row as an arithmetic sequence and sum the rows to find the total.
- use number patterns to rearrange the rows to a simpler configuration, then find the sum.

FACILITATE
Q How many chairs are in the last row? Explain. **[23; the number of chairs in each row increases by the same amount, so this is an arithmetic sequence with a common difference of 1.]**
Q Can the chairs be grouped in a different way to make your calculations easier? Explain. **[Yes; sample: Combine rows to get equal sums. The first and last row will sum to 27 chairs. The second row and next-to-last row will sum to 27 chairs, and so on.]**

ANSWER See Solve It in Answers on next page.
CONNECT THE MATH In the Solve It, students use arithmetic sequences to find a sum. In this lesson, students will use explicit formulas or a graphing calculator to find sums of finite arithmetic series.

2 Guided Instruction

Take Note

Q When you divide the formula for the sum of a finite arithmetic series by n, you get $\frac{a_1 + a_n}{2}$. What does this imply about the mean of all the terms in the series? **[The mean of all the terms in the series is the same as the mean of the first and last terms.]**

9-4 Preparing to Teach

BIG ideas   **Equivalence**   **UbD**
          Variable

ESSENTIAL UNDERSTANDINGS
- When two terms and the number of terms in a finite arithmetic sequence are known, the sum of the terms can be found.
- A sequence can be defined explicitly by describing its nth term with a formula using n or recursively by stating its first term and a formula for its nth term using the $(n - 1)$ term.

Math Background
A series is the sum of the terms in a sequence. If an arithmetic sequence is infinite, it follows that an arithmetic series is also infinite. However, it is often useful to find the partial sum of an arithmetic series. In this lesson, the partial sum of an

arithmetic series is referred to as a finite arithmetic series.

Finding the sum of a finite arithmetic sequence requires knowing two of the terms and the number of terms in the sequence. This sum can be thought of as the average of the first and last terms times the number of terms.

Students are introduced to summation notation using $\sum$ when writing arithmetic series. Index limits may vary, although most lower limits in this lesson will begin at 0 or 1. The limit values will affect the explicit formula. The number of terms of a finite sequence is one more than the difference of the limits.

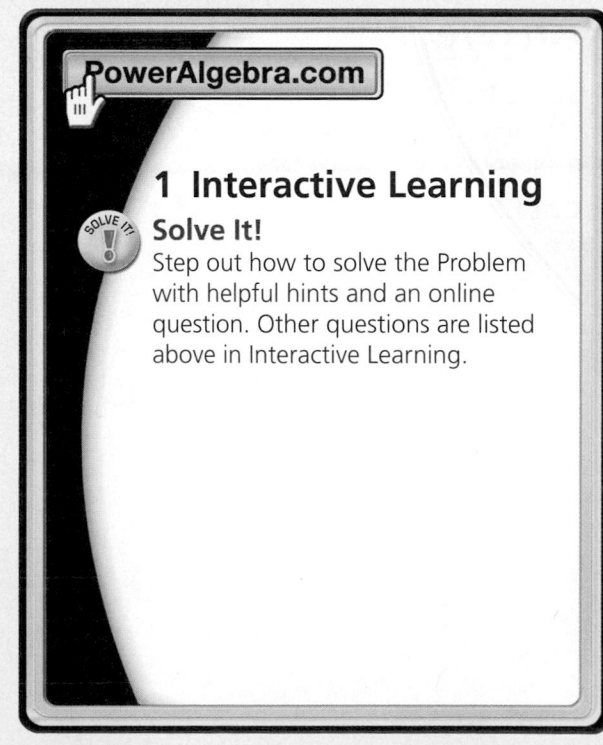

PowerAlgebra.com

1 Interactive Learning
Solve It!
Step out how to solve the Problem with helpful hints and an online question. Other questions are listed above in Interactive Learning.

Problem 1   ERROR PREVENTION

Students might assume the common difference is used in the formula because the formula contains the term $\frac{n}{2}$ and the common difference in 1A is 2. Point out the term $\frac{n}{2}$ is always used because you must find the mean of two terms, i.e. the first and last term.

> **Q** How is the common difference used to find the sum in 1A? in 1B? Explain. **[It does not have to be used in 1A because the number of terms can be determined by doubling 1, 2, 3, ... For 1B, it is used in the explicit formula to find the number of terms.]**
>
> **Q** How can you find the number of terms in 1B using subtraction? Explain your reasoning. **[The difference between 223 and 7 is 216. Dividing 216 by the common difference of 4 gives 54. Because the first term must also be counted, the number of terms is 55.]**

Got It?

> **Q** How can the terms in 1a be paired to help find the sum? Explain. **[1 + 99 = 100, 3 + 97 = 100 and so on. The sum of each pair times the number of pairs is equal to the total sum.]**

 **Problem 1**   Finding the Sum of Finite Arithmetic Series

What is the sum of each finite arithmetic series?

Ⓐ $2 + 4 + 6 + \cdots + 100$

Think

How many even integers are there from 2 to 100?
Double 1, 2, 3, ..., 50, and you get 2, 4, 6, ..., 100, the even integers from 2 to 100. There are 50 even integers.

This series is the sum of the even integers from 2 to 100. The first term is 2, the last (and 50th) term is 100, and the common difference is 2.

Use the sum formula.	$S_n = \frac{n}{2}(a_1 + a_n)$
Substitute 50 for n, 2 for a_1, and 100 for a_n.	$S_{50} = \frac{50}{2}(2 + 100)$
Simplify.	$= 25(102)$
Multiply.	$= 2550$

The sum is 2550.

Ⓑ $7 + 11 + 15 + \cdots + 223$

Hint

Before you can use the sum formula, you need to use the explicit formula for an arithmetic sequence to find the number of terms n.

Step 1   Find the number of terms in the series.

The first term is 7, the last term is 223, and the constant difference is $11 - 7 = 4$.

Use the explicit formula.	$a_n = a + (n - 1)d$
Substitute 223 for a_n, 7 for a, and 4 for d.	$223 = 7 + (n - 1)4$
Use the Distributive Property.	$223 = 7 + 4n - 4$
Isolate the variable term.	$220 = 4n$
Solve for n.	$55 = n$

There are 55 terms in the series.

Step 2   Find the sum of the series.

Use the sum formula.	$S_n = \frac{n}{2}(a_1 + a_n)$
Substitute 55 for n, 7 for a_1, and 223 for a_n.	$S_{55} = \frac{55}{2}(7 + 223)$
Simplify.	$= \frac{55}{2}(230)$
Multiply.	$= 6325$

The sum is 6325.

 Got It?   **1.** What is the sum of the finite arithmetic series?
     a. $1 + 3 + 5 + \cdots + 99$
     b. $4 + 9 + 14 + \cdots + 134$
     c. **Reasoning** Will the sum of a sequence of even numbers always be an even number? Will the sum of a sequence of odd numbers always be an odd number? Explain.

Answers

Solve It!

270 chairs; continue the pattern and add the number of chairs in each row.

Got It?

1. a. 2500
   b. 1863
   c. Yes; no; the sum of any number of even numbers is always even. The sum of an odd number of odd numbers is odd, but the sum of an even number of odd numbers is even.

2. 59 sales; 1725 sales

 PowerAlgebra.com

2 Guided Instruction

Each Problem is worked out and supported online.

> **Problem 1**
> Finding the Sum of a Finite Arithmetic Series
>   *Animated*

> **Alternative Problem 1**
> Finding the Sum of a Finite Arithmetic Series

> **Problem 2**
> Using the Sum of a Finite Arithmetic Series   *Animated*

> **Problem 3**
> Writing a Series in Summation Notation

> **Alternative Problem 4**
> Finding the Sum of a Series
>   *Animated*

> **Alternative Problem 5**
> Using a Graphing Calculator to Find the Sum of a Series

Support in Algebra 2 Companion
- Vocabulary
- Key Concepts
- Got It?

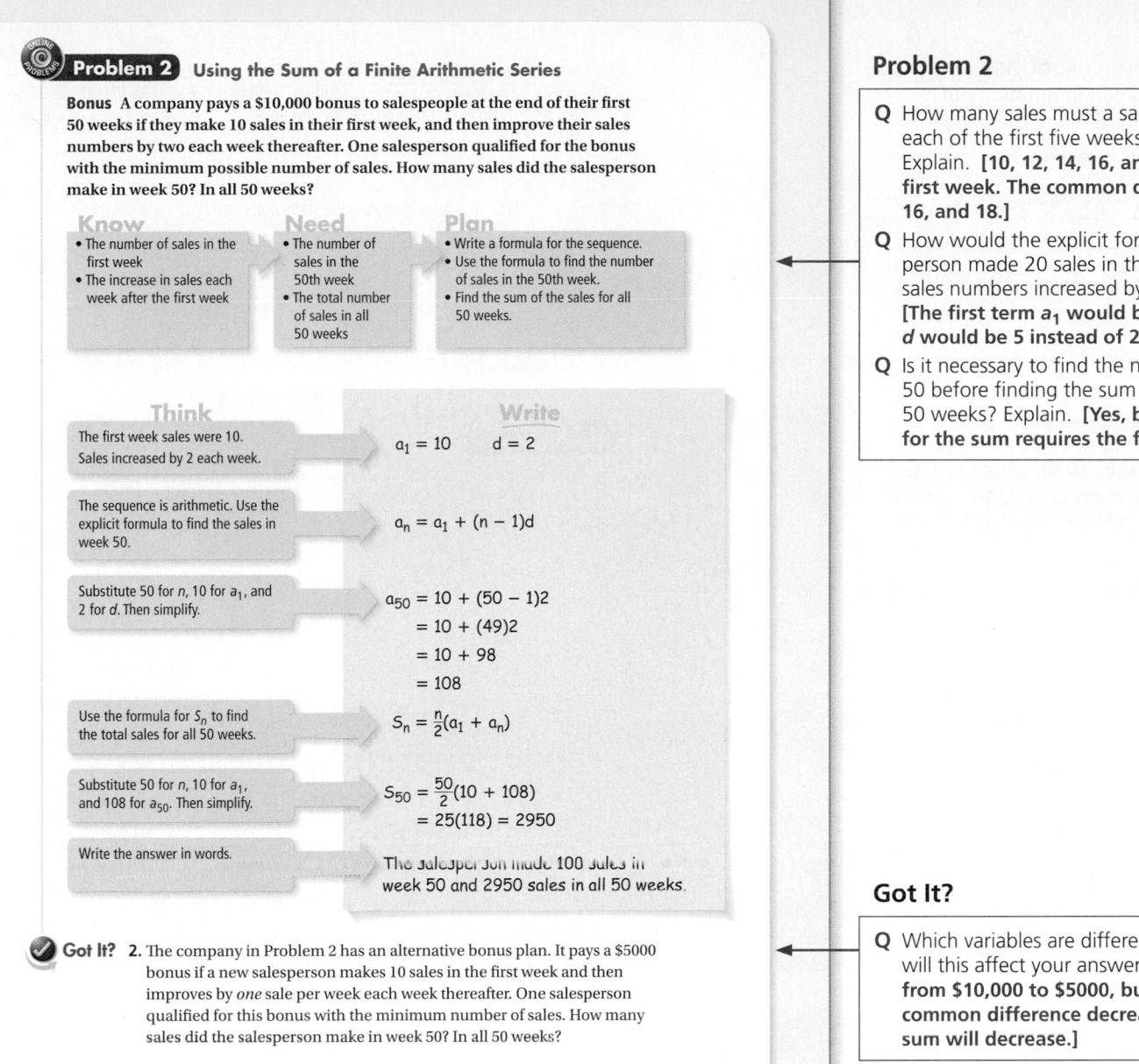

Problem 2 Using the Sum of a Finite Arithmetic Series

Bonus A company pays a $10,000 bonus to salespeople at the end of their first 50 weeks if they make 10 sales in their first week, and then improve their sales numbers by two each week thereafter. One salesperson qualified for the bonus with the minimum possible number of sales. How many sales did the salesperson make in week 50? In all 50 weeks?

Know
- The number of sales in the first week
- The increase in sales each week after the first week

Need
- The number of sales in the 50th week
- The total number of sales in all 50 weeks

Plan
- Write a formula for the sequence.
- Use the formula to find the number of sales in the 50th week.
- Find the sum of the sales for all 50 weeks.

Think

The first week sales were 10. Sales increased by 2 each week.

The sequence is arithmetic. Use the explicit formula to find the sales in week 50.

Substitute 50 for n, 10 for a_1, and 2 for d. Then simplify.

Use the formula for S_n to find the total sales for all 50 weeks.

Substitute 50 for n, 10 for a_1, and 108 for a_{50}. Then simplify.

Write the answer in words.

Write

$a_1 = 10 \qquad d = 2$

$a_n = a_1 + (n - 1)d$

$a_{50} = 10 + (50 - 1)2$
$= 10 + (49)2$
$= 10 + 98$
$= 108$

$S_n = \frac{n}{2}(a_1 + a_n)$

$S_{50} = \frac{50}{2}(10 + 108)$
$= 25(118) = 2950$

The salesperson made 108 sales in week 50 and 2950 sales in all 50 weeks.

✓ **Got It?** 2. The company in Problem 2 has an alternative bonus plan. It pays a $5000 bonus if a new salesperson makes 10 sales in the first week and then improves by *one* sale per week each week thereafter. One salesperson qualified for this bonus with the minimum number of sales. How many sales did the salesperson make in week 50? In all 50 weeks?

Problem 2

Q How many sales must a sales person make during each of the first five weeks to earn the bonus? Explain. **[10, 12, 14, 16, and 18; 10 sales made the first week. The common difference is 2 so 12, 14, 16, and 18.]**

Q How would the explicit formula change if the sales person made 20 sales in the first week? if their sales numbers increased by 5 each week? Explain. **[The first term a_1 would be 20 instead of 10; d would be 5 instead of 2.]**

Q Is it necessary to find the number of sales in week 50 before finding the sum of the sales in all 50 weeks? Explain. **[Yes, because the formula for the sum requires the first and last term.]**

Got It?

Q Which variables are different from Problem 2? How will this affect your answer? **[The bonus decreases from $10,000 to $5000, but this is not used. The common difference decreases from 2 to 1, so the sum will decrease.]**

Additional Problems

1. What is the sum of each finite arithmetic series?

a. $14 + 17 + 20 + 23 + \ldots + 116$?

b. $73 + 68 + 63 + 58 + \ldots + 18$?

ANSWERS

a. 2275

b. 546

2. There are 30 rows of seats in a large arena. The first row contains 10 seats. Each successive row increases by 3 seats. How many seats are in the last row? How many seats are there in all?

ANSWER 97; 1605

3. What is summation notation for the series?

a. $-19 + -14 + -9 + \ldots + 221 + 226$

b. $20 + 18 + 16 + \ldots + -24 + -26$

ANSWERS

a. $\sum_{n=1}^{50} (5n - 24)$

b. $\sum_{n=1}^{24} (-2n + 22)$

Problem 3

Practice reading the summation notation out loud so students understand the necessary parts.

For example, $\sum_{n=1}^{51}(4n + 3)$ is read as "The sum of $4n + 3$ for values of n from 1 to 51."

> **Q** Which answer choices represent a series with a common difference of 4? Explain. **[Choices A and B because the variable is multiplied by 4. So each successive term increases by 4.]**

> **Q** How would the summation notation for this problem be different if the lower limit began with $n = 0$? State the new summation notation. **[The explicit formula and the upper and lower limits would change. The summation notation would be $\sum_{n=0}^{50}(4n + 7)$.]**

Got It?

Watch for students who confuse n and a_n when writing a series using summation notation. The lower limit to the upper limit is the *number* of terms, not the *values* of the terms.

> **Q** Can the series be written correctly in summation notation in more than one way? Explain. **[Yes; for example, the first series can be written as $\sum_{n=0}^{39}(-5 + 7n)$ or as $\sum_{n=1}^{40}(-12 + 7n)$.]**

You can use the Greek capital letter sigma, Σ, to indicate a sum. With it, you use *limits* to indicate how many terms you are adding. **Limits** are the least and greatest values of n in the series. You write the limits below and above the Σ to indicate the first and last terms of the series.

For example, you can write the series $3^2 + 4^2 + 5^2 + \cdots + 108^2$ as $\sum_{n=3}^{108}n^2$.

> Upper limit: the series ends with $n = 108$.

$$\sum_{n=3}^{108}n^2$$ — The explicit formula for each term is n^2.

> Lower limit: the series begins with $n = 3$.

To find the number of terms in a series written in Σ form, subtract the lower limit from the upper limit and add 1.

The number of terms in the series above is $108 - 3 + 1 = 106$.

Problem 3 Writing a Series in Summation Notation

Multiple Choice What is summation notation for the series?

$7 + 11 + 15 + \cdots + 203 + 207$

Ⓐ $\sum_{n=1}^{51}(4n + 3)$ Ⓑ $\sum_{n=1}^{50}(4n + 3)$ Ⓒ $\sum_{n=1}^{50}(7n)$ Ⓓ $\sum_{n=1}^{51}(7n)$

Plan

What do you need to write a series in summation notation?
You need an explicit formula for the nth term and the lower and upper limits.

The sequence $7, 11, 15, \ldots, 203, 207$ is arithmetic with first term $a_1 = 7$ and common difference $d = 4$.

Use the explicit formula for an arithmetic sequence.	$a_n = a_1 + (n - 1)d$
Substitute 7 for a_1, and 4 for d.	$a_n = 7 + (n - 1)4$
Simplify.	$= 4n + 3$

An explicit formula for the nth term is $4n + 3$.

Use the explicit formula to find the value of n for the term 207.	$a_n = 4n + 3$
Substitute 207 for a_n.	$207 = 4n + 3$
Isolate the variable term.	$204 = 4n$
Solve for n.	$51 = n$

The upper limit is 51. You can write the series as $\sum_{n=1}^{51}(4n + 3)$.

The correct answer is A.

> ✅ **Got It? 3.** What is summation notation for the series?
> **a.** $-5 + 2 + 9 + 16 + \cdots + 261 + 268$
> **b.** $500 + 490 + 480 + \cdots + 20 + 10$

Answers

Got It? (continued)

3. a. $\sum_{n=1}^{40}(7n - 12)$

b. $\sum_{n=1}^{50}(510 - 10n)$

Focus Question What is an arithmetic series?

Answer An arithmetic series is a series whose terms form an arithmetic sequence. You can find the sum of a finite arithmetic series using a formula involving the first term, the last term, and the number of terms.

Lesson Check

Do you know HOW?

Find the sum of each finite arithmetic series.

1. $4 + 7 + 10 + 13 + 16 + 19 + 22$

2. $10 + 20 + 30 + \cdots + 110 + 120$

Write each arithmetic series in summation notation.

3. $3 + 6 + 9 + 12 + 15 + 18 + 21$

4. $1 + 5 + 9 + \cdots + 41 + 45$

Do you UNDERSTAND?

5. **Vocabulary** What is the difference between an arithmetic sequence and an arithmetic series?

6. **Error Analysis** A student writes the arithmetic series $3 + 8 + 13 + \cdots + 43$ in summation notation as
$$\sum_{n=3}^{8}(3 + 5n).$$ Describe and correct the error.

7. **Reasoning** Is more than one arithmetic series with four terms whose sum is 44 possible? Explain.

Practice and Problem-Solving Exercises

A Practice

Find the sum of each finite arithmetic series.

◆ See Problem 1.

8. $8 + 9 + 10 + \cdots + 15$

Guided Practice

To start, identify what you know.

The first term is 8, the last (and 8th) term is 15, and the common difference is 1.

9. $5 + 6 + 7 + \cdots + 11$

10. $1 + 4 + 7 + \cdots + 31$

11. $7 + 14 + 21 + \cdots + 105$

12. $1 + 4 + 9 + \cdots + 81$

13. $(-3) + (-6) + (-9) + \cdots + (-30)$

14. $105 + 97 + 89 + \cdots + (-71)$

15. **Grades** A student has taken three math tests so far this semester. His scores for the first three tests were 75, 79, and 83.

◆ See Problem 2.

a. Suppose his test scores continue to improve at the same rate. What will be his grade on the sixth (and final) test?
b. What will be his total score for all six tests?

Write each arithmetic series in summation notation.

◆ See Problem 3.

16. $4 + 8 + 12 + 16 + 20$

17. $7 + 9 + 11 + \cdots + 21$

18. $5 + 8 + 11 + \cdots + 38$

19. $100 + 90 + 80 + \cdots + 10$

---

3 Lesson Check

Do you know HOW?

- If students have difficulty getting started with Exercises 3 and 4, ask them to name the components they need to write the series in summation notation. Then ask them to identify which of those components are given.

Do you UNDERSTAND?

- For Exercise 5, if students have difficulty remembering the difference between a sequence and a series, encourage them to come up with some device to help them remember. For example, a series is the sum of a sequence. Both "series" and the phrase "sum of a sequence" contain the letter s twice.

Close

Q How are arithmetic series and sequences the same? How are they different? **[Sample: Both an arithmetic series and an arithmetic sequence consist of terms that change by a common difference; a sequence is the list of these terms, while a series is the sum of these terms.]**

Q How can the formula for the sum of a finite arithmetic series be explained using the concept of mean? **[Sample: The sum of any arithmetic sequence can be found by multiplying the mean value times the number of values; the mean of the first and last term is multiplied by the number of terms.]**

Lesson Check

1. 91
2. 780
3. $\displaystyle\sum_{n=1}^{7}3n$
4. $\displaystyle\sum_{n=1}^{12}(4n - 3)$
5. An arithmetic sequence is a list of numbers for which successive numbers have a common difference. An arithmetic series is an expression for the sum of the terms of an arithmetic sequence.
6. The lower limit should not be 3, it should be zero. The correct summation notation is $\displaystyle\sum_{n=0}^{8}(3 + 5n)$.
7. Yes; $44 = 2(a_1 + a_4)$, so any combination of a_1 and a_4 with a sum of 22 is a possible series.

Practice and Problem-Solving Exercises

8. 92
9. 56
10. 176
11. 840
12. 285
13. −165
14. 391
15. a. 95
      b. 510
16. $\displaystyle\sum_{n=1}^{5}4n$
17. $\displaystyle\sum_{n=1}^{8}(2n + 5)$
18. $\displaystyle\sum_{n=1}^{12}(2 + 3n)$
19. $\displaystyle\sum_{n=1}^{10}(110 - 10n)$

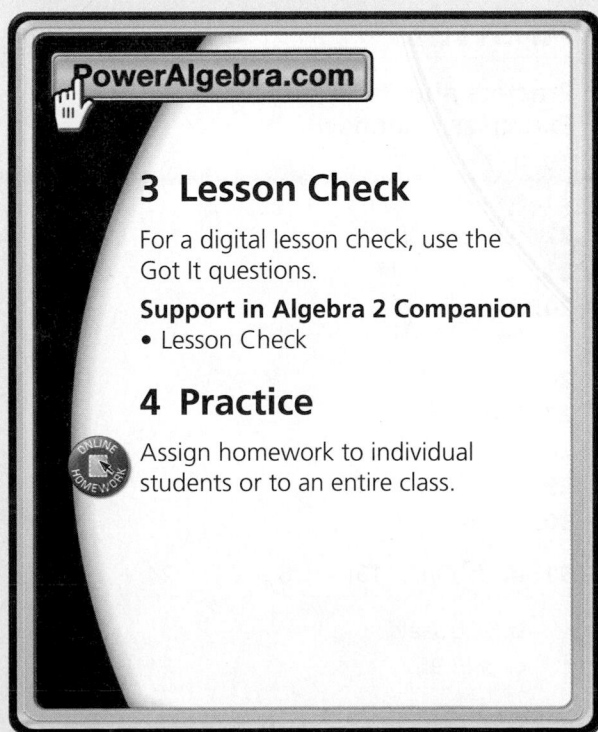

PowerAlgebra.com

3 Lesson Check

For a digital lesson check, use the Got It questions.

Support in Algebra 2 Companion
- Lesson Check

4 Practice

Assign homework to individual students or to an entire class.

4 Practice

ASSIGNMENT GUIDE

Basic: 8–22, 31

Average: 8–20, 21–33 odd

Standardized Test Prep: 36–40

Mixed Review: 41–49

Reasoning exercises have blue headings.

Applications exercises have red headings.

EXERCISE 31: Use the Think About a Plan worksheet in the **Student Companion** (also available in the Teaching Resources in print and online) to further support students' development in becoming independent learners.

HOMEWORK QUICK CHECK

To check students' understanding of key skills and concepts, go over Exercises 10, 15, 16, 20, and 31.

 Apply

20. Think About a Plan A meeting room is set up with 16 rows of seats. The number of seats in a row increases by two with each successive row. The first row has 12 seats. What is the total number of seats?
- How can you find the number of seats in each row using an explicit formula?
- What is the number of seats in the 16th row?
- How can you find the sum of the seats in 16 rows?

Determine whether each list is a *sequence* or a *series* and *finite* or *infinite*.

21. 1, 2, 4, 8, 16, 32, . . .

22. 1, 0.5, 0.25, 0.125, 0.0625

23. $-0.5 - 0.25 - 0.125 - \ldots$

24. $2.3 + 4.6 + 9.2 + 18.4$

Each sequence has eight terms. Evaluate each related series.

25. $\frac{1}{2}, \frac{3}{2}, \frac{5}{2}, \ldots, \frac{15}{2}$

26. $1, -1, -3, \ldots, -13$

27. 5, 13, 21, . . . , 61

28. $-3.5, -1.25, 1, \ldots, 12.25$

29. 1765, 1414, 1063, . . . , -692

30. $-13, -14.5, -16, \ldots, -23.5$

31. Architecture In a 20-row theater, the number of seats in a row increases by three with each successive row. The first row has 18 seats.
- **a.** Write an arithmetic series to represent the number of seats in the theater.
- **b.** Find the total seating capacity of the theater.
- **c.** Front-row tickets for a concert cost $60. After every 5 rows, the ticket price goes down by $5. What is the total amount of money generated by a full house?

32. a. Grocery A supermarket displays cans in a triangle. Write an explicit formula for the sequence of the number of cans.
- **b.** Use summation notation to write the related series for a triangle with 10 cans in the bottom row.
- **c.** Suppose the triangle had 17 rows. How many cans would be in the 17th row?
- **d. Reasoning** Could the triangle have 110 cans? 140 cans? Explain.

Evaluate each series to the given term.

33. $2 + 4 + 6 + 8 + \ldots$; 10th term

34. $-5 - 25 - 45 - \ldots$; 9th term

35. a. Open-Ended Write two explicit formulas for arithmetic sequences.
- **b.** Write the first five terms of each related series.
- **c.** Use summation notation to rewrite each series.
- **d.** Evaluate each series.

Answers

Practice and Problem-Solving Exercises (continued)

20. 432 seats

21. sequence; infinite

22. sequence; finite

23. series; infinite

24. series; finite

25. 32

26. -48

27. 264

28. 35

29. 4292

30. -146

31. a. $\sum_{n=1}^{20}(3n + 15)$, or $18 + 21 + 24 + \cdots + 75$

    b. 930 seats

    c. $46,950

32. a. $a_n = n + 1$

    b. $\sum_{n=1}^{9}(n + 1)$

    c. 18 cans

    d. No; no; 13 rows have 104 cans, 14 rows have 119 cans, 15 rows have 135 cans, and 16 rows have 152 cans. The number of rows would not be an integer for 110 cans or 140 cans.

33. 110

34. -765

35. a–d. Check students' work.

SAT/ACT

36. Which expression represents the series $14 + 20 + 26 + 32 + 38 + 44 + 50$?

    Ⓐ $\sum_{n=2}^{8}(7n - 1)$ Ⓑ $\sum_{n=3}^{8}(6n - 4)$ Ⓒ $\sum_{n=3}^{9}(6n - 4)$ Ⓓ $\sum_{n=8}^{14}(n + 6)$

37. What is the common ratio in the geometric sequence $\frac{9}{2}, 3, 2, \frac{4}{3}, \ldots$?

    Ⓕ $\frac{3}{2}$ Ⓖ $\frac{9}{2}$ Ⓗ $\frac{2}{3}$ Ⓘ $\frac{27}{2}$

38. Which expression is NOT equivalent to $\sqrt[4]{4n^2}$?

    Ⓐ $\left(4n^2\right)^{\frac{1}{4}}$ Ⓒ $\left(2|n|\right)^{\frac{1}{2}}$

    Ⓑ $2n^{\frac{1}{2}}$ Ⓓ $\sqrt{2|n|}$

39. The graph shows the inverse of which function?

    Ⓕ $y = 3x$ Ⓗ $y = 3^x$

    Ⓖ $y = -3^{2x}$ Ⓘ $y = 2^{3x}$

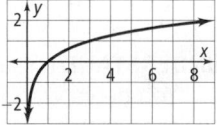

Short Response

40. Solve the equation $x^2 + 10x + 40 = 5$ by completing the square.

Mixed Review

Write an explicit formula for each geometric sequence. Then find the first three terms.   ◀ **See Lesson 9-3.**

41. $a_1 = 1, r = 2$ **42.** $a_1 = -1, r = -1$ **43.** $a_1 = 3, r = \frac{3}{2}$

Simplify each rational expression. State any restrictions on the variable.   ◀ **See Lesson 8-4.**

44. $\dfrac{x^2 + 4x + 3}{x^2 - 3x - 4}$ **45.** $\dfrac{c^2 - 8c + 12}{c^2 - 11c + 30}$ **46.** $\dfrac{3z^4 + 36z^3 + 60z^2}{3z^3 - 3z^2}$

Get Ready!   **To prepare for Lesson 9-5, do Exercises 47–49.**

Find the common ratio for each geometric sequence.   ◀ **See Lesson 9-3.**

47. $90, -30, 10, \ldots$ **48.** $64, 48, 36, \ldots$ **49.** $-9, 4.5, -2.25, \ldots$

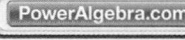

Standardized Test Prep

36. C

37. H

38. B

39. H

40. [2] $\left(\frac{b}{2}\right)^2 = \left(\frac{10}{2}\right)^2 = 25$

           $x^2 + 10x + 25 = -35 + 25$

                $(x + 5)^2 = -10$

                    $x + 5 = \pm i\sqrt{10}$

                      $x = -5 \pm i\sqrt{10}$

     [1] appropriate method, but with one computational error

Mixed Review

41. $a_n = 2^{n-1}$; $1, 2, 4$

42. $a_n = -1(-1)^{n-1}$; $-1, 1, -1$

43. $a_n = 3\left(\frac{3}{2}\right)^{n-1}$; $3, \frac{9}{2}, \frac{27}{4}$

44. $\dfrac{x + 3}{x - 4}$; $x \neq 4, x \neq -1$

45. $\dfrac{c - 2}{c - 5}$; $c \neq 5, c \neq 6$

46. $\dfrac{z^2 + 12z + 20}{z - 1}$; $z \neq 1, z \neq 0$

47. $-\dfrac{1}{3}$

48. $\dfrac{3}{4}$

49. $-\dfrac{1}{2}$

Additional Instructional Support

Algebra 2 Companion

Students can use the **Algebra 2 Companion** worktext (4 pages) as you teach the lesson. Use the Companion to support

- New Vocabulary
- Key Concepts
- Got It for each Problem
- Lesson Check

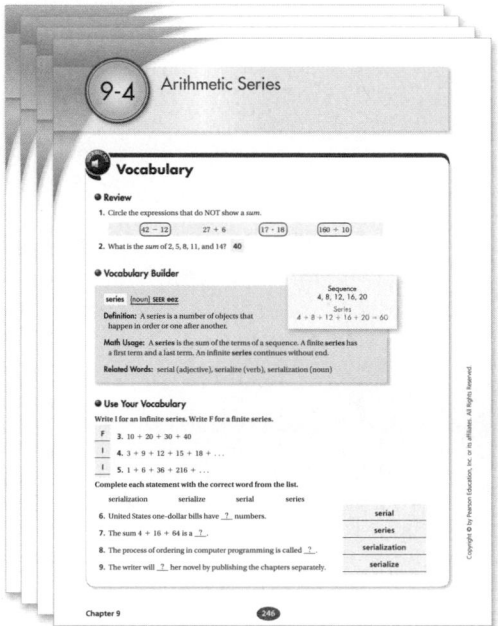

ELL Support

Focus on Language Have students use a dictionary to look up the terms *sequence* and *series*. A sequence is commonly defined as "a following of one thing after another." Students may have heard of the Fibonacci sequence. A series is commonly defined as "similar things happening one after the other." For example, several books are often printed as a series. Television shows are also referred to as series. Encourage students to discuss other examples of sequences and series in real life. Confirm that *sequence* and *series* are often used interchangeably outside of mathematics.

Explain that in mathematics, *sequence* and *series* cannot be used interchangeably. A sequence is an ordered list of numbers, while a series is the sum of the terms in a sequence. Write the words *sequence* and *series* on the board with examples of each. Point to each example, and have students practice saying the words.

5 Assess & Remediate

Lesson Quiz

1. What is the sum of the finite arithmetic series $-10 + (-8) + (-6) + (-4) + \ldots + 24$?

2. **Do you UNDERSTAND?** You are trying to save \$1500. You begin with \$5 and save \$3 more than the previous amount each week for 30 weeks. Will you meet your goal? Explain.

3. What is the summation notation for the series $-3 + 1 + 5 + \ldots + 169 + 173$?

4. What is $\sum\limits_{n=1}^{105} -2n + 10$?

ANSWERS TO LESSON QUIZ

1. 126

2. No; the first term is 5, and the common difference is 3. The amount saved in week 30 is $a_{30} = 5 + (30 - 1)3 = 92$. The sum for all 30 weeks is $S_{30} = \frac{30}{2}(5 + 92) = \$1455$.

3. $\sum\limits_{n=1}^{45} 4n - 7$

4. $-10{,}080$

PRESCRIPTION FOR REMEDIATION
Use the student work on the Lesson Quiz to prescribe a differentiated review assignment:

Points	Differentiated Remediation
0–2	Intervention
3	On-level
4	Extension

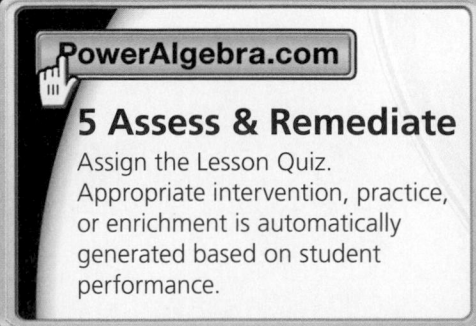

PowerAlgebra.com

5 Assess & Remediate
Assign the Lesson Quiz. Appropriate intervention, practice, or enrichment is automatically generated based on student performance.

Intervention

- **Reteaching** (2 pages) Provides reteaching and practice exercises for the key lesson concepts. Use with struggling students or absent students.

- **English Language Learner Support** Helps students develop and reinforce mathematical vocabulary and key concepts.

All-in-One Resources/Online
Reteaching

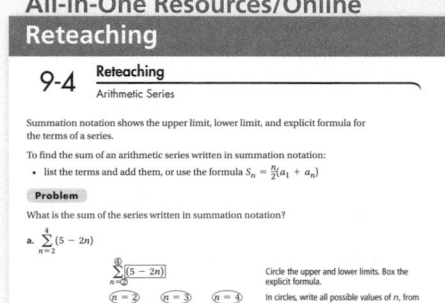

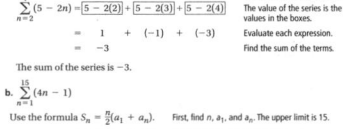

All-in-One Resources/Online
English Language Learner Support

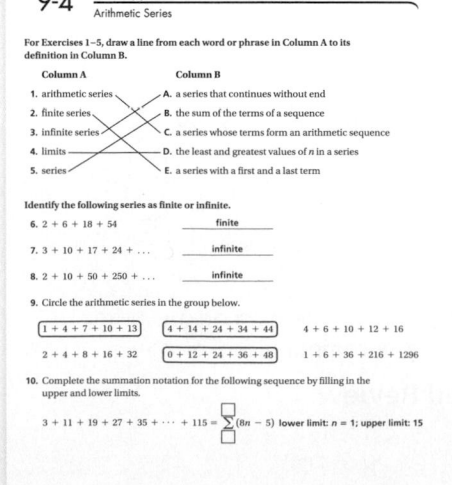

Differentiated Remediation *continued*

On-Level

- **Practice** (2 pages) Provides extra practice for each lesson. For more challenging practice exercises, use the Form G Practice pages found in the All-in-One Teaching Resources and online.

- **Think About a Plan** Helps students develop specific problem-solving skills and strategies by providing scaffolded guiding questions.

- **Standardized Test Prep** Focuses on all major exercises, all major question types, and helps students prepare for the high-stakes assessments.

Extension

- **Enrichment** Provides students with interesting problems and activities that extend the concepts of the lesson.

- **Activities, Games, and Puzzles** Worksheets that can be used for concepts development, enrichment, and for fun!

Student Companion/All-in-One Resources/Online
Practice page 1

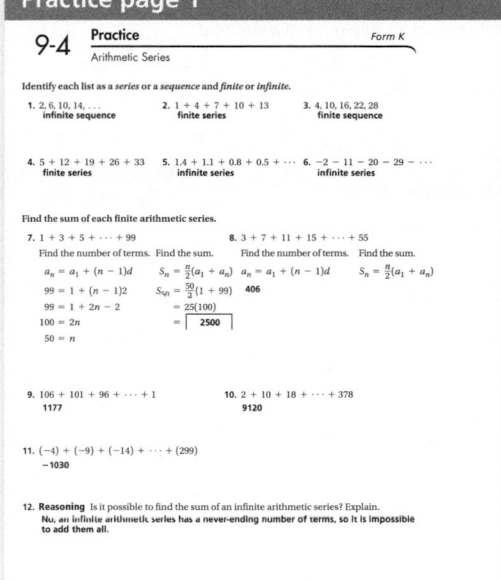

Student Companion/All-in-One Resources/Online
Practice page 2

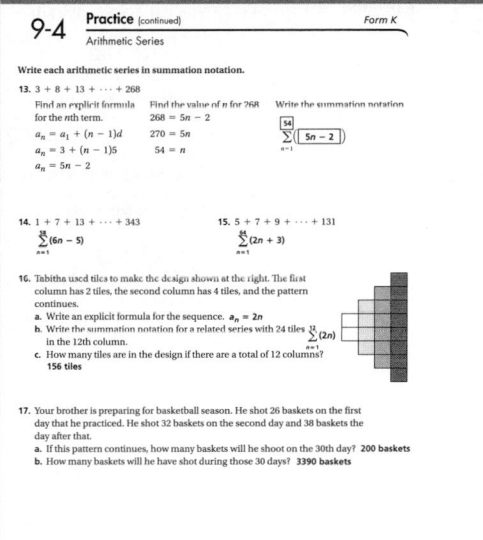

All-in-One Resources/Online
Enrichment

Student Companion/All-in-One Resources/Online
Think About a Plan

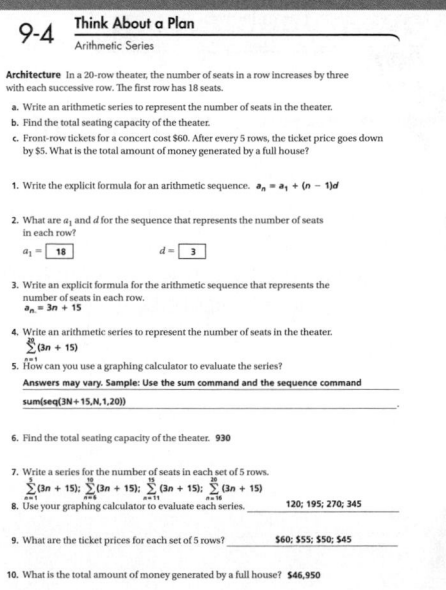

Student Companion/All-in-One Resources/Online
Standardized Test Prep

Online Teacher Resource Center
Activities, Games, and Puzzles

1 Interactive Learning

Solve It!

PURPOSE To use summation notation to find the sum of an infinite series

PROCESS Students may
- use a calculator to substitute a large value for the upper limit of the series.
- substitute each index value into the explicit formula to determine a pattern.

FACILITATE

Q What is ∞? **[the infinity symbol]**

Q Instead of 9, try 3 in the box. What pattern is in the sequence of the first four terms? What is their sum? **[0.3, 0.03, 0.003, 0.0003; 0.3333.]**

Q How do you write this pattern as a repeated decimal? **[$0.\overline{3}$]**

Q What fraction represents $0.\overline{3}$? **[$\frac{1}{3}$]**

ANSWER See Solve It in Answers on next page.
CONNECT THE MATH Students use their knowledge of series and geometric sequences to find the sum of the series in the Solve It. In this lesson, students will find the sum of finite and infinite geometric series when possible.

2 Guided Instruction

Take Note

Q For the sum S_n, why is the last term of the series $a_1 r^{n-1}$ and not $a_1 r^n$? **[The first term is a_1 and can also be written as $a_1 r^0$. Because the 0th term is counted as the first term, the last term must be to the power $n-1$.]**

Objective To define geometric series and find their sums

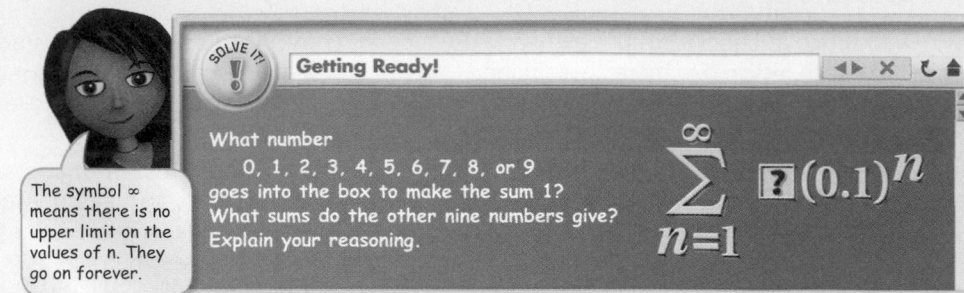

The symbol ∞ means there is no upper limit on the values of n. They go on forever.

Getting Ready!

What number 0, 1, 2, 3, 4, 5, 6, 7, 8, or 9 goes into the box to make the sum 1? What sums do the other nine numbers give? Explain your reasoning.

$$\sum_{n=1}^{\infty} \boxed{?}(0.1)^n$$

Lesson Vocabulary
- geometric series
- converge
- diverge

You can write any whole number that has the same digit in every place as the sum of the terms of a geometric sequence. For example,

$$4444 = 4(10)^0 + 4(10)^1 + 4(10)^2 + 4(10)^3$$

You can write any rational number as an infinite repeating decimal. For example, $\frac{47}{90} = 0.5222\ldots$.

Therefore, you can write any rational number as a number plus the sum of an infinite geometric sequence.

$$0.5222\ldots = 0.5 + 2(0.1)^2 + 2(0.1)^3 + 2(0.1)^4 + \ldots$$

Focus Question What is a geometric series?

A **geometric series** is the sum of the terms of a geometric sequence.

Key Concept Sum of a Finite Geometric Series

The sum S_n of a finite geometric series $a_1 + a_1 r + a_1 r^2 + \cdots + a_1 r^{n-1}, r \neq 1$, is

$$S_n = \frac{a_1(1 - r^n)}{1 - r}$$

where a_1 is the first term, r is the common ratio, and n is the number of terms.

Preparing to Teach

BIG idea Modeling **UbD**

ESSENTIAL UNDERSTANDINGS
- Just as with finite arithmetic series, the sum of a finite geometric series can be found using a formula. It is necessary to know the first term, the number of terms, and the common ratio.
- A geometric sequence can be modeled explicitly or recursively. The sum of its first n terms is $\frac{a_1(1 - r^n)}{1 - r}$.

Math Background

As with an arithmetic series, a geometric series is infinite. The sum of a finite number of terms can be found given the first term, the number of terms, and the common ratio. It is also possible to find the sum of an infinite geometric series when the series converges, when $|r| < 1$.

The sum of an infinite series is the number that the sequence of partial sums approaches. Find the sum of the first term, then the first two terms, then the first three terms, etc. The number approached by these partial sums as the number of terms increases is the sum of the infinite series. The sum of a finite series of real numbers is always a real number. The sum of an infinite series may be a real number; the series must converge.

A convergent series approaches a number similar to the way a graph approaches a horizontal asymptote. An arithmetic series always diverges because it is linear.

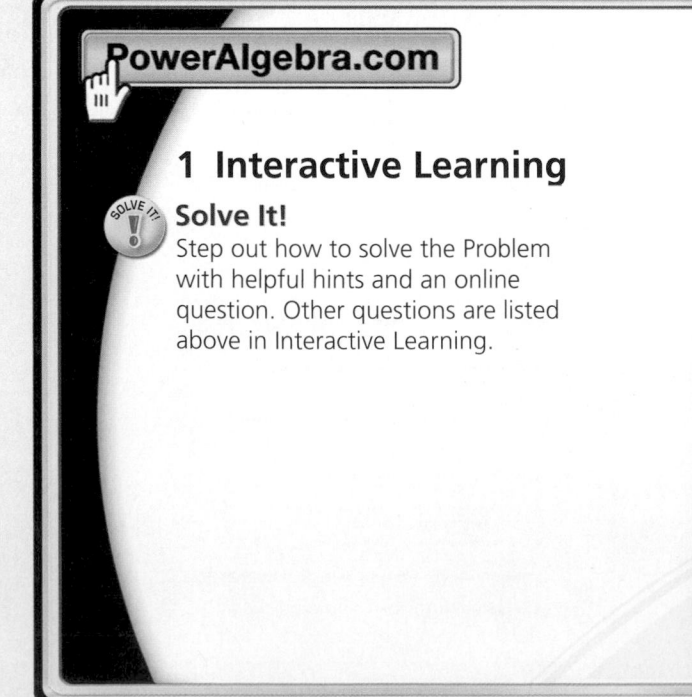

PowerAlgebra.com

1 Interactive Learning

Solve It!

Step out how to solve the Problem with helpful hints and an online question. Other questions are listed above in Interactive Learning.

Problem 1 Finding the Sums of Finite Geometric Series

Plan

What do you need to find the sum?
You need the first term, the common ratio, and the number of terms in the series.

What is the sum of the finite geometric series?

A $3 + 6 + 12 + 24 + \cdots + 3072$

The first term is 3. The common ratio is $\frac{6}{3} = 2$. The nth term is 3072.

Find the value of n.

Use the explicit formula.	$a_n = a_1 r^{n-1}$
Substitute 3 for a_1, 2 for r, and 3072 for a_n.	$3072 = 3 \cdot 2^{n-1}$
Divide each side by 3.	$1024 = 2^{n-1}$

1024 is 2^{10}, so $n - 1 = 10$ and $n = 11$.

Use the sum formula.	$S_n = \dfrac{a_1(1 - r^n)}{1 - r}$
Substitute 3 for a_1, 2 for r, and 11 for n.	$S_{11} = \dfrac{3(1 - 2^{11})}{1 - 2}$
Simplify.	$= 6141$

The sum of the series is 6141.

B $4 + 2 + 1 + \frac{1}{2} + \cdots + \frac{1}{128}$

The first term is 4. The common ratio is $\frac{2}{4} = \frac{1}{2}$. The nth term is $\frac{1}{128}$.

Find the value of n.

Use the explicit formula.	$a_n = a_1 r^{n-1}$
Substitute 4 for a_1, $\frac{1}{2}$ for r, and $\frac{1}{128}$ for a_n.	$\frac{1}{128} = 4\left(\frac{1}{2}\right)^{n-1}$
Divide each side by 4.	$\frac{1}{512} = \left(\frac{1}{2}\right)^{n-1}$

$\frac{1}{512}$ is $\left(\frac{1}{2}\right)^9$, so $n - 1 = 9$ and $n = 10$.

Use the sum formula.	$S_n = \dfrac{a_1(1 - r^n)}{1 - r}$
Substitute 4 for a_1, $\frac{1}{2}$ for r, and 10 for n.	$S_{10} = \dfrac{4\left(1 - \left(\frac{1}{2}\right)^{10}\right)}{1 - \frac{1}{2}}$
Simplify. Use a calculator.	≈ 8

The sum of the series is approximately 8.

 Got It? 1. What is the sum of the finite geometric series?
   a. $-15 + 30 - 60 + 120 - 240 + 480$
   b. $5 - 10 + 20 - 40 + \cdots - 2560$

Problem 1

Q How can you find the number of terms in the geometric series for 1A using a calculator? **[Enter 3, then Ans*2, and count the number of times you hit enter before getting the last term.]**

Q Will the terms of the geometric series in 1B increase or decrease? Explain. **[Decrease; the common ratio is $\frac{1}{2}$. This is less than 1, so the terms in the sequence will decrease.]**

EXTENSION

Q How can you rewrite the fractions in 1B using exponents to help you find the number of terms? Explain. **[Rewrite as $2^{-1} + \ldots + 2^{-7}$. So there are seven fractions and three whole number terms for a total of ten terms.]**

Q What is the sum of the first 20 terms of the series in 1B? Why is this sum not much greater than the sum of the first 10 terms? **[About 8; each successive term gets smaller, so additional terms will not greatly affect the sum.]**

Got It?

Q Why is the formula for the sum of a finite geometric series more useful in 1b than in 1a? **[In 1a, the series has six terms, so you can use a calculator instead of the formula to find the sum. In 1b, the number of terms is much larger, so calculator is not an efficient method to find the sum directly.]**

---

2 Guided Instruction

 Each Problem is worked out and supported online.

Problem 1
Finding the Sums of Finite Geometric Series
Animated

Alternative Problem 1
Finding the Sums of Finite Geometric Series
Animated

Problem 2
Using the Geometric Series Formula

Problem 3
Analyzing Infinite Geometric Series

Alternative Problem 3
Analyzing Infinite Geometric Series
Animated

Support in Algebra 2 Companion
• Vocabulary
• Key Concepts
• Got It?

Answers

Solve It!
9

$0.\overline{8}, 0.\overline{7}, 0.\overline{6}, 0.\overline{5}, 0.\overline{4}, 0.\overline{3}, 0.\overline{2}, 0.\overline{1}, 0$

Got It?
1. a. 315
   b. −1705

Problem 2   KINESTHETIC LEARNERS

Encourage students to use objects such as paper clips or centimeter cubes to demonstrate the grains of wheat on the chessboard. After each new square is filled in, have students find the sum of the new series.

> **Q** How can the common ratio be determined? **[The ratio is found by dividing one term by the previous term. The terms are 1, 2, 4, 8, etc., so the ratio is $\frac{2}{1} = 2$.]**

EXTENSION

> **Q** How can this series be written using summation notation? **[$\sum_{n=0}^{63} 2^n$ or $\sum_{n=1}^{64} 2^{n-1}$]**
>
> **Q** How many grains are on the last square? Explain. **[Because the first term is $2^0 = 1$, the last term is $2^{63} \approx 9.22 \times 10^{18}$.]**

Got It?   ERROR PREVENTION

Students sometimes think that because the increase is 10%, the value of r is 0.1. Point out that an r value of 0.1 would result in a decreasing sequence of terms or a lesser amount being put aside each month. Remind students to be sure their values make sense.

The Soldier's Reasonable Request A famous story involves a soldier who rescues his king in battle. The king grants him any prize "within reason" from the riches of the kingdom. The soldier asks for a chessboard with a single kernel of wheat on the first square, two kernels of wheat on the second square, then four, then eight, and so on for all 64 squares of the chessboard. The king decides that the request is reasonable.

 Problem 2 Using the Geometric Series Formula

According to the story above, how many total kernels of wheat did the soldier request?

Know	Need	Plan
The amount of wheat in the first 4 squares	The total amount of wheat	• Find the common ratio • Use the sum formula to find the total amount of wheat.

Step 1   Identify the first term, common ratio, and the number of terms.

$$a_1 = 1, r = 2, n = 64$$

Step 2   Use the sum formula.

Write the sum formula.	$S_n = \dfrac{a_1(1 - r^n)}{1 - r}$
Substitute for a_1, r, and n.	$S_{64} = \dfrac{1(1 - 2^{64})}{1 - 2}$
Simplify.	$= 2^{64} - 1$
Write in scientific notation.	$\approx 1.845 \times 10^{19}$

The soldier requested approximately 1.845×10^{19} kernels of wheat.

 Got It?   **2.** To save money for a vacation, you set aside \$100. For each month thereafter, you plan to set aside 10% more than the previous month. How much money will you save in 12 months?

Additional Problems

1. What is the sum of the geometric series?

  a. $4 + 12 + 36 + 108 + 324 + 972 + 2916$

  b. $\displaystyle\sum_{n=0}^{11} 3(-1.5)^n$

ANSWERS

  a. 4372

  b. about -154.50

2. A game show is offering a prize of 1¢ on the first day, 3¢ on the second day, 9¢ on the third day, etc. What is the total amount of money earned from this prize in two weeks?

  ANSWER \$23,914.84

3. Does the infinite series converge or diverge? If it converges, what is the sum?

  a. $-5 - \dfrac{5}{2} - \dfrac{5}{4} - \dfrac{5}{8} - \dfrac{5}{16} - \cdots$

  b. $\dfrac{1}{4} - \dfrac{3}{8} + \dfrac{9}{16} - \dfrac{27}{32} + \cdots$

  c. $\displaystyle\sum_{n=0}^{\infty} (0.8)^n$

ANSWERS

  a. converges; -10

  b. diverges

  c. converges; 5

Answers

Got It? (continued)

  2. about \$2138.43

The Rest of the Story A bushel of wheat contains about a million kernels. The total US output of wheat in a recent year was just over 2.1 billion bushels. How many years of production at that level would it take the United States to produce enough wheat to satisfy the soldier's "reasonable" request?

In Problem 2, you found that the terms of a geometric series grow rapidly when the common ratio is greater than 1. Likewise, they diminish rapidly when the common ratio is between 0 and 1. In fact, they diminish so rapidly that the infinite geometric series actually has a finite sum.

take note →

Key Concept Infinite Geometric Series

An infinite geometric series with first term a_1 and common ratio $|r| < 1$ has a finite sum S.

$$S = \frac{a_1}{1 - r}.$$

An infinite geometric series with $|r| \geq 1$ does not have a finite sum.

To say that an infinite series $a_1 + a_2 + a_3 + \ldots$ has a sum means that the *sequence of partial sums* $S_1 = a_1, S_2 = a_1 + a_2, S_3 = a_1 + a_2 + a_3, \ldots$, $S_n = a_1 + a_2 + \cdots + a_n, \ldots$ **converges** to a number S as n gets very large.

When an infinite series does not converge to a sum, the series **diverges**. An infinite geometric series with $|r| \geq 1$ diverges.

 Problem 3 Analyzing Infinite Geometric Series

Does the series *converge* or *diverge*? If it converges, what is the sum?

A $1 + \frac{1}{2} + \frac{1}{4} + \ldots$

The common ratio is $\frac{1}{2} \div 1 = \frac{1}{2}$. Since $|r| = \left|\frac{1}{2}\right| < 1$, the series converges.

Use the sum formula. $S = \frac{a_1}{1 - r}$

Substitute 1 for a_1 and $\frac{1}{2}$ for r. $= \frac{1}{1 - \frac{1}{2}}$

Simplify. $= \frac{1}{\frac{1}{2}} = 2$

The sum is 2.

Think

When does an infinite geometric series converge?
An infinite geometric series converges when the absolute value of the common ratio is less than 1.

Q As the value of r gets close to 1, what happens to the value of the denominator? The value of the sum? **[As r gets close to 1, the value of the denominator decreases; the value of the sum increases.]**

SYNTHESIZING

It is sometimes difficult for students to understand how an infinite series can have a sum. Point out that you are finding partial sums and then finding the number approached by an increasing number of partial sums.

Problem 3   VISUAL LEARNERS

Q How can you tell whether a series is finite or infinite? **[A finite series can have ... in the middle but always has a term at the end. An infinite series ends in ...]**

Q In 3A, the sum equals 2. How can you check that this is a reasonable answer? Explain. **[As the number of terms increases, the partial sums converge to 2. For example, $S_2 = 1.5$; $S_3 = 1.75$; $S_4 = 1.875$; $S_{10} \approx 1.9980$.]**

Got It?

Q Will the convergence or divergence of 3b change if all the terms are positive? Explain. **[No; the absolute value of _r_ determines whether the series converges or diverges, so changing the sign has no effect.]**

3 Lesson Check

Do you know HOW?   ERROR INTERVENTION

• If students have difficulty solving Exercises 1 and 2, remind them that they must find the common ratio by dividing the second term by the first.

Do you UNDERSTAND?

• If students have trouble answering Exercise 5, review the definitions of convergence and divergence. A series will converge only if _r_ is between −1 and 1. The ratio must be checked before applying the formula for infinite series.

Close

Q What are the similarities and differences between a geometric sequence and geometric series? **[Both have a common ratio. A sequence is the list of terms while a series is the sum of the terms.]**

Q What is the difference between finding the sum of a finite and infinite geometric series? **[A finite series is found by adding each term. An infinite series is found by adding the partial sums and then finding the number approached by the sequence of partial sums.]**

B $\frac{2}{3} - \frac{5}{6} + \frac{25}{24} - \frac{125}{96} + \ldots$

The common ratio is $-\frac{5}{6} \div \frac{2}{3} = -\frac{15}{12} = -\frac{5}{4}$.

Since $|r| = \left|-\frac{5}{4}\right| = \frac{5}{4} > 1$, the series diverges.

 Got It? **3.** Does the infinite series *converge* or *diverge*? If it converges, what is the sum?

  a. $\frac{1}{2} + \frac{3}{4} + \frac{9}{8} + \ldots$ **b.** $\frac{1}{3} - \frac{1}{9} + \frac{1}{27} - \frac{1}{81} + \ldots$

  c. Reasoning Will an infinite geometric series either converge or diverge? Explain.

Focus Question What is a geometric series?

Answer A geometric series is the sum of the terms of a geometric sequence. Find the sum of a finite geometric series using the first term, the number of terms, and the common ratio. You can also find the sum of an infinite geometric series if the common ratio $|r| < 1$.

Lesson Check

Do you know HOW?

Evaluate each finite geometric series.

1. $\frac{1}{5} + \frac{1}{10} + \frac{1}{20} + \frac{1}{40} + \frac{1}{80}$

2. $9 - 6 + 4 - \frac{8}{3} + \frac{16}{9}$

Determine whether each infinite geometric series *diverges* or *converges*.

3. $1 - \frac{1}{6} + \frac{1}{36} - \frac{1}{216} + \ldots$

4. $\frac{1}{64} + \frac{1}{32} + \frac{1}{16} + \ldots$

Do you UNDERSTAND?

5. Error Analysis A classmate uses the formula for the sum of an infinite geometric series to evaluate $1 + 1.1 + 1.21 + 1.331 + \ldots$ and gets −10. What error did your classmate make?

6. Writing Explain how you can determine whether an infinite geometric series has a sum.

7. Compare and Contrast How are the formulas for the sum of a finite arithmetic series and the sum of a finite geometric series similar? How are they different?

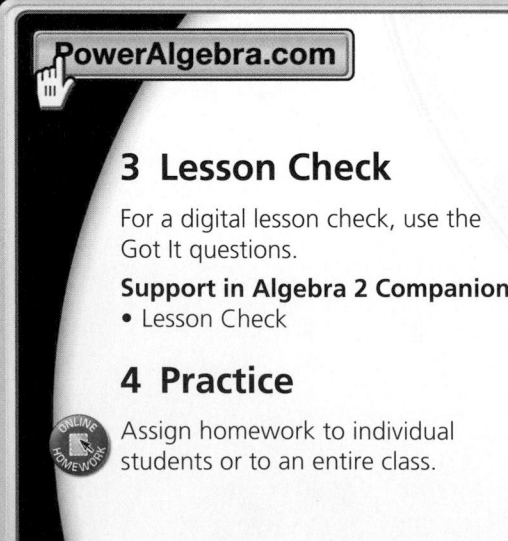

3 Lesson Check

For a digital lesson check, use the Got It questions.

Support in Algebra 2 Companion
• Lesson Check

4 Practice

Assign homework to individual students or to an entire class.

Answers

Got It? (continued)

3. a. diverges

  b. converges; $\frac{1}{4}$

  c. Yes; if $|r| < 1$, the series converges. If $|r| \geq 1$, the series diverges.

Lesson Check

1. $\frac{31}{80}$

2. $\frac{55}{9}$

3. converges

4. diverges

5. Since $r = 1.1 > 1$, the series diverges and does not have a sum.

6. An infinite geometric series has a sum only when $|r| < 1$.

7. The sum of a finite arithmetic series is $S_n = \frac{n}{2}(a_1 + a_n)$. The sum of a finite geometric series is $S_n = \frac{a_1(1 - r^n)}{1 - r}$. The formulas are similar in that each sum requires the first term and the number of terms in the series. The formulas are different in that the sum of a finite arithmetic series needs the last term, while the sum of a finite geometric series needs the common ratio.

Practice and Problem-Solving Exercises

A Practice   Evaluate the sum of the finite geometric series.   ◀ **See Problem 1.**

Guided Practice

> To start, use the explicit formula for a geometric sequence with $a_1 = 1$, $r = 2$ and $a_n = 128$.
>
> **8.** $1 + 2 + 4 + 8 + \cdots + 128$
>
> $a_n = a_1 r^{n-1}$
>
> $128 = 1 \cdot 2^{n-1}$

9. $4 + 12 + 36 + 108 + \cdots + 972$ **10.** $3 + 6 + 12 + 24 + \cdots + 768$

11. $-5 - 10 - 20 - 40 - \cdots - 2560$ **12.** $1 - 3 + 9 - 27 + \cdots - 2187$

13. Financial Planning In March, a family starts saving for a vacation they are planning for the end of August. The family expects the vacation to cost $1375. They start with $125. Each month they plan to deposit 20% more than the previous month. Will they have enough money for their trip? If not, how much more do they need?   ◀ **See Problem 2.**

Determine whether each infinite geometric series *diverges* or *converges*. If the series converges, state the sum.   ◀ **See Problem 3.**

Guided Practice

> **14.** $1 + \frac{1}{4} + \frac{1}{16} + \ldots$
>
> To start, find the common ratio. $\frac{1}{4} \div 1 = \frac{1}{4}$

15. $1 - \frac{1}{2} + \frac{1}{4} - \ldots$ **16.** $4 + 2 + 1 + \ldots$ **17.** $1 + 2 + 4 + \ldots$

18. $6 + 18 + 54 + \ldots$ **19.** $-54 - 18 - 6 - \ldots$ **20.** $1 - 1 + 1 - \ldots$

Evaluate each infinite geometric series.

21. $1.1 + 0.11 + 0.011 + \ldots$ **22.** $3 + 1 + \frac{1}{3} + \frac{1}{9} + \ldots$ **23.** $3 - 2 + \frac{4}{3} - \frac{8}{9} + \ldots$

B Apply   **24. Think About a Plan** The height a ball bounces is less than the height of the previous bounce due to friction. The heights of the bounces form a geometric sequence. Suppose a ball is dropped from one meter and rebounds to 95% of the height of the previous bounce. What is the total distance traveled by the ball when it comes to rest?
- Does the problem give you enough information to solve the problem?
- How can you write the general term of the sequence?
- What formula should you use to calculate the total distance?

4 Practice

ASSIGNMENT GUIDE

Basic: 8–18, 21–24, 31, 36

Average: 8–24, 25–31 odd, 33, 34, 36

Standardized Test Prep: 37–41

Mixed Review: 42–49

Reasoning exercises have blue headings.

Applications exercises have red headings.

EXERCISE 31: Use the Think About a Plan worksheet in the **Student Companion** (also available in the Teaching Resources in print and online) to further support students' development in becoming independent learners.

HOMEWORK QUICK CHECK

To check students' understanding of key skills and concepts, go over Exercises 9, 15, 24, 31, and 36.

Practice and Problem-Solving Exercises

8. 255

9. 1456

10. 1533

11. −5115

12. −1640

13. no; $133.76

14. converges; $\frac{4}{3}$

15. converges; $\frac{2}{3}$

16. converges; 8

17. diverges

18. diverges

19. converges; −81

20. diverges

21. $1.\overline{2}$

22. $\frac{9}{2}$

23. $\frac{9}{5}$

24. 39 m

Answers

25. geometric; 2046

26. arithmetic; 420

27. geometric; −1,627,605

28. geometric; ≈96.47

29. arithmetic; 500,500

30. geometric; 121.5

31. a.

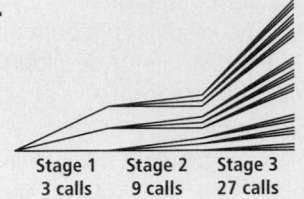

Stage 1	Stage 2	Stage 3
3 calls	9 calls	27 calls

b. 3 + 9 + 27 + 81 + 243 + 729

c. 1092

32. a. 20, 18, 16.2, 14.58

b. about 198.59

c. $S = \dfrac{20}{1 - 0.9} = 200$

d. Check students' work.

33. Check students' work.

34. a. 70th swing

b. 10,000 cm

35. choice (b); (a) yields $26,000; using the formula for finding the sum of a finite geometric series, (b) yields $1,342,177.26.

36. a. Answers may vary. Sample: The student used $r - 1$ instead of $1 - r$ in the formula for the sum of an infinite geometric series.

b. $\dfrac{1}{2}$

Determine whether each series is *arithmetic* or *geometric*. Then evaluate the finite series for the specified number of terms.

25. 2 + 4 + 8 + 16 + . . . ; $n = 10$

26. 2 + 4 + 6 + 8 + . . . ; $n = 20$

27. −5 + 25 − 125 + 625 − . . . ; $n = 9$

28. 6.4 + 8 + 10 + 12.5 + . . . ; $n = 7$

29. 1 + 2 + 3 + 4 + . . . ; $n = 1000$

30. 81 + 27 + 9 + 3 + . . . ; $n = 200$

31. Communications Many companies use a telephone chain to notify employees of a closing due to bad weather. Suppose a company's CEO calls three people. Then each of these people calls three others, and so on.
  a. Make a diagram to show the first three stages in the telephone chain. How many calls are made at each stage?
  b. Write the series that represents the total number of calls made through the first six stages.
  c. How many employees have been notified after stage six?

32. Graphing Calculator The graph models the sum of the first n terms in a geometric series with $a_1 = 20$ and $r = 0.9$.
  a. Write the first four sums of the series.
  b. Use the graph to evaluate the series to the 47th term.
  c. Write and evaluate the formula for the sum of the series.
  d. Graph the formula using the window values shown. Use the graph to verify your answer to part (b).

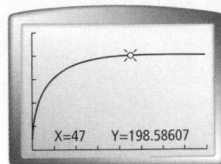

X=47   Y=198.58607

Xmin=0   Ymin=0
Xmax=94   Ymax=250
Xscl=10   Yscl=50

33. Open-Ended Write an infinite geometric series that converges to 3. Use the formula to evaluate the series.

34. Physics Because of friction and air resistance, each swing of a pendulum is a little shorter than the previous one. The lengths of the swings form a geometric sequence. Suppose the first swing of a pendulum has a length of 100 cm and the return swing is 99 cm.
  a. On which swing will the arc first have a length less than 50 cm?
  b. What is the total distance traveled by the pendulum when it comes to rest?

35. Writing Suppose you are to receive an allowance each week for the next 26 weeks. Would you rather receive (a) $1000 per week or (b) $.02 the first week, $.04 the second week, $.08 the third week, and so on for the 26 weeks? Justify your answer.

36. The sum of an infinite geometric series is twice its first term.
  a. Error Analysis A student says the common ratio of the series is $\frac{3}{2}$. What is the student's error?
  b. Find the common ratio of the series.

Standardized Test Prep

SAT/ACT

37. Solve $\sqrt{x} + \sqrt{2x} = 2$. Check for extraneous solutions.

38. Evaluate the infinite geometric series $\frac{2}{5} + \frac{4}{25} + \frac{8}{125} + \ldots$. Enter your answer as a fraction.

39. Use $\log_5 2 \approx 0.43$ and $\log_5 7 \approx 1.21$ and the properties of logarithms to approximate $\log_5 \sqrt{14}$ without using a calculator.

40. Use a calculator to solve the equation $7^{2x} = 75$. Round the answer to the nearest hundredth.

41. Use the Change of Base Formula and your calculator to solve $\log_9 x = \log_6 15$. Round the answer to the nearest tenth.

Mixed Review

Evaluate each series to the given term.   ◀ See Lesson 9-4.

42. $12.5 + 15 + 17.5 + 20 + 22.5 + \ldots$; 7th term

43. $-100 - 95 - 90 - 85 - \ldots$; 11th term

Add or subtract. Simplify where possible.   ◀ See Lesson 8-5.

44. $\frac{7}{2c} - \frac{2}{c^2}$ **45.** $\frac{5}{y+3} + \frac{15}{y-3}$ **46.** $\frac{4}{x^2-36} + \frac{x}{x-6}$

Use the properties of logarithms to evaluate each expression.   ◀ See Lesson 7-4.

47. $\log_2 \frac{1}{8} + \log_2 8$ **48.** $\log_{15} 25 + \log_{15} 9$ **49.** $3\log_9 3 - \frac{1}{4}\log_9 81$

Standardized Test Prep

37. 2

38. $\frac{2}{3}$

39. 0.82

40. 1.11

41. 27.7

Mixed Review

42. 140

43. −825

44. $\frac{7c-4}{2c^2}$

45. $\frac{10(2y+3)}{(y+3)(y-3)}$

46. $\frac{x^2+6x+4}{(x+6)(x-6)}$

47. 0

48. 2

49. 1

Additional Instructional Support

Algebra 2 Companion

Students can use the **Algebra 2 Companion** worktext (4 pages) as you teach the lesson. Use the Companion to support

- New Vocabulary
- Key Concepts
- Got It for each Problem
- Lesson Check

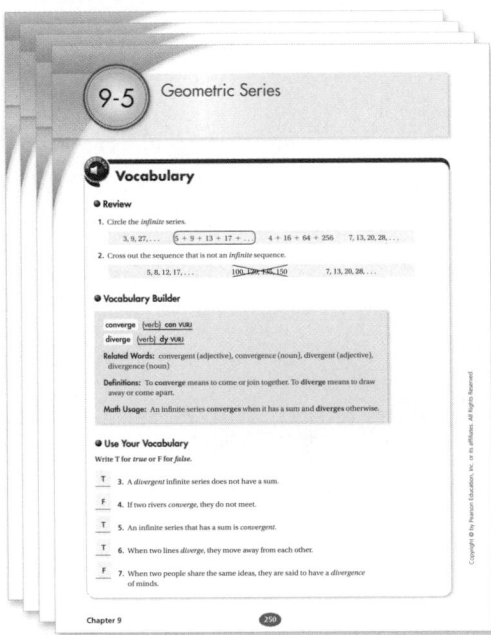

ELL Support

Focus on Graphic Organizer Write the words *finite*, *infinite*, *converge*, and *diverge* with definitions on the board. Then draw rectangles around the words *finite* and *infinite* and ovals around the words *converge* and *diverge*. Next have students copy the graphic organizer below.

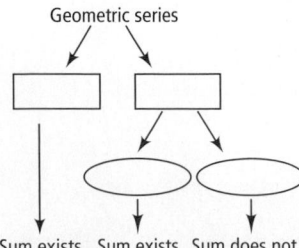

Geometric series

Sum exists   Sum exists   Sum does not exist

Have students fill in the organizer with the vocabulary words and state the information shown. For example, a student may say "I can look at a finite or infinite geometric series. A finite series has a sum. If an infinite series converges, it has a sum. If an infinite series diverges, the sum cannot be found."

5 Assess & Remediate

Lesson Quiz

1. What is the sum of the geometric series $\sum_{n=0}^{18} 3\left(\frac{3}{4}\right)^n$?

2. Do you UNDERSTAND? You saved $500 this year. Each year you plan to save 5% more than the previous year. How much do you expect to save after 8 more years?

3. Does the series converge or diverge? If it converges, what is the sum?

$2 + \frac{1}{2} + \frac{1}{8} + \frac{1}{32} + \dots$

ANSWERS TO LESSON QUIZ

1. about 11.95

2. $5513.28

3. converge; $\frac{8}{3}$

PRESCRIPTION FOR REMEDIATION

Use the student work on the Lesson Quiz to prescribe a differentiated review assignment:

Points	Differentiated Remediation
0–1	Intervention
2	On-level
3	Extension

PowerAlgebra.com

5 Assess & Remediate

Assign the Lesson Quiz. Appropriate intervention, practice, or enrichment is automatically generated based on student performance.

Intervention

- **Reteaching** (2 pages) Provides reteaching and practice exercises for the key lesson concepts. Use with struggling students or absent students.

- **English Language Learner Support** Helps students develop and reinforce mathematical vocabulary and key concepts.

All-in-One Resources/Online
Reteaching

9-5 Reteaching
Geometric Series

- The **sum of a finite geometric series** is $S_n = \frac{a_1(1 - r^n)}{1 - r}$, where a_1 is the first term, r is the common ratio, and n is the number of terms.

- The **sum of an infinite geometric series** with $|r| < 1$ is $S = \frac{a_1}{1 - r}$, where a_1 is the first term and r is the common ratio. If $|r| \geq 1$, then the series has no sum.

Problem

What is the sum of the first ten terms of the geometric series $8 + 16 + 32 + 64 + 128 + \dots$?

$a_1 = 8$	a_1 is the first term in the series.
$r = \frac{16}{8} = \frac{32}{16} = \frac{64}{32} = \frac{128}{64} = 2$	Simplify the ratio formed by any two consecutive terms to find r.
$n = 10$	n is the number of terms in the series to be added together.
$S_{10} = \frac{8(1 - 2^{10})}{1 - 2}$	Substitute $a_1 = 8$, $r = 2$, and $n = 10$ into the formula for the sum of a finite geometric series.
$= \frac{8(-1023)}{-1}$	Simplify inside the parentheses.
$= 8184$	Simplify.

Exercises

Evaluate the finite series for the specified number of terms.

1. $3 + 12 + 48 + 192 + \dots; n = 5$ **4095** **2.** $8 + 2 + \frac{1}{2} + \frac{1}{8} + \dots; n = 5$ $\frac{341}{32}$

3. $-10 - 5 - 2.5 - 1.25 - \dots; n = 7$ $-\frac{635}{32}$ **4.** $10 + (-5) + \frac{5}{2} + \left(-\frac{5}{4}\right) + \dots; n = 11$ $\frac{3415}{512}$

Evaluate each infinite geometric series.

5. $10 + 5 + 2.5 + \dots$ **20** **6.** $-1 + \frac{2}{11} - \frac{4}{121} + \dots$ $-\frac{11}{13}$ **7.** $\frac{1}{4} + \frac{7}{32} + \frac{49}{256} + \dots$ **2**

8. $\frac{1}{2} - \frac{1}{5} + \frac{2}{25} - \dots$ $\frac{5}{14}$ **9.** $-\frac{1}{6} + \frac{1}{12} - \frac{1}{24} + \dots$ $-\frac{1}{9}$ **10.** $20 + 16 + \frac{64}{5} + \dots$ **100**

11. $12 + 4 + \frac{4}{3} + \dots$ **18** **12.** $\frac{1}{4} - \frac{1}{8} + \frac{1}{16} - \dots$ $\frac{1}{6}$ **13.** $\frac{2}{3} + \frac{2}{15} + \frac{2}{75} + \dots$ $\frac{5}{6}$

All-in-One Resources/Online
English Language Learner Support

9-5 ELL Support
Geometric Series

Problem

What is the sum of the geometric series $2 + 6 + 18 + 54 + \dots + 1458$?

$\frac{6}{2} = \frac{18}{6} = \frac{54}{18} = 3$	Identify the common ratio and the nth term.
nth term $= 1458$	
$a_n = a_1 r^{n-1}$	Use the explicit formula.
$1458 = 2 \cdot 3^{n-1}$	Substitute 2 for a_1, 3 for r, and 1458 for a_n.
$729 = 3^{n-1}$	Divide each side by 2.
729 is 3^6, so $n - 1 = 6$ and $n = 7$	Use a calculator.
$S_n = \frac{a_1(1 - r^n)}{1 - r}$	Use the sum formula.
$S_7 = \frac{2(1 - 3^7)}{1 - 3}$	Substitute 2 for a_1, 3 for r, and 7 for n.
$S_7 = 2186$	

Exercise

What is the sum of the geometric series $1 + 4 + 16 + 64 + \dots + 1024$?

$\frac{4}{1} = \frac{16}{4} = \frac{64}{16} = 4$	Identify the common ratio and the nth term.
nth term $= 1024$	
$a_n = a_1 r^{n-1}$	Use the explicit formula
$1024 = 1 \cdot 4^{n-1}$	Substitute 1 for a_1, 4 for r, and 1024 for a_n
$1024 = 4^{n-1}$	Divide each side by 1
1024 is 4^5, so $n - 1 = 5$ and $n = 6$	Use a calculator
$S_n = \frac{a_1(1 - r^n)}{1 - r}$	Use the sum formula
$S_6 = \frac{1(1 - 4^6)}{1 - 4}$	Substitute 1 for a_1, 4 for r, and 6 for n
$S_6 = 1365$	

Differentiated Remediation *continued*

On-Level

- **Practice** (2 pages) Provides extra practice for each lesson. For more challenging practice exercises, use the Form G Practice pages found in the All-in-One Teaching Resources and online.

- **Think About a Plan** Helps students develop specific problem-solving skills and strategies by providing scaffolded guiding questions.

- **Standardized Test Prep** Focuses on all major exercises, all major question types, and helps students prepare for the high-stakes assessments.

Extension

- **Enrichment** Provides students with interesting problems and activities that extend the concepts of the lesson.

- **Activities, Games, and Puzzles** Worksheets that can be used for concepts development, enrichment, and for fun!

Student Companion/All-in-One Resources/Online
Practice page 1

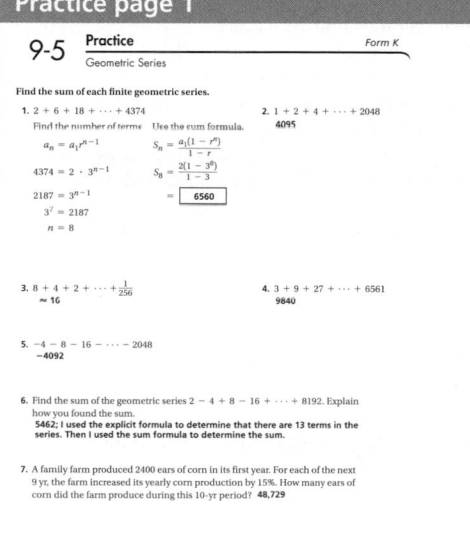

Student Companion/All-in-One Resources/Online
Practice page 2

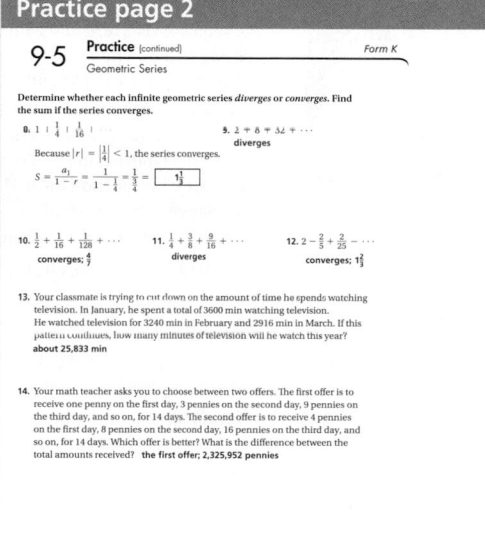

All-in-One Resources/Online
Enrichment

Student Companion/All-in-One Resources/Online
Think About a Plan

Student Companion/All-in-One Resources/Online
Standardized Test Prep

Online Teacher Resource Center
Activities, Games, and Puzzles

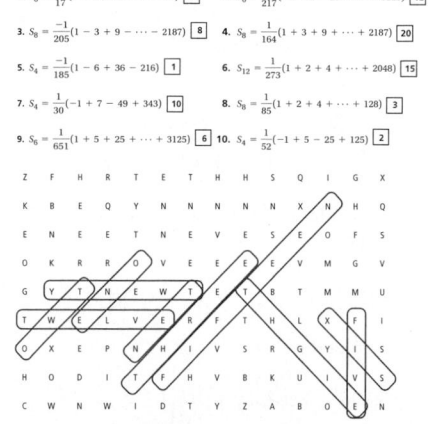

Performance Task UbD

Pull It All Together

The concepts and skills required to solve these problems are from several lessons within this chapter and from earlier chapters. As students solve these problems, they will demonstrate their reasoning strategies and their growth as independent problem solvers.

Task 1

Derive algebraic formulas from other formulas and expressions.

- If you know the first term and the common difference of an arithmetic sequence, what formula would you use to find the nth term of the sequence?
- If you group all of the a_1 terms, how many are there? If you factor d from the remaining terms, how would you write the sum of what was left?

Task 2

Express arithmetic and geometric sequences as functions and explain the relationship of the sequences to their respective parent functions.

- Which variable in the expressions $a_1 + (n - 1)d$ and $a_1 r^{n-1}$ will not be a constant value for any given sequence?

Task 3

Identify what quantities specific formula variables represent and explain the process of solving for an unknown variable when all other variable values are known.

- Does a subscript correspond to any mathematical operation?

To solve these problems, you will pull together concepts and skills related to sequences and series.

BIG idea Variable

You can represent quantities using variables and algebraic expressions.

Task 1

The sum S_n of a finite arithmetic series of n terms is $S_n = \frac{n}{2}(a_1 + a_n)$ where a_1 is the first term and a_n is the nth term.

a. Show that $S_n = na_1 + \frac{n(n-1)}{2}d$ by replacing a_n with its value in terms of a_1, n, and d in the above formula.

b. Explain why $S_n = na_1 + \frac{n(n-1)}{2}d$ makes sense by explaining how you can extract each of na_1 and $\frac{n(n-1)}{2}d$ from the sum $a_1 + (a_1 + d) + (a_1 + 2d) + \cdots + (a_1 + (n-1)d)$.

BIG idea Equivalence

You can represent any *function* in an unlimited number of ways, where all representations have the same domain and the same pairing of inputs with outputs.

Task 2

A sequence is a function with domain the natural numbers $1, 2, 3, \ldots$.
Using function notation, you can write the sequence $a_n = a_1 + (n-1)d$ as $a(n) = a_1 + (n-1)d$ and the sequence $a_n = a_1 r^{n-1}$ as $a(n) = a_1 r^{n-1}$.

a. Is $a(n) = a_1 + (n-1)d$ a linear function? Explain. If not, how can you adjust its definition so that it is a linear function? What is the slope?

b. What type of function does $a(n) = a_1 r^{n-1}$ suggest? To what family of functions does this function belong? Explain how it is related to the parent function of that family. Draw its graph.

c. What type of function is suggested by the sum sequence $S(n) = \frac{a_1(1-r^n)}{1-r}$? By $S(n) = \frac{n}{2}(a_1 + a(n))$? Explain each answer.

BIG idea Modeling

You can represent many real-world mathematical problems algebraically. These representations can lead to algebraic solutions.

Task 3

Each of these sequence or series formulas involves four quantities. For each formula, describe the four quantities. Then explain how you can find the fourth quantity if you know the values of the other three.

a. $a_n = a_1 + (n-1)d$

b. $S_n = \frac{n}{2}(a_1 + a_n)$

c. $a_n = a_1 r^{n-1}$

d. $S_n = \frac{a_1(1-r^n)}{1-r}$

Assess Performance  UbD

Pull It All Together

See p. 53 for a holistic scoring rubric to gauge a student's progress on Understanding the Problem, Planning a Solution, Getting an Answer, and Assessing Autonomy.

1. a. First step: Substitute $a_1 + (n-1)d$ for a_n in $S_n = \frac{n}{2}(a_1 + a_n)$.
$\left(S_n = \frac{n}{2}[a_1 + (a_1 + (n-1)d)]\right)$

Second step: Simplify $S_n = \frac{n}{2}[a_1 + (a_1 + (n-1)d)]$.

$\begin{aligned} \Big[S_n &= \frac{n}{2}[a_1 + a_1 + (n-1)d] \\ &= \frac{n}{2}(2a_1 + (n-1)d \\ &= na_1 + \frac{n(n-1)}{2}d \Big] \end{aligned}$

b. Possible plan: Evaluate $S_n = na_1 + \frac{n(n-1)}{2}$ for $n = 1$, $n = 2$ and $n = 3$. Look for a pattern that will help you to extract na_1 and $\frac{n(n-1)}{2}$ from each term of the sum.
[When $n = 1$, $S_n = a_1 + \frac{1(0)}{2}d = a_1$
When $n = 2$, $S_n = 2a_1 + \frac{2(1)}{2}d = 2a_1 + d = a_1 + (a_1 + d)$.
When $n = 3$, $S_n = 3a_1 + 3d = a_1 + (a_1 + d) + (a_1 + 2d)$.
And so on.]

2. a. Answers may vary. Sample: No, its graph is not a line but rather a set of points in a line. It is a linear function if you state its domain to be the set of real numbers. In the form $a(n) = dn + (a_1 - d)$, its slope clearly is d.

b. exponential; $a(n) = a_1 r^{n-1} = \frac{a_1}{r}r^n$, which is a stretch of the parent function $a(n) = r^n$ by the factor $\frac{a_1}{r}$.

c. exponential; $S(n) = \frac{a_1(1-r^n)}{1-r} = \frac{a_1(r^n-1)}{r-1} = \frac{a_1}{r-1}r^n - \frac{a_1}{r-1}$ which is a stretch or compression of $S(n) = r^n$ by the factor $\frac{a_1}{r-1}$ and then a horizontal translation by $\frac{a_1}{r-1}$.
quadratic; $S(n) = \frac{n}{2}(a_1 + a(n)) = na_1 + \frac{n(n-1)}{2}d$ (from Task 1b) $= \frac{d}{2}n^2 + \left(a_1 - \frac{d}{2}\right)n$.

3. a. This formula is used to find nth term of an arithmetic sequence. a_n is the nth term, a_1 is the first term, d is the common difference, and n is the number of the term you are looking for. To find a_n, you need to know a_1, d and n.

9 Chapter Review

Connecting BIG ideas and Answering the Essential Questions

1 Variable
You can define a sequence
- by describing its nth term with a formula using n.
- by stating its first term and a formula that relates the $n - 1$ and nth terms.

Mathematical Patterns and Arithmetic Sequences (Lessons 9-1 and 9-2)
$a_n = 2 - \frac{3}{4}(n - 1)$ and $a_1 = 2$, so $a_n = a_{n-1} - \frac{3}{4}$ represent the arithmetic sequence $2, \frac{5}{4}, \frac{2}{4}, -\frac{1}{4}, -1, \ldots$

Arithmetic Series (Lesson 9-4)
The sum $S_n = a_1 + a_2 + \cdots + a_n$ of an arithmetic series is $S_n = \frac{n}{2}(a_1 + a_n)$. The sum
$$S_6 = 2 + \frac{5}{4} + \frac{2}{4} - \frac{1}{4} - 1 - \frac{7}{4}$$
$$= 3\left(2 - \frac{7}{4}\right) = \frac{3}{4}.$$

2 Equivalence
$a_n = a + (n - 1)d$ and $a_1 = a$, $a_n = a_{n-1} + d$ for $n > 1$ define the same arithmetic sequence, $a, a + d, a + 2d, \ldots$

3 Modeling
You can model a geometric sequence explicitly or recursively. The sum of its first n terms is $\frac{a_1(1 - r^n)}{1 - r}$.

Mathematical Patterns and Geometric Sequences (Lessons 9-1 and 9-3)
$a_n = 2\left(-\frac{1}{2}\right)^{n-1}$ and $a_1 = 2$, so $a_n = \left(-\frac{1}{2}\right)a_{n-1}$ represents the geometric sequence $2, -1, \frac{1}{2}, -\frac{1}{4}, \frac{1}{8}, \ldots$.

Geometric Series (Lesson 9-5)
$S_n = \frac{a_1(1 - r^n)}{1 - r}$ is the sum of the first n terms of a geometric series. If the series is infinite with $|r| < 1$, the sum is $S = \frac{a_1}{1 - r}$.
For the geometric series,
$$a_1 = 2, a_n = \left(-\frac{1}{2}\right)a_{n-1},$$
$$S_6 = \frac{2\left(1 - \left(-\frac{1}{2}\right)^6\right)}{1 - \left(-\frac{1}{2}\right)}, \text{ or } \frac{21}{16}, \text{ and}$$
$$S = \frac{2}{1 - \left(-\frac{1}{2}\right)} = \frac{4}{3}.$$

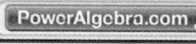

Chapter Vocabulary

- arithmetic mean (p. 594)
- arithmetic sequence (p. 592)
- arithmetic series (p. 607)
- common difference (p. 592)
- common ratio (p. 600)
- converge (p. 617)

- diverge (p. 617)
- explicit formula (p. 585)
- finite series (p. 607)
- geometric mean (p. 603)
- geometric sequence (p. 600)
- geometric series (p. 614)

- infinite series (p. 607)
- limits (p. 610)
- recursive formula (p. 586)
- sequence (p. 584)
- series (p. 607)
- term (p. 584)

Choose the vocabulary term that correctly completes each sentence.

1. When you use Σ to write a series, you can use _?_ to indicate how many terms you are adding.

2. An ordered list of terms is a _?_.

3. If an infinite geometric series _?_, then it must have a sum.

4. There is a constant _?_ between consecutive terms in a geometric sequence.

5. A formula that expresses the nth term of a sequence in terms of n is a(n) _?_.

PowerAlgebra.com | Chapter 9 Chapter Review | 623

---

b. This formula is used to find the nth term of a geometric sequence. a_n is the nth term, a_1 is the first term, r is the common ratio, and n is the number of the term you are looking for. To find the nth term, you need to know the first term, the common ratio and the number of the term you are looking for.

c. This formula is used to find the sum of a finite arithmetic series. S_n is the sum, n is the number of terms, a_1 is the first term and a_n is the last term. You need to know the first term, the last term, and the number of terms to find the sum of a finite arithmetic series.

d. This formula is used to find the sum of a finite geometric series. S_n is the sum, n is the number of terms, a_1 is the first term and r is the common ratio. You need to know the first term, the common ratio, and the number of terms to add.

Answers

Chapter Review

1. limits
2. sequence
3. converges
4. common ratio
5. explicit formula

Essential Questions

BIG idea Variable
ESSENTIAL QUESTIONS How can you represent the terms of a sequence explicitly? How can you represent them recursively?
ANSWER You can define a sequence
- by describing its nth term with a formula using n.
- by stating its first term and a formula that relates the $n - 1$ and nth terms.

BIG idea Equivalence
ESSENTIAL QUESTION What are equivalent explicit and recursive definitions for an arithmetic sequence?
ANSWER $a_n = a + (n - 1)d$ and $a_1 = a$, $a_n = a_{n-1} + d$ for $n > 1$ define the same arithmetic sequence, $a, a + d, a + 2d, \ldots$

BIG idea Modeling
ESSENTIAL QUESTIONS How can you model a geometric sequence? How can you model its sum?
ANSWER You can model a geometric sequence explicitly or recursively. The sum of its first n terms is $\frac{a_1(1 - r^n)}{1 - r}$.

Summative Questions

Use the following prompts as you review this chapter with your students. The prompts are designed to help you assess your students' understanding of the BIG ideas they have studied.

- Compare and contrast explicit formula and recursive definition. If you knew the first term, which would you use to find the 100th term?
- How can you find the common difference of a sequence? common ratio?
- When is it possible to find the sum of an arithmetic or geometric series?
- What does it mean for an infinite series to diverge? converge? Could an infinite arithmetic series ever converge?

Chapter Review 623

Answers

Chapter Review (continued)

6. $1, -1, -3, -5, -7$

7. $1, 0, -3, -8, -15$

8. $2, 3, 5, 9, 17$

9. $20, 10, 5, 2.5, 1.25$

10. $a_n = a_{n-1} + 17, a_1 = 5$

11. $a_n = a_{n-1} + 9, a_1 = -2$

12. $a_n = 1 + 3(n - 1)$

13. $a_n = 4 - 2.5(n - 1)$

14. no

15. yes; $d = 15, a_{32} = 468$

16. yes; $d = 3, a_{32} = 100$

17. no

18. 5

19. 101.5

20. 5

21. -4.9

22. $-10.5, -8, -5.5$

23. $1.4, 0.8, 0.2$

24. $a_n = -2 + 9(n - 1)$

25. $a_n = 62 - 3(n - 1)$

9-1 Mathematical Patterns

Quick Review

A **sequence** is an ordered list of numbers called **terms**.

A recursive definition gives the first term and defines the other terms using a **recursive formula** that relates each term after the first term to the one before it.

An **explicit formula** expresses the nth term of a sequence in terms of n, where n is a positive integer.

Example

A sequence has an explicit formula $a_n = n^2$. What are the first three terms of this sequence?

Substitute 1 for n and evaluate.	$a_1 = (1)^2 = 1$
Substitute 2 for n and evaluate.	$a_2 = (2)^2 = 4$
Substitute 3 for n and evaluate.	$a_3 = (3)^2 = 9$

The first three terms are 1, 4, and 9.

Exercises

Find the first five terms of each sequence.

6. $a_n = -2n + 3$

7. $a_n = -n^2 + 2n$

8. $a_n = 2a_{n-1} - 1$, where $a_1 = 2$

9. $a_n = \frac{1}{2}a_{n-1}$, where $a_1 = 20$

Write a recursive definition for each sequence.

10. $5, 22, 39, 56, \ldots$ **11.** $-2, 7, 16, 25, \ldots$

Write an explicit formula for each sequence.

12. $1, 4, 7, 10, \ldots$ **13.** $4, 1.5, -1, -3.5, \ldots$

9-2 Arithmetic Sequences

Quick Review

In an **arithmetic sequence**, the constant difference between consecutive terms is called the **common difference**.

For an arithmetic sequence, a is the first term, a_n is the nth term, n is the number of the term, and d is the common difference.

An explicit formula is $a_n = a + (n - 1)d$.

A recursive definition is $a_{n+1} = a_n + d$, with $a_1 = a$.

The **arithmetic mean** of two numbers x and y is the average of the two numbers $\frac{x + y}{2}$.

Example

What is the missing term of the arithmetic sequence $11, \blacksquare, 27, \ldots$?

Use the formula for the arithmetic mean.	arithmetic mean $= \frac{x + y}{2}$
Substitute 11 for x and 27 for y.	$= \frac{11 + 27}{2}$
Simplify.	$= \frac{38}{2} = 19$

The missing term is 19.

Exercises

Determine whether each sequence is arithmetic. If so, identify the common difference and find the 32nd term of the sequence.

14. $2, 4, 7, 10, \ldots$ **15.** $3, 18, 33, 48, \ldots$

16. $7, 10, 13, 16, \ldots$ **17.** $2, 5, 9, 14, \ldots$

Find the missing term(s) of each arithmetic sequence.

18. $1, \blacksquare, 9, \ldots$ **19.** $104, \blacksquare, 99, \ldots$

20. $-1, \blacksquare, 11, \ldots$ **21.** $-4.6, \blacksquare, -5.2, \ldots$

22. $-13, \blacksquare, \blacksquare, \blacksquare, -3, \ldots$ **23.** $2, \blacksquare, \blacksquare, \blacksquare, -0.4, \ldots$

Write an explicit formula for each arithmetic sequence.

24. $-2, 7, 16, 25, \ldots$ **25.** $62, 59, 56, 53, \ldots$

9-3 Geometric Sequences

Quick Review

In a **geometric sequence**, the ratio of consecutive terms is constant. This ratio is the **common ratio**. For a geometric sequence, a is the first term, a_n is the nth term, n is the number of the term, and r is the common ratio.

An explicit formula is $a_n = a \cdot r^{n-1}$.

A recursive definition is $a_n = a_{n-1} \cdot r$, with $a_1 = a$.

The geometric mean of two positive numbers x and y is $\sqrt{xy}$.

Example

What is the sixth term of the geometric sequence that begins $2, 6, 18, \ldots$?

The first term a is 2. The common ratio r is $6 \div 2 = 3$.

Use the explicit formula. $\qquad a_n = ar^{n-1}$

Substitute 6 for n, 2 for a, and 3 for r. $\quad a_6 = 2 \cdot 3^{6-1}$

Simplify. $\qquad\qquad\qquad\qquad\qquad = 486$

The sixth term is 486.

Exercises

Determine whether each sequence is geometric. If so, identify the common ratio and find the next two terms.

26. $1, \frac{1}{2}, \frac{1}{4}, \frac{1}{8}, \ldots$

27. $1, 3, 5, 7, \ldots$

28. $3, 3.6, 4.32, 5.184, \ldots$

Find the missing term(s) of each geometric sequence.

29. $3, \blacksquare, 12, \ldots$

30. $0.004, \blacksquare, 0.4, \ldots$

31. $-20, \blacksquare, \blacksquare, \blacksquare, -1.25, \ldots$

Write an explicit formula for each geometric sequence.

32. $1, 2, 4, 8, \ldots$

33. $25, 5, 1, \frac{1}{5}, \ldots$

Use an explicit formula to find the 10th term of each geometric sequence.

34. $5, 10, 20, 40, \ldots$ $\qquad$ **35.** $-3, 6, -12, 24, \ldots$

9-4 Arithmetic Series

Quick Review

A **series** is the expression for the sum of the terms of a sequence. An **arithmetic series** is the sum of the terms of an arithmetic sequence. The sum S_n of the first n terms of an arithmetic series is $S_n = \frac{n}{2}(a_1 + a_n)$.

Example

What is the sum of the arithmetic series?

$2 + 5 + 8 + 11 + 14 + 17 + 20$

The first term is 2, and the last (and 7th) term is 20.

Use the sum formula. $\qquad\qquad S_n = \frac{n}{2}(a_1 + a_n)$

Substitute 7 for n, 2 for a_1, and 20 for a_n. $\quad S_7 - \frac{7}{2}(2 + 20)$

Simplify. $\qquad\qquad\qquad\qquad\qquad\quad = 77$

Exercises

Use summation notation to write each arithmetic series for the specified number of terms. Then evaluate the sum.

36. $10 + 7 + 4 + \ldots ; n = 5$

37. $50 + 55 + 60 + \ldots ; n = 7$

38. $6 + 7.4 + 8.8 + \ldots ; n = 11$

39. $21 + 19 + 17 + \ldots ; n = 8$

PowerAlgebra.com

Chapter 9   Chapter Review $\qquad$ 625

---

26. yes; $r = \frac{1}{2}; \frac{1}{16}, \frac{1}{32}$

27. no

28. yes; $r = 1.2$; 6.2208, 7.46496

29. ± 6

30. ± 0.04

31. $\pm 10, -5, \pm 2.5$

32. $a_n = 2^{n-1}$

33. $a_n = 25\left(\frac{1}{5}\right)^{n-1}$

34. 2560

35. 1536

36. $\displaystyle\sum_{n=1}^{5}(13 - 3n)$; 20

37. $\displaystyle\sum_{n=1}^{7}(45 + 5n)$; 455

38. $\displaystyle\sum_{n=1}^{11}(4.6 + 1.4n)$; 143

39. $\displaystyle\sum_{n=1}^{8}(23 - 2n)$; 112

Answers

Chapter Review (continued)

40. 31

41. $53\frac{1}{8}$

42. $14\frac{7}{18}$

43. converges; $S = 187.5$

44. diverges

45. diverges

46. converges; $S = 2$

Quick Review

A **geometric series** is the sum of the terms of a geometric sequence. The sum S_n of the first n terms of a geometric series is $S_n = \frac{a_1(1 - r^n)}{1 - r}, r \neq 1$.

When an infinite series has a finite sum, the series **converges**. When the series does not converge, the series **diverges**.

For an infinite geometric series, when $|r| < 1$, the series converges to $S = \frac{a_1}{1 - r}$. When $|r| \geq 1$, the series diverges.

Example

What is the sum of the geometric series?

5 + 10 + 20 + 40 + 80 + 160

The first term is 5, and common ratio is $10 \div 5 = 2$.

There are 6 terms.

Use the sum formula. $S_n = \frac{a_1(1 - r^n)}{1 - r}$

Substitute 6 for n, 5 for a_1, and 2 for r. $S_6 = \frac{5(1 - 2^6)}{1 - 2}$

Simplify. $= 315$

The sum is 315.

Exercises

Evaluate each finite series for the specified number of terms.

40. $1 + 2 + 4 + \ldots; n = 5$

41. $80 - 40 + 20 - \ldots; n = 8$

42. $12 + 2 + \frac{1}{3} + \ldots; n = 4$

Determine whether each infinite geometric series *converges* or *diverges*. If the series converges, state the sum.

43. $150 + 30 + 6 + \ldots$

44. $2.2 + 2.42 + 2.662 + \ldots$

45. $-10 - 20 - 40 - \ldots$

46. $\frac{2}{3} + \frac{4}{9} + \frac{8}{27} + \ldots$

9 Chapter Test

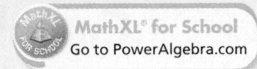

MathXL® for School
Go to PowerAlgebra.com

Do you know HOW?

Write a recursive definition and an explicit formula for each sequence. Then find a_{12}.

1. 7, 13, 19, 25, 31, . . .

2. 10, 20, 40, 80, 160, . . .

Determine whether each sequence is *arithmetic*, *geometric*, or *neither*. Then find the tenth term.

3. 23, 27, 31, 35, 39, . . .

4. −12, −5, 2, 9, 16, . . .

5. −5, 15, −45, 135, −405, . . .

6. $\frac{1}{4}$, 1, 4, 16, . . .

Find the missing term of each arithmetic sequence.

7. 4, ■, 12, . . .   **8.** −11, ■, 23, . . .

Determine whether each sequence is *arithmetic* or *geometric*. Then identify the common difference or common ratio.

9. 1620, 540, 180, 60, 20, . . .

10. 78, 75, 72, 69, 66, 63, 60, . . .

11. $\frac{3}{32}, \frac{3}{16}, \frac{3}{8}, \frac{3}{4}, \frac{3}{2}, 3, 6, \ldots$

a_1 is the first term of a sequence, r is the common ratio, and d is the common difference. Write the first five terms.

12. $a_1 = 2, r = -2$ **13.** $a_1 = 3, d = 7$

14. $a_1 = -100, r = \frac{1}{5}$ **15.** $a_1 = 19, d = -4$

Find the missing term of each geometric sequence.

16. 2, ■, 0.5, . . .   **17.** 2, ■, 8, . . .

Find the sum of each infinite geometric series.

18. 0.5 + 0.05 + 0.005 + . . .

19. $1 - \frac{1}{2} + \frac{1}{4} - \ldots$

20. $6 + 5 + \frac{25}{6} + \ldots$

Determine whether each series is *arithmetic* or *geometric*. Then evaluate the finite series for the specified number of terms.

21. 2 + 7 + 12 + . . . ; $n = 8$

22. 5000 + 1000 + 200 + . . . ; $n = 5$

23. 1 + 0.01 − 0.98 − . . . ; $n = 5$

24. 2 + 6 + 18 + . . . ; $n = 6$

Do you UNDERSTAND?

25. You have saved $50. Each month you add $10 more to your savings.
   a. Write an explicit formula to model the amount you have saved after n months.
   b. How much have you saved after six months?

26. **Open-Ended** Write an arithmetic sequence. Then write an explicit formula for it.

27. **Reasoning** How can you tell if a geometric series converges or diverges? Include examples of both types of series. Evaluate the series that converges.

28. A diamond is purchased for $2500. Suppose its value increases 5% each year.
   a. What is the value of diamond after 8 years?
   b. **Writing** Explain how you can write an explicit formula for a geometric sequence to answer the question.

PowerAlgebra.com   Chapter 9   Chapter Test   627

Answers

Chapter Test

1. $a_n = a_{n-1} + 6, a_1 = 7$;
$a_n = 7 + 6(n - 1)$

2. $a_n = a_{n-1} \cdot 2, a_1 = 10$;
$a_n = 10 \cdot 2^{n-1}$; 20,480

3. arithmetic; 59

4. arithmetic; 51

5. geometric; 98,415

6. geometric; 65,536

7. 8

8. 6

9. geometric; $r = \frac{1}{3}$

10. arithmetic; $d = -3$

11. geometric; $r = 2$

12. 2, −4, 8, −16, 32

13. 3, 10, 17, 24, 31

14. $-100, -20, -4, -\frac{4}{5}, -\frac{4}{25}$

15. 19, 15, 11, 7, 3

16. ±1

17. ±4

18. $\frac{5}{9}$

19. $\frac{2}{3}$

20. 36

21. arithmetic; 156

22. geometric; 6248

23. arithmetic; −4.9

24. geometric; 728

25. a. $S = 50 + 10n$ where S represents savings.
   b. $110

26. Answers may vary. Sample answer: 3, 5, 7, 9, . . . ; $a_n = 1 + 2n$

27. If the absolute value of the common ratio is less than 1, then it will converge; check students' work.

28. a. $3693.64
   b. $A_n = 2500(1.05)^n$;
   $A_8 = 2500(1.05)^8 \approx 3693.64$

PowerAlgebra.com

MathXL for School
Prepare students for the Mid-Chapter Quiz and Chapter Test with online practice and review.

Item Number	Lesson
1	5-2
2	9-2
3	9-3
4	5-3
5	5-2
6	5-2
7	8-4
8	9-4
9	6-6
10	6-6
11	6-4
12	7-4
13	8-4
14	4-4
15	9-3
16	4-1
17	9-4
18	9-4
19	7-4
20	3-2
21	6-6
22	2-4
23	4-8
24	2-4
25	9-3
26	9-4
27	6-7
28	7-4
29	9-3
30	5-3

Cumulative Test Prep

TIPS FOR SUCCESS

Read the question at the right. Then follow the tips to answer the sample question.

TIP 1

Find where y = 0. These are the x-intercepts of the graph.

TIP 2

Check your solutions in the original equation.

The graph below shows the quadratic function $y = 2x^2 + 2x - 4$. Use the graph to find the solutions of $2x^2 + 2x - 4 = 0$.

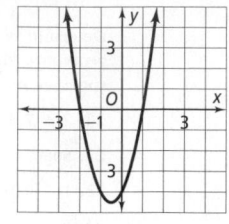

A) -4 and 0 C) -1 and 2
B) -2 and 1 D) 2 and -1

Think It Through

The x-intercepts of the graph are at $x = -2$ and $x = 1$.

Substitute to verify your answers.

$2(-2)^2 + 2(-2) - 4$
$= 2(4) - 4 - 4$
$= 0$
$2(1)^2 + 2(1) - 4$
$= 2 + 2 - 4$
$= 0$

The correct answer is B.

Vocabulary Builder

As you solve test items, you must understand the meanings of mathematical terms. Match each term with its mathematical meaning.

A. recursive formula

B. limit

C. explicit formula

D. sequence

I. a formula that expresses the nth term in terms of n

II. an ordered list of numbers

III. the least or greatest integer value of n in a series

IV. a formula that gives the first term in a sequence and defines the other terms by relating each term to the one before it

Multiple Choice

Read each question. Then write the letter of the correct answer on your paper.

1. What is the solution set of the equation $(2x - 4)(x + 6) = 0$?
A) $\{-4, 6\}$ C) $\{2, -6\}$
B) $\{-4, 6\}$ D) $\{-2, -6\}$

2. What are the first five terms of the sequence $a_n = 2n - 1$?
F) $0, 1, 2, 3, 4$ H) $2, 4, 6, 8, 10$
G) $1, 3, 5, 7, 9$ I) $3, 5, 7, 9, 11$

3. What is the common ratio in a geometric series if $a_2 = \frac{2}{5}$ and $a_5 = \frac{16}{135}$?
A) $\frac{2}{5}$ C) $\frac{6}{65}$
B) $\frac{2}{3}$ D) $\frac{8}{27}$

Answers

Cumulative Test Prep

A. IV

B. III

C. I

D. II

Multiple Choice

1. C

2. G

3. B

4. The total area of a sheet of paper can be represented by $27x^3 + 64y^3$. Which factors could represent the length times the width?

- Ⓕ $(3x + 4y)(3x^2 + 4y^2)$
- Ⓖ $(3x + 4y)(9x^2 - 12xy + 16y^2)$
- Ⓗ $(3x - 4y)(9x^2 - 12xy + 16y^2)$
- Ⓘ $(3x + 4y)(3x^2 - 3xy + 4y^2)$

5. The graph below shows the quadratic function $y = x^2 + 2x - 3$. Use the graph to find all the solutions of $x^2 + 2x - 3 = 0$.

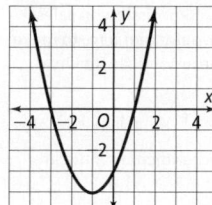

- Ⓐ -3
- Ⓒ -3 and 1
- Ⓑ -1
- Ⓓ 3 and -1

6. The table shows ordered pairs that satisfy the equation $y = -x^2 + 2x + 15$.

x	-3	0	2	3	5
y	0	15	15	12	0

Based on this table, what is the solution set of the equation $-x^2 + 2x + 15 = 0$?

- Ⓕ $\{0, 15\}$
- Ⓗ $\{5, 0\}$
- Ⓖ $\{-3, 15\}$
- Ⓘ $\{-3, 5\}$

7. What is the product of $\frac{x^2 + 5x + 4}{(x - 1)(x + 1)}$ and $\frac{x^2 - 5x + 6}{x - 2}$?

- Ⓐ $\frac{x^2 + 7x + 12}{x - 1}$ for $x \neq 1$
- Ⓑ $\frac{x^2 + x - 12}{x - 1}$ for $x \neq -1, 1,$ or 2
- Ⓒ $\frac{x^2 + x - 12}{x - 1}$ for $x \neq 1$
- Ⓓ $\frac{x^2 + 7x + 12}{x - 1}$ for $x \neq -1, 1,$ or 2

8. What is the sum of the infinite geometric series $\frac{1}{4} + \frac{1}{16} + \frac{1}{64} + \frac{1}{256} + \dots$?

- Ⓕ $\frac{1}{4}$
- Ⓗ $\frac{1}{2}$
- Ⓖ $\frac{1}{3}$
- Ⓘ 3

9. If $f(x) = 4x^4 - 9$ and $g(x) = 2x^2 + 3$, what is $\left(\frac{f}{g}\right)(x)$?

- Ⓐ $2x^2 - 3$
- Ⓑ $2x + 3$
- Ⓒ $2x - 3$
- Ⓓ $2x^2 + 3$

10. Marisol wants to start saving money for college. She sees the advertisement below in her local newspaper.

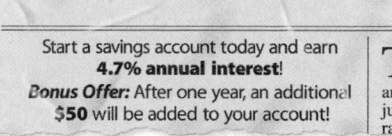

Start a savings account today and earn **4.7% annual interest**!
Bonus Offer: After one year, an additional $50 will be added to your account!

For x dollars in this savings account, $I(x) = 1.047x$ is the value of the account after one year. $B(x) = x + 50$ is the value of the account after the one-year bonus. $(B \circ I)(x)$ models the value of this account after one year of investment time and the one-year bonus. Marisol opens a savings account by depositing $120. What is the value of the account after one year?

- Ⓕ $175.64
- Ⓗ $226.40
- Ⓖ $182.58
- Ⓘ $249.90

11. What is the area of the parallelogram below?

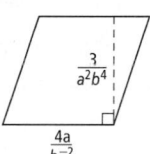

$\frac{3}{a^2 b^4}$

$\frac{4a}{b^{-2}}$

- Ⓐ $\frac{12}{ab^2}$
- Ⓒ $\frac{12b^2}{a}$
- Ⓑ $\frac{3}{ab^2}$
- Ⓓ $\frac{3b^5}{4a^3}$

4. G
5. C
6. I
7. B
8. G
9. A
10. F
11. A

Answers

Cumulative Test Prep
(continued)

12. I

13. D

14. G

15. C

16. G

17. 341

18. 224

19. 4

20. 20

21. 9

22. 2

23. [2] 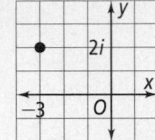 ;

$|-3 + 2i| = \sqrt{(-3)^2 + (2)^2} = \sqrt{13}$

[1] correct graph, but incorrect abs. value OR correct abs. value, but incorrect graph

24. [2] $m = \frac{1 - 5}{7 - 3} = -1$, $y - 5 = -(x - 3)$ OR equivalent eq.

[1] correct eq., without work shown

25. [2] $a_n = 6\left(\frac{1}{2}\right)^{n-1}$; $6, 3, \frac{3}{2}, \frac{3}{4}, \frac{3}{8}$

[1] one of the five terms is incorrect

26. [2] $78 = \frac{30}{2}(a_1 + 4.4)$, $a_1 = 0.8$

[1] correct answer, without work shown

27. [2] $x = \sqrt{y - 5}$, $x^2 = y - 5$, $y = x^2 + 5$ for $x \geq 0$

[1] correct inverse function, without work shown

28. [4] $\log 45 = \log (5 \cdot 9) = \log 5 + \log 9$; Product Prop.

$\log 45 = \log (5 \cdot 3^2) = \log 5 + 2 \log 3$; Product and Power Prop.

$\log 45 = \log \frac{90}{2} = \log 90 - \log 2$; Quotient Prop.

$\log 45 = \log 2025^{\frac{1}{2}} = \frac{1}{2} \log 2025$; Power Prop.

[3] log 45 written in only three diff. ways, correct prop.

[2] log 45 written in only two diff. ways, correct prop. OR log 45 written in four diff. ways, with two incorrect prop.

[1] log 45 written in only two diff. ways, without correct prop.

---

12. If log 5 ≈ 0.69897 and log 6 ≈ 0.77815, what is the approximate value of log 150?

Ⓕ 0.34188

Ⓖ 0.38017

Ⓗ 1.20412

Ⓘ 2.17609

13. What is $\frac{4x^2 - 1}{2x^2 - 5x - 3} \cdot \frac{x^2 - 6x + 9}{2x^2 + 5x - 3}$?

Ⓐ 1

Ⓑ $x + 3$

Ⓒ $x - 3$

Ⓓ $\frac{x - 3}{x + 3}$

14. Which is the factored form of $0.81p^2 - 0.09$?

Ⓕ $(0.9p + 0.045)(0.9p - 0.045)$

Ⓖ $(0.9p + 0.3)(0.9p - 0.3)$

Ⓗ $(0.9p + 0.03)(0.9p - 0.03)$

Ⓘ $(0.9p + 0.81)(0.9p - 0.81)$

15. Which arithmetic sequence does NOT include the term 33?

Ⓐ 1, 5, 9, 13, . . .

Ⓑ 3, 9, 15, . . .

Ⓒ 1, 11, 21, . . .

Ⓓ 85, 72, 59, . . .

16. The graph shows a transformation of which parent function?

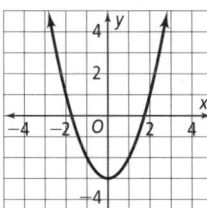

Ⓕ $y = x$ ⠀⠀ Ⓗ $y = |x|$

Ⓖ $y = x^2$ ⠀⠀ Ⓘ $y = \frac{1}{x}$

---

17. What is the sum of the following finite geometric series?

$1 + 4 + 16 + 64 + 256$

18. What is the sum of the following finite arithmetic series?

$14 + 20 + 26 + 32 + 38 + 44 + 50$

19. What is the value of $\log_4 256$?

20. Rita works a part-time job at a clothing store and earns $7 per hour. Juan works at another clothing store and earns $6 per hour plus a 10% commission on sales. How many sales, in dollars, would Juan have to make in two hours to earn the same amount as Rita in a two-hour shift?

21. Let $f(x) = x + 1$ and $g(x) = x^2$. What is $(g \circ f)(2)$?

22. What is the slope of a line perpendicular to the line $y = -\frac{1}{2}x + 5$?

Short Response

23. What is the graph and absolute value of $-3 + 2i$?

24. What is an equation of the line passing through points $(3, 5)$ and $(7, 1)$?

25. Write an explicit formula for the geometric sequence for which $a_1 = 6$ and $r = \frac{1}{2}$. Then generate the first five terms.

26. The 30th term of a finite arithmetic series is 4.4. The sum of the first 30 terms is 78. What is the first term of the series?

27. What is the inverse of $y = \sqrt{x - 5}$?

Extended Response

28. Use the properties of logarithms to write log 45 in four different ways. Name each property you use.

29. In a geometric sequence, $a_1 = 2$ and $a_5 = 162$. Explain how to use the geometric mean to find the missing terms a_2, a_3, and a_4.

30. What are all the solutions to $27x^4 + 8x = 0$? Show your work.

---

29. [4] $a_3 = \sqrt{a_1 \cdot a_5} = \sqrt{2(162)} = 18$

Likewise,

$a_2 = \pm\sqrt{a_1 \cdot a_3} = \pm\sqrt{2(18)} = \pm 6$

and

$a_4 = \pm\sqrt{a_3 \cdot a_5} = \pm\sqrt{18(162)} = \pm 54$

[3] one computational error

[2] only pos. values are found for a_2 and a_4.

[1] correct values, without work shown

30. [4] $27x^4 + 8x = 0$

$x(27x^3 + 8) = 0$

$x(3x + 2)(9x^2 - 6x + 4) = 0$

$x = 0, -\frac{2}{3}$, or $\frac{1 \pm i\sqrt{3}}{3}$

[3] one computational error

[2] only the real solutions are found

[1] correct solutions, without work shown

Get Ready!

Lesson 4-1 ◆ **Graphing Quadratic Functions**

Graph each function.

1. $y = -x^2$ **2.** $y = \frac{1}{3}x^2$

3. $y = 2x^2 + 5$ **4.** $y = x^2 + 6x + 8$

Lesson 4-3 ◆ **Identifying Quadratic Functions**

Determine whether each function is *linear* or *quadratic*. Identify the quadratic, linear, and constant terms.

5. $y = 6x - x^2 + 1$ **6.** $f(x) = -2(3 + x)^2 + 2x^2$ **7.** $y = 2x - y - 13$

8. $y = 4x(7 - 2x)$ **9.** $g(x) = -2x^2 - 3(x - 2)$ **10.** $y = x - 2(x + 5)$

Lesson 4-6 ◆ **Completing the Square**

Complete the square.

11. $x^2 + 8x +$ ■   **12.** $x^2 - 5x +$ ■   **13.** $x^2 + 14x +$ ■

Rewrite each equation in vertex form. Then graph the function.

14. $y = x^2 + 6x + 7$ **15.** $y = 2x^2 - 4x + 10$ **16.** $y = -3x^2 + x$

Lesson 4-1 ◆ **Graphing Quadratic Functions in Vertex Form**

Graph each function.

17. $y = 2(x - 3)^2 + 1$ **18.** $y = -1(x + 7)^2 - 4$

Lesson 2-7 ◆ **Graphing Absolute Value Functions**

Graph each function.

19. $y = 2|x|$ **20.** $y = |x| + 2$

 Looking Ahead Vocabulary

21. The word *radius* is a Latin word for the spoke of a wheel. It is also the source of the word "radio" because electromagnetic rays radiate from a radio in every direction. Why do you think mathematicians use the term radius to label any line segment from the center of a circle to any point on the circle?

22. In geometry, you learned that a *vertex* is typically a corner or point where two lines intersect. The four corners of a square are called vertices. Using this information, what can you conclude about the vertex of a parabola?

Get Ready!

Assign this diagnostic assessment to determine if students have the prerequisite skills for Chapter 10.

Lesson	Skill
4-1	Graph Quadratic Functions
4-3	Identify Quadratic Functions
4-6	Complete the Square
4-1	Graph Quadratic Functions in Vertex Form
2-7	Graph Absolute Value Functions

To remediate students, select from these resources (available for every lesson).
- Online Problems (PowerAlgebra.com)
- Reteaching (All-in-One Teaching Resources)
- Practice (All-in-One Teaching Resources)

Why Students Need These Skills

GRAPHING QUADRATIC FUNCTIONS
Graphing quadratic functions is essential to graphing conic sections.

IDENTIFYING QUADRATIC FUNCTIONS
Students will extend their skills identifying quadratic functions to identifying functions of various conic sections.

COMPLETING THE SQUARE
Completing the square is essential to writing the equations of some conic sections in standard form.

GRAPHING QUADRATIC FUNCTIONS IN VERTEX FORM
Students will graph quadratic functions in vertex form when graphing parabolas.

GRAPHING ABSOLUTE VALUE FUNCTIONS
Students will extend graphing absolute value functions to graphing conic section functions.

Looking Ahead Vocabulary

RADIUS Ask students what is true about all of the radii in any circle.

VERTEX A parabola is neither made up of lines nor does it contain a corner. However, like the vertex of a square, the vertex of a parabola is the most protruding point.

Answers

Get Ready!

1.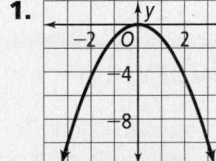

2.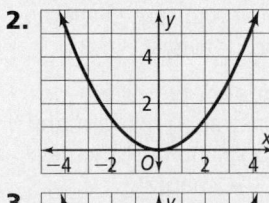

3.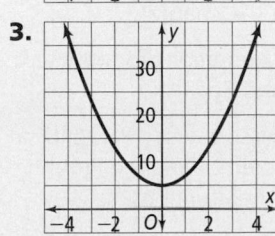

4.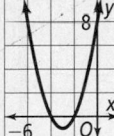

5. quadratic; $-x^2$, $6x$, 1

6. linear; none, $-12x$, -18

7. linear; none, x, $-\frac{13}{2}$

8. quadratic; $-8x^2$, $28x$, none

9. quadratic; $-2x^2$, $-3x$, 6

10. linear; none, $-x$, -10

11. 16   **12.** $\frac{25}{4}$ **13.** 49

14. $y = (x + 3)^2 - 2$

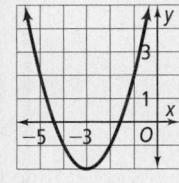

15–22. See back of book.

Chapter 10 Overview

UbD Understanding by Design

Chapter 10 expands on students' understandings and skills related to expressions, equations, and inequalities. In this chapter, students will develop the answers to the Essential Questions posed on the student page as they learn the concepts and skills bulleted below.

BIG idea Modeling

ESSENTIAL QUESTION What is the intersection of a cone and a plane parallel to a line along the side of a cone?

• Students will identify the possible conic sections formed depending on the angle of intersection of a cone and plane.

BIG idea Equivalence

ESSENTIAL QUESTION What is the graph of $\frac{x^2}{9} + \frac{y^2}{9} = 1$?

• Students will graph circles.
• Students will identify conic sections based on their equations.

BIG idea Coordinate Geometry

ESSENTIAL QUESTION What is the difference between the algebraic representations of ellipses and hyperbolas?

• Students will differentiate between ellipses and hyperbolas algebraically and graphically.

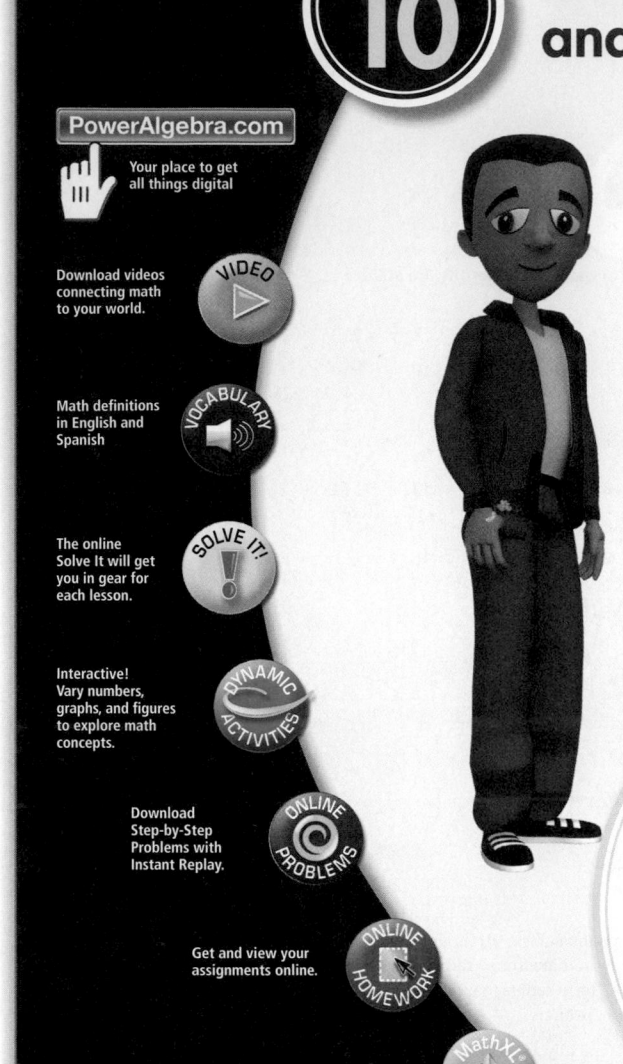

PowerAlgebra.com

Your place to get all things digital

Download videos connecting math to your world.

Math definitions in English and Spanish

The online Solve It will get you in gear for each lesson.

Interactive! Vary numbers, graphs, and figures to explore math concepts.

Download Step-by-Step Problems with Instant Replay.

Get and view your assignments online.

Extra practice and review online

In this chapter you will learn how to work with curves that you can trace along the surface of a cone. These curves are called <u>conic sections</u>.

People can manufacture these curves to make beautiful architecture, as shown on the next page.

Vocabulary

English/Spanish Vocabulary Audio Online:

English	Spanish
center of a circle, p. 649	centro de un círculo
circle, p. 649	círculo
conic section, p. 634	sección cónica
directrix, p. 641	directriz
ellipse, p. 658	elipse
hyperbola, p. 666	hipérbola
radius, p. 649	radio
standard form of an equation of a circle, p. 650	forma normal de la ecuación de un círculo

PowerAlgebra.com

Chapter 10 Overview

Use these online assets to engage your students. These include support for the Solve It and step-by-step solutions for Problems.

 Show the student-produced video demonstrating relevant and engaging applications of the new concepts in the chapter.

 Find online definitions for new terms in English and Spanish.

 Start each lesson with an attention-getting Problem. View the Problem online with helpful hints.

My Math Video

BIG ideas

1 **Modeling**
Essential Question What is the intersection of a cone and a plane parallel to a line along the side of the cone?

2 **Equivalence**
Essential Question What is the graph of $\frac{x^2}{9} + \frac{y^2}{9} = 1$?

3 **Coordinate Geometry**
Essential Question What is the difference between the algebraic representations of ellipses and hyperbolas?

Chapter Preview

PowerAlgebra.com Chapter 10 Quadratic Relations and Conic Sections 633

My Math Video

Use this photo to introduce students to the shapes of some conic sections. The photo depicts the Webb Bridge in Australia. It is a bridge for pedestrians and cyclists.

Q This bridge was designed to be symbolic of reconciliation with the area's indigenous history. How would you describe the resemblance to aboriginal eel traps, baskets, and the flow of the water? **[The curves recall the rounded shape of a netted trap or basket and the smooth flow of water.]**

Q How would you describe the curves depicted? Can you name any of them? **[From the photo shown, the curves resemble parabolas connected by straight segments. If they curved all the way around, they would be circles or ellipses.]**

EXTENSION

Have students research other cases where conic sections have been incorporated into architecture or structural engineering. Have them identify the shapes used, and if possible, the reasons behind choosing those shapes.

 Increase students' depth of knowledge with interactive online activities.

 Show problems from each lesson solved step by step. Instant replay allows students to go at their own pace when studying online.

 Prepare students for the Mid-Chapter Quiz and Chapter Test with online practice and review.

Math Background

Modeling

BIG idea Many real-world mathematical problems can be represented algebraically. These representations can lead to algebraic solutions. A function that models a real-world situation can then be used to make estimates or predictions about future occurrences.

ESSENTIAL UNDERSTANDINGS

10-2 Each point of a parabola is equidistant from a point called the focus and a line called the directix.

Equivalence

BIG idea A single quantity may be represented by many different expressions. The facts about a quantity may be expressed by many different equations (or inequalities).

ESSENTIAL UNDERSTANDINGS

10-3 An equation of a circle with center $(0, 0)$ and radius r in the coordinate plane is $x^2 + y^2 = r^2$.

Coordinate Geometry

BIG idea A coordinate system in a plane is formed by two perpendicular number lines, called the x- and y-axes, and the quadrants they form. The coordinate plane can be used to graph many functions and relations.

ESSENTIAL UNDERSTANDINGS

10-1 There are four types of curves known as conic sections: parabolas, circles, ellipses, and hyperbolas. Each curve has its own distinct shape and properties.

10-4 A circle is a set of points a fixed distance from one point. An ellipse "stretches" a circle and is the set of points that have a total fixed distance from two points.

10-5 The shape of a hyperbola is guided by asymptotes.

Parabolas and Circles

Parabolas

A parabola is formed when a plane intersects a cone parallel to a side of the cone.

Parabola With Vertex (h, k)

Equation: $y = \frac{1}{4c}(x - h)^2 + k$

focus: $(h, k + c)$

directrix: $y = k - c$

The parabola with the form $y = ax^2 + bx + c$ can be changed to an equation in vertex form by completing the square.

Example: What are the vertex, focus, and directrix of the parabola with equation $y = x^2 - 6x + 11$? Sketch the graph.

Step 1) Complete the square.

$$y = (x^2 - 6x + 9) + 11 - 9$$
$$y = (x - 3)^2 + 2$$

Step 2) Find the vertex, focus, and directrix.

Because $\frac{1}{4c} = 1$, $c = \frac{1}{4}$, so

vertex: $(3, 2)$

focus: $\left(3, 2\frac{1}{4}\right)$

directrix: $y = 1\frac{3}{4}$

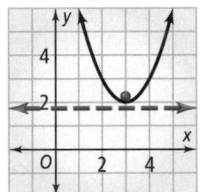

Circles

A circle is formed when a plane intersects a cone perpendicular to the axis of the cone.

Circle With Center (h, k)

Equation: $(x - h)^2 + (y - k)^2 = r^2$

center: (h, k)

radius: r

Example: What is the graph of $(x - 2)^2 + (y - 4)^2 = 9$?

• center: $(2, 4)$
• radius: 3

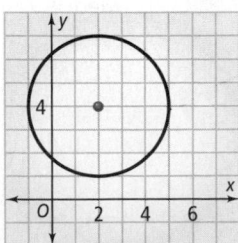

Common Errors With Parabolas and Circles

To help students avoid **errors when graphing parabolas**, have them verify the following: the parabola should open away from the directrix, and the vertex should be half the distance between the focus and the directrix.

Circle errors occur when students mistakenly use r^2 as the radius rather than r. Remind students that in the equation $x^2 + y^2 = 25$, the radius is 5.

Ellipses

An ellipse is formed when a plane intersects a cone making a closed curve, while not being perpendicular to its axis.

Ellipse With Center (0, 0)

Horizontal Ellipse

Equation: $\frac{x^2}{a^2} + \frac{y^2}{b^2} = 1, a > b > 0$

vertices: $(\pm a, 0)$

co-vertices: $(0, \pm b)$

foci: $(\pm c, 0)$ where $c^2 = a^2 - b^2$

Vertical Ellipse

Equation: $\frac{x^2}{b^2} + \frac{y^2}{a^2} = 1, a > b > 0$

vertices: $(0, \pm a)$

co-vertices: $(\pm b, 0)$

foci: $(0, \pm c)$ where $c^2 = a^2 - b^2$

Example: What are the vertices and foci of the ellipse with equation $9x^2 + 16y^2 = 144$? Sketch the graph.
- standard form: $\frac{x^2}{16} + \frac{y^2}{9} = 1$
- major axis is horizontal
- vertices: $(4, 0)$ and $(-4, 0)$
- co-vertices: $(0, 3)$ and $(0, -3)$
- foci: $(\sqrt{7}, 0)$ and $(-\sqrt{7}, 0)$

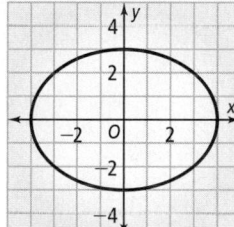

Horizontal Ellipse With Center (h, k)

Equation: $\frac{(x - h)^2}{a^2} + \frac{(y - k)^2}{b^2} = 1$

vertices: $(h \pm a, k)$

co-vertices: $(h, k \pm b)$

foci: $(h \pm c, k)$, where $c^2 = a^2 - b^2$

Example: What are vertices and foci of the ellipse with equation $\frac{(x - 3)^2}{16} + \frac{(y - 1)^2}{9} = 1$? Sketch the graph.
- $h = 3, k = 1, a = 4, b = 3$
- vertices: $(7, 1)$ and $(-1, 1)$
- co-vertices: $(3, 4)$ and $(3, -2)$
- foci: $(3 + \sqrt{7}, 1)$ and $(3 - \sqrt{7}, 1)$

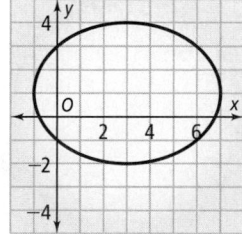

Common Errors With Ellipses

Students are often confused between the relationship for a, b, and c in an ellipse and the Pythagorean Theorem. Point out that c does not represent a hypotenuse as it is the distance between the center and the foci.

Hyperbolas

A hyperbola is formed when a plane intersects a cone parallel to the axis.

Horizontal Hyperbola With Center (0, 0)

Equation: $\frac{x^2}{a^2} - \frac{y^2}{b^2} = 1$

vertices: $(\pm a, 0)$

foci: $(\pm c, 0)$, where $c^2 = a^2 + b^2$

asymptotes: $y = \pm \frac{b}{a}x$

Example: What are the vertices, foci, and asymptotes of the hyperbola with equation $4x^2 - 9y^2 = 36$? Sketch the graph.
- standard form: $\frac{x^2}{9} - \frac{y^2}{4} = 1$
- vertices: $(3, 0)$ and $(-3, 0)$
- foci: $(\sqrt{13}, 0)$ and $(-\sqrt{13}, 0)$
- asymptotes: $y = \pm \frac{2}{3}x$
- use the central rectangle and asymptotes to graph.

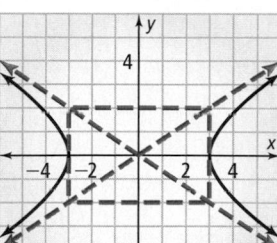

Vertical Hyperbola With Center (0, 0)

Equation: $\frac{y^2}{a^2} - \frac{x^2}{b^2} = 1$

vertices: $(0, \pm a)$

foci: $(0, \pm c)$, where $c^2 = a^2 + b^2$

asymptotes: $y = \pm \frac{a}{b}x$

Example: What are the vertices, foci, and asymptotes of the hyperbola with equation $9y^2 - 16x^2 = 144$? Sketch the graph.
- standard form: $\frac{y^2}{16} - \frac{x^2}{9} = 1$
- vertices: $(0, 4)$ and $(0, -4)$
- foci: $(0, 5)$ and $(0, -5)$
- asymptotes: $y = \pm \frac{4}{3}x$
- Use the central rectangle and asymptotes to graph.

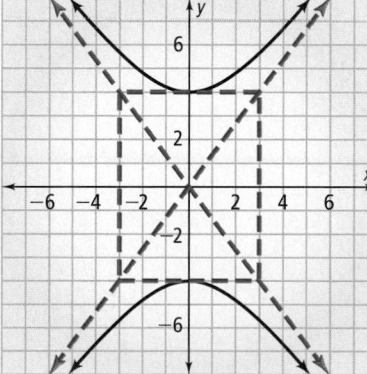

Common Errors With Hyperbolas

Because of similarities with an ellipse, hyperbola errors most often occur with **orienting the hyperbola** and **finding the foci**. Remind students that a hyperbola is horizontal if the x^2 term is positive, vertical if the y^2 term is positive, and the relationship between a, b, and c is $c^2 = a^2 + b^2$.

QUADRATIC RELATIONS AND CONIC SECTIONS
Pacing and Assignment Guide

		TRADITIONAL		BLOCK
Lesson	**Teaching Day(s)**	**Basic**	**Average**	**Block**
10-1	1	Problems 1–3 Exs. 7–19, 24, 26, 27, 33, 36, 38–50	Problems 1–3 Exs. 7–35 odd, 36, 38–50	**Day 1** Problems 1–3 Exs. 7–35 odd, 36, 38–50
10-2	1	Problems 1–3 Exs. 7–17, 38–47	Problems 1–5 Exs. 7–25 odd, 26, 27–35 odd, 38–47	Problems 1–5 Exs. 7–25 odd, 26, 27–35 odd, 38–47
	2	Problems 4–5 Exs. 18–23, 26, 27		
10-3	1	Problems 1–5 Exs. 7–10, 13–29, 37, 51–68	Problems 1–3 Exs. 7–49 odd, 51–68	**Day 2** Problems 1–5 Exs. 7–49 odd, 51–68
10-4	1	Problems 1–4 Exs. 7–18, 21–29, 34, 39, 48–61	Problems 1–4 Exs. 7–33 odd, 34–39, 41–47 odd, 48–61	Problems 1–4 Exs. 7–33 odd, 34–39, 41–47 odd, 48–61
10-5	1	Problems 1–3 Exs. 8–17, 20, 21, 30, 34, 34–46	Problems 1–3 Exs. 9–19 odd, 20–30, 34, 35–46	**Day 3** Problems 1–3 Exs. 9–19 odd, 20–30, 34, 35–46
Review	1	Chapter 10 Review	Chapter 10 Review	**Day 4** Chapter 10 Review Chapter 10 Test
Assess	1	Chapter 10 Test	Chapter 10 Test	
Total		**8 Days**	**7 Days**	**4 Days**

Note: Pacing does not include Concept Bytes and other feature pages.

Resources

	For the Chapter	10-1	10-2	10-3	10-4	10-5
Planning						
Teacher Center Online Planner & Grade Book	I	I	I	I	I	I
Interactive Learning & Guided Instruction						
My Math Video	I					
Solve It!		I TM	I TM	I TM	I TM	I TM
Student Companion (SP)*		P M	P M	P M	P M	P M
Vocabulary Support		I P M	I P M	I P M	I P M	I P M
Got It? Support		I P	I P	I P	I P	I P
Dynamic Activity		I	I	I	I	
Online Problems		I	I	I	I	I
Additional Problems		M	M	M	M	M
English Language Learner Support (TR)		E P M	E P M	E P M	E P M	E P M
Activities, Games, and Puzzles		E M	E M	E M	E M	E M
Teaching With TI Technology With CD-ROM						
TI-Nspire™ Support CD-ROM		✓	✓	✓	✓	✓
Lesson Check & Practice						
Student Companion (SP)*		P M	P M	P M	P M	P M
Lesson Check Support		I P	I P	I P	I P	I P
Think About a Plan (TR)*		E P M	E P M	E P M	E P M	E P M
Practice Form K (TR)*		E P M	E P M	E P M	E P M	E P M
Standardized Test Prep (TR)*		P M	P M	P M	P M	P M
Practice *Form G* (TR)*		E P M	E P M	E P M	E P M	E P M
Extra Practice	E M					
Find the Errors!	M					
Enrichment (TR)		E P M	E P M	E P M	E P M	E P M
Answers and Solutions CD-ROM	✓	✓	✓	✓	✓	✓
Assess & Remediate						
ExamView CD-ROM	✓	✓	✓	✓	✓	✓
Lesson Quiz		I TM	I TM	I TM	I TM	I TM
Quizzes and Tests *Form K* (TR)*	E P M			E P M		E P M
Quizzes and Tests *Form G* (TR)*	E P M			E P M		E P M
Reteaching (TR)		E P M	E P M	E P M	E P M	E P M
Performance Tasks (TR)*	P M					
Cumulative Review (TR)*	P M					
Progress Monitoring Assessments	I P M					

(TR) Available in All-In-One Teaching Resources   * Spanish available

1 Interactive Learning

Solve It!

PURPOSE To visualize the intersection of a plane and a cone

PROCESS Students may
- use a foam cup or paper model and scissors to determine the shapes formed.
- list possible shapes and use visualization to determine if any of the shapes can be formed.

FACILITATE

Q What is a planar cut? Give an example. **[slicing something with a plane; for example, using a large flat knife to cut a block of cheese]**

Q What shapes do the ends of the foam cup form? **[They both form circles.]**

Q Is it possible to get a line segment using a plane and the foam cup? Explain. **[Samples: Yes, theoretically, a plane tangent to the cone will form a line. No, lines have no width, so it is impossible to actually get a line segment using a foam cup.]**

Q Is it possible to create a polygon using a plane and a cone? Explain. **[No; a polygon is a closed figure made of a finite number of line segments. Because the cone is curved, it is not possible to get a polygon.]**

ANSWER See Solve It in Answers on next page.

CONNECT THE MATH In the Solve It, students visualize the intersection of a plane and cone. These shapes are conic sections, which students will identify and graph in this lesson.

10-1 Exploring Conic Sections

Objective To graph and identify conic sections

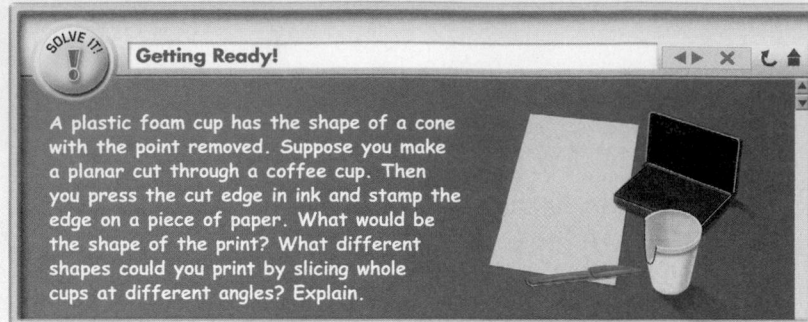

Getting Ready!

A plastic foam cup has the shape of a cone with the point removed. Suppose you make a planar cut through a coffee cup. Then you press the cut edge in ink and stamp the edge on a piece of paper. What would be the shape of the print? What different shapes could you print by slicing whole cups at different angles? Explain.

In Chapter 4, you studied parabolas. Geometrically, a parabola has the shape of a cross section of a cone that you cut in a particular way. Parabolas form a family of curves that belong to a larger family known as *conic sections*.

Focus Question What is a conic section?

Lesson Vocabulary
• conic section

Key Concept Conic Sections

A **conic section** is a curve you get by intersecting a plane and a double cone. By changing the inclination of the plane, you can get a circle, a parabola, an ellipse, or a hyperbola.

Hint

Cone comes from the Indo-European word for "sharpen." *Section* comes from the word for "cut."

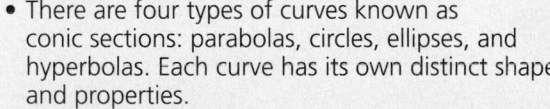

10-1 Preparing to Teach

BIG idea Coordinate Geometry   **UbD**

ESSENTIAL UNDERSTANDINGS
- There are four types of curves known as conic sections: parabolas, circles, ellipses, and hyperbolas. Each curve has its own distinct shape and properties.
- A conic section is a curve obtained by intersecting a plane and a double cone.

Math Background

Although students may be familiar with parabolas, ellipses, circles, and hyperbolas, this lesson reintroduces these shapes as *conic sections*. Conic sections are shapes formed by the intersection of a plane and a double cone. The angle at which the plane intersects the cone determines the shape.

In a coordinate plane, the graph of a quadratic equation in two variables is always a conic section. The signs of the equations and the coefficients of the variable terms determine the shape.

Future lessons go into greater detail for each conic section. This lesson focuses on using a table of values to graph each conic section in the coordinate plane. From there it is possible to identify lines of symmetry, the center of the figure, domain and range, and the *x*- and *y*-intercepts.

Support Student Learning

Use the **Algebra 2 Companion** to engage and support students during instruction. See Lesson Resources at the end of this lesson for details.

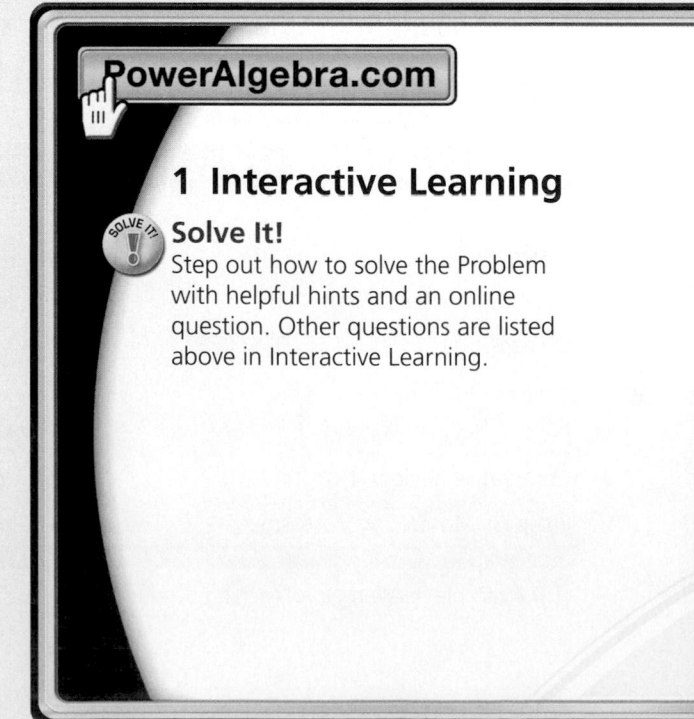

PowerAlgebra.com

1 Interactive Learning

Solve It!

Step out how to solve the Problem with helpful hints and an online question. Other questions are listed above in Interactive Learning.

You can use lines of symmetry to graph a conic section.

 **Problem 1** Graphing a Circle

What is the graph of $x^2 + y^2 = 25$? What are its lines of symmetry? What are the domain and range?

Know	Need	Plan
An equation	The lines of symmetry of the graph, the domain and range of the relation	• Plot points and connect them with a smooth curve. • Look for lines of symmetry on the graph. • Determine the domain and range.

Think

Can you find values of x and y that satisfy the equation? Yes; find the x- and y-intercepts. Then look for other values of x and y that make the calculations easy.

Make a table of values. Plot the points and connect them with a smooth curve.

x	y
-5	0
-4	± 3
-3	± 4
0	± 5
3	± 4
4	± 3
5	0

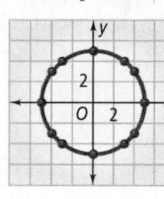

The graph is a circle with radius 5. Its center is the origin.
Every line through the center is a line of symmetry.

The domain is the set of real numbers x with $-5 \le x \le 5$.
The range is the set of real numbers y with $-5 \le y \le 5$.

 Got It? 1. a. What is the graph of $x^2 + y^2 = 9$? What are its lines of symmetry? What are the domain and range?
   b. **Reasoning** In Problem 1, why is there no point on the graph with x-coordinate 6?

2 Guided Instruction

Problem 1

Q Can you solve for y to help find values? Explain. **[Yes; solve the equation for y, and then substitute values of x to determine y.]**

Q What is the definition of line of symmetry? How can you check that a line of symmetry is correct? **[A line of symmetry divides an object into 2 congruent parts. To check, fold the graph along the line of symmetry and verify that all parts match.]**

Got It?

Q Can you use algebra to check that your domain is correct in 1a? Explain. **[Sample: Yes; solve the equation for y to get $y = \pm\sqrt{9 - x^2}$. The radicand cannot be negative, so $-3 \le x \le 3$.]**

---

2 Guided Instruction

 Each Problem is worked out and supported online.

Problem 1
Graphing a Circle
                        Animated

Problem 2
Graphing an Ellipse
                        Animated

Problem 3
Graphing a Hyperbola
                        Animated

Alternative Problem 4
Identifying Graphs of Conic Sections

Alternative Problem 5
Using Models

Support in Algebra 2 Companion
• Vocabulary
• Key Concepts
• Got It?

Answers

Solve It!
If you cut the cup in a plane parallel to the base of the cup, you will get a circle; if the plane is not quite parallel to the base of the cup, you will get an ellipse; if you tilt the plane a little bit more, so that it is parallel to one of the sides of the cup, you will get a parabola; if you tilt the plane even further, so that it is perpendicular to the base of the cup, you will get one branch of a hyperbola.

Got It?
1. a. The graph is a circle with center $(0, 0)$ and radius 3. lines of sym.: every line through the origin; domain: $-3 \le x \le 3$, range: $-3 \le y \le 3$

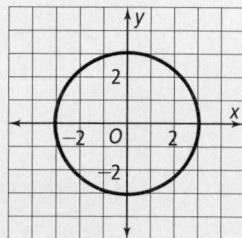

b. 6 is outside the domain of x.

Lesson 10-1   635

Problem 2

Q How are the domain and range related to the x- and y-intercepts? **[The greatest and least values of the domain are the x-intercepts. The greatest and least values of the range are the y-intercepts.]**

Q Are the points in the table exact values? Explain. **[The x- and y-intercepts are exact values. For**

$$x = \pm 3, \ y = \pm\sqrt{\frac{144 - 9(\pm 3)^2}{16}} \approx \pm 1.9843, \text{ so}$$

the y-values ± 2.0 are approximations.]

Got It?

Q What values should you substitute for x? How did you choose these values? **[Answers may vary. Sample: $-3, -2, -1, 0, 1, 2,$ and 3; I needed to choose both positive and negative numbers.]**

Its many lines of symmetry make a circle a special kind of an *ellipse*. In general, an ellipse has only two lines of symmetry.

Problem 2 Graphing an Ellipse

What is the graph of $9x^2 + 16y^2 = 144$? What are its lines of symmetry? What are the domain and range?

Think
What values should you substitute for x? Substitute both positive and negative values for x.

Step 1 Make a table of values. Plot the points and connect them with a smooth curve.

x	y
-4	0
-3	± 2
0	± 3
3	± 2
4	0

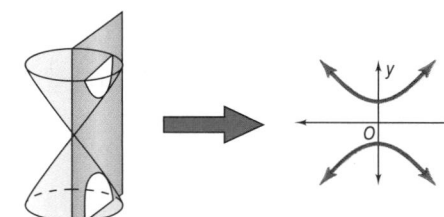

Step 2 Identify lines of symmetry.

The graph is an ellipse. The center is the origin.
The ellipse has two lines of symmetry: the x-axis and the y-axis.

Step 3 Identify the domain and range.

The domain is the set of real numbers x with $-4 \le x \le 4$.
The range is the set of real numbers y with $-3 \le y \le 3$.

Got It? 2. What is the graph of $2x^2 + y^2 = 18$? What are its lines of symmetry? What are the domain and range?

You are probably familiar with the conic sections explored in Problems 1 and 2, the circle and the ellipse. You should also recall the parabola from your work with quadratic functions in Chapter 4. You probably have not encountered the last conic section, the hyperbola. It is unique because it consists of two separate curves called branches.

Hint
You will learn more about hyperbolas in Lesson 10-5.

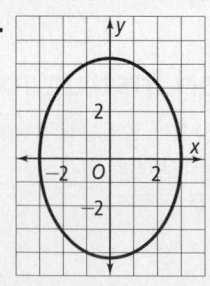

Additional Problems

1. What is the graph of $x^2 + y^2 = 16$? What are its lines of symmetry? What are the domain and range?

ANSWER Every line through the center is a line of symmetry. Domain: the set of real numbers with $-4 \le x \le 4$ Range: the set of real numbers with $-4 \le y \le 4$

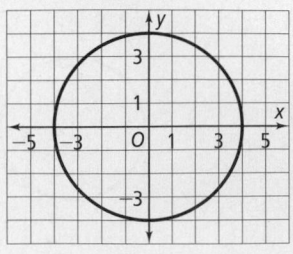

2. What is the graph of $27x^2 + 3y^2 = 27$? What are its lines of symmetry? What are the domain and range?

ANSWER Lines of symmetry: x- and y-axes Domain: the set of real numbers with $-1 \le x \le 1$ Range: the set of real numbers with $-3 \le y \le 3$

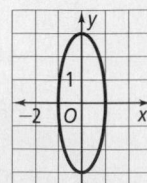

3. What is the graph of $y^2 - x^2 = 36$? What are its lines of symmetry? What are the domain and range?

ANSWER Lines of symmetry: x- and y-axis. Domain: all real numbers Range: the set of real numbers with $y \le -6$ or $y \ge 6$

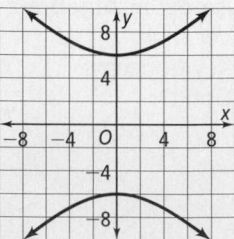

Answers

Got It? (continued)

2.

lines of sym.: x-axis and y-axis; domain: $-3 \le x \le 3$, range: $-3\sqrt{2} \le y \le 3\sqrt{2}$

Problem 3 Graphing a Hyperbola

What is the graph of $x^2 - y^2 = 9$? What are its lines of symmetry? What are the domain and range?

Make a table of values.

x	−5	−4	−3	−2	−1	0	1	2	3	4	5
y	±4	±2.6	0	—	—	—	—	—	0	±2.6	±4

Think

How will you know which points to connect?
Plot enough points so you see a pattern. Only connect points if you know that the points between them satisfy the equation.

Plot the points and connect them with smooth curves.

The graph is a hyperbola that consists of two branches. Its center is the origin. It has two lines of symmetry: the x-axis and the y-axis.

The domain is the set of real numbers x with $x \le -3$ or $x \ge 3$.
The range is the set of real numbers.

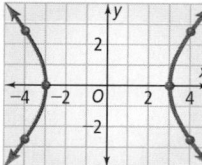

 Got It? 3. What is the graph of $x^2 - y^2 = 16$? What are its lines of symmetry? What are the domain and range?

Focus Question What is a conic section?
Answer A conic section is a curve that is formed by the intersection of a plane and a double cone. The four types of conic sections are circles, parabolas, ellipses, and hyperbolas.

 Lesson Check

Do you know HOW?

Graph each equation. Find the lines of symmetry, the domain, and the range.

1. $x^2 + 4y^2 = 36$ **2.** $4x^2 - 9y^2 = 36$

Identify the domain and range.

3. 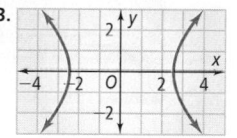   **4.**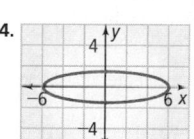

Do you UNDERSTAND?

5. Vocabulary Identify the type of conic section graphed.

a. 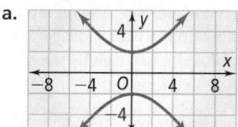   **b.**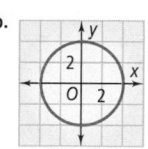

6. Compare and Contrast How is the domain of an ellipse different from the domain of a hyperbola?

Problem 3

Q The equations of circles and ellipses contain a sum of variables, while the equation of a hyperbola contains a difference. What figure would be represented by the equation if it were changed to a sum? How do the domain and range change? **[The equation would represent a circle whose domain is the set of real numbers $-3 \le x \le 3$ and whose range is the set of real numbers $-3 \le y \le 3$.]**

Q How are the domain and range of a hyperbola different from that of an ellipse? **[Depending on the orientation of the hyperbola, either the domain or range is the set of all real numbers. The domain and range of an ellipse are bounded.]**

Got It?   VISUAL LEARNERS
When students make the table of values by solving for a variable, they sometimes forget to take the negatives into account. Solving for y yields the equation $y = \pm\sqrt{x^2 - 16}$.

3 Lesson Check

Do you know HOW?   ERROR INTERVENTION
• If students have difficulty solving Exercises 1 and 2, have them make a list of the characteristics of the conic sections and their equations.

Do you UNDERSTAND?
• If students have trouble comparing domains, graph an ellipse and a hyperbola as a class.

Close

Q What two conic sections are formed when a plane intersects a cone? Explain how each is formed. **[Sample: Circle: the plane is perpendicular to the axis of the cone. Hyperbola: the plane is parallel to the axis.]**

Got It? (continued)

3.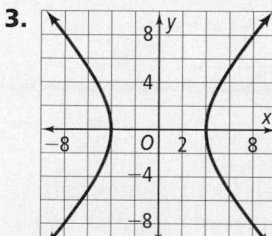

The graph is a hyperbola with center (0, 0). lines of sym.: x-axis and y-axis; domain: $x \le -4$ or $x \ge 4$, range: all real numbers

Lesson Check

1.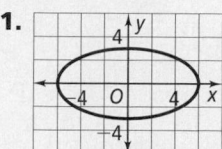

lines of sym.: x-axis and y-axis; domain: $-6 \le x \le 6$, range: $-3 \le y \le 3$

2.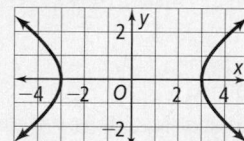

lines of sym.: x-axis and y-axis; domain: $x \le -3$ or $x \ge 3$, range: all real numbers

3. domain: $x \le -2.5$ or $x \ge 2.5$, range: all real numbers

4. domain: $-6 \le x \le 6$, range: $-1.5 \le y \le 1.5$

5. a. hyperbola
   b. circle

6. Answers may vary. Sample: The domain of an ellipse is an interval of two real numbers, such as $-a \le x \le a$. The domain of a hyperbola is two intervals, such as $x \le -a$ or $x \ge a$, if there are x-intercepts, or all real numbers if there are no x-intercepts.

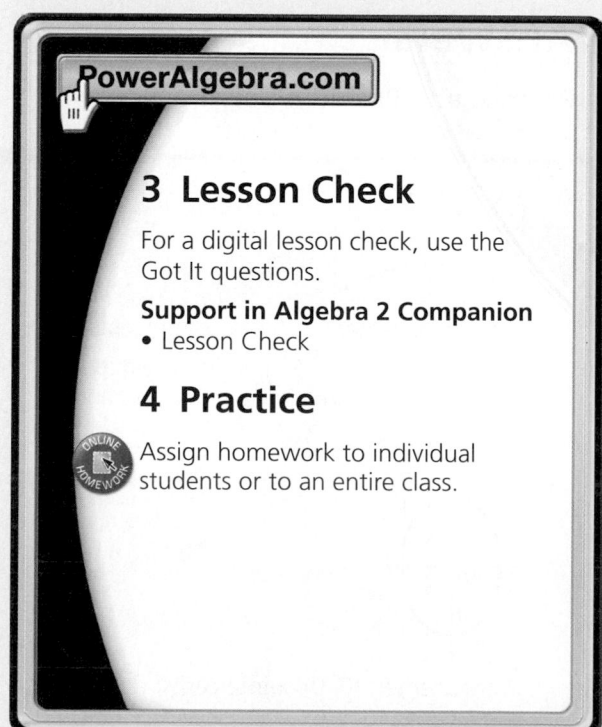

PowerAlgebra.com

3 Lesson Check

For a digital lesson check, use the Got It questions.

Support in Algebra 2 Companion
• Lesson Check

4 Practice

Assign homework to individual students or to an entire class.

4 Practice

ASSIGNMENT GUIDE

Basic: 7–19, 24, 26, 27, 33, 36

Average: 7–35 odd, 36

Standardized Test Prep: 38–41

Mixed Review: 42–50

Reasoning exercises have blue headings.

Applications exercises have red headings.

EXERCISE 36: Use the Think About a Plan worksheet in the Student Companion (also available in the Teaching Resources in print and online) to further support students' development in becoming independent learners.

HOMEWORK QUICK CHECK

To check students' understanding of key skills and concepts, go over Exercises 9, 11, 24, 33, and 36.

Practice and Problem-Solving Exercises

 **Practice**   Graph each equation. Identify the conic section and describe the graph and its lines of symmetry. Then find the domain and range.   ◀ See Problems 1, 2, and 3.

 Guided Practice

7. $3y^2 - x^2 = 25$

To start, make a table of values.

x	y
−3	±3.37
−2	±3.11
−1	±2.94
0	±2.89
1	±2.94
2	±3.11
3	±3.37

8. $2x^2 + y^2 = 36$

9. $x^2 + y^2 = 16$

10. $3y^2 - x^2 = 9$

11. $4x^2 + 25y^2 = 100$

12. $x^2 + y^2 = 49$

13. $x^2 - y^2 + 1 = 0$

14. $x^2 - 2y^2 = 4$

15. $6x^2 + 6y^2 = 600$

16. $x^2 + y^2 - 4 = 0$

17. $6x^2 + 24y^2 - 96 = 0$

18. $4x^2 + 4y^2 - 20 = 0$

19. $x^2 + 9y^2 = 1$

Ⓑ Apply   Graph each equation. Describe the graph and its lines of symmetry. Then find the domain and range.

20. $9x^2 - y^2 = 144$

21. $11x^2 + 11y^2 = 44$

22. $-8x^2 + 32y^2 - 128 = 0$

23. $25x^2 + 16y^2 - 320 = 0$

24. Think About a Plan The light emitted from a lamp with a shade forms a shadow on the wall. How can you turn the lamp in relation to the wall so that the shadow cast by the shade forms a parabola and a circle?
- How can a drawing or model help you solve this problem?
- Can you form a hyperbola and an ellipse? If so, explain how.

25. a. Writing Describe the relationship between the center of a circle and the axes of symmetry of the circle.
   b. Make a Conjecture Where is the center of an ellipse or a hyperbola located in relation to the axes of symmetry? Verify your conjecture with examples.

Graph each circle with the given radius or diameter so that the center is at the origin. Then write the equation for each graph.

26. radius 6

27. radius $\frac{1}{2}$

28. diameter 8

29. diameter 2.5

Answers

Practice and Problem-Solving Exercises

7.

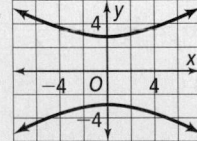

hyperbola; center: (0, 0); no x-intercepts, y-intercepts: $\left(0, \pm\frac{5\sqrt{3}}{3}\right)$; lines of sym.: x-axis and y-axis; domain: all real numbers, range: $y \leq -\frac{5\sqrt{3}}{3}$ or $y \geq \frac{5\sqrt{3}}{3}$

8.

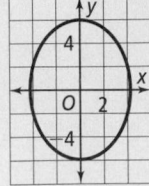

ellipse; center: (0, 0); x-intercepts: $(\pm 3\sqrt{2}, 0)$, y-intercepts: $(0, \pm 6)$; lines of sym.: x-axis and

y-axis; domain: $-3\sqrt{2} \leq x \leq 3\sqrt{2}$, range: $-6 \leq y \leq 6$

9.

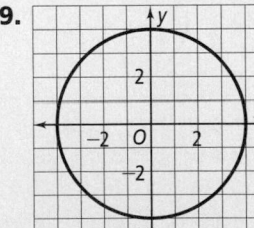

circle; center: (0, 0); radius: 4; x-intercepts: $(\pm 4, 0)$, y-intercepts: $(0, \pm 4)$; infinitely many lines of sym.; domain: $-4 \leq x \leq 4$, range: $-4 \leq y \leq 4$

10.

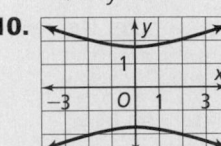

hyperbola; center: (0, 0); no x-intercepts, y-intercepts: $(0, \pm\sqrt{3})$; lines of sym.: x-axis and y-axis;

domain: all real numbers, range: $y \leq -\sqrt{3}$ or $y \geq \sqrt{3}$

11.

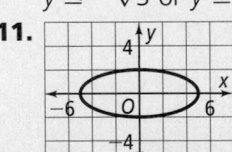

ellipse; center: (0, 0); x-intercepts: $(\pm 5, 0)$, y-intercepts: $(0, \pm 2)$; lines of sym.: x-axis and y-axis; domain: $-5 \leq x \leq 5$, range: $-2 \leq y \leq 2$

12.

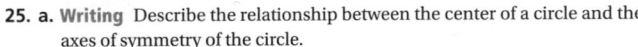

circle; center: (0, 0); radius: 7; x-intercepts: $(\pm 7, 0)$, y-intercepts: $(0, \pm 7)$; infinitely many lines of sym.; domain: $-7 \leq x \leq 7$, range: $-7 \leq y \leq 7$

13–29. See back of book.

Mental Math Each given point is on the graph of the given equation. Use symmetry to find at least one more point on the graph.

30. $(2, -4), y^2 = 8x$

31. $(-\sqrt{2}, 1), x^2 + y^2 = 3$

32. $(2, 2\sqrt{2}), x^2 + 4y^2 = 36$

33. $(-2, 0), 9x^2 + 9y^2 - 36 = 0$

34. $(-3, -\sqrt{51}), 6y^2 - 9x^2 - 225 = 0$

35. $(0, \sqrt{7}), x^2 + 2y^2 = 14$

36. Sound An airplane flying faster than the speed of sound creates a cone-shaped pressure disturbance in the air. This is heard by people on the ground as a sonic boom. What is the shape of the path on the ground?

37. Open-Ended Describe any other figures you can see that can be formed by the intersection of a plane and another shape, such as a sphere.

50.

x	-3	-2	-1	0	1
y	-2	-3	-4	-3	-2

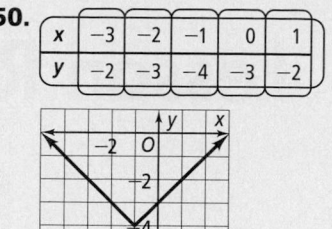

Standardized Test Prep

38. Which expression can be simplified to $\frac{x-1}{x-3}$?

Ⓐ $\frac{x^2 - x - 6}{x^2 - x - 2}$
Ⓑ $\frac{x^2 - 2x + 1}{x^2 + 2x - 3}$
Ⓒ $\frac{x^2 - 3x - 4}{x^2 - 7x + 12}$
Ⓓ $\frac{x^2 - 4x + 3}{x^2 - 6x + 9}$

39. Which product is NOT equal to 13?

Ⓕ $(4 + \sqrt{3})(4 - \sqrt{3})$
Ⓗ $(6 + \sqrt{23})(6 - \sqrt{23})$
Ⓖ $(5 - 2\sqrt{3})(5 + 2\sqrt{3})$
Ⓘ $(7 - \sqrt{6})(7 + \sqrt{6})$

40. Which function represents exponential growth?

Ⓐ $y = 35x^{1.35}$
Ⓑ $y = 35 \cdot (0.35)^x$
Ⓒ $y = 35 \cdot (1.35)^x$
Ⓓ $y = 35 \div (1.35)^x$

41. What is an explicit formula for the sequence $4, 9, 16, 25, 36, \ldots$? What is the ninth term in this sequence?

Mixed Review

Determine whether each geometric series *diverges* or *converges*. If the series converges, state the sum.
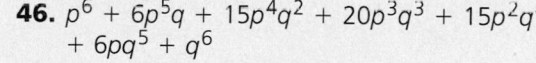 See Lesson 9-5.

42. $1 + 3 + 9 + \cdots$
43. $1 + \frac{4}{3} + \frac{16}{9} + \cdots$
44. $\frac{1}{2} + \frac{1}{4} + \frac{1}{8} + \cdots$

Expand each binomial. See Lesson 5-7.

45. $(x - y)^3$
46. $(p + q)^6$
47. $(x - 2)^4$

Get Ready! To prepare for Lesson 10-2, do Exercises 48–50.

Make a table of values for each equation. Then graph the equation. See Lesson 2-7.

48. $y = |x| + 3$
49. $y = |x - 2|$
50. $y = |x + 1| - 4$

30. $(2, 4)$
31. $(\sqrt{2}, 1)$
32. $(-2, 2\sqrt{2})$
33. $(2, 0)$
34. $(3, \sqrt{51})$
35. $(0, -\sqrt{7})$
36. one branch of a hyperbola
37. Check students' work.

46. $p^6 + 6p^5q + 15p^4q^2 + 20p^3q^3 + 15p^2q^4 + 6pq^5 + q^6$

47. $x^4 - 8x^3 + 24x^2 - 32x + 16$

48.

x	-2	-1	0	1	2
y	5	4	3	4	5

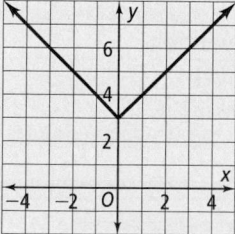

49.

x	0	1	2	3	4
y	2	1	0	1	2

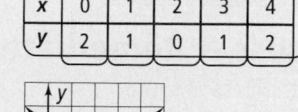

Standardized Test Prep

38. D
39. I
40. C
41. [2] $a_n = (n + 1)^2; a_9 = (9 + 1)^2 = 100$
[1] correct explicit formula, incorrect ninth term

Mixed Review

42. diverges
43. diverges
44. converges
45. $x^3 - 3x^2y + 3xy^2 - y^3$

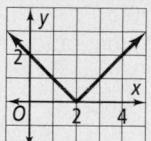

Additional Instructional Support

Algebra 2 Companion

Students can use the **Algebra 2 Companion** worktext (4 pages) as you teach the lesson. Use the Companion to support

- New Vocabulary
- Key Concepts
- Got It for each Problem
- Lesson Check

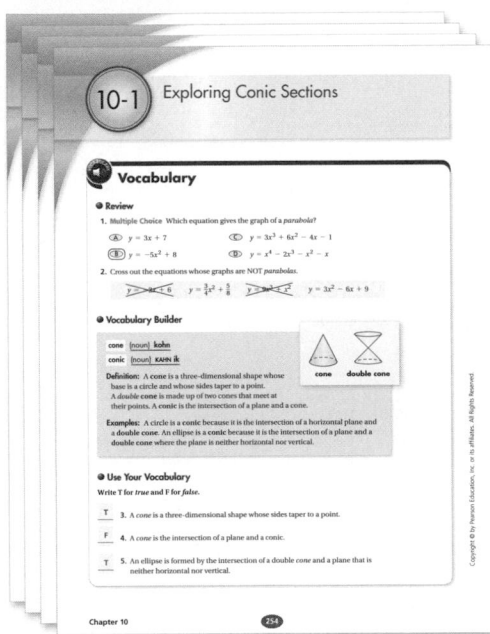

ELL Support

Focus on Language Have students write the words *ellipse*, *circle*, *parabola*, and *hyperbola* on index cards. On the back of each card tell students to draw a representation of each figure in a coordinate plane. If possible, have students write the equation of the figure. Allow students to page through the lesson so they may use equations and graphs from the examples and practice problems if needed. Next, put students in pairs and have one student place his or her cards on the desk with the graphs showing. The other student must take his or her own cards showing only the name of the figure and place them on top of the appropriate shapes. Tell students to state each conic section as they point to the name and the graph. Have students switch partners so they can practice identifying and saying each conic section with several different graphs.

5 Assess & Remediate

Lesson Quiz

1. What is the graph of $25x^2 + 4y^2 = 100$? What are its lines of symmetry? What are the domain and range?

2. Name the conic section in question 1. What are the center and intercepts?

3. **Do you UNDERSTAND?** Of the three equations listed, which equation might be a model for each situation?
$x^2 + y^2 = 81$; $10x^2 + y^2 = 100$; $x^2 - y^2 = 4$

   a. the path of the Earth around the Sun
   b. the circumference of a dinner plate
   c. a conic section consisting of two smooth curves intersecting the x-axis

ANSWERS TO LESSON QUIZ

1. Lines of symmetry: x- and y-axes; domain: the set of real numbers with $-2 \leq x \leq 2$; range: the set of real numbers with $-5 \leq y \leq 5$

2. ellipse; center: $(0, 0)$; x-intercepts: $(-2, 0)$, $(2, 0)$; y-intercepts: $(0, -5)$, $(0, 5)$

3. **a.** ellipse; $10x^2 + y^2 = 100$.
   b. circle; $x^2 + y^2 = 81$
   c. hyperbola; $x^2 - y^2 = 4$

PRESCRIPTION FOR REMEDIATION

Use the student work on the Lesson Quiz to prescribe a differentiated review assignment:

Points	Differentiated Remediation
0–1	Intervention
2	On-level
3	Extension

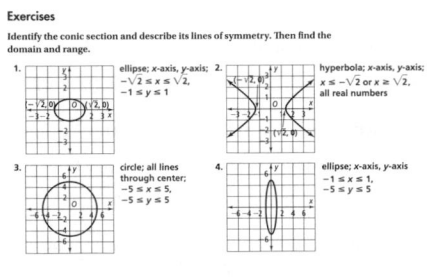

5 Assess & Remediate

Assign the Lesson Quiz. Appropriate intervention, practice, or enrichment is automatically generated based on student performance.

Intervention

- **Reteaching** (2 pages) Provides reteaching and practice exercises for the key lesson concepts. Use with struggling students or absent students.

- **English Language Learner Support** Helps students develop and reinforce mathematical vocabulary and key concepts.

All-in-One Resources/Online
Reteaching

All-in-One Resources/Online
English Language Learner Support

Differentiated Remediation *continued*

On-Level

- **Practice** (2 pages) Provides extra practice for each lesson. For more challenging practice exercises, use the Form G Practice pages found in the All-in-One Teaching Resources and online.

- **Think About a Plan** Helps students develop specific problem-solving skills and strategies by providing scaffolded guiding questions.

- **Standardized Test Prep** Focuses on all major exercises, all major question types, and helps students prepare for the high-stakes assessments.

Extension

- **Enrichment** Provides students with interesting problems and activities that extend the concepts of the lesson.

- **Activities, Games, and Puzzles** Worksheets that can be used for concepts development, enrichment, and for fun!

Student Companion/ All-in-One Resources/Online
Practice page 1

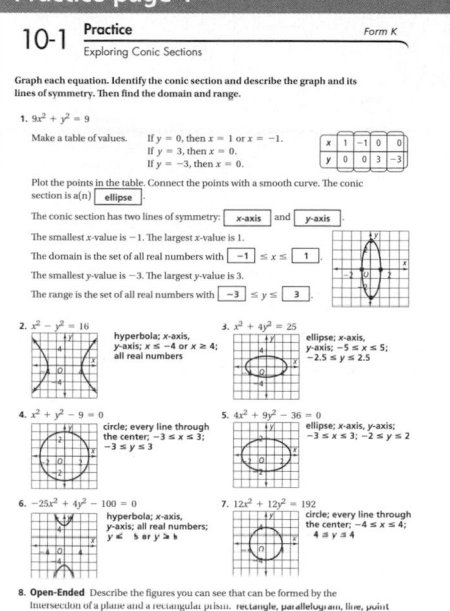

Student Companion/ All-in-One Resources/Online
Practice page 2

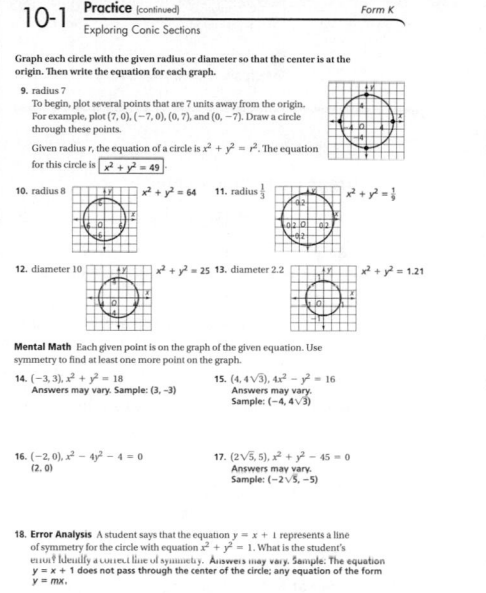

All-in-One Resources/Online
Enrichment

Student Companion/ All-in-One Resources/Online
Think About a Plan

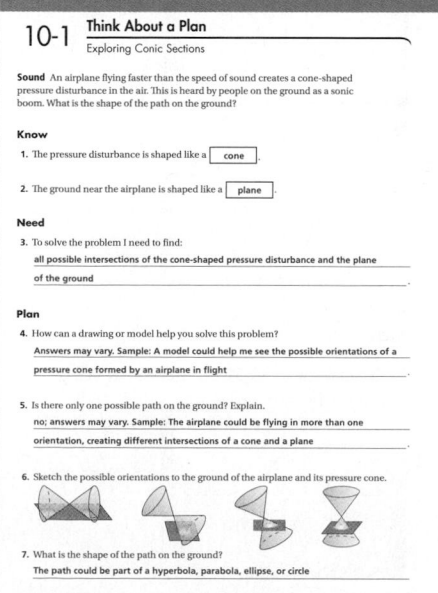

Student Companion/ All-in-One Resources/Online
Standardized Test Prep

Online Teacher Resource Center
Activities, Games, and Puzzles

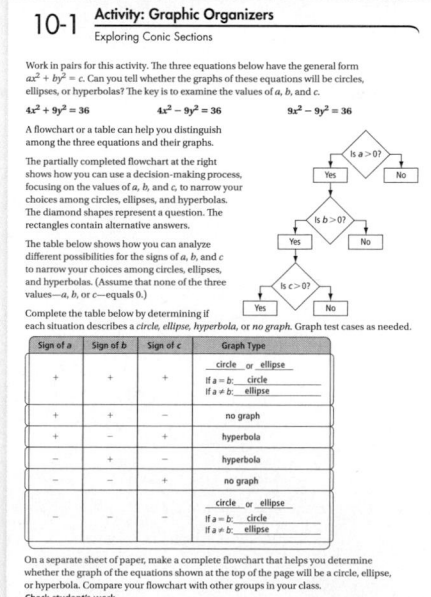

Guided Instruction

PURPOSE To graph conic sections with a graphing calculator

PROCESS Students will
- solve equations for y.
- find the square roots of polynomials.
- find appropriate windows for viewing the conic sections.

DISCUSS Because a graphing calculator allows you to input only an equation solved for y, it can only graph functions. By separating equations for conic sections into two parts, it is possible to graph conic sections. Elicit that
- graphing two functions can result in a figure that looks like a conic section.
- gaps can appear in the graph of a conic section on a graphing calculator due to rounding.

Example

Q What information is in the table in the graphing calculator but not in the graph? **[The trace key can find the y-intercepts, but there are gaps for the x-intercepts in the graph. The table gives values for both.]**

Q Is it possible to write the equation of the ellipse without fractions? Explain. **[Yes; multiplying the entire equation by 144 yields $9x^2 + 16y^2 = 144$.]**

Q What happens when the equations in the calculator are changed to $y = \pm\sqrt{1 + \frac{x^2}{16}}$?
Explain. **[The conic section is a hyperbola. The x term is negative on the left side of the equation.]**

Concept Byte
For Use With Lesson 10-1
TECHNOLOGY

Graphing Conic Sections

You can use your graphing calculator to graph relations that are not functions.

Example

Graph the ellipse $\frac{x^2}{16} + \frac{y^2}{9} = 1$.

Step 1 Solve the equation for y.

$$\frac{x^2}{16} + \frac{y^2}{9} = 1$$

$$\frac{y^2}{9} = 1 - \frac{x^2}{16}$$

$$y^2 = 9\left(1 - \frac{x^2}{16}\right)$$

$$y = \pm 3\sqrt{1 - \frac{x^2}{16}}$$

Step 2 Enter the equations as Y_1 and Y_2.

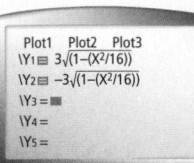

Step 3 Select a square window.

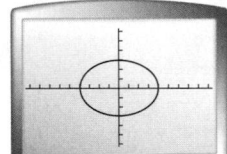

Step 4 Graph.

Exercises

Graph each conic section.

1. $x^2 + y^2 = 25$
2. $4x^2 + y^2 = 16$
3. $9x^2 - 16y^2 = 144$
4. $x^2 - y^2 = 3$
5. $\frac{x^2}{4} - \frac{y^2}{9} = 1$
6. $x^2 + \frac{y^2}{4} = 16$

7. **a.** Graph $y = \sqrt{\frac{81}{4} - x^2}$ and $y = -\sqrt{\frac{81}{4} - x^2}$.
   b. Estimate the x-intercepts and find the y-intercepts.
   c. Adjust the window to $-9.3 \le x \le 9.5$. What are the x-intercepts?
   d. What conic section does the graph represent?

Graph each conic section. Find the x- and y-intercepts.

8. $4x^2 + y^2 = 25$
9. $x^2 + y^2 = 30$
10. $9x^2 - 4y^2 = 72$

11. **Reasoning** Which conic sections can you graph using only one equation? Explain.

Answers

Exercises

1.

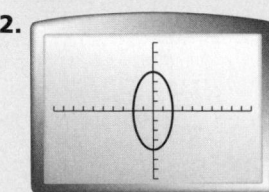

2.

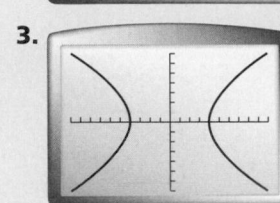

3.

4.

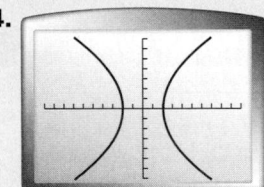

5.

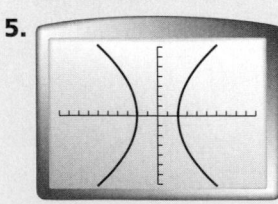

6. (x and y-scales set to two units)

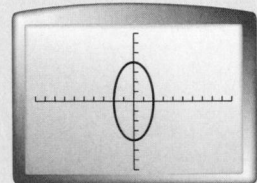

7–11. See back of book.

10-2 Parabolas

Objective To write the equation of a parabola and to graph parabolas

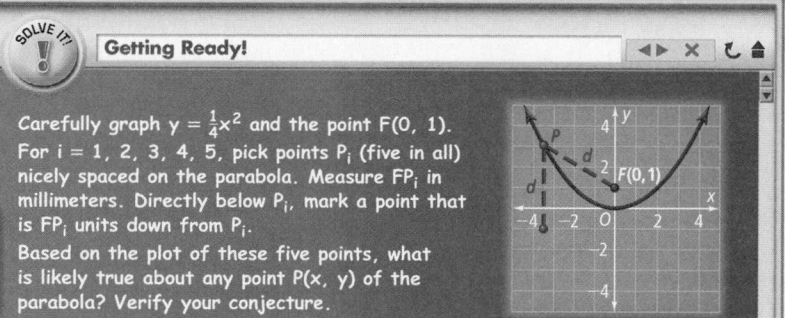

SOLVE IT!

Getting Ready!

Carefully graph $y = \frac{1}{4}x^2$ and the point $F(0, 1)$. For $i = 1, 2, 3, 4, 5$, pick points P_i (five in all) nicely spaced on the parabola. Measure FP_i in millimeters. Directly below P_i, mark a point that is FP_i units down from P_i.

Based on the plot of these five points, what is likely true about any point $P(x, y)$ of the parabola? Verify your conjecture.

P_i, $i = 1$ to 5, stands for the five points P_1, P_2, P_3, P_4, and P_5.

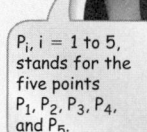
Dynamic Activity Parabolas

From Chapter 4, you know that a parabola has a vertex and an axis of symmetry. A parabola also has other special characteristics.

Focus Question What are the focus and directrix of a parabola?

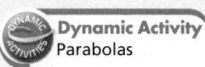

Lesson Vocabulary
• focus of a parabola
• directrix
• focal length

take note

Key Concept Parabola

Definition
A parabola is the set of all points in a plane that are the same distance from a fixed line and a fixed point not on the line.
The fixed point is called the **focus of a parabola**.
The fixed line is called the **directrix**.
The distance between the vertex and the focus is the **focal length** of the parabola.

Graph
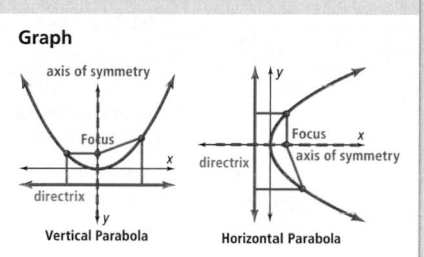

Vertical Parabola   Horizontal Parabola

In this lesson, you will consider vertical parabolas (each of which has a vertical axis of symmetry and a horizontal directrix) and horizontal parabolas (each of which has a horizontal axis of symmetry and a vertical directrix).

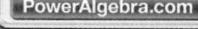
1 Interactive Learning

Solve It!
PURPOSE To use measurement to explore the definition of a parabola
PROCESS Students may
• measure the distances from point F to a point on the parabola and from the point on the parabola to a point directly below.
• work with a partner to determine whether the choice of points affects their conjecture.

FACILITATE

Q The coordinates of which point on the parabola result in the shortest distance between F and P_i? **[The shortest distance is between F and $(0, 0)$, which is the vertex of the parabola.]**

Q In this activity, what will be true about all the points drawn directly below each point in the parabola? **[The points form a horizontal line.]**

ANSWER See Solve It in Answers on next page.
CONNECT THE MATH In the Solve It, students use measurement and geometry to help them understand the definition of a parabola. In this lesson, students will use the focus and directrix to define parabola and write their equations.

2 Guided Instruction

Take Note
The previous lesson showed how a parabola was formed by the intersection of a cone and a plane parallel to the side of the cone. This definition uses the focus and directrix to define this conic section in a coordinate plane.

10-2 Preparing to Teach

BIG idea Modeling   UbD
ESSENTIAL UNDERSTANDINGS
• Each point of a parabola is equidistant from a point called the focus and a line called the directrix.
• The intersection of a cone and a plane parallel to a line along its side is a parabola.

Math Background
Students are familiar with parabolas as nonlinear functions. In this lesson, parabolas are introduced as conic sections. In this context, the lesson shows that a parabola is not always a function. A parabola can have any orientation. This lesson focuses on horizontal parabolas (which are not functions) and vertical parabolas (which are functions).
• A parabola can be formed by the intersection of a cone and a plane parallel to a side of the cone.

• A parabola is defined as the set of all points in a plane that are the same distance from a fixed line (directrix) and a fixed point not on the line (focus).

The vertex equation for a parabola allows you to determine the vertex, focus, and directrix without graphing.
For a vertical parabola,
• equation: $y = \frac{1}{4c}(x - h)^2 + k$
• focus: $(h, k + c)$
• directrix: $y = k - c$.

When the vertex is at $(0, 0)$, the equation simplifies to $y = \frac{1}{4c}x^2$ so the focus is $(0, c)$, and the directrix is $y = -c$.

Support Student Learning
Use the **Algebra 2 Companion** to engage and support students during instruction. See Lesson Resources at the end of this lesson for details.

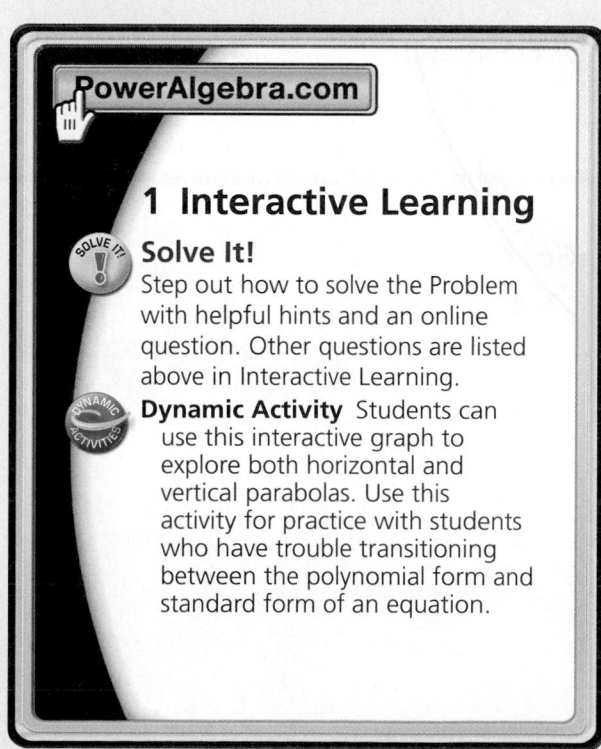

PowerAlgebra.com

1 Interactive Learning

SOLVE IT! **Solve It!**
Step out how to solve the Problem with helpful hints and an online question. Other questions are listed above in Interactive Learning.

DYNAMIC ACTIVITIES **Dynamic Activity** Students can use this interactive graph to explore both horizontal and vertical parabolas. Use this activity for practice with students who have trouble transitioning between the polynomial form and standard form of an equation.

Here's Why It Works — TACTILE LEARNERS

The relationship between the focus and the directrix determines the size and orientation of a parabola. To demonstrate, have students follow these steps using paper:
1) Draw one point near the bottom of the paper.
2) Fold the bottom of the paper until it meets the point and make a crease.
3) Unfold and repeat for 20–30 other folds. A parabola will be formed by the creases.

 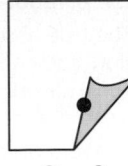 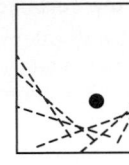

Step 1   Step 2   Step 3

Encourage students to change the distance of the point (focus) from the bottom of the paper (directrix) to change the parabola.

Problem 1 — EXTENSION

Q What is the relationship between the axis of symmetry and the focus and directrix? **[The axis of symmetry is perpendicular to the directrix. The focus is a point on the axis of symmetry.]**

Q In 1B, is it possible to find the vertex of a parabola not at the origin if given the focus and directrix? Explain. **[Yes; the distance from the focus to the vertex is equal to the distance from the vertex to the directrix, so the midpoint formula can be used.]**

You can find the equation of a vertical parabola with its vertex at the origin by using the geometric definition. If the focus is the point $(0, c)$, the directrix is the line with equation $y = -c$.

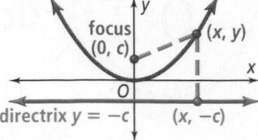

Here's Why It Works Any point (x, y) on the parabola must be equidistant from the focus and the directrix. Use the Distance Formula.

Use the Distance Formula.	$\sqrt{(x - 0)^2 + (y - c)^2} = \sqrt{(x - x)^2 + (y - (-c))^2}$
Square each side.	$x^2 + (y - c)^2 = 0^2 + (y + c)^2$
Expand.	$x^2 + y^2 - 2cy + c^2 = y^2 + 2cy + c^2$
Subtract y^2 and c^2 from each side.	$x^2 - 2cy = 2cy$
Add $2cy$ to each side.	$x^2 = 4cy$
Write in standard quadratic form.	$y = \frac{1}{4c}x^2$

Note that the equation has the expected quadratic form $y = ax^2$ for a vertical parabola with vertex at $(0, 0)$. The coefficient $a = \frac{1}{4c}$ determines both the focus $(0, c)$ and the directrix $y = -c$. This is the key to shifting between the algebraic and geometric representations of a parabola.

Problem 1 — Parabolas with Equation $y = ax^2$

A What is an equation of the parabola with vertex at the origin and focus $(0, 2)$?

The focus is directly above the vertex. This is a vertical parabola with vertex at the origin. The focus is $(0, c)$, so $c = 2$.

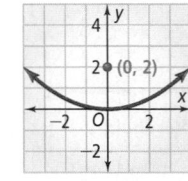

Write the standard form.	$y = \frac{1}{4c}x^2$
Substitute 2 for c.	$= \frac{1}{4(2)}x^2$
Simplify.	$= \frac{1}{8}x^2$

B What are the vertex, focus, and directrix of the parabola with equation $y = -\frac{1}{12}x^2$?

This is a vertical parabola. The vertex is at the origin and $a = -\frac{1}{12}$. Find c.

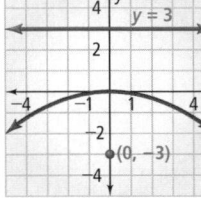

Write the equation relating a and c.	$a = \frac{1}{4c}$
Substitute $-\frac{1}{12}$ for a.	$-\frac{1}{12} = \frac{1}{4c}$
Write the cross products.	$4c = -12$
Divide each side by 4.	$c = -3$

Since $c = -3$ and the vertex is at the origin, you can conclude that the focus is the point $(0, -3)$ and the directrix is the line with equation $y = 3$.

Answers

Solve It!

Any pt. on the parabola will be equidistant from point F and the line formed by connecting pts. that are FP_i units down from P_i.

Got It?

1. a. $y = -\frac{1}{6}x^2$

  b. vertex: $(0, 0)$; focus: $(0, 1)$; directrix: $y = -1$

  c. As the distance between the vertex and focus increases, the width of the parabola increases.

2. a. $x = \frac{1}{10}y^2$

  b. vertex: $(0, 0)$; focus: $\left(-\frac{1}{16}, 0\right)$; directrix: $x = \frac{1}{16}$

PowerAlgebra.com

2 Guided Instruction

Each Problem is worked out and supported online.

Problem 1
Parabolas with Equation $y = ax^2$
Animated

Problem 2
Parabolas with Equation $x = ay^2$

Problem 3
Using Parabolas to Solve Problems
Animated

Problem 4
Analyzing a Parabola
Animated

Problem 5
Writing an Equation of a Parabola

Support in Algebra 2 Companion
• Vocabulary
• Key Concepts
• Got It?

Got It? **1. a.** What is an equation of the parabola with vertex (0, 0) and focus (0, −1.5)?

b. What are the focus and directrix of the parabola with equation $y = \frac{x^2}{4}$?

c. Reasoning How does the distance of the focus from the vertex affect the shape of a parabola?

The quadratic equation $x = ay^2$ determines a *horizontal parabola* with vertex at (0, 0). The coefficient $a = \frac{1}{4c}$ determines both the focus $(c, 0)$ and the directrix $x = -c$.

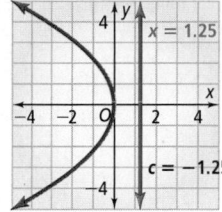

directrix $x = -c$

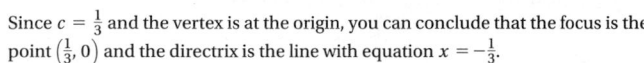

Problem 2 Parabolas with Equation $x = ay^2$

A What is an equation of a parabola with vertex at the origin and directrix $x = 1.25$?

The directrix lies directly to the right of the vertex. The parabola is horizontal. The directrix has equation $x = -c$, so $c = -1.25$.

Write the general equation of a horizontal parabola. $x = \frac{1}{4c} y^2$

Substitute −1.25 for c. $= \frac{1}{4(-1.25)} y^2$

Simplify. $= -\frac{1}{5} y^2$

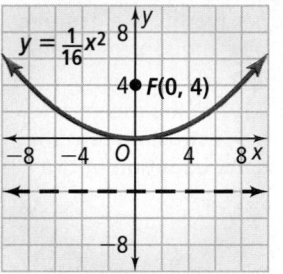

Check for Reasonableness

The graph is reasonable since it opens in the negative direction and $a < 0$.

B What are the vertex, focus, and directrix of the parabola with equation $x = 0.75y^2$?

This is a horizontal parabola. The vertex is at the origin and $a = 0.75$. Find c.

Write the equation relating a and c. $a = \frac{1}{4c}$

Substitute $0.75 = \frac{3}{4}$ for a. $\frac{3}{4} = \frac{1}{4c}$

Write the cross products. $12c = 4$

Divide each side by 12 and simplify. $c = \frac{4}{12} = \frac{1}{3}$

Since $c = \frac{1}{3}$ and the vertex is at the origin, you can conclude that the focus is the point $\left(\frac{1}{3}, 0\right)$ and the directrix is the line with equation $x = -\frac{1}{3}$.

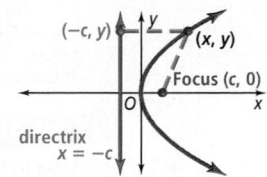

 Got It? **2. a.** What is an equation of the parabola with vertex at the origin and directrix $x = -\frac{5}{2}$?

b. What are the vertex, focus, and directrix of the parabola with equation $x = -4y^2$?

Plan

How can you tell if this is a vertical or a horizontal parabola?
The directrix is parallel to the *y*-axis, so this is a horizontal parabola.

Think

What does the sign of *a* tell you about the graph?
Since *a* is positive, the parabola opens to the right.

Got It?

Q Is the parabola in 1b vertical or horizontal? **[vertical]**

Q The equation of the parabola in 1b is in the form $y = ax^2$. What does that tell you about the vertex of this parabola? **[The vertex is (0, 0).]**

If students have difficulty with this problem, refer them to Lesson 4-1 to refresh their basic understanding of parabolas.

ERROR PREVENTION

Students sometimes reverse the *x*- and *y*-coordinates of the focus. A parabola with focus (0, 4) and directrix $y = -4$ is different from a parabola with focus (4, 0) and the same directrix. Although both are vertical and facing up, the shapes and locations are different.

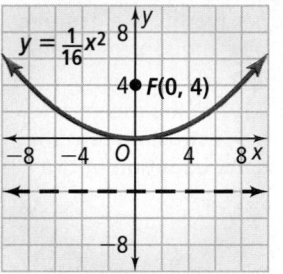

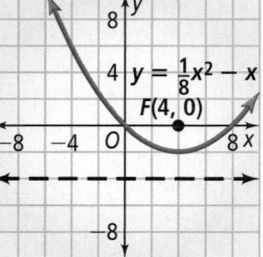

Problem 2

Q Is it possible to graph the parabola in 2A on a graphing calculator? Explain. **[Yes; solving for y, $y = \pm\sqrt{-5x}$, which is defined for negative values of x.]**

 | Lesson 10-2 Parabolas | 643

Additional Problems

1. a. What is an equation of the parabola with vertex at the origin and focus $\left(0, \frac{1}{2}\right)$?

b. What are the focus and directrix of the parabola with equation $y = 6x^2$?

ANSWERS

a. $y = \frac{1}{2}x^2$

b. focus: $\left(0, \frac{1}{24}\right)$; directrix: $y = -\frac{1}{24}$

2. a. What is an equation of a parabola with vertex at the origin and directrix $x = -\frac{1}{8}$?

b. What are the vertex, focus, and directrix of the parabola with equation $x = \frac{3}{5}y^2$?

ANSWERS

a. $x = 2y^2$

b. vertex: (0, 0); focus: $\left(\frac{5}{12}, 0\right)$; directrix: $x = -\frac{5}{12}$

3. The mirrored reflector of a flashlight is 16 cm across and 10 cm deep. How far from the vertex should the light bulb be positioned?

ANSWER 1.6 cm

4. What are the vertex, focus, and directrix of the parabola with equation $y = x^2 - 6x + 15$?

ANSWER vertex: (3, 6); focus: (3, 6.25); directrix: $y = 5.75$

5. Multiple Choice Which is an equation of the parabola with vertex (10, 2) and focus (10, 1)?

A. $y = -\frac{1}{4}(x + 10)^2 - 2$

B. $y = -\frac{1}{4}(x - 10)^2 + 2$

C. $y = -\frac{1}{4}(x + 10)^2 + 2$

D. $y = -\frac{1}{4}(x - 10)^2 - 2$

ANSWER B

Lesson 10-2 **643**

Got It?

Q What does the equation for the directrix tell you about the parabola in 2a? **[The directrix is a vertical line, so the parabola is horizontal.]**

Q Can you describe the direction the parabola faces in 2b before finding the vertex, focus, and directrix? Explain. **[Yes; the x term is linear, so the parabola is horizontal. The a term is negative, so it opens to the left.]**

Problem 3

Q Must the vertex of this parabola be at $(0, 0)$? Explain. **[No; the vertex could be anywhere on the coordinate plane. For easier computation, the vertex is placed at $(0, 0)$.]**

Q Why can you use either point to find the value of c? **[Because the x-value is squared, the positive or negative x-value will give the same answer.]**

Q What is the equation of the parabola representing the satellite dish? Explain. **[$y = \frac{1}{8}x^2$; the vertex is at the origin and $c = 2$. Substituting into the equation $y = \frac{1}{4c}x^2$ yields the equation of the parabola.]**

Got It?

Q How can you find two ordered pairs on the parabola? **[The reflector is 8 cm across, so the distance between the x-values must be 8 units. Placing the vertex at the origin, the ordered pairs are $(-4, 4)$ and $(4, 4)$.]**

The geometry of a parabola implies a very important reflective property that gives real-world meaning to the word "focus."

As the diagram of a *parabolic reflector* shows, lines from the focus reflect off the parabola along lines parallel to the axis of symmetry. This is how a flashlight works.

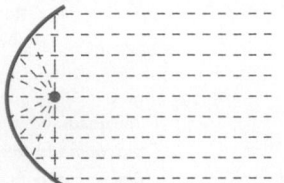

Conversely, lines parallel to the axis of symmetry reflect off the parabola directly into the focus. This is how a satellite dish works.

Problem 3 Using Parabolas to Solve Problems

Solar Reflector The parabolic solar reflector pictured has a depth of 2 feet at the center. How far from the vertex is the focus? (What is the focal length?)

Graph the parabola in a coordinate system with vertex $(0, 0)$. The vertical parabola has the form $y = \frac{1}{4c}x^2$. Substitute one of the points: $(4, 2)$.

Think What is the shape of the solar reflector? A cross section is part of a parabola and is 8 ft across.

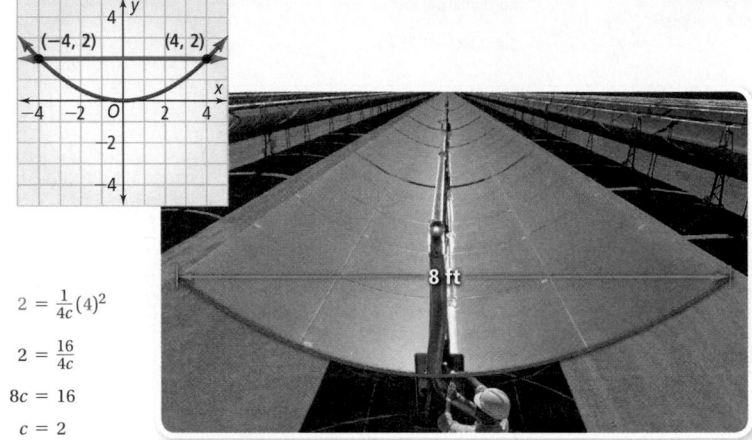

$$2 = \frac{1}{4c}(4)^2$$

$$2 = \frac{16}{4c}$$

$$8c = 16$$

$$c = 2$$

Therefore, the focus is at $(0, 2)$, 2 ft from the vertex. The focal length is 2 ft.

 Got It? 3. The mirrored reflector of a flashlight is 8 cm across and 4 cm deep. How far from the vertex should the light bulb be positioned?

Answers

Got It? (continued)

3. 1 cm

In Chapter 4, you studied how to translate a parabola with vertex $(0, 0)$ to one with vertex (h, k). For such a translation, all of the other features—axis of symmetry, focus, and directrix—translate along with the parabola and its vertex.

take note

Key Concept   Transformations of a Parabola

Vertical Parabola	Vertex (0, 0)	Vertex (h, k)
Equation	$y = \frac{1}{4c}x^2$	$y = \frac{1}{4c}(x - h)^2 + k$
Focus	$(0, c)$	$(h, k + c)$
Directrix	$y = -c$	$y = k - c$
Horizontal Parabola	**Vertex (0, 0)**	**Vertex (h, k)**
Equation	$x = \frac{1}{4c}y^2$	$x = \frac{1}{4c}(y - k)^2 + h$
Focus	$(c, 0)$	$(h + c, k)$
Directrix	$x = -c$	$x = h - c$

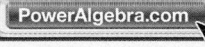

Problem 4   Analyzing a Parabola

What are the vertex, focus, and directrix of the parabola with equation $y = x^2 - 4x + 8$?

Know	Need	Plan
The equation of the parabola	• vertex • focus • directrix	• Find c, h, and k. • Use these values to find the vertex, focus, and directrix.

First, complete the square to get the equation in vertex form.

Write the original equation.	$y = x^2 - 4x + 8$
Add $\left(\frac{1}{2} \cdot -4\right)^2$ inside parentheses; subtract it outside.	$y = (x^2 - 4x + 4) + 8 - 4$
Factor and simplify.	$y = (x - 2)^2 + 4$

Next, compare the resulting equation to the vertex form of a vertical parabola.

Write the general form.	$y = \frac{1}{4c}(x - h)^2 + k$
Write the vertex form.	$y = 1 \cdot (x - 2)^2 + 4$

Note that, in this case, $\frac{1}{4c} = 1$, so $c = 0.25$.

The vertex (h, k) is $(2, 4)$. The focus $(h, k + c)$ is $(2, 4.25)$.
The directrix $y = k - c$ is $y = 3.75$.

✔ **Got It? 4.** What are the vertex, focus, and directrix of the parabola with equation $y = x^2 + 8x + 18$?

Think

How can you change the equation to an equivalent form?
Subtract the same value outside the parentheses that you added inside the parentheses.

Hint

To complete the square for $x^2 + bx$, you need to find the value of $\left(\frac{b}{2}\right)^2$.

Take Note

Unlike the standard form $y = ax^2 + bx + c$, the vertex form allows you to find the vertex, focus, and directrix without graphing.

Q What methods can you use to help you remember the equations shown in the box? **[Sample: Use equations for the vertex of a vertical parabola. Substitute 0 for h and k to make an equation for a parabola with vertex at the origin. Horizontal parabola equations are made by switching x and y and switching h and k.]**

Problem 4

Q How can you determine the value of $\frac{1}{4c}$? **[The coefficient of the squared term in the equation is 1, so $\frac{1}{4c} = 1$.]**

Got It?

Q What is the vertex form of the equation? **[$y = (x + 4)^2 + 2$]**

Q How can you algebraically check that your vertex is correct? [The equation is in standard form, so use $\frac{-b}{2a}$ to find the x-value, then substitute to find y.]

4. vertex: $(-4, 2)$; focus: $\left(-4, 2\frac{1}{4}\right)$;
directrix: $y = 1\frac{3}{4}$

Problem 5

> **Q** How can you use the vertex to help you eliminate one of the answers? **[The vertex is a point on the parabola, so (3, 7) must be a solution to the equation. This point is not a solution to answer D, so D is incorrect.]**

Got It?

> **Q** What is the orientation of this parabola? Explain. **[The focus is above the vertex, so this is a vertical parabola opening upward.]**

3 Lesson Check

Do you know HOW?
- For Exercises 1 and 2, suggest to students that they first determine whether the parabola is vertical or horizontal.

Do you UNDERSTAND?
- If students have trouble with Exercise 6, remind them that a parabola can have any orientation. This lesson focused on vertical and horizontal parabolas facing upward, downward, rightward, or leftward. Have students sketch these four types of parabolas each with vertex at the origin.

Close

> **Q** What is true about the set of points on a parabola, its focus, and its directrix? **[A parabola is the set of all points that are the same distance from the directrix and the focus.]**
>
> **Q** What can you determine about the orientation of a parabola by looking at its vertex equation? **[If the y-term is linear, the parabola is vertical. If the x-term is linear, the parabola is horizontal. If $\frac{1}{4c}$ is positive, it opens upward or rightward. If negative, it opens downward or leftward.]**

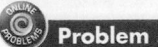 **Problem 5** Writing an Equation of a Parabola

Multiple Choice Which is an equation of the parabola with vertex $(3, 7)$ and focus $(5, 7)$?

- Ⓐ $x = \frac{1}{4}(y - 7)^2 + 3$
- Ⓒ $x = \frac{1}{8}(y - 7)^2 + 3$
- Ⓑ $y = \frac{1}{8}(x - 7)^2 + 3$
- Ⓓ $x = \frac{1}{8}(y + 7)^2 - 3$

Plan

How do you determine which equation to use?
Use the focus and the vertex to determine the orientation of the parabola.

The focus is to the right of the vertex, so the parabola is horizontal. Use the equation. $x = \frac{1}{4c}(y - k)^2 + h$.

The vertex (h, k) is $(3, 7)$ and the focus $(h + c, k)$ is $(5, 7)$. So, $h = 3$, $k = 7$, and $c = 2$.

Substitute into the general equation and simplify.

$$x = \frac{1}{4(2)}(y - 7)^2 + 3$$
$$= \frac{1}{8}(y - 7)^2 + 3$$

The correct answer is C.

 Got It? 5. What is an equation of the parabola with vertex $(1, 4)$ and focus $(1, 6)$?

Focus Question What are the focus and directrix of a parabola?

Answer Each point of a parabola is equidistant from a fixed point called the focus and a fixed line (not containing the focus) called the directrix. Use the focus and directrix to write the equation of a parabola given its graph.

 Lesson Check

Do you know HOW?
Write an equation of a parabola with the given information.

1. vertex $(0, 0)$, focus $\left(0, \frac{1}{2}\right)$

2. vertex $(3, 2)$, focus $(4, 2)$

Find the vertex, focus, and the directrix of each parabola.

3. $x = \frac{1}{16}y^2$

4. $y = x^2 + 6x + 5$

Do you UNDERSTAND?

5. Vocabulary If the vertex of a parabola is 3 units from the focus, how far is the focus from the directrix?

6. Error Analysis The vertex of a parabola is at the origin, one unit away from the focus. A student concludes that the equation is $y = \frac{1}{4}x^2$. Identify at least two ways in which the student's equation might be in error.

PowerAlgebra.com

3 Lesson Check

For a digital lesson check, use the Got It questions.

Support in Algebra 2 Companion
- Lesson Check

4 Practice

Assign homework to individual students or to an entire class.

Answers

Got It? (continued)

5. $y = \frac{1}{8}(x - 1)^2 + 4$

Lesson Check

1. $y = \frac{1}{2}x^2$

2. $x = \frac{1}{4}(y - 2)^2 + 3$

3. vertex: $(0, 0)$; focus: $(4, 0)$; directrix: $x = -4$

4. vertex: $(-3, -4)$; focus: $(-3, -3.75)$; directrix: $y = -4.25$

5. 6 units

6. With the focus one unit away from the vertex of a parabola at the origin, $c = \pm 1$. Given this information, the student cannot tell whether the parabola opens in the vert. direction, with one of the eqs. $y = \frac{1}{4}x^2$ or $y = -\frac{1}{4}x^2$, or whether the parabola opens in the horizontal direction, with one of the eqs. of $x = \frac{1}{4}y^2$ or $x = -\frac{1}{4}y^2$.

Practice and Problem-Solving Exercises

7. $x = \frac{1}{24}y^2$

8. $y = -\frac{1}{16}x^2$

9. $x = -\frac{1}{4}y^2$

10. vertex: $(0, 0)$; focus: $(0, -2)$; directrix: $y = 2$

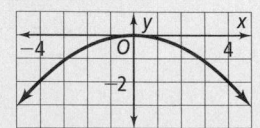

11. vertex: $(0, 0)$; focus: $\left(0, \frac{1}{16}\right)$; directrix: $y = -\frac{1}{16}$

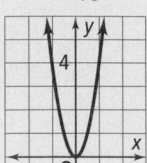

Practice and Problem-Solving Exercises

A Practice   Write an equation of a parabola with vertex at the origin and the given focus.   ◀ See Problem 1.

7. focus at $(6, 0)$ **8.** focus at $(0, -4)$ **9.** focus at $(-1, 0)$

Identify the vertex, the focus, and the directrix of the parabola with the   ◀ See Problems 1 and 2.
given equation. Then sketch the graph of the parabola.

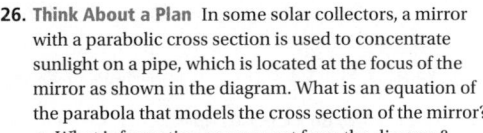

Guided Practice

To start, identify the orientation and vertex of the parabola.

10. $y = -\frac{1}{8}x^2$

This is a vertical parabola with vertex at $(0, 0)$.

11. $y = 4x^2$ **12.** $x = y^2$ **13.** $x = \frac{1}{2}y^2$

Write an equation of a parabola with vertex at the origin and the given directrix.   ◀ See Problem 2.

14. directrix $x = -3$ **15.** directrix $y = 5$ **16.** directrix $x = 9$

17. Optics A cross section of a flashlight reflector is a parabola. The bulb is located   ◀ See Problem 3.
at the focus. Suppose the bulb is located $\frac{1}{4}$ in. from the vertex of the reflector.
Model a cross section of the reflector by writing an equation of a parabola that
opens upward and has its vertex at the origin. What is an advantage of this
parabolic design?

Identify the vertex, the focus, and the directrix of the parabola with the given   ◀ See Problem 4.
equation. Then sketch the graph of the parabola.

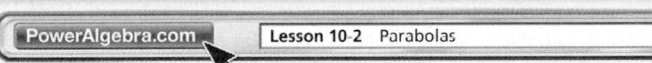

Guided Practice

To start, complete the square by adding and subtracting $\left(\frac{b}{2}\right)^2 = \left(\frac{4}{2}\right)^2 = 4$.

18. $y = x^2 + 4x + 3$
$y = (x^2 + 4x + 4) + 3 - 4$

19. $y = x^2 - 6x + 11$ **20.** $y - x^2 - 2x - 4$ **21.** $y = 2x^2 + 4x - 2$

Write an equation of a parabola with the given vertex and focus.   ◀ See Problem 5.

22. vertex $(4, 1)$; focus $(6, 1)$ **23.** vertex $(0, 3)$; focus $(-8, 3)$

24. vertex $(-5, 4)$; focus $(-5, 0)$ **25.** vertex $(7, 2)$; focus $(7, -2)$

B Apply   **26. Think About a Plan** In some solar collectors, a mirror
with a parabolic cross section is used to concentrate
sunlight on a pipe, which is located at the focus of the
mirror as shown in the diagram. What is an equation of
the parabola that models the cross section of the mirror?
- What information can you get from the diagram?
- What information do you need to be able to write an
  equation that models the cross section of the mirror?

12. vertex: $(0, 0)$; focus: $\left(\frac{1}{4}, 0\right)$; directrix: $x = -\frac{1}{4}$
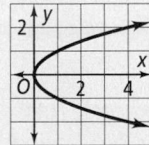

13. vertex: $(0, 0)$; focus: $\left(\frac{1}{2}, 0\right)$; directrix: $x = -\frac{1}{2}$
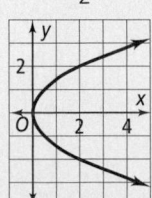

14. $x = \frac{1}{12}y^2$

15. $y = -\frac{1}{20}x^2$

16. $x = -\frac{1}{36}y^2$

17. Answers may vary. Sample: $y = x^2$.
The light produced by the bulb will
reflect off the parabolic mirror in
parallel rays.

18. vertex: $(-2, -1)$; focus: $\left(-2, -\frac{3}{4}\right)$; directrix: $y = -\frac{5}{4}$
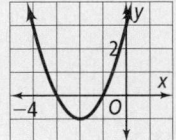

19. vertex: $(3, 2)$; focus: $\left(3, \frac{9}{4}\right)$; directrix: $y = \frac{7}{4}$
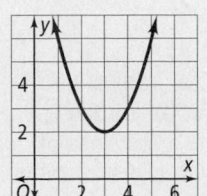

20. vertex: $(1, -5)$; focus: $\left(1, -4\frac{3}{4}\right)$; directrix: $y = -5\frac{1}{4}$
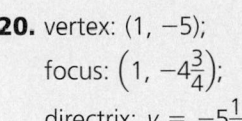
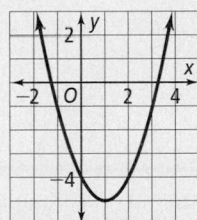

21. vertex: $(-1, -4)$; focus: $\left(-1, -3\frac{7}{8}\right)$; directrix: $y = -4\frac{1}{8}$
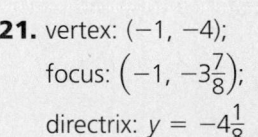
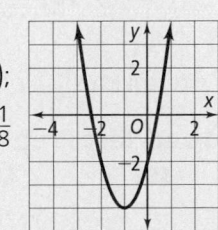

22. $x = \frac{1}{8}(y - 1)^2 + 4$ **23.** $x = -\frac{1}{32}(y - 3)^2$

24. $y = -\frac{1}{16}(x + 5)^2 + 4$

25. $y = -\frac{1}{16}(x - 7)^2 + 2$

26. $y = \frac{1}{24}x^2$; the focal distance;
the focus and the vertex

4 Practice

ASSIGNMENT GUIDE
Basic: 7–23, 26, 27
Average: 7–25 odd, 26, 27–35 odd
Standardized Test Prep: 38–41
Mixed Review: 42–47

Reasoning exercises have blue headings.
Applications exercises have red headings.

EXERCISE 27: Use the Think About a Plan
worksheet in the **Student Companion** (also
available in the Teaching Resources in print and
online) to further support students' development in
becoming independent learners.

HOMEWORK QUICK CHECK
To check students' understanding of key skills and
concepts, go over Exercises 11, 17, 19, 26, and 27.

Answers

Practice and Problem-Solving Exercises (continued)

27. 3.5 in.

28. vertex: $(0, 0)$; focus: $\left(\frac{25}{4}, 0\right)$; directrix: $x = -\frac{25}{4}$

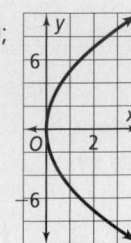

29. vertex: $(0, 0)$; focus: $(0, -1)$; directrix: $y = 1$

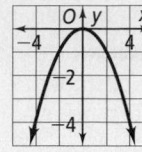

30. vertex: $(2, 0)$; focus: $(2, 1)$; directrix: $y = -1$

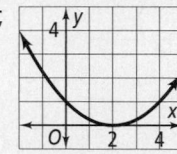

31. vertex: $(0, 0)$; focus: $(-2, 0)$; directrix: $x = 2$

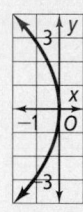

32. vertex: $(-3, 0)$; focus: $\left(-\frac{3}{2}, 0\right)$; directrix: $x = -\frac{9}{2}$

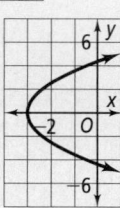

33. vertex: $(4, 0)$; focus: $(4, -6)$; directrix: $y = 6$

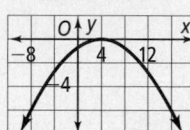

34. $y = \frac{1}{6}(x - 1)^2 + 1$

35. $x = -\frac{1}{2}(y - 1)^2 + 1$

36. $y = -\frac{1}{4}(x - 1)^2 + 1$

37. Answers may vary. Sample: Write the eq. in the form $x = \frac{1}{4\left(\frac{1}{8}\right)}y^2$. The distance from the focus to the directrix is $2\left(\frac{1}{8}\right)$, or $\frac{1}{4}$.

Standardized Test Prep

38. D   **39.** F   **40.** D

41. **[4]** $\log 12 = \log 3 \cdot 4 = \log 3 + \log 4$;
Product Prop.
$\log 12 = \log 3 \cdot 2^2 = \log 3 + 2 \log 2$;
Product and Power Prop.
$\log 12 = \log \frac{24}{2} = \log 24 - \log 2$;
Quotient Prop.
$\log 12 = \log 144^{\frac{1}{2}} = \frac{1}{2} \log 144$;
Power Prop.

[3] log 12 written in only three diff. ways, correct prop.

[2] log 12 written only in two diff. ways, correct prop. OR log 12 written in four diff. ways, with two incorrect prop.

[1] log 12 written in only two diff. ways, without correct prop

Mixed Review

42.

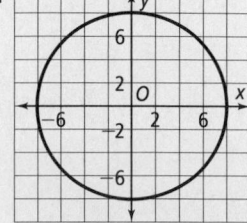

circle: center $(0, 0)$, radius 8; x-intercepts: $(\pm 8, 0)$, y-intercepts: $(0, \pm 8)$; infinitely many lines of sym.; domain: $-8 \le x \le 8$, range: $-8 \le y \le 8$

43.

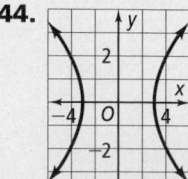

ellipse: center $(0, 0)$; x-intercepts: $(\pm 3, 0)$, y-intercepts: $(0, \pm 1)$; lines of sym.: x-axis and y-axis; domain: $-3 \le x \le 3$, range: $-1 \le y \le 1$

44.

hyperbola: center $(0, 0)$; x-intercepts $(\pm 3, 0)$, no y-intercept; lines of sym.: x-axis and y-axis; domain: $x \le -3$ or $x \ge 3$, range: all real numbers

45. 1   **46.** 25   **47.** 9

---

27. **Sound** Broadcasters use a parabolic microphone on football sidelines to pick up field audio for broadcasting purposes. A certain parabolic microphone has a reflector dish with a diameter of 28 inches and a depth of 14 inches. If the receiver of the microphone is located at the focus of the reflector dish, how far from the vertex should the receiver be positioned?

Identify the vertex, the focus, and the directrix of a parabola with each equation. Then sketch a graph of the parabola with the given equation.

28. $y^2 - 25x = 0$ **29.** $x^2 = -4y$ **30.** $(x - 2)^2 = 4y$

31. $-8x = y^2$ **32.** $y^2 - 6x = 18$ **33.** $x^2 + 24y - 8x = -16$

Write an equation of a parabola with vertex at $(1, 1)$ and the given information.

34. directrix $y = -\frac{1}{2}$ **35.** directrix $x = \frac{3}{2}$ **36.** focus at $(1, 0)$

37. **Writing** Explain how to find the distance from the focus to the directrix of the parabola $x = 2y^2$.

Standardized Test Prep

SAT/ACT

38. What is the equation of a parabola with vertex at the origin and focus at $\left(0, \frac{5}{2}\right)$?

Ⓐ $x = -\frac{1}{10}y^2$ Ⓑ $x = \frac{1}{10}y^2$ Ⓒ $x = -\frac{1}{10}x^2$ Ⓓ $y = \frac{1}{10}x^2$

39. Use the information in the graph to find the equation for the graph.

Ⓕ $y^2 + 6x = 0$ Ⓗ $x^2 + 6y = 0$

Ⓖ $y^2 - 6x = 0$ Ⓘ $x^2 - 6y = 0$

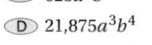

Directrix, $x = \frac{3}{2}$

40. What is the fifth term in the expansion of $(a - 5b)^7$?

Ⓐ $35a^3b^4$ Ⓒ $625a^3b^4$

Ⓑ $-175a^3b^4$ Ⓓ $21{,}875a^3b^4$

Extended Response

41. Use the properties of logarithms to write log 12 in four different ways. Name each property you use.

Mixed Review

Graph each equation. Identify the conic section and describe the graph and its lines of symmetry. Then find the domain and range.   ◀ See Lesson 10-1.

42. $x^2 + y^2 = 64$ **43.** $x^2 + 9y^2 = 9$ **44.** $4x^2 - 9y^2 = 36$

Get Ready! To prepare for Lesson 10-3, do Exercises 45–47.

Complete the square.   ◀ See Lesson 4-6.

45. $x^2 - 2x + \blacksquare$ **46.** $x^2 + 10x + \blacksquare$ **47.** $x^2 - 6x + \blacksquare$

Lesson Resources

Additional Instructional Support

Algebra 2 Companion

Students can use the **Algebra 2 Companion** worktext (4 pages) as you teach the lesson. Use the Companion to support

- New Vocabulary
- Key Concepts
- Got It for each Problem
- Lesson Check

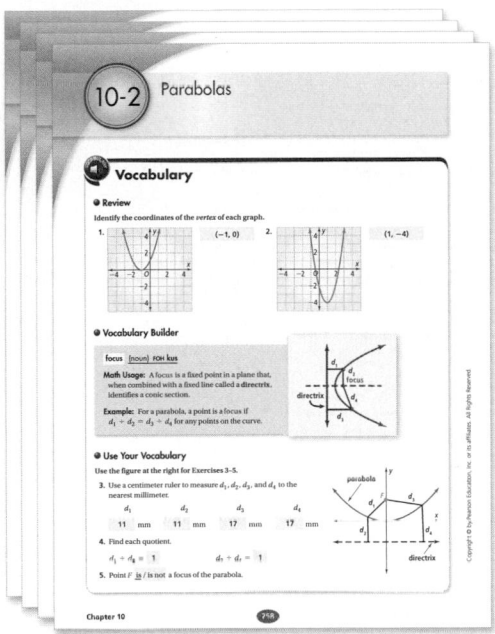

ELL Support

Focus on Language Sketch a parabola on the board. It is not necessary to draw the parabola on a coordinate plane because the focus of this activity is to become familiar with the vocabulary.

Ask, "What is the name of this figure?" [parabola] Place a point at the approximate location of the focus. Point to the focus and ask, "What is the name of this point?" [focus] Draw a line at the approximate location of the directrix. Point to the line and ask, "What is this line?" [directrix]

Next, have several students come to the board and sketch parabolas of varying orientations. Parabolas can be vertical, horizontal, or at any angle. Ask each student to draw the approximate focus and directrix. Have students stand in front of their drawing and point to each object saying "parabola, focus, directrix." Next, have students move in front of a different sketch and name each part on the new drawing.

5 Assess & Remediate

Lesson Quiz

1. What is an equation of the parabola with vertex at the origin and focus (0, 0.75)?

2. What is an equation of the parabola with vertex at the origin and directrix $x = \frac{1}{8}$?

3. **Do you UNDERSTAND?** A convex lens has a diameter of 30 mm and a depth of 5 mm at the center. How far from the vertex is the focus?

4. What are the vertex, focus, and directrix of the parabola with equation $y = x^2 + 10x + 12$?

5. What is an equation of the parabola with vertex (6, 7) and focus (7, 7)?

ANSWERS TO LESSON QUIZ

1. $y = \frac{1}{3}x^2$

2. $x = -2y^2$

3. 11.25 mm

4. vertex: $(-5, -13)$; focus: $(-5, -12.75)$; directrix: $y = -13.25$

5. $x = \frac{1}{4}(y - 7)^2 + 6$

PRESCRIPTION FOR REMEDIATION

Use the student work on the Lesson Quiz to prescribe a differentiated review assignment:

Points	Differentiated Remediation
0–2	Intervention
3–4	On-level
5	Extension

PowerAlgebra.com

5 Assess & Remediate

Assign the Lesson Quiz. Appropriate intervention, practice, or enrichment is automatically generated based on student performance.

Intervention

- **Reteaching** (2 pages) Provides reteaching and practice exercises for the key lesson concepts. Use with struggling students or absent students.

- **English Language Learner Support** Helps students develop and reinforce mathematical vocabulary and key concepts.

All-in-One Resources/Online
Reteaching

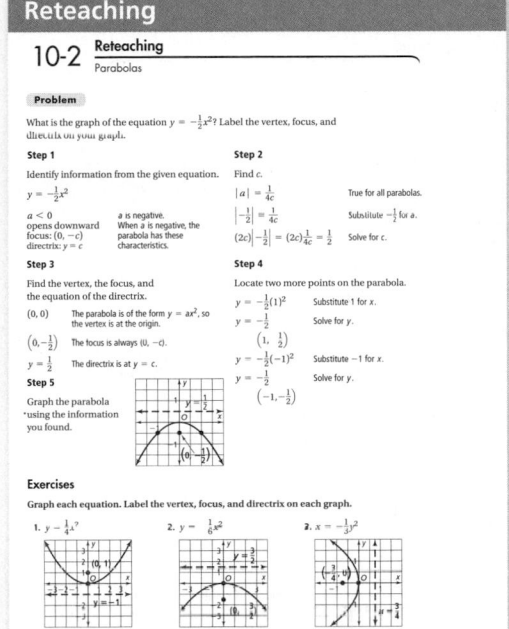

All-in-One Resources/Online
English Language Learner Support

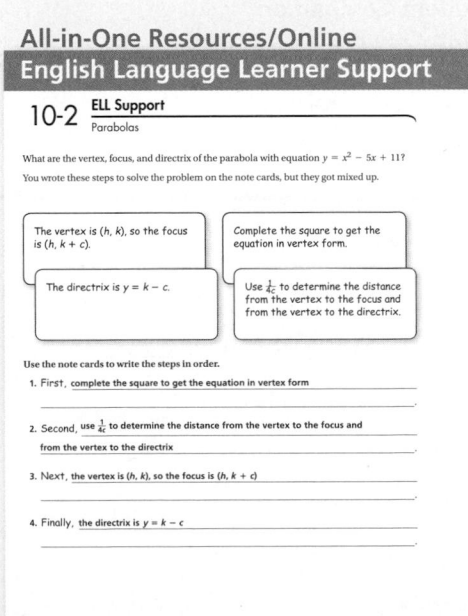

Differentiated Remediation *continued*

On-Level

- **Practice** (2 pages) Provides extra practice for each lesson. For more challenging practice exercises, use the Form G Practice pages found in the All-in-One Teaching Resources and online.

- **Think About a Plan** Helps students develop specific problem-solving skills and strategies by providing scaffolded guiding questions.

- **Standardized Test Prep** Focuses on all major exercises, all major question types, and helps students prepare for the high-stakes assessments.

Extension

- **Enrichment** Provides students with interesting problems and activities that extend the concepts of the lesson.

- **Activities, Games, and Puzzles** Worksheets that can be used for concepts development, enrichment, and for fun!

Student Companion/All-in-One Resources/Online
Practice page 1

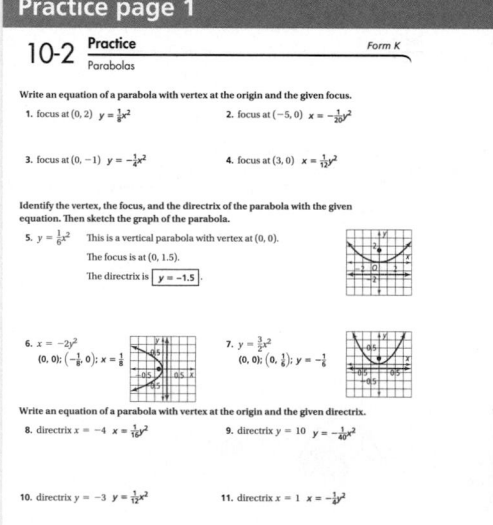

Student Companion/All-in-One Resources/Online
Practice page 2

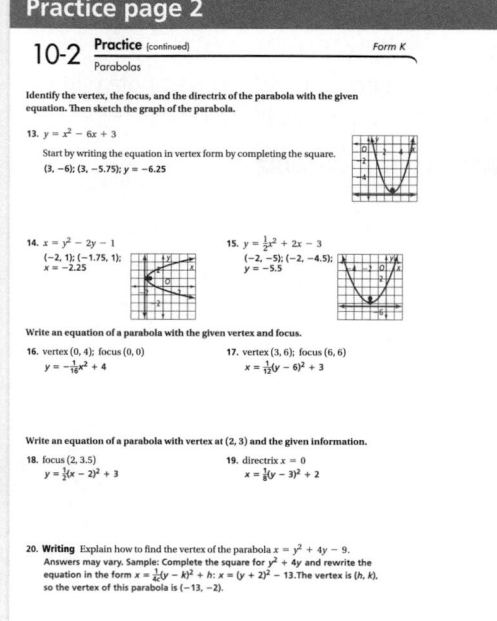

All-in-One Resources/Online
Enrichment

10-2 Enrichment — Parabolas

Quadratic Maxima and Minima

Consider the equation of a parabola in standard form, $y = a(x - h)^2 + k$. If $a > 0$, then the parabola opens upward and the vertex (h, k) represents the lowest point, or minimum value, on the graph. Similarly, if $a < 0$, the parabola opens downward and the vertex (h, k) represents the highest point, or maximum value, on the graph.

Suppose that a rancher has 100 yd of fencing with which to construct a rectangular field in such a way that the total area enclosed is a maximum.

1. If ℓ represents the length of the field and w its width, what equation expresses the area A of the field? **$A = \ell w$**

2. How would you express the fact that the perimeter P of the field must be 100 yd? **$P = 2\ell + 2w = 100$**

3. Solve the perimeter equation for ℓ in terms of w, and substitute into the area equation. What is the equation for A in terms of w? **$A = (50 - w)w = 50w - w^2$**

4. Write your equation in standard form for a parabola. **$A = -(w - 25)^2 + 625$**

5. For which value of w is the area a maximum? **$w = 25$ yd**

6. What is the corresponding length ℓ? **$\ell = 25$ yd**

7. What is the area of the field? **625 yd²**

8. What is its shape? **square**

Repeat the exercises above assuming that the rancher has 200 yd of fencing.

9. What are the dimensions of the field enclosing the maximum area? **50 yd by 50 yd**

10. On the basis of your results, what might you infer? **The largest rectangle with a fixed perimeter is a square.**

11. What type of geometric figure might enclose the most area given a fixed perimeter? Explain. **A circle; its ratio of area to perimeter is even greater than a square's.**

Student Companion/All-in-One Resources/Online
Think About a Plan

10-2 Think About a Plan — Parabolas

Sound Broadcasters use a parabolic microphone on football sidelines to pick up field audio for broadcasting purposes. A certain parabolic microphone has a reflector dish with a diameter of 28 inches and a depth of 14 inches. If the receiver of the microphone is located at the focus of the reflector dish, how far from the vertex should the receiver be positioned?

Understanding the Problem

1. What is the diameter of the reflector dish? **28 in.**

2. What is the depth of the reflector dish? **14 in.**

3. What is the problem asking you to determine? **the distance between the receiver and the vertex of the dish**

Planning the Solution

4. Sketch a graph of a vertical parabola to represent the reflector dish. Place the vertex at the origin.

5. You know the coordinates of two other points on the parabola. Plot and label them on your graph.

6. What is the equation for a vertical parabola with vertex at the origin? **$y = \frac{1}{4c}x^2$**

7. How can you find the location of the focus from the equation for the parabola? **Substitute the point (14, 14) or (−14, 14) into the equation. Solve for c. The focus is at (0, c)**

Getting an Answer

8. What is the location of the focus? **(0, 3.5)**

9. If the receiver of the microphone is located at the focus of the reflector dish, how far from the vertex should the receiver be positioned? **3.5 in.**

Student Companion/All-in-One Resources/Online
Standardized Test Prep

10-2 Standardized Test Prep — Parabolas

Multiple Choice

For Exercises 1–5, choose the correct letter.

1. Which is an equation of the parabola with the vertex at the origin and focus (0, 3)? **B**
   - Ⓐ $y = \frac{1}{4}x^2$ Ⓑ $y = \frac{1}{12}x^2$ Ⓒ $x = \frac{1}{12}y^2$ Ⓓ $x = \frac{1}{3}y^2$

2. What is the focus of the parabola with the equation $y = -\frac{1}{16}x^2$? **F**
   - Ⓕ $(0, -4)$ Ⓖ $(-4, 0)$ Ⓗ $\left(0, -\frac{1}{16}\right)$ Ⓘ $\left(-\frac{1}{4}, 0\right)$

3. Which is the equation of a parabola with vertex at the origin and directrix $x = 2.5$? **A**
   - Ⓐ $x = -\frac{1}{10}y^2$ Ⓑ $x = \frac{1}{10}y^2$ Ⓒ $x = \frac{1}{2}y^2$ Ⓓ $x = -\frac{5}{2}y^2$

4. What is the directrix of $x = 2.25y^2$? **I**
   - Ⓕ $x = \frac{1}{4}$ Ⓖ $x = -\frac{1}{4}$ Ⓗ $x = \frac{1}{9}$ Ⓘ $x = -\frac{1}{9}$

5. What is the vertex of $y = x^2 - 8x + 10$? **D**
   - Ⓐ $(-4, 8)$ Ⓑ $(8, 10)$ Ⓒ $(10, 16)$ Ⓓ $(4, -6)$

Short Response

6. What are the vertex, focus, and directrix of the parabola with equation $y = x^2 - 14x + 5$? Show your work.
   [2] $y = x^2 - 14x + 5$; $y = (x^2 - 14x + 49) + 5 - 49$; $y = (x - 7)^2 - 44$; vertex $(h, k) = (7, -44)$; focus $(h, k + c) = (7, -43.75)$; directrix $(y = k - c)$ is $y = -44.25$
   [1] incorrect vertex OR incorrect focus OR incorrect directrix OR correct answers, without work shown
   [0] incorrect answers and no work shown OR no answers given

Online Teacher Resource Center
Activities, Games, and Puzzles

10-2 Game: A Parabolic Race — Parabolas

This is a game for two players. Each player uses one of the parabolic racetracks provided. For each item below, decide whether the parabola described *opens up, down, to the right,* or *to the left.* Write your answer to the right of each item.

- Move from one point to the next for each correct answer.
- Players must agree on the accuracy of each answer.
- The first player to cross the finish line wins. If neither player crosses, then the player who advances farthest wins.

1. focus: $F(-2, 1)$; directrix: $y = 3$ — **down**
2. vertex: $V(2, 7)$; focus: $F(-2, 7)$ — **left**
3. $y = -x^2 + 2x + 5$ — **down**
4. $A(0, 3)$, $B(4, 7)$, $C(4, -7)$ — **right**
5. $y = 3(x - 2)^2 + 1$ — **up**
6. vertex: $V(5, 2)$; directrix: $x = 6$ — **left**
7. vertex: $V(0, 7)$; focus: $F(0, 0)$ — **down**
8. $x = -5y^2$ — **left**
9. $A(-3, 6)$, $B(0, 1)$, $C(4, 8)$ — **up**
10. $x = 2(y - 1)^2 + 2$ — **right**
11. focus: $F(2, 8)$; directrix: $x = 0$ — **right**
12. vertex: $V(-3, 1)$; directrix: $y = 2$ — **down**
13. $y = 0.3x^2 + 1$ — **up**
14. focus: $F(2.2, 2)$; vertex: $V(5, 2)$ — **left**
15. $x = -(y + 1)^2 - 3$ — **left**
16. $K(3, 6)$, $L(0, 3)$, $M(3, -6)$ — **right**

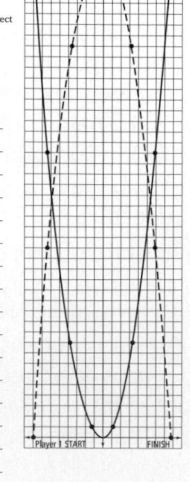

Objectives To write and graph the equation of a circle
To find the center and radius of a circle and use them to graph the circle

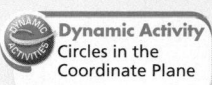

Lesson Vocabulary
- circle
- center of a circle
- radius
- standard form of an equation of a circle

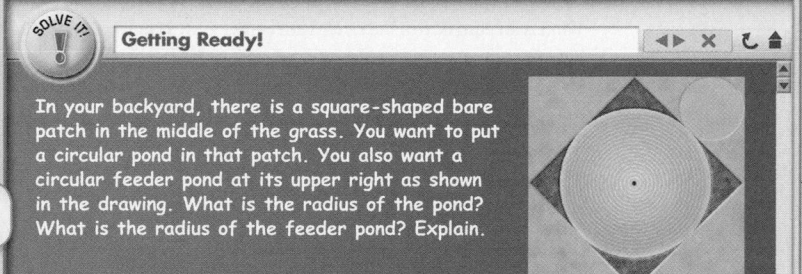

Getting Ready!

In your backyard, there is a square-shaped bare patch in the middle of the grass. You want to put a circular pond in that patch. You also want a circular feeder pond at its upper right as shown in the drawing. What is the radius of the pond? What is the radius of the feeder pond? Explain.

You've seen these shapes before.

⟵ 80 ft ⟶

A **circle** is the set of all points in a plane that are a distance *r* from a given point, the **center of a circle**. The distance *r* is the **radius** of the circle. The use of *distance* in these definitions makes the Distance Formula

$d = \sqrt{(x_2 - x_1)^2 + (y_2 - y_1)^2}$ a useful tool for describing a circle in the coordinate plane.

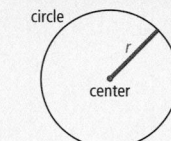

circle

r

center

Focus Question How is the equation of a circle related to its graph?

An equation of a circle with center (0, 0) and radius *r* in the coordinate plane is $x^2 + y^2 = r^2$. Not every circle has its center at the origin. Suppose a circle with radius *r* has center (*h*, *k*). Then *r* is the distance from (*h*, *k*) to any point (*x*, *y*) on the circle.

Use the Distance Formula. $r = \sqrt{(x - h)^2 + (y - k)^2}$
Square each side. $r^2 = (x - h)^2 + (y - k)^2$

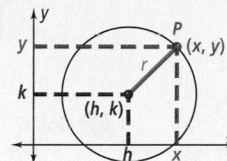

1 Interactive Learning

Solve It!
PURPOSE To apply geometric properties of circles, squares, and right triangles
PROCESS Students may
- use the Pythagorean Theorem or distance formula to find the radius of the pond.
- use properties of right triangles, squares, and congruent triangles to find the radius of the feeder pond.

FACILITATE
Q How can the radius of the pond be measured? **[Draw a diameter perpendicular to a tangent line at the point of tangency. The radius is half the length of the diameter.]**
Q Where is the tangency point of the ponds located? **[in the middle of the upper right side of the patch]**

ANSWER See Solve It in Answers on next page.
CONNECT THE MATH In the Solve It, students find the radii of two circles. In the lesson, students will define a circle as the set of points in a plane a fixed distance—the radius—from a center point.

10-3 Preparing to Teach

BIG idea Equivalence   **UbD**
ESSENTIAL UNDERSTANDINGS
- An equation of a circle with center (0, 0) and radius *r* in the coordinate plane is $x^2 + y^2 = r^2$.
- Not every circle has its center at the origin. Suppose a circle with radius *r* has center (*h*, *k*). Then *r* is the distance from (*h*, *k*) to any point (*x*, *y*) on the circle. The equation is $r^2 = (x - h)^2 + (y - k)^2$.
- $\frac{x^2}{r^2} + \frac{y^2}{r^2} = 1$ is an equation of a circle centered at the origin with radius *r*. Multiply each side by r^2 to get $x^2 + y^2 = r^2$.

Math Background
A circle is the conic section obtained when a cross section of a cone is taken perpendicularly to the cone's axis.

A circle is defined as the set of all points that are equidistant from a given point, called the center. In the coordinate plane, the standard form of an equation of a circle is given by
$(x - h)^2 + (y - k)^2 = r^2$, where

- *h* is the horizontal translation of the center from the origin,
- *k* is the vertical translation of the center from the origin, and
- *r* is the radius, or the distance from the center to any point on the circle.

The lesson shows how to derive the standard equation of a circle from the distance formula. Deriving it using the Pythagorean Theorem is a good activity for interested students. For example, use the same diagram for the distance formula on page 649. Sketch the two legs of a right triangle with *r* as the hypotenuse and the third vertex as (*x*, *k*).

The length of one leg is *x* − *h*, and the length of the second leg is *y* − *k*. Thus by the Pythagorean Theorem, $(x - h)^2 + (y - k)^2 = r^2$.

Support Student Learning
Use the **Algebra 2 Companion** to engage and support students during instruction. See Lesson Resources at the end of this lesson for details.

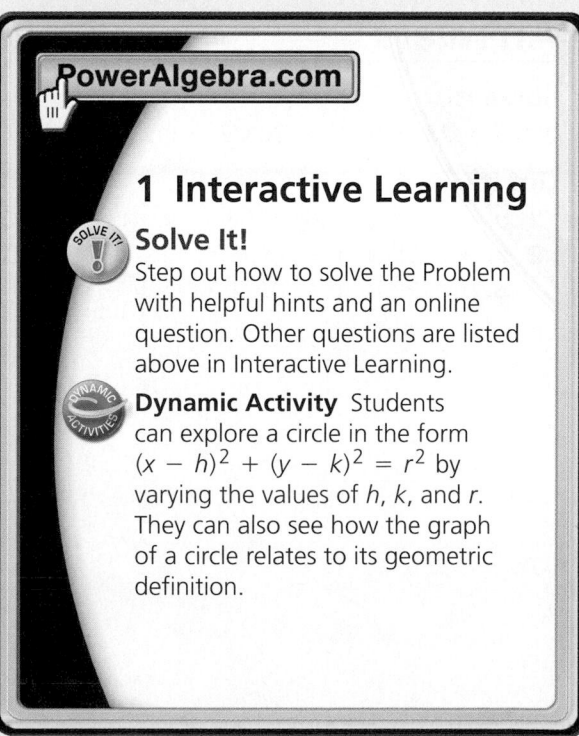

PowerAlgebra.com

1 Interactive Learning

Solve It!
Step out how to solve the Problem with helpful hints and an online question. Other questions are listed above in Interactive Learning.

Dynamic Activity Students can explore a circle in the form $(x - h)^2 + (y - k)^2 = r^2$ by varying the values of *h*, *k*, and *r*. They can also see how the graph of a circle relates to its geometric definition.

2 Guided Instruction

Take Note

Q What information do you need to write the equation of a circle? **[the center or the horizontal and vertical translations of the center from the origin, and the radius]**

Problem 1

Q In the standard form of the equation of a circle, why do you subtract h and k rather than add them? **[Sample: The formula for a circle is derived from the distance formula, in which the variables are subtracted, not added.]**

EXTENSION

Q What does r^2 correspond to in the Pythagorean Theorem? **[r^2 is the square of the length of the hypotenuse.]**

Got It?

Q How can checking the graph of an equation of a circle help you find what errors you may have made in writing the equation? **[Samples: If the center is in the wrong quadrant, one or more signs may be incorrect in the equation; if the radius is too small, it may not have been squared in the equation.]**

Key Concept   Standard Form of an Equation of a Circle

The **standard form of an equation of a circle** with center (h, k) and radius r is $(x - h)^2 + (y - k)^2 = r^2$.

You can use the center and the radius of a circle to write an equation for the circle.

Plan

How do you know which equation to use?
Since this circle is not centered at the origin, use the standard form equation.

Problem 1   Writing an Equation of a Circle

What is an equation of the circle with center $(-4, 3)$ and radius 4? Check your answer.

Use the standard form.	$(x - h)^2 + (y - k)^2 = r^2$
Substitute -4 for h, 3 for k, and 4 for r.	$(x - (-4))^2 + (y - 3)^2 = 4^2$
Simplify.	$(x + 4)^2 + (y - 3)^2 = 16$

An equation of the circle is $(x + 4)^2 + (y - 3)^2 = 16$.

Check   Solve the equation for y.

Write the equation.	$(x + 4)^2 + (y - 3)^2 = 16$
Subtract $(x + 4)^2$ from each side.	$(y - 3)^2 = 16 - (x + 4)^2$
Find the square root of each side.	$y - 3 = \pm\sqrt{16 - (x + 4)^2}$
Add 3 to each side.	$y = \pm\sqrt{16 - (x + 4)^2} + 3$

Enter both functions into your graphing calculator.

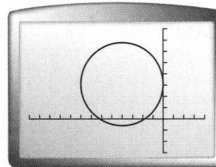

The graph shows a circle with center $(-4, 3)$ and radius 4. ✔

 Got It? 1. What is an equation of the circle with center $(5, -2)$ and radius 8? Check your answer.

Answers

Solve It!
$20\sqrt{2} \approx 28.28$ ft; $40 - 20\sqrt{2} \approx 11.72$ ft

Got It?
1. $(x - 5)^2 + (y + 2)^2 = 64$
2. a. $(x + 5)^2 + (y + 3)^2 = 1$
    b. $(x - 2)^2 + (y - 3)^2 = 9$

PowerAlgebra.com

2 Guided Instruction

 Each Problem is worked out and supported online.

Problem 1
Writing an Equation of a Circle
Animated

Problem 2
Using Translations to Write an Equation
Animated

Problem 3
Using a Graph to Write an Equation

Problem 4
Finding the Center and Radius
Animated

Problem 5
Graphing a Circle Using Center and Radius

Support in Algebra 2 Companion
- Vocabulary
- Key Concepts
- Got It?

You can use the standard form of an equation of a circle to graph a circle.

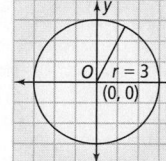 **Problem 2** Using Translations to Write an Equation

What is an equation for the translation of $x^2 + y^2 = 9$ by
4 units left and 3 units up? Draw the graph.

Know

An equation that is
translated 4 units left
and 3 units up

Need

The equation
and graph of the
translation

Plan

• Use the standard form to write the
  equation of the translation.
• Graph the translation.

Step 1 Write the equation of the translation.

Write the original equation. $x^2 + y^2 = 9$

Translate 4 units left
and 3 units up. $(x - (-4))^2 + (y - 3)^2 = 9$

Simplify. $(x + 4)^2 + (y - 3)^2 = 3^2$

Think

How does the
translation help you
draw the graph?
Use the translation
to determine the new
center coordinates.

Step 2 Graph the equation of the translation.

The radius is 3.

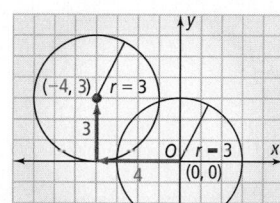

✓ **Got It?** 2. What is an equation for each translation? Draw the graph.
   a. $x^2 + y^2 = 1$; left 5 units and down 3 units
   b. $x^2 + y^2 = 9$; right 2 units and up 3 units

Problem 2

Q Does a translation change the radius? Explain.
**[No; a translation only relocates the graph of the
circle; it does not stretch or shrink the graph of
the circle.]**

Got It?

Q How can you check whether your equation for
the translation of the circle is correct? **[Sketch the
translation without using the translated equation,
and then graph the translated equation using
your graphing calculator. Compare the graphs.]**

Additional Problems

1. What is an equation of a
circle with center $(3, -5)$ and
radius 2?

ANSWER
$(x - 3)^2 + (y + 5)^2 = 4$

2. What is an equation for the
translation of $x^2 + y^2 = 10$
by 2 units right and 5 units
down?

ANSWER
$(x - 2)^2 + (y + 5)^2 = 10$

3. You row a boat from the
water's edge to the center
of a circular pond, located
30 feet north and 80 feet
west of your starting point.
If the location where you
began rowing is the origin,
what equation represents

the water's edge around the
pond?

ANSWER
$(x + 80)^2 + (y - 30)^2 = 7300$

4. What are the center and
radius of the circle with the
equation
$x^2 + y^2 + 2x - 6y = 6$?

ANSWER center $(-1, 3)$,
radius 4

5. What is the graph of
$x^2 + (y - 1)^2 = 16$?

ANSWER

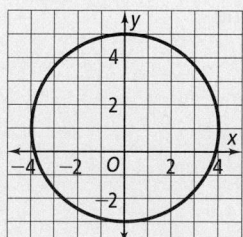

Take Note

Q What are the center and radius of the unit circle?
[(0, 0); 1 unit]

Q What values of r will stretch the unit circle? What values of r will shrink the unit circle? **[values of $r > 1$; values of r such that $0 < r < 1$]**

Problem 3

Q What reason or reasons can you give to eliminate each of the choices B, C, and D? **[For choice B, the values for h and k are reversed, and the signs on h and k are incorrect; for choice C, the radius is not squared; for choice D, the radius is not squared, and the signs on h and k are incorrect.]**

EXTENSION

Q What would be an equation of the circle representing the edge of the field if it were centered at (0, 0)? **[$x^2 + y^2 = 160,000$]**

Got It?

Q What errors might someone make writing the equation of the circular field described in 3a? **[Samples: You might not square the radius; you might add h and k instead of subtracting them; you might forget the square notation; you might reverse the positions of h and k in the equation.]**

Hint
The <u>unit circle</u> is centered at the origin and has radius 1.

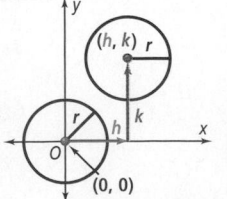

Key Concept   Transforming a Circle

You can use the parameter r to stretch or shrink the unit circle $x^2 + y^2 = 1$ to the circle $x^2 + y^2 = r^2$ with radius r.

You can use the parameters h and k to translate the circle $x^2 + y^2 = r^2$ with center (0, 0) to the circle $(x - h)^2 + (y - k)^2 = r^2$ with center (h, k).

Plan
What information do you need to write an equation for the circle?
You need the center and radius of the circle.

Problem 3   Using a Graph to Write an Equation

Multiple Choice Which equation models the circular irrigation field?

Ⓐ $(x - 450)^2 + (y - 500)^2 = 160,000$ Ⓒ $(x - 450)^2 + (y - 500)^2 = 400$

Ⓑ $(x + 500)^2 + (y + 450)^2 = 160,000$ Ⓓ $(x + 450)^2 + (y + 500)^2 = 400$

According to the photograph, this circular irrigation field has radius 400 and center at the point (450, 500).

Use the standard form.	$(x - h)^2 + (y - k)^2 = r^2$
Substitute the values of h, k, and r from the photograph.	$(x - 450)^2 + (y - 500)^2 = 400^2$
Simplify.	$(x - 450)^2 + (y - 500)^2 = 160,000$

The correct answer is A.

✓ **Got It?** **3. a.** What is an equation of the circle for a circular irrigation field that has radius 12 and center $(7, -10)$?

b. Reasoning Will the graph of every equation of the form $(x - h)^2 + (y - k)^2 = r^2$, where h, k, and r are real numbers, be a circle? Explain your reasoning.

(450, 500)

400 ft

Answers

Got It? (continued)

3. a. $(x - 7)^2 + (y + 10)^2 = 144$

b. Yes; the values of h and k determine the position of the circle, and r determines the size of the circle.

You can find the center and radius of a circle by rewriting the equation in standard form. In some cases, you may need to complete the square.

 Problem 4 Finding the Center and Radius

Plan

What do you need to do to the equation to find the center and radius of the circle?
Write the equation in standard form.

What are the center and radius of the circle with the given equation?

A $(x - 16)^2 + (y + 9)^2 = 144$

Rewrite the equation in standard form.	$(x - 16)^2 + (y - (-9))^2 = 12^2$
Identify h, k, and r.	$h = 16 \qquad k = -9 \qquad r = 12$

The center of the circle is $(16, -9)$. The radius is 12.

B $x^2 + y^2 + 8x - 10y = 8$

Set up to complete the squares.	$(x^2 + 8x) + (y^2 - 10y) = 8$
Complete the squares and balance the equation.	$(x^2 + 8x + 16) + (y^2 - 10y + 25) = 8 + 16 + 25$
Simplify.	$(x + 4)^2 + (y - 5)^2 = 49$
Rewrite in standard form.	$(x - (-4))^2 + (y - 5)^2 = 7^2$
Identify h, k, and r.	$h = -4 \qquad k = 5 \qquad r = 7$

The center of the circle is $(-4, 5)$. The radius is 7.

✔ **Got It? 4.** What are the center and radius of the circle with the given equation?
a. $(x + 8)^2 + (y + 3)^2 = 121$ **b.** $x^2 + y^2 - 6x + 14y = 8$

You can use the center and the radius to graph a circle.

 Problem 5 Graphing a Circle Using Center and Radius

Plan

What information do you need to graph a circle?
You need the center and radius of the circle.

What is the graph of $(x + 1)^2 + (y - 3)^2 = 25$?

Step 1 Identify the center and radius.

Write the original equation.	$(x + 1)^2 + (y - 3)^2 = 25$
Rewrite the equation in standard form.	$(x - (-1))^2 + (y - 3)^2 = 5^2$
Identify h, k, and r.	$h = -1 \qquad k = 3 \qquad r = 5$ **Step 2**

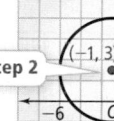

Step 2 Plot the center, $(-1, 3)$.

Step 3 Draw a circle of radius 5.

✔ **Got It? 5.** What is the graph of $(x - 4)^2 + (y + 2)^2 = 49$?

Problem 4

Q What error can be avoided by writing the equation of the circle in 4A in standard form to find the center and the radius? **[The radius will not be mistaken for 144, and the center will be identified correctly.]**

Q In Problem 4B, why do you add 16 to the x^2 and x terms and 25 to the y^2 and y terms? **[to form perfect square trinomials]**

Q Is $(x + 4)^2 + (y - 5)^2 = 49$ in standard form? Explain. **[No; $(x + 4)^2$ is not written as $(x - h)^2$ and 49 is not written as r^2; standard form would be written as $(x - (-4))^2 + (y - 5) = 7^2$.]**

Got It?

Q Is the radius of the circle for 4b equal to the square root of 8? Explain. **[No; the value on the right side of the equation changes after you complete the square and balance the equation.]**

Problem 5

Q How can you check your graph? **[Sample: Solve the equation for y and use a graphing calculator.]**

Q How would you describe the translation of this equation from the parent equation, $x^2 + y^2 = 25$? **[left one, up three]**

Got It?

Q How is $(x - 4)^2 + (y + 2)^2 = 49$ translated from $x^2 + y^2 = 49$? **[right 4, down 2]**

4. a. center $(-8, -3)$, radius 11
b. center $(3, -7)$, radius $\sqrt{66}$

5.

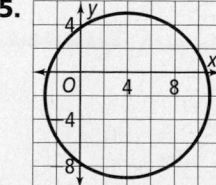

3 Lesson Check

Do you know HOW?

- If students have difficulty writing the equations for Exercises 1–4, then have them identify the values of h, k, and r in each problem and then use the standard form of the equation of a circle.

Do you UNDERSTAND?

- If students have difficulty locating the error in Exercise 5, have them identify several translations such as $(x - 4)^2$, $(x - (-4))^2$, and $(x + 4)^2$. Then have them identify the translation in the problem without looking at the student's answer.
- If students have difficulty completing Exercise 6, then suggest they sketch a picture of the conditions and then sketch a right triangle with one vertex at the origin, one vertex on the circle, and the right angle on the x-axis.

Close

> **Q** What is the standard form of an equation of a circle, and what do the variables h, k, and r represent? **[$(x - h)^2 + (y - k)^2 = r^2$; h and k are the x- and y-coordinates of the center, and r is the radius of the circle.]**

Focus Question How is the equation of a circle related to its graph?

Answer The standard form of the equation of a circle with center (h, k) and radius r is $(x - h)^2 + (y - k)^2 = r^2$. Use the graph of a circle to write its equation, or use the equation of a circle to draw its graph.

 Lesson Check

Do you know HOW?

Use the given information to write an equation of a circle.

1. center at $(-1, -5)$, radius 2

2. center at $(0, 0)$, radius 6

Write an equation for each translation.

3. $x^2 + y^2 = 121$; up 3 units

4. $x^2 + y^2 = 16$; left 5 units and down 3 units

Do you UNDERSTAND?

5. Error Analysis A student claims that the circle $(x + 7)^2 + (y - 7)^2 = 8$ is a translation of the circle $x^2 + y^2 = 8$, 7 units right and 7 units down. What is the student's mistake?

6. Reasoning Let $P(x, y)$ be any point on the circle with center $(0, 0)$ and radius r. Prove that $x^2 + y^2 = r^2$ is an equation for the circle.

 Practice and Problem-Solving Exercises

**Practice**   Write an equation of a circle with the given center and radius. Check your answers.   ◆ **See Problem 1.**

7. center $(0, 0)$, radius 10   **8.** center $(-4, -6)$, radius 7

9. center $(2, 3)$, radius 4.5   **10.** center $(-6, 10)$, radius 1

11. center $(1, -3)$, radius 10   **12.** center $(-1.5, -3)$, radius 2

Write an equation for each translation.   ◆ **See Problem 2.**

Guided Practice

To start, translate left 1 unit.

13. $x^2 + y^2 = 81$; left 1 unit and up 3 units

$(x - (-1))^2 + y^2 = 81$

14. $x^2 + y^2 = 9$; down 1 unit   **15.** $x^2 + y^2 = 25$; right 2 units and down 4 units

16. $x^2 + y^2 = 100$; down 5 units   **17.** $x^2 + y^2 = 49$; right 3 units and up 2 units

---

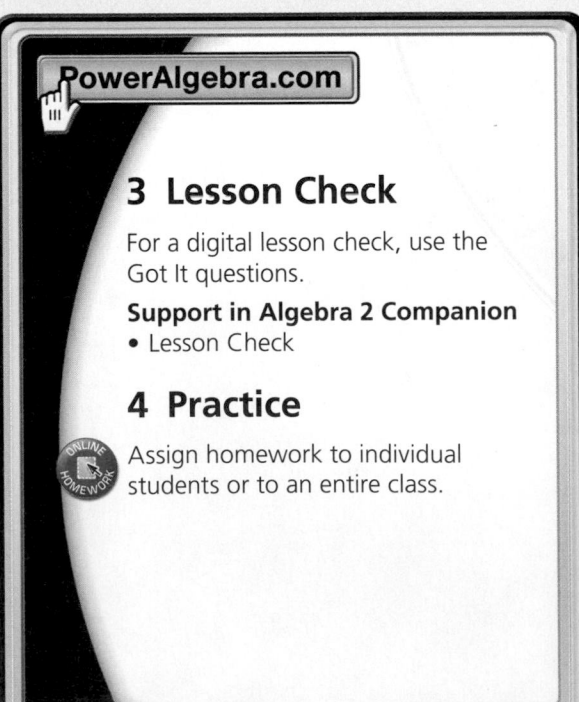

PowerAlgebra.com

3 Lesson Check

For a digital lesson check, use the Got It questions.

Support in Algebra 2 Companion
- Lesson Check

4 Practice

Assign homework to individual students or to an entire class.

Answers

Lesson Check

1. $(x + 1)^2 + (y + 5)^2 = 4$

2. $x^2 + y^2 = 36$

3. $x^2 + (y - 3)^2 = 121$

4. $(x + 5)^2 + (y + 3)^2 = 16$

5. The circle with equation $(x + 7)^2 + (y - 7)^2 = 8$ is a translation of the circle with equation $x^2 + y^2 = 8$ as 7 units left and 7 units up, not right and down.

6. If $P(x, y)$ is one of the pts. $(r, 0)$, $(-r, 0)$, $(0, r)$, or $(0, -r)$, subst. shows that $x^2 + y^2 = r^2$. If $P(x, y)$ is any other pt. on the circle, drop a perpendicular $\overline{PK}$ from P to K on the x-axis. $\triangle OPK$ is a rt. triangle with legs of lengths $|x|$ and $|y|$ and with hypotenuse of length r. By the Pythagorean Thm., $|x|^2 + |y|^2 = r^2$, so $x^2 + y^2 = r^2$.

Practice and Problem-Solving Exercises

7. $x^2 + y^2 = 100$

8. $(x + 4)^2 + (y + 6)^2 = 49$

9. $(x - 2)^2 + (y - 3)^2 = 20.25$

10. $(x + 6)^2 + (y - 10)^2 = 1$

11. $(x - 1)^2 + (y + 3)^2 = 100$

12. $(x + 1.5)^2 + (y + 3)^2 = 4$

13. $(x + 1)^2 + (y - 3)^2 = 81$

14. $x^2 + (y + 1)^2 = 9$

15. $(x - 2)^2 + (y + 4)^2 = 25$

16. $x^2 + (y + 5)^2 = 100$

17. $(x - 3)^2 + (y - 2)^2 = 49$

Write an equation for each circle. Each interval represents one unit. ◀ See Problem 3.

18.

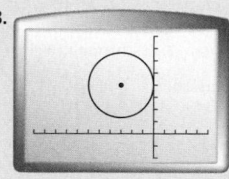

Guided Practice

To start, identify the values of h, k, and r from the graph.

$h = -3$ $\quad k = 4$ $\quad r = 3$

19.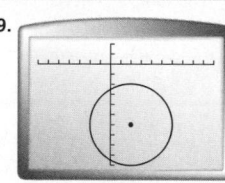

20.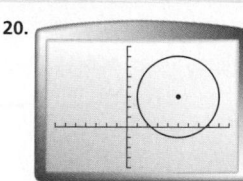

For each equation, find the center and radius of the circle. ◀ See Problem 4.

21. $(x - 1)^2 + (y - 1)^2 = 1$

22. $(x - 3)^2 + (y + 1)^2 = 36$

23. $x^2 + (y + 3)^2 = 25$

24. $(x + 6)^2 + y^2 = 121$

Use the center and the radius to graph each circle. ◀ See Problem 5.

25. $(x + 4)^2 + (y - 4)^2 = 4$

26. $(x - 6)^2 + y^2 = 64$

27. $(x - 7)^2 + (y - 1)^2 = 100$

28. $x^2 + (y + 4)^2 = 144$

 Apply

29. Think About a Plan Three gears of radii 6 in., 4 in., and 2 in. mesh with each other in a motor assembly as shown at the right. What is the equation of each circle in standard form?
  • How can the diagram of the gears in the coordinate plane help you solve this problem?
  • How can you write an equation for each circle?

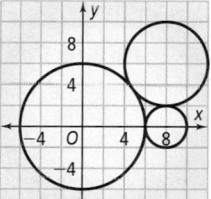

30. Open-Ended Write two functions that together represent a circle.

Write the equation of the circle that passes through the given point and has a center at the origin.

31. $(0, 4)$

32. $(0, -3)$

33. $(4, -3)$

34. $(-2, 3)$

35. $(1, -5)$

36. $(-6, -4)$

> **Hint** Use the Distance Formula to find the radius.

37. Machinery Three gears, A, B, and C, mesh with each other in a motor assembly. Gear A has a radius of 4 in., B has a radius of 3 in., and C has a radius of 1 in. If the largest gear is centered at $(-7, 0)$, the smallest gear is centered at $(4, 0)$, and Gear B is centered at the origin, what is the equation of each circle in standard form?

18. $(x + 3)^2 + (y - 4)^2 = 9$
19. $(x - 2)^2 + (y + 6)^2 = 16$
20. $(x - 5)^2 + (y - 3)^2 = 16$
21. center $(1, 1)$, radius 1
22. center $(3, -1)$, radius 6
23. center $(0, -3)$, radius 5
24. center $(-6, 0)$, radius 11
25.
26.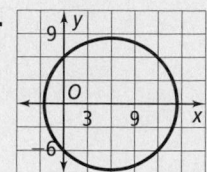

27.

28.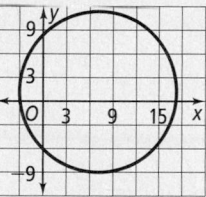

29. $x^2 + y^2 = 36$,
$(x - 8)^2 + (y - 6)^2 = 16$,
$(x - 8)^2 + (y)^2 = 4$
30. Answers may vary. Sample:
$y = \sqrt{25 - x^2}$ and $y = -\sqrt{25 - x^2}$.
31. $x^2 + y^2 = 16$
32. $x^2 + y^2 = 9$
33. $x^2 + y^2 = 25$
34. $x^2 + y^2 = 13$
35. $x^2 + y^2 = 26$
36. $x^2 + y^2 = 52$

37. Gear A: $(x + 7)^2 + y^2 = 16$,
Gear B: $x^2 + y^2 = 9$,
Gear C: $(x - 4)^2 + y^2 = 1$

ASSIGNMENT GUIDE
Basic: 7–10, 13–29, 37
Average: 7–49 odd
Standardized Test Prep: 51–55
Mixed Review: 56–68
Reasoning exercises have blue headings.
Applications exercises have red headings.
EXERCISE 37: Use the Think About a Plan worksheet in the **Student Companion** (also available in the Teaching Resources in print and online) to further support students' development in becoming independent learners.

HOMEWORK QUICK CHECK
To check students' understanding of key skills and concepts, go over Exercises 7, 15, 19, 29, and 39.

Answers

Practice and Problem-Solving Exercises (continued)

38. $(x + 6)^2 + (y - 13)^2 = 49$

39. $(x - 1)^2 + (y + 2)^2 = 10$

40. $(x - 2)^2 + (y - 1)^2 = 25$

41. $(x - 6)^2 + (y - 4)^2 = 25$

42. $(x + 1)^2 + (y + 7)^2 = 36$

43. center $(0, 0)$, radius $\sqrt{2}$

44. center $(0, -1)$, radius $\sqrt{5}$

45. center $(-5, 0)$, radius $3\sqrt{2}$

46. center $(-2, -4)$, radius $5\sqrt{2}$

47. center $(-3, 5)$, radius $\sqrt{38}$

48. center $(-1, 0)$, radius 2

49. center $(3, 1)$, radius $\sqrt{6}$

50. center $(0, 2)$, radius $2\sqrt{5}$

Standardized Test Prep

51. 12

52. 1.45

53. 5

54. $\frac{2}{3}$

55. 0.42

Mixed Review

56. $x = -\frac{1}{12}y^2$

57. at $x = -1$

58. at $x = 2$ and $x = 3$

59. no points of discontinuity

60. 4

61. 2

62. −3

63. 4

64. $\frac{1}{2}$

65. 1

66. −2, −9

67. 0, ±4, ±4i

68. ±2, ±2$\sqrt{2}$

Use the given information to write an equation of the circle.

38. radius 7, center $(-6, 13)$

39. center $(1, -2)$, through $(0, 1)$

40. center $(2, 1)$, through $(6, 4)$

41. center $(6, 4)$, through $(2, 1)$

42. translation of $(x - 1)^2 + (y + 3)^2 = 36$, 2 units left and 4 units down

Find the center and the radius of each circle.

43. $x^2 + y^2 = 2$

44. $x^2 + (y + 1)^2 = 5$

45. $(x + 5)^2 + y^2 = 18$

46. $(x + 2)^2 + (y + 4)^2 = 50$

47. $(x + 3)^2 + (y - 5)^2 = 38$

48. $x^2 + 2x + 1 + y^2 = 4$

49. $x^2 + y^2 - 6x - 2y + 4 = 0$

50. $x^2 + y^2 - 4y - 16 = 0$

Standardized Test Prep

GRIDDED RESPONSE

SAT/ACT

51. What is the radius of the circle with equation $(x + 5)^2 + (y - 3)^2 = 144$?

52. Find the positive zero of the function $y = x^2 + 2x - 5$ by graphing. Enter your answer as a decimal to the nearest hundredth.

53. What is the distance between $T(9, -5)$ and the center of the circle with equation $(x - 6)^2 + (y + 1)^2 = 10$?

54. What is the common ratio in a geometric series if $a_2 = \frac{2}{5}$ and $a_5 = \frac{16}{135}$? Enter your answer as a fraction.

55. Evaluate the sum $\sum_{n=1}^{3}\left(\frac{1}{n+1}\right)^2$. Enter your answer as a decimal to the nearest hundredth.

Mixed Review

56. What is an equation of a parabola opening left with vertex $(0, 0)$ and focus $(-3, 0)$?

See Lesson 10-2.

For each rational function, find any points of discontinuity.

See Lesson 8-3.

57. $y = \frac{2}{x + 1}$

58. $y = \frac{1}{x^2 - 5x + 6}$

59. $y = \frac{2x - 1}{x^2 + 4}$

Evaluate each logarithm.

See Lesson 7-3.

60. $\log_2 16$

61. $\log_5 25$

62. $\log_3 \frac{1}{27}$

63. $\log 10,000$

64. $\log_{36} 6$

65. $\log_{100} 100$

Get Ready!   To prepare for Lesson 10-4, do Exercises 66–68.

Solve each equation.

See Lesson 5-3.

66. $x^2 + 11x = -18$

67. $m^5 - 256m = 0$

68. $p^4 + 32 = 12p^2$

Additional Instructional Support

Algebra 2 Companion

Students can use the **Algebra 2 Companion** worktext (4 pages) as you teach the lesson. Use the Companion to support

- New Vocabulary
- Key Concepts
- Got It for each Problem
- Lesson Check

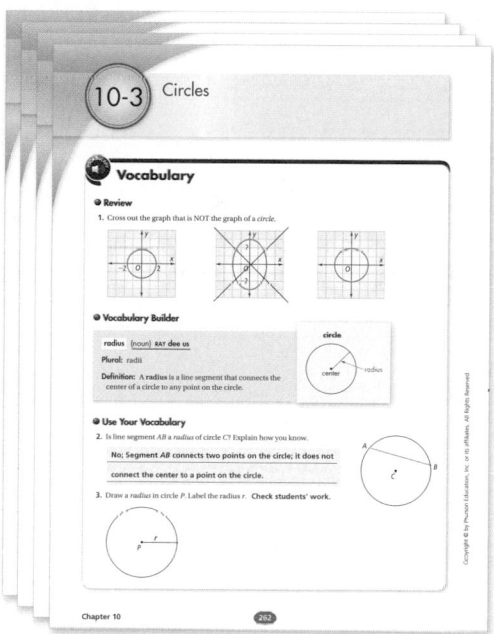

ELL Support

Focus on Language Give students a coordinate plane, and have them write and graph an equation of a circle that fits in the coordinate plane and uses only integers. In pairs, have students try to guess the other person's equation. When a student misses, he or she may ask a question about the horizontal translation, vertical translation, or radius. The other student should answer the question with, for example, "My circle is translated farther left than that." The students should take turns until they have both figured out the other student's equation. Monitor to make sure the students are using correct vocabulary to describe the translations and changes in radius.

5 Assess & Remediate

Lesson Quiz

1. What is an equation of a circle with center $(-2, -1)$ and radius 3?

2. What is an equation for the translation of $x^2 + y^2 = 3.6$ by 1 unit left and 2 units down?

3. **Do you UNDERSTAND?** You have a tree in your yard 4 ft to the left of and 5 ft in front of the corner of your porch. A circular fence 3 ft in radius has its center at the tree. If the corner of your porch is the origin and forward is the positive y direction, what equation represents the circle formed by the fence in your yard?

4. What are the center and radius of the circle with equation $x^2 + 12x + y^2 + 4y = -31$?

5. What is the graph of $(x + 1)^2 + (y + 3)^2 = 25$?

ANSWERS TO LESSON QUIZ

1. $(x + 2)^2 + (y + 1)^2 = 9$
2. $(x + 1)^2 + (y + 2)^2 = 3.6$
3. $(x + 4)^2 + (y - 5)^2 = 9$
4. center $(-6, -2)$, radius 3
5.

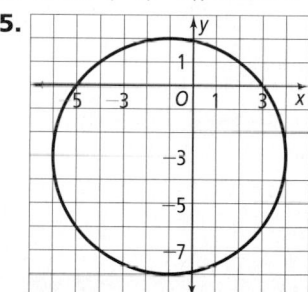

PRESCRIPTION FOR REMEDIATION

Use the student work on the Lesson Quiz to prescribe a differentiated review assignment:

Points	Differentiated Remediation
0–2	Intervention
3–4	On-level
5	Extension

PowerAlgebra.com

5 Assess & Remediate

Assign the Lesson Quiz. Appropriate intervention, practice, or enrichment is automatically generated based on student performance.

Intervention

- **Reteaching** (2 pages) Provides reteaching and practice exercises for the key lesson concepts. Use with struggling students or absent students.

- **English Language Learner Support** Helps students develop and reinforce mathematical vocabulary and key concepts.

All-in-One Resources/Online
Reteaching

10-3 Reteaching
Circles

- When working with circles, begin by writing the equation in standard form:
$(x - h)^2 + (y - k)^2 = r^2$
- Unlike equations of parabolas, which include either x^2 or y^2, the equation of a circle will include both x^2 and y^2.

Problem

What is the center and radius of the circle with the equation $x^2 + y^2 - 4x + 6y = 12$?

| $(x^2 - 4x)$ | + | $(y^2 + 6y) = 12$ | Rearrange and group the terms by variable. |

$\frac{b}{2} = \frac{-4}{2} = -2$ $\frac{b}{2} = \frac{6}{2} = 3$ To complete each square, find $\frac{b}{2}$ for each group.

$\left(\frac{b}{2}\right)^2 = (-2)^2 = 4$ $\left(\frac{b}{2}\right)^2 = (3)^2 = 9$ Find $\left(\frac{b}{2}\right)^2$ for each expression.

$(x^2 - 4x + 4) + (y^2 + 6y + 9) = 12 + 4 + 9$ Add $\left(\frac{b}{2}\right)^2$ for each expression to both sides.

$(x - 2)^2 + (y + 3)^2 = 25$ Write the expressions as perfect squares; simplify.

$(x - 2)^2 + (y - (-3))^2 = 5^2$ Write the equation in standard form.

$h = 2, k = -3, r = 5$ Compare the equation to $(x - h)^2 + (y - k)^2 = r^2$.

The center of the circle is $(2, -3)$. The radius of the circle is 5.

Exercises

Find the center and radius of each circle.

1. $x^2 + y^2 - 10y = 0$ (0, 5); 5
2. $x^2 + y^2 = 225$ (0, 0); 15
3. $x^2 + y^2 + 2x - 6y = 15$ (-1, 3); 5
4. $x^2 + y^2 + 12x + 14y = -84$ (-6, -7); 1
5. $x^2 + y^2 + 2x + 4y = 31$ (-1, -2); 6
6. $x^2 + y^2 - 10x - 4y = -20$ (5, 2); 3
7. $x^2 + y^2 + 16x - 8y = -72$ (-8, 4); $2\sqrt{2}$
8. $x^2 + y^2 - 8x + 6y = -5$ (4, -3); $2\sqrt{5}$
9. $x^2 + y^2 - 4x - 6y = 0$ (2, 3); 3
10. $x^2 + y^2 + 8x = 47$ (-4, 0); $3\sqrt{7}$

All-in-One Resources/Online
English Language Learner Support

10-3 ELL Support
Circles

Concept List

center	circle	complete the square
distance formula	parameter	parent graph of a circle
radius		standard from of a circle	translation

Choose the concept from the list below that best represents the item in each box.

1. $x^2 + y^2 = r^2$ parent graph of a circle	2. the set of all points in a plane that are a distance r from a given point circle	3. the method used to change an equation of a circle into standard form complete the square
4. h, k, and r in the equation of a circle parameters	5. $d = \sqrt{(x_2 - x_1)^2 + (y_2 - y_1)^2}$ distance formula	6. the distance r from the center of a circle to a point on the circle radius
7. all points on a circle are equidistant from this point center	8. $(x - h)^2 + (y - k)^2 = r^2$ standard form of a circle	9. movement of the parent graph horizontally or vertically translation

Differentiated Remediation *continued*

On-Level

- **Practice** (2 pages) Provides extra practice for each lesson. For more challenging practice exercises, use the Form G Practice pages found in the All-in-One Teaching Resources and online.

- **Think About a Plan** Helps students develop specific problem-solving skills and strategies by providing scaffolded guiding questions.

- **Standardized Test Prep** Focuses on all major exercises, all major question types, and helps students prepare for the high-stakes assessments.

Extension

- **Enrichment** Provides students with interesting problems and activities that extend the concepts of the lesson.

- **Activities, Games, and Puzzles** Worksheets that can be used for concepts development, enrichment, and for fun!

Student Companion/All-in-One Resources/Online
Practice page 1

10-3 Practice Form K
Circles

Write an equation of a circle with the given center and radius. Check your answers.

1. center (1, 1), radius 4
$(x - 1)^2 + (y - 1)^2 = 16$

2. center (−2, 0), radius 6
$(x + 2)^2 + y^2 = 36$

3. center (5, −3), radius 1
$(x - 5)^2 + (y + 3)^2 = 1$

4. center (−1, −5), radius 5
$(x + 1)^2 + (y + 5)^2 = 25$

Write an equation for each translation.

5. $x^2 + y^2 = 16$; left 2 units and down 1 unit

Translate left 2 units:
$(x - (-2))^2 + y^2 = 16$
$(x + 2)^2 + y^2 = 16$

Translate down 1 unit:
$(x + 2)^2 + (y - \boxed{-1})^2 = 16$
$(x + 2)^2 + (y + \boxed{1})^2 = 16$

6. $x^2 + y^2 = 81$; right 4 units
$(x - 4)^2 + y^2 = 81$

7. $x^2 + y^2 = 1$; left 1 unit and up 1 unit
$(x + 1)^2 + (y - 1)^2 = 1$

8. $x^2 + y^2 = 4$; up 7 units
$x^2 + (y - 7)^2 = 4$

9. $x^2 + y^2 = 36$; right 5 units and down 2 units
$(x - 5)^2 + (y + 2)^2 = 36$

Write an equation for each circle. Each interval represents one unit.

10.
First, identify the center. (4, −3)
Then find the radius. The circle is 4 units wide, so the radius is 2.
Use the standard form $(x - h)^2 + (y - k)^2 = r^2$.
$(x - 4)^2 + (y + 3)^2 = 4$

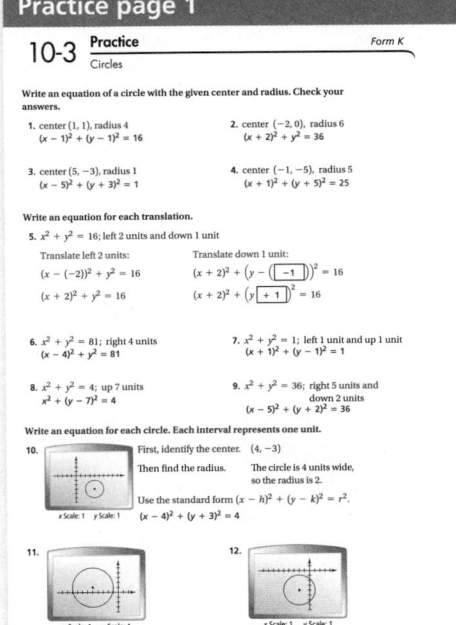

11. x Scale: 1 y Scale: 1
$(x + 5)^2 + (y - 1)^2 = 16$

12. x Scale: 1 y Scale: 1
$(x + 2)^2 + (y + 4)^2 = 9$

Student Companion/All-in-One Resources/Online
Practice page 2

10-3 Practice (continued) Form K
Circles

For each equation, find the center and radius of the circle.

13. $(x + 2)^2 + (y + 2)^2 = 64$
(−2, −2); 8

14. $x^2 + (y - 5)^2 = 16$
(0, 5); 4

15. $(x + 6)^2 + y^2 = 9$
(−6, 0); 3

16. $(x - 7)^2 + (y + 1)^2 = 81$
(7, −1); 9

Use the center and the radius to graph each circle.

17. $(x + 3)^2 + (y - 3)^2 = 16$

Rewrite the equation in standard form. $(x - (-3))^2 + (y - 3)^2 = 4^2$
Find the center and radius from the equation. center (−3, 3), radius 4
Plot the center and draw a circle with the given radius.

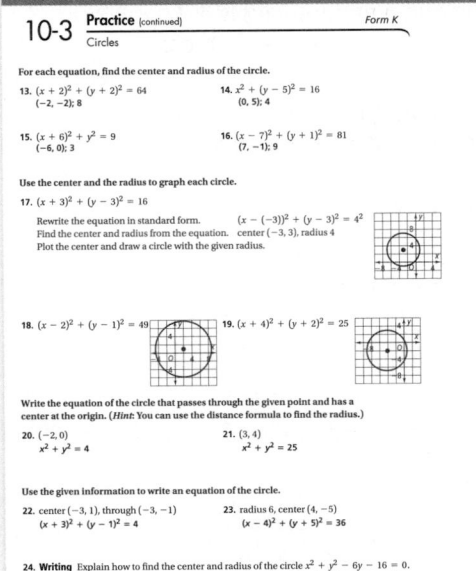

18. $(x - 2)^2 + (y - 1)^2 = 49$

19. $(x + 4)^2 + (y + 2)^2 = 25$

Write the equation of the circle that passes through the given point and has a center at the origin. (*Hint:* You can use the distance formula to find the radius.)

20. (−2, 0)
$x^2 + y^2 = 4$

21. (3, 4)
$x^2 + y^2 = 25$

Use the given information to write an equation of the circle.

22. center (−3, 1), through (−3, −1)
$(x + 3)^2 + (y - 1)^2 = 4$

23. radius 6, center (4, −5)
$(x - 4)^2 + (y + 5)^2 = 36$

24. **Writing** Explain how to find the center and radius of the circle $x^2 + y^2 - 6y - 16 = 0$.
Answers may vary. Sample: Complete the square for $y^2 - 6y$ and rewrite the equation in the form $(x - h)^2 + (y - k)^2 = r^2$: $(x - 0)^2 + (y - 3)^2 = 5^2$. The center is (h, k), so the center of this circle is (0, 3). The radius is 5.

All-in-One Resources/Online
Enrichment

10-3 Enrichment
Circles

In geometry, you learned that a tangent to a circle is a line that intersects the circle in exactly one point. The tangent is also perpendicular to the radius at the point of tangency. Use these facts, along with what you know about the equation of a circle, to solve the problems below.

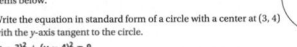

1. Write the equation in standard form of a circle with a center at (3, 4) with the y-axis tangent to the circle.
$(x - 3)^2 + (y - 4)^2 = 9$

2. Write the equation of a circle with radius 2 units with both the x-axis and the y-axis tangent to the circle. Explain why there is more than one equation to describe this circle.
Answers may vary. Sample: $(x - 2)^2 + (y - 2)^2 = 4$; this circle could be located in any quadrant where the centers could be (2, 2), (2, −2), (−2, 2), or (−2, −2).

3. Write the equation in standard form of a circle that is tangent to the y-axis, tangent to the horizontal line $y = 5$, and tangent to the vertical line $x = -4$.
$(x + 2)^2 + (y - 3)^2 = 4$

4. Write the equation in standard form of a circle with a diameter that has endpoints (−1, −3) and (3, −3).
$(x - 1)^2 + (y + 3)^2 = 4$

5. Write the equation in standard form of a circle with center at (−2, 3) that passes through the point (−2, 7).
$(x + 2)^2 + (y - 3)^2 = 17$

6. Write the equation in standard form of a circle with center in the fourth quadrant with the x-axis, the vertical line $x = 4$, and the vertical line $x = 6$ tangent to the circle.
$(x - 5)^2 + (y + 1)^2 = 1$

7. Write the equation of a circle with center on the line $y = 2x$, radius 2, and is tangent to the y-axis.
$(x - 2)^2 + (y - 4)^2 = 4$ or $(x + 2)^2 + (y + 4)^2 = 4$

Student Companion/All-in-One Resources/Online
Think About a Plan

10-3 Think About a Plan
Circles

Machinery Three gears, A, B, and C, mesh with each other in a motor assembly. Gear A has a radius of 4 in., B has a radius of 3 in., and C has a radius of 1 in. If the largest gear is centered at (−4, 0), the smallest gear is centered at (4, 0), and Gear B is centered at the origin, what is the equation of each circle in standard form?

Understanding the Problem

1. The radius of gear $A = \boxed{4}$ in.

2. The radius of gear $B = \boxed{3}$ in.

3. The radius of gear $C = \boxed{1}$ in.

4. The centers of the gears are at what points? (−4, 0), (0, 0), and (4, 0)

5. What is the problem asking you to determine?
an equation for a circle that represents each gear

Planning the Solution

6. What do you need to find an equation for each gear?
the radius and center of each gear

Getting an Answer

7. Fill in the table below to find the equation of the circle that represents each gear.

Gear	(h, k)	r	Equation
A	(−4, 0)	4	$(x + 4)^2 + y^2 = 16$
B	(0, 0)	3	$x^2 + y^2 = 9$
C	(4, 0)	1	$(x - 4)^2 + y^2 = 1$

Student Companion/All-in-One Resources/Online
Standardized Test Prep

10-3 Standardized Test Prep
Circles

Multiple Choice

For Exercises 1–5, choose the correct letter.

1. Which is an equation of the circle with center at the origin and radius 3? C
   A. $x^2 + y^2 = 9$
   B. $x^2 + y^2 = 81$
   C. $x^2 + y^2 = 9$
   D. $(x - 3)^2 + (y - 3)^2 = 9$

2. What is the equation for the translation of $x^2 + y^2 = 16$ two units left and one unit down? I
   F. $x^2 + y^2 = 16$
   G. $(x - 2)^2 + (y - 1)^2 = 16$
   H. $2x^2 + y^2 = 16$
   I. $(x + 2)^2 + (y + 1)^2 = 16$

3. Which equation represents a circle with a center at (7, −9) and a diameter of 8? C
   A. $(x - 7)^2 + (y - 9)^2 = 64$
   B. $(x - 7)^2 + (y + 9)^2 = 16$
   C. $(x - 7)^2 + (y + 9)^2 = 64$
   D. $(x + 7)^2 + (y - 9)^2 = 16$

4. What is the center of the circle $(x - 3)^2 + (y + 2)^2 = 81$? G
   F. (−3, 2)
   G. (3, −2)
   H. (3, 2)
   I. (9, 9)

5. What is the radius of the circle $(x + 8)^2 + (y - 3)^2 = 100$? A
   A. 10
   B. 20
   C. 50
   D. 100

Short Response

6. What are the radius and center of a circle with the equation $(x + 7)^2 + (y - 8)^2 = 144$?
[2] The radius is 12; the center is (−7, 8).
[1] incorrect radius OR center
[0] no answers given

Online Teacher Resource Center
Activities, Games, and Puzzles

10-3 Puzzle: Circles In Squares
Circles

Here is a puzzle about circles in the coordinate plane. You will need a compass.

Draw circles in the grid that meet all of the conditions described below. Use a compass to lightly draw different combinations of circles until you find a correct answer.

- No circle extends beyond the boundary of the puzzle grid.
- All circles have centers whose coordinates are integers.
- There must be two circles with a radius of 3 units, one circle with a radius of 4 units, and one circle with a radius of 5 units.
- No two circles intersect at more than one point.

Answers may vary. Sample graph:

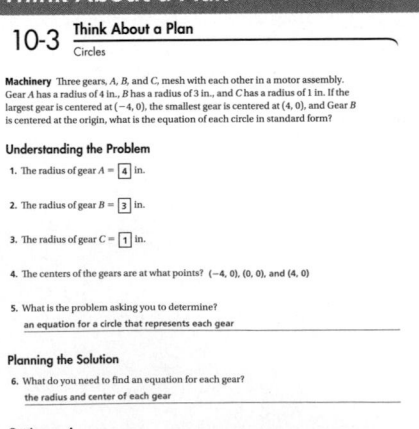

There are different combinations of circles that can be used to find the solution. Use the space below to write the equation for each circle in your solution.
Answers may vary. Sample: $(x + 3)^2 + (y - 3)^2 = 5^2$; $(x - 4)^2 + (y + 4)^2 = 4^2$; $(x - 5)^2 + (y - 4)^2 = 3^2$; $(x + 4)^2 + (y + 5)^2 = 3^2$

On the grid below, insert a point at the center of each circle. Then form a polygon by drawing segments between the centers of the circles. Classify the polygon by the number of sides. Is the polygon *equilateral*, *equiangular*, *regular*, or *none of these*? Explain.
Answers may vary. Sample: Quadrilateral; the polygon is equilateral because all sides are the same length.

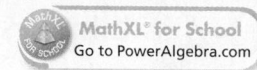

MathXL® for School
Go to PowerAlgebra.com

Do you know HOW?

Graph each equation. Identify the conic section and describe the graph and its lines of symmetry. Then find the domain and range.

1. $y^2 - 2x^2 = 16$

2. $3x^2 + 3y^2 - 12 = 0$

3. $9x^2 - 25y^2 = 225$

4. $36 - 4x^2 - 9y^2 = 0$

Identify the vertex, focus, and directrix of each parabola. Then graph the parabola.

5. $y = 3x^2$

6. $x = 4(y + 2)^2$

7. $y + 1 = (x - 3)^2$

Write an equation for the parabola with the given vertex and focus.

8. vertex $(-5, 4)$; focus $(-5, 0)$

9. vertex $(7, 2)$; focus $(7, -2)$

10. vertex $(0, 0)$; focus $(-7, 0)$

11. vertex $(2, 4)$; focus $(1, 4)$

12. Write an equation that models the graph below.

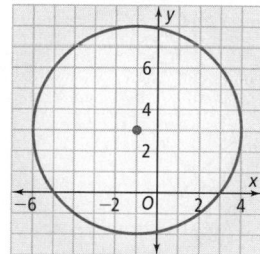

Write an equation in standard form of the circle with the given center and radius.

13. center $(-6, 3)$, radius 8

14. center $(1, 1)$, radius 1.5

Do you UNDERSTAND?

Determine whether each point lies on the graph of the conic section with the given equation.

15. $x^2 + y^2 = 36$
   a. $(-6, 0)$
   b. $(-2, -\sqrt{3})$
   c. $(0, \sqrt{2})$

16. $4x^2 - y^2 - 4 = 0$
   a. $(-1, 0)$
   b. $(2, 2)$
   c. $(1, 0)$

17. **Writing** Suppose that $x^2 = 4py$ and $y = ax^2$ represent the same parabola. Explain how a and p are related.

Reasoning Without graphing, describe how each graph differs from the graph of $y = x^2$.

18. $y = 2x^2$ 19. $y = -x^2$

20. $y = x^2 + 2$ 21. $y = \frac{1}{3}x^2$

22. A circle has center $(0, 0)$ and radius 1. Write an equation that represents the translation of the circle 7 units left and 8 units up. Then graph the equation.

Write the standard form of the equation of the circle that passes through the given point and whose center is at the origin.

23. $(-6, 0)$ 24. $(0, 5)$

25. $(-11, -11)$ 26. $(-8, 14)$

5. vertex: $(0, 0)$;
   focus: $\left(0, \frac{1}{12}\right)$;
   directrix: $y = -\frac{1}{12}$
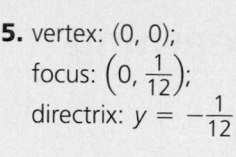

6. vertex: $(0, -2)$;
   focus: $\left(\frac{1}{16}, -2\right)$;
   directrix: $x = -\frac{1}{16}$
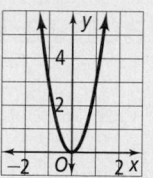

7. vertex: $(3, -1)$;
   focus: $\left(3, -\frac{3}{4}\right)$;
   directrix: $y = -\frac{5}{4}$
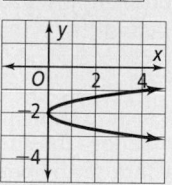

8. $y = -\frac{1}{16}(x + 5)^2 + 4$

9. $y = -\frac{1}{16}(x - 7)^2 + 2$

10. $x = -\frac{1}{28}y^2$

11. $x = -\frac{1}{4}(y - 4)^2 + 2$

12. $(x + 1)^2 + (y - 3)^2 = 25$

13. $(x + 6)^2 + (y - 3)^2 = 64$

14. $(x - 1)^2 + (y - 1)^2 = 2.25$

15. a. yes   b. no   c. no

16. a. yes   b. no   c. yes

17. Solve $y = ax^2$ for x^2. You get $x^2 = \frac{y}{a}$. Then using the transitive property, you get $4py = \frac{y}{a}$. Solving for a, you will find that $a = \frac{1}{4p}$. So, a and p vary inversely.

18. stretch by a factor of 2

19. reflect across the x-axis

20. translated up 2 units

21. compress by a factor of $\frac{1}{3}$

22. $(x + 7)^2 + (y - 8)^2 = 1$
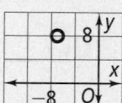

23. $x^2 + y^2 = 36$

24. $x^2 + y^2 = 25$

25. $x^2 + y^2 = 242$

26. $x^2 + y^2 = 260$

Answers

Mid-Chapter Quiz

1.
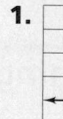
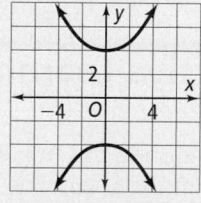

hyperbola: center: $(0, 0)$; no x-intercept, y-intercepts $(0, \pm 4)$; lines of sym.: x-axis and y-axis; domain: all real numbers, range: $y \leq -4$ or $y \geq 4$

2.
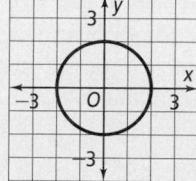

circle: center: $(0, 0)$, radius 2; x-intercepts: $(\pm 2, 0)$, y-intercepts: $(0, \pm 2)$; infinitely many lines of sym.;

domain: $-2 \leq x \leq 2$, range: $-2 \leq y \leq 2$

3.
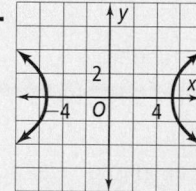

hyperbola: center: $(0, 0)$; x-intercepts $(\pm 5, 0)$, no y-intercepts; lines of sym.: x-axis and y-axis; domain: $x \leq -5$ or $x \geq 5$, range: all real numbers

4.
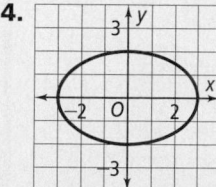

ellipse: center: $(0, 0)$; x-intercepts: $(\pm 3, 0)$, y-intercepts: $(0, \pm 2)$; lines of sym.: x-axis and y-axis; domain: $-3 \leq x \leq 3$, range: $-2 \leq y \leq 2$

1 Interactive Learning

Solve It!

PURPOSE To model an ellipse
PROCESS Students may
- solve the problem physically.
- use algebra and the Pythagorean Theorem.

FACILITATE

Q Make a sketch to show the pencil on the positive *x*-axis. What does the string look like? **[It stretches from one tack to the pencil point and then doubles back to the other tack.]**

Q Let *n* equal the length from the tack on the positive *x*-axis to the pencil point when it is on the *x*-axis. Find the length of the string in terms of *n*. What equation can you write to solve for *n*? **[2*n* + 8; 2*n* + 8 = 10]**

Q How can you use the Pythagorean Theorem to find the *y*-intercept? **[When the pencil is on the *y*-axis, the string forms two right triangles. The hypotenuse is half the length of the string, 5. The distance on the *x*-axis is 4, so the distance on the *y*-axis is 3.]**

ANSWER See Solve It in Answers on next page.
CONNECT THE MATH In the Solve It, students use algebra to identify the *x*- and *y*-intercepts of an ellipse. In the lesson, students will use the definition of an ellipse to identify parts of ellipses and write their equations.

2 Guided Instruction

Take Note

You may want to explain the notation. *P* is any point on the ellipse. The symbol PF_1 refers to the distance from any point *P* to F_1, and F_1F_2 is the distance between F_1 and F_2.

10-4 Ellipses

Objectives To write the equation of an ellipse
To find the foci of an ellipse
To graph an ellipse

Getting Ready!

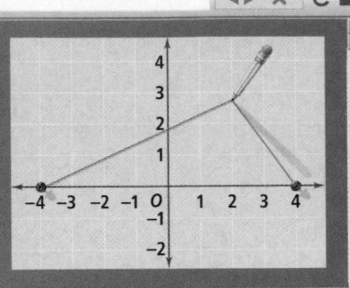

Suppose you have a piece of string 10 units long. You tack down its ends as shown. You place your pencil against the string and, keeping the string taut, you draw a smooth curve.

Where would your pencil hit each axis? Explain your reasoning.

It's not quite a circle.

Points on the smooth curve in the Solve It have a total distance of 10 units to the points $(-4, 0)$ and $(4, 0)$. In fact, all of the points on the smooth curve have a total distance of 10 units to the two fixed points. You can describe this smooth curve with an equation.

Focus Question What is an ellipse?

Lesson Vocabulary
- ellipse
- focus of an ellipse
- major axis
- center of an ellipse
- minor axis
- vertices of an ellipse
- co-vertices of an ellipse

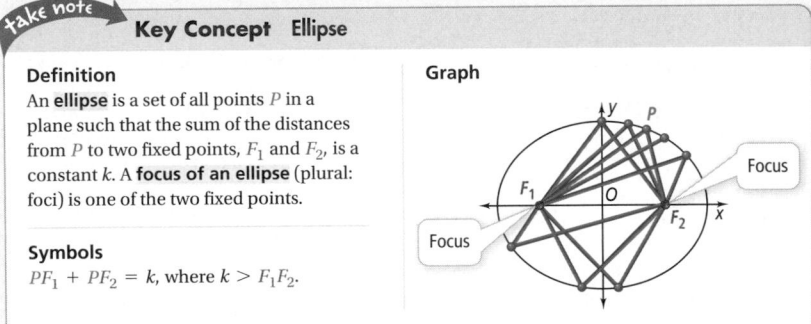

Key Concept Ellipse

Definition
An **ellipse** is a set of all points *P* in a plane such that the sum of the distances from *P* to two fixed points, F_1 and F_2, is a constant *k*. A **focus of an ellipse** (plural: foci) is one of the two fixed points.

Graph

Symbols
$PF_1 + PF_2 = k$, where $k > F_1F_2$.

10-4 Preparing to Teach

BIG idea Coordinate Geometry   **UbD**

ESSENTIAL UNDERSTANDINGS
- A circle is the set of points a fixed distance from one point. An ellipse "stretches" a circle in one direction and is the set of points that have a total fixed distance from two points.
- In the algebraic equation for an ellipse, the x^2 and y^2 terms are both positive. For a hyperbola, one term is negative.

Math Background

An ellipse is a conic section formed by a plane intersecting a cone at a slant, crossing through both sides to form a bounded figure.

The sum of the distances from any point on an ellipse to both foci is a constant.
By convention, the length of the major axis is 2*a* and the length of the minor axis is 2*b*. Therefore, the standard equation of an ellipse depends on its orientation.

- For a horizontal ellipse, the standard equation is $\frac{x^2}{a^2} + \frac{y^2}{b^2} = 1$ because the major axis is the *x*-axis.
- For a vertical ellipse, the standard equation is $\frac{x^2}{a^2} + \frac{y^2}{b^2} = 1$ because the major axis is the *y*-axis.

A circle is a special case of an ellipse in which the major axis and the minor axis have the same length. Therefore, $a = b$ and $c = 0$, and the foci of a circle centered at the origin coincide at the origin, which is also the center of the circle. The radius of the circle is *a* or *b*.

Support Student Learning

Use the **Algebra 2 Companion** to engage and support students during instruction. See Lesson Resources at the end of this lesson for details.

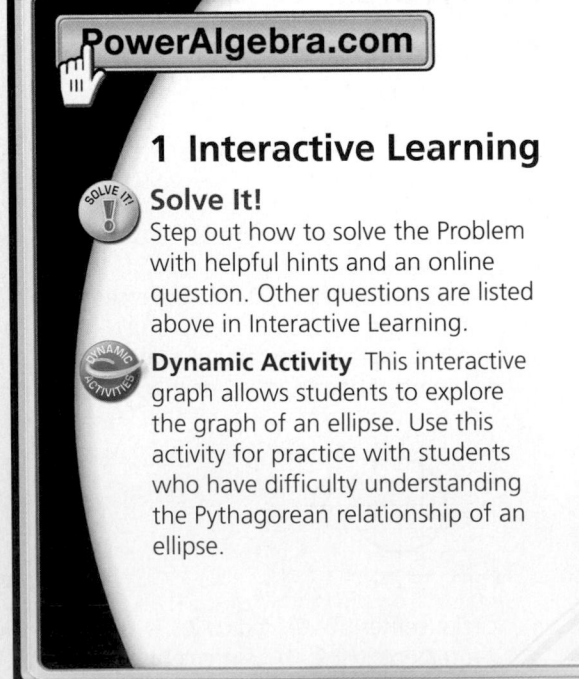

PowerAlgebra.com

1 Interactive Learning

Solve It!
Step out how to solve the Problem with helpful hints and an online question. Other questions are listed above in Interactive Learning.

Dynamic Activity This interactive graph allows students to explore the graph of an ellipse. Use this activity for practice with students who have difficulty understanding the Pythagorean relationship of an ellipse.

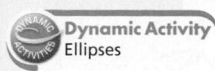

The **major axis** is the segment that contains the foci and has its endpoints on the ellipse. Its midpoint is the **center of the ellipse**. The **minor axis** is perpendicular to the major axis at the center. The **vertices of an ellipse** (singular: *vertex*) are the endpoints of the major axis. The **co-vertices of an ellipse** are the endpoints of the minor axis.

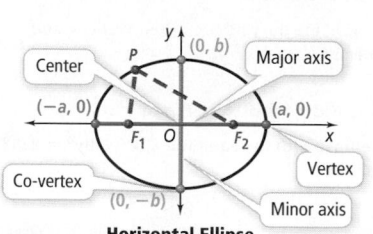

Horizontal Ellipse

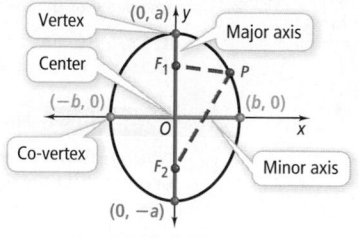

Vertical Ellipse

 Key Concept   **Properties of Ellipses with Center (0, 0)**

	Horizontal Ellipses	Vertical Ellipses
Standard Equation	$\frac{x^2}{a^2} + \frac{y^2}{b^2} = 1, a > b > 0$	$\frac{x^2}{b^2} + \frac{y^2}{a^2} = 1, a > b > 0$
Major Axis	horizontal	vertical
Vertices	$(\pm a, 0)$	$(0, \pm a)$
Co-vertices	$(0, \pm b)$	$(\pm b, 0)$
Foci	$(\pm c, 0)$ on x-axis	$(0, \pm c)$ on y-axis

The length of the major axis is $2a$ and the length of the minor axis is $2b$.
For any point P on an ellipse, $PF_1 + PF_2 = 2a$.

Problem 1   **Writing an Equation of an Ellipse**

What is an equation in standard form of an ellipse centered at the origin with a vertex at $(-6, 0)$ and a co-vertex at $(0, 3)$?

Since one vertex is at $(-6, 0)$, the other vertex is at $(6, 0)$. The major axis is horizontal. Since one co-vertex is $(0, 3)$, the other co-vertex is $(0, -3)$. The minor axis is vertical. So $a = 6$, $b = 3$, $a^2 = 36$, and $b^2 = 9$.

Write the standard form of a horizontal ellipse. $\frac{x^2}{a^2} + \frac{y^2}{b^2} = 1$

Substitute for a^2 and b^2. $\frac{x^2}{36} + \frac{y^2}{9} = 1$

 Got It? 1. What is the equation in standard form of an ellipse centered at the origin with a vertex at $(0, 5)$ and a co-vertex at $(2, 0)$?

Think
What is the orientation of the ellipse?
Since the vertices $(-6, 0)$ and $(6, 0)$ are aligned horizontally, the ellipse is horizontal.

Q Besides containing the foci, what do you notice about the major axis? **[It is always the longer axis.]**

Take Note

Q How does the orientation of the ellipse affect the vertices? **[For horizontal ellipses, the vertices are *x*-intercepts. For vertical ellipses, vertices are *y*-intercepts.]**

Q Why must $a > b > 0$? **[If either *a* or *b* were equal to zero, there would be no major or minor axis and thus no ellipse. If $b > a$, the major and minor axes would be reversed. Since the length of the major axis is 2*a* and minor axis is 2*b*, *a* and *b* cannot be negative.]**

Problem 1

Q What information do you need to find the equation of an ellipse centered at the origin? Explain. **[To write the standard form equation you need a^2 and b^2. Since *a* is a coordinate of the vertex and *b* is a coordinate of the co-vertex, you need the vertex and co-vertex.]**

Got It?

Q The foci of this ellipse are on which axis? How do you know? **[The foci are on the *y*-axis. The foci of an ellipse are always on the major axis. Because 5 > 2 and the ellipse is centered at the origin, the *y*-axis must be the major axis.]**

2 Guided Instruction

 Each Problem is worked out and supported online.

Problem 1
Writing an Equation of an Ellipse
Animated

Problem 2
Finding the Foci of an Ellipse
Animated

Problem 3
Using the Foci of an Ellipse

Problem 4
Using the Foci of an Ellipse
Animated

Support in Algebra 2 Companion
• Vocabulary
• Key Concepts
• Got It?

Answers

Solve It!
It would hit the *x*-axis at $(\pm 5, 0)$; the distance between the pts. where the string is attached is 8 units. The string can go at most 1 unit past both 4 and -4. It would hit the *y*-axis at $(0, \pm 3)$.

Got It?
1. $\frac{x^2}{4} + \frac{y^2}{25} = 1$

You may want to show why $PF_1 + PF_2 = 2a$. By definition, the distances from any point on the ellipse to each focus sums to a constant k. Therefore, the sum of the distances from $P(0, b)$ to each focus equals the sum of the distances from $(a, 0)$ to each focus. By inspection, the sum of the distances from $(a, 0)$ to each focus equals $2a$:

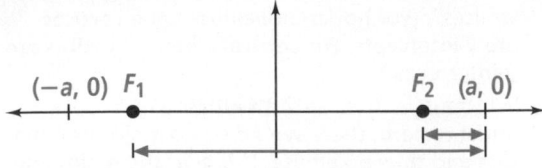

Therefore, $PF_1 + PF_2 = 2a$.

Problem 2

Q What are the characteristics of the standard form of the equation of an ellipse? **[Answers may vary. Sample: The variables are squared and are in the numerators, the two fractions are added, and their sum is 1.]**

Q Can the distance from the foci to the origin of an ellipse ever be less than the distance from the co-vertices to the origin? Give an example.

[yes; $\frac{x^2}{16} + \frac{y^2}{25} = 1$; $c = 3$ and $b = 4$]

EXTENSION

Q What reflective property do you think a circle has? Explain your reasoning. **[A circle is a special case of an ellipse in which the foci coincide at the center. Thus a line emanating from the center of a circle will be reflected back to the center.]**

Hint

The Pythagorean Theorem states that the sum of the squares of the legs of a right triangle is equal to the square of the hypotenuse.

Since the co-vertex $P(0, b)$ is on the ellipse, $PF_1 + PF_2 = 2a$. If you denote the distance from each focus to the center of the ellipse by c, then a, b, and c are the lengths of the sides of a right triangle, as shown in the ellipse at the right. Thus, the distances from the center to each vertex, to each co-vertex, and to each focus are related by the Pythagorean Theorem.

If $(\pm a, 0)$, $(0, \pm b)$, and $(\pm c, 0)$ are the vertices, the co-vertices, and the foci of an ellipse, respectively, then $c^2 = a^2 - b^2$.

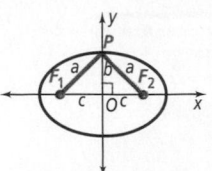

Problem 2 Finding the Foci of an Ellipse

What are the foci of the ellipse with the equation $25x^2 + 9y^2 = 225$? Graph the foci and the ellipse.

Know	Need	Plan
The equation of an ellipse	The coordinates of the vertices, co-vertices, and foci	• Write the equation in standard form to find a^2 and b^2. Use $c^2 = a^2 - b^2$ to find c. • Use a, b, and c to draw the ellipse.

Step 1 Write the equation in standard form.

Write the original equation.	$25x^2 + 9y^2 = 225$
Divide each side by 225.	$\frac{25x^2}{225} + \frac{9y^2}{225} = 1$
Simplify.	$\frac{x^2}{9} + \frac{y^2}{25} = 1$

Think

Is the major axis vertical or horizontal? Since $25 > 9$ and 25 is with y^2, the major axis is vertical.

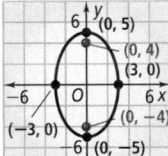

Step 2 Identify the foci.

Identify a^2 and b^2 from the standard equation for a vertical ellipse.	$a^2 = 25$ and $b^2 = 9$
Find the value of c.	$c^2 = a^2 - b^2$
Substitute 25 for a^2 and 9 for b^2.	$c^2 = 25 - 9$
Simplify.	$c^2 = 16$
Find square roots.	$c = \pm 4$

The foci are $(0, 4)$ and $(0, -4)$.

Step 3 Plot points for the vertices, co-vertices, and foci. Then, graph the ellipse.

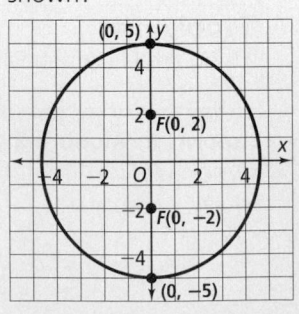

Additional Problems

1. What is an equation of an ellipse in standard form centered at the origin with a vertex at $(8, 0)$ and a co-vertex at $(0, 5)$?

ANSWER $\frac{x^2}{64} + \frac{y^2}{25} = 1$

2. What are the foci of the ellipse with the equation $4x^2 + 36y^2 = 144$? Graph the ellipse.

ANSWER $(-4\sqrt{2}, 0)$ and $(4\sqrt{2}, 0)$

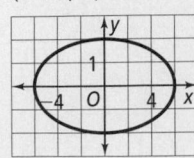

3. Many road-racing tracks in the U.S. are oval, with an asphalt surface in the shape of an ellipse or a flattened ellipse around a grassy infield. If an elliptical track has a major axis of 3400 ft and a minor axis of 1600 ft, how far apart are the foci?

ANSWER 3000 ft

4. What is the standard form equation of the ellipse shown?

ANSWER $\frac{x^2}{21} + \frac{y^2}{25} = 1$

Got It? 2. a. What are the coordinates of the foci of the ellipse with the equation $36x^2 + 100y^2 = 3600$? Graph the ellipse.

    b. Reasoning What happens to the foci as c gets closer to 0? What would the graph of an ellipse be if $c = 0$?

Like parabolas, ellipses have an important reflective property related to their foci: Any line emanating from one focus of an ellipse will reflect off the ellipse directly into the other focus. This property is related to the two-focus definition of an ellipse and is shown in the picture.

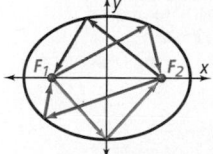

 Problem 3 Using the Foci of an Ellipse

Whispering Gallery A room with an elliptical ceiling (called an *ellipsoid*, since it is 3-dimensional) forms a "whispering gallery." Thanks to the reflective property of the ellipse, a whispered message at one focus can be heard clearly by someone standing across the room at the other focus. If the elliptical ceiling has a major axis of 120 feet and a minor axis of 72 feet, how far apart are the foci?

Plan

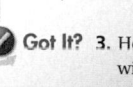

How can you find the distance between foci, given the major and minor axes?
Find the values of a and b. Then, use a^2 and b^2 to solve for c. The distance between the foci is $2c$.

The major axis has length $2a = 120$, so $a = 60$.
The minor axis has length $2b = 72$, so $b = 36$.

$$c = \sqrt{a^2 - b^2}$$
$$= \sqrt{60^2 - 36^2}$$
$$= 48$$

Thus, the foci are $2c = 96$ feet apart.

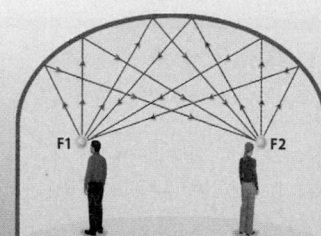

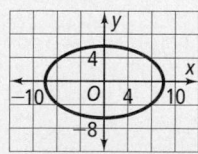 **Got It?** 3. How far apart are the foci of an ellipse with a major axis of 26 ft and a minor axis of 10 ft?

Got It? ERROR PREVENTION

In 2a, check to make sure students find
$c = \sqrt{a^2 - b^2} = \sqrt{100 - 36} = 8$ and not
$c = \sqrt{a^2} - \sqrt{b^2} = \sqrt{100} - \sqrt{36} = 4$.

Problem 3

Q How do you know that the foci are 2c apart? [The calculated value **c** is the distance from the center to one focus. Thus the distance from one focus to the other is 2c.]

Got It?

Q Do you need to know whether the ellipse is horizontal or vertical? Explain. [No; you only need to find the distance between the foci, which does not depend on the orientation.]

Answers

Got It? (continued)

2. a. (± 8, 0).

b. The vertex and co-vertex approach the same distance from the center of the ellipse; a circle

3. 24 ft

Problem 4

Q What are the coordinates of the co-vertices of this ellipse? Do they make sense? **[(0, √39) and (0, −√39); yes; √39 is slightly greater than √36 = 6, and the co-vertices are just above y = 6 and just below y = −6.]**

Got It?

Q Is the major axis of this ellipse horizontal or vertical? **[Vertical; the foci are on the y-axis and co-vertices on the x-axis.]**

Q What are the lengths of the major and minor axes? **[major: 2√53 units; minor: 12 units]**

3 Lesson Check

Do you know HOW?
- For Exercise 1, students could see that the co-vertices are on the y-axis. Therefore, the y-axis is the minor axis and the x-axis is the major axis with vertices (±8, 0).
- For Exercise 2, students should begin by dividing each side of the equation by 100 to put the equation in standard form.

ERROR INTERVENTION
- For Exercise 4, point out that the distance between foci, not the distance from focus to center, is needed.

Do you UNDERSTAND?
- For Exercise 6, challenge students to explain in terms of the standard-form equations and in terms of planes intersecting cones.

Close

Q The distances from the foci to a point on an ellipse are 3 and 5 units. What are other possible whole number values for these distances? **[4 and 4 units; 2 and 6 units]**

How can you write the equation of an ellipse given a focus and a vertex?
Find the values of a and c. Use a^2 and c^2 to find b^2.

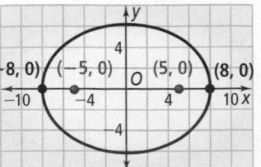

Problem 4 Using the Foci of an Ellipse

What is the standard form equation of the ellipse shown?

The foci are on the x-axis, so the major axis is horizontal.

Since $c = 5$ and $a = 8$, $c^2 = 25$ and $a^2 = 64$.

Relate the values of a, b, and c.	$c^2 = a^2 - b^2$
Substitute.	$25 = 64 - b^2$
Solve.	$b^2 = 39$
Write the standard form of a horizontal ellipse.	$\frac{x^2}{a^2} + \frac{y^2}{b^2} = 1$
Substitute.	$\frac{x^2}{64} + \frac{y^2}{39} = 1$

Got It? 4. What is the standard form equation of an ellipse with foci at $(0, \pm\sqrt{17})$ and co-vertices at $(\pm 6, 0)$?

Focus Question What is an ellipse?
Answer An ellipse is the set of all points P such that the sum of the distances from two fixed points F_1 and F_2 (the foci of the ellipse) is a given constant k.

Lesson Check

Do you know HOW?
1. What is an equation in standard form of an ellipse with co-vertices $(0, \pm 6)$ and major axis with length 16?

2. What are the coordinates of the foci of an ellipse with the equation $4x^2 + 25y^2 = 100$?

3. What is an equation in standard form of an ellipse centered at the origin with vertices $(\pm 13, 0)$ and foci $(\pm 12, 0)$?

4. How far apart are the foci of an ellipse with a major axis of 32 ft and minor axis of 14 ft?

Do you UNDERSTAND?
5. **Error Analysis** A student claims that an equation of the ellipse shown is $\frac{x^2}{41} + \frac{y^2}{29} = 1$. Describe the student's error. What is the correct equation in standard form of the ellipse?

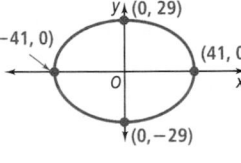

6. **Reasoning** Explain why a circle is a special case of an ellipse.

Answers

Got It? (continued)
4. $\frac{x^2}{36} + \frac{y^2}{53} = 1$

Lesson Check
1. $\frac{x^2}{64} + \frac{y^2}{36} = 1$

2. $(\pm\sqrt{21}, 0)$

3. $\frac{x^2}{169} + \frac{y^2}{25} = 1$

4. $6\sqrt{23}$ ft ≈ 28.77 ft

5. The student used a and b instead of a^2 and b^2; $\frac{x^2}{1681} + \frac{y^2}{841} = 1$

6. The eq. of an ellipse with center at the origin is $\frac{x^2}{a^2} + \frac{y^2}{b^2} = 1$. For a circle, the major axis and the minor axis are of equal length such that $a = b = r$. Thus, by subst., $\frac{x^2}{r^2} + \frac{y^2}{r^2} = 1$ or $x^2 + y^2 = r^2$.

Practice and Problem-Solving Exercises
7. $\frac{x^2}{16} + \frac{y^2}{9} = 1$

8. $\frac{x^2}{4} + y^2 = 1$

9. $\frac{x^2}{9} + y^2 = 1$

Practice and Problem-Solving Exercises

A Practice

Write an equation of an ellipse in standard form with center at the origin and with the given vertex and co-vertex listed respectively.

◆ See Problem 1.

Guided Practice

To start, identify both vertices and co-vertices.

7. $(4, 0), (0, 3)$
Vertices: $(4, 0)$ and $(-4, 0)$
Co-vertices: $(0, 3)$ and $(0, -3)$

8. $(2, 0), (0, 1)$ **9.** $(3, 0), (0, -1)$ **10.** $(0, 6), (1, 0)$

11. $(0, -7), (4, 0)$ **12.** $(-6, 0), (0, 5)$ **13.** $(0, 5), (-3, 0)$

Find the foci for each equation of an ellipse. Then graph the ellipse.

◆ See Problem 2.

Guided Practice

To start, write the equation in standard form.

14. $x^2 + 4y^2 = 16$
$\dfrac{x^2}{16} + \dfrac{y^2}{4} = 1$

15. $\dfrac{x^2}{4} + \dfrac{y^2}{9} = 1$ **16.** $\dfrac{x^2}{9} + \dfrac{y^2}{25} = 1$ **17.** $\dfrac{x^2}{81} + \dfrac{y^2}{49} = 1$

18. $\dfrac{x^2}{25} + \dfrac{y^2}{16} = 1$ **19.** $\dfrac{x^2}{64} + \dfrac{y^2}{100} = 1$ **20.** $3x^2 + y^2 = 9$

Find the distance between the foci of an ellipse. The lengths of the major and minor axes are listed respectively.

◆ See Problem 3.

21. 40 and 24   **22.** 10 and 8   **23.** 16 and 10

24. 20 and 16   **25.** 18 and 14   **26.** 8 and 6

Write an equation of an ellipse for the given foci and co-vertices.

◆ See Problem 4.

27. foci $(\pm 5, 0)$, co-vertices $(0, \pm 8)$ **28.** foci $(0, \pm 4)$, co-vertices $(\pm 2, 0)$

29. Miniature Golf The figure at the right represents a miniature golf green. The green is elliptical with the tee at one focus and the hole at the other.
a. How far is the hole from the tee?
b. Knowing that the border is elliptical, how should you aim your putt from the tee?

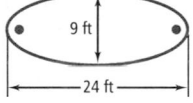
9 ft
24 ft

Practice and Problem-Solving Exercises

10. $x^2 + \dfrac{y^2}{36} = 1$

11. $\dfrac{x^2}{16} + \dfrac{y^2}{49} = 1$

12. $\dfrac{x^2}{36} + \dfrac{y^2}{25} = 1$

13. $\dfrac{x^2}{9} + \dfrac{y^2}{25} = 1$

14. $(\pm 2\sqrt{3}, 0)$

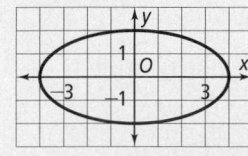

15. $(0, \pm\sqrt{5})$

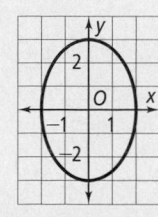

16. $(0, \pm 4)$

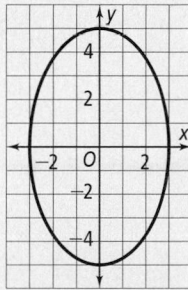

17. $(\pm 4\sqrt{2}, 0)$

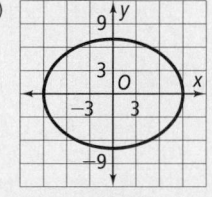

18. $(\pm 3, 0)$

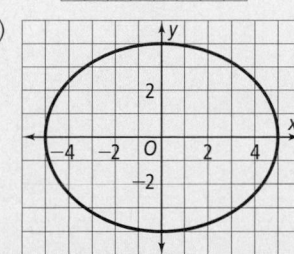

19. $(0, \pm 6)$

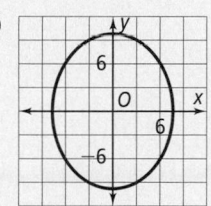

20. $(0, \pm\sqrt{6})$

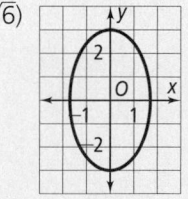

21. 32   **22.** 6   **23.** $2\sqrt{39}$
24. 12   **25.** $8\sqrt{2}$ **26.** $2\sqrt{7}$

27. $\dfrac{x^2}{89} + \dfrac{y^2}{64} = 1$ **28.** $\dfrac{x^2}{4} + \dfrac{y^2}{20} = 1$

29. a. about 22.25 ft
b. Due to the reflective prop. of an ellipse, you can aim your putt at any part of the border. The ball will reflect off the border and go directly into the hole.

ASSIGNMENT GUIDE
Basic: 7–18, 21–29, 34, 39
Average: 7–33 odd, 34–39, 41–47 odd
Standardized Test Prep: 48–51
Mixed Review: 52–61

Reasoning exercises have blue headings.

Applications exercises have red headings.

EXERCISE 39: Use the Think About a Plan worksheet in the **Student Companion** (also available in the Teaching Resources in print and online) to further support students' development in becoming independent learners.

HOMEWORK QUICK CHECK
To check students' understanding of key skills and concepts, go over Exercises 9, 15, 21, 34, and 39.

Answers

Practice and Problem-Solving
Exercises (continued)

30. $(\pm\sqrt{5}, 0)$

31. $(0, \pm2\sqrt{3})$

32. $(\pm4\sqrt{2}, 0)$

33. $(0, \pm1)$

34. $\dfrac{x^2}{279{,}841} + \dfrac{y^2}{203{,}401} = 1$

35. a. 0.9

    b. 0.1

    c. The shape is close to a circle.

    d. The shape is close to a line segment.

36. $\dfrac{x^2}{9} + \dfrac{y^2}{4} = 1$

37. $\dfrac{x^2}{16} + y^2 = 1$

38. Check students' work.

39. $\dfrac{x^2}{1681} + \dfrac{y^2}{841} = 1$

40. $\dfrac{x^2}{4} + \dfrac{y^2}{3} = 1$

41. $\dfrac{x^2}{25} + \dfrac{y^2}{4} = 1$

42. $\dfrac{x^2}{121} + \dfrac{y^2}{81} = 1$

43. $\dfrac{x^2}{169} + \dfrac{y^2}{144} = 1$

44. $\dfrac{x^2}{256} + \dfrac{y^2}{324} = 1$

45. $\dfrac{x^2}{16} + \dfrac{y^2}{12} = 1$

46. $\dfrac{x^2}{39} + \dfrac{y^2}{64} = 1$

47. $\dfrac{x^2}{36} + \dfrac{y^2}{27} = 1$

 Apply

Find the foci for each equation of an ellipse.

30. $4x^2 + 9y^2 = 36$

31. $16x^2 + 4y^2 = 64$

32. $36x^2 + 4y^2 = 144$

33. $25x^2 + 24y^2 = 600$

34. Think About a Plan The open area south of the White House is known as the Ellipse, or President's Park South. It is 902 ft wide and 1058 ft long. Assume the origin is at the center of the President's Park South. What is the equation of the ellipse in standard form?
- How does the length and width of the ellipse relate to the equation?
- What does the center at the origin tell you?
- How can you write the equation of the ellipse in standard form?

35. The eccentricity of an ellipse is a measure of how nearly circular it is. Eccentricity is defined as $\frac{c}{a}$, where c is the distance from the center to a focus and a is the distance from the center to a vertex.
- **a.** Find the eccentricity of an ellipse with foci $(\pm9, 0)$ and vertices $(\pm10, 0)$.
- **b.** Find the eccentricity of an ellipse with foci $(\pm1, 0)$ and vertices $(\pm10, 0)$.
- **c.** Describe the shape of an ellipse that has an eccentricity close to 0.
- **d.** Describe the shape of an ellipse that has an eccentricity close to 1.

Write an equation for each ellipse.

36.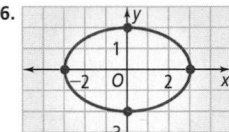

37.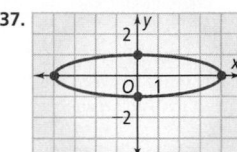

38. Open-Ended Find a real-world design that uses ellipses. Place a coordinate grid over the design and write an equation of the ellipse.

39. Aerodynamics Scientists used the Transonic Tunnel at NASA Langley Research Center, Virginia, to study the dynamics of air flow. The elliptical opening of the Transonic Tunnel is 82 ft wide and 58 ft high. What is an equation of the ellipse?

Write an equation of an ellipse in standard form with center at the origin and with the given characteristics.

40. focus $(1, 0)$, width 4

41. $a = 5$, $b = 2$, width 10

42. vertex $(-11, 0)$, co-vertex $(0, 9)$

43. focus $(-5, 0)$, co-vertex $(0, -12)$

44. $c^2 = 68$, vertex $(0, -18)$

45. focus $(2, 0)$, x-intercept 4

46. focus $(0, -5)$, y-intercept 8

47. focus $(3, 0)$, x-intercept -6

48. Which equation is represented by the circle shown?

   Ⓐ $(x - 1)^2 + (y + 2)^2 = 4$ Ⓒ $(x + 2)^2 + (y - 1)^2 = 4$

   Ⓑ $(x + 1)^2 + (y - 2)^2 = 4$ Ⓓ $(x - 2)^2 + (y + 1)^2 = 4$

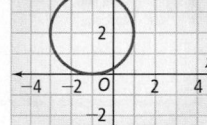

49. What is the center of the circle with equation $(x + 3)^2 + (y - 2)^2 = 49$?

   Ⓕ $(3, -2)$ Ⓖ $(-3, 2)$ Ⓗ $(3, 2)$ Ⓘ $(-3, -2)$

50. The graph of which equation contains all the points in the table below?

x	−4	−2	0	2	4
y	0	$\pm\sqrt{3}$	± 2	$\pm\sqrt{3}$	0

   Ⓐ $x^2 + 4y^2 = 16$ Ⓑ $4x^2 + 16y^2 = 144$ Ⓒ $4x^2 + 25y^2 = 64$ Ⓓ $9x^2 + 4y^2 = 81$

51. Find the horizontal asymptote of $y = \frac{5x + 7}{x + 3}$ by dividing the numerator by the denominator. Explain your steps.

Mixed Review

Write an equation of a circle with the given center and radius.   ◀ See Lesson 10-3.

52. center $(1, -5)$, radius 3   **53.** center $(-2, 4)$, radius 9

Simplify each expression. State any restrictions on the variable.   ◀ See Lesson 8-4.

54. $\frac{3x}{6x^2 - 9x^5}$ **55.** $\frac{x^2 - 36}{x^2 + 5x - 6}$ **56.** $\frac{x^2 - 3x - 10}{x^3 + 8}$

Write each expression as a single logarithm.   ◀ See Lesson 7-4.

57. $\log 3 + \log 5$ **58.** $\log_3 12 - \log_3 2$ **59.** $3 \log 2 - \log 4$

Get Ready!   To prepare for Lesson 10-5, do Exercises 60 and 61.

Write an equation of a line in slope-intercept form using the given information.   ◀ See Lesson 2-3.

60. $m = 2$ and the y-intercept is 4   **61.** passes through $(3, 1)$ and $(9, 3)$

Standardized Test Prep

48. B

49. G

50. A

51. [2]
$$x + 3 \overline{)\begin{array}{r} 5 \\ 5x + 7 \end{array}}$$
$$\underline{5x + 15}$$
$$-8$$
$y = 5 - \frac{8}{x + 3}$;
horizontal asymptote at $y = 5$

   [1] correct asymptote, without work shown

Mixed Review

52. $(x - 1)^2 + (y + 5)^2 = 9$

53. $(x + 2)^2 + (y - 4)^2 = 81$

54. $\frac{1}{2x - 3x^4}$; $x \neq 0$ or $\sqrt[3]{\frac{2}{3}}$

55. $\frac{x - 6}{x - 1}$; $x \neq 1$ or -6

56. $\frac{x - 5}{x^2 - 2x + 4}$; $x \neq -2$

57. $\log 15$

58. $\log_3 6$

59. $\log 2$

60. $y = 2x + 4$

61. $y = \frac{1}{3}x$

Additional Instructional Support

Algebra 2 Companion

Students can use the **Algebra 2 Companion** worktext (4 pages) as you teach the lesson. Use the Companion to support

- New Vocabulary
- Key Concepts
- Got It for each Problem
- Lesson Check

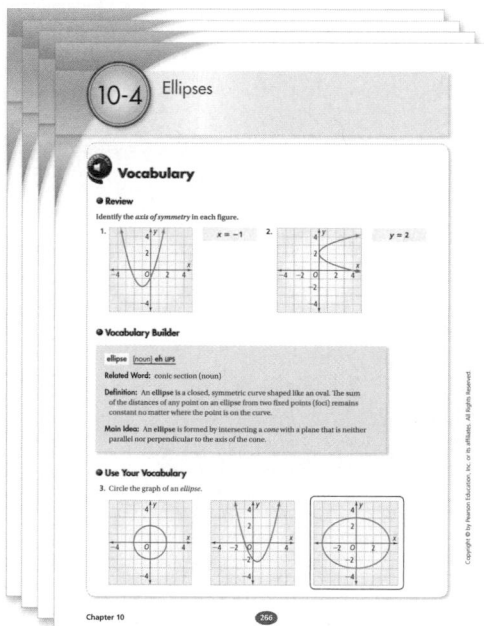

ELL Support

Focus on Language Ask the following questions:

- The plural form of a noun refers to more than one thing. For instance, this is a book. These are books. How did the word *book* change when plural?
- What are two vocabulary words in today's lesson that you do not add an *s* to when making the word plural?
- The plural of *vertex* is *vertices*. The *-ex* becomes *-ices*. With a partner, look through the table of contents of your math textbook to find two other words that end in *-ex*. When you find one, say the word and the plural form to your partner.
- What did you find? What are the plural forms?
- Another math word like this is *axis* and its plural *axes*.
- The plural of *focus* is *foci*. The *-us* becomes *-i*. Try to think of some words that end in *–us*, and say the plural form to your partner. You might think about types of animals.

5 Assess & Remediate

Lesson Quiz

1. What is an equation in standard form of an ellipse centered at the origin with a vertex at (0, 4) and a co-vertex at (−1, 0)?

2. What are the foci of the ellipse with the equation $81x^2 + 1681y^2 = 136{,}161$? Graph the ellipse.

3. **Do you UNDERSTAND?** The planets in our solar system have elliptical orbits with the sun at one focus. The major axis of Mercury's orbit is about 11.6 million km long. The foci of Mercury's orbit are about 2.4 million km apart. About how long is the minor axis of Mercury's orbit?

4. What is the standard form equation of the ellipse centered at the origin with co-vertices (0, ±20) and foci (±15, 0)?

ANSWERS TO LESSON QUIZ

1. $\dfrac{x^2}{1} + \dfrac{y^2}{16} = 1$

2. (−40, 0) and (40, 0)

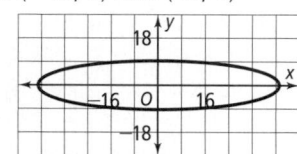

3. about 11.3 million km

4. $\dfrac{x^2}{625} + \dfrac{y^2}{400} = 1$

PRESCRIPTION FOR REMEDIATION
Use the student work on the Lesson Quiz to prescribe a differentiated review assignment:

Points	Differentiated Remediation
0–2	Intervention
3	On-level
4	Extension

PowerAlgebra.com

5 Assess & Remediate

Assign the Lesson Quiz. Appropriate intervention, practice, or enrichment is automatically generated based on student performance.

Intervention

- **Reteaching** (2 pages) Provides reteaching and practice exercises for the key lesson concepts. Use with struggling students or absent students.
- **English Language Learner Support** Helps students develop and reinforce mathematical vocabulary and key concepts.

All-in-One Resources/Online
Reteaching

10-4   Reteaching
   Ellipses

All-in-One Resources/Online
English Language Learner Support

10-4   ELL Support
   Ellipses

Differentiated Remediation *continued*

On-Level

- **Practice** (2 pages) Provides extra practice for each lesson. For more challenging practice exercises, use the Form G Practice pages found in the All-in-One Teaching Resources and online.

- **Think About a Plan** Helps students develop specific problem-solving skills and strategies by providing scaffolded guiding questions.
- **Standardized Test Prep** Focuses on all major exercises, all major question types, and helps students prepare for the high-stakes assessments.

Extension

- **Enrichment** Provides students with interesting problems and activities that extend the concepts of the lesson.
- **Activities, Games, and Puzzles** Worksheets that can be used for concepts development, enrichment, and for fun!

Student Companion/All-in-One Resources/Online
Practice page 1

10-4 Practice — Form K
Ellipses

Write an equation of an ellipse in standard form with center at the origin with the given vertex and co-vertex listed. (Note that the vertex is listed first and the co-vertex is listed second.)

1. (3, 0), (0, 1)   Because one vertex is at (3, 0), the other vertex is at (−3, 0).
The major axis is horizontal.
Because one co-vertex is at (0, 1), the other co-vertex is at (0, −1).
The minor axis is vertical.
$a = \boxed{3}$, $b = \boxed{1}$, $a^2 = \boxed{9}$, and $b^2 = \boxed{1}$.
Write the standard form of a horizontal ellipse $\frac{x^2}{a^2} + \frac{y^2}{b^2} = 1$
Substitute for a^2 and b^2. $\frac{x^2}{9} + y^2 = 1$

2. (0, −7), (2, 0) $\frac{x^2}{4} + \frac{y^2}{49} = 1$ 3. (−5, 0), (0, −4) $\frac{x^2}{25} + \frac{y^2}{16} = 1$

Find the foci for each equation of an ellipse. Then graph the ellipse.

4. $16x^2 + 25y^2 = 400$
Write the equation in standard form. $\frac{x^2}{25} + \frac{y^2}{16} = 1$
Find the vertices, co-vertices, and foci   vertices: (−5, 0) and (5, 0)
from the equation.   co-vertices: (0, −4) and (0, 4)
foci: (−3, 0) and (3, 0)
Plot the points to graph the ellipse.

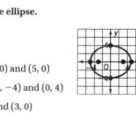

5. $\frac{x^2}{4} + \frac{y^2}{16} = 1$ (0, 2√3), (0, −2√3)   6. $4x^2 + 16y^2 = 16$ (√3, 0), (−√3, 0)

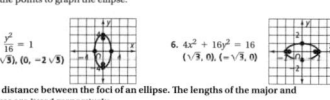

Find the distance between the foci of an ellipse. The lengths of the major and minor axes are listed respectively.

7. 26, 24 **10**   8. 30, 18 **24**   9. 18, 12 **6√5**

Student Companion/All-in-One Resources/Online
Practice page 2

10-4 Practice (continued) — Form K
Ellipses

Write an equation of an ellipse for the given foci and co-vertices.

10. foci (0, ±3), co-vertices (±1, 0)
The foci are on the y-axis, so the major axis is vertical.
Because $c = 3$ and $b = 1$, $c^2 = 9$ and $b^2 = 1$.
$c^2 = a^2 − b^2$
Find a^2: $9 = a^2 − 1$ Write the equation: $\frac{x^2}{b^2} + \frac{y^2}{a^2} = 1$
$a^2 = \boxed{10}$ $x^2 + \frac{y^2}{10} = 1$

11. foci (±1, 0), co-vertices (0, ±5) $\frac{x^2}{26} + \frac{y^2}{25} = 1$ 12. foci (0, ±4), co-vertices (±4, 0) $\frac{x^2}{16} + \frac{y^2}{32} = 1$

13. The decorative arch of a bridge is shaped like an ellipse. The arch is 120 ft wide and the foci are 48 ft from the center of the arch. What is the height of the arch? **36 ft**

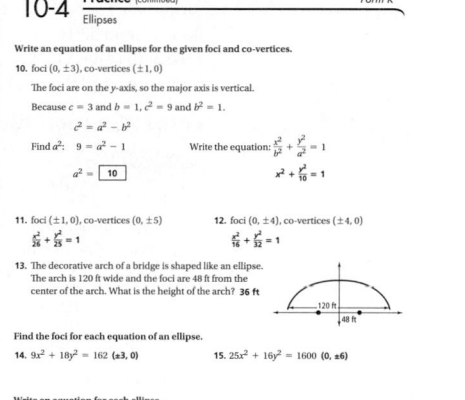
120 ft / 48 ft

Find the foci for each equation of an ellipse.

14. $9x^2 + 18y^2 = 162$ (±3, 0)   15. $25x^2 + 16y^2 = 1600$ (0, ±6)

Write an equation for each ellipse.

16. $\frac{x^2}{9} + \frac{y^2}{4} = 1$ 17. $\frac{x^2}{4} + y^2 = 1$

18. **Reasoning** How are the major and minor axes of an ellipse similar? How are they different? **Answers may vary. Sample: The major and minor axes both pass through the center of the ellipse and are both lines of symmetry of the ellipse. The length of the major axis is greater than the length of the minor axis and the foci lie on the major axis.**

All-in-One Resources/Online
Enrichment

10-4 Enrichment
Ellipses

The orbit, or path, of a planet around the sun can be described by an ellipse with the sun as one of the foci. The point in its orbit at which a planet is closest to the sun is called the perihelion. The point at which the planet is farthest from the sun is called the aphelion.

Solve

1. Suppose that a planet's distance from the sun at aphelion and at perihelion are the same. What is the shape of the planet's orbit? **circle**

2. Suppose that a coordinate plane is superimposed on the planet's orbit centered at the origin. If the aphelion and perihelion both lie on the x-axis and the perihelion is located on the positive x-axis, where is the aphelion located? **on the negative x-axis, beyond the negative focus**

3. In terms of the location of the aphelion and the perihelion, where is the center of the ellipse located? **midway between aphelion and perihelion**

4. If the distance from a planet to the sun at aphelion is A and the perihelion distance is P, what is the distance from the sun to the center in terms of A and P? $\frac{A − P}{2}$

5. Suppose the aphelion and the perihelion of a planet both lie on the x-axis. What is the minimum number of additional points needed to determine the equation of the orbit? **1**

6. Suppose that the aphelion distance is A and the perihelion distance is P, and suppose that d represents the maximum distance of the planet from the x-axis. What is the orbital equation of the planet? $\frac{4x^2}{(A + P)^2} + \frac{y^2}{d^2} = 1$

7. When the planet reaches point D, what is the distance from the planet to the sun in terms of A, P, and d? $\sqrt{d^2 + \left(\frac{A − P}{2}\right)^2}$

8. Why must the distance from D to the sun be greater than P and less than A? **No point on the ellipse may be closer than the perihelion or farther than the aphelion**

Student Companion/All-in-One Resources/Online
Think About a Plan

10-4 Think About a Plan
Ellipses

Aerodynamics Scientists used the Transonic Tunnel at NASA Langley Research Center, Virginia, to study the dynamics of air flow. The elliptical opening of the Transonic Tunnel is 82 ft wide and 58 ft high. What is an equation of the ellipse?

Know

1. The width of the tunnel opening is $\boxed{82 \text{ ft}}$.

2. The height of the tunnel opening is $\boxed{58 \text{ ft}}$.

Need

3. To solve the problem I need to find:
an equation for the ellipse that represents the opening of the Transonic Tunnel

Plan

4. How can a drawing help you solve this problem?
Answers may vary. Sample: A drawing could help me relate the dimensions of the tunnel opening to the features of an ellipse

5. Make a sketch of an ellipse that represents the tunnel opening. Where should you put the origin? **at the center of the ellipse**

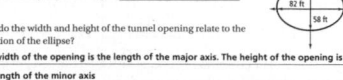
82 ft / 58 ft

6. How do the width and height of the tunnel opening relate to the equation of the ellipse?
The width of the opening is the length of the major axis. The height of the opening is the length of the minor axis

7. How can you write the equation of the ellipse in standard form?
Find a from the length of the major axis: $a = \frac{82}{2} = 41$. Find b from the length of the minor axis: $b = \frac{58}{2} = 29$. The origin is (0, 0), so h = 0 and k = 0

8. Write the equation of the ellipse in standard form. $\frac{x^2}{41^2} + \frac{y^2}{29^2} = 1$

Student Companion/All-in-One Resources/Online
Standardized Test Prep

10-4 Standardized Test Prep
Ellipses

Gridded Response

Solve each exercise and enter your answer on the grid provided.

1. In the equation for a horizontal ellipse $\frac{x^2}{16} + \frac{y^2}{9} = 1$, what is the positive value of the x-coordinates of the vertices?

2. What is the positive y-coordinate of the foci of the ellipse with the equation $25x^2 + 16y^2 = 400$?

3. In the equation for a vertical ellipse $\frac{x^2}{49} + \frac{y^2}{100} = 1$, what is the positive value of the y-coordinates of the vertices?

4. An ellipse has foci at (±7, 0) and vertices at (±16, 0). What is the value of c?

5. Suppose you are planning a party at an elliptical park with one game at each foci. The major axis of the ellipse is 80 yd and the minor axis is 28 yd. How many yards will the games be from one another? Round to the nearest whole number.

Answers

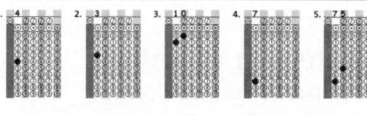

Online Teacher Resource Center
Activities, Games, and Puzzles

10-4 Game: Eccentricity of Ellipses
Ellipses

Provide the host with the following questions and answers.

Round 1	Far from, Close to, or Circle?	Player 1	Player 2
1.	$\frac{x^2}{400} + \frac{y^2}{4} = 1$ Answer: far from		
2.	$\frac{x^2}{1} + \frac{y^2}{2^2} = 1$ Answer: close to		
3.	$\frac{x^2}{1.3} + \frac{y^2}{1.3} = 1$ Answer: circle		
4.	$\frac{x^2}{2.3^2} + \frac{y^2}{3.8^2} = 1$ Answer: close to		
5.	$\frac{x^2}{36} + \frac{y^2}{1} = 1$ Answer: far from		
6.	$\frac{x^2}{8.73^2} + \frac{y^2}{2.01^2} = 1$ Answer: far from		

Round 2	Lengths of the major and minor axes?	Player 1	Player 2
1.	$\frac{x^2}{400} + \frac{y^2}{4} = 1$ Answer: 40, 4		
2.	$\frac{x^2}{1} + \frac{y^2}{9} = 1$ Answer: 2, 6		
3.	$\frac{x^2}{4} + \frac{y^2}{25} = 1$ Answer: 4, 10		
4.	$\frac{x^2}{100} + \frac{y^2}{100} = 1$ Answer: 20, 20		

1 Interactive Learning

Solve It!
PURPOSE To find distances between the graphs of one part of a hyperbola and semicircle

PROCESS Students may
- graph the functions on a graphing calculator and use the table feature.
- solve the following equations for x:
$$\sqrt{1+x^2} - \sqrt{2} = \sqrt{1-x^2} \text{ and}$$
$$\sqrt{1+x^2} - 1 = \sqrt{1-x^2}.$$

FACILITATE
Q Where would you look for the values on a table? **[between $x = 1$ and $x = -1$]**

Q What parts of the graph can you ignore? Why? **[$x = 0$, $x > 1$, $x < -1$; the graphs intersect at $x = 0$, and $y = \sqrt{1-x^2}$ does not exist at $x > 1$, $x < -1$]**

ANSWER See Solve It in Answers on next page.

CONNECT THE MATH In the Solve It, students find fixed distances between points on a hyperbola and semicircle. In the lesson, students will define, graph and write equations of hyperbolas using fixed points and distances.

2 Guided Instruction

A model can demonstrate the various hyperbolas that are possible at different cutting angles.

Take Note

Q How is the definition of a hyperbola different from the definition of an ellipse? **[For an ellipse, the *sum* of the distances from a point to the foci is a constant, while for a hyperbola, the absolute value of the *difference* of the distances from a point to the foci is a constant.]**

10-5 Hyperbolas

Objectives To graph hyperbolas
To find and use the foci of a hyperbola

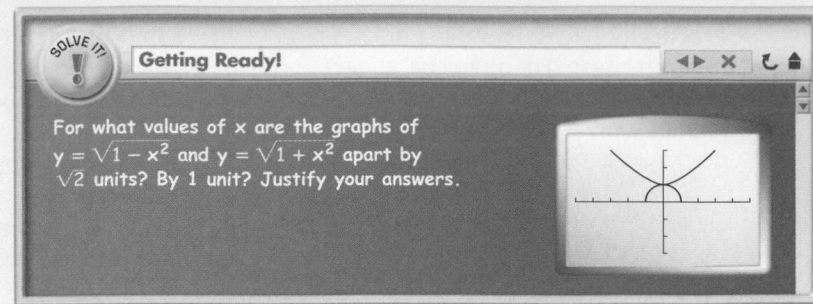

Dynamic Activity Hyperbolas

Lesson Vocabulary
- hyperbola
- focus of the hyperbola
- vertex of a hyperbola
- transverse axis
- axis of symmetry
- center of a hyperbola
- conjugate axis

In the Solve It, you saw the top halves of two different conic sections. You can complete each conic section by graphing $y = -\sqrt{1-x^2}$ and $y = -\sqrt{1+x^2}$ respectively.

Recall from Lesson 10-1, that you can get a variety of conic sections by slicing the double cone with a plane. Changing the angle at which the plane slices the double cone determines the shape of the curve and whether or not the plane will slice both cones. If the plane is parallel to the axis of the double cone, it slices both cones and the result is a *hyperbola*.

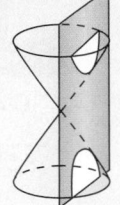

Focus Question What is a hyperbola?

take note
Key Concept Hyperbola

A **hyperbola** is the set of points P in a plane such that the absolute value of the difference between the distances from P to two fixed points F_1 and F_2 is a constant k.

$$|PF_1 - PF_2| = k, \text{ where } k < F_1F_2$$

Each fixed point F is a **focus of the hyperbola**.

Since F_1 and F_2 are the foci of the hyperbola, the long and short segments in each of the two colored paths differ in length by k.

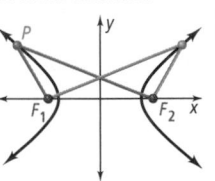

10-5 Preparing to Teach

BIG idea **Coordinate Geometry**   **UbD**

ESSENTIAL UNDERSTANDINGS
- The shape of a hyperbola is guided by asymptotes.
- The x^2 and y^2 terms of the algebraic form of an ellipse are both positive. For a hyperbola, one term is negative.

Math Background
It may be helpful to relate the hyperbola to the ellipse and highlight the similarities and differences.

DEFINITION
Instead of the sum of the distances from any point to two foci being a constant, the absolute value of the difference between the distances from any point to two foci is a constant.

ELEMENTS
For both, the foci and vertices lie on the major axis called the transverse axis for the hyperbola.

STANDARD EQUATIONS
The standard equations for a horizontal or vertical hyperbola with center $(0, 0)$ are identical to the corresponding ellipse equations with one important exception: the term containing the variable of the conjugate axis is subtracted, not added.

When graphing hyperbolas, make sure students always sketch the central rectangle and asymptotes. The central rectangle guides the location of the asymptotes, and the asymptotes guide the shape of the graph.

Support Student Learning
Use the **Algebra 2 Companion** to engage and support students during instruction. See Lesson Resources at the end of this lesson for details.

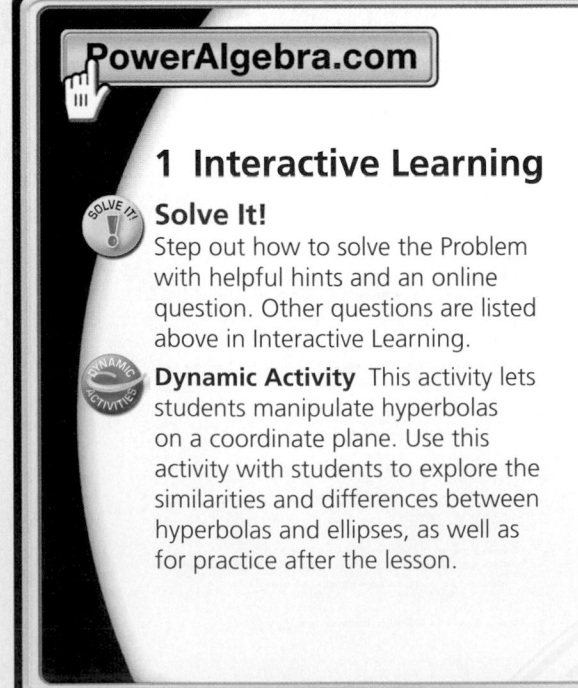

PowerAlgebra.com

1 Interactive Learning

Solve It!
Step out how to solve the Problem with helpful hints and an online question. Other questions are listed above in Interactive Learning.

Dynamic Activity This activity lets students manipulate hyperbolas on a coordinate plane. Use this activity with students to explore the similarities and differences between hyperbolas and ellipses, as well as for practice after the lesson.

A hyperbola consists of two smooth branches. The turning point of each branch is a **vertex of the hyperbola**. The segment connecting the two vertices is the **transverse axis**, which lies on the **axis of symmetry**. The two foci also lie on the axis of symmetry. The **center of the hyperbola** is the midpoint between the two vertices, which also is the midpoint between the two foci.

Just as for an ellipse, if the foci are $(\pm c, 0)$, the distance between the two foci is $2c$. If the vertices are $(\pm a, 0)$, the distance between the two vertices is $2a$.

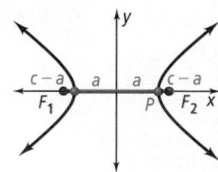

Since vertex P is on the hyperbola, it must satisfy the equation $|PF_1 - PF_2| = k$, but you can also see that

$$|PF_1 - PF_2| = |[2a + (c - a)] - (c - a)|$$
$$= |2a + c - a - c + a|$$
$$= |2a| = 2a$$

Therefore, $k = 2a$.

In a standard hyperbola, c is related to a and b by the equation $c^2 = a^2 + b^2$. The length of the **conjugate axis** is $2b$. The transverse and conjugate axes determine a rectangle that lies between the vertices, and the diagonals of that central rectangle determine the asymptotes of the hyperbola. The branches of the hyperbola approach the asymptotes.

Hint

Recall that an asymptote is a line that a graph approaches but never intersects.

take note

Key Concept   Properties of Hyperbolas with Center (0, 0)

Horizontal Hyperbola

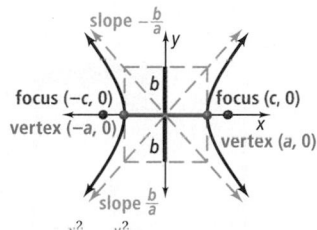

Equation: $\dfrac{x^2}{a^2} - \dfrac{y^2}{b^2} = 1$

Transverse axis: Horizontal

Vertices: $(\pm a, 0)$

Foci: $(\pm c, 0)$, where $c^2 = a^2 + b^2$

Asymptotes: $y = \pm \dfrac{b}{a}x$

Vertical Hyperbola

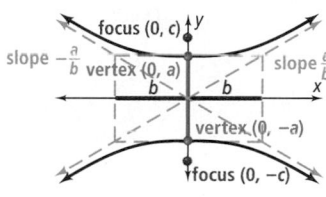

Equation: $\dfrac{y^2}{a^2} - \dfrac{x^2}{b^2} = 1$

Transverse axis: Vertical

Vertices: $(0, \pm a)$

Foci: $(0, \pm c)$, where $c^2 = a^2 + b^2$

Asymptotes: $y = \pm \dfrac{a}{b}x$

While the transverse axis is the axis of symmetry, a hyperbola, like an ellipse, has two lines of symmetry.

Note that for both an ellipse and a hyperbola, the distance between the foci is by definition $2c$.

Q Which axis of a hyperbola—the transverse axis or the conjugate axis—corresponds to the major axis of an ellipse? Why? **[Transverse axis; like the major axis, it contains the vertices and the foci.]**

Take Note

Q How does the position of the transverse axis determine the orientation of the hyperbola? **[If the transverse axis is along the x-axis, the hyperbola is horizontal. If it is along the y-axis, the hyperbola is vertical.]**

Q What are the x-intercepts of a horizontal hyperbola with a center at the origin? y-intercepts? **[(−a, 0) and (a, 0); there are none because the hyperbola does not intersect the y-axis]**

Q What are the x-intercepts of a vertical hyperbola with a center at the origin? y-intercepts? **[There are none because the hyperbola does not intersect the x-axis; (0, −a) and (0, a).]**

Q Where do the asymptotes intersect the central rectangle of a horizontal hyperbola? vertical hyperbola? **[at the vertices of the rectangle; horizontal: (a, b), (−a, b); (−a, −b), (a, −b); vertical: (b, a), (−b, a), (−b,−a), (b, −a)]**

Q How is the relationship between a and c different for a hyperbola than for an ellipse? **[Unlike an ellipse, in a hyperbola, c is greater than a.]**

2 Guided Instruction

Each Problem is worked out and supported online.

Problem 1
Writing and Graphing the Equation of a Hyperbola
Animated

Problem 2
Analyzing a Hyperbola from Its Equation
Animated

Problem 3
Modeling with a Hyperbola
Animated

Support in Algebra 2 Companion
• Vocabulary
• Key Concepts
• Got It?

Answers

Solve It!
± 1; ± 0.93; If you substitute 1 or −1 into both equations the distance between the results will be $\sqrt{2}$. If you substitute 0.93 or −0.93 into both equations, the distance between the results will be 1.

Problem 1 SYNTHESIZING

Q What information do you need to write the standard equation of a hyperbola with a center at (0, 0)? How does this problem provide it? **[To write the standard equation you need to know a^2 and b^2 and whether it is horizontal or vertical. You are given the vertices and a focus, so you have a and c, and you know the transverse axis is horizontal. To find b^2, solve $b^2 = c^2 - a^2$.]**

Q Is the central rectangle part of the graph of the hyperbola? What is it for? **[No; it defines the asymptotes and assists in graphing.]**

Q In 1B, suppose you only graphed Y_1 on the graphing calculator. What would the graph look like? Would it be sufficient to check? **[The graph would not include any points where y is negative. It would look like two curves starting at the x-axis and curving outward. Since the hyperbola is symmetric in the x-axis, it would be sufficient to compare the top part and check for symmetry.]**

Got It?

Q For 1c, how do the dimensions of the rectangle affect the asymptotes? Could the asymptotes ever be parallel? Why or why not? **[The diagonals of the rectangle determine the asymptotes. A long narrow horizontal rectangle would yield asymptotes close together and almost horizontal. However, no rectangle has diagonals that are parallel, so the asymptotes could never be parallel.]**

Because of symmetry, for both the ellipse and a hyperbola, the value of c is half the distance between the two foci.

Problem 1 Writing and Graphing the Equation of a Hyperbola

A hyperbola centered at (0, 0) has vertices $(\pm 4, 0)$ and one focus (5, 0).

A What is the standard-form equation of the hyperbola?

First, find a, b, and c. The vertices are $(\pm 4, 0)$, so $a = 4$. One focus is (5, 0), so $c = 5$.

The transverse axis is horizontal. Use $c^2 = a^2 + b^2$ to find b: $5^2 = 4^2 + b^2$, so $b = 3$.

Then write the equation of a horizontal hyperbola in standard form $\frac{x^2}{a^2} - \frac{y^2}{b^2} = 1$.

Substitute values for a and b. $\frac{x^2}{4^2} - \frac{y^2}{3^2} = 1$

Simplify. $\frac{x^2}{16} - \frac{y^2}{9} = 1$

Think
Is the transverse axis horizontal or vertical?
The vertices and focus are on a horizontal line. The transverse axis is horizontal.

B Sketch the hyperbola. Use a graphing calculator to check.

Step 1 Draw the horizontal transverse axis, vertices, and central rectangle. This rectangle shares a center with the hyperbola and in this case has a height of $2b$ and a width of $2a$. If the hyperbola were vertical, the dimensions would be reversed.

Hint
The central rectangle guides the drawing of the graph.

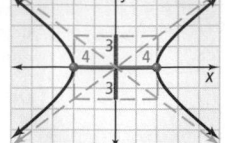

Step 2 Extend the diagonals of the rectangle to show the asymptotes.

Step 3 Sketch the branches from the vertices.

Check Solve for y.

$$\frac{x^2}{16} - \frac{y^2}{9} = 1$$
$$\frac{y^2}{9} = \frac{x^2}{16} - 1$$
$$y^2 = 9\left(\frac{x^2}{16} - 1\right)$$
$$y = \pm 3\sqrt{\frac{x^2}{16} - 1}$$

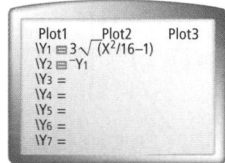 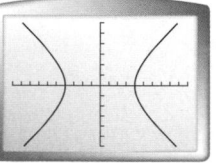

Got It? **1. a.** What is the standard-form equation of the hyperbola with vertices $(0, \pm 4)$ and foci $(0, \pm 5)$?
   b. Sketch the hyperbola. Use a graphing calculator to check.
   c. **Reasoning** Under what circumstances are the asymptotes of the graph of a hyperbola perpendicular?

Additional Problems

1. A hyperbola centered at (0, 0) has vertices $(\pm 2, 0)$ and one focus (3, 0).
   a. What is the standard-form equation of the hyperbola?
   b. Sketch the hyperbola.
   ANSWERS
   a. $\frac{x^2}{4} - \frac{y^2}{5} = 1$
   b.
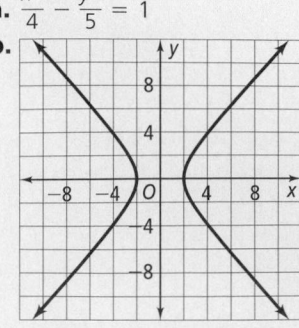

2. What are the vertices, foci, and asymptotes of the hyperbola with equation $4y^2 - x^2 = 16$? Sketch the graph.
   ANSWERS
   vertices: $(0, \pm 2)$
   foci: $(0, \pm 2\sqrt{5})$
   Asymptotes: $y = \pm 0.5x$
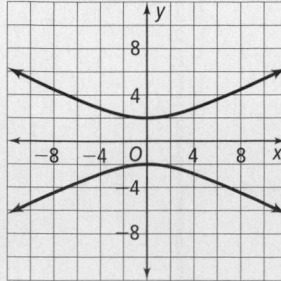

3. If a vertex of a hyperbola is (0, 10) and the equations of the asymptotes are $y = \pm 0.5x$, what is the equation of an hyperbola?
   ANSWER $\frac{y^2}{100} - \frac{x^2}{400} = 1$

Answers

Got It?

1. a. $\frac{y^2}{16} - \frac{x^2}{9} = 1$

b.
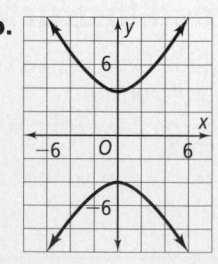

c. when $a = b$

Problem 2 Analyzing a Hyperbola from Its Equation

What are the vertices, foci, and asymptotes of the hyperbola with equation $9y^2 - 7x^2 = 63$? Sketch the graph.

Think	Write
Write the original equation.	$9y^2 - 7x^2 = 63$
In standard form, the right side must be 1. Divide each side by 63.	$\dfrac{9y^2}{63} - \dfrac{7x^2}{63} = 1$
Simplify. Since y^2 has the positive coefficient, the hyperbola is vertical. The vertices and foci are on the y-axis.	$\dfrac{y^2}{7} - \dfrac{x^2}{9} = 1$
Compare to $\dfrac{y^2}{a^2} - \dfrac{x^2}{b^2} = 1$ to find a^2 and b^2.	$a^2 = 7$ and $b^2 = 9$ $a = \pm\sqrt{7}$ $b = \pm 3$
Find c^2. Use $c^2 = a^2 + b^2$.	$c^2 = 7 + 9$, so $c = \pm\sqrt{7+9}$ $c = \pm 4$
You know a, b, and c. You can answer the questions and draw the graph. $\sqrt{7} \approx 2.65$	Vertices: $(0, \pm\sqrt{7})$, Foci: $(0, \pm 4)$. Slopes of asymptotes: $m = \pm\dfrac{\sqrt{7}}{3}$ Asymptotes: $y = \pm\dfrac{\sqrt{7}}{3}x$

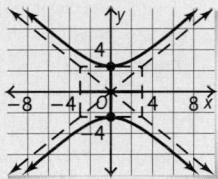

Hint
Use a graphing calculator to check your graph. Define $Y1 = \sqrt{(7(X^2/9+1))}$ and $Y2 = -Y1$.

✓ **Got It?** **2.** What are the vertices, foci, and asymptotes of the hyperbola with equation $9x^2 - 4y^2 = 36$? Sketch a graph.

Problem 2

Q What information can you get directly from an equation in standard form? How can you use it to find what you need? [a^2 **and** b^2 **and the transverse axis; use** a^2 **to find the vertices,** a^2 **and** b^2 **to solve for** c^2 **and find the foci, and** $\pm\dfrac{a}{b}$ **to find the equations of the asymptotes.**]

Q What information do you need to graph the hyperbola? Explain. [**You need** a **to plot the vertices and start the central rectangle, and you need** b **to finish the central rectangle to sketch the asymptotes. The graph of the hyperbola follows the asymptotes, so you do not need** c.]

EXTENSION

Q Are the asymptotes perpendicular? How could you determine this just by looking at the standard equation? [**No; the asymptotes are perpendicular only if the denominators in the standard equation are equal which happens only when** $a = b$.]

Got It?

Q What are three basic steps for finding the values of a, b, and c for this hyperbola? [**1) Rewrite the equation in standard form, 2) identify** a^2 **and** b^2 **and use them to solve for** c^2, **and 3) take the square root of each to find** a, b, **and** c.]

---

2. vertices: $(\pm 2, 0)$; foci: $(\pm\sqrt{13}, 0)$;
asymptotes: $y = \pm\dfrac{3}{2}x$

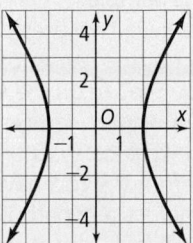

Problem 3

Q How is this reflection different from a reflection within an ellipse? **[Samples: A reflection in an ellipse passes through both foci. The foci are internal in an ellipse.]**

Q On this graph, where is the origin located? **[between the foci]**

Q Is the first reflector part of the graph of the hyperbola? Explain. **[No; it is facing the wrong direction, so it could not be part of the second branch.]**

Got It?

Q How does changing the location of the foci and the second reflector change its equation? **[The foci are closer together and the vertex is farther from the first focus, so the value of a decreases. The denominator of the x term will be smaller.]**

The *reflection property of a hyperbola* is important in optics. As with an ellipse, the reflection property of a hyperbola involves both foci, but only one branch reflects. Any ray on the *external side* of a branch directed at its internal focus will reflect off the branch toward the *external focus*.

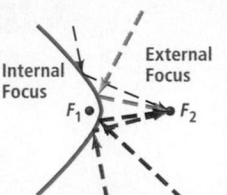

Problem 3 Modeling with a Hyperbola

Communications The graph shows a 2-dimensional view of a satellite dish. The focus is located at F_1 but the receiving device is located on the bottom of the dish at the point F_2. The rays are reflected by the first reflector (the black curve), toward F_1 and then reflected by the second reflector (the blue curve) toward F_2.

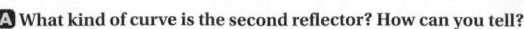

Think
What information does the diagram give you?
It helps you see the relative positions of the reflectors and foci.

A What kind of curve is the second reflector? How can you tell?

The second reflector is a hyperbola because it reflects rays aimed at its internal focus toward its external focus.

B The vertex of the second reflector is 3 in. from F_1 and 21 in. from F_2. What is an equation for the second reflector? Assume the conic is horizontal and centered at the origin.

Step 1 Determine the standard-form equation of the conic. The conic is a horizontal hyperbola centered at the origin.
$$\frac{x^2}{a^2} - \frac{y^2}{b^2} = 1$$

Step 2 Find c.
The distance between the foci is $3 + 21 = 24$ in. Since c is half this distance, $c = 12$.

Step 3 Find a.
The distance from the internal focus to the vertex of the reflector is 3 in. So, $c - a = 12 - a = 3$ and $a = 9$.

Step 4 Use c and a to find b^2.
Relate a^2, b^2, and c^2. $b^2 = c^2 - a^2$
Substitute. $= 12^2 - 9^2$
Simplify. $= 63$

Step 5 Use a^2 and b^2 to write the equation.
An equation is $\frac{x^2}{81} - \frac{y^2}{63} = 1$.

 Got It? 3. Suppose the vertex of the second reflector in Problem 3 were 4 in. from F_1 and 18 in. from F_2. What is the equation for the second reflector? Assume the conic is horizontal and centered at the origin.

Answers

Got It? (continued)

3. $\frac{x^2}{49} - \frac{y^2}{72} = 1$

Lesson Check

1. vertices: $(\pm 6, 0)$; foci: $(\pm \sqrt{61}, 0)$; slopes of asymptotes: $\pm\frac{5}{6}$

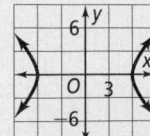

2. vertices: $(0, \pm 4)$; foci: $(0, \pm \sqrt{41})$; slopes of asymptotes: $\pm\frac{4}{5}$

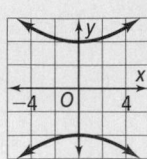

3. vertices: $(0, \pm 2)$; foci: $(0, \pm 2\sqrt{5})$; slopes of asymptotes: $\pm\frac{1}{2}$

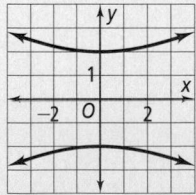

4. vertices: $(\pm 5, 0)$; foci: $(\pm \sqrt{41}, 0)$; slopes of asymptotes: $\pm\frac{4}{5}$

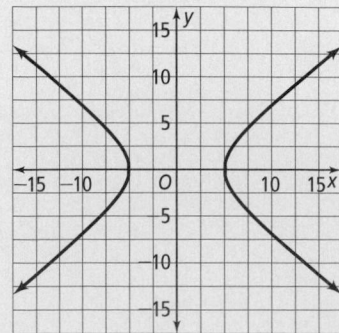

5. $\frac{x^2}{25} - \frac{y^2}{24} = 1$

6. Answers may vary. Sample: Similarities—Both have two axes of sym. that intersect at the center of the figure and two foci that lie on the same line as the two "principal" vertices. Differences—An ellipse consists of pts. whose distances from the foci have a constant sum, whereas a hyperbola consists of pts. whose distances from the foci have a constant diff.

7. Answers may vary. Sample: A hyperbola is vert. or horizontal depending on whether it has a positive coefficient, not because the larger denominator is under the y^2-term.

Practice and Problem-Solving Exercises

8. $\frac{x^2}{9} - \frac{y^2}{16} = 1$ **9.** $\frac{x^2}{144} - \frac{y^2}{25} = 1$

10. $\frac{x^2}{19} - \frac{y^2}{81} = 1$ **11.** $\frac{x^2}{144} - \frac{y^2}{25} = 1$

Focus Question What is a hyperbola?

Answer A hyperbola is the set of points P such that the absolute value of the difference between the distances from P to two fixed points F_1 and F_2 (the foci of the hyperbola) is a constant k.

Lesson Check

Do you know HOW?

Find the vertices and foci of each equation. Write the slopes of the asymptotes. Then graph the equation.

1. $\frac{x^2}{36} - \frac{y^2}{25} = 1$ **2.** $\frac{y^2}{16} - \frac{x^2}{25} = 1$

3. $4y^2 - x^2 = 16$ **4.** $16x^2 - 25y^2 = 400$

5. What is an equation of a hyperbola with vertices $(\pm 5, 0)$ and focus $(7, 0)$?

Do you UNDERSTAND?

6. Compare and Contrast How is graphing a hyperbola like graphing an ellipse? How is it different?

7. Error Analysis Your friend says that a graph must be a vertical hyperbola because the larger denominator is under the y^2 term. What error did your friend make?

Practice and Problem-Solving Exercises

A Practice

Write an equation of a hyperbola with the given values, foci, or vertices. Assume that the transverse axis is horizontal.

◆ See Problem 1.

8. $a = 3, b = 4$

$\frac{x^2}{a^2} - \frac{y^2}{b^2} = 1$

Guided Practice

To start, write the equation of a horizontal hyperbola in standard form.

9. $a = -12, c = 13$ **10.** $b = 9, c = 10$

11. foci $(\pm 13, 0)$, vertices $(\pm 12, 0)$ **12.** foci $(\pm 3, 0)$, vertices $(\pm 2, 0)$

Find the vertices, foci, and asymptotes of each hyperbola. Then sketch the graph.

◆ See Problem 2.

13. $\frac{y^2}{81} - \frac{x^2}{16} = 1$

y^2 has the positive coefficient. The hyperbola is vertical. The vertices and foci are on the y-axis.

Guided Practice

To start, identify the location of the vertices and foci.

14. $\frac{x^2}{121} - \frac{y^2}{144} = 1$ **15.** $\frac{y^2}{25} - \frac{x^2}{100} = 1$

16. $81y^2 - 9x^2 = 729$ **17.** $4y^2 - 25x^2 = 100$

18. $36x^2 - 8y^2 = 288$ **19.** $14y^2 - 28x^2 = 448$

---

12. $\frac{x^2}{4} - \frac{y^2}{5} = 1$

13. vertices: $(0, \pm 9)$; foci: $(0, \pm\sqrt{97})$; asymptotes: $y = \pm\frac{9}{4}x$

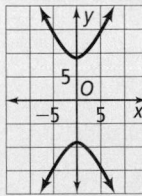

14. vertices: $(\pm 11, 0)$; foci: $(\pm\sqrt{265}, 0)$; asymptotes: $y = \pm\frac{12}{11}x$

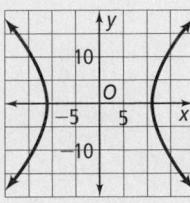

15. vertices: $(0, \pm 5)$; foci: $(0, \pm 5\sqrt{5})$; asymptotes: $y = \pm\frac{1}{2}x$

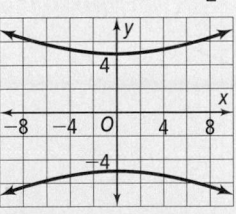

16. vertices: $(0, \pm 3)$; foci: $(0, \pm 3\sqrt{10})$; asymptotes: $y = \pm\frac{1}{3}x$

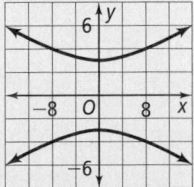

17–19. See next page.

Do you know HOW?

• To assist graphing Exercises 1–4, students should note whether the hyperbola is vertical or horizontal.

Do you UNDERSTAND?

• For Exercise 6, suggest students compare the axes and a and b in both conics.

Close

Q What parts of a hyperbola must be included on its graph? **[the vertices]**

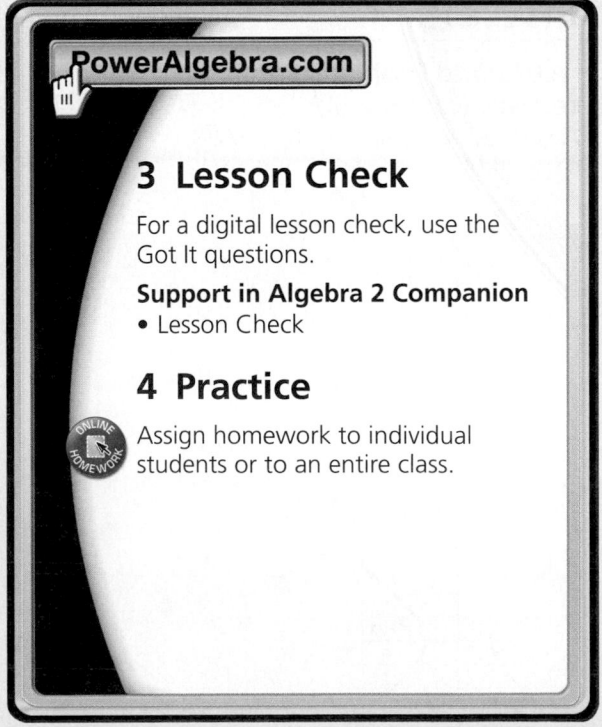

PowerAlgebra.com

3 Lesson Check

For a digital lesson check, use the Got It questions.

Support in Algebra 2 Companion
• Lesson Check

4 Practice

Assign homework to individual students or to an entire class.

4 Practice

20. Satellite Dish The diagram at the right models a satellite dish and the small reflector inside it. Suppose F_1 and F_2 are 7 meters apart, and F_1 is 1 meter from the vertex of the small reflector. What equation best models the small reflector?

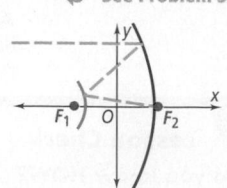

⬦ See Problem 3.

B Apply

21. Think About a Plan The path that Voyager 2 made around Jupiter followed one branch of a hyperbola. Find an equation that models the path of Voyager 2 around Jupiter, given that $a = 2{,}184{,}140$ km and $c = 2{,}904{,}906.2$ km. Use the horizontal model.
- What information do you need to write the equation?
- How can you use the given information to find the information you need?

Write an equation of a hyperbola with the given foci and vertices.

22. foci $(\pm 5, 0)$, vertices $(\pm 3, 0)$

23. foci $(0, \pm 13)$, vertices $(0, \pm 5)$

24. foci $(0, \pm 2)$, vertices $(0, \pm 1)$

25. foci $(\pm \sqrt{5}, 0)$, vertices $(\pm 2, 0)$

Write an equation of a hyperbola from the given information. Assume the center of each hyperbola is (0, 0).

26. Transverse axis is vertical and is 9 units; central rectangle is 9 units by 4 units

27. Perimeter of central rectangle is 16 units; vertices are $(0, 3)$ and $(0, -3)$

Graphing Calculator Solve each equation for y. Graph each relation on your graphing calculator. Use the TRACE feature to locate the vertices.

28. $x^2 - 2y^2 = 4$

29. $3x^2 - y^2 = 2$

30. Comets The path of a comet around the sun followed one branch of a hyperbola. Find an equation that models its path around the sun, given that $a = 40$ million miles and $c = 250$ million miles. Use the horizontal model.

31. Open-Ended Choose two points on an axis to be the vertices of a hyperbola. Choose two other points on the same axis to be the foci. Write the equation of your hyperbola and draw its graph.

Graph each equation.

32. $5x^2 - 12y^2 = 120$

33. $16x^2 - 20y^2 = 560$

34. Error Analysis On a test, a student found that the foci of the hyperbola with equation $\frac{y^2}{100} - \frac{x^2}{21} = 1$ were $(0, \pm \sqrt{79})$. The teacher credited the student three points out of a possible five. What did the student do right? What did the student do wrong?

Answers

Practice and Problem-Solving Exercises (continued)

17. vertices: $(0, \pm 5)$; foci: $(0, \pm \sqrt{29})$; asymptotes: $y = \pm \frac{5}{2}x$

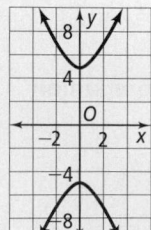

18. vertices: $(\pm 2\sqrt{2}, 0)$; foci: $(\pm 2\sqrt{11}, 0)$; asymptotes: $y = \pm \frac{3\sqrt{2}}{2}x$

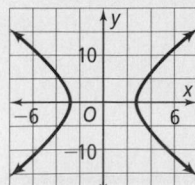

19. vertices: $(0, \pm 4\sqrt{2})$; foci: $(0, \pm 4\sqrt{3})$; asymptotes: $y = \pm \sqrt{2}x$

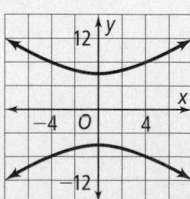

20. $\frac{x^2}{6.25} - \frac{y^2}{6} = 1$

21. $\frac{x^2}{4.770 \times 10^{12}} - \frac{y^2}{3.668 \times 10^{12}} = 1$

22. $\frac{x^2}{9} - \frac{y^2}{16} = 1$

23. $\frac{y^2}{25} - \frac{x^2}{144} = 1$

24. $y^2 - \frac{x^2}{3} = 1$

25. $\frac{x^2}{4} - y^2 = 1$

26. $\frac{y^2}{20.25} - \frac{x^2}{4} = 1$

27. $\frac{y^2}{9} - x^2 = 1$

28. $y = \pm \sqrt{\frac{x^2}{2} - 2}$; $(\pm 2, 0)$

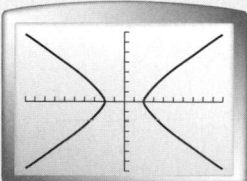

29. $y = \pm \sqrt{3x^2 - 2}$; $(\pm 0.816, 0)$

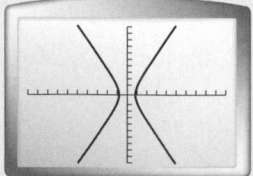

30. $\frac{x^2}{1.6 \times 10^{15}} - \frac{y^2}{6.09 \times 10^{16}} = 1$

31. Check students' work.

Standardized Test Prep

SAT/ACT

35. The graph of $\frac{x^2}{16} - \frac{y^2}{4} = 1$ is a hyperbola. Which set of equations represents the asymptotes of the hyperbola's graph?

Ⓐ $y = \frac{1}{2}x, y = -\frac{1}{2}x$ Ⓒ $x = \frac{1}{2}y, x = -\frac{1}{2}y$

Ⓑ $y = 2x, y = -2x$ Ⓓ $y = \frac{1}{4}x, y = -\frac{1}{4}x$

36. Simplify $\dfrac{\frac{1}{y} - \frac{1}{x}}{\frac{1}{xy} - 1}$.

Ⓕ $-\dfrac{y - x}{xy - 1}$ Ⓖ $\dfrac{x - y}{1 - xy}$ Ⓗ $\dfrac{x + y}{1 + xy}$ Ⓘ $x + y$

37. How is the graph of $y = 4 \cdot \left(\frac{1}{2}\right)^{x-3}$ translated from the graph of $y = 4 \cdot \left(\frac{1}{2}\right)^{x}$?

Ⓐ 3 units right   Ⓑ 3 units left   Ⓒ 3 units down   Ⓓ 3 units up

Short Response

38. Using sigma notation, what is an expression for the sum of a 6-term arithmetic sequence with first term of 3 and a common difference of 4? What is the sum?

Mixed Review

Find the foci for each equation of an ellipse. Then graph the ellipse.   ◀ See Lesson 10-4.

39. $\frac{x^2}{34} + \frac{y^2}{25} = 1$ **40.** $3x^2 + 2y^2 = 6$ **41.** $25x^2 + 16y^2 = 1600$

Solve each equation. Check your answers.   ◀ See Lesson 7-5.

42. $8^{2x} = 4$ **43.** $\log 8x = 3$ **44.** $2\log_3 x - \log_3 4 = 2$

Get Ready!   **To prepare for Lesson 11-1, do Exercises 45 and 46.**

Evaluate each expression for the given value of the variable.   ◀ See Lesson 1-3.

45. $x + 5x - x - 9$; $x = -2$ **46.** $(n - 4)^2 + n$; $n = 5$

Mixed Review

39. foci: $(\pm 3, 0)$

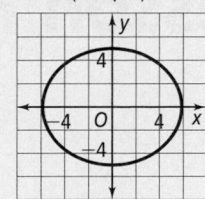

40. foci: $(0, \pm 1)$

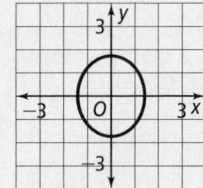

41. foci: $(0, \pm 6)$

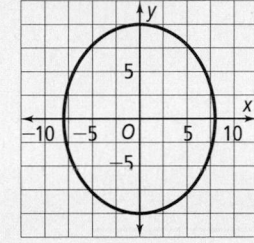

42. $\frac{1}{3}$

43. 125

44. 6

45. -19

46. 6

32.

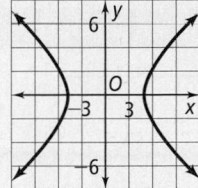

33.

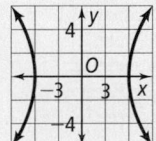

34. right: the foci are located on the vert. axis; wrong: $c^2 = 100 + 21 = 121$, so the foci are $(0, \pm 11)$, not $(0, \pm\sqrt{79})$

38. **[2]** $\displaystyle\sum_{n=1}^{6}(-1 + 4n)$ OR equivalent expression;

$a_6 = 3 + (6 - 1)4 = 23$,

$S_6 = 6\dfrac{(3 + 23)}{2} = 78$

[1] correct expression, but incorrect sum OR correct sum, but incorrect expression

Standardized Test Prep

35. A

36. G

37. A

Additional Instructional Support

Algebra 2 Companion

Students can use the **Algebra 2 Companion** worktext (4 pages) as you teach the lesson. Use the Companion to support

- New Vocabulary
- Key Concepts
- Got It for each Problem
- Lesson Check

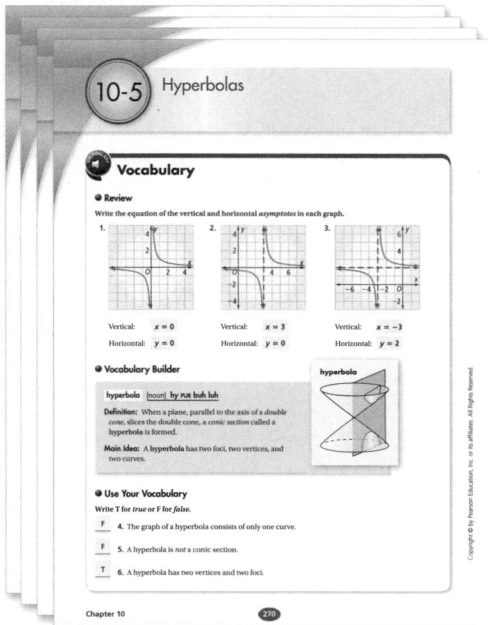

ELL Support

Focus on Language Have one pair of students sit with another pair. Distribute index cards, half with graphs of hyperbolas and the other half with equations to match the graphs. Have each pair work together to match the graph with the equation. Give students additional blank index cards. While one student examines a graph and one student examines an equation, both students discuss how to find *a*, *b*, *c*, vertices, foci, transverse axis and length, conjugate axis and length, dimensions of the central rectangle, and asymptotes. They then record this information on a blank card. If the pair finds that the graph does not match the equation, the graph card is set aside and another graph is chosen. When the activity ends, students should have 3 cards per problem to present to the class.

5 Assess & Remediate

Lesson Quiz

1. What is the standard-form equation of the hyperbola centered at (0, 0) with vertices (0, ±7) and one focus (0, 25)?

2. What are the vertices, foci, and asymptotes of the hyperbola with equation $36x^2 - 25y^2 = 900$? Sketch the graph.

3. **Do you UNDERSTAND?** As a comet shoots through space, it follows a hyperbolic path. The central rectangle is a square, the distance from focus to center is 50, and the hyperbola is horizontal, centered at the origin. What is the equation of the hyperbola?

ANSWERS TO LESSON QUIZ

1. $\dfrac{y^2}{49} - \dfrac{x^2}{576} = 1$;

2. vertices: (±5, 0); foci: (±$\sqrt{61}$, 0); asymptotes: $y = \pm 1.2x$

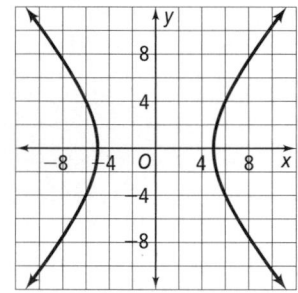

3. $\dfrac{x^2}{1250} - \dfrac{y^2}{1250} = 1$

PRESCRIPTION FOR REMEDIATION

Use the student work on the Lesson Quiz to prescribe a differentiated review assignment:

Points	Differentiated Remediation
1	Intervention
2	On-level
3	Extension

PowerAlgebra.com

5 Assess & Remediate

Assign the Lesson Quiz. Appropriate intervention, practice, or enrichment is automatically generated based on student performance.

Differentiated Remediation

Intervention

- **Reteaching** (2 pages) Provides reteaching and practice exercises for the key lesson concepts. Use with struggling students or absent students.

- **English Language Learner Support** Helps students develop and reinforce mathematical vocabulary and key concepts.

All-in-One Resources/Online
Reteaching

10-5 **Reteaching**
Hyperbolas

All-in-One Resources/Online
English Language Learner Support

10-5 **ELL Support**
Hyperbolas

Differentiated Remediation *continued*

On-Level

- **Practice** (2 pages) Provides extra practice for each lesson. For more challenging practice exercises, use the Form G Practice pages found in the All-in-One Teaching Resources and online.

- **Think About a Plan** Helps students develop specific problem-solving skills and strategies by providing scaffolded guiding questions.

- **Standardized Test Prep** Focuses on all major exercises, all major question types, and helps students prepare for the high-stakes assessments.

Extension

- **Enrichment** Provides students with interesting problems and activities that extend the concepts of the lesson.

- **Activities, Games, and Puzzles** Worksheets that can be used for concepts development, enrichment, and for fun!

Student Companion/All-in-One Resources/Online
Practice page 1

10-5 Practice — Form K
Hyperbolas

Find the equation of a hyperbola with the given values, foci, or vertices. Assume that the transverse axis is horizontal.

1. $b = 3, c = 4$
Use the equation $c^2 = a^2 + b^2$ to find a^2. $\quad 4^2 = a^2 + 3^2$
$\quad a^2 = \boxed{7}$
Substitute values for a^2 and b^2. $\quad \frac{x^2}{7} - \frac{y^2}{9} = 1$

2. $b = 9, c = 12$
$\frac{x^2}{63} - \frac{y^2}{81} = 1$

3. foci $(\pm 8, 0)$, vertices $(\pm 2, 0)$
$\frac{x^2}{4} - \frac{y^2}{60} = 1$

Find the vertices, foci, and asymptotes of each hyperbola. Then sketch the graph.

4. $\frac{x^2}{25} - \frac{y^2}{11} = 1$
Compare to $\frac{x^2}{a^2} - \frac{y^2}{b^2} = 1$: $a^2 = 25, b^2 = 11$. $\quad a = \pm 5, b = \pm\sqrt{11}$
The vertices are given by $(\pm a, 0)$. $\quad (-5, 0)$ and $(5, 0)$
Use the formula $c^2 = a^2 + b^2$ to find c. $\quad c = \pm 6$
The foci are given by $(\pm c, 0)$. $\quad (-6, 0)$ and $(6, 0)$
Asymptotes $\left(y = \pm\frac{b}{a}x\right)$: $\boxed{y = \pm\frac{\sqrt{11}}{5}x}$
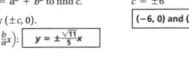

5. $\frac{x^2}{4} - \frac{y^2}{4} = 1$
$(\pm 2, 0), (\pm 2\sqrt{2}, 0),$
$y = \pm x$

6. $4y^2 - 36x^2 = 144$
$(0, \pm 6), (0, \pm 2\sqrt{10})$
$y = \pm 3x$

Student Companion/All-in-One Resources/Online
Practice page 2

10-5 Practice (continued) — Form K
Hyperbolas

7. The diagram at the right models a satellite dish and the small reflector inside it. Suppose F_1 and F_2 are 10 ft apart, and F_1 is 2 ft from the vertex of the small reflector. What equation best models the small reflector?
$\frac{x^2}{9} - \frac{y^2}{16} = 1, -4 \le x \le -3$
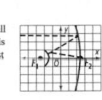

Write the equation of a hyperbola with the given foci and vertices.

8. foci $(0, \pm 10)$, vertices $(0, \pm 8)$
$\frac{y^2}{64} - \frac{x^2}{36} = 1$

9. foci $(\pm 3, 0)$, vertices $(\pm 2, 0)$
$\frac{x^2}{4} - \frac{y^2}{5} = 1$

Write an equation of a hyperbola with the given information. Assume the center of each hyperbola is (0, 0).

10. The transverse axis is horizontal and is 8 units; the central rectangle is 8 units by 2 units.
$\frac{x^2}{16} - \frac{y^2}{1} = 1$

11. The perimeter of central rectangle is 44 units; the vertices are at (6, 0) and (−6, 0).
$\frac{x^2}{36} - \frac{y^2}{25} = 1$

Graphing Calculator Solve each equation for y. Graph each relation on your graphing calculator. Use the TRACE feature to locate the vertices.

12. $4y^2 - x^2 = 12 \quad (0, \pm 1.73)$

13. $2y^2 - 5x^2 = 4 \quad (0, \pm 1.41)$

Graph each equation.

14. $4x^2 - y^2 = 4$
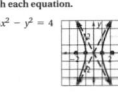

15. $32y^2 - 18x^2 = 288$

All-in-One Resources/Online
Enrichment

10-5 Enrichment
Hyperbolas

Rectangular Hyperbolas
The graphs of equations of the form $xy = c$, where c is a nonzero constant, are also hyperbolas, sometimes referred to as rectangular hyperbolas. Graph the following and compare.

1. Draw the graph of $\frac{x^2}{4} - \frac{y^2}{4} = 1$ on the coordinate grid below.

2. Draw the graph of $xy = 2$ on the coordinate grid below.

3. Compare the two graphs. How are they similar? **They are the same shape.**

4. How are the two graphs different? **The second graph is rotated 45° counterclockwise from the first graph.**

5. Find the asymptotes for the hyperbola in Exercise 1. $y = x; y = -x$

6. Find the asymptotes for the hyperbola in Exercise 2. x-axis; y-axis

7. Describe the graph of $xy = c$ if $c > 0$. What can you say about the x- and y-intercepts? What are the asymptotes? **It is a hyperbola with a horizontal transverse axis and equation $x^2 - y^2 = 2c$ rotated 45° counterclockwise; there are no x- or y-intercepts; x- and y-axes are asymptotes.**

8. Describe the graph of $xy = c$ if $c < 0$. What can you say about the x- and y-intercepts? What are the asymptotes? **It is a hyperbola with a horizontal transverse axis and equation $x^2 - y^2 = 2c$ rotated 45° clockwise; there are no x- or y-intercepts; x- and y-axes are asymptotes.**

9. Draw the graph of $xy = -2$ on the coordinate axis at the right.

10. Compare the graph in Exercise 1 to the graph in Exercise 9. What do you notice? **It is the same shape but rotated 45° clockwise.**

Student Companion/All-in-One Resources/Online
Think About a Plan

10-5 Think About a Plan
Hyperbolas

Comets The path of a comet around the sun followed one branch of a hyperbola. Find an equation that models its path around the sun, given that $a = 40$ million miles and $c = 250$ million miles. Use the horizontal model.

Know

1. a is equal to $\boxed{40 \times 10^6 \text{ mi}}$.

2. c is equal to $\boxed{250 \times 10^6 \text{ mi}}$.

Need

3. To solve the problem I need to find:
an equation that models the comet's path around the sun using the
horizontal model

Plan

4. What is the equation for a horizontal hyperbola? $\frac{x^2}{a^2} - \frac{y^2}{b^2} = 1$

5. What do you need in order to write an equation for the hyperbola that models the comet? a^2 and b^2

6. What is the relationship between a, b, and c in a hyperbola? $c^2 = a^2 + b^2$

7. How can you use the relationship between a, b, and c to find an equation for the hyperbola? I can solve the equation for b^2 since I know a and c

8. Write an equation for a horizontal hyperbola that models the path of the comet.
$\frac{x^2}{1600 \times 10^{12}} - \frac{y^2}{60,900 \times 10^{12}} = 1$

Student Companion/All-in-One Resources/Online
Standardized Test Prep

10-5 Standardized Test Prep
Hyperbolas

Multiple Choice

For Exercises 1–4, choose the correct letter.

1. A hyperbola has vertices $(\pm 5, 0)$ and one focus at $(6, 0)$. What is the equation of the hyperbola in standard form? **D**
Ⓐ $\frac{x^2}{25} + \frac{y^2}{11} = 1$ Ⓒ $\frac{x^2}{11} - \frac{y^2}{25} = 1$
Ⓑ $\frac{x^2}{5} - \frac{y^2}{11} = 1$ Ⓓ $\frac{x^2}{25} - \frac{y^2}{11} = 1$

2. A hyperbola with a horizontal transverse axis has asymptotes $y = \pm\frac{3}{4}x$. Which of the following could be the equation of the hyperbola in standard form? **G**
Ⓕ $\frac{x^2}{3} + \frac{y^2}{4} = 1$ Ⓗ $\frac{x^2}{4} - \frac{y^2}{3} = 1$
Ⓖ $\frac{x^2}{16} - \frac{y^2}{9} = 1$ Ⓘ $\frac{x^2}{9} - \frac{y^2}{16} = 1$

3. What are the vertices of the hyperbola with the equation $8x^2 - 9y^2 = 72$? **A**
Ⓐ $(\pm 3, 0)$ Ⓑ $(\pm 2\sqrt{2}, 0)$ Ⓒ $(\pm 8, 0)$ Ⓓ $(\pm 9, 0)$

4. What are the foci of the hyperbola with the equation $\frac{y^2}{12} - \frac{x^2}{5} = 1$? **I**
Ⓕ $(0, \pm 5)$ Ⓖ $(0, \pm 12)$ Ⓗ $(0, \pm\sqrt{13})$ Ⓘ $(0, \pm\sqrt{17})$

Short Response

5. What are the vertices, foci, and asymptotes of the hyperbola with the equation $4y^2 - 16x^2 = 64$?
[2] vertices: $(0, \pm 4)$; foci: $(0, \pm 2\sqrt{5})$; asymptotes: $y = \pm 2x$
[1] incorrect vertices OR foci OR asymptotes
[0] no answers given

Online Teacher Resource Center
Activities, Games, and Puzzles

10-5 Activity: Closer and Closer . . .
Hyperbolas

Work with a partner. Select one of the three equations and sketch the graph of it on the grid shown.
- Draw the axes and foci.
- Sketch the asymptotes.
- Write the equations for the asymptotes of your hyperbola below.

A. $\frac{x^2}{5^2} - \frac{y^2}{2^2} = 1 \qquad y = \pm\frac{2}{5}x$

B. $\frac{x^2}{3^2} - \frac{y^2}{2^2} = 1 \qquad y = \pm\frac{2}{3}x$

C. $\frac{x^2}{1^2} - \frac{y^2}{1^2} = 1 \qquad y = \pm x$

Use a graphing calculator to graph your hyperbola and its asymptotes. Then complete the information for your hyperbola below. The answers to the first row are shown. Record only positive values.

x	A y-value curve	A y-value asymptote	x	B y-value curve	B y-value asymptote	x	C y-value curve	C y-value asymptote
50	19.90	20	50	33.27	33.33	50	49.99	50
100	39.95	40	100	66.64	66.67	100	99.995	100
200	79.97	80	200	133.32	133.33	200	199.997	200
500	199.99	200	500	333.327	333.333	500	499.999	500
1000	399.995	400	1000	666.664	666.667	1000	999.999	1000

Is there any value of x for which the curve touches the asymptote? Explain.
No; for every value of x, for example when $x > 0$, the asymptote in the first quadrant is higher up than the curve. But, the distance between them for a given value of x gets smaller and smaller.

What will be the smallest distance between the curve and the asymptote? Where will this distance be found? Explain.
Zero; the distance between the curve and the asymptote becomes zero as x approaches infinity.

As a class, discuss your findings for each of the three given hyperbolas.

Performance Task

Pull It All Together

The concepts and skills required to solve these problems are from several lessons within this chapter and from earlier chapters. As students solve these problems, they will demonstrate their reasoning strategies and their growth as independent problem solvers.

Task 1

Visualize transformations of a conic section and write algebraic representations of the visual transformations.

• If the vertex of the parabola remained constant, which value in the vertex form of the equation of a parabola would effect the transformation described in part b?

Task 2

Describe the relationship between an ellipse and a circle in multiple ways.

• What is the shape of the base of a right cone?
• What happens to the shape of an ellipse as the foci move away from the center?

Task 3

Find an equation to represent the distance relationship between the foci of a hyperbola and an ellipse inscribed in the hyperbola's central rectangle.

• What is the distance between $(c_e, 0)$ and $(c_h, 0)$ in terms of c_e and c_h?

To solve these problems, you will pull together concepts and skills related to conic sections.

BIG idea Modeling

You can represent many real-world mathematical problems algebraically.

TASK 1

Imagine a plane and a cone intersecting to form a parabola.

a. Explain why the plane has to intersect the axis of the cone.

b. Imagine the plane moving so that it keeps the same angle, but its point of intersection with the axis moves in the direction of the apex of the cone and eventually passes through the apex. Describe what happens to the parabola and write equations that describe how the parabola changes.

BIG idea Equivalence

You can represent any relationship in an infinite number of ways, where each representation has the same domain and the same pairing of inputs with outputs.

TASK 2

You can define an ellipse using a cone, a set of points, or algebra. For each kind of definition, explain how to describe a circle as a special case of an ellipse.

 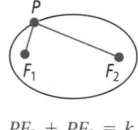 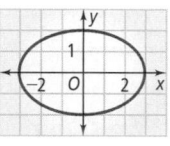

$$PF_1 + PF_2 = k$$

$$\frac{x^2}{9} + \frac{y^2}{4} = 1$$

BIG idea Coordinate Geometry

You can use a coordinate system to represent and analyze geometric relationships.

TASK 3

The focus of the hyperbola $\frac{x^2}{a^2} - \frac{y^2}{b^2} = 1$ is c_h units from $(0, 0)$. Imagine the ellipse inscribed in the central rectangle of the hyperbola. Its focus is c_e units from $(0, 0)$. How far apart are the foci $(c_e, 0)$ and $(c_h, 0)$? Give the distance in terms of a and b.

Assess Performance

Pull It All Together

See p. 53 for a holistic scoring rubric to gauge a student's progress on Understanding the Problem, Planning a Solution, Getting an Answer, and Assessing Autonomy.

SOLUTION OUTLINES

1. a. If the plane does not intersect the axis of the cone, it is parallel to the axis and the conic section formed is a hyperbola.

b. The plane is parallel to the "far edge" of the cone. The plane stays parallel as it moves toward the apex. When the plane intersects the apex, its intersection with the cone is a line—the "far edge" itself. By the continuous nature of the movement, the parabola is getting narrower and narrower with the two branches converging, in a sense, on the line. If $y = ax^2$ is the equation for a parabola, the above change in the shape of the parabola corresponds to $|a|$ increasing without bound. The

equation of the "degenerate" parabola would be $x = 0$. And as the plane proceeds away from the apex after intersecting it, the equation would again be $y = ax^2$ with a having values opposite those for the parabola on the other side of the vertex. (If students have studied Dandelin spheres, point out that the focus is getting close to the vertex of the parabola, and hence to the directrix. The locus description of the parabola thus would force the points of the parabola closer and closer to the parabola's axis.)

2. Using a cone: If the plane intersects the cone perpendicular to the axis, the intersection is a circle.

Using a set of points: If the two fixed points used to define an ellipse are the same point, the figure is a circle.

Using algebra: If $\frac{x^2}{a^2} + \frac{y^2}{b^2} = 1$ and $a = b$, the graph is a circle.

3. First step: Write the coordinate of one foci of the hyperbola in terms of a and b. [The foci of the hyperbola are located at $(\pm c, 0)$ and $c = \sqrt{a^2 + b^2}$. So, the focus of the hyperbola is located at $(\sqrt{a^2 + b^2}, 0)$.]

Second step: Write the coordinate of one foci of the ellipse in terms of a and b. [The foci of the ellipse are located at $(\pm c, 0)$ and $c = \sqrt{a^2 - b^2}$. So, the focus of the hyperbola is located at $(\sqrt{a^2 - b^2}, 0)$.]

Third step: Find the distance between $(c_e, 0)$ and $(c_h, 0)$ by subtracting c_e from c_h.

$$(c_h - c_e = \sqrt{a^2 + b^2} - \sqrt{a^2 - b^2})$$

Connecting BIG ideas and Answering the Essential Questions

1 Modeling
The intersection of a cone and a plane parallel to the side of a cone is a parabola.

→

Parabolas (Lesson 10-2)
Centered at the origin,
- a parabola has equation $y = ax^2$, or $x = ay^2$.

2 Equivalence
$\frac{x^2}{9} + \frac{y^2}{9} = 1$ is an equation of a circle centered at the origin with radius 3. Multiply each side by 9 to get $x^2 + y^2 = 9$.

→

Circles (Lesson 10-3)
Centered at the origin,
- a circle with radius r has equation $x^2 + y^2 = r^2$.

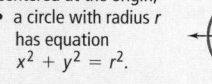

3 Coordinate Geometry
The x^2 and y^2 terms of the algebraic form of an ellipse are both positive. For a hyperbola, one term is negative.

→

Ellipses and Hyperbolas (Lessons 10-4 and 10-5)
Centered at the origin,
- an ellipse has equation $\frac{x^2}{a^2} + \frac{y^2}{b^2} = 1$
- a hyperbola has equation $\frac{x^2}{a^2} - \frac{y^2}{b^2} = 1$ or $\frac{y^2}{a^2} - \frac{x^2}{b^2} = 1$.

Chapter Vocabulary

- axis of symmetry (p. 667)
- center of a circle (p. 649)
- center of an ellipse (p. 659)
- center of a hyperbola (p. 667)
- circle (p. 649)
- conic section (p. 634)
- conjugate axis (p. 667)
- co-vertices of an ellipse (p. 659)
- directrix (p. 641)
- ellipse (p. 658)
- focal length (p. 641)
- focus of a parabola (p. 641)
- foci of an ellipse (p. 658)
- foci of a hyperbola (p. 666)
- hyperbola (p. 666)
- major axis (p. 659)
- minor axis (p. 659)
- radius (p. 649)
- standard form of an equation of a circle (p. 650)
- transverse axis (p. 667)
- vertices of an ellipse (p. 659)
- vertices of a hyperbola (p. 667)

Fill in the blanks.

1. In the definition of a parabola, a point on the curve is equidistant from the focus and the ? .

2. The vertices of an ellipse are on its ? .

3. $(x - h)^2 + (y - k)^2 = r^2$ is the ? .

4. The distance from a point on a circle to its center is the ? of the circle.

5. The vertices of a hyperbola are on its ? .

Essential Questions

BIG idea Modeling
ESSENTIAL QUESTIONS What is the intersection of a cone and a plane parallel to a line along the side of a cone?
ANSWER The intersection of a cone and a plane parallel to the side of the cone is a parabola.

BIG idea Equivalence
ESSENTIAL QUESTION What is the graph of $\frac{x^2}{9} + \frac{y^2}{9} = 1$?
ANSWER $\frac{x^2}{9} + \frac{y^2}{9} = 1$ is an equation of a circle centered at the origin with radius 3. Multiply each side by 9 to get $x^2 + y^2 = 9$.

BIG idea Coordinate Geometry
ESSENTIAL QUESTIONS What is the difference between the algebraic representations of ellipses and hyperbolas?
ANSWER The x^2- and y^2-terms of the algebraic form of an ellipse are both positive. For a hyperbola, one term is negative.

Answers

Chapter Review
1. directrix
2. major axis
3. standard form of an eq. of a circle
4. radius
5. transverse axis

Summative Questions

Use the following prompts as you review this chapter with your students. The prompts are designed to help you assess your students' understanding of the BIG ideas they have studied.

- Does the graph of a conic section ever intersect its focus or foci?
- Which conic sections are symmetric? How can you identify their axes of symmetry?
- Which is the only conic section without a center? Why does it not have one?
- Compare the standard-form equations of the conic sections. How can you identify each type of conic from the equation?

Answers

Chapter Review (continued)

6.
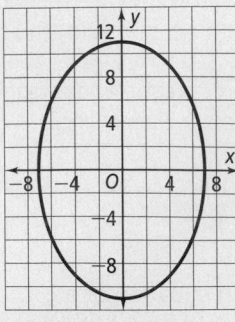

ellipse; lines of sym.: *x*-axis and *y*-axis; domain: $-7 \le x \le 7$, range: $-11 \le y \le 11$

7.
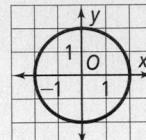

circle; lines of sym.: every line through the center; domain: $-2 \le x \le 2$, range: $-2 \le y \le 2$

8.
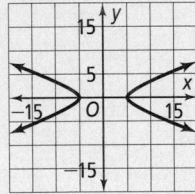

hyperbola; lines of sym.: *x*-axis and *y*-axis; domain: $x \le -5$ or $x \ge 5$, range: all real numbers

9.
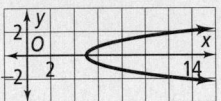

parabola; line of sym.: *x*-axis; domain: $x \ge 5$, range: all real numbers

10. center $(0, 0)$; domain: $x \le -4$ or $x \ge 4$, range: all real numbers

11. center $(0, 0)$; domain: $-3 \le x \le 3$, range: $-2 \le y \le 2$

12. $x = \frac{1}{20}y^2$

13. $y = -\frac{1}{20}x^2$

14. $y = \frac{1}{24}x^2$

15. $y = \frac{1}{10}x^2$

16. $y = 3x^2$

17. $y = \frac{1}{8}x^2 + 1$

18. $x = -\frac{1}{12}y^2 + 1$

19. focus: $\left(0, \frac{1}{20}\right)$, directrix: $y = -\frac{1}{20}$

676 Chapter 10

10-1 Exploring Conic Sections

Quick Review

A **conic section** is formed by the intersection of a plane and a double cone. Circles, ellipses, parabolas, and hyperbolas are all conic sections.

Example

Graph the equation $x^2 + y^2 = 9$. Identify the conic section and the domain and range.

Plot points that satisfy the equation. Connect them with a smooth curve.

The graph is a circle with center $(0, 0)$ and radius 3.

The domain is $-3 \le x \le 3$.

The range is $-3 \le y \le 3$.

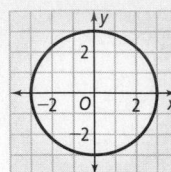

Exercises

Graph each equation. Identify the conic section, any lines of symmetry, and the domain and range.

6. $\dfrac{x^2}{49} + \dfrac{y^2}{121} = 1$ **7.** $x^2 + y^2 = 4$

8. $\dfrac{x^2}{25} - \dfrac{y^2}{4} = 1$ **9.** $x = 2y^2 + 5$

Identify the center and domain and range of each graph.

10. 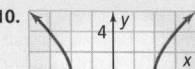   **11.**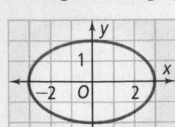

10-2 Parabolas

Quick Review

In a plane, a parabola is the set of all points that are the same distance, *c*, from a fixed point, the **focus**, and a fixed line, the **directrix**.

For $y = ax^2$, if $a > 0$, the parabola opens up, and has focus $(0, c)$ and directrix $y = -c$; if $a < 0$, the parabola opens down, and has focus $(0, -c)$ and directrix $y = c$.

For $x = ay^2$, if $a > 0$, the parabola opens right, and has focus $(c, 0)$ and directrix $x = -c$; if $a < 0$, the parabola opens left, and has focus $(-c, 0)$ and directrix $x = c$. In all cases, $a = \frac{1}{4c}$.

Example

Write an equation of a parabola that opens up, with vertex at the origin and focus 1 unit from the vertex.

Since the parabola opens up, use $y = ax^2$. Since the focus is 1 unit from the vertex, $c = 1$.

$$a = \frac{1}{4c} = \frac{1}{4(1)} = \frac{1}{4}$$

An equation for the parabola is $y = \frac{1}{4}x^2$.

Exercises

Write an equation of a parabola with vertex at the origin and the given focus.

12. $(5, 0)$ **13.** $(0, -5)$ **14.** $(0, 6)$

Write an equation of a parabola that opens up, with vertex at the origin and a focus as described.

15. focus is 2.5 units from the vertex

16. focus is $\frac{1}{12}$ of a unit from the vertex

Write an equation of a parabola with the given focus and directrix.

17. focus: $(0, 3)$; directrix: $y = -1$

18. focus: $(-2, 0)$; directrix: $x = 4$

Find the focus and the directrix of the graph of each equation. Sketch the graph.

19. $y = 5x^2$ **20.** $x = 2y^2$ **21.** $x = -\frac{1}{8}y^2$

20. focus: $\left(\frac{1}{8}, 0\right)$, directrix: $x = -\frac{1}{8}$

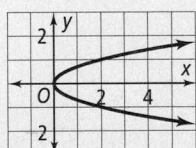

21. focus: $(-2, 0)$, directrix: $x = 2$

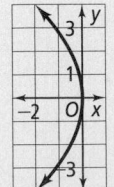

10-3 Circles

Quick Review

In a plane, a **circle** is the set of all points that are a given distance, the **radius**, r, from a given point, the **center**, (h, k).

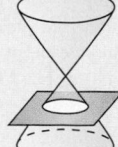

Example

Write an equation in standard form of a circle with center $(-3, 4)$ and radius 2.

Use the standard form of the equation of a circle. Substitute -3 for h, 4 for k, and 2 for r.

$$(x - h)^2 + (y - k)^2 = r^2$$
$$(x - (-3))^2 + (y - 4)^2 = 2^2$$
$$(x + 3)^2 + (y - 4)^2 = 4$$

An equation for the circle is $(x + 3)^2 + (y - 4)^2 = 4$.

Exercises

Write an equation in standard form of a circle with the given center and radius.

22. center $(0, 0)$; radius 4

23. center $(8, 1)$; radius 5

Write an equation for each translation of $x^2 + y^2 = r^2$ with the given radius.

24. left 3 units, up 2 units; radius 10

25. right 5 units, down 3 units; radius 8

Find the center and the radius of each circle. Graph each circle. Describe the translation from center $(0, 0)$.

26. $(x - 1)^2 + y^2 = 64$

27. $(x + 7)^2 + (y + 3)^2 = 49$

10-4 Ellipses

Quick Review

An **ellipse** is the set of all points P, where the sum of the distances between P and two fixed points, the **foci**, is constant. The **major axis** contains the foci, and its endpoints are the **vertices of the ellipse**. For $a > b$, there are two standard forms of ellipses centered at the origin. If $\frac{x^2}{a^2} + \frac{y^2}{b^2} = 1$, the major axis is horizontal with vertices $(\pm a, 0)$, foci $(\pm c, 0)$, and co-vertices $(0, \pm b)$. If $\frac{x^2}{b^2} + \frac{y^2}{a^2} = 1$, the major axis is vertical with vertices $(0, \pm a)$, foci $(0, \pm c)$, and co-vertices $(\pm b, 0)$.
In either case, $c^2 = a^2 - b^2$.

Example

Write an equation of an ellipse with foci $(\pm 5, 0)$ and co-vertices $(0, \pm 3)$.

Since the foci are $(\pm 5, 0)$, the major axis is horizontal. Since $c = 5$ and $b = 3$, $c^2 = 25$ and $b^2 = 9$. Using the equation $c^2 = a^2 - b^2$, $a^2 = 34$.
An equation of the ellipse is $\frac{x^2}{34} + \frac{y^2}{9} = 1$.

Exercises

Write an equation of an ellipse centered at the origin, satisfying the given conditions.

28. foci $(\pm 1, 0)$; co-vertices $(0, \pm 4)$

29. vertex $(0, \sqrt{29})$; co-vertex $(-5, 0)$

30. focus $(0, 1)$; vertex $(0, \sqrt{10})$

31. foci $(\pm 2, 0)$; co-vertices $(0, \pm 6)$

32. Write an equation of an ellipse centered at the origin with height 8 units and width 16 units.

33. Find the foci of the graph of $\frac{x^2}{4} + \frac{y^2}{9} = 1$. Graph the ellipse.

30. $\frac{x^2}{9} + \frac{y^2}{10} = 1$

31. $\frac{x^2}{40} + \frac{y^2}{36} = 1$

32. $\frac{x^2}{64} + \frac{y^2}{16} = 1$

33. foci: $(0, \pm\sqrt{5})$

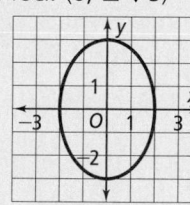

22. $x^2 + y^2 = 16$

23. $(x - 8)^2 + (y - 1)^2 = 25$

24. $(x + 3)^2 + (y - 2)^2 = 100$

25. $(x - 5)^2 + (y + 3)^2 = 64$

26. center $(1, 0)$, radius 8

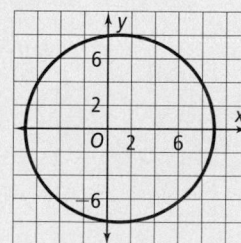

circle with radius 8 translated 1 unit to the rt.

27. center $(-7, -3)$, radius 7

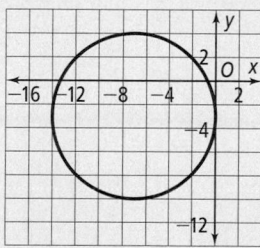

circle with radius 7 translated 7 units to the left and 3 units down

28. $\frac{x^2}{17} + \frac{y^2}{16} = 1$

29. $\frac{x^2}{25} + \frac{y^2}{29} = 1$

Answers

Chapter Review (continued)

34. foci: $(\pm 3\sqrt{29}, 0)$

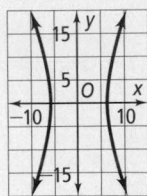

35. foci: $(0, \pm\sqrt{569})$

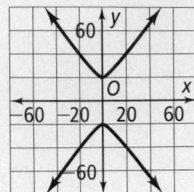

36. foci: $(\pm\sqrt{202}, 0)$

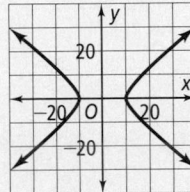

37. $\dfrac{x^2}{64} - \dfrac{y^2}{225} = 1$

38. $\dfrac{y^2}{49} - \dfrac{x^2}{576} = 1$

39. $\dfrac{x^2}{1.148 \times 10^{10}} - \dfrac{y^2}{3.395 \times 10^{10}} = 1$

10-5 Hyperbolas

Quick Review

A **hyperbola** is the set of all points P such that the absolute value of the difference of the distances from P to two fixed points, the **foci**, is constant. There are two standard forms of hyperbolas centered at the origin. If $\dfrac{x^2}{a^2} - \dfrac{y^2}{b^2} = 1$, the asymptotes are $y = \pm\dfrac{b}{a}x$, the **transverse axis** is horizontal with vertices $(\pm a, 0)$, and the foci are $(\pm c, 0)$. If $\dfrac{y^2}{a^2} - \dfrac{x^2}{b^2} = 1$, the asymptotes are $y = \pm\dfrac{a}{b}x$, the transverse axis is vertical with vertices $(0, \pm a)$, and the foci are $(0, \pm c)$. In either case, $c^2 = a^2 + b^2$.

Example

Find the foci of the graph of $\dfrac{x^2}{25} - \dfrac{y^2}{9} = 1$.

The equation is in the form $\dfrac{x^2}{a^2} - \dfrac{y^2}{b^2} = 1$, so the transverse axis is horizontal; $a^2 = 25$ and $b^2 = 9$.

Using the Pythagorean Theorem to find c,
$c = \sqrt{25 + 9} = \sqrt{34} \approx 5.8$.
The foci, $(\pm c, 0)$, are approximately $(5.8, 0)$ and $(-5.8, 0)$.

Exercises

Find the foci of each hyperbola. Graph the hyperbola.

34. $\dfrac{x^2}{36} - \dfrac{y^2}{225} = 1$

35. $\dfrac{y^2}{400} - \dfrac{x^2}{169} = 1$

36. $\dfrac{x^2}{121} - \dfrac{y^2}{81} = 1$

Write an equation of a hyperbola with the given foci and vertices.

37. foci $(\pm 17, 0)$, vertices $(\pm 8, 0)$

38. foci $(0, \pm 25)$, vertices $(0, \pm 7)$

39. Find an equation that models the hyperbolic path of a spacecraft around a planet if $a = 107{,}124$ km and $c = 213{,}125.9$ km.

10 Chapter Test

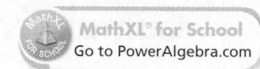

Do you know HOW?

Graph each equation. Identify the conic section and describe the graph and its lines of symmetry. Then find the domain and range.

1. $36 - 9x^2 - 4y^2 = 0$

2. $9x^2 - 4y^2 - 36 = 0$

3. $x^2 + 4y^2 = 4$

4. $4x^2 + 36 = 9y^2$

Identify the focus and the directrix of the graph of each equation.

5. $y = 3x^2$

6. $x = -2y^2$

7. $x + 5y^2 = 0$

8. $9x^2 - 2y = 0$

Write an equation of a parabola with its vertex at the origin and the given characteristics.

9. focus at $(0, -2)$

10. focus at $(3, 0)$

11. directrix $x = 7$

12. directrix $y = -1$

For each equation, find the center and radius of the circle. Graph the circle.

13. $(x - 2)^2 + (y - 3)^2 = 36$

14. $(x + 5)^2 + (y + 8)^2 = 100$

15. $(x - 1)^2 + (y + 7)^2 = 81$

16. $(x + 4)^2 + (y - 10)^2 = 121$

Write an equation of an ellipse for each given height and width. Assume that the center of the ellipse is $(0, 0)$.

17. height 10 units; width 16 units

18. height 2 units; width 12 units

19. height 9 units; width 5 units

Find the foci of each ellipse. Then graph the ellipse.

20. $x^2 + \dfrac{y^2}{49} = 1$

21. $4x^2 + y^2 = 4$

Find the foci of each hyperbola. Then graph the hyperbola.

22. $\dfrac{x^2}{64} - \dfrac{y^2}{4} = 1$

23. $y^2 - \dfrac{x^2}{225} = 1$

Write an equation of an ellipse centered at the origin with the given characteristics.

24. horizontal major axis of length 8; minor axis of length 6

25. vertical major axis of length 12; minor axis of length 10

Write an equation of a hyperbola with the given characteristics.

26. vertices $(\pm 3, 0)$; foci $(\pm 5, 0)$

27. vertices $(0, \pm 5)$; foci $(0, \pm 7)$

Do you UNDERSTAND?

28. **Reasoning** Suppose you graph a conic section that has two foci and a range of all real numbers. What type of conic section did you graph? Explain.

29. **Reasoning** What shape is an ellipse whose height and width are equal?

30. **Open-Ended** Write an equation of a hyperbola whose transverse axis is on the x-axis.

Answers

Chapter Test

1.
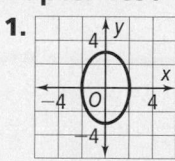

ellipse: center $(0, 0)$; x-intercepts: $(\pm 2, 0)$, y-intercepts: $(0, \pm 3)$; lines of sym.: x-axis and y-axis; domain: $-2 \le x \le 2$, range: $-3 \le y \le 3$

2.
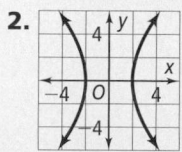

hyperbola: center $(0, 0)$; x-intercepts $(\pm 2, 0)$, no y-intercepts; lines of sym.: x-axis and y-axis; domain: $x \le -2$ or $x \ge 2$, range: all real numbers

3.
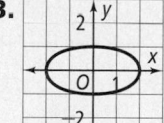

ellipse: center $(0, 0)$; x-intercepts: $(\pm 2, 0)$, y-intercepts: $(0, \pm 1)$; lines of sym.: x-axis and y-axis; domain: $-2 \le x \le 2$, range: $-1 \le y \le 1$

4.
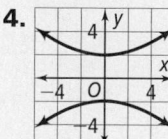

hyperbola: center $(0, 0)$; no x-intercepts, y-intercepts $(0, \pm 2)$; lines of sym.: x-axis and y-axis; domain: all real numbers, range: $y \le -2$ or $y \ge 2$

5. focus: $\left(0, \dfrac{1}{12}\right)$, directrix: $y = -\dfrac{1}{12}$

6. focus: $\left(-\dfrac{1}{8}, 0\right)$, directrix: $x = \dfrac{1}{8}$

7. focus: $\left(-\dfrac{1}{20}, 0\right)$, directrix: $x = \dfrac{1}{20}$

8. focus: $\left(0, \dfrac{1}{18}\right)$, directrix: $y = -\dfrac{1}{18}$

9. $y = -\dfrac{1}{8}x^2$

10. $x = \dfrac{1}{12}y^2$

11. $x = -\dfrac{1}{28}y^2$

12. $y = \dfrac{1}{4}x^2$

13. center $(2, 3)$, radius 6
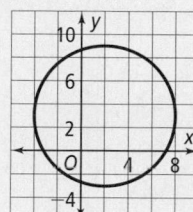

14. center $(-5, -8)$, radius 10
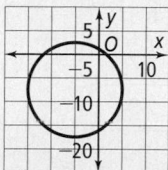

15. center $(1, -7)$, radius 9
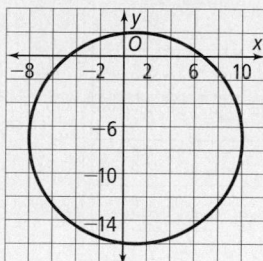

16. center $(-4, 10)$, radius 11
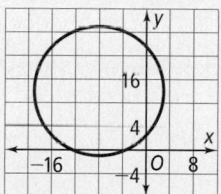

17. $\dfrac{x^2}{64} + \dfrac{y^2}{25} = 1$

18. $\dfrac{x^2}{36} + y^2 = 1$

19. $\dfrac{x^2}{6.25} + \dfrac{y^2}{20.25} = 1$

20–30. See back of book.

Item Number	Lesson
1	10-5
2	2-3
3	4-1
4	7-1
5	2-2
6	4-5
7	10-5
8	4-5
9	8-4
10	4-1
11	10-3
12	8-6
13	8-5
14	2-2
15	2-3
16	10-3
17	9-3
18	8-4
19	4-5
20	7-2
21	6-8
22	4-5
23	7-1

10 Cumulative Test Prep

TIPS FOR SUCCESS

Read the question at the right. Then follow the tips to answer the multiple choice question.

A stone falls from a 56-foot cliff. The graph shows the height of the stone h, in feet, after t seconds. In about how many seconds does the stone reach the ground?

TIP 1

Read the labels on the axes to understand the meaning of a point on the graph.

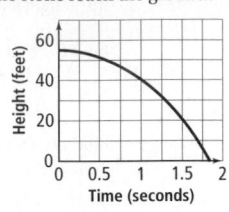

TIP 2

Use the graph to determine when $h = 0$.

Think It Through

Find the point where the graph crosses the horizontal axis.

The graph crosses the horizontal axis at about $(1.9, 0)$. So the stone reaches the ground in about 1.9 seconds.

The correct answer is D.

- Ⓐ 0.9 second
- Ⓑ 1.0 second
- Ⓒ 1.5 seconds
- Ⓓ 1.9 seconds

Vocabulary Builder

As you solve test items, you must understand the meanings of mathematical terms. Match each term with its mathematical meaning.

A. conic section

B. hyperbola

C. directrix

D. ellipse

E. circle

I. a set of points P in a plane such that the absolute value of the difference between the distances from P to two fixed points F_1 and F_2 is a constant k

II. a set of points P in a plane such that the sum of the distances from P to two fixed points F_1 and F_2 is a constant k

III. the set of all points in a plane that are a distance r from a given point

IV. a curve formed by the intersection of a plane and a double cone

V. the fixed line equidistant with the focus from each point on a parabola

Multiple Choice

Read each question. Then write the letter of the correct answer on your paper.

1. The graph of $\frac{x^2}{21} - \frac{y^2}{4} = 1$ is a hyperbola. Which set of coordinates represents the foci?
- Ⓐ $(0, 5)$ and $(0, -5)$
- Ⓑ $(5, 0)$ and $(0, -5)$
- Ⓒ $(0, 5)$ and $(-5, 0)$
- Ⓓ $(5, 0)$ and $(-5, 0)$

2. If the equation $y = 4x$ is graphed, which of the following values of x would produce a point on the x-axis?
- Ⓕ 3
- Ⓖ 0
- Ⓗ 1
- Ⓘ 4

Answers

Cumulative Test Prep

A. IV

B. I

C. V

D. II

E. III

1. D

2. G

3. An acrobat landed on a teeterboard and launched his partner into the air. The graph below shows the height h of the partner, in yards, at t seconds after the launch.

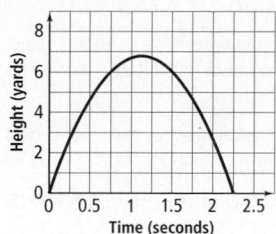

Which value is the best approximation of the maximum height of the partner?

(A) 6.0 yards   (C) 6.8 yards

(B) 6.4 yards   (D) 7.2 yards

4. The bacteria in a petri dish are growing exponentially with time, as shown in the table below.

Bacteria Growth

Day	Bacteria
0	50
1	150
2	450

Which of the following equations expresses the number of bacteria y present on day x?

(F) $y = (3)^x$

(G) $y = 50 + (3)^x$

(H) $y = 50 \cdot (3)^x$

(I) $y = 150 \cdot (3)^x$

5. A truck driver traveled 120 miles in 2.5 hours. How far can he drive in 2 hours?

(A) 48 miles   (C) 96 miles

(B) 72 miles   (D) 144 miles

6. Alexandra dives from a 30-foot board into a swimming pool. The graph below shows her height h, in feet, t seconds after jumping.

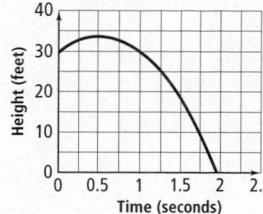

After leaving the board, in how many seconds is Alexandra at the height of 30 feet again?

(F) 0.5 second   (H) 1.5 seconds

(G) 1 second   (I) 2 seconds

7. What is the standard form of the equation of the conic section given below?

$$25x^2 - 49y^2 - 1225 = 0$$

(A) $\dfrac{x^2}{49} - \dfrac{y^2}{25} = 1$

(B) $\dfrac{x^2}{49} + \dfrac{y^2}{25} = 1$

(C) $25x^2 - 49y^2 = 1225$

(D) $49x^2 - 25y^2 = 1$

8. Owen threw a ball straight up into the air from an initial height of 5 feet. The graph below shows the height h of the ball, in feet, at t seconds after Owen threw it. Of the following times, when was the ball closest to the ground?

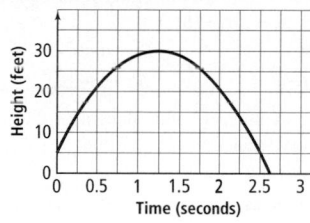

(F) 0.6 second   (H) 1.6 seconds

(G) 1 second   (I) 2 seconds

3. C
4. H
5. C
6. G
7. A
8. I

Answers

Cumulative Test Prep (continued)

9. D

10. I

11. A

12. G

13. $\frac{7}{10}$

14. 9.90

15. −3.5

16. 10

17. [2] $a_n = -5(3^{n-1})$; −5, −15, −45, −135, −405

   [1] $a_n = -5(3^{n-1})$ without the first five terms OR −5, −15, −45, −135, −405 without the explicit formula.

18. [2] $\frac{14x^2}{3}$

   [1] $\frac{560x^3}{120x}$ OR other correct simplification (but not on simplest form) of the division problem such as $\frac{28x^2}{6}$.

19. [2] $x^2 - 2x = 0$
      $x(x - 2) = 0$
      $x = 0, 2$

   [1] $x = 0, 2$ with no work shown

20. [4] $10,671.59; $13,840.31

   [3] $10,671.59 OR $13,840.31

   [2] Both answers with minor miscalculations with rounding (such as $10,671 and $13,841).

   [1] One of the answers with a minor miscalculation with rounding (such as $13,841).

21. [4] The graph of $y = \sqrt{x} - 3$ is the graph of $y = \sqrt{x}$ translated down 3 units.

   [3] The graph of $y = \sqrt{x} - 3$ is the graph of $y = \sqrt{x}$ translated down.

   [2] The graph of $y = \sqrt{x} - 3$ is the graph of $y = \sqrt{x}$ translated up 3 units.

   [1] The graph of $y = \sqrt{x} - 3$ is the graph of $y = \sqrt{x}$ translated up.

22. [4] $100 - 4(k)(25) = 0$; $100k = 100$; $k = 1$

   [3] $100 - 4(k)(25) = 0$; $100k = 100$

   [2] $100 - 4(k)(25) = 0$

   [1] $100 - 4(k)(25) = 0$; $100k = 100$; $k = 100$ (contains correct procedure but gives incorrect final response based on a miscalculation error).

23. [4] For $y = ab^x$, if $b > 1$, the exponential function represents exponential growth; if $0 < b < 1$, the exponential function represents exponential decay.

   [3] For $y = ab^x$, if $b > 1$, the exponential function represents exponential growth.

   [2] For $y = ab^x$, if $0 < b < 1$, the exponential function represents exponential growth; if $b > 1$, the exponential function represents exponential decay.

   [1] For $y = ab^x$, if $b > 1$, the exponential function represents exponential decay.

---

9. Which is the first *incorrect* step in simplifying?

$$\frac{4}{(x - 1)^{-1}(x^2 + 3x - 4)}$$

Step 1: $\dfrac{4(x - 1)}{x^2 + 3x - 4}$

Step 2: $\dfrac{4(x - 1)}{(x + 4)(x - 1)}$

Step 3: $\dfrac{4(x - 1)}{(x + 4)(x - 1)} \div \dfrac{x - 1}{x - 1}$

Step 4: $\dfrac{4}{x + 4} \div \dfrac{4}{4} = \dfrac{1}{x}$

(A) Step 1   (C) Step 3

(B) Step 2   (D) Step 4

10. Which of the following is the graph of the quadratic parent function?

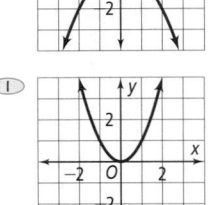

11. Which conic section is represented by the equation $x^2 + y^2 = 6x - 14y - 9$?

(A) circle   (C) ellipse

(B) parabola   (D) hyperbola

12. If x is a real number, for what values of x is the equation $(3x - 6)(x - 2)^{-1} = 3$ true?

(F) all values of x

(G) some values of x

(H) no values of x

(I) impossible to determine

---

13. What is the value of $\dfrac{1 - \frac{1}{8}}{2 - \frac{3}{4}}$?

14. A copy center charges $4.26 to make 71 copies. At that rate, how much will the copy center charge for 165 copies?

15. What is the y-coordinate of the y-intercept of the line with equation $-6x - 2y = 7$?

16. What is the distance between $(-3, 2)$ and $(5, -4)$?

Short Response

17. Write an explicit formula for the geometric sequence for which $a_1 = -5$ and $r = 3$. Then generate the first five terms.

18. Write the expression $\dfrac{35x^3}{24} \div \dfrac{5x}{16}$ in simplest form.

19. Find the zeros of the function $y = x^2 - 2x$. Show your work.

Extended Response

20. Suppose you put $10,000 in an account that pays 6.5% annual interest compounded continuously. How much will be in the account after one year? After five years?

21. Explain how to graph $y = \sqrt{x} - 3$ by translating the graph of $y = \sqrt{x}$.

22. Find a nonzero value for k such that the equation $kx^2 - 10x + 25 = 0$ has one solution. Show your work.

23. Explain when the function $y = a \cdot b^x$ models exponential growth and when it models exponential decay.

---

   [2] For $y = ab^x$, if $0 < b < 1$, the exponential function represents exponential growth; if $b > 1$, the exponential function represents exponential decay.

   [1] For $y = ab^x$, if $b > 1$, the exponential function represents exponential decay.

Get Ready!

Skills Handbook, page 865

◆ Finding Percent

Write each number as a percent.

1. $\frac{5}{6}$ **2.** $\frac{7}{36}$ **3.** $\frac{48}{52}$ **4.** 0.3056

Skills Handbook, page 868

◆ Simplifying Expressions

Simplify each expression.

5. $8 \cdot 7 \cdot 6 \cdot 5 \cdot 4$ **6.** $\frac{52 \cdot 51 \cdot 50}{3 \cdot 2 \cdot 1}$ **7.** $\frac{5 \cdot 4 \cdot 3 \cdot 2 \cdot 1}{3 \cdot 2 \cdot 1 \cdot 2 \cdot 1}$

Lesson 5-7

◆ Expanding Binomials

Use Pascal's Triangle to expand each binomial.

8. $(a + b)^5$ **9.** $(j + 3k)^3$ **10.** $(m + 0.7)^2$

11. $(2 + t)^4$ **12.** $(m + n)^2$ **13.** $(x + 3y)^4$

Lesson 6-1

◆ Finding Real Roots

Find the real square roots of each number.

14. $\frac{1}{100}$ **15.** $\frac{1}{400}$ **16.** $\frac{1}{196}$

17. $\frac{1}{4}$ **18.** $\frac{1}{9}$ **19.** $\frac{1}{576}$

Looking Ahead Vocabulary

20. In a history class, students may learn about history through a *simulation*. How do you think simulations might be used in a math class?

21. When you describe the likelihood that it will rain tomorrow given that it rained today, you are giving a *conditional probability*. What is the condition in this situation?

22. When you give a value to represent the typical data value in a data set, you are giving a *measure of central tendency* of the data set. What value do you think best represents the following data set? Explain.

$\{1, 3, 3, 3, 4, 10, 20, 30, 40\}$

Answers

Get Ready!

1. $83.\overline{3}\%$

2. $19.\overline{4}\%$

3. $\approx 92.308\%$

4. 30.56%

5. 6720

6. $22{,}100$

7. 10

8. $a^5 + 5a^4b + 10a^3b^2 + 10a^2b^3 + 5ab^4 + b^5$

9. $j^3 + 9j^2k + 27jk^2 + 27k^3$

10. $m^2 + 1.4m + 0.49$

11. $16 + 32t + 24t^2 + 8t^3 + t^4$

12. $m^2 + 2mn + n^2$

13. $x^4 + 12x^3y + 54x^2y^2 + 108xy^3 + 81y^4$

14. $\pm\frac{1}{10}$

15. $\pm\frac{1}{20}$

16. $\pm\frac{1}{14}$

17. $\pm\frac{1}{2}$

18. $\pm\frac{1}{3}$

19. $\pm\frac{1}{24}$

20. In a math class, when actual trials are difficult to conduct, you can find experimental probability by using a simulation which is a model of one or more events.

21. It rained today.

22. The mean, $12.\overline{6}$; the data are fairly evenly distributed around the mean, which makes the mean the best representation of the data given.

Get Ready!

Assign this diagnostic assessment to determine if students have the prerequisite skills for Chapter 11.

Lesson	Skill
Skills Handbook, p. 865	Finding Percent
Skills Handbook, p. 868	Simplifying Expressions
5-7	Expanding Binomials
6-1	Finding Real Roots

To remediate students, select from these resources (available for every lesson).
- Online Problems (PowerAlgebra.com)
- Reteaching (All-in-One Teaching Resources)
- Practice (All-in-One Teaching Resources)

Why Students Need These Skills

FINDING PERCENT
Finding percents is essential to expressing probabilities.

SIMPLIFYING EXPRESSIONS
Simplifying expressions is essential for using formulas to calculate probability.

EXPANDING BINOMIALS
Students' skills of expanding binomials are extended with another variation of the Binomial Theorem.

FINDING REAL ROOTS
Finding real roots is essential to finding standard deviation from the variance.

Looking Ahead Vocabulary

SIMULATION Elicit that a simulation can be a way to replay an event or events so that more data can be derived.

CONDITIONAL PROBABILITY Ask students whether the probability is dependent on the given condition.

MEASURE OF CENTRAL TENDENCY Ask students what criteria they are looking for that makes a data value the most typical.

Chapter 11 Overview

UbD Understanding by Design

Chapter 11 expands on students' understandings and skills related to probability and statistics. In this chapter, students will develop the answers to the Essential Questions posed on the student page as they learn the concepts and skills bulleted below.

BIG idea Probability

ESSENTIAL QUESTION What is the difference between a permutation and a combination?
- Students will find permutations and combinations of data sets using formulas.

BIG idea Probability

ESSENTIAL QUESTION What is the difference between experimental and theoretical probability?
- Students will use simulation to model experimental probability.
- Students will find the theoretical probability of events using a formula.

BIG idea Data Collection and Analysis

ESSENTIAL QUESTION How are measures of central tendency different from standard deviation?
- Students will find and analyze the measures of central tendency of given data sets.
- Students will find the standard deviation of given data sets.

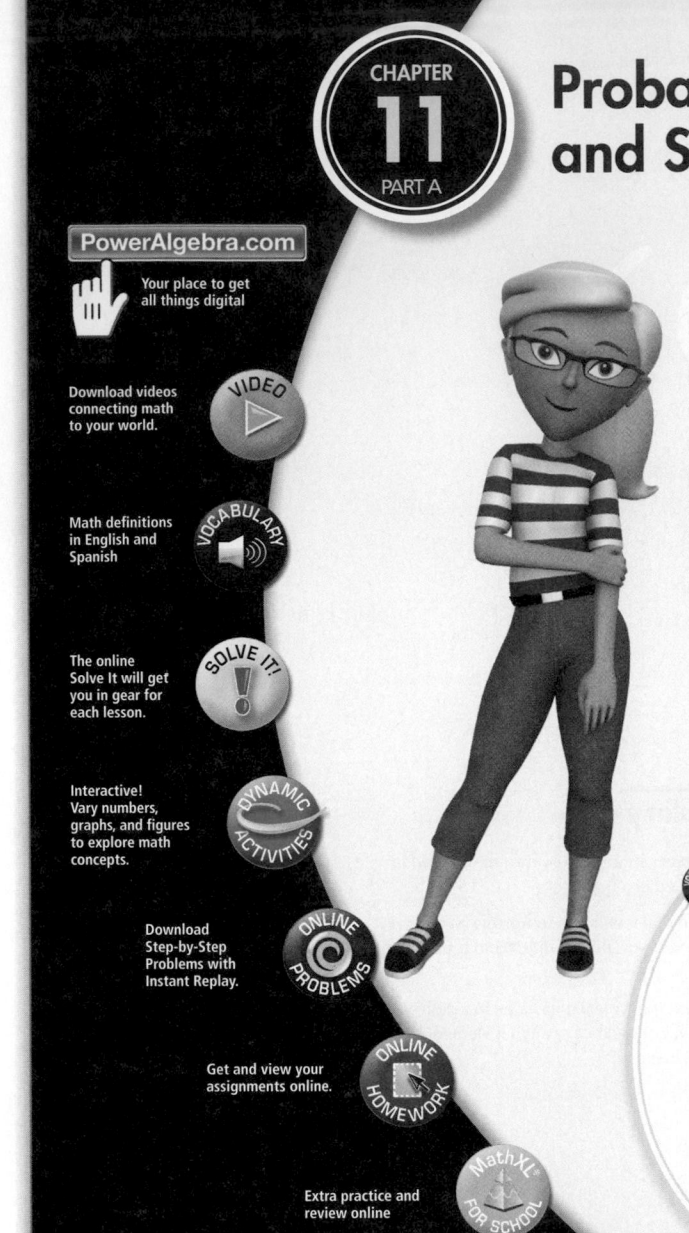

CHAPTER 11 PART A

Probability and Statistics

PowerAlgebra.com

Your place to get all things digital

VIDEO Download videos connecting math to your world.

VOCABULARY Math definitions in English and Spanish

SOLVE IT! The online Solve It will get you in gear for each lesson.

DYNAMIC ACTIVITIES Interactive! Vary numbers, graphs, and figures to explore math concepts.

ONLINE PROBLEMS Download Step-by-Step Problems with Instant Replay.

ONLINE HOMEWORK Get and view your assignments online.

MathXL FOR SCHOOL Extra practice and review online

In this chapter you will learn about probability and statistics.

What's the probability of scoring in soccer on a penalty kick? Do statistics from past games help you decide? How do you apply theoretical and experimental probabilities? How can you compare data sets? You will learn how in this chapter.

Vocabulary for Part A

English/Spanish Vocabulary Audio Online:

English	Spanish
combination, p. 690	combinación
conditional probability, p. 711	probabilidad condicional
experimental probability, p. 695	probabilidad experimental
mutually exclusive events, p. 705	sucesos mutuamente excluyentes
permutation, p. 687	permutación
simulation, p. 696	simulación
theoretical probability, p. 698	probabilidad teórica

PowerAlgebra.com

Chapter 11 Overview

Use these online assets to engage your students. These include support for the Solve It and step-by-step solutions for Problems.

 VIDEO Show the student-produced video demonstrating relevant and engaging applications of the new concepts in the chapter.

 VOCABULARY Find online definitions for new terms in English and Spanish.

 SOLVE IT! Start each lesson with an attention-getting Problem. View the Problem online with helpful hints.

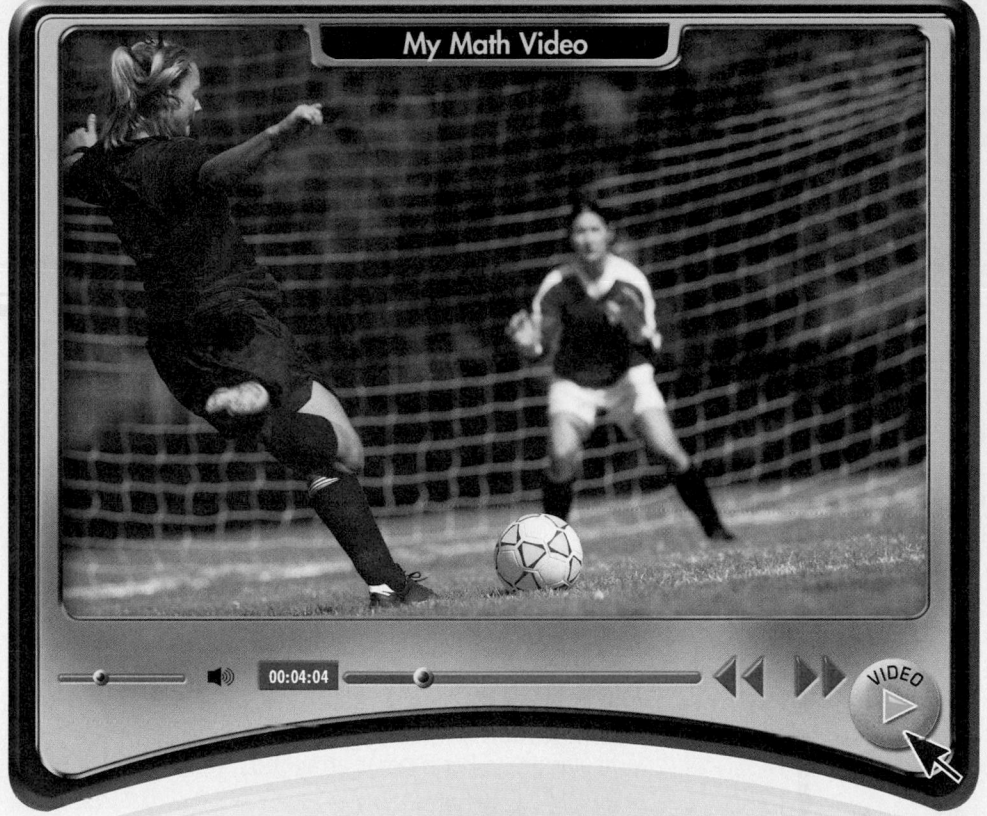

My Math Video

My Math Video

Use this photo to introduce the concept of probability. Statistically, the kicker is more likely to score than the goalie is to save, so the probability of scoring should be greater than 50%, or greater than 0.5.

Q What factors affect the chances of the kicker scoring? **[the skill of the kicker and of the goalie]**

Q How could you examine these factors? **[You could look at the kicker's past percentage of scoring on a penalty kick and the goalie's percentage of saving a penalty kick.]**

Q Statistics show that it is significantly more likely to score on a penalty kick than to save it. What does this tell you about the probabilities of each? **[The probability of scoring on a penalty kick is greater than the probability of saving the penalty kick.]**

EXTENSION

Have students research the statistics of one or more soccer players and compare the likelihood of each scoring.

BIG ideas

1 **Probability**
Essential Question What is the difference between a permutation and a combination?

2 **Probability**
Essential Question What is the difference between experimental and theoretical probability?

3 **Data Collection and Analysis**
Essential Question How are measures of central tendency different from standard deviation?

Chapter Preview for Part A

PowerAlgebra.com   Chapter 11 Probability and Statistics   685

 Increase students' depth of knowledge with interactive online activities.

 Show problems from each lesson solved step by step. Instant replay allows students to go at their own pace when studying online.

 Prepare students for the Chapter Test for Part A and the Chapter Test for Part B with online practice and review.

UbD

Probability

BIG idea Probability expresses the likelihood that a particular event will occur. Data can be used to calculate an experimental probability, and mathematical properties can be used to determine a theoretical probability. Either experimental or theoretical probability can be used to make predictions or decisions about future events. Various counting methods can be used to develop theoretical probabilities.

ESSENTIAL UNDERSTANDINGS

11-1 You can use multiplication to quickly count the number of ways certain things can happen.

11-2 The probability of an impossible event is 0 (or 0%). The probability of a certain event is 1 (or 100%). Otherwise, the probability of an event is a number between 0 and 1 (or a percent between 0% and 100%).

11-3 To find the probability of two events occurring together, you have to decide whether one event occurring affects the other event.

11-4 Conditional probability is when two events are dependent.

11-8 You can use binomial probabilities in situations involving two possible outcomes.

Data Collection and Analysis

BIG idea Sampling techniques are used to gather data from real-world situations. If the data are representative of the larger population, inferences can be made about that population. Biased sampling techniques yield data unlikely to be representative of the larger population. Sets of numerical data are described using measures of central tendency and dispersion.

ESSENTIAL UNDERSTANDINGS

11-5 You can describe and compare sets of data using various statistical measures, depending on what characteristics you want to study.

11-6 Standard deviation is a measure of how far the numbers in a data set deviate from the mean.

11-7 You can get good statistical information about a population by studying a sample of the population.

11-8 You can use binomial probabilities in situations involving two possible outcomes.

11-9 Many common statistics (such as human height, weight, and blood pressure) gathered from samples in the natural world tend to have a *normal distribution* about their mean.

Probability

The probability of an event is a number from 0 to 1 that measures how likely it is for the event to occur. If events are equally likely, then the probability of an event A is

$$P(A) = \frac{\text{number of outcomes in event } A}{\text{total number of outcomes}}.$$

Counting Methods

Counting methods help determine the number of events and the number of outcomes.

- The **Fundamental Counting Principle** states that if event A can happen m ways and event B can happen n ways, then Event A followed by Event B can happen in $m \times n$ ways.

- A **permutation** is an arrangement of items in a particular order. For n items arranged r at a time, $_nP_r = \frac{n!}{(n-r)!}$, where $0 \le r \le n$.

- A **combination** is used if the order of the items is not important. $_nC_r = \frac{n!}{r!(n-r)!}$ for $0 \le r \le n$.

Probability Rules

Independent events have no effect on each other. Events are dependent if they do have an effect on each other.

$P(A \text{ and } B) = P(A) \cdot P(B)$ for independent events.

$P(A \text{ or } B) = P(A) + P(B) - P(A \text{ and } B)$

- For the special case of **mutually exclusive events** (events that cannot happen at the same time), then $P(A \text{ and } B) = 0$.

- $P(B \mid A) = \frac{P(A \text{ and } B)}{P(A)}$

- Conditional probability is the probability that an event will occur given that another event has already occurred.

Common Errors When Finding Probability

Counting errors occur when students choose the wrong counting formula for a situation. Encourage students to begin a list of items to determine whether they are finding permutations or combinations.

Probability rules are used incorrectly when students do not verify conditions. Require students to state whether events are independent, dependent, or mutually exclusive before applying probability rules.

PROGRAM ORGANIZATION · BIG IDEA · ESSENTIAL UNDERSTANDING · PROGRAM ORGANIZATION

Using Data

Descriptive Measures

The most common measures used to describe data are measures of central tendency and measures of variation.

Measures of Central Tendency

Measures of central tendency include the **mean, median,** and **mode.** In a normal distribution, these measures are very similar. However, outliers can cause one measure to better represent the data than another measure. An **outlier** is a value substantially different from the rest of the data.

Example: Which measure of central tendency best represents the data? 78, 82, 95, 80, 14, 91, 88

The mean is about 75.4, median is 82, and there is no mode. The value 14 differs greatly from the other values, so it might be considered an outlier. The outlier causes the mean to be much lower than the median, so the median is a better choice.

Measures of Variation

Measures of variation include the **range, quartiles,** and the **interquartile range (IQR).** Quartiles are the values that separate the data into four parts. The IQR is the difference between Q_3 and Q_1.

Standard deviation is a measure of how far the data values in a set deviate from the mean and is given by the formula $\sigma = \sqrt{\frac{\Sigma(x - \bar{x})^2}{n}}$, where $\bar{x}$ is the mean and n is the number of values.

Gathering Data

A **sample** is a subset of a population. A random sample is most representative of a population because each member has an equal chance of being selected. Due to time and cost restraints, convenience samples, self-selected samples, and systematic samples are often used, although they can introduce bias. **Bias** is a systematic error that results in the sample not being a true representation of the population.

Common Errors When Using Data

Errors occur with interpretation of **data descriptors** rather than calculations. Ask, for example, what students know about data if the mean is greater than the median. Discuss conclusions rather than calculations.

Acknowledge that **designing samples and surveys** without bias is quite challenging. Help students identify bias by using newspaper articles or other sources of current events.

Binomial and Normal Distributions

A probability distribution is a function that gives the probability of each outcome in a sample space. Two common types of probability distributions are binomial distributions and normal distributions.

Binomial Experiment

A binomial experiment is characterized by:
• trials with exactly two outcomes (success or failure)
• independent trials (probability remains the same)

The individual probability in a binomial experiment can be calculated using the formula $P(x) = {}_nC_x p^x q^{n-x}$

Example: A coin is flipped six times. What is the probability of getting exactly two heads?

Answer: The two outcomes are heads and tails. The trials are independent; probability is always 50%. The number of trials is six. So $P(\text{two heads}) = {}_6C_2\, 0.5^2 0.5^4 \approx 0.23$

Binomial Distribution

A binomial distribution is a discrete probability distribution because it has a finite number of possible events or values. It is created from the individual binomial probabilities.

Normal Distribution

A normal distribution is a continuous probability distribution because its values are in an interval of real numbers. Standard deviation is shown on the normal curve and is used to determine what percent of the population falls within certain values.

Example: The average score on a test is 82 with a standard deviation of 4. In a group of 30 students about how many would you expect to score between 78 and 86?

Answer: This is within one standard deviation, so $0.68 \cdot (30)$ is about 20 students.

Common Errors When Using Binomial and Normal Distributions

Binomial Distribution Errors occur when the binomial distribution is used with situations that do not satisfy the conditions of a binomial experiment. Before applying the binomial formula, have students ask themselves: Are the events independent? Are there exactly two outcomes?

Normal Distribution Errors are made when students use the incorrect intervals. Remind them that within one standard deviation of the mean requires adding and subtracting the standard deviation from the mean. Encourage students to sketch the normal graph in each situation to help them determine correct intervals.

PROBABILITY AND STATISTICS
Pacing and Assignment Guide

		TRADITIONAL		BLOCK
Lesson	Teaching Day(s)	Basic	Average	Block
11-1	1	Problems 1–3 Exs. 5–14, 15–21 odd	Problems 1–3 Exs. 5–14, 15–27 odd	**Day 1** Part 1 Problems 1–3 Exs. 5–14, 15–27 odd Part 2 Problems 4–5 Exs. 7–21, 23–35
	2	Problems 4-5 Exs. 7–18, 20, 23–35	Problems 4–5 Exs. 7–21, 23–35	
11-2	1	Problems 1–2 Exs. 5–10	Problems 1–2 Exs. 5–10	**Day 2** Part 1 Problems 1–2 Exs. 5–10 Part 2 Problems 3–5 Exs. 4–25, 27–41
	2	Problems 3–5 Exs. 4–18, 20, 25, 27–41	Problems 3–5 Exs. 4–25, 27–41	
11-3	1	Problems 1–3 Exs. 9–17, 37–54	Problems 1–3 Exs. 9–14, 16, 37–54	**Day 3** Problems 1–5 Exs. 9–14, 16–26 even, 27–35, 37–54
	2	Problems 4–5 Exs. 18–26, 31	Problems 4–5 Exs. 18–26 even, 27–35	
11-4	1	Problems 1–4 Exs. 8–17, 19, 22, 26–35	Problems 1–4 Exs. 8–23, 26–35	Problems 1–4 Exs. 8–23, 26–35
Review	1	Chapter Review for Part A	Chapter Review for Part A	**Day 4** Chapter Review for Part A Chapter Test for Part A
Assess	1	Chapter Test for Part A	Chapter Test for Part A	
11-5	1	Problems 1–3 Exs. 5–9, 23–34	Problems 1–3 Exs. 5–9, 23–34	**Day 5** Problems 1–5 Exs. 5–21, 23–34
	2	Problems 4–5 Exs. 10–13, 16, 17, 20	Problems 4–5 Exs. 10–21	
11-6	1	Problems 1–3 Exs. 5–13, 17–29	Problems 1–3 Exs. 5–29	Problems 1–3 Exs. 5–29
11-7	1	Problems 1–3 Exs. 6–12, 17, 23, 26–37	Problems 1–3 Exs. 6–12, 13–25 odd, 26–37	**Day 6** Problems 1–3 Exs. 6–12, 13–25 odd, 26–37
11-8	1	Problems 1–3 Exs. 8–20, 31–47	Problems 1–3 Exs. 8–18 even, 19–28, 30–47	Problems 1–3 Exs. 8–18 even, 19–28, 30–47
11-9	1	Problems 1–3 Exs. 7–16, 18, 20, 26, 28–40	Problems 1–3 Exs. 7–15 odd, 16–26, 28–40	**Day 7** Problems 1–3 Exs. 7–15 odd, 16–26, 28–40
Review	1	Chapter Review for Part B	Chapter Review for Part B	**Day 8** Chapter Review for Part B Chapter Test for Part B
Assess	1	Chapter Test for Part B	Chapter Test for Part B	
Total		**17 Days**	**17 Days**	**8 Days**

Note: Pacing does not include Concept Bytes and other feature pages.

Resources

	For the Chapter	11-1	11-2	11-3	11-4	11-5	11-6	11-7	11-8	11-9
Planning										
Teacher Center Online Planner & Grade Book	I	I	I	I	I	I	I	I	I	I
Interactive Learning & Guided Instruction										
My Math Video	I									
Solve It!		I TM	I TM	I TM	I TM	I TM	I TM	I TM	I TM	I TM
Student Companion (SP)*		P M	P M	P M	P M	P M	P M	P M	P M	P M
Vocabulary Support		I P M	I P M	I P M	I P M	I P M	I P M	I P M	I P M	I P M
Got It? Support		I P	I P	I P	I P	I P	I P	I P	I P	I P
Dynamic Activity			I	I		I			I	
Online Problems		I	I	I	I	I	I	I	I	I
Additional Problems		M	M	M	M	M	M	M	M	M
English Language Learner Support (TR)		E P M	E P M	E P M	E P M	E P M	E P M	E P M	E P M	E P M
Activities, Games, and Puzzles		E M	E M	E M	E M	E M	E M	E M	E M	E M
Teaching With TI Technology With CD-ROM										
TI-Nspire™ Support CD-ROM		✓	✓	✓	✓	✓	✓	✓	✓	✓
Lesson Check & Practice										
Student Companion (SP)*		P M	P M	P M	P M	P M	P M	P M	P M	P M
Lesson Check Support		I P	I P	I P	I P	I P	I P	I P	I P	I P
Think About a Plan (TR)*		E P M	E P M	E P M	E P M	E P M	E P M	E P M	E P M	E P M
Practice Form K (TR)*		E P M	E P M	E P M	E P M	E P M	E P M	E P M	E P M	E P M
Standardized Test Prep (TR)*		P M	P M	P M	P M	P M	P M	P M	P M	P M
Practice *Form G* (TR)*		E P M	E P M	E P M	E P M	E P M	E P M	E P M	E P M	E P M
Extra Practice	E M									
Find the Errors!	M									
Enrichment (TR)		E P M	E P M	E P M	E P M	E P M	E P M	E P M	E P M	E P M
Answers and Solutions CD-ROM	✓	✓	✓	✓	✓	✓	✓	✓	✓	✓
Assess & Remediate										
ExamView CD-ROM	✓	✓	✓	✓	✓	✓	✓	✓	✓	✓
Lesson Quiz		I TM	I TM	I TM	I TM	I TM	I TM	I TM	I TM	I TM
Quizzes and Tests *Form K* (TR)*	E P M				E P M					E P M
Quizzes and Tests *Form G* (TR)*	E P M				E P M					E P M
Reteaching (TR)		E P M	E P M	E P M	E P M	E P M	E P M	E P M	E P M	E P M
Performance Tasks (TR)*	P M									
Cumulative Review (TR)*	P M									
Progress Monitoring Assessments	I P M									

(TR) Available in All-In-One Teaching Resources   * Spanish available

1 Interactive Learning

Solve It!

PURPOSE To use counting techniques to determine the number of possible lunches

PROCESS Students may make a list or use a tree diagram to list the possible choices.

FACILITATE

Q Can you begin with a simpler problem? Explain. **[Yes; reduce the number of choices for each menu item and calculate the total number of lunch combinations. There are two combinations with one sandwich and two sides, four combinations with two sandwiches and two sides, etc.]**

Q Do you notice a pattern? Explain. **[Yes; the number of lunch combinations is the product of the number of options for each menu item.]**

ANSWER See Solve It in Answers on next page.

CONNECT THE MATH Students develop counting techniques to find the number of lunch combinations in the Solve It. In this lesson, students use the Fundamental Counting Principle, permutations, and combinations to count the number of ways certain events can happen.

2 Guided Instruction

Take Note   VISUAL LEARNERS

It may help students to compare the example in the Take Note to the Solve It. Have them explain what the two situations have in common, and what is different about them.

Here's Why It Works

Have students make a similar tree diagram for the Solve It.

11-1 Permutations and Combinations
PART 1

Objectives To use the Fundamental Counting Principle
To count permutations

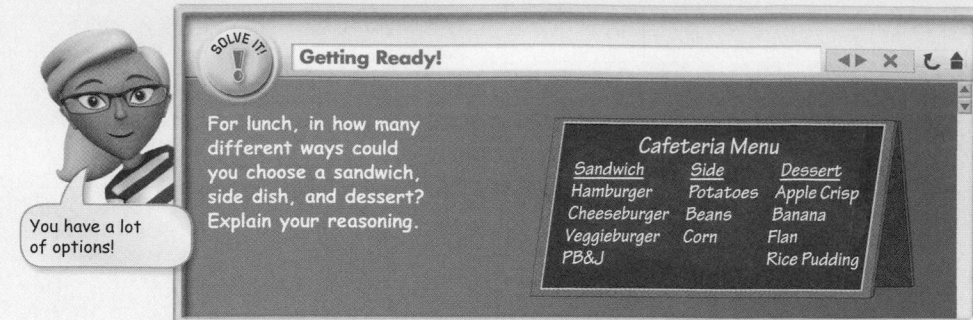

For lunch, in how many different ways could you choose a sandwich, side dish, and dessert? Explain your reasoning.

You have a lot of options!

Cafeteria Menu

Sandwich	Side	Dessert
Hamburger	Potatoes	Apple Crisp
Cheeseburger	Beans	Banana
Veggieburger	Corn	Flan
PB&J		Rice Pudding

It is fairly easy to count the ways you can pick items from a short list. But, sometimes there are so many choices that counting the possibilities is impractical.

Focus Question What is a permutation?

The **Fundamental Counting Principle** describes the method of using multiplication to count the number of ways certain things can happen.

Lesson Vocabulary
- Fundamental Counting Principle
- permutation
- *n* factorial

> **Key Concept   Fundamental Counting Principle**
>
> If event M can occur in m ways and is followed by event N that can occur in n ways, then event M followed by event N can occur in $m \cdot n$ ways.
>
> **Example** 3 pairs of pants and 2 shirts give $3 \cdot 2 = 6$ possible outfits.

Hint
This diagram assumes you choose the pants first. You could instead choose a shirt first and obtain 2 groups of 3 outfits, or $2 \cdot 3 = 6$ outfits.

Here's Why It Works Making a tree diagram, you can see that there are 3 groups of 2 outfits, or $3 \cdot 2 = 6$ outfits.

You can extend the Fundamental Counting Principle to three or more events.

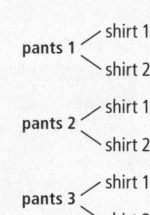

pants 1 — shirt 1
     — shirt 2

pants 2 — shirt 1
     — shirt 2

pants 3 — shirt 1
     — shirt 2

686   Chapter 11 Probability and Statistics

11-1 Preparing to Teach

PART 1

BIG idea Probability   **UbD**

ESSENTIAL UNDERSTANDING

Multiplication can be used to count the number of ways that certain things can happen.

Math Background

This chapter introduces several important counting techniques that are useful in probability, statistics, and combinatorics.

FUNDAMENTAL COUNTING PRINCIPLE

- The number of ways that two or more events can occur is equal to the product of the number of ways each event can occur separately.

NUMBER OF PERMUTATIONS

- The permutation formula calculates the number of ways to order r objects selected from a set of n objects. The same objects selected in a different order count as an individual permutation.

- The number of permutations of a set of n items arranged r items at a time is $\frac{n!}{(n-r)!}$ for $0 \leq r \leq n$.

Support Student Learning

Use the **Algebra 2 Companion** to engage and support students during instruction. See Lesson Resources at the end of this lesson for details.

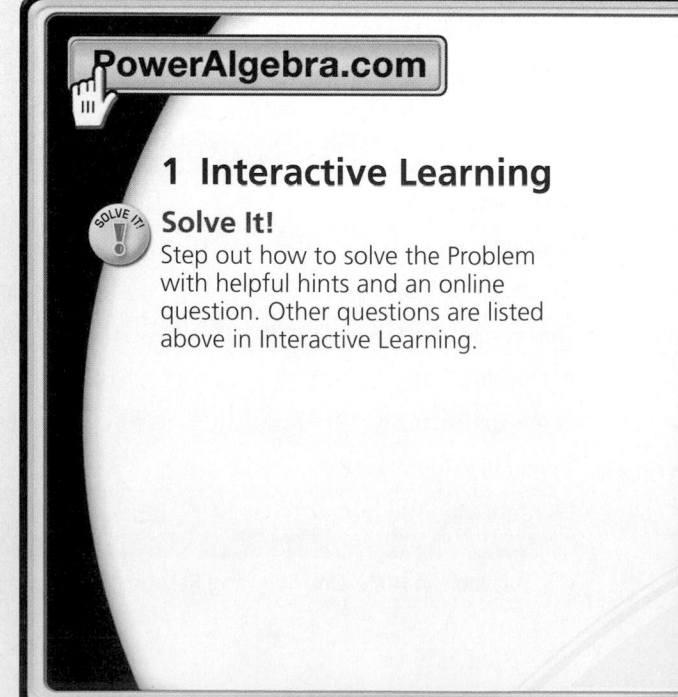

PowerAlgebra.com

1 Interactive Learning

Solve It!

Step out how to solve the Problem with helpful hints and an online question. Other questions are listed above in Interactive Learning.

 **Problem 1** Using the Fundamental Counting Principle

Motor Vehicles The photos show Maryland license plates in 2004 and 1912. How many more 2004-style license plates were possible than 1912-style plates?

 Think

How many digits are in our number system? How many letters are in our alphabet?
There are 10 digits and 26 letters.

The 2004 license plates had places for three letters and three digits.

Number of possible 2004 license plates:

$26 \cdot 26 \cdot 26 \cdot 10 \cdot 10 \cdot 10 = 17{,}576{,}000$

The 1912 license plates had places for four digits.

Number of possible 1912 license plates:

$10 \cdot 10 \cdot 10 \cdot 10 = 10{,}000$

Find the difference. $17{,}576{,}000 - 10{,}000 = 17{,}566{,}000$

There were 17,566,000 more 2004-style license plates possible than 1912-style plates.

 Got It? 1. In 1966, one type of Maryland license plate had two letters followed by four digits. How many of this type of license plate were possible?

Hint

A special case is zero factorial:
$0! = 1$

A **permutation** is an arrangement of items in a particular order. Suppose you want to find the number of ways to order three items. There are 3 ways to choose the first item, 2 ways to choose the second, and 1 way to choose the third. By the Fundamental Counting Principle, there are $3 \cdot 2 \cdot 1 = 6$ permutations.

Using *factorial* notation, you can write $3 \cdot 2 \cdot 1$ as 3!, read "three factorial." For any positive integer n, **n factorial** is $n! = n \cdot (n - 1) \cdot \ldots \cdot 3 \cdot 2 \cdot 1$.

Plan

What strategy can you use to help you see how to solve?
Act it out and you will see how many options you have at each step.

 **Problem 2** Finding the Number of Permutations of n Items

In how many ways can you file 12 folders, one after another, in a drawer?

Use the Fundamental Counting Principle to count the number of permutations of 12 items. There are 12 ways to select the first folder, 11 ways to select the next folder, and so on. The total number of permutations is

$12! = 12 \cdot 11 \cdot \ldots \cdot 2 \cdot 1 = 479{,}001{,}600.$

There are 479,001,600 ways to file 12 folders in a drawer.

 Got It? 2. In how many ways can you arrange 8 shirts on hangers in a closet?

Sometimes you are interested in the number of permutations possible ordering just a few objects from a set at a time. You can still use the Fundamental Counting Principle or factorial notation.

---

2 Guided Instruction

Each Problem is worked out and supported online.

Problem 1
Using the Fundamental Counting Principle

Problem 2
Finding the Number of Permutations of n Items

Problem 3
Finding $_nP_r$
Animated

Support in Algebra 2 Companion
• Vocabulary
• Key Concepts
• Got It?

Problem 1

Q Suppose the numbers in the 2007 license plate were placed in the first three spaces, followed by the letters. Would the number of possible license plates change? Explain. **[No; the factors remain the same regardless of the order.]**

Got It?

Q How does the 1966 license plate differ from the 1912 and 2007 license plates? **[The 1912 plate has four digits, the 1966 plate has four digits and two letters, the 2007 plate has one fewer digit but one more letter.]**

Q How can you use the information from Problem 1 to check your answer? Explain. **[The 1966 plate should have more possibilities than the 1912 plate but fewer than the 2007 plate.]**

Problem 2   VISUAL LEARNERS

Q If you exchanged the first and second folder in a particular arrangement, would the result be a different permutation of the folders? Explain. **[Yes; two permutations of a set are different if the order of their elements is different.]**

Got It?
To check their work, have students divide their answers into the answer in Problem 2. Discuss why the quotient should equal
$12 \cdot 11 \cdot 10 \cdot 9 = 11{,}880.$

Answers

Solve It!

48 ways; there are four sandwiches to choose from, three sides, and four desserts; $4 \cdot 3 \cdot 4 = 48$.

Got It?

1. 6,760,000

2. 40,320

688 Chapter 11

Take Note

Q What happens when you simplify the formula when $r = n$? [**The formula becomes $\frac{n!}{0!} = \frac{n!}{1} = n!$**]

Q Why must r be less than or equal to n in the formula? [**You cannot order more than n items.**]

Problem 3

Q How is Method 1 related to Method 2? [**Sample: If you cancel out the common factors in the numerator and denominator in Method 2, the result is the expression in Method 1.**]

Got It?

Q Why might there be an advantage to using the Fundamental Counting Principle instead of the permutation formula when solving this problem? Explain. [**Sample: Using this principle only requires you to multiply three numbers.**]

3 Lesson Check

Do you know HOW?   ERROR INTERVENTION

• If students have difficulty with Exercises 1–3, encourage them to use the method that makes the most sense to them for all three problems.

Do you UNDERSTAND?

• If students have trouble with Exercise 4, have them look back at the Problems in the lesson and change the numbers to match this problem.

Close

Q How are the Fundamental Counting Principle and the formula for permutations related? [**The formula for counting permutations is an application of the Fundamental Counting Principle.**]

Hint
You can rewrite 10! as $10 \cdot 9!$ or $10 \cdot 9 \cdot 8!$ and so on. Use these equivalent expressions to simplify.

Plan
How many numbers will you need to multiply together? You will multiply three numbers together to represent the possibilities of finishing first, second, and third.

Hint
Notice that the permutation formula reduces to the same calculation you get using the Fundamental Counting Principle.

 Key Concept   Number of Permutations

The number of permutations of n items of a set arranged r items at a time is

$$_nP_r = \frac{n!}{(n-r)!} \text{ for } 0 \le r \le n.$$

Example $_{10}P_4 = \frac{10!}{(10-4)!} = \frac{10!}{6!} = 5040$

 Problem 3 Finding $_nP_r$

Track Ten students are in a race. First, second, and third places will win medals. In how many ways can 10 runners finish first, second, and third (no ties allowed)?

Method 1 Use the Fundamental Counting Principle.

$$10 \cdot 9 \cdot 8 = 720$$

Method 2 Use the permutation formula.

There are $n = 10$ runners to arrange $r = 3$ at a time.

Use the formula for permutations.	$_nP_r = \frac{n!}{(n-r)!}$
Substitute 10 for n and 3 for r.	$_{10}P_3 = \frac{10!}{(10-3)!}$
Subtract in the denominator. Then, rewrite 10! to find common factors.	$= \frac{10!}{7!} = \frac{10 \cdot 9 \cdot 8 \cdot 7!}{7!}$
Remove the common factors and simplify.	$= 10 \cdot 9 \cdot 8 = 720$

There are 720 ways that 10 runners can finish in first, second, and third places.

 Got It? 3. a. In how many ways can 15 runners finish first, second, and third?
b. Reasoning In Problem 3, is the number of ways for runners to finish first, second, and third the same as the number of ways to finish eighth, ninth, and tenth? Explain.

Focus Question What is a permutation?
Answer A permutation is an arrangement of items in a particular order. Use the permutation formula to quickly count the number of ways to order n items r at a time.

Lesson Check

Do you know HOW?
Evaluate each expression.

1. $_6P_3$ **2.** $_9P_4$ **3.** $_5P_2$

Do you UNDERSTAND?

4. Open-Ended Describe a situation in which the number of outcomes is given by $_9P_2$.

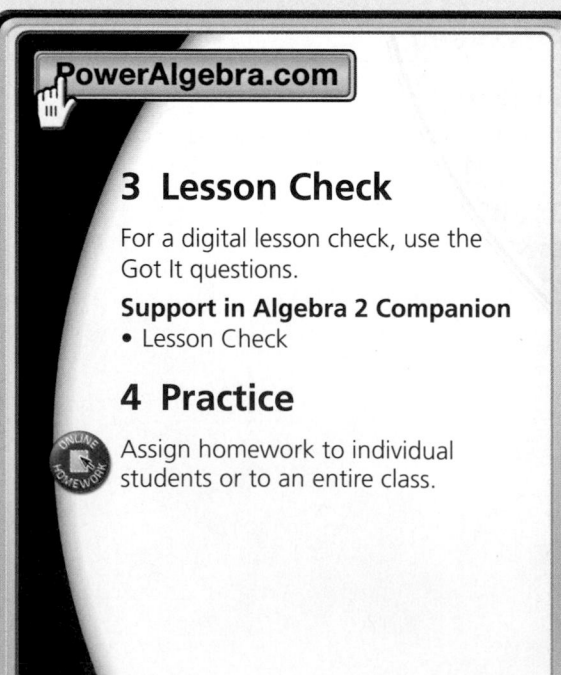

PowerAlgebra.com

3 Lesson Check

For a digital lesson check, use the Got It questions.

Support in Algebra 2 Companion
• Lesson Check

4 Practice

Assign homework to individual students or to an entire class.

Additional Problems

1. An old website requires a four-character password consisting of three numbers and one letter. A new website requires a six-character password consisting of three numbers and three letters. How many more passwords can be made for the new website?
ANSWER 17,550,000

2. In how many ways can you arrange nine CD's one after another on a shelf?
ANSWER 362,880

3. In how many ways can a first, second, and third baseman be selected from eight players?
ANSWER 336

Answers

Got It? (continued)

3. a. 2730

b. Yes; because $n = 10$ and $r = 3$ in the formula $_nP_r$ for both cases.

Lesson Check

1. 120

2. 3024

3. 20

4. Check students' answers.

Practice and Problem-Solving Exercises

 **Practice**

Use the Fundamental Counting Principle to solve each problem.

◀ See Problem 1.

 Guided Practice

5. To make an entry code, you need to first choose a letter and then choose three single-digit numbers. How many different entry codes are possible?

To start, record what you know.   Number of letters: 26
Number of digits: 10

Describe what you need to find.   The number of codes possible using one letter and three digits

6. The prom committee has four sites available for the banquet and three sites for the dance. How many arrangements are possible for the banquet and dance?

Evaluate each expression.

◀ See Problem 2.

7. $5!$

8. $10!$

9. $5!3!$

10. $\frac{12!}{6!}$

11. $\frac{10!}{7!3!}$

12. $\frac{15!}{10!5!}$

13. Automobiles You should rotate tires on a car at regular intervals.
    a. In how many ways can four tires be arranged on a car?
    b. If a spare tire is included, how many arrangements are possible?

Evaluate each expression.

◀ See Problem 3.

Guided Practice

To start, write the formula for permutations.

14. $_8P_1$

$$_nP_r = \frac{n!}{(n-r)!}$$

15. $_8P_2$

16. $_8P_3$

17. $_8P_4$

18. $_3P_2$

19. $_7P_4$

20. $_9P_6$

21. Scheduling Fifteen students ask to visit a college admissions counselor. Each scheduled visit includes one student. In how many ways can ten time slots be assigned?

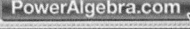 **Apply**

Assume a and b are positive integers. Determine whether each statement is *true* or *false*. If it is true, explain why. If it is false, give a counterexample.

22. $a! + b! = b! + a!$

23. $a!(b!c!) = (a!b!)c!$

24. $(a+b)! = a! + b!$

25. $(ab)! = a!b!$

26. $(a!)! = (a!)^2$

27. $(a!)^b = a^{(b!)}$

28. Writing In how many ways is it possible to arrange the two numbers a and b in an ordered pair? Explain why such a pair is called an *ordered* pair.

Practice and Problem-Solving Exercises

5. 26,000
6. 12
7. 120
8. 3,628,800
9. 720
10. 665,280
11. 120
12. 3003
13. a. 24
    b. 120
14. 8
15. 56
16. 336
17. 1680
18. 6
19. 840
20. 60,480
21. 10,897,286,400

22. true; Comm. Prop. of Add.
23. true; Assoc. Prop. of Mult.
24. false; answers may vary. Sample:
    $(3+2)! = 120$ and $3! + 2! = 8$
25. false; answers may vary. Sample:
    $(3 \cdot 2)! = 6! = 720$ and $3! \cdot 2! = 6 \cdot 2 = 12$
26. false; answers may vary. Sample:
    $(3!)! = 6! = 720$ and $(3!)^2 = 6^2 = 36$
27. false; answers may vary. Sample:
    $(3!)^2 = 6^2 = 36$ and $3^{(2!)} = 3^2 = 9$
28. Two ways, because order matters.

4 Practice

ASSIGNMENT GUIDE
Basic: 5–14, 15–21 odd
Average: 5–14, 15–27 odd

Reasoning exercises have blue headings.

Applications exercises have red headings.

HOMEWORK QUICK CHECK
To check students' understanding of key skills and concepts, go over Exercises 6, 7, 13, 15, and 21.

1 Launch

CONNECT THE MATH In Part 1 of this lesson students worked with permutations of objects. In a permutation the order of the objects chosen is important. In Part 2, students will work with combinations. In a combination, the order of the objects chosen is not important.

FOCUS QUESTION

Q During the student council election, ten people are running for the offices of President, Vice President, and Treasurer. Is the order the offices are filled important? Explain. **[Yes; an order with one person being elected President is different than an order with the same person elected Vice President.]**

Q Two team members are to be elected as captains for the softball team. Is the order the captains are chosen important? Explain. **[No; it does not matter if a person is elected as the first team captain or the second team captain.]**

---

2 Guided Instruction

Take Note

Q What is the difference between the formulas for permutations and combinations? **[The combinations formula has a factor of $r!$ in the denominator.]**

Permutations and Combinations

11-1 PART 2

Objectives To count permutations
To count combinations

Connect to What You Know

In Part 1 of the lesson, you learned how to find the number of arrangements of items when order is important.

Here you will learn to find the number of ways to select items when order does not matter.

Lesson Vocabulary
• combination

Focus Question What is a combination?

In Problem 3, you found the number of ways that 10 runners can finish in first, second, and third places. Suppose instead that the three runners who finish first, second, and third in a race advance to a championship race. In this case, the order in which the first three runners cross the finish line does not matter. A selection in which order does not matter is called a **combination**.

As with permutations, you can use a formula to find the number of combinations of n items chosen r at a time.

Hint
The formula for combinations is similar to the formula for permutations. This formula has an additional factorial in the denominator.

Key Concept   **Number of Combinations**

The number of combinations of n items of a set chosen r items at a time is

$$_nC_r = \frac{n!}{r!(n-r)!} \text{ for } 0 \le r \le n.$$

Example $_5C_3 = \frac{5!}{3!(5-3)!} = \frac{5!}{3! \cdot 2!} = \frac{120}{6 \cdot 2} = 10$

Preparing to Teach

PART 2

BIG idea Probability   **UbD**

ESSENTIAL UNDERSTANDING

Multiplication can be used to count the number of ways that certain things can happen.

Math Background

This chapter introduces several important counting techniques.

NUMBER OF COMBINATIONS

• Counts the number of ways to choose r items from a set of n items, when the order of the r items does not matter.
• The number of combinations of a set of n items chosen r items at a time is $\frac{n!}{r!(n-r)!}$ for $0 \le r \le n$.

The number of permutations is a direct application of the Fundamental Counting Principle. The number of combinations is derived from the number of permutations by dividing by $r!$.

Support Student Learning

Use the **Algebra 2 Companion** to engage and support students during instruction. See Lesson Resources at the end of this lesson for details.

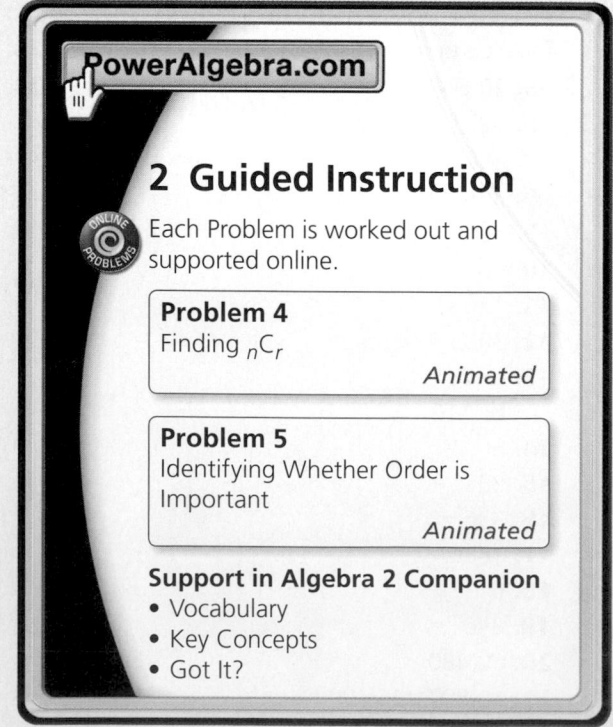

PowerAlgebra.com

2 Guided Instruction

Each Problem is worked out and supported online.

Problem 4
Finding $_nC_r$
Animated

Problem 5
Identifying Whether Order is Important
Animated

Support in Algebra 2 Companion
• Vocabulary
• Key Concepts
• Got It?

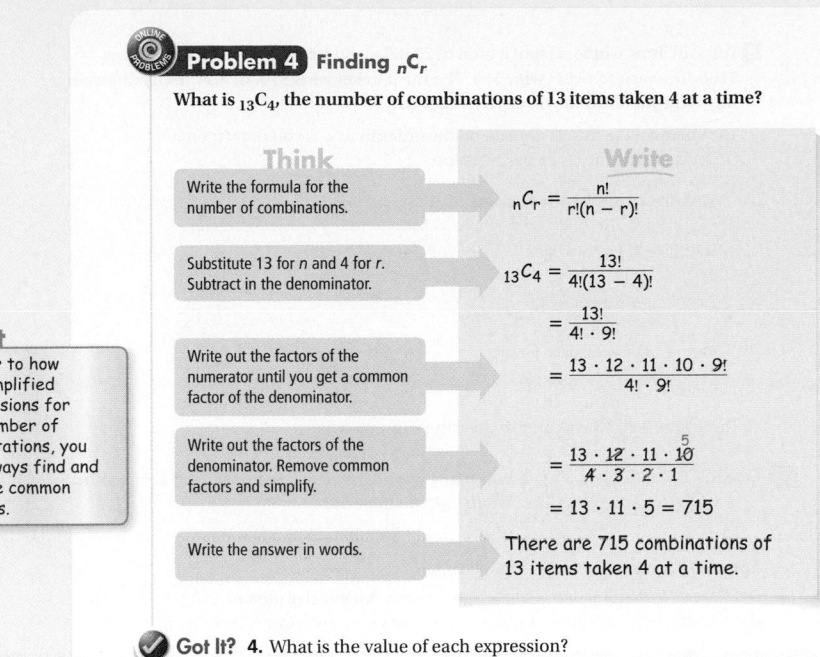

Problem 4 Finding $_nC_r$

What is $_{13}C_4$, the number of combinations of 13 items taken 4 at a time?

Think	Write
Write the formula for the number of combinations.	$_nC_r = \dfrac{n!}{r!(n-r)!}$
Substitute 13 for n and 4 for r. Subtract in the denominator.	$_{13}C_4 = \dfrac{13!}{4!(13-4)!}$
	$= \dfrac{13!}{4! \cdot 9!}$
Write out the factors of the numerator until you get a common factor of the denominator.	$= \dfrac{13 \cdot 12 \cdot 11 \cdot 10 \cdot 9!}{4! \cdot 9!}$
Write out the factors of the denominator. Remove common factors and simplify.	$= \dfrac{13 \cdot \cancel{12} \cdot 11 \cdot \overset{5}{\cancel{10}}}{\cancel{4} \cdot \cancel{3} \cdot \cancel{2} \cdot 1}$
	$= 13 \cdot 11 \cdot 5 = 715$
Write the answer in words.	There are 715 combinations of 13 items taken 4 at a time.

Hint

Similar to how you simplified expressions for the number of permutations, you can always find and remove common factors.

✓ **Got It? 4.** What is the value of each expression?

a. $_8C_3$ b. $_9C_2$ c. $_{15}C_5$

Problem 5 Identifying Whether Order is Important

For each situation, determine whether you should use a permutation or combination. What is the answer to each question?

A A chemistry teacher divides his class into eight groups. Each group submits one drawing of the molecular structure of water. He will select four of the drawings to display. In how many different ways can he select the drawings?

Write the formula for combinations.	$_nC_r = \dfrac{n!}{r!(n-r)!}$	There is no reason why order is important. Use a combination.
Substitute 8 for n and 4 for r.	$_8C_4 = \dfrac{8!}{4!(8-4)!}$	
Subtract in the denominator.	$= \dfrac{8!}{4! \cdot 4!}$	
Rewrite to show common factors.	$= \dfrac{8 \cdot 7 \cdot 6 \cdot 5 \cdot 4!}{4 \cdot 3 \cdot 2 \cdot 1 \cdot 4!}$	
Simplify.	$= \dfrac{8 \cdot 7 \cdot 6 \cdot 5}{4 \cdot 3 \cdot 2 \cdot 1} = 70$	

There are 70 ways to select the drawings.

Plan

How will you solve? If order is important, use the formula $_nP_r = \dfrac{n!}{(n-r)!}$. If order is not important, use the formula $_nC_r = \dfrac{n!}{r!(n-r)!}$.

Problem 4

Q For given values of n and r, are there more combinations or permutations? **[The number of permutations is greater by a factor of $r!$.]**

Q If $_{13}C_4 = 715$, how can you find $_{13}P_4$ without using a formula? Explain. **[The only difference between the formulas is 4! in the denominator of $_{13}C_4$. Multiply $715 \times 4! = 17{,}160$ which equals $_{13}P_4$.]**

Got It?   ERROR PREVENTION

Q Is $\dfrac{15!}{3!}$ equal to 5!? Explain. **[No; $15! = 15 \times 14 \times \ldots \times 2 \times 1$, while $3! = 3 \times 2 \times 1$, so $\dfrac{15!}{3!} = 15 \times 14 \times \ldots \times 5 \times 4$.]**

Problem 5

Q What is an example of a situation in which order does not matter? **[Sample: In choosing members for a committee, only the final set of members matters. The order in which they are chosen does not matter.]**

Additional Problems

4. What is $_{15}C_6$ (the number of combinations of 15 items taken 6 at a time)?

ANSWER 5005

5. a. You have 20 songs on your MP3 player. You have time to listen to four of the songs. In how many different ways can you select the four songs?

b. A raffle at a school carnival awards prizes of $100, $50, $25, and $10. If 25 raffle tickets are sold, how many different ways can the prizes be distributed?

ANSWERS

a. 4845

b. 303,600

Answers

Got It?

4. a. 56   **b.** 36   **c.** 3003

Got It?

ERROR PREVENTION

Suggest to students that they list a few of the possibilities in each scenario to help them decide whether combinations or permutations should be used. If the order is switched and the outcomes are the same, use combinations. If they are different, use permutations.

3 Lesson Check

Do you know HOW?　　ERROR INTERVENTION

• For Exercise 5, have students begin making a list by choosing 9 students out of 16 in their class. Ask questions such as "Who is going to bat first?" and "Who is going to bat last?" to help them determine whether combinations or permutations should be used.

Do you UNDERSTAND?

• If students have trouble with Exercise 5, have them look back and compare the Problems in Parts 1 and 2 of the lesson.

Close

> **Q** Which type of situation requires combinations?
> **[when a certain number of items is chosen from a larger set and order does not matter]**

 You will draw winners from a total of 25 tickets in a raffle. The first ticket wins $100. The second ticket wins $50. The third ticket wins $10. In how many different ways can you draw the three winning tickets?

The values of the tickets depend on the order in which you draw them. Order is important. Use a permutation.

Hint
When determining whether to use a permutation or combination, you must decide whether order is important.

Write the formula for permutations.　　$_nP_r = \dfrac{n!}{(n-r)!}$

Substitute 25 for n and 3 for r.　　$_{25}P_3 = \dfrac{25!}{(25-3)!}$

Subtract in the denominator.　　$= \dfrac{25!}{22!}$

Rewrite to show common factors.　　$= \dfrac{25 \cdot 24 \cdot 23 \cdot 22!}{22!}$

Simplify.　　$= 25 \cdot 24 \cdot 23 = 13{,}800$

There are 13,800 ways you can draw the winning tickets.

 Got It? 5. In Problem 5(a), in how many ways can the teacher select and arrange the four drawings from left to right on the wall?

Focus Question What is a combination?
Answer A combination is a selection of items for which order does not matter. Use the combination formula to find the number of groups of n items chosen r at a time.

Lesson Check

Do you know HOW?

Evaluate each expression.

1. $_5C_2$　　　　**2.** $_7C_5$　　　　**3.** $_4C_3$

4. Sports How many different nine-player batting orders can be chosen from a baseball team of 16?

Do you UNDERSTAND?

5. Vocabulary Explain the difference between permutations and combinations.

6. Open-Ended Describe a situation in which the number of outcomes is given by $_4C_2$.

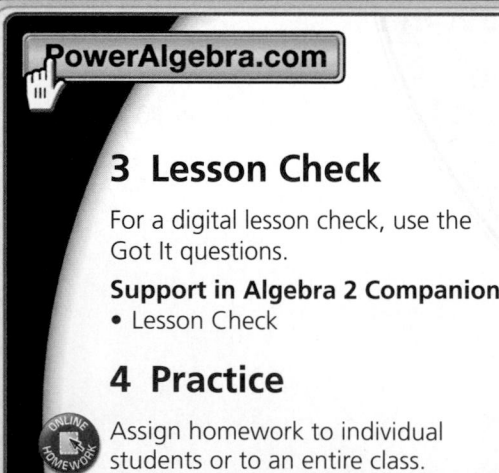

PowerAlgebra.com

3 Lesson Check

For a digital lesson check, use the Got It questions.

Support in Algebra 2 Companion
• Lesson Check

4 Practice

Assign homework to individual students or to an entire class.

Answers

Got It? (continued)
5. 1680

Lesson Check
1. 10
2. 21
3. 4
4. 4,151,347,200
5. A permutation is an arrangement of items in a particular order; order is important. A grouping in which order does not matter is a combination.
6. Check students' answers.

Practice and Problem-Solving Exercises

See Problem 4.

A Practice Evaluate each expression.

Guided Practice

7. $_6C_2$

To start, write the formula for combinations.

$$_nC_r = \frac{n!}{r!(n-r)!}$$

8. $_8C_5$ **9.** $_4C_4$ **10.** $_7C_3$

11. $3(_5C_4)$ **12.** $_6C_2 + _6C_3$ **13.** $\frac{_7C_4}{_9C_4}$

14. Awards There are eight swimmers in a competition where the top three swimmers advance. In how many ways can three swimmers advance?

For each situation, determine whether to use a permutation or a combination. Then solve the problem.

See Problem 5.

15. How many different teams of 11 players can be chosen from a soccer team of 16?

16. Suppose you find seven equally useful articles related to the topic of your research paper. In how many ways can you choose five articles to read?

17. A salad bar offers eight choices of toppings for a salad. In how many ways can you choose four toppings?

B Apply **18. Think About a Plan** You and your friends are picking up videos at a video store. You have selected 7 videos but will only have time to watch 3 videos together. How many different ways can you select the 3 videos to watch?
- Does the order in which the videos are selected make a difference?
- What formula should you use?

19. Security A car door lock has a five-button keypad. Each button has two numerals. The entry code 21914 uses the same button sequence as the code 11023. How many different five-button patterns are possible? You can use a button more than once.

Ⓐ 120 Ⓑ 720 Ⓒ 3125 Ⓓ 5555

20. Consumer Issues A consumer magazine rates televisions by identifying two levels of price, five levels of repair frequency, three levels of features, and two levels of picture quality. How many different ratings are possible?

21. Reasoning Determine whether the statement $_nC_r = _nP_r$ is *always*, *sometimes*, or *never* true. Explain your reasoning.

ASSIGNMENT GUIDE

Basic: 7–18, 20

Average: 7–21

Standardized Test Prep: 23–26

Mixed Review: 27–35

Reasoning exercises have blue headings.

Applications exercises have red headings.

EXERCISE 20: Use the Think About a Plan worksheet in the **Student Companion** (also available in the Teaching Resources in print and online) to further support students' development in becoming independent learners.

HOMEWORK QUICK CHECK

To check students' understanding of key skills and concepts, go over Exercises 9, 14, 15, 18, and 20.

Practice and Problem-Solving Exercises

7. 15

8. 56

9. 1

10. 35

11. 15

12. 35

13. $\frac{5}{18}$

14. 56

15. combination; 4368

16. combination; 21

17. combination; 70

18. 35

19. C

20. 60

21. Sometimes; $_nC_r = _nP_r$ when $\frac{n!}{r!(n-r)!} = \frac{n!}{(n-r)!}$, that is when $r! = 1$, or $r = 1$, or $r = 0$.

Answers

Practice and Problem-Solving Exercises (continued)

22. a. 2
  b. 6
  c. $(n - 1)!$

Standardized Test Prep

23. D
24. H
25. D
26. G

Mixed Review

27. foci: $(\pm\sqrt{85}, 0)$;
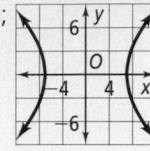

28. foci: $(0, \pm\sqrt{21})$;
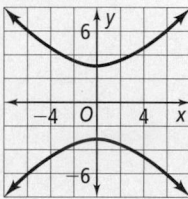

29. foci: $(0, \pm2\sqrt{26})$;
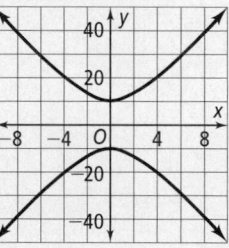

30. $4(x - 1)^2$
31. $-(x + 3)^2$
32. $3(x - 5)(x + 5)$
33. 30,240
34. $\dfrac{4}{5}$
35. 210

---

22. There are 3!, or 6, arrangements of 3 objects. Consider the number of clockwise arrangements possible for objects placed in a loop, without a beginning or end.

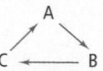

ABC, BCA, and CAB are all parts of one possible clockwise loop arrangement of the letters A, B, and C.

  a. Find the number of clockwise loop arrangements possible for letters A, B, and C.
  b. Use the diagram at the right to help find the number of loop arrangements possible for A, B, C, and D.
  c. Write an expression for the number of clockwise loop arrangements for n objects.

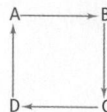

Standardized Test Prep

23. What is the value of $_7C_2$?
  A 2520   **B** 49   **C** 42   **D** 21

24. What are all the solutions of $\dfrac{3}{x^2 - 1} + \dfrac{4x}{x + 1} = \dfrac{1.5}{x - 1}$?
  F 1, −1   **G** 1, 0.375   **H** 0.375   **I** 0.375, 3

25. Use a calculator to solve $-x^2 - 3x + 7 = 0$. Round to the nearest hundredth.
  A −0.76, 4.76   **B** 0.76, 5.76   **C** −1.54, 4.54   **D** −4.54, 1.54

26. What is the center of the circle with equation $(x - 5)^2 + (y + 1)^2 = 81$?
  F (5, 1)   **G** (5, −1)   **H** (−5, 1)   **I** (−5, −1)

Mixed Review

Find the foci of each hyperbola. Draw the graph.   ◀ See Lesson 10-5.

27. $\dfrac{x^2}{49} - \dfrac{y^2}{36} = 1$ **28.** $8y^2 - 6x^2 = 72$ **29.** $4y^2 - 100x^2 = 400$

Factor each expression completely.   ◀ See Lesson 4-4.

30. $4x^2 - 8x + 4$ **31.** $-x^2 - 6x - 9$ **32.** $3x^2 - 75$

Get Ready! To prepare for Lesson 11-2, do Exercises 33–35.

Simplify each expression.   ◀ See Lesson 11-1.

33. $10 \cdot 9 \cdot 8 \cdot 7 \cdot 6$ **34.** $\dfrac{4 \cdot 3 \cdot 2}{6 \cdot 5}$ **35.** $\dfrac{7 \cdot 6 \cdot 5 \cdot 4 \cdot 3 \cdot 2 \cdot 1}{4 \cdot 3 \cdot 2 \cdot 1}$

Lesson Resources

Additional Instructional Support

Algebra 2 Companion

Students can use the **Algebra 2 Companion** worktext (4 pages) as you teach the lesson. Use the Companion to support

- New Vocabulary
- Key Concepts
- Got It for each Problem
- Lesson Check

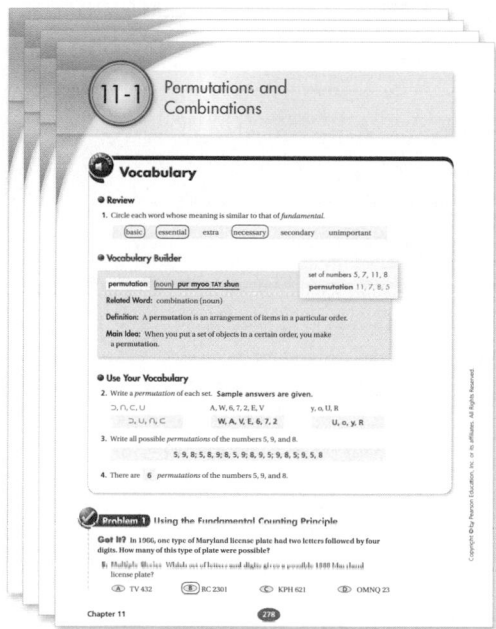

ELL Support

Focus on Language Write the words *permutation*, *combination*, and *order* on the board. Explain that *order* refers to how something is arranged. Demonstrate by placing several objects (or people) from tallest to shortest in a line. Then tell students the objects are in order from tallest to shortest. Mix up the objects and tell them the objects are not in order.

Select several students to act out a race. As three students cross the finish line, give them pieces of paper that say first, second, and third. Place the students in order for first, second, and third. Point to the word *permutation* on the board and say: *The order matters. Use permutations.* Ask students to state the word. Next, have students act out the race again, but give the first three students pieces of paper that say *winner*. Place the students in any order and then switch them around. Point to the word combination and say: *The order does not matter. Use combinations.*

5 Assess & Remediate

Lesson Quiz

1. Students used to have four-digit ID codes. Now ID codes consist of five digits and one letter. How many more ID codes are there now than there used to be?

2. In how many ways can you arrange 10 paintings, one after another, on a wall?

3. The drama club has 14 members. Three students are needed to sell tickets, design programs, and handle refreshments. In how many ways can three members be chosen from a group of 14 for helping with tickets, programs, and refreshments?

4. What is $_{15}C_8$ (the number of combinations of 15 items taken eight at a time)?

5. **Do you UNDERSTAND?** Three students are selected from a class of 12 to be president, vice president, and secretary of the music club. How many ways can these positions be filled?

ANSWERS TO LESSON QUIZ

1. 2,590,000
2. 3,628,800
3. 2184
4. 6435
5. Because the positions are different, the order of the selections matters. This is a permutation, so $_{12}P_3 = 1320$.

A PRESCRIPTION FOR REMEDIATION
Use the student work on the Lesson Quiz to prescribe a differentiated review assignment:

Points	Differentiated Remediation
0–2	Intervention
3–4	On-level
5	Extension

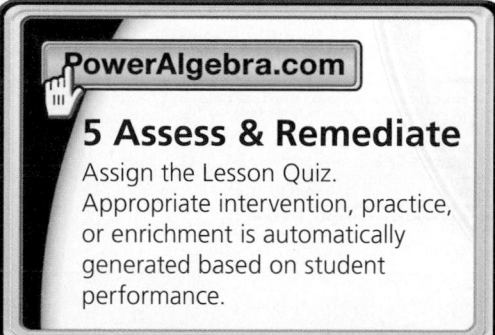

PowerAlgebra.com

5 Assess & Remediate

Assign the Lesson Quiz. Appropriate intervention, practice, or enrichment is automatically generated based on student performance.

Intervention

- **Reteaching** (2 pages) Provides reteaching and practice exercises for the key lesson concepts. Use with struggling students or absent students.

- **English Language Learner Support** Helps students develop and reinforce mathematical vocabulary and key concepts.

All-in-One Resources/Online
Reteaching

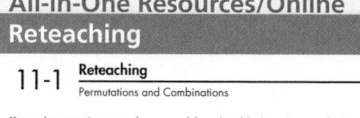

11-1 Reteaching
Permutations and Combinations

If you select some items out of a group and the order of the items in your selection is important, then your selection is a *permutation* of the group.

For example, suppose Ana, Bob, Cal, and Dan enter a local essay contest. Here are some possible ways for the judges to select the first-prize and second-prize winners.

First Prize	Second Prize
Ana	Bob
Dan	Cal
Bob	Ana
Bob	Dan

"Ana, Bob" means Ana is first and Bob is second.

"Bob, Ana" means Bob is first and Ana is second.

The order of the names in the selection is important. The selection "Ana, Bob" is a *permutation* of the group of contestants.

The number of permutations of n items of a set arranged r items at a time is
$$_nP_r = \frac{n!}{(n-r)!}, (0 \le r \le n)$$

Problem

In how many ways can the judges select the first-prize and second-prize winners in the essay contest described above?

Step 1 Is the order of the names in each selection important?
Yes. "Ana, Bob" is not the same as "Bob, Ana." You are looking for the total number of permutations of 2 items each selected from a group of 4 items.

Step 2 Describe n and r.
There are 4 people in the group of contestants. $n = 4$
There are 2 people in each selection of prize winners. $r = 2$

Step 3 Substitute for each variable in the formula.
$$_nP_r = {_4}P_2 = \frac{n!}{(n-r)!} = \frac{4!}{(4-2)!} = \frac{4!}{2!} = \frac{4 \cdot 3 \cdot 2 \cdot 1}{2 \cdot 1} = 12$$
There are 12 ways for the judges to choose the first-prize and second-prize winners.

Exercises

1. In how many ways can you choose 6 letters for a password from the set A, B, E, L, N, O, S, T, Y? 60,480

2. In how many ways can a club with 15 members elect a president, vice president, secretary, and treasurer? 32,760

3. In how many ways can a family of 6 line up in 1 row for a photograph? 720

All-in-One Resources/Online
English Language Learner Support

11-1 ELL Support
Permutations and Combinations

Fundamental Counting Principle
If event M can occur in m ways and is followed by event N that can occur in n ways, then event M followed by event N can occur in $m \cdot n$ ways.

Example 4 different fruits and 6 different vegetables give $4 \cdot 6$ possible fruit and vegetable combinations.

Solve.

1. Hector has 6 computers and 7 printers to choose from. How many possible computer-printer combinations can he make? 42

2. Raymond and Jasmine have 8 sofas and 14 chairs to choose between. How many possible sofa-chair combinations can they make? 112

Number of Permutations
The number of permutations of n items of a set arranged r items at a time is
$$_nP_r = \frac{n!}{(n-r)!} \text{ for } 0 \le r \le n$$

Example
$$_8P_3 = \frac{8!}{(8-3)!} = \frac{8!}{5!} = 336$$

Evaluate each expression.

3. $_7P_4$ 840
4. $_9P_5$ 15,120

Number of Combinations
The number of combinations of n items of a set chosen r items at a time is
$$_nC_r = \frac{n!}{r!(n-r)!} \text{ for } 0 \le r \le n$$

Example
$$_7C_3 = \frac{7!}{3!(7-3)!} = \frac{7!}{3! \cdot 4!} = \frac{7!}{6 \cdot 24} = 35$$

Evaluate each expression.

5. $_8C_5$ 56
6. $_9C_3$ 84

Differentiated Remediation *continued*

On-Level

- **Practice** (2 pages) Provides extra practice for each lesson. For more challenging practice exercises, use the Form G Practice pages found in the All-in-One Teaching Resources and online.

- **Think About a Plan** Helps students develop specific problem-solving skills and strategies by providing scaffolded guiding questions.
- **Standardized Test Prep** Focuses on all major exercises, all major question types, and helps students prepare for the high-stakes assessments.

Extension

- **Enrichment** Provides students with interesting problems and activities that extend the concepts of the lesson.
- **Activities, Games, and Puzzles** Worksheets that can be used for concepts development, enrichment, and for fun!

Student Companion/ All-in-One Resources/Online
Practice page 1

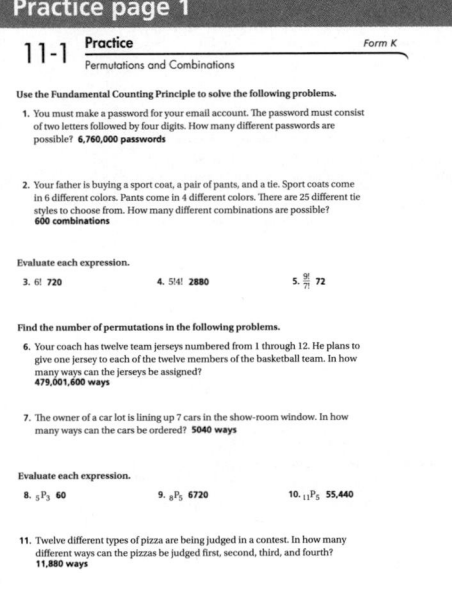

11-1 Practice   *Form K*
Permutations and Combinations

Use the Fundamental Counting Principle to solve the following problems.

1. You must make a password for your email account. The password must consist of two letters followed by four digits. How many different passwords are possible? **6,760,000 passwords**

2. Your father is buying a sport coat, a pair of pants, and a tie. Sport coats come in 6 different colors. Pants come in 4 different colors. There are 25 different tie styles to choose from. How many different combinations are possible? **600 combinations**

Evaluate each expression.

3. $6!$ **720** 4. $5!4!$ **2880** 5. $\frac{9!}{7!}$ **72**

Find the number of permutations in the following problems.

6. Your coach has twelve team jerseys numbered from 1 through 12. He plans to give one jersey to each of the twelve members of the basketball team. In how many ways can the jerseys be assigned? **479,001,600 ways**

7. The owner of a car lot is lining up 7 cars in the show-room window. In how many ways can the cars be ordered? **5040 ways**

Evaluate each expression.

8. $_5P_3$ **60** 9. $_8P_5$ **6720** 10. $_{11}P_5$ **55,440**

11. Twelve different types of pizza are being judged in a contest. In how many different ways can the pizzas be judged first, second, third, and fourth? **11,880 ways**

Student Companion/ All-in-One Resources/Online
Practice page 2

11-1 Practice (continued)   *Form K*
Permutations and Combinations

Evaluate each expression.

12. $_7C_2$ **21** 13. $_9C_5$ **126** 14. $_{12}C_7$ **792**

15. $_8C_6$ **28** 16. $5(_6C_3)$ **100** 17. $_{10}C_7 + _5C_2$ **130**

Decide whether to use a permutation or a combination for each situation. Then solve the problem.

18. An ice cream parlor offers 14 different types of ice cream. In how many different ways can you select 5 types of ice cream to sample? **combination; 2002 ways**

19. Eleven groups entered a science fair competition. In how many ways can the groups finish first, second, and third? **permutation; 990 ways**

20. Your aunt is ordering appetizers for her and her family. The restaurant offers 10 different appetizers. She will select 4 appetizers. How many different combinations of appetizers can your aunt possibly select? **combination; 210 combinations**

21. **Error Analysis** Your friend is shopping for blue jeans. The clothing store offers 18 different types of blue jeans, and your friend will buy 5 different types. Your friend believes that she has 1,028,160 different combinations that she could possibly select. What error did your friend make? How many different combinations could she possibly select? **Your friend used a permutation when she should have used a combination. She could possibly select 8568 different combinations.**

All-in-One Resources/Online
Enrichment

11-1 Enrichment
Permutations and Combinations

Dinner at a Chinese Restaurant

A typical Chinese restaurant will often feature a Special Dinner, in which the customer has the choice of ordering one appetizer and one entree.

1. If there are 8 appetizers and 11 entrees, how many different Special Dinners are there? **88**

2. If there are 12 appetizers and 7 entrees, how many different Special Dinners are there? **84**

3. If there are A appetizers and E entrees, how many different Special Dinners are there? **AE**

4. There are 12 appetizers; 4 are soups; 6 contain meat, and 2 do not. In how many different orders can 3 different appetizers be brought to the table? **1320**

5. In how many different orders can 5 different appetizers of the 12 be brought to the table? **95,040**

6. Do Exercises 1–5 involve permutations or combinations? **permutations**

7. Assume that 3 customers arrive and order different appetizers to share from a choice of 12 appetizers.
   a. Does this problem involve permutations or combinations? **combinations**
   b. Why? **order doesn't matter**
   c. In how many possible ways can this be done? $_{12}C_3 =$ **220**

8. Suppose that 5 customers arrive, and each orders a different appetizer to share from a choice of 12 appetizers. In how many ways can this be done? $_{12}C_5 =$ **792**

9. Suppose that 7 customers arrive, and each orders a different appetizer to share from a choice of 12 appetizers.
   a. In how many ways can this be done? $_{12}C_7 =$ **792**
   b. Why is this answer the same as the number of ways that 5 customers can order different appetizers? $_nC_r = _nC_{n-r}$, or $_{12}C_5 = _{12}C_7$

Student Companion/ All-in-One Resources/Online
Think About a Plan

11-1 Think About a Plan
Permutations and Combinations

Consumer Issues A consumer magazine rates televisions by identifying two levels of price, five levels of repair frequency, three levels of features, and two levels of picture quality. How many different ratings are possible?

Understanding the Problem

1. How many levels of price are possible? **2**

2. How many levels of repair frequency are possible? **5**

3. How many levels of features are possible? **3**

4. How many levels of picture quality are possible? **2**

5. What is the problem asking you to determine? **the number of different ratings that are possible**

Planning the Solution

6. What is the Fundamental Counting Principle? **If an event M can occur in m ways and is followed by event N that can occur in n ways, then event M followed by event N can occur in $m \cdot n$ ways**

7. How can the Fundamental Counting Principle help you solve the problem? **Answers may vary. Sample: Each rating type is an event, and I know the possible number of ways each event can occur. So by the Fundamental Counting Principle, the total number of ratings is the product of the number of ways each event can occur**

Getting an Answer

8. Write an expression for the number of different ratings that are possible. $2 \cdot 5 \cdot 3 \cdot 2$

9. How many different ratings are possible? **60**

Student Companion/ All-in-One Resources/Online
Standardized Test Prep

11-1 Standardized Test Prep
Permutations and Combinations

Multiple Choice

For Exercises 1–5, choose the correct letter.

1. You choose 5 apples from a case of 24 apples. Which best represents the number of ways you can make your selection? **B**
   (A) $_5C_{19}$ (B) $_{24}C_5$ (C) $_5P_{24}$ (D) $_{19}P_5$

2. Which is equivalent to $_7P_3$? **H**
   (F) 28 (G) 35 (H) 210 (I) 840

3. A traveler can choose from three airlines, five hotels, and four rental car companies. How many arrangements of these services are possible? **B**
   (A) 12 (B) 60 (C) 220 (D) 495

4. Which is equivalent to $a!(b!)$? **I**
   (F) $(ab)!$ (G) $(ab!)!$ (H) $ba!$ (I) $b!(a!)$

5. Which is equivalent to $_9C_5$? **A**
   (A) 126 (B) 3024 (C) 15,120 (D) 45,000

Short Response

6. You have a $1 bill, a $5 bill, a $10 bill, a $20 bill, a quarter, a dime, a nickel, and a penny. How many different total amounts can you make by choosing 6 bills and coins? Show your work.

   [2] $_8C_6 = \frac{8!}{6!(8-6)!}$
   $= \frac{8 \cdot 7 \cdot 6!}{6!(2 \cdot 1)}$
   $= \frac{56}{2}$
   $= 28$
   [1] incorrect or incomplete work shown
   [0] incorrect answer and no work shown OR no answer given

Online Teacher Resource Center
Activities, Games, and Puzzles

11-1 Activity: Word Analysis
Permutations and Combinations

This activity is for groups of two to four students. Parts A and B should be done as a group and Part C should be done individually. Your teacher will determine whether or not you use a calculator.

Part A

1. Find the number of distinct three-letter combinations of the letters that make up the word COMBINE. **35**

2. Find the number of distinct three-letter permutations of the letters that make up the word COMBINE. **210**

3. Which of these two values is larger? Explain. Support your answer with numbers and actual examples from the word COMBINE. **Permutations; order matters, and for each three-letter combination, there are six distinct orderings: 35 · 6 = 210; for example: COM = COM, CMO, OCM, OMC, MCO, and MOC.**

Part B

4. Find the number of distinct three-letter combinations of the letters that make up the word PERMUTE. **20**

5. Find the number of distinct three-letter permutations of the letters that make up the word PERMUTE. **120**

6. How does Part B differ from Part A? Explain what you had to do to resolve the difference. **The letter E appears twice in the word PERMUTE. For uniqueness, we can only consider six letters.**

7. Write the statement for Part B that parallels 35 · 6 = 210 from Part A. **20 · 6 = 120**

Part C

Using the letters in your first, middle, and last names, find the following:

8. The number of distinct four-letter combinations. **Check students' work.**

9. The number of distinct five-letter permutations. **Check students' work.**

10. Try to find two English words of four or more letters using the distinct letters in your name. **Check students' work.**

Bonus: How many of the four-letter combinations from Exercise 8 contain a vowel? **Check students' work.**

11-2
PART 1

Probability

Objective To find the probability of an event using experimental and simulation methods

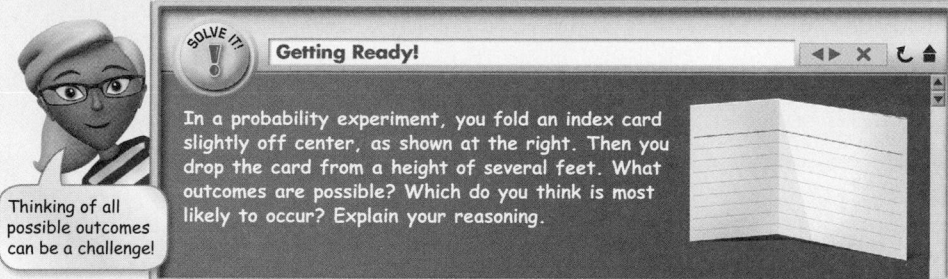

Getting Ready!

In a probability experiment, you fold an index card slightly off center, as shown at the right. Then you drop the card from a height of several feet. What outcomes are possible? Which do you think is most likely to occur? Explain your reasoning.

Thinking of all possible outcomes can be a challenge!

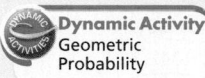
Dynamic Activity
Geometric Probability

Lesson Vocabulary
• experimental probability
• simulation

Probability measures how likely it is for an event to occur. The probability of an impossible event is 0 (or 0%). The probability of a certain event is 1 (or 100%). Other events have probabilities between 0 and 1 (or between 0% and 100%).

Focus Question How can you find the probability that a given event occurs?

When you gather data from observations, you can calculate an *experimental probability*. Each observation is called an experiment or a trial.

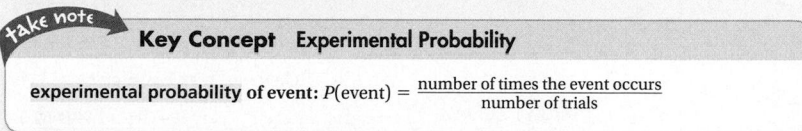

Key Concept Experimental Probability

experimental probability of event: $P(\text{event}) = \dfrac{\text{number of times the event occurs}}{\text{number of trials}}$

Think

What is a trial? What is an event?
A trial is a vehicle parking in the lot. An event is the vehicle being a truck.

Problem 1 Finding Experimental Probability

Gridded Response Of the 60 vehicles in a teachers' parking lot today, 15 are pickup trucks. What is the experimental probability that a vehicle in the lot is a pickup truck?

Use the formula. $P(\text{pickup truck}) = \dfrac{\text{number of pickup trucks}}{\text{number of vehicles}}$

Substitute and simplify. $= \dfrac{15}{60} = 0.25$

The probability that a vehicle in the lot is a pickup truck is 0.25, or 25%.

 Got It? 1. A softball player got a hit in 20 of her last 50 times at bat. What is the experimental probability that she will get a hit in her next at bat?

 PowerAlgebra.com   Lesson 11-2   Probability   695

11-2 Preparing to Teach

PART 1

BIG idea Probability   UbD

ESSENTIAL UNDERSTANDINGS
• The probability, *p*, of an event is a number such that $0 \le p \le 1$.
• The probability of an impossible event is 0.
• The probability of a certain event is 1.

Math Background

This chapter applies counting techniques that are useful in probability, statistics, and combinatorics. The probability of an event is never less than zero or more than one. The experimental probability of an event is found using a number of trials or a simulation.

Experimental Probability is determined by dividing the number of times the event occurred by the total number of trials. Data is gathered from actual trials or a simulation.

Support Student Learning

Use the **Algebra 2 Companion** to engage and support students during instruction. See Lesson Resources at the end of this lesson for details.

---

1 Interactive Learning

Solve It!

PURPOSE To use different strategies to determine the number of possible outcomes
PROCESS Students may
• replicate the experiment by dropping an index card to determine the possible outcomes.
• visualize and list the possible outcomes.

FACILITATE

Q What type of outcome is not possible when dropping the index card? **[Sample: The card will not land on a single corner.]**

Q Is it possible to find all possible outcomes? Explain. **[No; although the card can land on different sides, you can also look at the possible orientations of the folded edge.]**

ANSWER See Solve It in Answers on next page.
CONNECT THE MATH Students use an experiment and visualization to determine possible outcomes in the Solve It. In this lesson, students learn to find probability using different methods.

2 Guided Instruction

Take Note

Experimental probability is often called *empirical probability*.

Problem 1

Q If the experimental probability was 0%, can you conclude that no teachers ever drive pickup trucks to school? Explain. **[No; 0% means there were no trucks that day.]**

Got It?

Q What is the trial? the event? **[an at bat; a hit]**

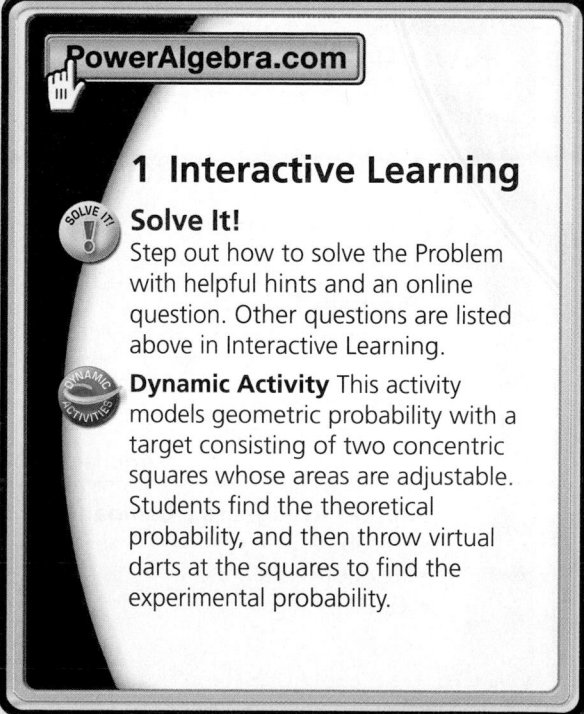

PowerAlgebra.com

1 Interactive Learning

Solve It!
Step out how to solve the Problem with helpful hints and an online question. Other questions are listed above in Interactive Learning.

Dynamic Activity This activity models geometric probability with a target consisting of two concentric squares whose areas are adjustable. Students find the theoretical probability, and then throw virtual darts at the squares to find the experimental probability.

Problem 2

ERROR PREVENTION

Q Can other digits be chosen for the simulation? Explain. [Yes, as long as one digit represents the correct answer and three represent incorrect answers. For example, 5, 6, 7, 8 where 7 represents the correct answer.]

Q How could you answer this question using experimental probability without a calculator? [Sample: Use three red marbles (wrong answer) and one blue marble (correct answer). Randomly select a marble 10 times to determine the number of correct answers. Repeat 20 times.]

SYNTHESIZING

Students recreating the simulation may find that none of their tests have six or more correct answers. They might conclude the probability of passing is 0%, although they intuitively know the probability is more than 0%. Explain that simulation and experimental probability yield better results with more trials.

Got It?

EXTENSION

Q How does the simulation change if the passing score is 50% or better? How does it stay the same? [The digits and number of trials stay the same. The passing test must consist of five or more 1's.]

Sometimes actual trials are difficult or unreasonable to conduct. In these situations, you can estimate the experimental probability of an event by using a simulation. A **simulation** is a model of the event.

Problem 2 Using a Simulation

Testing On a multiple-choice test, each item has 4 choices, but only one choice is correct. How can you simulate guessing the answers? What is the probability that you will pass the test by guessing at least 6 of 10 answers correctly?

Plan

How do you simulate guessing one out of four?
You can pick at random from four numbers, specifying that one of them will be the "correct" answer.

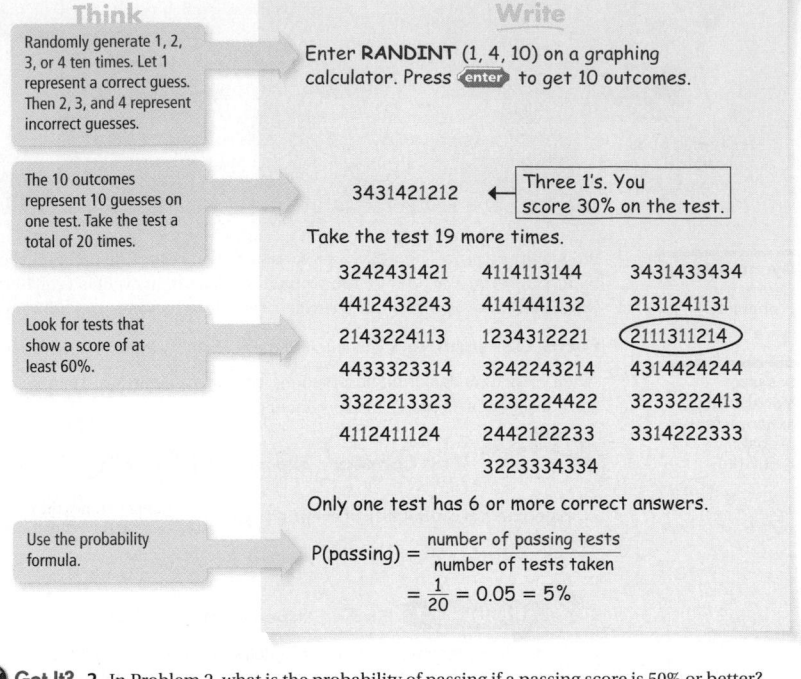

Think

Randomly generate 1, 2, 3, or 4 ten times. Let 1 represent a correct guess. Then 2, 3, and 4 represent incorrect guesses.

The 10 outcomes represent 10 guesses on one test. Take the test a total of 20 times.

Hint

A score of 60% is equivalent to six 1's out of 10 guesses.

Look for tests that show a score of at least 60%.

Use the probability formula.

Write

Enter **RANDINT** (1, 4, 10) on a graphing calculator. Press **enter** to get 10 outcomes.

3431421212 ← Three 1's. You score 30% on the test.

Take the test 19 more times.

3242431421 4114113144 3431433434
4412432243 4141441132 2131241131
2143224113 1234312221 (2111311214)
4433323314 3242243214 4314424244
3322213323 2232224422 3233222413
4112411124 2442122233 3314222333
            3223334334

Only one test has 6 or more correct answers.

$$P(\text{passing}) = \frac{\text{number of passing tests}}{\text{number of tests taken}}$$
$$= \frac{1}{20} = 0.05 = 5\%$$

Got It? **2.** In Problem 2, what is the probability of passing if a passing score is 50% or better?

Focus Question How can you find the probability that a given event occurs?
Answer Gather data from observations or simulations to find the experimental probability of an event.

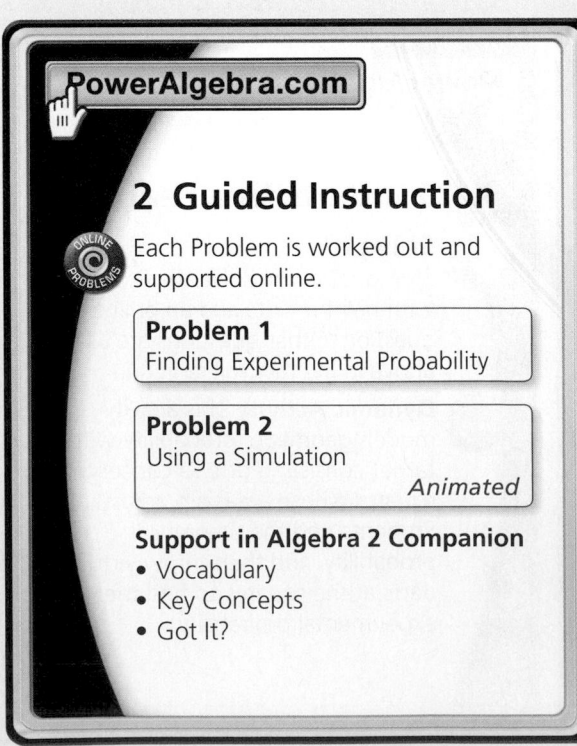

2 Guided Instruction

Each Problem is worked out and supported online.

Problem 1
Finding Experimental Probability

Problem 2
Using a Simulation
Animated

Support in Algebra 2 Companion
• Vocabulary
• Key Concepts
• Got It?

Additional Problems

1. You observe 119 animals at a zoo, and nine of them have wings. What is the experimental probability that an animal at this zoo has wings?

ANSWER 0.16

2. On a multiple-choice test, each item has three choices, but only one choice is correct. How can you simulate guessing the answers? What is the probability that you will pass the test by guessing at least five of ten answers correctly?

ANSWER Sample: Use digit 1 to represent the correct answer and digits 2 and 3 to represent incorrect answers.

Answers

Solve It!

The index card can fall in various ways, such as on its longer side, shorter side, back, front, like a tent or one edge; its top or bottom side.

Answers may vary. Sample: Most likely, the index card will fall on its back since it has a greater area than any of the other possibilities.

Got It?

1. 0.40, or 40%   **2.** 0.20, or 20%

Lesson Check

1. 0.75, or 75%   **2.** 0.80, or 80%

3. Answers may vary. Samples: Flip a coin; generate random numbers on a calculator; roll a die with odd numbers as true and even numbers as false.

4. Because you are averaging over more samples, you are getting a more accurate average.

Lesson Check

Do you know HOW?

1. What is the probability a quarterback will complete his next pass if he has completed 30 of his last 40 passes?

2. What is the probability a quarterback will complete his next pass if he has completed 36 of his last 45 passes?

Do you UNDERSTAND?

3. **Writing** List three ways you could simulate answering a true-false question.

4. **Reasoning** Why is a simulation better the more times you perform it?

Practice and Problem-Solving Exercises

Ⓐ **Practice**

Find each experimental probability. ◀ See Problem 1.

Guided Practice

5. A class tossed coins and recorded 161 heads and 179 tails. What is the experimental probability of heads? Of tails?

To start, write the formula for experimental probability.

$P(\text{heads}) = \dfrac{\text{number of heads}}{\text{number of tosses}}$

6. A class rolled number cubes. Their results are shown in the table. What is the experimental probability of rolling each number?

Number	1	2	3	4	5	6
Occurrences	42	44	45	44	47	46

 Graphing Calculator For Exercises 7–9, define a simulation by telling how you represent correct answers, incorrect answers, and the quiz. Use your simulation to find each experimental probability. ◀ See Problem 2.

7. If you guess the answers at random, what is the probability of getting at least two correct answers on a five-question true-or-false quiz?

8. If you guess the answers at random, what is the probability of getting at least three correct answers on a five-question true-or-false quiz?

9. A five-question multiple-choice quiz has five choices for each answer. What is the probability of correctly guessing at random exactly one correct answer? Exactly two correct answers? Exactly three correct answers? (*Hint:* You could let any two digits represent correct answers, and the other digits represent wrong answers.)

Ⓑ **Apply**

10. **a. Sports** Out of four games, team A has won one game and team B has won three games in a championship series. What is the experimental probability that team A wins the next game? That team B wins the next game?

    b. Reasoning Do you think that experimental probability is a good predictor of the winner of the next game? Explain.

---

3 Lesson Check

Do you know HOW?   ERROR INTERVENTION

• If students have difficulty solving Exercises 1–2, remind them they must determine which number represents the event and which number represents the number of trials.

Do you UNDERSTAND?

• If students have trouble with Exercise 4, have them find the probability using only the first 5 trials. Point out that using fewer trials does not allow as many possibilities to occur.

Close

> **Q** What is the difference between a simulation and experimental probability? **[Experimental probability is found using data from actual experiments. A simulation is the experiment.]**

4 Practice

ASSIGNMENT GUIDE

Basic: 5–10

Average: 5–10

Reasoning exercises have blue headings.

Applications exercises have red headings.

HOMEWORK QUICK CHECK

To check students' understanding of key skills and concepts, go over Exercises 6, 7, 8, 9, and 10.

Practice and Problem-Solving Exercises

5. $\dfrac{161}{340} \approx 47\%$; $\dfrac{179}{340} \approx 53\%$

6. the number 1: $\dfrac{21}{134} \approx 15.7\%$;
   the number 2: $\dfrac{11}{67} \approx 16.4\%$;
   the number 3: $\dfrac{45}{268} \approx 16.8\%$;
   the number 4: $\dfrac{11}{67} \approx 16.4\%$;
   the number 5: $\dfrac{47}{268} \approx 17.5\%$;
   the number 6: $\dfrac{23}{134} \approx 17.2\%$

7. Answers may vary. Sample: Generate random numbers between 0 and 1 using a graphing calculator. Examine the first five digits of each random number. Let even digits represent correct answers and odd digits incorrect answers. If there are two or more even digits, make a tally mark for that number. The total number of tally marks for 100 numbers, as a percent, gives the experimental probability. The simulated probability should be about 0.8.

8. Answers may vary. Sample: Toss 5 coins. Keep a tally of the times three or more heads are tossed. (A head represents a correct answer.) Do this 100 times. The total number of tally marks, as a percent, gives the experimental probability. The simulated probability should be about 50%.

9. Answers may vary. Sample: Randomly generate a 1, 2, 3, 4, or 5 five times. Let 1 represent a correct guess and 2–5 represent incorrect guesses. Tally the recorded numbers with exactly one digit that represents a correct answer. Tally the recorded numbers with exactly two digits that represent correct answers. Tally the recorded numbers with exactly three digits that represent correct answers. The tally totals, as percents, give the experimental probabilities. They should be in the neighborhood of 40%, 20%, and 5%, respectively.

10. a. 25%; 75%

    b. No; there were too few trials.

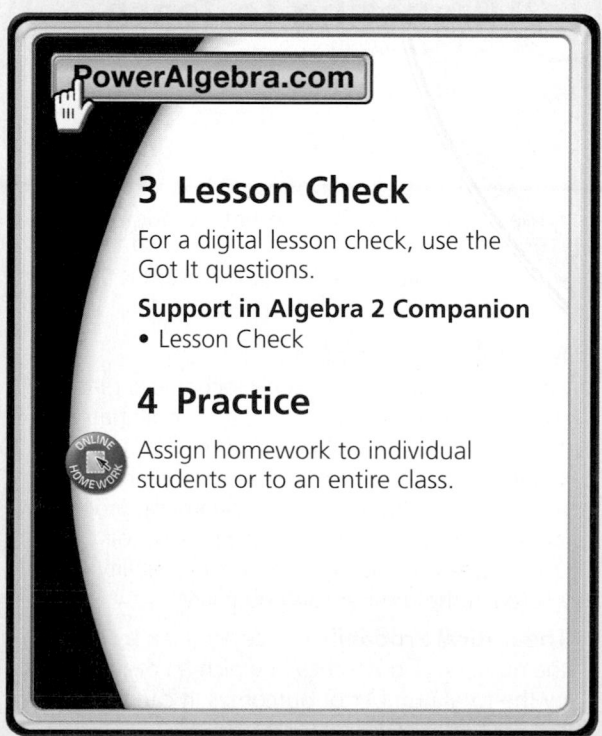

PowerAlgebra.com

3 Lesson Check

For a digital lesson check, use the Got It questions.

Support in Algebra 2 Companion
• Lesson Check

4 Practice

Assign homework to individual students or to an entire class.

1 Launch

CONNECT THE MATH In Part 1 of this lesson, students used simulations to find experimental probability. In Part 2 of the lesson, students will apply the knowledge of probability they gained by investigating experimental probability to find theoretical probability.

FOCUS QUESTION

Q What happens to the experimental probability if the number of trials you use in a simulation is small? **[The data may not be adequate to find a relevant experimental probability.]**

Q Would it be reasonable to expect 1,000 trials to collect the data to determine experimental probability? Why or why not? **[No; while it would produce an accurate probability it would take too much time.]**

2 Guided Instruction

Take Note

Help students understand the difference between experimental probability and theoretical probability by discussing coin flips. The experimental probability of a coin landing heads is found by flipping a coin many times and recording whether it lands heads or tails. The theoretical probability of a coin landing heads is found by knowing there are two equally likely outcomes, one of which is heads.

Problem 3

Q How can you be sure the sample space consists of equally likely outcomes? **[The problem states that the number cube is fair. A fair number cube is one in which each side has an equal probability of occurring.]**

Objective To find the probability of an event using theoretical methods

> In Part 1 of the lesson, you learned how to find experimental probability based on observations and simulations.

Connect to What You Know

> Here you will find probabilities based on the number and likelihood of outcomes in a sample space.

Lesson Vocabulary
- sample space
- equally likely outcomes
- theoretical probability

Focus Question What is theoretical probability?

The set of all possible outcomes to an experiment or activity is a **sample space**. When each outcome in a sample space has the same chance of occurring, the outcomes are **equally likely outcomes**.

For one roll of a standard number cube, there are six equally likely outcomes in the sample space. You can calculate *theoretical probability* as a ratio of outcomes.

take note   Key Concept   Theoretical Probability

If a sample space has n equally likely outcomes and an event A occurs in m of these outcomes, then the **theoretical probability** of event A is $P(A) = \frac{m}{n}$.

> Sample space: n outcomes
> Event A: m outcomes

Problem 3   Finding Theoretical Probability

What is the theoretical probability of each event?

A getting a 5 on one roll of a standard number cube

There are six equally likely outcomes: 1, 2, 3, 4, 5, and 6. A 5 occurs in only one way.

$$P(5) = \frac{1}{6}$$

B getting a sum of 5 on one roll of two standard number cubes

There are 36 possible equally likely outcomes. The favorable outcomes are those with a sum of 5.

$$P(\text{sum } 5) = \frac{4}{36} = \frac{1}{9}$$

Plan

How many outcomes are there?
Each cube has six numbers on it, so there are
$6 \cdot 6 = 36$ outcomes.

PART 2

BIG idea Probability   **UbD**

ESSENTIAL UNDERSTANDINGS
- The probability, p, of an event is a number such that $0 \le p \le 1$.
- The probability of an impossible event is 0.
- The probability of a certain event is 1.

Math Background

This chapter applies counting techniques that are useful in probability, statistics, and combinatorics. The probability of an event is never less than zero or more than one. The experimental probability of an event may differ from the theoretical probability because of randomness. As the number of trials increases, the experimental probability will approach the theoretical probability.

Theoretical Probability is determined by dividing the number of outcomes in which an event occurs by the total number of outcomes. It can be used to predict the experimental probability.

Geometric Probability is a type of theoretical probability in geometry problems involving length, area or volume.

Support Student Learning

Use the **Algebra 2 Companion** to engage and support students during instruction. See Lesson Resources at the end of this lesson for details.

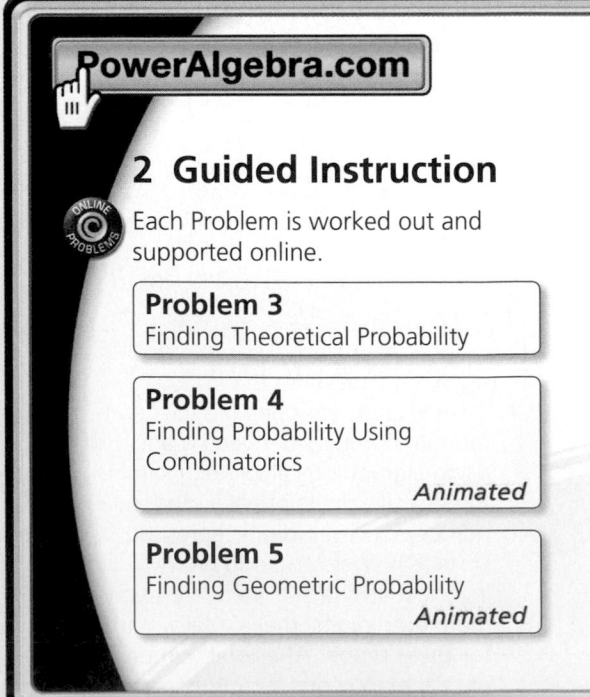

PowerAlgebra.com

2 Guided Instruction

Each Problem is worked out and supported online.

Problem 3
Finding Theoretical Probability

Problem 4
Finding Probability Using Combinatorics
Animated

Problem 5
Finding Geometric Probability
Animated

b. Reasoning Without calculating the probability, is it more likely to get an even or odd number on one roll of a standard number cube? Explain.

It can be easier to use *combinatorics* to find theoretical probability rather than listing and counting all the equally likely outcomes. Combinatorics include the Fundamental Counting Principle and other ways to count permutations and combinations.

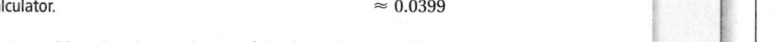

Problem 4 Finding Probability Using Combinatorics

Plan

Should you use permutations or combinations?
Order does not matter.
Use combinations.

What is the theoretical probability of being dealt exactly two 7's in a 5-card hand from a standard 52-card deck?

Step 1 Find the number of ways to get a hand with exactly two 7's.

A hand with exactly 2 sevens also has exactly 3 non-sevens.

Find the number of ways to choose exactly 2 sevens from 4 possible sevens. $\quad _4C_2$

Find the number of ways to choose exactly 3 non-sevens from the 48 remaining cards. $\quad _{48}C_3$

The product is the number of ways to get exactly 2 sevens. $\quad _4C_2 \cdot {}_{48}C_3$

Step 2 Find the number of possible 5-card hands.

Find the number of ways to choose exactly 5 cards from 52 possible cards. $\quad _{52}C_5$

Step 3 Find the probability.

Use the formula for probability. $\quad P(\text{hand with two 7's}) = \dfrac{\text{number of hands with two 7's}}{\text{total number of possible hands}}$

Substitute. $\quad = \dfrac{_4C_2 \cdot {}_{48}C_3}{_{52}C_5}$

Simplify. $\quad = \dfrac{103,776}{2,598,960}$

Use a calculator. $\quad \approx 0.0399$

The probability of a 5-card hand with exactly two 7's is about 0.04, or 4%.

Got It? **4.** What is the theoretical probability of being dealt all four 7's in a 5-card hand?

Got It?

Q Is the sum of two odd numbers odd or even? two even numbers? an even and an odd number? **[The sum of two odd numbers is even. The sum of two even numbers is even. The sum of an even and an odd number is odd.]**

Q How does this information help you find the possible favorable outcomes? **[Count only the sums of even and odd numbers.]**

Problem 4

Q Why is it necessary to count the number of combinations of 3 non-seven cards? **[Being dealt exactly two 7's means you must also have exactly 3 non-sevens. Multiply the number of ways to choose 7's by the number of ways to choose non-sevens.]**

Got It?

Q What is the meaning of the denominator when determining this probability? **[The denominator is the sample space or all the possible outcomes. It is all the possible ways to get five cards in a deck of 52.]**

Q How is the Fundamental Counting Principle used to find the probability in this problem? **[The numerator is the number of ways to get four 7's times the number of ways to get one non-seven.]**

Support in Algebra 2 Companion
- Vocabulary
- Key Concepts
- Got It?

Additional Problems

3. What is the theoretical probability of getting a number less than 3 on one roll of a fair number cube? getting a sum that is a multiple of 4 on one roll of two fair number cubes?

ANSWERS $\frac{1}{3}; \frac{1}{4}$

4. What is the theoretical probability of being dealt exactly three 8's in a five-card hand from a standard 52-card deck?

ANSWER about 0.0017%

5. A carnival game consists of throwing darts at a circular board as shown. What is the geometric probability that a dart thrown at random will hit the shaded circle?

ANSWER about 14%

Answers

Got It?

3. a. $\frac{1}{2}$

b. The likelihoods of getting an even or odd are the same, i.e. $\frac{1}{2}$.

4. $\dfrac{48}{2,598,960}$ or ≈ 0.0000184689 or $\approx 0.00185\%$

Problem 5

"At random" in this problem means that the probability of the ball being thrown to a certain point in the strike zone is the same for any point in the strike zone.

Q What is the probability that a baseball thrown at random in the strike zone will NOT be in the high-inside strike zone? Explain. **[The probability of not being in that area is 1 − 0.064 or 0.936 which is 93.6%.]**

Q How is area related to sample space? **[Sample space is the set of all possible outcomes. The area can be thought of as the set of all possible points.]**

Got It?

VISUAL LEARNERS

Q If the low inside strike zone is the same area as a high inside strike zone, will the probabilities be different? Explain. **[No; it does not matter where in the total area the event area occurs. If the areas of the different events are the same, the probabilities will be the same.]**

Sometimes you can use areas to find a theoretical probability.

 Problem 5 Finding Geometric Probability

Geometry A batter's strike zone depends on the height and stance of the batter. What is the geometric probability that a baseball thrown at random within the batter's strike zone, as shown in the figure below, will be a high-inside strike (one of the hardest pitches to hit)?

Think

What are the favorable outcomes? All outcomes?
Favorable outcomes are points in the high-inside region. All outcomes are points in the strike zone.

Use the formula for probability.

$$P(\text{high-inside strike}) = \frac{\text{area of high-inside strike zone}}{\text{area of total strike zone}}$$

Substitute.

$$= \frac{4 \cdot 6}{17 \cdot 22}$$

Use a calculator.

$$\approx 0.064$$

For a baseball thrown at random in the batter's strike zone, the probability that it will be a high-inside strike is about 6.4%.

 Got It? 5. Suppose a batter's strike zone is 15 in.-by-20 in. and the high-inside strike zone is 3 in.-by-5 in. What is the probability that a baseball thrown at random within the strike zone will be a high-inside strike?

Answers

Got It? (continued)
5. 0.05 or 5%

Focus Question What is theoretical probability?

Answer The theoretical probability of an event A is $P(A) = \frac{m}{n}$, where the sample space has n equally likely outcomes and the event A occurs in m of the outcomes.

Lesson Check

Do you know HOW?

Find the theoretical probability of each event when rolling a standard number cube.

1. $P(3)$ **2.** $P(2 \text{ or } 4)$

Do you UNDERSTAND?

3. Vocabulary Explain the difference between experimental probability, theoretical probability, and geometric probability.

Practice and Problem-Solving Exercises

A Practice

A jar contains 30 red marbles, 50 blue marbles, and 20 white marbles. You pick one marble from the jar at random. Find each theoretical probability.

⬅ **See Problem 3.**

> **Guided Practice**
>
> | | **4.** $P(\text{red})$ |
> |---|---|
> | To start, find the total number of outcomes. | $30 + 50 + 20 = 100$ |

5. $P(\text{blue})$ **6.** $P(\text{not blue})$

7. $P(\text{not white})$ **8.** $P(\text{red or blue})$

A bag contains 36 red blocks, 48 green blocks, 22 yellow blocks, and 19 purple blocks. You pick one block from the bag at random. Find each theoretical probability.

9. $P(\text{green})$ **10.** $P(\text{purple})$

11. $P(\text{not yellow})$ **12.** $P(\text{green or yellow})$

13. $P(\text{yellow or not green})$ **14.** $P(\text{purple or not red})$

15. Games A group of 30 students from your school is part of the audience for a TV game show. The total number of people in the audience is 150. What is the theoretical probability of 3 students from your school being selected as contestants out of 9 possible contestant spots?

⬅ **See Problem 4.**

---

3 Lesson Check

Do you know HOW? ERROR INTERVENTION

• If students have difficulty solving Exercises 1–2, remind them the total number of outcomes, or the sample space, is the number in the denominator of the probability fraction.

Do you UNDERSTAND?

• If students have trouble with Exercise 3, have them make three columns headed with the titles experimental probability, theoretical probability, and geometric probability. Then have them go back through the lesson and write characteristics about each type of probability in the appropriate columns.

Close

> **Q** When might you choose to use experimental probability rather than theoretical probability? Give an example. **[when you do not know the sample space; example: determining the most common color of marble in a bag of marbles when you are unaware of the total number or colors]**
>
> **Q** What are the maximum and minimum values of a theoretical probability? Explain. **[1 and 0; the probability of an event is a number between 0 (impossible) and 1 (certain), inclusive.]**

Lesson Check

1. $\frac{1}{6}$

2. $\frac{1}{3}$

3. Experimental probabilities are calculated on the basis of data from an experiment, actual or simulated. Given equally likely outcomes, the basis for calculating theoretical probability is being able to determine the no. of ways that an event can occur within these outcomes. Comparisons of measures such as length and area are the basis of geometric probability.

Practice and Problem-Solving Exercises

4. $\frac{3}{10}$, or 30%

5. $\frac{1}{2}$, or 50%

6. $\frac{1}{2}$, or 50%

7. $\frac{4}{5}$, or 80%

8. $\frac{4}{5}$, or 80%

9. $\frac{48}{125}$, or 38.4%

10. $\frac{19}{125}$, or 15.2%

11. $\frac{103}{125}$, or 82.4%

12. $\frac{14}{25}$, or 56%

13. $\frac{77}{125}$, or 61.6%

14. $\frac{89}{125}$, or 71.2%

15. $\frac{{}_{30}C_3 \cdot {}_{120}C_6}{{}_{150}C_9} \approx 0.17879 \approx 17.9\%$

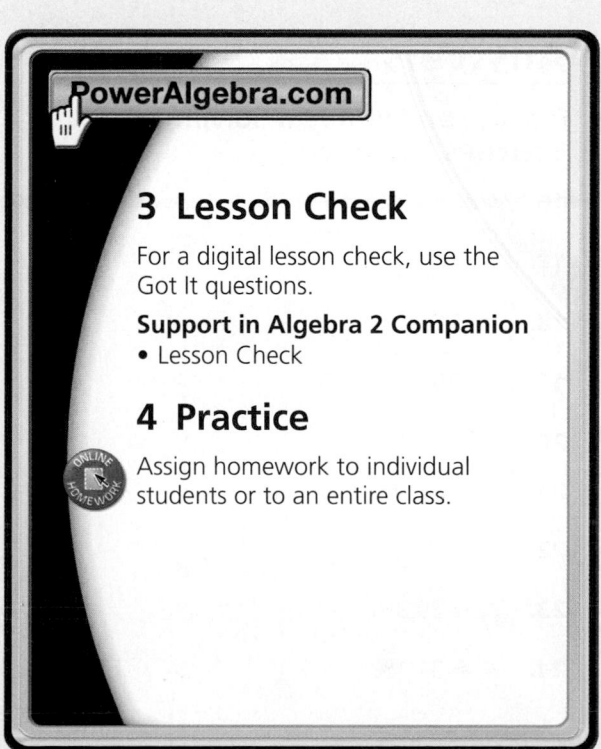

PowerAlgebra.com

3 Lesson Check

For a digital lesson check, use the Got It questions.

Support in Algebra 2 Companion
• Lesson Check

4 Practice

Assign homework to individual students or to an entire class.

4 Practice

ASSIGNMENT GUIDE

Basic: 4–18, 20, 25

Average: 4–25

Standardized Test Prep: 27–31

Mixed Review: 32–41

Reasoning exercises have blue headings.

Applications exercises have red headings.

EXERCISE 25: Use the Think About a Plan worksheet in the **Student Companion** (also available in the Teaching Resources in print and online) to further support students' development in becoming independent learners.

HOMEWORK QUICK CHECK

To check students' understanding of key skills and concepts, go over Exercises 5, 15, 17, 20, and 25.

Geometry Suppose that a dart lands at random on the dartboard shown at the right. Find each theoretical probability.

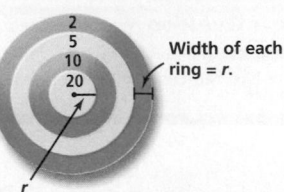

Width of each ring = r.

◀ See Problem 5.

> **Guided Practice**
>
> **16.** The dart lands in the bull's eye.
>
> To start, find the area of the bull's eye region. $A = \pi r^2$

17. The dart lands in a green region.

18. The dart scores at least 10 points.

19. The dart scores fewer than 10 points.

Ⓑ Apply

20. Think About a Plan Suppose you roll two standard number cubes. What is the theoretical probability of getting a sum of 7?
- What is the sample space?
- How many outcomes are there?

In a class of 147 students, 95 are taking math (M), 73 are taking science (S), and 52 are taking both math and science. One student is picked at random. Find each probability.

21. P(taking math or science or both)

22. P(not taking math)

23. P(taking math but not science)

24. P(taking neither math nor science)

M   S

43   52   21

31

25. Lottery A lottery has 53 numbers from which five are drawn at random. Each number can only be drawn once. What is the probability of your lottery ticket matching all five numbers in any order?

26. Writing Explain what you would need to know to determine the theoretical probability of a five-digit postal ZIP code ending in 1.

Answers

Practice and Problem-Solving Exercises (continued)

16. $\frac{1}{16}$, or 6.25%

17. $\frac{5}{8}$, or 62.5%

18. $\frac{1}{4}$, or 25%

19. $\frac{3}{4}$, or 75%

20. $\frac{1}{6}$

21. $\frac{116}{147} \approx 78.9\%$

22. $\frac{52}{147} \approx 35.4\%$

23. $\frac{43}{147} \approx 29.3\%$

24. $\frac{31}{147} \approx 21.1\%$

25. 1 chance in 2,869,685 or $\approx 0.00003485\%$

26. if there are any restrictions on the last digit of a ZIP code

Standardized Test Prep

27. What is the theoretical probability of getting a 2 or a 3 when rolling a standard number cube?

   (A) $\frac{1}{2}$ (B) $\frac{1}{3}$ (C) $\frac{1}{4}$ (D) $\frac{1}{6}$

28. Which expression is equivalent to $\left(n^{\frac{3}{2}} \div n^{-\frac{1}{6}}\right)^{-3}$?

   (F) n^{27} (G) n^{-27} (H) n^{-4} (I) n^{-5}

29. How can you rewrite the equation $x^2 + 12x + 5 = 3$ so the left side of the equation is in the form $(x + a)^2$?

   (A) $(x - 6)^2 = 28$ (C) $(x + 6)^2 = 39$

   (B) $(x + 6)^2 = 34$ (D) $(x + 12)^2 = -2$

30. How many ways are there to select 25 books from a collection of 27 books?

   (F) 702   (G) 5.4×1027 (H) 351   (I) 675

31. Use the center and radius to graph the circle with equation $(x + 4)^2 + (y - 2)^2 = 16$.

Mixed Review

Evaluate each expression.   ◀ **See Lesson 11-1.**

32. $_5P_2$ **33.** $_7P_4$ **34.** $_5C_3$ **35.** $_{10}C_8$

Add or subtract. Simplify where possible.   ◀ **See Lesson 8-5.**

36. $\frac{5}{a^2b} - \frac{7a}{5b^2}$ **37.** $\frac{3}{p} + \frac{7}{q}$ **38.** $\frac{x}{x - 5} + \frac{x}{5 - x}$

Get Ready! **To prepare for Lesson 11-3, do Exercises 39–41.**

A bag contains 24 green marbles, 22 blue marbles, 14 yellow marbles,   ◀ **See Lesson 11-2.**
and 12 red marbles. Suppose you pick one marble at random.
What is each probability?

39. $P(\text{yellow})$ **40.** $P(\text{not blue})$ **41.** $P(\text{green or red})$

Standardized Test Prep

27. B

28. I

29. B

30. H

31. [2]

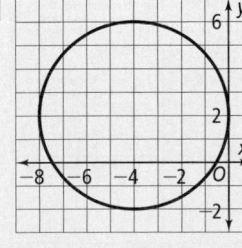

  [1] circle has correct center, but incorrect radius

Mixed Review

32. 20

33. 840

34. 10

35. 45

36. $\frac{25b - 7a^3}{5a^2b^2}$

37. $\frac{3q + 7p}{pq}$

38. 0

39. $\frac{7}{36} = 19.\overline{4}\%$

40. $\frac{25}{36} = 69.\overline{4}\%$

41. $\frac{1}{2}$, or 50%

Differentiated Remediation

Additional Instructional Support

Algebra 2 Companion

Students can use the **Algebra 2 Companion** worktext (4 pages) as you teach the lesson. Use the Companion to support

- New Vocabulary
- Key Concepts
- Got It for each Problem
- Lesson Check

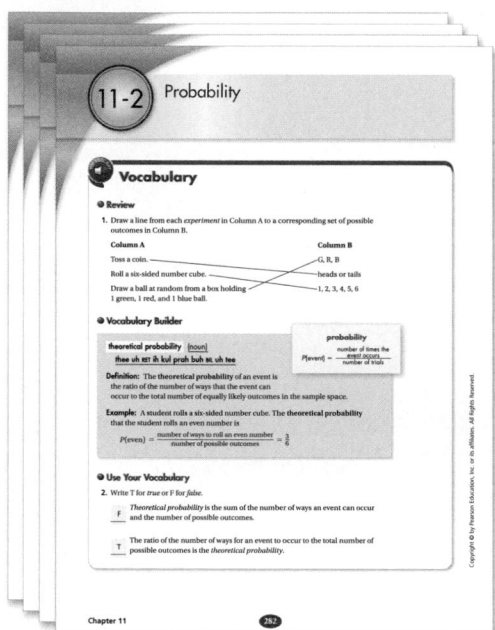

ELL Support

Use Manipulatives Provide students with number cubes and coins to help them learn the difference between experimental and theoretical probability as well as find the sample space of events discussed in this lesson.

Write *experimental probability* on the board. Provide students with one number cube; have them roll the cube 20 times and record their results. Say: *This is an experiment.* Have students find the experimental probability of rolling a 3. Write the different probabilities found under *experimental probability*.

Next write *theoretical probability* on the board. Have students look at the number cube and record the sample space. Then have them count the number of 3s on the cube. Say: *This is theoretical probability.* Have the students find the theoretical probability of rolling a 3. Compare the theoretical probabilities with the experimental probabilities.

5 Assess & Remediate

Lesson Quiz

1. Of 24 movies shown in a theater, three are rated G. What is the experimental probability that a movie chosen at random at the theater is rated G?

2. **Do you UNDERSTAND?** A multiple-choice test consists of five answer choices for each item. How can you use simulation to determine the experimental probability of passing the test with at least 5 out of 10 answers correct?

3. What is the theoretical probability of getting a sum of 7 on one roll of two fair number cubes?

4. What is the theoretical probability of being dealt exactly one ace in a five-card hand from a standard 52-card deck?

5. A rectangular landing pad measures $20' \times 25'$ with a rectangular target on the pad measuring $6' \times 8'$. What is the geometric probability that a model rocket falling randomly on the pad will land in the target?

ANSWERS TO LESSON QUIZ

1. 12.5%
2. Use random digits 1, 2, 3, 4, 5 ten times with 1 representing the correct answer. Repeat 20 times. Count the number of times the simulation shows 5 or more 1's.
3. $\frac{1}{6}$
4. 29.9%
5. 9.6%

A PRESCRIPTION FOR REMEDIATION

Use the student work on the Lesson Quiz to prescribe a differentiated review assignment:

Points	Differentiated Remediation
0–2	Intervention
3–4	On-level
5	Extension

PowerAlgebra.com

5 Assess & Remediate

Assign the Lesson Quiz. Appropriate intervention, practice, or enrichment is automatically generated based on student performance.

Intervention

- **Reteaching** (2 pages) Provides reteaching and practice exercises for the key lesson concepts. Use with struggling students or absent students.

- **English Language Learner Support** Helps students develop and reinforce mathematical vocabulary and key concepts.

All-in-One Resources/Online
Reteaching

11-2 Reteaching
Probability

Probability is a measure of how likely a specific event is to occur. To find the *experimental probability* of a specific event, you conduct an experiment, or simulation of the experiment, multiple times. Each time you run the experiment or simulation, you are conducting a *trial*. You count the number of times the event you are looking for occurs. The experimental probability is the ratio of the number of times the event occurs to the number of trials.

$$P(\text{event}) = \frac{\text{\# of times the event occurs}}{\text{\# of trials}}$$

Problem

You toss a coin 12 times and record each result: H, T, T, H, H, H, T, T, H, T, H, T. What is the experimental probability of tails?

Step 1 Determine the total number of trials, the event you are looking for, and the number of times the event occurred during the trials.
One toss of the coin is one trial. You did 12 trials.
The event you are looking for is tails. Tails occurred 5 times.

Step 2 Use the formula for experimental probability.
$$P(\text{tails}) = \frac{\text{\# of tails}}{\text{\# of tosses}} = \frac{5}{12} \approx 0.42, \text{ or } 42\%$$
The experimental probability of tails is about 0.42.

Exercises

In a telephone survey of 150 households, 75 people answered "yes" to a particular question, 50 answered "no," and 25 were "not sure." Find each experimental probability.

1. $P(\text{yes})$ $\frac{1}{2}$ or 50%
2. $P(\text{no})$ $\frac{1}{3} \approx 0.33$, or 33%
3. $P(\text{not sure})$ $\frac{1}{6} \approx 0.17$, or 17%
4. $P(\text{not yes})$ $\frac{1}{2}$, or 50%
5. $P(\text{yes or no})$ $\frac{5}{6} \approx 0.83$, or 83%
6. $P(\text{yes and not sure})$ 0, or 0%

All-in-One Resources/Online
English Language Learner Support

11-2 ELL Support
Probability

Complete the vocabulary chart by filling in the missing information.

Word or Phrase	Definition	Example
experimental probability	1. the number of times the event occurs divided by the number of trials	You take 12 marbles from a bag and 3 of them are blue. The experimental probability of pulling a blue marble from the bag is $\frac{3}{12} = 0.25 = 25\%$.
simulation	2. a *simulation* is a model of an event	You can simulate guessing on a set of true or false questions by flipping a coin.
sample space	a list of all possible outcomes to an experiment or activity	3. The sample space for a flip of a coin is heads or tails.
equally likely sample space	4. a sample space in which each outcome has the same chance of occurring	The sample space for randomly selecting a card from a deck of 52 cards includes all of the cards in the deck, and each outcome has an equal chance of occurring.
theoretical probability	If an event A occurs in *m* out of *n* equally likely outcomes, then the theoretical probability of A is $\frac{m}{n}$.	5. The theoretical probability of pulling an Ace from a deck of 52 cards is $\frac{4}{52} = \frac{1}{13}$

Differentiated Remediation *continued*

On-Level

- **Practice** (2 pages) Provides extra practice for each lesson. For more challenging practice exercises, use the Form G Practice pages found in the All-in-One Teaching Resources and online.

- **Think About a Plan** Helps students develop specific problem-solving skills and strategies by providing scaffolded guiding questions.
- **Standardized Test Prep** Focuses on all major exercises, all major question types, and helps students prepare for the high-stakes assessments.

Extension

- **Enrichment** Provides students with interesting problems and activities that extend the concepts of the lesson.
- **Activities, Games, and Puzzles** Worksheets that can be used for concepts development, enrichment, and for fun!

Student Companion/All-in-One Resources/Online
Practice page 1

11-2 Practice *Form K*
Probability

Find each experimental probability.

1. A baseball player got a hit in 12 of his last 40 at bats. What is the probability that he will get a hit in his next at bat? 0.3 or 30%

2. A pitcher struck out 8 of the last 32 batters that he faced. What is the probability that he will strike out the next batter that he faces? 0.25 or 25%

3. A student rolled a six-sided number cube 60 times. She rolled the number 4 nine times. What is the experimental probability of rolling a 4? 0.15 or 15%

4. **Reasoning** There are 50 cars in a used car lot. The experimental probability that a car in the lot has two doors is 0.12. How many cars in the lot have two doors? 6 cars

Explain how you could simulate each situation. Then use your simulation to find each experimental probability.

5. A quiz consists of 12 true-or-false questions. If you guess the answers at random, what is the probability of getting at least 8 correct answers?
Answers may vary. Sample: Use a coin and allow heads to represent a correct answer and tails to represent an incorrect answer. Flip the coin 12 times to represent the quiz, and record the number of correct answers. Represent the quiz 20 times, and record the number of times there are at least 8 correct answers. The probability is about 20%.

6. There are 15 multiple-choice questions on a test. Each question has four answer choices, and only one choice is correct. What is the probability of passing the test by guessing at least 7 of the 15 answers correctly?
Answers may vary. Sample: Pick at random from four numbers, and select one of them to represent a correct answer. Pick 15 times to represent one test, and represent the test 20 times. The probability is about 5%.

7. **Writing** Explain why simulations are sometimes preferable to conducting actual trials.
Answers may vary. Sample: Sometimes it is impractical to conduct actual trials. For example, a teacher would not ask her students to guess all of the answers on a test. In such cases, it makes sense to use a simulation.

Student Companion/All-in-One Resources/Online
Practice page 2

11-2 Practice (continued) *Form K*
Probability

Find each of the following theoretical probabilities.

8. Your classmate rolls a fair number cube. What is the theoretical probability that she will roll a number greater than 4? 33⅓%

9. Shawn rolls a pair of fair number cubes. What is the theoretical probability that he will roll a sum of 3? about 6%

10. A box contains 24 green markers, 16 red markers, and 10 blue markers.
   a. P(red) 32%
   b. P(green or blue) 68%
   c. P(not green) 52%

Use combinatorics to find the following theoretical probability.

11. Six of the 32 players on the football team are left-handed. There are 5 starting offensive linemen. What is the theoretical probability that 2 of the starting offensive linemen are left-handed? about 19%

Use area to find the following theoretical probabilities.

12. The floor in your friend's house covers 1400 ft². The floor in her bedroom is 14 ft by 10 ft. What is the probability that a randomly selected point on the floor of the house is in your friend's bedroom? 10%

13. A garden is 15 ft by 12 ft. Tomatoes fill a 5 foot by 4 foot section of the garden. A squirrel leaps from a tree into the garden. What is the theoretical probability that the squirrel will land in the tomato section of the garden? about 11%

Student Companion/All-in-One Resources/Online
Think About a Plan

11-2 Think About a Plan
Probability

Lottery A lottery has 53 numbers from which five are drawn at random. Each number can only be drawn once. What is the probability of your lottery ticket matching all five numbers in any order?

Know

1. The lottery has [53] possible numbers that can be drawn.

2. Each number can be drawn [1] time(s).

3. A total of [5] numbers will be drawn.

Need

4. To solve the problem I need to find:
the theoretical probability of the numbers on a lottery ticket matching the
numbers drawn in any order

Plan

5. Because order does not matter, the size of the sample space is a [combination]

6. What is the sample space?
all combinations of 53 numbers chosen 5 at a time

7. What is the size of the sample space? $_{53}C_5 = 2,869,685$

8. How many of the events in the sample space represent your ticket? 1

9. What is the probability of your lottery ticket matching all five numbers in any order? $\frac{1}{2,869,685} \approx 0.00000035$

Student Companion/All-in-One Resources/Online
Standardized Test Prep

11-2 Standardized Test Prep
Probability

Gridded Response

For Exercises 1–3, find each theoretical probability based on one roll of two number cubes. Enter each answer in the grid as a whole percent.

1. P(sum 9)   2. P(one even, one odd)

3. P(sum > 12)

For Exercises 4–5, find each theoretical probability based on one marble drawn at random from a bag of 14 red marbles, 10 pink marbles, 18 blue marbles, and 6 gold marbles. Enter each answer in the grid as a fraction in simplest form.

4. P(not pink)   5. P(blue or gold)

Answers

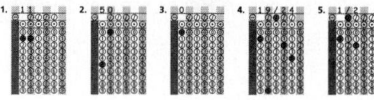

All-in-One Resources/Online
Enrichment

11-2 Enrichment
Probability

Biologists use a Punnett Square to predict the gene combinations that are possible for an offspring when the genes of the parents are known. Each parent organism carries two genes, or alleles, for a particular trait. For example, a parent might have the genotype *Bb* for dimples. A capital *B* represents the dominant trait, which is having dimples. A lower case *b* represents the recessive trait, which is not having dimples.

1. Both parents contribute one allele to their offspring. For example, if both parents have the genotype *Bb*, an offspring could inherit the genotype of *BB* with each parent contributing one dominant *B* allele. What are the other possible combinations? *Bb, bB, bb*

2. This information can be displayed in a Punnett Square. Each side of the square represents the genotype of one parent. The Punnett Square for the offspring of the parents who both have the genotype *Bb* is shown at the right. If the dominant allele is present it will be the trait that appears. What is the probability that this offspring will not have dimples? ¼

3. Create a Punnett Square to show the possible gene combinations for the offspring if one parent has the genotype *bb* and the other has the genotype *BB*.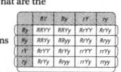

4. What is the probability that the offspring of parents with *Bb* and *BB* will have dimples? 1

5. You can show more complicated crosses when you consider two or more genes that are independent of each other. For example, pea pods can either be round (*R*) or wrinkled (*r*), yellow (*Y*) or green (*y*). What are the possible combinations of shape and color?
RY, Ry, rY, ry

6. Create a Punnett Square to show the possible gene combinations for the pea pods.

7. What is the probability that a pea pod with both parents *RrYy* will be round and yellow? In other words, what is the probability that there is an *R* and a *Y* present? 9/16

8. What is the probability that a pea pod with both parents *RrYy* will be wrinkled and yellow? 3/16

9. What is the probability that a pea pod with both parents *RrYy* will be wrinkled and green? 1/16

Online Teacher Resource Center
Activities, Games, and Puzzles

11-2 Activity: Colors and Probability
Probability

This activity is best done in groups of two to three students.

Materials
A small container of colored plastic chips Set up a container with no one color less than 1/20 of the total.

Special Instruction
Do not look inside the container until Part 1 has been completed.

Part 1: Experimental Probability
- Select one member of the group to record the colors drawn.
- Thoroughly mix the chips.
- Draw one chip and record its color.
- Replace the chip and thoroughly mix the chips.
- Repeat 50 times.
- Record your results in the space below.
- Use your results to calculate the experimental probabilities of drawing each color.

Results: Check students' work.

Experimental Probabilities: Check students' work.

Part 2: Theoretical Probability
- Examine the contents of the container and record the number of each color below.
- Calculate the theoretical probabilities of drawing each color.

Results: Check students' work.

Theoretical Probabilities: Check students' work.

Part 3: Compare/Contrast
- Use a separate sheet of paper to write a paragraph comparing and contrasting your results from Parts 1 and 2. Was there any difference in your results? Explain. Which type of probability might be more useful? When? What are the advantages and disadvantages of calculating these different types of probabilities? Check students' work.

1 Interactive Learning

Solve It!

PURPOSE To use counting principles to find probabilities
PROCESS Students may
- make lists to determine the sample spaces.
- find individual probabilities and make predictions about which score is likely.

FACILITATE

Q Can you add the points to find the total number of turns? Why or why not? **[No; some turns do not result in points, so if you only count points, you will undercount the number of turns.]**

ANSWER See Solve It in Answers on next page.
CONNECT THE MATH Students use probability to determine the number of trials and the most likely event in the Solve It. In this lesson, students find probabilities of multiple events that may or may not have an effect on each other.

2 Guided Instruction

Problem 1

Q Consider the sample space from which the first card is chosen. How is the sample space different when choosing the second card? **[The first card's sample space is 52. The second card's sample space is 51.]**

Got It?

Q Does the sample space change for each coin selected? Explain. **[No; since the coin is replaced, the sample space remains the same.]**

Objectives To find the probability of the event A and B
To find the probability of the event A or B

Getting Ready!

You and your friend take turns rolling two standard number cubes. If you roll a sum that is either odd or a prime number, you score a point. If your friend rolls a sum that is both odd and a prime number, she scores a point. Which score is likely yours? About how many turns have each of you taken? Explain.

An integer is prime if it is greater than 1 and has only itself and 1 as positive integer factors.

You can find the probabilities of multiple events occurring by using the probabilities of the individual events.

Focus Question How do you find the probability of multiple events?

Before you can find the probability of two events occurring together, you have to decide whether one event occurring affects the other event. When the occurrence of one event affects how a second event can occur, the events are **dependent events**. Otherwise, the events are **independent events**.

Lesson Vocabulary
- dependent events
- independent events
- mutually exclusive events

Problem 1 Classifying Events

Is each pair of events dependent or independent?

A Roll a number cube. Then spin a spinner.

The two events do not affect each other. They are independent.

B Pick one flash card, then another from a stack of 30 flash cards.

Picking the first card affects the possible outcomes of picking the second card. The events are dependent.

Think
What must you ask yourself?
Does the first event have an effect on the outcome of the second event?

 Got It? 1. You select a coin at random from your pocket. You replace the coin and select again. Are your selections independent events? Explain.

704 Chapter 11 Probability and Statistics

BIG idea Probability

UbD

ESSENTIAL UNDERSTANDING

To find the probability of two events occurring together, it is necessary to determine whether the occurrence of one event affects the probability that the other event will occur.

Math Background

If the occurrence of one event affects the probability that another event will occur, then the events are *dependent*. Otherwise, they are *independent*.

EXAMPLES OF INDEPENDENT EVENTS
- choosing one object each out of two different containers
- choosing an object from a container, replacing it, and then choosing another object

EXAMPLES OF DEPENDENT EVENTS
- choosing two objects out of one container
- choosing an object and then choosing a second object without replacing the first

704 Chapter 11

For any two events A and B, the probability that either A or B occurs, P(A or B), is given by the equation
$P(A \text{ or } B) = P(A) + P(B) - P(A \text{ and } B)$.
This equation says to add the probability that A occurs with the probability that B occurs, and then subtract the probability that both A and B occur.

Support Student Learning

Use the **Algebra 2 Companion** to engage and support students during instruction. See Lesson Resources at the end of this lesson for details.

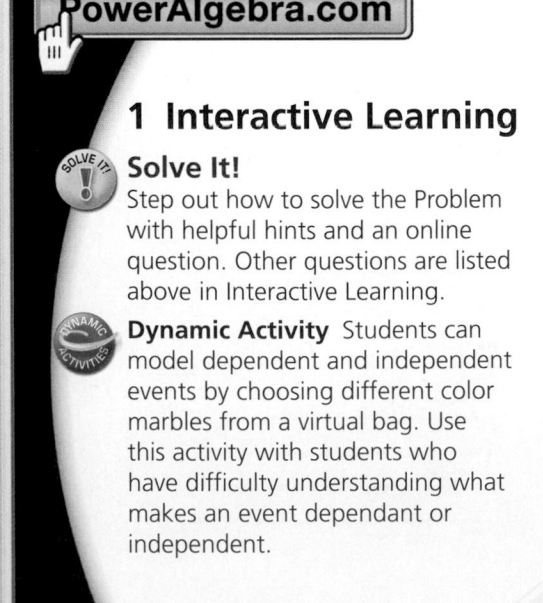

PowerAlgebra.com

1 Interactive Learning

Solve It!

Step out how to solve the Problem with helpful hints and an online question. Other questions are listed above in Interactive Learning.

Dynamic Activity Students can model dependent and independent events by choosing different color marbles from a virtual bag. Use this activity with students who have difficulty understanding what makes an event dependant or independent.

Multiply to find the probability that two independent events will both occur.

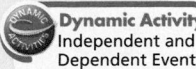
Dynamic Activity
Independent and Dependent Events

 Key Concept Probability of *A* and *B*

If *A* and *B* are independent events, then $P(A \text{ and } B) = P(A) \cdot P(B)$.

 Problem 2 Finding the Probability of Independent Events

Picnic At a picnic there are 10 diet drinks and 5 regular drinks. There are also 8 bags of fat-free chips and 12 bags of regular chips. If you grab a drink and a bag of chips without looking, what is the probability that you get a diet drink and fat-free chips?

Event *A* = picking a diet drink   Event *B* = picking fat-free chips

A and *B* are independent. Picking a drink has no effect on picking the chips.

Think
Is it important that you don't look?
Yes; probability is based on random events. It is not random if you look.

Hint
The probability that <u>both</u> events occur is always less than or equal to the probability of each individual event.

Use the formula.	$P(A \text{ and } B) = P(A) \cdot P(B)$
Write the probability of each event.	$= \dfrac{\text{number of diet drinks}}{\text{total number of drinks}} \cdot \dfrac{\text{number of bags of fat-free chips}}{\text{total number of bags of chips}}$
Substitute.	$= \dfrac{10}{15} \cdot \dfrac{8}{20}$
Simplify and use a calculator.	$= \dfrac{4}{15} \approx 0.267$

The probability that you get a diet drink and fat-free chips is about 0.267, or 26.7%.

 Got It? **2.** In Problem 2, what is the probability that you get a regular drink and regular chips?

Two events that cannot happen at the same time are **mutually exclusive events**. If *A* and *B* are mutually exclusive events, then $P(A \text{ and } B) = 0$.

 Problem 3 Mutually Exclusive Events

You roll a standard number cube. Are the events mutually exclusive? Explain.

A rolling a 2 and a 3

You cannot roll a 2 and 3 at the same time. These events are mutually exclusive.

B rolling an even number and a multiple of 3

The even numbers on a number cube are 2, 4, and 6. The multiples of 3 on a number cube are 3 and 6. There is one possible outcome that is both an even number *and* a multiple of 3, namely 6. These events are not mutually exclusive.

Think
Can you roll a 2 and a 3 at the same time?
No; only one number comes up on one roll of one number cube.

 Got It? **3.** You roll a standard number cube. Are the events mutually exclusive? Explain.
   a. rolling an even number and rolling a prime number
   b. rolling an even number and rolling a number less than 2

Take Note

Q How does finding the probability of two independent events use the Fundamental Counting Principle? **[Multiplying the numerators in the probability fractions uses it to find the number of ways that events A and B can happen. Multiplying the denominators uses it to find the entire sample space.]**

Problem 2

Q Will the probability be the same for the next person who chooses a drink and bag of chips? Explain. **[No; once a drink and bag of chips has been chosen, the sample space changes.]**

Got It?   EXTENSION

Q Can you find the probability for Got It 2 by taking 1 minus the probability in Problem 2? Explain. **[No; there are more possible outcomes.]**

Problem 3   VISUAL LEARNERS

Q How many mutually exclusive events can occur at one time? Explain. **[One; if one mutually exclusive event occurs, the other cannot occur.]**

Got It?

Have students create a Venn diagram to determine whether events are mutually exclusive. For example, the Venn diagram for 3a would be:

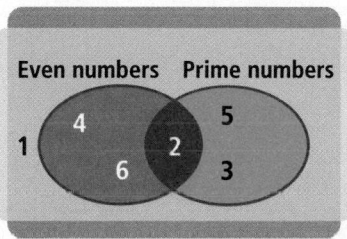

2 Guided Instruction

Each Problem is worked out and supported online.

Problem 1
Classifying Events

Problem 2
Finding the Probability of Independent Events
Animated

Problem 3
Mutually Exclusive Events

Problem 4
Finding Probability for Mutually Exclusive Events
Animated

Problem 5
Finding Probability
Animated

Support in Algebra 2 Companion
• Vocabulary
• Key Concepts
• Got It?

Answers

Solve It!
Your probability of winning is $\frac{19}{36}$. Your friend's is $\frac{14}{36}$. Your scores are likely those on the left. To estimate the number of turns *x*, solve the equations $18 = \frac{19}{36}x$ and $15 = \frac{14}{36}x$. You each had between 34 and 38 turns.

Got It?

1. Independent; the number of coins is the same after the coin is replaced.

2. 0.20, or 20%

3. a. Not mutually exclusive; 2 is a prime number and an even number.

    b. Mutually exclusive; there is no even number less than 2 in the roll of a number cube.

Take Note

Q Why does the equation
$P(A \text{ or } B) = P(A) + P(B) - P(A \text{ and } B)$ change if
the events are mutually exclusive? Explain. **[The
events cannot happen at the same time, so
$P(A \text{ and } B) = 0.$]**

Problem 4

Q Would the answer be different if students were
allowed to take more than one foreign language?
Explain. **[Yes; the events would not be mutually
exclusive. You would subtract the probability
that a student was enrolled in both Spanish and
French.]**

Q Is it possible for 50% of the students at the school
to be enrolled in Latin? Explain. **[No; because
students are limited to one foreign language, the
sum of the probabilities cannot exceed 1.]**

Got It?

Q What is the probability that a student is not taking
Spanish, French, or Mandarin Chinese? Explain
your reasoning. **[Students are either taking
one of these languages or they are not. These
are all possible events, so P(not taking these
languages) = 1 − 0.61 = 0.39 = 39%.]**

To find the probability of either event A or event B occurring, you need to determine
whether events A and B are mutually exclusive.

 take note

Key Concept Probability of A or B

$P(A \text{ or } B) = P(A) + P(B) - P(A \text{ and } B)$

If A and B are mutually exclusive events, then $P(A \text{ or } B) = P(A) + P(B)$.

Problem 4 Finding Probability for Mutually Exclusive Events

Languages At your high school, a student can take one foreign language each term.
About 37% of the students take Spanish. About 15% of the students take French.
What is the probability that a student chosen at random is taking Spanish or French?

Know	Need	Plan
• The percentages of students taking Spanish or French	The probability that a student is taking Spanish or French	Use the correct formula for $P(A \text{ or } B)$.
• Students can take one foreign language at a time.		

One foreign language each term means a student cannot take both Spanish and French.
The events are mutually exclusive.

$P(A \text{ or } B) = P(A) + P(B)$ for mutually exclusive events.

$P(\text{Spanish or French}) = P(\text{Spanish}) + P(\text{French})$

Substitute. $\approx 0.37 + 0.15$

Simplify. $= 0.52$

The probability that a student chosen at random is taking Spanish or French is
about 0.52, or about 52%.

Hint
Remember that 37%
can be written as a
decimal, 0.37, or as a
fraction, $\frac{37}{100}$.

✓ **Got It? 4. a.** In Problem 4, about 9% of the students take Mandarin Chinese. What
is the probability that a student chosen at random is taking Spanish,
French, or Mandarin Chinese?
b. Reasoning Without knowing the number of students in the school
in Problem 4, can you determine which language most students
take? Explain.

Additional Problems

1. Is each pair of events
dependent or independent?
  a. Flip a coin. Then roll a
  number cube.
  b. Choose a marble from
  a bag. Keep the marble,
  and then choose another
  marble from the same
  bag.
ANSWERS
a. independent
b. dependent

2. What is the probability of
rolling a 6 on a fair number
cube and flipping a coin and
getting tails?
ANSWER about 8.3%

3. You select one card from
a standard 52-card deck.

Are the events mutually
exclusive? Explain.
  a. choosing a red card and
  an even numbered card
  b. choosing a red card and a
  black card
ANSWERS
a. not mutually exclusive
  because a card can be red
  and an even number at
  the same time
b. mutually exclusive because
  the card cannot be red
  and black at the same
  time

4. Students choose one elective
each school year. About 18%
chose woodworking and
about 38% chose music.
What is the probability that

a student chosen at random
has selected woodworking or
music as an elective?
ANSWER 56%

5. The numbers 1 through 10
are written on index cards
and placed in a box. What
is the probability that a card
chosen at random has a
number that is greater than 7
or that it is even?
A. 30%
B. 50%
C. 60%
D. 80%
ANSWER C

Answers

Got It? (continued)
  4. a. 0.61, or 61%
    b. Yes; the percentage
    of students tells which
    language is chosen by
    more students.

When events *A* and *B* are *not* mutually exclusive, *P(A)* and *P(B)* may have common outcomes. You need to subtract the probability of these common outcomes to find *P(A or B)*.

Multiple Choice Suppose you reach into the dish and select a token at random. What is the probability that the token is round or green?

(A) $\frac{2}{9}$ (B) $\frac{3}{9}$ (C) $\frac{6}{9}$ (D) $\frac{8}{9}$

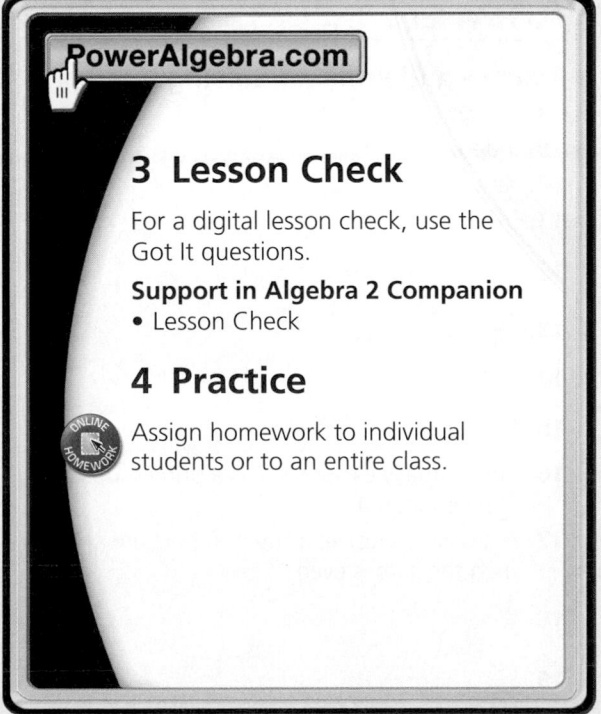

These events are not mutually exclusive.
Use the formula $P(A \text{ or } B) = P(A) + P(B) - P(A \text{ and } B)$.

Think
Are the events mutually exclusive? No; it is possible to have a round *and* green token.

Write the formula. $P(\text{round or green})$
$= P(\text{round}) + P(\text{green}) - P(\text{round and green})$

Determine the probability for each type of token and substitute.

5 round tokens

3 green tokens

2 round and green tokens

$= \frac{5}{9} + \frac{3}{9} - \frac{2}{9}$

9 tokens in all

Simplify. $= \frac{6}{9}$

Hint
The probability that *either* event occurs is always greater than or equal to the probability of each individual event.

The probability of selecting a round or green token is $\frac{6}{9}$, or $\frac{2}{3}$. The correct answer is C.

✓ Got It? 5. Suppose you select a token at random from the dish above. What is each probability?
  a. the token is square or red   **b.** the token is green or square

Focus Question How do you find the probability of multiple events?
Answer If *A* and *B* are independent events, then $P(A \text{ and } B) = P(A) \cdot P(B)$ and $P(A \text{ or } B) = P(A) + P(B) - P(A \text{ and } B)$.

✓ Lesson Check

Do you know HOW?

A and *B* are independent events. Find *P(A and B)*.

1. $P(A) = \frac{1}{6}, P(B) = \frac{2}{5}$ **2.** $P(A) = \frac{9}{20}, P(B) = \frac{3}{4}$

C and *D* are mutually exclusive events. Find *P(C or D)*.

3. $P(C) = \frac{2}{5}, P(D) = \frac{3}{5}$ **4.** $P(C) = \frac{1}{2}, P(D) = \frac{3}{8}$

5. Events *A* and *B* are not mutually exclusive. If $P(A) = \frac{1}{2}$, $P(B) = \frac{1}{4}$, and $P(A \text{ and } B) = \frac{1}{8}$, find $P(A \text{ or } B)$.

Do you UNDERSTAND?

6. Vocabulary Explain the difference between independent events and mutually exclusive events.

7. Error Analysis The weather forecast for the weekend is a 30% chance of rain on Saturday and a 70% chance of rain on Sunday. Your friend says that means there is a 100% chance of rain this weekend. What error did your friend make?

8. Open-Ended Describe two events that are mutually exclusive.

---

5. a. $\frac{5}{9}$

   b. $\frac{5}{9}$

Lesson Check

1. $\frac{1}{15}$, or $6.\overline{6}\%$

2. $\frac{27}{80}$, or 33.75%

3. 1, or 100%

4. $\frac{7}{8}$, or 87.5%

5. $\frac{5}{8}$, or 62.5%

6. Events A and B are independent if the outcomes of A do not affect the outcomes of B. The events are mutually exclusive if A and B cannot occur at the same time. For independent events, $P(A \text{ and } B) = P(A) \cdot P(B)$. For mutually exclusive events, $P(A \text{ and } B) = 0$. For any events, $P(A \text{ or } B) = P(A) + P(B) - P(A \text{ and } B)$.

7. Since these are not mutually exclusive events, $P(A \text{ and } B) \neq 0$. The student should have calculated $P(A \text{ or } B) = P(A) + P(B) - P(A \text{ and } B)$, which is 0.79, or 79%.

8. Check students' work.

Problem 5   VISUAL LEARNERS

Q Give an example of an event using the same tokens that is mutually exclusive. [Sample: selecting a token that is yellow or a square]

Got It?

Q Are the events in 5a mutually exclusive? Explain. [No; a token can be both square and red.]

3 Lesson Check

Do you know HOW?   ERROR INTERVENTION
• If students have difficulty solving Exercises 1–2, remind them that the probability of independent events can be multiplied.
• For Exercises 3–4, students might have difficulty choosing between the expressions for *P(A or B)*. Remind them that $P(A \text{ and } B) = 0$ for mutually exclusive events.

Do you UNDERSTAND?
• If students have trouble with Exercise 6, remind them that mutually exclusive events cannot happen at the same time. Have students apply this fact to the definition of independent events to help them answer the question.

Close

Q In what situation do you multiply probabilities? In what situation do you add them? Explain. [Multiply if finding *P(A and B)* and they are independent events. Add if finding *P(A or B)* and they are mutually exclusive.]

Q What is the difference between independent and dependent events? [Events are dependent if one event affects the probability that another event occurs. Otherwise, they are independent.]

PowerAlgebra.com

3 Lesson Check
For a digital lesson check, use the Got It questions.

Support in Algebra 2 Companion
• Lesson Check

4 Practice
Assign homework to individual students or to an entire class.

4 Practice

ASSIGNMENT GUIDE

Basic: 9–26, 31

Average: 9–15, 16–26 even, 27–35

Standardized Test Prep: 37–42

Mixed Review: 43–54

Reasoning exercises have blue headings.

Applications exercises have red headings.

EXERCISE 37: Use the Think About a Plan worksheet in the **Student Companion** (also available in the Teaching Resources in print and online) to further support students' development in becoming independent learners.

HOMEWORK QUICK CHECK

To check students' understanding of key skills and concepts, go over Exercises 14, 16, 20, 26, and 31.

Practice and Problem-Solving Exercises

Ⓐ Practice

Classify each pair of events as *dependent* or *independent*.
◀ See Problem 1.

9. A month is selected at random; a number from 1 to 30 is selected at random.

10. A month is selected at random; a day of that month is selected at random.

11. A letter of the alphabet is selected at random; one of the remaining letters is selected at random.

Q and R are independent events. Find $P(Q$ and $R)$.
◀ See Problem 2.

Guided Practice

To start, write the formula for the probability of independent events.

12. $P(Q) = \frac{1}{4}, P(R) = \frac{2}{3}$
$$P(Q \text{ and } R) = P(Q) \cdot P(R)$$

13. $P(Q) = \frac{12}{17}, P(R) = \frac{3}{8}$

14. $P(Q) = 0.6, P(R) = 0.9$

15. **Reading** Suppose you have five books in your book bag. Three are novels, one is a biography, and one is a poetry book. Today you grab one book out of your bag without looking, and return it later. Tomorrow you do the same thing. What is the probability that you grab a novel both days?

Two fair number cubes are rolled. State whether the events are mutually exclusive. Explain your reasoning.
◀ See Problem 3.

16. The sum is a prime number; the sum is less than 4.

17. The numbers are equal; the sum is odd.

S and T are mutually exclusive events. Find $P(S$ or $T)$.
◀ See Problem 4.

Guided Practice

To start, write the formula for the probability of mutually exclusive events.

18. $P(S) = \frac{5}{8}, P(T) = \frac{1}{8}$
$$P(S \text{ or } T) = P(S) + P(T)$$

19. $P(S) = \frac{3}{5}, P(T) = \frac{1}{3}$

20. $P(S) = 12\%, P(T) = 27\%$

21. **Population** About 30% of the U.S. population is under 20 years old. About 17% of the population is over 60. What is the probability that a person chosen at random is under 20 or over 60?

Answers

Practice and Problem-Solving Exercises

9. independent

10. dependent

11. dependent

12. $\frac{1}{6}$

13. $\frac{9}{34}$

14. 0.54

15. $\frac{2}{7}$

16. not mutually exclusive; 2 is a prime number and less than 4

17. mutually exclusive; if the numbers are equal, then the sum is even

18. $\frac{3}{4}$

19. $\frac{14}{15}$

20. 39%

21. 47%

A standard number cube is tossed. Find each probability.  See Problem 5.

22. $P(3 \text{ or odd})$

23. $P(\text{even or less than } 4)$

24. $P(\text{odd or greater than } 2)$

25. $P(\text{odd or prime})$

26. Think About a Plan A multiple-choice test has four choices for each answer. Suppose you make a random guess on three of the ten test questions. What is the probability that you will answer all three correctly?
- Is each guess a dependent event or an independent event?
- What is the probability that a random guess on one question will yield the correct answer?

27. Suppose a number from 1 to 100 is selected at random. What is the probability that a multiple of 4 or 5 is chosen?

Statistics The graph at the right shows the types of jobs held by people in the U.S. Find each probability.

28. A person is in a service occupation.

29. A person is in service or sales and office.

30. A person is neither in service nor in sales and office.

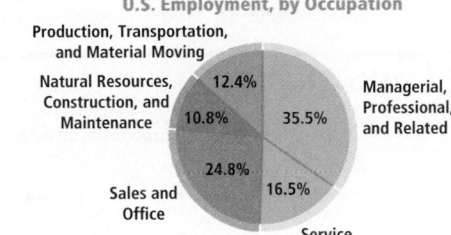

U.S. Employment, by Occupation

Production, Transportation, and Material Moving 12.4%

Natural Resources, Construction, and Maintenance 10.8%

Managerial, Professional, and Related 35.5%

Sales and Office 24.8%

Service 16.5%

Source: U.S. Census Bureau

A jar contains four blue marbles and two red marbles. Suppose you choose a marble at random, and do not replace it. Then you choose a second marble. Find the probability of each event.

31. You select a blue marble and then a red marble.

32. You select a red marble and then a blue marble.

33. One of the marbles you select is blue and the other is red.

34. Both of the marbles you select are red.

For each set of probabilities, determine if the events A and B are mutually exclusive.

35. $P(A) = \frac{1}{2}$, $P(B) = \frac{1}{3}$, $P(A \text{ or } B) = \frac{2}{3}$

36. $P(A) = \frac{1}{6}$, $P(B) = \frac{3}{8}$, $P(A \text{ or } B) = \frac{13}{24}$

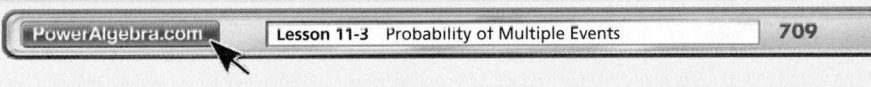

22. $\frac{1}{2}$

23. $\frac{5}{6}$

24. $\frac{5}{6}$

25. $\frac{2}{3}$

26. $\frac{1}{64}$

27. $\frac{2}{5}$

28. 14.5%

29. 38%

30. 62%

31. $\frac{4}{15}$

32. $\frac{4}{15}$

33. $\frac{8}{15}$

34. $\frac{1}{15}$

35. not mutually exclusive

36. mutually exclusive

Answers

Standardized Test Prep

37. $\frac{8}{11}$

38. $\frac{1}{3}$

39. 8

40. $\frac{1}{3}$

41. 5

42. 6720

Mixed Review

43. $\frac{1}{6}$

44. $\frac{1}{2}$

45. $\frac{1}{2}$

46. $\frac{3}{7}$

47. $-\frac{3}{2}$, 2

48. $\frac{1}{6}$

49. 500

50. 500,000

51. ± 100

52. $\frac{1}{16}$

53. $\frac{1}{16}$

54. $\frac{3}{16}$

 SAT/ACT

37. A bag contains 5 red marbles, 1 blue marble, 3 yellow marbles, and 2 green marbles. One marble is drawn from the bag. What is the probability that the marble is red or yellow?

38. What is the theoretical probability of getting a 1 or 6 when rolling a standard number cube?

39. The first term of an arithmetic series is 123. The common difference is 12 and the sum 1320. How many terms are in the series?

40. What is the slope of the graph of the equation $6x - 18y = -24$?

41. What is the radius of the circle with equation $x^2 - 4x + y^2 - 21 = 0$?

42. How many five-letter permutations can you form from the letters of the word COMPUTER?

Mixed Review

Find the theoretical probability of each event when rolling a standard number cube.   ◆ See Lesson 11-2.

43. $P(5)$ | **44.** $P(\text{an even number})$ | **45.** $P(\text{less than 4})$

Solve each equation. Check each solution.   ◆ See Lesson 8-6.

46. $\frac{1}{2} - x = \frac{x}{6}$ | **47.** $\frac{2}{2x-1} = \frac{x}{3}$ | **48.** $\frac{3}{2x} - \frac{2}{3x} = 5$

Solve each equation. Check your answers.   ◆ See Lesson 7-5.

49. $\log 2x = 3$ | **50.** $\log x + \log 2 = 6$ | **51.** $\log x^2 + 1 = 5$

Get Ready! To prepare for Lesson 11-4, do Exercises 52–54.

A spinner has four equal sections that are red, blue, green, and yellow. Find each probability for two spins.   ◆ See Lesson 11-3.

52. $P(\text{blue, then blue})$ | **53.** $P(\text{red, then yellow})$ | **54.** $P(\text{not yellow, then green})$

Additional Instructional Support

Algebra 2 Companion

Students can use the **Algebra 2 Companion** worktext (4 pages) as you teach the lesson. Use the Companion to support

• New Vocabulary

• Key Concepts

• Got It for each Problem

• Lesson Check

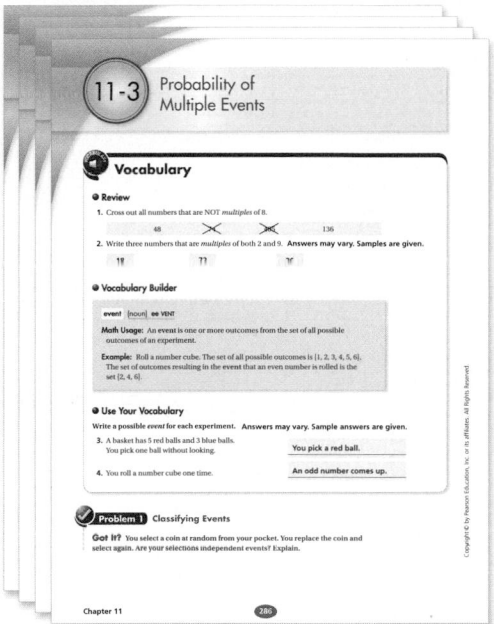

ELL Support

Focus on Language Have students make a vocabulary page for the words *independent* and *dependent*. Direct students to underline the prefix *in-*. Then say: *The prefix in- sometimes represents the opposite of the root word. The opposite of dependent is independent.*

Have students add examples of other words that follow this rule. Examples include *incomplete, incorrect, indirect,* and *informal.*

Explore the meaning of *dependent* by writing sentences using this word. For example: The score on his test was dependent on how much he studied. Her paycheck was dependent on the hours she worked.

5 Assess & Remediate

Lesson Quiz

1. You pick two marbles from a bag and record their colors. How can you make your selections independent events? Dependent events?

2. Suppose you toss a coin four times. What is the probability that you get heads on the second, third, and fourth tosses?

3. **Do you UNDERSTAND?** The numbers 20 through 30 are written on cards and placed in a box. Explain whether the events of choosing a number that is a multiple of 3 or choosing a number that is a multiple of 4 are mutually exclusive.

4. Students choose one area of science for a project. About 26% choose biology. About 18% choose botany. What is the probability that a student chosen at random has selected a project in the field of biology or botany?

5. What is the probability of getting an even sum or a sum less than 7 on one roll of two fair number cubes?

ANSWERS TO LESSON QUIZ

1. Replace marbles after picking them; do not replace marbles.

2. 12.5%

3. Not mutually exclusive because 24 is a multiple of 3 and 4.

4. 44%

5. $66.\overline{6}\%$

PRESCRIPTION FOR REMEDIATION

Use the student work on the Lesson Quiz to prescribe a differentiated review assignment:

Points	Differentiated Remediation
0–2	Intervention
3–4	On-level
5	Extension

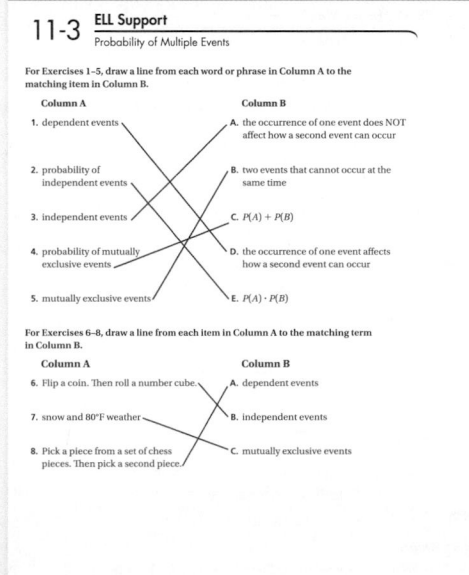

PowerAlgebra.com

5 Assess & Remediate

Assign the Lesson Quiz. Appropriate intervention, practice, or enrichment is automatically generated based on student performance.

Intervention

• **Reteaching** (2 pages) Provides reteaching and practice exercises for the key lesson concepts. Use with struggling students or absent students.

• **English Language Learner Support** Helps students develop and reinforce mathematical vocabulary and key concepts.

All-in-One Resources/Online
Reteaching

11-3 Reteaching
Probability of Multiple Events

• If Event *A* can change the way Event *B* occurs, then the events are *dependent*.
• If Event *A* cannot change the way Event *B* occurs, then the events are *independent*.

If Event *A* and Event *B* are independent, the probability of Event *A* and Event *B* both occurring is the product of their individual probabilities.

$$P(A \text{ and } B) = P(A) \cdot P(B)$$

Problem

A pet store has two cages of mice. The first cage has 10 white mice—4 females and 6 males. The second cage has 10 gray mice—6 females and 4 males. Suppose you randomly choose 1 mouse from each cage. What is the probability that you choose 2 female mice?

Step 1 Determine the events.
Event *A* is "you choose a white female mouse."
Event *B* is "you choose a gray female mouse."
You are looking for the probability of Event *A* and Event *B*.

Step 2 Decide if the events are independent.
Your choice of a white mouse does not affect your choice of a gray mouse. The events are independent.

Step 3 Use the formula.

$$P(\text{white female and gray female}) = P(\text{white female}) \cdot P(\text{gray female})$$
$$= \frac{4}{10} \cdot \frac{6}{10} = \frac{24}{100} = 0.24 = 24\%$$

The probability of choosing 2 female mice is 24%.

Exercises

Use the information from the problem above. You choose one mouse at random from each cage. Find each probability.

1. *P*(white male and gray male) **24%**
2. *P*(white mouse and gray male) **40%**
3. *P*(white male and gray female) **36%**
4. *P*(white male and white female) **0%**
5. *P*(white mouse and white mouse) **0%**
6. *P*(white female and gray male) **16%**

All-in-One Resources/Online
English Language Learner Support

11-3 ELL Support
Probability of Multiple Events

For Exercises 1–5, draw a line from each word or phrase in Column A to the matching item in Column B.

Column A	Column B
1. dependent events	a. the occurrence of one event does NOT affect how a second event can occur
2. probability of independent events	b. two events that cannot occur at the same time
3. independent events	c. $P(A) + P(B)$
4. probability of mutually exclusive events	d. the occurrence of one event affects how a second event can occur
5. mutually exclusive events	e. $P(A) \cdot P(B)$

For Exercises 6–8, draw a line from each item in Column A to the matching term in Column B.

Column A	Column B
6. Flip a coin. Then roll a number cube.	A. dependent events
7. snow and 80°F weather	B. independent events
8. Pick a piece from a set of chess pieces. Then pick a second piece.	C. mutually exclusive events

Differentiated Remediation *continued*

On-Level

- **Practice** (2 pages) Provides extra practice for each lesson. For more challenging practice exercises, use the Form G Practice pages found in the All-in-One Teaching Resources and online.

- **Think About a Plan** Helps students develop specific problem-solving skills and strategies by providing scaffolded guiding questions.

- **Standardized Test Prep** Focuses on all major exercises, all major question types, and helps students prepare for the high-stakes assessments.

Extension

- **Enrichment** Provides students with interesting problems and activities that extend the concepts of the lesson.

- **Activities, Games, and Puzzles** Worksheets that can be used for concepts development, enrichment, and for fun!

Student Companion/ All-in-One Resources/Online
Practice page 1

11-3 Practice *Form K*
Probability of Multiple Events

Classify each pair of events as *dependent* or *independent*.

1. Roll a number cube. Then roll it again. **independent**
2. Pull a card from a deck of playing cards. Then pull a second card. **dependent**
3. Randomly choose a student from your class. Then choose another student. **dependent**
4. Flip a coin. Then spin a spinner. **independent**

Use the table shown below to answer the following questions.

Movie Collection	Video	DVD
Action	12	26
Comedy	14	8
Drama	4	16

5. You randomly pick a video and a DVD. What is the probability that you pick an action video and a comedy DVD? **about 6%**
6. Your friend randomly picks a video and a DVD. What is the probability that she picks a comedy video and an action DVD? **about 24%**
7. What is the probability of randomly picking a drama video and a comedy DVD? **about 2%**
8. **Writing** Explain the difference between independent events and dependent events.
   Answers may vary. Sample: Events are dependent when the occurrence of one event affects how a second event can occur. Events are independent when the occurrence of one event does not affect how the other event can occur.

Student Companion/ All-in-One Resources/Online
Think About a Plan

11-3 Think About a Plan
Probability of Multiple Events

Marbles A jar contains four blue marbles and two red marbles. Suppose you choose a marble at random, and do not replace it. Then you choose a second marble. Find the probability that you select a blue marble and then a red marble.

Understanding the Problem
1. How many marbles are blue? **4**
2. How many marbles are red? **2**
3. How many marbles are in the jar? **6**
4. What is the problem asking you to determine?
   the probability that you select a blue marble and then a red marble

Planning the Solution
5. What is the probability that you choose a blue marble from the jar? $\frac{4}{6} = \frac{2}{3}$
6. Assuming you choose a blue marble and do not replace it, how many marbles of each color remain in the jar? What is the total number of marbles in the jar?
   3 blue marbles and 2 red marbles; 5 marbles
7. What is the probability that you now choose a red marble from the jar? $\frac{2}{5}$
8. How can you find the probability that you select a blue marble and then a red marble? **Answers may vary. Sample: The probability is the product of the probabilities for each event**

Getting an Answer
9. What is the probability that you select a blue marble and then a red marble? $\frac{2}{3} \cdot \frac{2}{5} = \frac{4}{15}$

Student Companion/ All-in-One Resources/Online
Practice page 2

11-3 Practice (continued) *Form K*
Probability of Multiple Events

Two fair number cubes are rolled. State whether the following events are mutually exclusive.

9. The sum is odd. The sum is less than 5. **not mutually exclusive**
10. The difference is 1. The sum is even. **mutually exclusive**
11. The sum is a multiple of 4. The sum is odd. **mutually exclusive**

Find the probability for the following mutually exclusive events.

12. Students can either participate in track and field or play baseball. About 13% of students participate in track and field. About 8% play baseball. What is the probability that a student chosen at random either participates in track and field or plays baseball? **about 21%**
13. About $\frac{1}{3}$ of a town's population has black hair. About $\frac{2}{7}$ of the population has blonde hair. What is the probability that a person chosen at random from this town will have either black hair or blonde hair? **about 49%**

Use the diagram at the right to answer the following questions.

14. Suppose you randomly select a shape from this circle. What is the probability that the shape is black or has five points? **70%**
15. What is the probability of randomly selecting a shape that is black or has four points? **80%**

Student Companion/ All-in-One Resources/Online
Standardized Test Prep

11-3 Standardized Test Prep
Probability of Multiple Events

Multiple Choice

For Exercises 1–4, choose the correct letter.

A store display shows two red shirts, one blue shirt, and three shirts with red and white stripes. The display also shows two pairs of blue jeans, one pair of white pants, and one pair of white shorts.

1. What is the probability of randomly selecting an item with white or red on it? D
   Ⓐ $\frac{1}{4}$ Ⓑ $\frac{3}{5}$ Ⓒ $\frac{1}{2}$ Ⓓ $\frac{7}{10}$

2. What is the probability of randomly selecting two items and getting a pair of blue jeans, putting them back in the display, and then randomly selecting a blue shirt? F
   Ⓕ $\frac{1}{50}$ Ⓖ $\frac{1}{45}$ Ⓗ $\frac{2}{10}$ Ⓘ $\frac{3}{10}$

3. What is the probability of randomly selecting a complete outfit (one shirt and one pair of jeans, pants, or shorts) on two picks? C
   Ⓐ $\frac{1}{24}$ Ⓑ $\frac{1}{5}$ Ⓒ $\frac{6}{25}$ Ⓓ $\frac{4}{15}$

4. What is the probability of selecting an item with red or blue on it? I
   Ⓕ $\frac{3}{20}$ Ⓖ $\frac{7}{10}$ Ⓗ $\frac{3}{5}$ Ⓘ $\frac{4}{5}$

Short Response

5. There is a 50% chance of thunderstorms on Monday, a 50% chance on Tuesday, and a 50% chance on Wednesday. Assume these are independent events. What is the probability that there will be thunderstorms on Monday, Tuesday, and Wednesday? Show your work.
   [2] P(M and T and W) = P(M) · P(T) · P(W)
   = 0.50 · 0.50 · 0.50
   = 0.125
   There is a 12.5% probability of thunderstorms on Monday, Tuesday, and Wednesday.
   [1] incorrect or incomplete work shown
   [0] incorrect answer and no work shown OR no answer given

All-in-One Resources/Online
Enrichment

11-3 Enrichment
Probability of Multiple Events

Tree Diagrams

Complex problems involving probability are often easier to visualize and solve using tree diagrams. For example, suppose that Alice, Bob, and Carol are running for president of the Math Club. Alice has a 0.45 probability of being elected, while Bob has 0.35 probability and Carol has a 0.2 probability of being elected. Sue and Ted are the candidates for vice president. If Alice becomes president, the probability is 0.7 that she will choose Sue as her vice president. If Bob becomes president, the probability that he will choose Sue is 0.4, while if Carol becomes president, the probability is 0.6 that she will choose Sue.

Examine the following tree diagram that represents the given information.

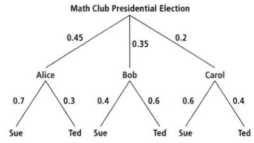

Math Club Presidential Election

The probability that Alice will be elected president and choose Sue as her vice president can be found by multiplying the probabilities found along the "branches" of the tree. Thus, the Alice-Sue combination has a probability of $0.45 \times 0.7 = 0.315$ of occurring.

1. What is the probability of the Bob-Sue combination? **0.14** of Carol-Sue? **0.12**

Use a tree diagram to compute the probabilities of each of the following events.

2. The probability that a random student at Elmville College is a freshman is 0.3; a sophomore, 0.25; and a junior or senior, 0.45. The probability that a freshman will major in engineering is 0.15; a sophomore, 0.2; and a junior or senior, 0.3. What is the probability that a random student at this college majors in engineering? **0.23**
3. The Adams' restaurant specializes in beef, chicken, and seafood. Of its customers, 32% order beef and 41% order chicken. Of those who order beef, 73% also order dessert. Of those who order chicken, 62% also order dessert. If 65% of the customers order dessert, what is the probability that someone who orders seafood will also order dessert? **about 0.60**

Online Teacher Resource Center
Activities, Games, and Puzzles

11-3 Game: The Probability Path
Probability of Multiple Events

Provide the host with the following questions and answers (shown in brackets).

What is the probability of the following?

1. rolling a 2 on your first turn and a 6 on your second turn [1/36]
2. rolling a 3 on your first turn and a 3 on your second turn [1/36]
3. rolling an even number on your first turn and a 2 on your second turn [1/12]
4. rolling a 1 on your first turn and a 3 or 5 on your second turn [1/18]
5. landing on a space with an even denominator [1/2]
6. landing on a space with an odd denominator [2/5]
7. landing on a $\frac{2}{9}$ or a space with an identical neighbor on each side [7/15]
8. landing on a $\frac{1}{3}$ or a space with an identical neighbor on each side [1/3]
9. from the $\frac{1}{12}$ in the middle, the next move landing on another $\frac{1}{12}$ [1/3]
10. moving "forward two spaces" after being on a $\frac{1}{4}$ [1/6]
11. landing on $\frac{1}{6}$ on your second move [1/12]
12. landing on $\frac{1}{3}$ on your second move [1/6]
13. landing on a $\frac{1}{4}$ or a $\frac{1}{2}$ [7/30]
14. landing on a $\frac{1}{3}$ or $\frac{1}{5}$ [2/15]
15. the finishing roll being a 3 [0]
16. landing on $\frac{1}{12}$ on your second move [1/9]
17. landing on a $\frac{1}{6}$ or "forward two spaces" [7/30]
18. landing on a $\frac{2}{5}$ or "back two spaces" [2/5]
19. landing on a space with an even denominator or an odd denominator [9/10]
20. landing on a space with an even denominator or requiring the piece to move two spaces [3/5]
21. landing on a space with an odd denominator or requiring the piece to move two spaces [1/2]
22. landing on a space with a 1 or a 2 in the numerator [9/10]
23. landing on a $\frac{1}{4}$ after being on a corner space and then landing on a $\frac{1}{12}$ [1/18]
24. landing on a "forward two spaces" after being on a $\frac{1}{4}$ and then landing on a $\frac{1}{6}$ on the next turn [1/18]
25. landing on a $\frac{1}{6}$ on your first two moves [1/36]
26. landing on $\frac{1}{3}$ on your last two moves [0]
27. landing on two $\frac{1}{5}$s in a row [0]
28. from the $\frac{1}{3}$ in the right corner landing on $\frac{1}{12}$ [1/2]
29. rolling a 4 and landing on a $\frac{1}{6}$ at some point in the game [1/10]
30. rolling a 3 and landing on a $\frac{1}{6}$ at some point in the game [1/6]

11-4 Conditional Probability

Objectives To find conditional probabilities
To use tables and tree diagrams to determine conditional probabilities

This sounds like a great idea for a television game show!

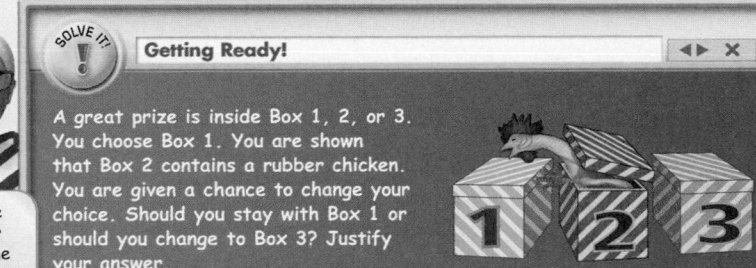

SOLVE IT!

Getting Ready!

A great prize is inside Box 1, 2, or 3. You choose Box 1. You are shown that Box 2 contains a rubber chicken. You are given a chance to change your choice. Should you stay with Box 1 or should you change to Box 3? Justify your answer.

Lesson Vocabulary
• conditional probability

The probability that an event, *B*, will occur given that another event, *A*, has already occurred is called a **conditional probability**. You can use conditional probability when two events are dependent.

Focus Question How do you find conditional probability?

You write the conditional probability of event *B*, given that event *A* occurs, as $P(B \mid A)$. You read $P(B \mid A)$ as "the probability of event *B*, given event *A*."

For example, suppose you select a tile from those shown and get a circle. You want to know the probability that the circle you have selected is orange.

You can describe the above as "the probability the tile is orange, given that it is a circle" and represent it as $P(\text{orange} \mid \text{circle})$. Of the 5 tiles that are circles, 2 are orange. So, $P(\text{orange} \mid \text{circle}) = \frac{2}{5}$.

11-4 Preparing to Teach

BIG idea Probability   **UbD**
ESSENTIAL UNDERSTANDING
A conditional probability is the probability that one event occurs, given that another event has occurred.

Math Background
Conditional probability is the probability that one event will occur given that another event has occurred. For two events *A* and *B*, the conditional probability that *B* will occur, given that *A* has occurred, is written $P(B|A)$.

Once it is known that an event *A* has occurred, the sample space is restricted to the subset of events that include *A*. For example, if you are rolling a number cube, then the original sample space is {1, 2, 3, 4, 5, 6}. If *A* is the event that an even number is rolled, and you know that

A occurs, then the new sample space is {2, 4, 6}. If *B* is the event that a 2 or 4 is rolled, then $P(B) = \frac{1}{3}$. However, $P(B|A) = \frac{2}{3}$.

Recall that if two events are independent, then the occurrence of one event does not affect the probability that the second event will occur. Thus, if *C* and *D* are independent events, then $P(D|C) = P(D)$.

Support Student Learning
Use the **Algebra 2 Companion** to engage and support students during instruction. See Lesson Resources at the end of this lesson for details.

Solve It!
PURPOSE To analyze a conditional probability situation
PROCESS Students may
• act out the situation.
• draw a branching tree diagram.

FACILITATE

Q What is the probability that you originally guessed the correct door? In this case, what wins the prize? **[$\frac{1}{3}$; staying with Box 1]**

Q What is the probability now that you did not guess the correct box? In this case, what wins the prize? **[$\frac{2}{3}$; switching boxes]**

Q How does the probability of winning by switching compare to the probability of winning by not switching? **[The probability of winning by switching is twice that of not switching.]**

ANSWER See Solve It in Answers on next page.
CONNECT THE MATH In the Solve It, students calculate conditional probability based on an initial choice. In the lesson, students will find conditional probability of situations using formulas and tree diagrams.

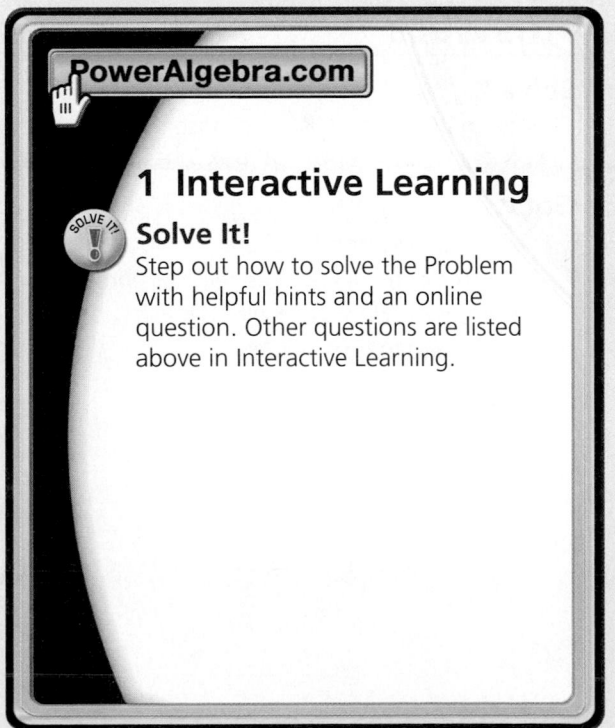

PowerAlgebra.com

1 Interactive Learning

SOLVE IT!

Solve It!
Step out how to solve the Problem with helpful hints and an online question. Other questions are listed above in Interactive Learning.

2 Guided Instruction

Problem 1

> **Q** Multiply the probabilities of selecting a female and selecting a graduate student. Is the product the same as the probability in 1A? Explain. **[No; it is much lower, about 0.11. Selecting a grad student is a given in 1A, so that part of the probability is 100%.]**
>
> **Q** In 1B, is 0.57 a reasonable answer? Explain. **[Yes; the number of females is greater than the number of males in every row of the table, so the probability of picking a female must be greater than 50%.]**

Got It?

> **Q** How would you translate 1a into a question using only words? **[What is the probability that a student attends a four-year college, given that the student is male?]**

Problem 2

> **Q** Based on the answer, how would you find the probability that a sample of recycled waste is *not* paper without calculating? **[The probability of recycled waste that is not paper is all the recycled waste minus the probability of recycled waste that is paper: 100% − 57% = 43%.]**

Got It?

> **Q** Does the question "What is the probability that a sample of waste is recycled glass?" differ from the question in 2b? Explain. **[Yes; in 2b, it is a given that the sample is recycled.]**

Tables and tree diagrams can help you find conditional probabilities.

 Problem 1 Finding Conditional Probability

Education The table shows students by gender at two- and four-year colleges, and graduate schools, in 2005. You pick a student at random.

Student Genders

	Males (in thousands)	Females (in thousands)
Two-year colleges	1866	2462
Four-year colleges	4324	5517
Graduate schools	1349	1954

SOURCE: U.S. Census Bureau

A What is $P(\text{female} \mid \text{graduate school})$?

Think
What's the condition?
The student is at a graduate school.

The condition that the person selected is at graduate school limits the sample space. There are $1349 + 1954 = 3303$ thousand students at graduate schools. Of those 3303 thousand students, 1954 thousand are female.

$$P(\text{female} \mid \text{graduate school}) = \frac{1954}{3303} \approx 0.59$$

B What is $P(\text{female})$?

$$P(F) = \frac{\text{total number of females}}{\text{total number of students}} = \frac{2462 + 5517 + 1954}{1866 + 2462 + 4324 + 5517 + 1349 + 1954}$$

$$= \frac{9933}{17,472} \approx 0.57$$

Got It? **1. a.** In Problem 1, what is $P(\text{four-year} \mid \text{male})$?
  b. Reasoning Without calculating, given a student is enrolled in a four-year college is it more likely for the student to be male or female? Explain.

Problem 2 Conditional Probability in Statistics

Multiple Choice Americans recycle increasing amounts through municipal waste collection. The table shows the collection data for 2007. What is the probability that a sample of recycled waste is paper?

Ⓐ 16% Ⓒ 33%
Ⓑ 28% Ⓓ 57%

Think
What's the condition?
The waste sample has to be recycled waste.

The given condition is that the waste is *recycled*. A favorable outcome is that the recycled waste is paper.

$$P(\text{paper} \mid \text{recycled}) = \frac{45.2}{45.2 + 7.2 + 3.2 + 2.1 + 21.7}$$

$$\approx 0.57$$

Municipal Waste Collected (millions of tons)

Material	Recycled	Not Recycled
Paper	45.2	37.8
Metal	7.2	13.6
Glass	3.2	10.4
Plastic	2.1	28.6
Other	21.7	46.3

SOURCE: U.S. Environmental Protection Agency

The probability that the recycled waste is paper is about 57%. The correct answer is D.

Got It? **2. a.** What is the probability that a sample of recycled waste is plastic?
  b. What is the probability that a sample of recycled waste is glass?

Answers

Solve It!

Change to box 3; there is a $\frac{1}{3}$ chance that box 1 has the prize and a $\frac{2}{3}$ chance that box 3 has the prize.

Got It?

1. a. ≈ 0.57355 or $\approx 57.355\%$
  b. Female; there are more females enrolled.

2. a. ≈ 0.026448 or $\approx 2.64\%$
  b. ≈ 0.040302 or $\approx 4.03\%$

PowerAlgebra.com

2 Guided Instruction

Each Problem is worked out and supported online.

Problem 1
Finding Conditional Probability
Animated

Problem 2
Conditional Probability in Statistics

Problem 3
Using the Conditional Probability Formula
Animated

Problem 4
Using a Tree Diagram
Animated

Support in Algebra 2 Companion
• Vocabulary
• Key Concepts
• Got It?

You can also use a formula to find conditional probability.

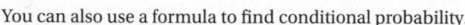

take note | Key Concept Conditional Probability

For any two events A and B with $P(A) \neq 0$,

$$P(B \mid A) = \frac{P(A \text{ and } B)}{P(A)}$$

Using the formula above, you can calculate a conditional probability from other probabilities.

Problem 3 Using the Conditional Probability Formula

Market Research A utility company asked 50 of its customers whether they pay their bills online or by mail. What is the probability that a customer pays the bill online, given that the customer is male?

Bill Payment

	Online	By Mail
Male	12	8
Female	24	6

Think

To use the formula, you need P(male and online) and P(male).

Write the formula for conditional probability.

Substitute and simplify.

Write the answer in words.

Write

$P(\text{male and online}) = \frac{12}{50}$ $P(\text{male}) = \frac{20}{50}$

$P(\text{online} \mid \text{male}) = \frac{P(\text{male and online})}{P(\text{male})}$

$= \frac{\frac{12}{50}}{\frac{20}{50}}$

$= \frac{12}{20} = \frac{3}{5} = 0.6$

The probability that a customer pays online, given that the customer is male, is 0.6, or 60%.

✔ **Got It?** 3. Researchers asked shampoo users whether they apply shampoo directly to the head, or indirectly using a hand. What is the probability that a respondent applies shampoo directly to the head, given that the respondent is female?

Applying Shampoo

	Directly Onto Head	Into Hand First
Male	2	18
Female	6	24

Take Note

Q In the formula for conditional probability, is A or B the given condition? **[A is the given condition.]**

Q Why must $P(A)$ not equal zero? **[Division by zero is not allowed.]**

Problem 3

Another approach to Problem 3 is to recognize that once it is given that the costumer is male, the sample space is restricted to the first row of the table. To find the size of the new sample space, add the entries in the first column: $12 + 8 = 20$. This is the total number of males in the sample space. The number of males who pay online is 12. Dividing, you get $\frac{12}{20} = 0.6$.

Q Suppose you know that a costumer pays by mail. Is it more likely that the costumer is male or female? **[14 costumers pay by mail. Of these, eight are male and six are female. Therefore, the probability that a costumer is male is $\frac{8}{14} \approx 0.57$. Thus, it is more likely that a costumer is male, given that the costumer pays by mail, even though there are more females in the original sample space.]**

Got It?

Q What two probabilities do you need to find to solve this problem? **[P(female and directly onto head) and P(female)]**

Q Without using the formula, how would you find $P(\text{directly on head} \mid \text{female})$? **[Divide the number in the female-and-onto-head box by the total in the female row.]**

Additional Problems

1. The table shows the number of male and female freshmen who chose to play one of the three intramural sports offered at a small college.

	Male	Female
Basketball	54	40
Soccer	36	61
Volleyball	10	12

What is $P(\text{soccer} \mid \text{female})$?

ANSWER about 0.54

2. A student compiled the following table comparing the amounts of land area and water area, in square miles, in various U.S. states.

	Land	Water
Alaska	571,936	91,332
Florida	54,018	11,777
Texas	262,100	6721
California	156,002	7694

What is the probability that a point chosen at random on a map is water, given that the map is of Florida?

ANSWER about 17.9%

3. The table below shows the number of male and female customers at a favorite café on a certain day. Each customer drank either a soda or an iced tea.

	Soda	Iced Tea
Male	21	29
Female	28	42

What is the probability that a customer drank a soda, given that the customer was male?

ANSWER 0.42

4. The chance of rain for the next evening is 60%. If it rains, the chance of lightning is 80%. If it does not rain, the chance of lighting is 5%. What is the probability that it will not rain and there will be no lightning?

ANSWER 38%

Answers

Got It? (continued)

3. 0.2

Problem 4

A tree diagram is an alternative way to represent a sample space. The advantage of a tree diagram is that you can mark different probabilities for each branch; in an ordered-list sample space, the probability of each item in the set is assumed to be equal, and it is the number of combinations of items that determines probability.

Q The information given in the problem states the probability that a student graduated from high school. How was the probability that a student did not graduate found? **[Every student either graduated or did not graduate, so the total probability must be 1, and 1 − 0.85 = 0.15.]**

Q The tree diagram shows four paths. What do you think the sum of the probabilities for all four paths should be? Explain and verify your answer. **[The sum of the probabilities for all four paths represents everything that could happen, so the probability should be 100%. P(H and G) + P(NH and G) + P(H and NG) + P(NH and NG) = 0.765 + 0.085 + 0.09 + 0.06 = 1.]**

Got It?

Q Which of the four paths did you follow to answer this question? What is the probability of each section of the path? **[The path is "not graduated" and "is happy." P(NG) = 0.15 and P(H|NG) = 0.6]**

Q If the graduating class contained 600 students, how many students would you expect did not graduate and are happy with their present jobs? **[54 students]**

Another way to write the formula for conditional probability $P(B \mid A) = \frac{P(A \text{ and } B)}{P(A)}$ is $P(A \text{ and } B) = P(A) \cdot P(B \mid A)$.

You can use this rule along with a tree diagram to find probabilities of dependent events.

Problem 4 Using a Tree Diagram

Education A school system compiled the following information from a survey it sent to people who were juniors 10 years earlier.

- 85% of the students graduated from high school.
- Of the students who graduated from high school, 90% are happy with their present jobs.
- Of the students who did not graduate from high school, 60% are happy with their present jobs.

What is the probability that a member of the junior class 10 years ago graduated from high school and is happy with his or her present job?

Make a tree diagram to help organize the information.

Let G = graduated, NG = not graduated, H = happy with present job, and NH = not happy with present job.

Think
What are the branches at each point?
The tree first branches at "graduated" and "not graduated." Each of these paths branches at "happy" and "not happy."

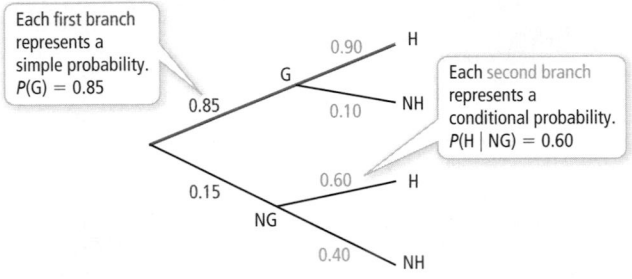

Hint
Follow the path along the graduated branch then the happy with present job branch.

The blue highlighted path represents $P(\text{G and H})$.

Use the formula for conditional probability.	$P(\text{G and H}) = P(\text{G}) \cdot P(\text{H} \mid \text{G})$
Substitute.	$= 0.85 \cdot 0.90$
Simplify.	$= 0.765$

The probability that a person from the junior class 10 years ago graduated and is happy with his or her present job is 0.765, or 76.5%.

 Got It? 4. What is the probability that a student from the junior class 10 years ago in Problem 4 did not graduate and is happy with his or her present job?

Answers

Got It? (continued)

4. 9%

Focus Question How do you find conditional probability?

Answer For any two events A and B with $P(A) \neq 0$, the conditional probability of event B, given that event A occurs is $P(B \mid A) = \frac{P(A \text{ and } B)}{P(A)}$. Use conditional probability when two events are dependent.

Lesson Check

Do you know HOW?

A card is drawn from a standard deck of cards. Find each probability, given that the card drawn is black.

1. $P(\text{club})$ **2.** $P(4)$ **3.** $P(\text{diamond})$

4. The probability that a car has two doors, given that it is red is 0.6. The probability that a car has two doors *and* is red is 0.2. What is the probability that a car is red?

Do you UNDERSTAND?

5. Reasoning Using the tree diagram in Problem 4, explain why the probabilities on each pair of branches must add up to 1.

6. Open-Ended Describe a situation in which you would use conditional probability to find the answer.

7. Compare and Contrast How are the Fundamental Counting Principle and tree diagrams alike? How are they different?

Practice and Problem-Solving Exercises

Ⓐ Practice   Use the table to find each probability.   ◀ See Problem 1.

Characteristics of Job Applicants

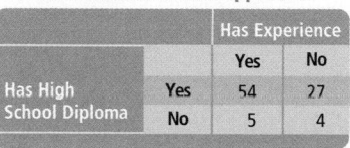

		Has Experience	
		Yes	No
Has High School Diploma	Yes	54	27
	No	5	4

Guided Practice ➡

To start, find the total number of job applicants with a diploma.

8. $P(\text{has diploma})$
$54 + 27 = 81$

9. $P(\text{has diploma and experience})$

10. $P(\text{has no diploma} \mid \text{has experience})$

Use the table to find each probability.   ◀ See Problem 2.

11. $P(\text{The degree is a bachelor's.})$

12. $P(\text{The recipient is female, given that the degree is an associate's.})$

13. $P(\text{The degree is } not \text{ an associate's, given that the recipient is male.})$

Projected Number of Degree Recipients in 2010 (thousands)

Degree	Male	Female
Associate's	245	433
Bachelor's	598	858

Source: U.S. National Center for Education Statistics

Lesson Check

1. $\frac{1}{2}$

2. $\frac{1}{13}$, or about 7.7%

3. 0%

4. 50%

5. The sum of the probability of an event happening and the probability of an event not happening is 1. Each branch represents either the event happening or the event not happening.

6. Check students' work.

7. Answers may vary. Sample: Tree diagrams apply to cases in which more than one event occurs in a sequence. The Fundamental Counting Principle applies to situations in which there are multiple outcomes of a single event.

With a tree diagram, but not with the Fundamental Counting Principle, you can determine probabilities of dependent events, or conditional probabilities.

Practice and Problem-Solving Exercises

8. 0.9

9. 0.6

10. ≈0.085

11. ≈0.682

12. ≈0.639

13. ≈0.709

3 Lesson Check

Do you know HOW?

- For Exercises 1–3, students must understand that it is given that the drawn card is black. That fact does not need to be calculated. Therefore, the denominator for calculating these probabilities should be 26 rather than 52.

- For Exercise 4, students may benefit from drawing a tree diagram. They should determine that the first branches are for illustrated/not-illustrated and the second branches are for hardback/not-hardback.

Do you UNDERSTAND?

- In Exercise 5, students may think that the sum of the probabilities of paired branches should equal the probability of the preceding branch in the diagram. Explain that the smaller branches contain 100% (all) of the preceding branch, which is the same as a part of the entire diagram.

- For Exercise 6, the situation must have at least two choices or events, and the first should be given.

Close

Q What is a simple probability experiment that shows how the probability of an outcome changes when a part is given? **[Answers may vary. Sample: Flipping a coin twice and getting two heads has a probability of one fourth. If the first coin flip is given as heads, then the probability of getting two heads is one half. The probability doubled.]**

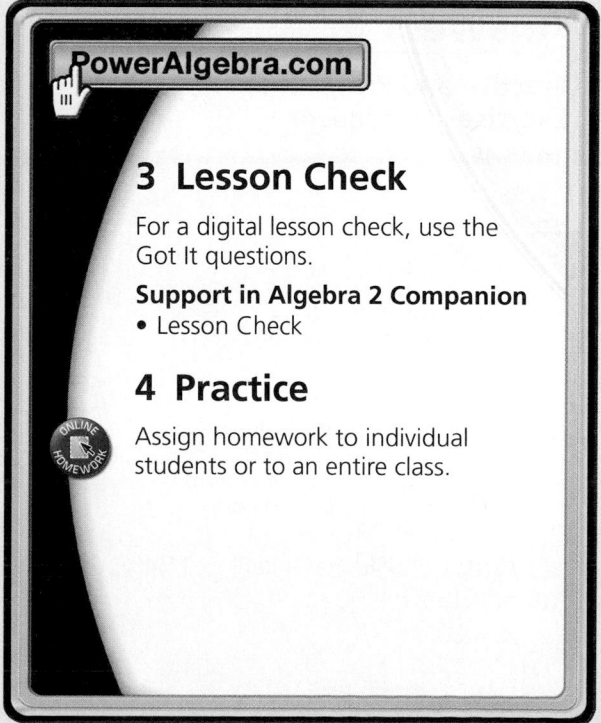

PowerAlgebra.com

3 Lesson Check

For a digital lesson check, use the Got It questions.

Support in Algebra 2 Companion
- Lesson Check

4 Practice

Assign homework to individual students or to an entire class.

4 Practice

ASSIGNMENT GUIDE
Basic: 8–17, 19, 22

Average: 8–23

Standardized Test Prep: 26–29

Mixed Review: 30–35

Reasoning exercises have blue headings.

Applications exercises have red headings.

EXERCISE 22: Use the Think About a Plan worksheet in the **Student Companion** (also available in the Teaching Resources in print and online) to further support students' development in becoming independent learners.

HOMEWORK QUICK CHECK
To check students' understanding of key skills and concepts, go over Exercises 9, 13, 15, 19, and 22.

Use the survey results for Exercises 14 and 15.
◀ See Problem 3.

14. Find the probability that a respondent has a pet, given that the respondent has had a pet.

15. Find the probability that a respondent has never had a pet, given that the respondent does not have a pet now.

> 39% have a pet now and have had a pet.
>
> 61% do not have a pet now.
>
> 86% have had a pet.
>
> 14% do not have a pet now and have never had a pet.

Make a tree diagram to find each conditional probability.
◀ See Problem 4.

16. **Sports** A football team has a 70% chance of winning when it doesn't snow, but only a 40% chance of winning when it snows. Suppose there is a 50% chance of snow. Find the probability that the team will win.

17. The results of a survey are given below. Find P(a female respondent is left-handed) and P(a respondent is both male and right-handed).
    - Of all the respondents, 17% are male.
    - Of the male respondents, 33% are left-handed.
    - Of female respondents, 90% are right-handed.

Ⓑ Apply

18. Suppose A and B are independent events, with $P(A) = 0.60$ and $P(B) = 0.25$. Find each probability.
    - **a.** $P(A \text{ and } B)$
    - **b.** $P(A \mid B)$
    - **c.** What do you notice about $P(A)$ and $P(A \mid B)$?
    - **d. Reasoning** One way to describe A and B as independent events is *The occurrence of B has no effect on the probability of A.* Explain how the answer to part (c) illustrates this relationship.

19. **Think About a Plan** A math teacher gives her class two tests. 60% of the class passes both tests and 80% of the class passes the first test. What percent of those who pass the first test also pass the second test?
    - What conditional probability are you looking for?
    - How can a tree diagram help you solve this problem?

Weather Use probability notation to describe the chance of each event. Let **S, C, W,** and **R** represent sunny, cloudy, windy, and rainy weather, respectively.

20. sunny and windy weather
21. rainy weather if it is windy

22. **Transportation** You can take Bus 65 or Bus 79. You take the first bus that arrives. The probability that Bus 65 arrives first is 75%. There is a 40% chance that Bus 65 picks up passengers along the way. There is a 60% chance that Bus 79 picks up passengers. Your bus picked up passengers. What is the probability that it was Bus 65?

Answers

Practice and Problem-Solving Exercises (continued)

14. ≈45%

15. ≈23%

16.

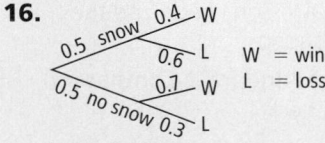

$P(W) = 55\%$

17.

M = male
F = female
R = right-handed
L = left-handed

$P(L \mid F) = 10\%$, $P(M \text{ and } R) \approx 11.4\%$

18. a. 0.15

   b. 0.60

c–d. Since $P(A) = P(A \mid B)$, the probability of A is the same, regardless of the occurrence of B.

19. 75%

20. $P(S \text{ and } W)$

21. $P(R \mid W)$

22. $\frac{2}{3}$, or $66.\overline{6}\%$

The tree diagram relates snowfall and school closings. Find each probability. Let H, L, O, and C represent heavy snowfall, light snowfall, schools open, and schools closed, respectively.

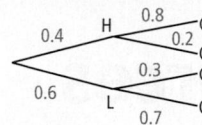

23. $P(\text{H and O})$ **24.** $P(\text{H} \mid \text{C})$ **25.** $P(\text{L} \mid \text{O})$

Standardized Test Prep

 SAT/ACT

Use the table for Exercises 26 and 27. A school library classifies its books as hardback or paperback, fiction or nonfiction, and illustrated or non-illustrated.

		Illustrated	Non-Illustrated
Hardback	Fiction	420	780
	Nonfiction	590	250
Paperback	Fiction	150	430
	Nonfiction	110	880

26. What is the probability that a book selected at random is a paperback, given that it is illustrated?

   Ⓐ $\frac{260}{3610}$ Ⓑ $\frac{150}{1270}$ Ⓒ $\frac{260}{1270}$ Ⓓ $\frac{110}{150}$

27. What is the probability that a book selected at random is nonfiction, given that it is a non-illustrated hardback?

   Ⓕ $\frac{250}{2040}$ Ⓖ $\frac{780}{1030}$ Ⓗ $\frac{250}{1030}$ Ⓘ $\frac{250}{780}$

28. Which of the following expressions is equivalent to $3(n-3)(n+4)$?

   Ⓐ $3n^2 + 3n - 36$ Ⓒ $3n^2 - 3n - 36$

   Ⓑ $3n^2 - 3n + 36$ Ⓓ $3n^2 - 36$

Short Response

29. What is the sample space for spinning the spinner twice? Are all the outcomes equally likely?

Mixed Review

Q and R are independent events. Find $P(Q \text{ and } R)$.   ◀ See Lesson 11-3.

30. $P(Q) = \frac{3}{4}$; $P(R) = \frac{4}{9}$ **31.** $P(Q) = \frac{17}{20}$; $P(R) = \frac{5}{19}$

Write an equation of a parabola with the given vertex and focus.   ◀ See Lesson 10-2.

32. vertex $(5, 2)$; focus $(6, 2)$ **33.** vertex $(-2, 3)$; focus $(-2, 6)$

Get Ready!   To prepare for Lesson 11-5, do Exercises 34 and 35.

Order each set of values from least to greatest. Then find the middle value.   ◀ See Lesson 1-2.

34. 0.2 0.3 0.6 1.2 0.7 0.9 0.8   **35.** 11 23 15 17 21 18 21

---

23. 0.08, or 8%

24. 0.64

25. 0.84

Standardized Test Prep

26. C

27. H

28. A

29. [2] (1, 1), (1, 2), (1, 3), (2, 1), (2, 2) (2, 3), (3, 1), (3, 2), (3, 3); yes

   [1] correct sample space only

Mixed Review

30. $\frac{1}{3} = 33.\overline{3}\%$

31. $\frac{17}{76} \approx 0.22368 \approx 22.37\%$

32. $x = \frac{1}{4}(y - 2)^2 + 5$

33. $y = \frac{1}{12}(x + 2)^2 + 3$

34. 0.2, 0.3, 0.6, 0.7, 0.8, 0.9, 1.2; 0.7

35. 11, 15, 17, 18, 21, 21, 23; 18

Additional Instructional Support

Algebra 2 Companion

Students can use the **Algebra 2 Companion** worktext (4 pages) as you teach the lesson. Use the Companion to support

- New Vocabulary
- Key Concepts
- Got It for each Problem
- Lesson Check

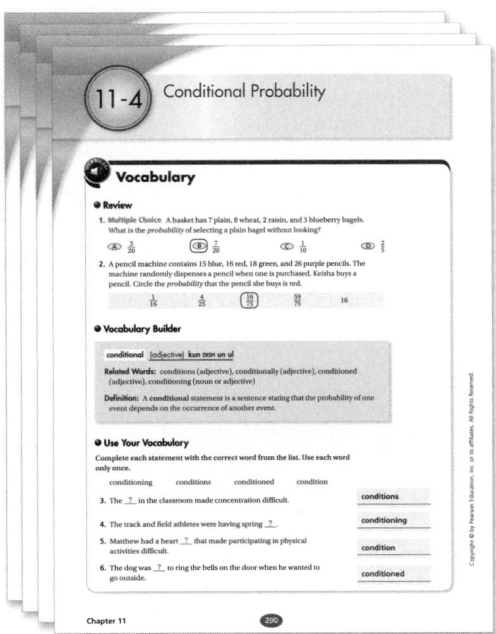

ELL Support

Focus on Communication Divide students into small groups or pairs. Ask each group to develop a table similar to the tables from Problems 1 and 3 in the lesson. Every group should divide its table into columns for "Female" and "Male." Allow each group to pick a way to divide the class into categories based on a single characteristic. Any non-offensive characteristic is acceptable as long as every student in the class will fit into one of the categories in every table.

After each group has decided on a characteristic, allow them to count students and fill in their tables.

Groups should ask each other probability questions of three types about the tables:
- Simple probability: What is the chance a student has brown hair?
- Compound probability: What is the chance a student has brown hair *and* is female?
- Conditional probability: What is the chance a student has brown hair, *given* that the student is female?

5 Assess & Remediate

Lesson Quiz

1. Do you UNDERSTAND? The table shows the number of male and female students in a certain classroom who take notes using different methods.

	Male	Female
Laptop Computer	27	33
Voice Recorder	2	1
Pencil and Paper	42	28

What is $P(\text{laptop} \mid \text{male})$?

2. You have two ways to drive home from work: Route A is usually quicker; Route B is scenic but slower. You choose Route A on 80% of your days and this gets you home by 6:00 P.M. 90% of the time. When you choose Route B you get home by 6:00 P.M. only 60% of the time. What is the probability that you choose Route B and get home by 6:00 P.M.?

3. A box contains 10 blue cubes, 5 red cubes, 5 blue marbles, and 10 red marbles. You randomly pick a blue shape out of the box. What is the probability that you picked a cube?

ANSWERS TO LESSON QUIZ

1. about 0.38
2. 12%
3. 0.67, or 67%

PRESCRIPTION FOR REMEDIATION
Use the student work on the Lesson Quiz to prescribe a differentiated review assignment:

Points	Differentiated Remediation
0–2	Intervention
3	On-level
4	Extension

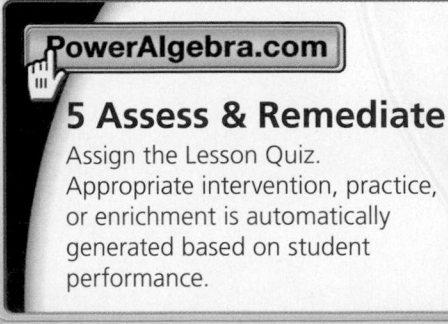

5 Assess & Remediate
Assign the Lesson Quiz. Appropriate intervention, practice, or enrichment is automatically generated based on student performance.

Intervention

- **Reteaching** (2 pages) Provides reteaching and practice exercises for the key lesson concepts. Use with struggling students or absent students.
- **English Language Learner Support** Helps students develop and reinforce mathematical vocabulary and key concepts.

All-in-One Resources/Online
Reteaching

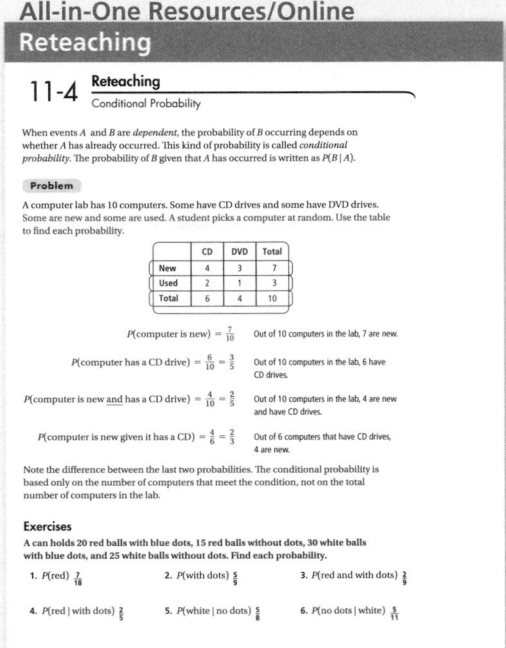

All-in-One Resources/Online
English Language Learner Support

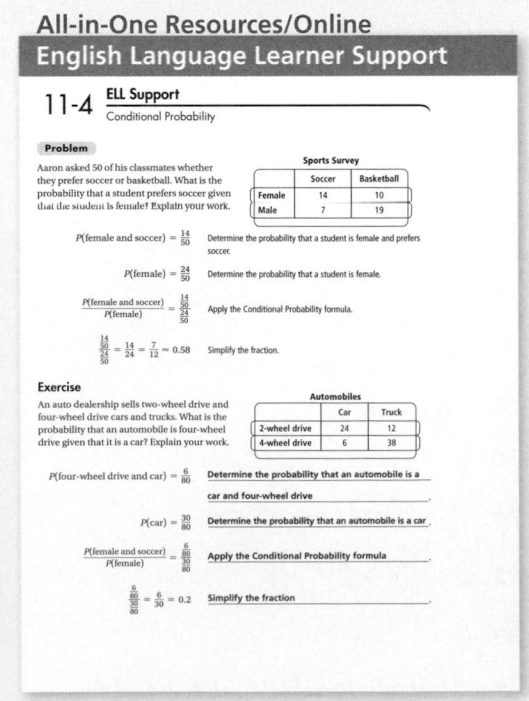

Differentiated Remediation continued

On-Level

- **Practice** (2 pages) Provides extra practice for each lesson. For more challenging practice exercises, use the Form G Practice pages found in the All-in-One Teaching Resources and online.

- **Think About a Plan** Helps students develop specific problem-solving skills and strategies by providing scaffolded guiding questions.
- **Standardized Test Prep** Focuses on all major exercises, all major question types, and helps students prepare for the high-stakes assessments.

Extension

- **Enrichment** Provides students with interesting problems and activities that extend the concepts of the lesson.
- **Activities, Games, and Puzzles** Worksheets that can be used for concepts development, enrichment, and for fun!

Student Companion/ All-in-One Resources/Online
Practice page 1

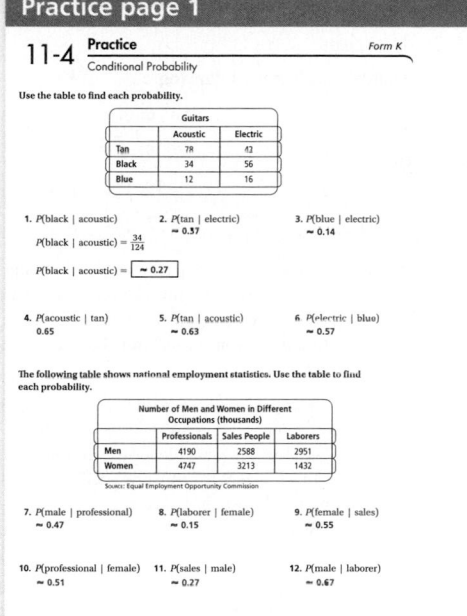

Student Companion/ All-in-One Resources/Online
Practice page 2

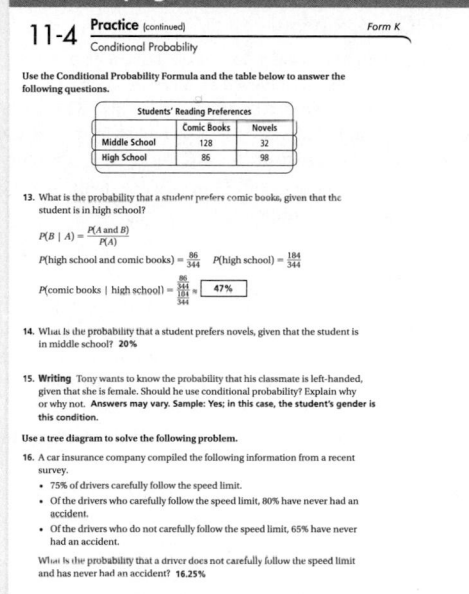

All-in-One Resources/Online
Enrichment

Student Companion/ All-in-One Resources/Online
Think About a Plan

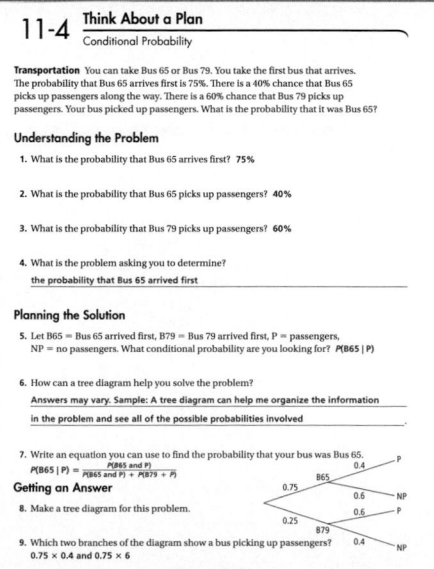

Student Companion/ All-in-One Resources/Online
Standardized Test Prep

Online Teacher Resource Center
Activities, Games, and Puzzles

Essential Questions UbD

BIG idea   Probability

ESSENTIAL QUESTION What is the difference between a permutation and a computation?
ANSWER A permutation is an arrangement of items in a particular order. A combination is an arrangement where order does not matter.

BIG idea   Probability

ESSENTIAL QUESTION What is the difference between experimental and theoretical probability?
ANSWER You compute an experimental probability from collected data. You find theoretical probability by considering the likelihood of every possible outcome.

BIG idea   Data Collection and Analysis

ESSENTIAL QUESTION How are measures of central tendency different from standard deviation?
ANSWER Measures of central tendency are ways to describe a "middle" value of a data set. Standard deviation describes how data are spread out from a particular middle value.

---

11 Chapter Review for Part A

Chapter Vocabulary

- combination (p. 690)
- conditional probability (p. 711)
- dependent events (p. 704)
- equally likely outcomes (p. 698)
- experimental probability (p. 695)
- Fundamental Counting Principle (p. 686)
- independent events (p. 704)
- mutually exclusive events (p. 705)
- n factorial (n!) (p. 687)
- permutation (p. 687)
- sample space (p. 698)
- simulation (p. 696)
- theoretical probability (p. 698)

Choose the correct term to complete each sentence.

1. A (*combination/permutation*) is an arrangement of items in a particular order.

2. (*Conditional/Theoretical*) probability refers to the probability that an event will occur given that another event has already occurred.

3. You can use a (*sample space/simulation*) to model an event when it is difficult or unreasonable to conduct numerous trials.

4. Two events that cannot occur at the same time are called (*dependent/mutually exclusive*) events.

11-1 Permutations and Combinations

Quick Review

If event M can occur in m ways and event N can occur in n ways, then M followed by N can occur in $m \cdot n$ ways. The notation **n! (n factorial)** means $n \cdot (n-1) \cdot \ldots \cdot 3 \cdot 2 \cdot 1$. The number of ways to choose r items from a set of n items, without regard to order, is $_nC_r = \frac{n!}{r!(n-r)!}$. The number of ways to choose r items from a set of n items and place those items in some order is $_nP_r = \frac{n!}{(n-r)!}$.

Example

A vacationer making travel preparations chooses 3 books from a shelf containing 15 books. How many ways are there to choose 3 books without regard to order? How many ways are there to choose one book for the trip to the destination, one for the stay, and one for the homeward trip?

Ignoring order, there are $_{15}C_3 = \frac{15!}{3!12!} = 455$ ways to choose 3 books.

There are $_{15}P_3 = \frac{15!}{12!} = 2730$ ways to choose 3 books to read in a particular order.

Exercises

Evaluate each of the following.

5. 3!

6. 9!

7. $\frac{4!}{2!}$

8. $\frac{5!}{2!2!}$

9. $_7C_2$

10. $_4C_3 + _6C_5$

11. $_6P_2$

12. $_4P_3 + _6P_5$

13. Camping On a camping trip, you bring 12 items for 4 dinners. For each dinner, you use 3 items. In how many ways can you choose the 3 items for the first dinner? For the second? For the third? For the fourth?

14. Advertising A newspaper ad includes a telephone number 1-555-DIAL VSW. How many 7-letter arrangements are possible for the phone number using the 26 letters of the alphabet if no letter is used more than once? Express your answer using scientific notation.

Summative Questions UbD

Use the following prompts as you review this chapter with your students. The prompts are designed to help you assess your students' understanding of the BIG ideas they have studied.

- Compare and contrast combinations and permutations. For a given set of data, are there more combinations or permutations?
- Can mutually exclusive events be dependent?
- What can you determine about data using the measures of central tendency? using measures of variance?
- How can sample and study methods influence the results of a study?
- What is the difference between a discrete probability distribution and a continuous probability distribution? Give an example of each.

Answers

Chapter Review for Part A

1. permutation

2. Conditional

3. simulation

4. mutually exclusive

5. 6

6. 362,880

7. 12

8. 30

9. 21

10. 10

11. 30

12. 744

13. 220; 84; 20; 1

14. 3.315312×10^9

11-2 Probability

Quick Review

Experimental probability is based on successes during repeated trials, while **theoretical probability** is based on number of occurrences in a **sample space** of equally likely outcomes. When an actual event cannot easily be repeated through numerous trials, you can use a **simulation** to obtain an experimental probability.

Example

What is the probability that a person chosen at random was born on a Thursday?

Since a random person had an equal chance of being born on any one of the 7 days of the week, the probability that the person was born on a Thursday is $\frac{1}{7}$.

Exercises

15. How many possible outcomes are there when a standard number cube is rolled three times?

16. You flipped a coin 70 times and recorded 23 heads. What is the experimental probability of flipping tails?

Find the probability of each event.

17. A fair number cube rolls a 13.

18. A number picked at random from the numbers 1 through 15 is prime.

19. **Writing** Suppose you have 20 tiles with the numbers 1 through 20. The theoretical probability that a tile chosen at random is a 5 is $\frac{1}{20}$. If you pick a tile randomly, 20 times, replacing the chosen tile each time, will you get a 5 exactly once? Explain.

11-3 Probability of Multiple Events

Quick Review

For any events A and B,
$P(A \text{ or } B) = P(A) + P(B) - P(A \text{ and } B)$.

When the occurrence of one event affects how a second event can occur, the events are **dependent**.

When A and B are **independent**, $P(A \text{ and } B) = P(A) \cdot P(B)$. For **mutually exclusive events**, $P(A \text{ and } B) = 0$, so $P(A \text{ or } B) = P(A) + P(B)$.

Example

You roll a standard number cube. Are the following events mutually exclusive: rolling a 1 and rolling an even number? Explain.

You cannot roll a 1 and an even number at the same time. The events are mutually exclusive.

Exercises

Classify each pair of events as *dependent* or *independent*.

20. A student in your algebra class is selected at random. One of the remaining students is then selected at random.

21. You select a number 1 through 6 by tossing a standard number cube. You select a second number by tossing the number cube again.

Calculate each probability, given that $P(A) = 0.3$, $P(B) = 0.7$, and A and B are independent.

22. $P(A \text{ and } B)$

23. $P(A \text{ or } B)$

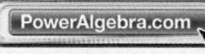

15. 216

16. $\frac{47}{70}$

17. 0

18. $\frac{2}{5}$

19. Not necessarily; you may pick a 5 zero times, one time, or more than once. Each time you pick, the prob. that it will be a 5 is $\frac{1}{20}$.

20. dependent

21. independent

22. 0.21

23. 0.79

Answers

Chapter Review for Part A (continued)

24. 0.3

25. 0.7

26. $\frac{1}{4}$

27. $\frac{1}{5}$

28. $\frac{1}{8}$

11-4 Conditional Probability

Quick Review

The probability that event B will occur, given that A has already occured, is the **conditional probability** $P(B \mid A) = \frac{P(A \text{ and } B)}{P(A)}$.

Example

A standard number cube is rolled twice. If the first number rolled is a and the second is b, find $P(a$ is even and $b > 2)$ and $P(b$ is even $\mid b > 3)$.

Number cube rolls are independent events.

$$P(a \text{ is even and } b > 2) = P(a \text{ is even}) \cdot P(b > 2)$$

$$= \frac{1}{2} \cdot \frac{2}{3} = \frac{1}{3}$$

$$P(b \text{ is even} \mid b > 3) = \frac{P(b > 3 \text{ and } b \text{ is even})}{P(b > 3)}$$

$$= \frac{P(4 \text{ or } 6)}{P(4 \text{ or } 5 \text{ or } 6)}$$

$$= \frac{\frac{2}{6}}{\frac{3}{6}} = \frac{2}{3}$$

Exercises

Calculate each probability, given that $P(A) = 0.3$, $P(B) = 0.7$, and A and B are independent.

24. $P(A \mid B)$

25. $P(B \mid A)$

Calculate each probability, given that $P(A) = 0.5$, $P(B) = 0.4$, and $P(A \text{ and } B) = 0.1$.

26. $P(A \mid B)$

27. $P(B \mid A)$

28. $P(A \text{ and } B \mid A \text{ or } B)$

Chapter Test for Part A

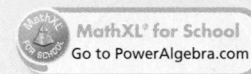
MathXL® for School
Go to PowerAlgebra.com

Do you know HOW?

Evaluate each expression.

1. $4!$
2. $6!$
3. $\frac{5!}{3!}$
4. $\frac{6!}{4!2!}$
5. $_7C_3$
6. $_9C_8$
7. $_5P_2$
8. $_{11}P_9$
9. $_4C_4$
10. $_4P_4$

Indicate whether each situation involves a combination or permutation. Then solve.

11. How many ways are there to select 5 actors from a troupe of 9 to improvise a scene?

12. How many different 3-student study groups can be formed from a class of 15?

13. Your teacher is looking for a new apartment. There are 5 apartments available. In how many ways can your teacher inspect the apartments?

Suppose you select a number at random from the sample space {5, 6, 7, 8, 9, 10, 11, 12, 13, 14}. Find each probability.

14. $P(7)$

15. $P(5 \text{ or } 13)$

16. $P(\text{greater than } 10)$

17. $P(\text{multiple of } 30)$

18. $P(\text{less than } 7 \text{ or greater than } 10)$

19. $P(\text{greater than } 6 \text{ and less than } 12)$

20. $P(\text{integer})$

21. $P(\text{less than } 10 \mid \text{less than } 13)$

22. $P(\text{greater than } 8 \mid \text{less than } 11)$

23. $P(\text{greater than } 7 \mid \text{greater than } 12)$

Two standard number cubes are tossed. State whether the events are mutually exclusive. Then find $P(A \text{ or } B)$.

24. A means their sum is 12; B means both are odd.

25. A means they are equal; B means their sum is a multiple of 3.

Do you UNDERSTAND?

26. **Vocabulary** Explain the difference between experimental probability and theoretical probability.

27. Suppose you select a number at random from the set {90, 91, 92, . . . , 99}. Event A is selecting a multiple of 2. Event B is selecting a multiple of 3.
   a. **Writing** Are events A and B mutually exclusive? Are they independent? Explain your answers.
   b. Find $P(A)$ and $P(B)$.
   c. Find $P(A \text{ and } B)$.
   d. Find $P(A \text{ or } B)$.
   e. Find $P(A \mid B)$ and $P(B \mid A)$.

28. **Reasoning** Let F and G be mutually exclusive events. Event F occurs more frequently than event G. Write the following in order from least to greatest: $P(F), P(G), P(F \text{ or } G), P(G \mid F)$.

29. **Error Analysis** For two events A and B, a student calculates the probabilities shown. Explain how you can tell that the student made a mistake.

$$P(A \text{ and } B) = 0.35$$
$$P(A \mid B) = 0.29$$

30. **Open-Ended** Your teacher selects at random two days out of every five days to give a "pop" quiz. Define a simulation to find the experimental probability that you will get a pop quiz on two consecutive days. Then use your simulation to find the probability.

27. a. not mutually exclusive since 90 and 96 are both multiples of 2 and 3; independent since each event A or B does not affect the outcome of the other event
   b. $P(A) = \frac{1}{2}$; $P(B) = \frac{2}{5}$
   c. $\frac{1}{5}$
   d. $\frac{7}{10}$
   e. $P(A \mid B) = \frac{1}{2}$; $P(B \mid A) = \frac{2}{5}$

28. $P(G \mid F), P(G), P(F), P(F \text{ or } G)$

29. $P(A \mid B) = \frac{P(B \text{ and } A)}{P(B)}$; since $P(A \text{ and } B) = 0.35$ and $P(A \mid B) = 0.29$, $0.29 = \frac{0.35}{P(B)}$ and $P(B) = \frac{0.35}{0.29} > 1$ which is not possible

30. Check students' work.

Answers

Chapter Test for Part A

1. 24
2. 720
3. 20
4. 15
5. 35
6. 9
7. 20
8. 19,958,400
9. 1
10. 24
11. combination; 126 ways
12. combination; 455 groups
13. permutation; 120 ways
14. $\frac{1}{10}$
15. $\frac{1}{5}$
16. $\frac{2}{5}$
17. 0
18. $\frac{3}{5}$
19. $\frac{1}{2}$
20. 1
21. $\frac{5}{8}$
22. $\frac{1}{3}$
23. 1
24. mutually exclusive; $\frac{5}{18}$
25. not mutually exclusive; $\frac{4}{9}$
26. Experimental probabilities are calculated on the basis of data from an experiment, actual or simulated. Given equally likely outcomes, the basis for calculating theoretical probability is being able to determine the no. of ways that an event can occur within these outcomes.

PowerAlgebra.com

MathXL for School

Prepare students for the Chapter Test for Part A with online practice and review.

Chapter 11 Overview

UbD Understanding by Design

Chapter 11 expands on students' understandings and skills related to probability and statistics. In this chapter, students will develop the answers to the Essential Questions posed on the student page as they learn the concepts and skills bulleted below.

BIG idea Probability

ESSENTIAL QUESTION What is the difference between a permutation and a combination?
- Students will find permutations and combinations of data sets using formulas.

BIG idea Probability

ESSENTIAL QUESTION What is the difference between experimental and theoretical probability?
- Students will use simulation to model experimental probability.
- Students will find the theoretical probability of events using a formula.

BIG idea Data Collection and Analysis

ESSENTIAL QUESTION How are measures of central tendency different from standard deviation?
- Students will find and analyze the measures of central tendency of given data sets.
- Students will find the standard deviation of given data sets.

•

CHAPTER 11 PART B

Probability and Statistics

In Part A, you learned to calculate permutations, combinations, and probability. Now you will analyze data using measures of central tendency and variation.

Vocabulary for Part B

English/Spanish Vocabulary Audio Online:

English	Spanish
mean, *p. 723*	media
measure of central tendency, *p. 723*	medida de tendencia central
median, *p. 723*	mediana
mode, *p. 723*	moda
normal distribution, *p. 752*	distribución normal
outlier, *p. 724*	valor extremo
sample, *p. 738*	muestra
standard deviation, *p. 732*	desviación típica

BIG ideas

1 Probability
Essential Question What is the difference between a permutation and a combination?

2 Probability
Essential Question What is the difference between experimental and theoretical probability?

3 Data Collection and Analysis
Essential Question How are measures of central tendency different from standard deviation?

Chapter Preview for Part B

722 Chapter 11 Probability and Statistics

PowerAlgebra.com

Chapter 11 Overview

Use these online assets to engage your students. There is support for the Solve It and step-by-step solutions for problems.

Show the student-produced video demonstrating relevant and engaging applications of the new concepts in this chapter.

Find online definitions for new terms in English and Spanish.

Start each lesson with an attention-getting Problem. View the Problem online with helpful hints.

Increase students' depth of knowledge with interactive online activities.

Show problems from each lesson solved step by step. Instant replay allows students to go at their own pace when studying online.

Prepare students for the Chapter Test for Part A and the Chapter Test for Part B with online practice and review.

11-5 Analyzing Data

Objectives To calculate measures of central tendency
To draw and interpret box-and-whisker plots

1 Interactive Learning

Solve It!
PURPOSE To estimate a weighted average
PROCESS Students may
- draw an annotated diagram showing the number of hours driving each way.
- make a table of distance and number of hours traveling east, west, and in total.

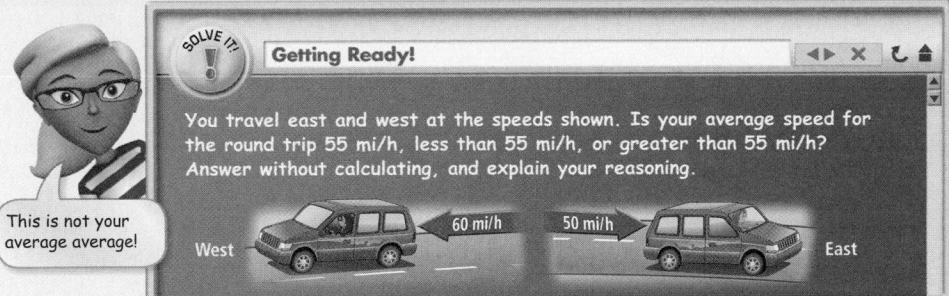

SOLVE IT! **Getting Ready!**

You travel east and west at the speeds shown. Is your average speed for the round trip 55 mi/h, less than 55 mi/h, or greater than 55 mi/h? Answer without calculating, and explain your reasoning.

West — 60 mi/h   50 mi/h — East

This is not your average average!

FACILITATE
Q Why is the total average speed different from the average of the two speeds? **[The traveling time in each direction is not the same.]**
Q What is a similar question using the same speeds that would have an answer of 55 mph? **[Answers may vary. Sample: What is the average speed of a car that traveled for 5 hours at 50 mph and for 5 hours at 60 mph?]**

ANSWER See Solve It in Answers on next page.
CONNECT THE MATH Students analyzed the meaning of *average* in the Solve It. In the lesson, students will analyze data sets and use measures of central tendency.

People often refer to the mean as the *average*. The mean is only one of the measures considered the average, a measure of the center of a set of data.

Focus Question How can you compare and describe sets of data?

Statistics is the study, analysis, and interpretation of data. One way to analyze data is by finding a *measure of central tendency*. A **measure of central tendency** indicates the "middle" of a data set. The *mean, median,* and *mode* are the most common measures of central tendency.

Dynamic Activity
Box-and-Whisker Plots

Lesson Vocabulary
- measure of central tendency
- mean
- median
- mode
- bimodal
- outlier
- range of a set of data
- quartile
- interquartile range
- box-and-whisker plot
- percentile

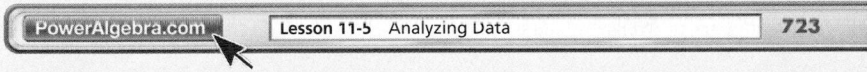

Key Concepts   Measures of Central Tendency

Measure	Definition	Example, using 1, 2, 3, 3, 4, 5, 5, 9
Mean	$\dfrac{\text{sum of the data values}}{\text{number of data values}}$	$\dfrac{1+2+3+3+4+5+5+9}{8} = 4$
Median	for a data set listed in order: the middle value for an odd number of data values; the mean of the two middle values for an even number of data values	For 1, 2, 3, 3, 4, 5, 5, 9, the middle two values are 3 and 4. The median is the mean of these values: $\dfrac{3+4}{2} = 3.5$.
Mode	the most frequently occurring value(s)	Two modes: In 1, 2, 3, 3, 4, 5, 5, 9, both 3 and 5 occur twice.

2 Guided Instruction

Take Note   ELL SUPPORT
The *mode* in statistics is an English word that comes from French and means "fashionable" or "popular." For instance, pie *à la mode* (pie with ice cream) literally means "pie in the popular way." This may help students remember that the mode is the *most frequent* data value.

11-5 Preparing to Teach

BIG idea Probability   **UbD**
ESSENTIAL UNDERSTANDING
Data sets can be described using various statistical measures, depending on what characteristics are being studied.

Math Background
There are numerous statistical measures for describing and comparing sets of data.

Measures of Central Tendency indicate the "middle" of a data set.
- mean: the sum of all the data values divided by the number of terms, commonly called the average
- median: the value in the middle of the ordered data, or the mean of the two middle numbers
- mode: the value that occurs most frequently

Measures of Variation determine the variation within a set of data.
- range: the difference between the greatest and the least values

- interquartile range: the difference between the third and first quartiles
In the next lesson, two more measures of variation are introduced: *variance* and *standard deviation*.

An *outlier* is a value that is significantly greater or less than any other value in the set. They may cause statistical analysis of the data to be misleading.

Support Student Learning
Use the **Algebra 2 Companion** to engage and support students during instruction. See Lesson Resources at the end of this lesson for details.

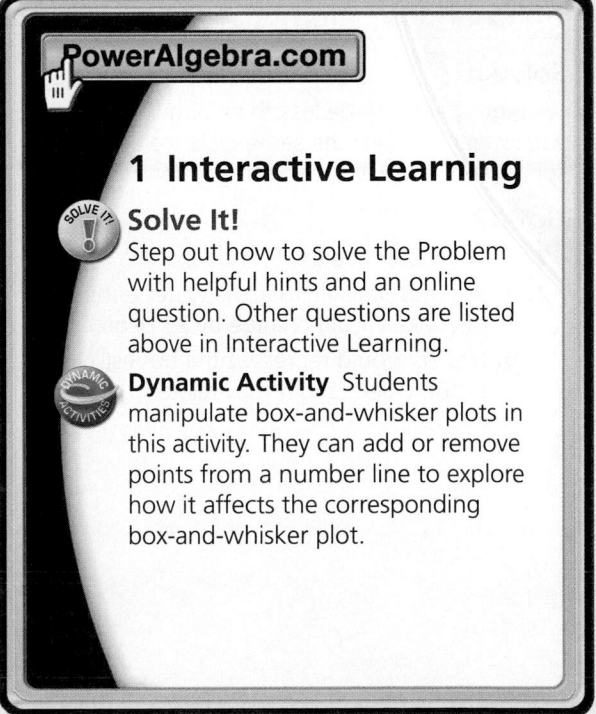

PowerAlgebra.com

1 Interactive Learning

SOLVE IT! **Solve It!**
Step out how to solve the Problem with helpful hints and an online question. Other questions are listed above in Interactive Learning.

Dynamic Activity Students manipulate box-and-whisker plots in this activity. They can add or remove points from a number line to explore how it affects the corresponding box-and-whisker plot.

Problem 1

Q About how many job offers do you think a student should expect? Explain your answer. **[Answers may vary. Sample: A student should expect 2 or 3 job offers. The mean is 2.2. A student could not be offered 0.2 of a job, so this can be interpreted as 2 or 3. The median and the mode also indicate 2 or 3 job offers.]**

Got It?

Q In an expression such as "trees per yard," what does *per* mean? **[*Per* means "in each" or "for every."]**

Q The mean of this data set is the ratio of what two quantities? **[the total number of trees to the total number of yards]**

If a data set has more than two modes, then the modes are probably not statistically useful.

A **bimodal** data set has two modes. If no value occurs more frequently than any other, then there is no mode.

Problem 1 Finding Measures of Central Tendency

Career The frequency table shows the number of job offers received by each student within two months of graduating with a mathematics degree from a small college. What are the mean, median, and mode for the job offers per student?

Job Offers	0	1	2	3	4
Students	2	2	4	5	2

Use the formula to find the mean.

Think

How do you find the total number of job offers? Add the products of each number of job offers and the number of students who received that many job offers.

Write the formula. The symbol $\bar{x}$, read "x bar," represents the mean.

$$\bar{x} = \frac{\text{sum of the data values}}{\text{number of data values}}$$

Substitute.

$$= \frac{2(0) + 2(1) + 4(2) + 5(3) + 2(4)}{15}$$

Simplify.

$$= \frac{33}{15} = 2.2$$

The mean is 2.2.

List the data set in order to find the median.

List each value the number of times it occurs. Arrange them in order.

0, 0, 1, 1, 2, 2, 2, 2, 3, 3, 3, 3, 3, 4, 4

Identify the middle value.

↑
2

The median is 2.

Hint

Remember median as the middle and mode as the most.

Identify repeated values to find the mode(s).

The mode is the number of job offers received by the greatest number of students.

0, 0, 1, 1, 2, 2, 2, 2, 3, 3, 3, 3, 3, 4, 4

↑
3

Five students received 3 job offers each.

The mode is 3.

Got It? 1. The frequency table shows the number of trees in the yard of each house on one street. What are the mean, median, and mode for the trees per yard?

Trees	3	4	5	6	7	8
Yards	1	5	7	4	1	2

Hint

An outlier can significantly affect the mean of a data set. Discard any outliers before calculating the mean.

An **outlier** is a value that is substantially different from the rest of the data set. If the data is arranged in order, outliers can occur at the "ends." Sometimes an outlier is an important part of the data. At other times it can be misleading because it affects measures of central tendency.

Answers

Solve It!

Average speed will be less than 55 mi/h; it takes you longer to travel the same distance at a lower speed, so the lower speed has greater weight.

Got It?

1. mean: 5.25, median: 5, mode: 5

2. a. Yes; it is unlikely that the water temperature of a lake would change by 25 degrees.

   b. No; 98 would represent the busiest night of the week, and it may relate to a weekly event.

 PowerAlgebra.com

2 Guided Instruction

Each Problem is worked out and supported online.

Problem 1
Finding Measures of a Central Tendency
Animated

Problem 2
Identifying an Outlier
Animated

Problem 3
Comparing Data Sets
Animated

Problem 4
Using a Box-and-Whisker Plot

Problem 5
Finding Percentiles

Support in Algebra 2 Companion
• Vocabulary
• Key Concepts
• Got It?

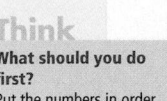

Problem 2 Identifying an Outlier

Multiple Choice Which is an outlier for this data set: 56 65 73 59 98 65 59?

  (A) 42   (B) 65   (C) 98   (D) 59

Think
What should you do first?
Put the numbers in order.

Order the data.

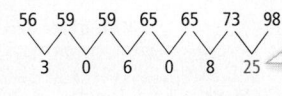

Find differences between adjacent values.

| 56 | 59 | 59 | 65 | 65 | 73 | 98 |

3 0 6 0 8 25

> This difference is significantly larger than the others. The value 98 is an outlier.

The correct answer is C.

 **Got It? 2.** Suppose the values in Problem 2 are the data for the situations below. Would you discard the outlier? Explain.
  a. water temperature of a lake at seven locations
  b. the number of customers in a restaurant each night in one week

The **range of a set of data** is the difference between the greatest and least values. If you order data from least value to greatest value, the median divides the data into two parts. The median of each part divides the data further and you have four parts in all. The values separating the four parts are **quartiles**. The **interquartile range** is the difference between the third and first quartiles.

For example, consider the ordered data set: 56 61 68 73 79 83 86

The median is the middle number, 73. The median is also the value of the second quartile, Q_2.

56 61 68 (73) 79 83 86

The median of the set of numbers *below* the median is the value of the first quartile: $Q_1 = 61$.

56 (61) 68 (73) 79 83 86

The median of the set of numbers *above* the median is the value of the third quartile: $Q_3 = 83$.

56 (61) 68 (73) 79 (83) 86

The range is the difference between the greatest and least values.

$$86 - 56 = 30$$

The interquartile range is the difference between Q_3 and Q_1.

$$83 - 61 = 22$$

A *box-and-whisker plot* uses minimum and maximum values, the median, and the first and third quartiles to display the spread, or variability, in a data set.

take note **Key Concept** Box-and-Whisker Plot

Definition	Graph
A **box-and-whisker plot** is a way to display data that uses • quartiles to bound the center box and • the minimum and maximum values to form the whiskers.	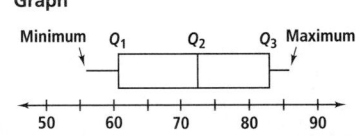

Problem 2
In some situations, you may choose to discard the outliers from the data set.

Q How does finding the difference between values help find an outlier? **[A difference that is much larger than all the other differences may indicate an outlier.]**

Q Can an outlier be a value other than the first or last value in an ordered data set? Explain. **[No; if a possible outlier is not first or last, then there must be more values near it and the value is by definition not an outlier.]**

Got It?

Q What is an explanation for 2a in which 98 might not be an error? **[Answers may vary. Sample: if that data value were recorded at a different time of year]**

Take Note

Q What measures of central tendency cannot be read from a box-and-whisker plot? **[mean and mode]**

Additional Problems

1. The frequency table shows the number of textbooks in several students' book bags.

Textbooks	0	1	2	3	4
Students	1	6	10	4	4

What are the mean, median, and mode for textbooks per student?

ANSWERS mean: 2.16; median: 2; mode: 2

2. Which is an outlier for this data set:
22 35 12 28 46 30 31 15 19?

ANSWER 46

3. The table shows population density by square mile for counties in three of Florida's eight regions, according to the 2000 U.S. Census.

Southwest	Southeast	Central East
204.2	228.1	401.9
13.7	573.0	467.7
548.6	1346.5	224.4
31.4	1157.9	46.4
124.1	79.8	336.6

What are the mean, mode, range, quartiles, and interquartile range for the Southwest and Southeast population density data?

ANSWERS Southwest:
mean = 184.4; mode = none;
range = 534.9; $Q_1 = 22.55$,
$Q_2 = 124.1$, $Q_3 = 376.4$;
IQR = 353.85

Southeast: mean = 677.06;
mode = none; range =
1266.7; $Q_1 = 153.95$,

$Q_2 = 573$, $Q_3 = 1252.2$;
IQR = 1098.25

4. What are the quartiles of the Central East region population density data in the preceding table? Use a graphing calculator box-and-whisker plot.

ANSWERS $Q_1 = 135.4$,
$Q_2 = 336.6$, $Q_3 = 434.8$

5. The data shows the number of hours in a week that students in a class spent doing homework. What value is at the 45th percentile?

0 3 4 4 4 4.25 4.5 4.5 4.75
5 5

5.25 5.5 5.5 6 6.25 6.25 6.5
7 9

ANSWER 4.75

Problem 3

Note that the median is always the middle value or mean of two middle values, and the quartiles are found by *not* including the median in the "half" data set.

> **Q** Each data set contains 12 values, one for each month of the year. Why is Q_3 of the St. Petersburg data equal to a value in the data set? **[Q_3 of St. Petersburg is the mean of two identical values, 84 and 84.]**
>
> **Q** Which measure of the ordered data tells the maximum change in water temperature over the year? **[the range]**

Problem 3 Comparing Data Sets

Temperature The table shows average monthly water temperatures for four locations on the Gulf of Mexico. How can you compare the 12 water temperatures from St. Petersburg with the 12 water temperatures from Key West?

Gulf of Mexico Eastern Coast Water Temperatures (°F)

Location	J	F	M	A	M	J	J	A	S	O	N	D
St. Petersburg, Florida	62	64	68	74	80	84	86	86	84	78	70	64
Key West, Florida	69	70	75	78	82	85	87	87	86	82	76	72
Dauphin Island, Alabama	51	53	60	70	75	82	84	84	80	72	62	56
Grand Isle, Louisiana	61	61	64	70	77	83	85	85	83	77	70	65

SOURCE: National Oceanographic Data Center

Know → Water temperatures near the two cities

Need → The means, medians, modes, ranges, and interquartile ranges

Plan → Order the data. Find the means, medians, modes, minimums, maximums, quartiles, range, and interquartile range.

St. Petersburg:

Find the mean.

$$\bar{x} = \frac{62 + 64 + 64 + 68 + 70 + 74 + 78 + 80 + 84 + 84 + 86 + 86}{12}$$

$$= \frac{900}{12} = 75$$

Find the mode(s). 64, 84, and 86

Find the range. Minimum: 62; Maximum: 86
Range: $86 - 62 = 24$

Median $(Q_2) = 76$

Hint
For an even number of data values, the median is the mean of the two middle values.

Order the data and find the median and quartiles. 62 64 (64 68) 70 (74 78) 80 (84 84) 86 86

Median of lower part $(Q_1) = 66$ Median of upper part $(Q_3) = 84$

Find the interquartile range. $Q_3 - Q_1 = 84 - 66$
$= 18$

St. Petersburg

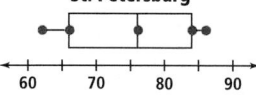

Key West:

Find the mean.
$$\bar{x} = \frac{69 + 70 + 72 + 75 + 76 + 78 + 82 + 82 + 85 + 86 + 87 + 87}{12}$$
$$= \frac{949}{12} \approx 79.1$$

Find the mode(s).　　82 and 87

Find the range.　　Minimum: 69; Maximum: 87
Range: $87 - 69 = 18$

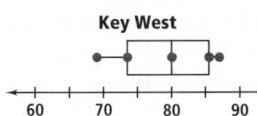
Median (Q_2) = 80

Order the data and find the median and quartiles.　　69 70 72 75 76 78 82 82 85 86 87 87

Median of lower part (Q_1) = 73.5　　Median of upper part (Q_3) = 85.5

Find the interquartile range.　　$Q_3 - Q_1 = 85.5 - 73.5 = 12$

Key West

The range and the interquartile range show the temperatures varying less at Key West than at St. Petersburg. Also, the temperatures at Key West are generally higher.

Got It? 3. How can you compare the 12 water temperatures in Problem 3 from Dauphin Island with the 12 water temperatures from Grand Isle?

Problem 4 Using a Box-and-Whisker Plot

How can you use a graphing calculator box-and-whisker plot to find quartiles for the water temperature data of St. Petersburg from Problem 3?

Step 1 For St. Petersburg, use **STAT EDIT** to enter the temperature data in **L1**.

Step 2 In **STAT PLOT**, select a box-and-whisker plot. Enter **L1** for the St. Petersburg data. Enter the window values. Draw the box-and-whisker plot.

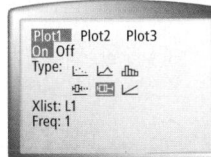
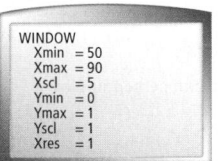
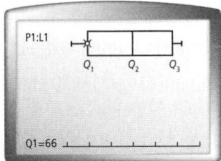

Step 3 Use **TRACE** to find the quartiles: $Q_1 = 66$, $Q_2 = 76$, and $Q_3 = 84$.

Q Does it make sense that Key West has a smaller range than St. Petersburg? Explain. **[Answers may vary. Samples: Yes; Key West is 200 miles south of St. Petersburg, and seasonal temperatures vary less towards the equator. Key West is surrounded by the ocean, and large bodies of water tend to resist temperature changes.]**

Q The measures of central tendency give information about water temperature over a full year. If you wanted to compare how water temperature changes during the year, how would you show the data? **[Answers may vary. Sample: A dual-line plot of the monthly temperature data with one line for St. Petersburg and one line for Key West would show how the temperature changes during a year.]**

Got It?

Q Is the mode an important measure for these data sets? Why or why not? **[Sample: No; the most common water temperature does not seem to be important. Dauphin Island has one mode, but it is far from the mean and median. Grand Isle has five modes.]**

Problem 4　　EXTENSION

Have students repeat the steps from Problem 4, but enter the data for Key West into L2.

Q What are some conclusions about the water temperatures in St. Petersburg and Key West that can be read off the box-and-whisker plots? **[Answers may vary. Samples: St. Petersburg has a greater range than Key West. Every measure of Key West is farther to the left than the measures of St. Petersburg.]**

Answers

Got It? (continued)

3. Dauphin Island: mean: $69.08\overline{3}$, mode: 84, range: 33, $Q_1 = 58$, median: 71, $Q_3 = 81$, interquartile range: 23; Grand Isle: mean: $73.41\overline{6}$, modes: 61, 70, 77, 83, 85, range: 24, $Q_1 = 64.5$, median: 73.5, $Q_3 = 83$, interquartile range: 18.5; The range and the interquartile range show the temperatures varying less at Grand Isle than at Dauphin Island. Also, the temperatures at Grand Isle are generally higher.

Got It?

Q Do you think any value in the water temperature data is an outlier? Why or why not? **[No; no temperature varies greatly from the others.]**

Problem 5

Q At about what percentiles do you think Q_1, Q_2, and Q_3 are? Verify your answer. **[25th, 50th, and 75th percentile: 25th = 67 and Q_1 = 70; 50th = 77 and Q_2 = 78; 75th = 89 and Q_3 = 91]**

Q When would Q_1, Q_2, and Q_3 equal the 25th, 50th, and 75th percentiles? **[with an odd number of data]**

Got It?

Q How do you find the value at the 95th percentile? **[20 · 0.95 = 19. Then find the 19th data value.]**

3 Lesson Check

Do you know HOW?
• For Exercise 4, calculating the percentiles will not return an integer value (e.g., $13 \times 0.4 = 5.2$). Students should round to the nearest integer to find the closest data value.

Do you UNDERSTAND?
• If students have trouble spotting the error in Exercise 6, encourage them to write out the full data set.

Close

Q When is the mean the most useful measure of central tendency? the median? the mode? **[Sample: mean: when a data set has a small range; median: when a data set has a larger range or an outlier; mode: for finding the most common value]**

 Got It? 4. a. How can you use graphing calculator box-and-whisker plots to find water temperature quartiles for other Gulf Coast sites from Problem 3 and Got It 3?
   b. Reasoning Is a box-and-whisker plot a useful graphical display for data with an outlier? Explain.

A **percentile** is a number from 0 to 100 that you can associate with a value x from a data set. It shows the percent of the data that are less than or equal to x. For example, if x is at the 63rd percentile, then 63% of the data are less than or equal to x.

Problem 5 Finding Percentiles

Testing Here is an ordered list of midterm test scores for a Spanish class. What value is at the 65th percentile?

41	54	61	65	67	73	74
77	77	77	79	80	82	88
89	93	97	98	98	100	

Of these 20 values, 65% fall at or below the value at the 65th percentile.

Find 65% of 20. $20 \cdot 65\% = 20 \cdot 0.65 = 13$

So, there are 13 values at or below the 65% percentile. Count to find the 13th value in the ordered data set: 82.

The value at the 65% percentile is 82.

 Got It? 5. What is the value at each percentile for the data in Problem 5?
   a. 55th percentile   **b.** 95th percentile

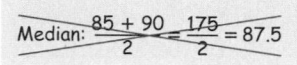
Plan
What should you do first to find percentiles? Make sure the data is in order.

Focus Question How can you compare and describe sets of data?
Answer Use the different measures of central tendency, as well as the range and interquartile range to compare and describe sets of data. Find the mean, median, and mode(s), and take any outliers into consideration.

Lesson Check

Do you know HOW?

Identify the outlier in the data set. Then find the mean, median, and mode of the data set both when the outlier is included and when it is not.

1. 16 19 21 18 18 54 20 22 23 17

2. 90 100 110 40 98 102 112 90 92

3. Find the values at the 40th and 80th percentiles for the values below.

   58 53 35 60 58 42 57 60 43 44 51 49 58

Do you UNDERSTAND?

4. Error Analysis A student found the median of the data set below. Explain and correct the student's error.

Score	80	85	90	95
Frequency	6	4	10	1

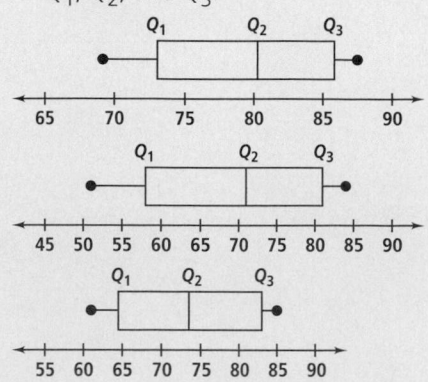

$$\text{Median:} \frac{85 + 90}{2} = \frac{175}{2} = 87.5$$

728   Chapter 11 Probability and Statistics

Answers

Got It? (continued)

4. a. Use STAT PLOT, select a box-and-whisker plot. Enter data for the three remaining Gulf Coast sites. Enter the window values. Draw the box-and-whisker plots. Use TRACE on the plot to find quartiles Q_1, Q_2, and Q_3.

b. Yes, a box-and-whisker plot uses minimum and maximum values, the median, and the first and third quartiles to display the variability in a data set.

5. a. 79
   b. 98

Lesson Check

1. outlier: 54; outlier included: mean: 22.8, median: 19.5, mode: 18; outlier not included: mean: $19.\overline{3}$, median: 19, mode: 18

2. outlier: 40; outlier included: mean: $92.\overline{6}$, median: 98, mode: 90; outlier not included: mean: 99.25, median: 99, mode: 90

3. 40%: 51 and below; 80%: 58 and below

4. The error is in how to calculate the median. The median is the middle value, or the 11th value, which is 90.

Practice and Problem-Solving Exercises

A Practice

Find the mean, median, and mode of each set of values. ◀ **See Problem 1.**

5. Time spent on Internet per day (in minutes): 75 68 43 120 65 180 95 225 140

6.

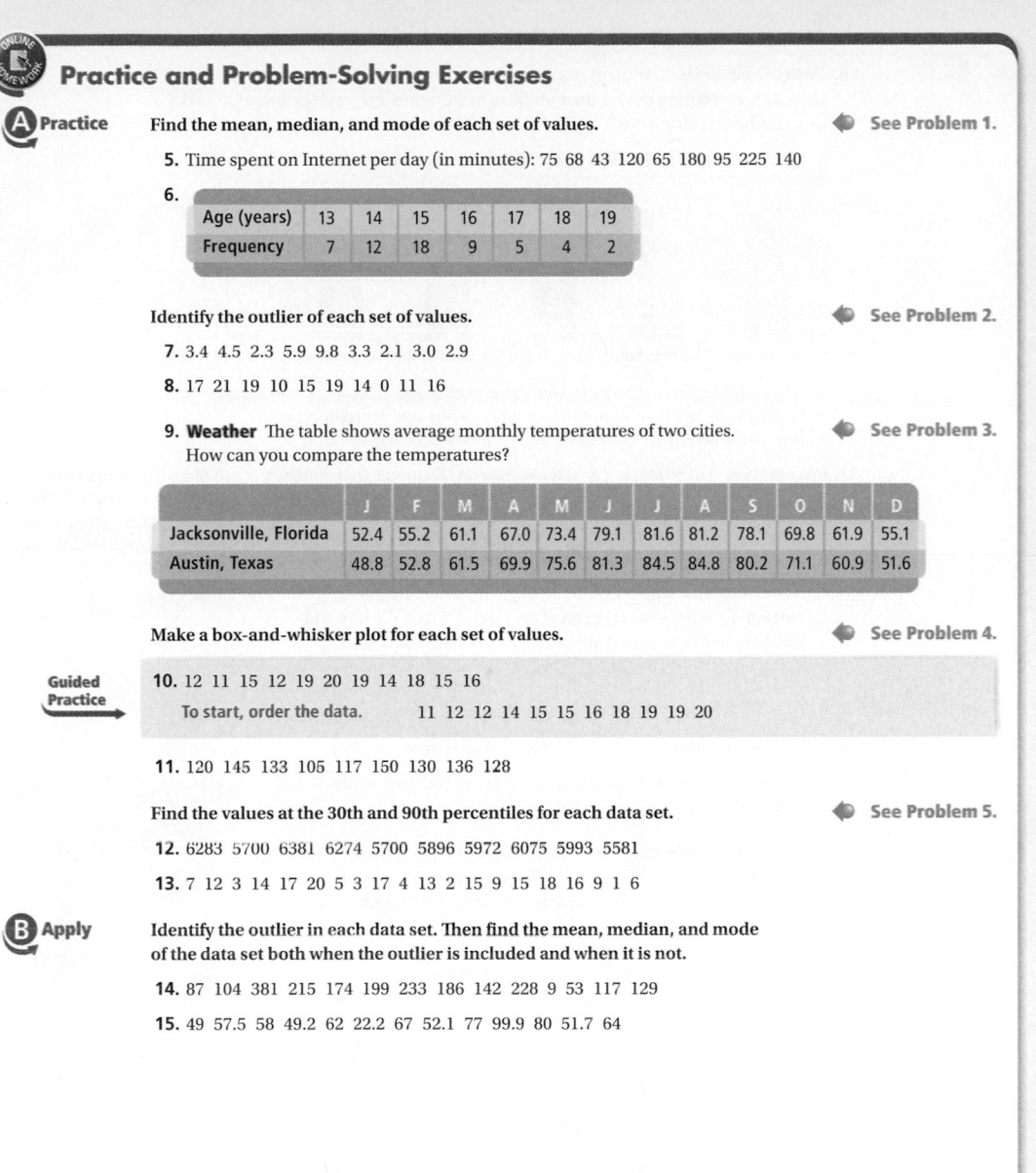

Age (years)	13	14	15	16	17	18	19
Frequency	7	12	18	9	5	4	2

Identify the outlier of each set of values. ◀ **See Problem 2.**

7. 3.4 4.5 2.3 5.9 9.8 3.3 2.1 3.0 2.9

8. 17 21 19 10 15 19 14 0 11 16

9. **Weather** The table shows average monthly temperatures of two cities. How can you compare the temperatures? ◀ **See Problem 3.**

	J	F	M	A	M	J	J	A	S	O	N	D
Jacksonville, Florida	52.4	55.2	61.1	67.0	73.4	79.1	81.6	81.2	78.1	69.8	61.9	55.1
Austin, Texas	48.8	52.8	61.5	69.9	75.6	81.3	84.5	84.8	80.2	71.1	60.9	51.6

Make a box-and-whisker plot for each set of values. ◀ **See Problem 4.**

Guided Practice ▶

10. 12 11 15 12 19 20 19 14 18 15 16

To start, order the data.   11 12 12 14 15 15 16 18 19 19 20

11. 120 145 133 105 117 150 130 136 128

Find the values at the 30th and 90th percentiles for each data set. ◀ **See Problem 5.**

12. 6283 5700 6381 6274 5700 5896 5972 6075 5993 5581

13. 7 12 3 14 17 20 5 3 17 4 13 2 15 9 15 18 16 9 1 6

B Apply

Identify the outlier in each data set. Then find the mean, median, and mode of the data set both when the outlier is included and when it is not.

14. 87 104 381 215 174 199 233 186 142 228 9 53 117 129

15. 49 57.5 58 49.2 62 22.2 67 52.1 77 99.9 80 51.7 64

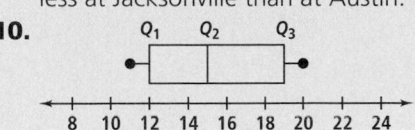
---

4 Practice

ASSIGNMENT GUIDE
Basic: 5–16, 16, 17, 20
Average: 5–21
Standardized Test Prep: 23–26
Mixed Review: 27–34

Reasoning exercises have blue headings.

Applications exercises have red headings.

EXERCISE 17: Use the Think About a Plan worksheet in the **Student Companion** (also available in the Teaching Resources in print and online) to further support students' development in becoming independent learners.

HOMEWORK QUICK CHECK
To check students' understanding of key skills and concepts, go over Exercises 7, 11, 16, 17, and 20.

Practice and Problem-Solving Exercises

5. mean: 112.$\overline{3}$, median: 95, mode: none

6. mean: ≈15.23, median: 15, mode: 15

7. 9.8

8. 0

9. Jacksonville: mean: 67.991$\overline{6}$, mode: none, range: 29.2, Q_1 = 58.15, median: 68.4, Q_3 = 78.6, interquartile range: 20.45; Austin: mean: 68.58$\overline{3}$, mode: none, range: 36, Q_1 = 56.85, median: 70.5, Q_3 = 80.75, interquartile range: 23.9; the range and the interquartile range show the temperatures varying less at Jacksonville than at Austin.

10.
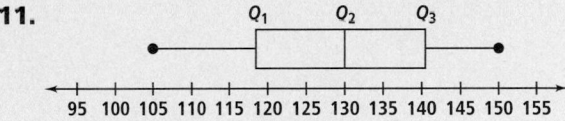

11.
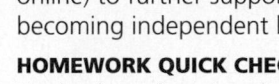

12. 5700; 6283

13. 5; 17

14. outlier: 381; outlier included: mean: ≈161.214, median: 158, mode: none; outlier not included: mean: ≈144.308, median: 142, mode: none

15. outliers: 22.2 and 99.9; outliers included: mean: ≈60.74, median: 58, mode: none; both outliers not included: mean: 60.6$\overline{81}$, median: 58, mode: none

Answers

Practice and Problem-Solving Exercises (continued)

16.

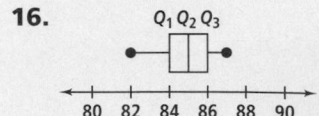

17. a.

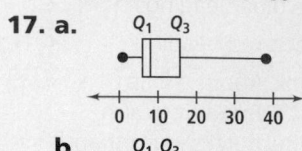

b.

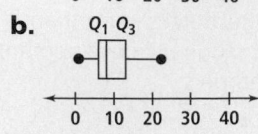

c. The main effect of removing the outlier is a shortening of the long whisker. The median decreases from 8.5 to 8.

18. 30th

19. 65th

20. 89 is at the 100th percentile since 100% of the values are less than or equal to 89.

21. a. mean: $1047.88, median: $1049.50, mode: $695

b. mode; it gives the lowest price

c. median; when extreme values (outliers) are involved ($695 and $1499), the median gives a more accurate measure of central tendency

22. a. 7

b. 4

c. 4

---

16. Think About a Plan Use the water temperature data for the eastern coast of the Gulf of Mexico during the summer months, as shown in the graph below. Find the quartiles by graphing a box-and-whisker plot of the data.

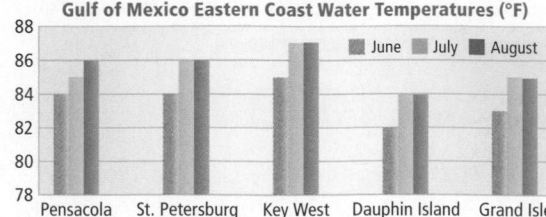

- What information can you get from the graph?
- How can you use that information to make a box-and-whisker plot?
- How can you find the quartiles using your box-and-whisker plot?

17. Meteorology On May 3, 1999, 59 tornadoes hit Oklahoma in the largest tornado outbreak ever recorded in the state. Sixteen of these were classified as strong (F2 or F3) or violent (F4 or F5).

a. Make a box-and-whisker plot of the data for length of path.

b. Identify the outliers. Remove them from the data set and make a revised box-and-whisker plot.

c. Writing How does the removal of the outliers affect the box-and-whisker plot? How does it affect the median of the data set?

For Exercises 18–20, use the set of values below.

1 1 1 1 1 1 2 3 5 8 13 21 34 55 89 89 89 89 89 89

18. At what percentile is 1? **19.** At what percentile is 34?

20. Error Analysis A student claims that 89 is at the 70th percentile. Explain the student's error.

21. Advertising An electronics store placed an ad in the newspaper showing flat-screen TVs for sale. The ad says "Our flat-screen TVs average $695." The prices of the flat-screen TVs are $1200, $999, $1499, $895, $695, $1100, $1300, and $695.

a. Find the mean, median, and mode of the prices.

b. Which measure is the store using in its ad? Why did they choose it?

c. As a consumer, which measure would you want to see advertised? Explain your reasoning.

22. The table displays the frequency of scores for one Calculus class on the Advanced Placement Calculus exam. The mean of the exam scores is 3.5.

a. What is the value of f in the table?

b. What is the mode of all of the exam scores?

c. What is the median of all of the exam scores?

Score	1	2	3	4	5
Frequency	1	3	f	12	3

Major Tornadoes in Oklahoma, May 3, 1999

Length of Path (miles)	Intensity
6	F3
9	F3
4	F2
37	F5
7	F2
12	F3
8	F2
7	F2
15	F4
39	F4
1	F2
22	F3
15	F3
8	F2
13	F3
2	F2

Source: National Oceanic & Atmospheric Administration

Standardized Test Prep

SAT/ACT

23. Use a calculator to solve $2x^2 - 7x - 5 = 0$. Round answers to the nearest hundredth.

    Ⓐ $-1.56, -4.44$ Ⓑ $-5.44, 1.56$ Ⓒ $-0.61, 4.11$ Ⓓ $-5.56, -1.44$

24. Which function generates the table of values at the right?

x	y
−2	$\frac{27}{8}$
−1	$\frac{9}{2}$
0	6
1	8
2	$\frac{32}{3}$

    Ⓕ $y = 27\left(\frac{2}{3}\right)^x$ Ⓗ $y = \left(\frac{8}{3}\right)^x$

    Ⓖ $y = 6\left(\frac{4}{3}\right)^x$ Ⓘ $y = 6\left(\frac{3}{4}\right)^x$

25. A homeroom class consists of 6 boys whose last name begins with S, 8 boys whose last name begins with T, 4 girls whose last name begins with S, and 11 girls whose last name begins with T. A student is chosen at random from the class. What is the probability that the student is a girl or has a last name that begins with S?

    Ⓐ $\frac{18}{29}$ Ⓒ $\frac{23}{29}$

    Ⓑ $\frac{21}{29}$ Ⓓ $\frac{25}{29}$

Short Response

26. In a library, the probability that a book is a hardback, given that it is illustrated, is 0.40. The probability that a book is hardback *and* illustrated is 0.20. Find the probability that a book is illustrated.

Mixed Review

Of all the respondents to a survey, 59% are girls. Of the girls, 61% read horror stories. Of the boys, 49% read horror stories. Find each probability.

◀ See Lesson 11-4.

27. P(boy and reads horror stories)   **28.** P (reads horror stories)

Determine whether each sequence is arithmetic. If it is, identify the common difference.

◀ See Lesson 9-2.

29. $16, 7, -2, \ldots$ **30.** $34, 51, 68, \ldots$ **31.** $2, 2.2, 2.22, \ldots$

Get Ready!   To prepare for Lesson 11-6, do Exercises 32–34.

Find all real square roots of each number.

◀ See Lesson 6-1.

32. 256   **33.** 0.0001   **34.** $\frac{121}{16}$

Standardized Test Prep

23. C

24. G

25. B

26. [2] $P(H|I) = 0.40$, $P(H \text{ and } I) = 0.20$

$$P(H|I) = \frac{P(H \text{ and } I)}{P(I)}$$

$$0.40 = \frac{0.20}{P(I)}$$

$$P(I) = 0.50$$

[1] appropriate method, but with one computational error OR correct probability, without work shown

Mixed Review

27. ≈0.20

28. ≈0.56

29. yes; −9

30. yes; 17

31. no

32. ±16

33. ±0.09

34. $\pm\frac{11}{4}$

Additional Instructional Support

Algebra 2 Companion

Students can use the **Algebra 2 Companion** worktext (4 pages) as you teach the lesson. Use the Companion to support

- New Vocabulary
- Key Concepts
- Got It for each Problem
- Lesson Check

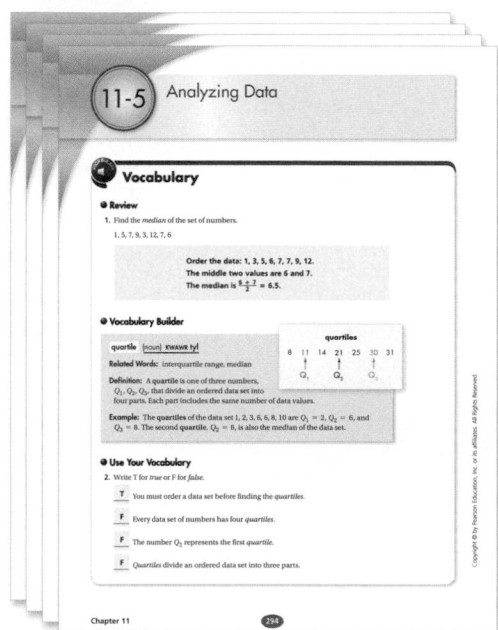

ELL Support

Use Graphic Organizers Have students work in groups of two or three. Have each group research a small data set with at least eight values. This could be real-world data like the population of South American countries, or data about classmates, like a frequency table of birth months.

Have students make a large table with four rows: *mean*, *median*, *mode*, and *range*. In the first column, students write a brief description of each measure of central tendency. In the second column, students write the data set in order and show the mathematical operations to arrive at the desired measure: adding and dividing for the mean, circling the middle number(s) for the median, underlining the most common numbers for the mode, subtracting greatest and least for the range.

5 Assess & Remediate

Lesson Quiz

1. Which is an outlier for this data set:
170 210 192 105 188 179 195?

2. Do you UNDERSTAND? The table shows the heights in inches of men's tennis rosters. How can you compare the heights?

Florida	Florida State
76	69
74	74
74	69
74	73
73	68
74	71
71	71
75	70
70	74

3. The data shows the ages of passengers on a city bus. What value is at the 75th percentile?
8 9 12 15 19 22 28 35
35 39 44 45 45 47 48
50 52 55 56

ANSWERS TO LESSON QUIZ

1. 105

2. Florida: mean 73.4; mode 74; range 6; median 74; Q_1 72; Q_2 74; Q_3 74.5; IQR 2.5

Florida State: mean 71; modes 69, 71, 74; range 6; median 71; Q_1 69; Q_2 71; Q_3 73.5; IQR 4.5

3. 47

PRESCRIPTION FOR REMEDIATION

Use the student work on the Lesson Quiz to prescribe a differentiated review assignment:

Points	Differentiated Remediation
0–1	Intervention
2	On-level
3	Extension

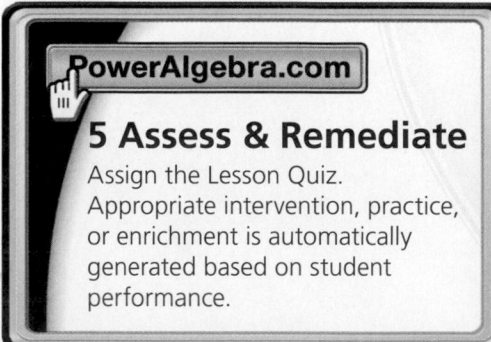

PowerAlgebra.com

5 Assess & Remediate

Assign the Lesson Quiz. Appropriate intervention, practice, or enrichment is automatically generated based on student performance.

Intervention

- **Reteaching** (2 pages) Provides reteaching and practice exercises for the key lesson concepts. Use with struggling students or absent students.

- **English Language Learner Support** Helps students develop and reinforce mathematical vocabulary and key concepts.

All-in-One Resources/Online
Reteaching

11-5 **Reteaching**
Analyzing Data

- The *mean* is the average of the values.
- The *median* is the middle value(s) when the values are listed in order.
- The *mode* is the most common value(s).

Problem

What are the mean, median, and mode for the data set below?

2 2 5 5 1 3 6 6 3 5 3 4 3 2 4 4 5 2 4 1 3 5 5 3 5 3 4 3 5 3 3 1 5 6

Step 1 Find the mean. The mean is the average of the values. Add all the values, and then divide the sum by the number of values.
$\frac{124}{34} \approx 3.65$

Step 2 Find the median. Write the values in numerical order. For an odd number of values, the median is the middle value. For an even number of values, the median is the mean of the middle two values.

1 1 1 2 2 2 2 3 3 3 3 3 3 3 3 3 | 3 4 | 4 4 4 4 5 5 5 5 5 5 5 5 5 6 6 6
    16 values   2 values   16 values

The mean of the middle two values is $\frac{3+4}{2} = \frac{7}{2} = 3.5$.

Step 3 Find the mode(s). If no value occurs more than once, then the data set has no mode. How many times does each value occur in the data set?
  1: three times   2: four times   3: ten times
  4: five times   5: nine times   6: three times
The most common value is 3.

The mean is about 3.65, the median is 3.5, and the mode is 3.

Exercises

Find the mean, median, and mode of each set of values.

1. 872 888 895 870 882 878 891 890 888 about 883.8; 888; 888

2. 2020 2040 2068 2120 2015 2301 2254 about 2116.9; 2068; no mode

3. 25 27 26 33 28 26 24 30 26 28 24 27 27; 26.5; 26

4. 4.4 5.6 1.5 2.1 3.8 1.9 4.7 2.5 4.7 2.8 3.4; 3.3; 4.7

5. 194 502 413 768 986 616 259 351 825 546; 502; no mode

6. 36 37 38 37 38 37 26 36 39 40 40 40 35 about 36.9; 38 and 40

All-in-One Resources/Online
English Language Learner Support

11-5 **ELL Support**
Analyzing Data

Concept List

bimodal	box-and-whisker plot	interquartile range
mean	median	mode
outlier	quartiles	range of a data set

Choose the concept from the list above that best represents the item in each box.

1. 12, 36, 45, 12, 52, 27, 12 mode	2. 29, 7, 35, 29, 56, 12, 75, 26, 39, 8 $Q_3 - Q_1 = 39 - 12 = 27$ interquartile range	3. 4, 7, 2, 9, 14, 8, 46 outlier
4. 34, 72, 29, 25, 13, 81, 56 $81 - 13 = 68$ range of a data set	5. 15, 17, 19, 19, 21, 23, 24 median	6. 20 30 40 50 60 70 80 box-and-whisker plot
7. 54, 74, 15, 91, 23, 54, 21, 15 bimodal	8. 44, 15, 76, 34, 91 $44 + 15 + 76 + 34 + 91 = 260$ $260 \div 5 = 52$ mean	9. 7, 9, 17, 26, 38, 40, 45, 53, 55, 62 $Q_1 = 17$ $Q_2 = 39$ $Q_3 = 53$ $Q_4 = 62$ quartiles

Differentiated Remediation *continued*

On-Level

- **Practice** (2 pages) Provides extra practice for each lesson. For more challenging practice exercises, use the Form G Practice pages found in the All-in-One Teaching Resources and online.

- **Think About a Plan** Helps students develop specific problem-solving skills and strategies by providing scaffolded guiding questions.

- **Standardized Test Prep** Focuses on all major exercises, all major question types, and helps students prepare for the high-stakes assessments.

Extension

- **Enrichment** Provides students with interesting problems and activities that extend the concepts of the lesson.

- **Activities, Games, and Puzzles** Worksheets that can be used for concepts development, enrichment, and for fun!

Student Companion/All-in-One Resources/Online
Practice page 1

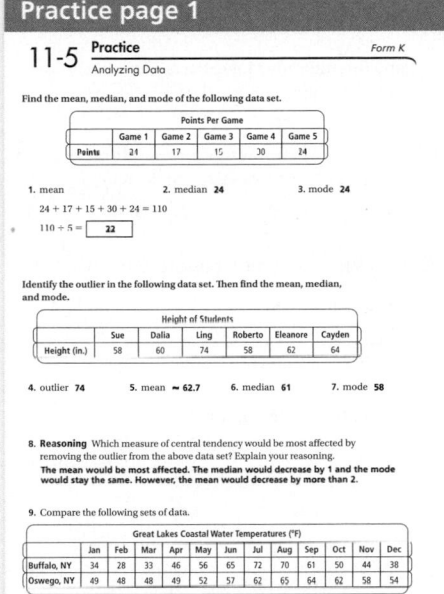

Student Companion/All-in-One Resources/Online
Practice page 2

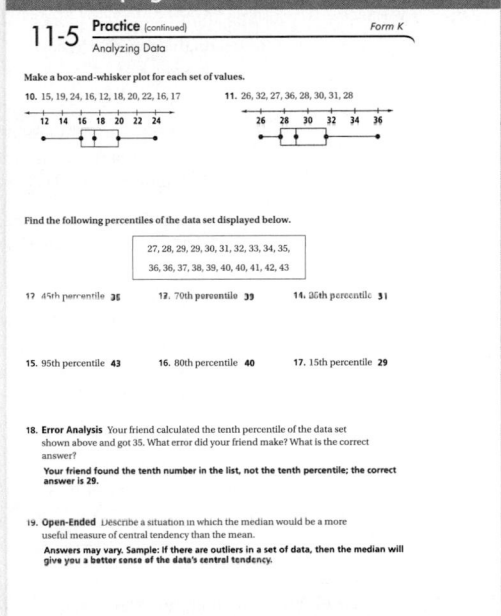

All-in-One Resources/Online
Enrichment

11-5 Enrichment — Analyzing Data

Moments to Remember

Student Companion/All-in-One Resources/Online
Think About a Plan

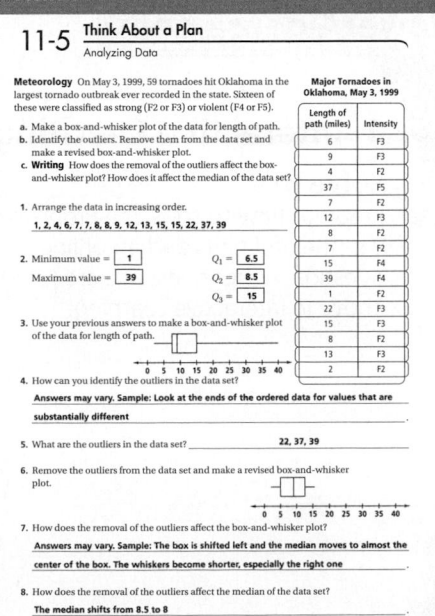

Student Companion/All-in-One Resources/Online
Standardized Test Prep

11-5 Standardized Test Prep — Analyzing Data

Online Teacher Resource Center
Activities, Games, and Puzzles

11-5 Puzzle: Can We Set a Data? — Analyzing Data

1 Interactive Learning

Solve It!
PURPOSE To compare the results of two summations

PROCESS Students may
- substitute the same nonnegative numbers for x in both expressions and compare results.
- find the length of the diagonal of the rectangular prism using $d = \sqrt{\ell^2 + w^2 + h^2}$.

FACILITATE

Q For which summation expression does it matter whether x_i is nonnegative? Explain. **[The first expression; negative numbers affect the sum. In the second expression, squaring negates the effects of negatives.]**

ANSWER See Solve It in Answers on next page.

CONNECT THE MATH In the Solve It, students compare a sum of data values to the square root of the sum of the squares of those data values. In the lesson, students use the square root of the sum of the differences of data values from the mean to find the standard deviation.

2 Guided Instruction

Take Note

Q If all the values in a data set are equal, what is the standard deviation of the set? **[0]**

Q Suppose each data value in the set is increased by the same amount. How are the mean and the standard deviation of the set affected? **[The mean increases by that number, but the standard deviation does not change.]**

Objectives To find the standard deviation and variance of a set of values
To apply standard deviation and variance

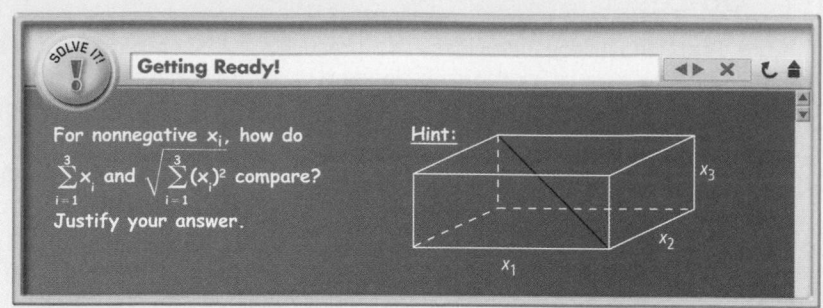

Getting Ready!

For nonnegative x_i, how do $\sum_{i=1}^{3} x_i$ and $\sqrt{\sum_{i=1}^{3} (x_i)^2}$ compare? Justify your answer.

Hint:

Lesson Vocabulary
- measure of variation
- variance
- standard deviation

You learned about summation notation in Chapter 9. To find the mean of a data set, you add the data values and divide by the number of data values. You can use summation to measure how data deviates from the mean.

Focus Question What are standard deviation and variance?

In the previous lesson you studied range and interquartile range. Each of these is a **measure of variation**. A measure of variation describes how the data in a data set are spread out.

Variance and **standard deviation** are measures showing how much data values deviate from the mean. The Greek letter σ (sigma) represents standard deviation. σ^2 (sigma squared) is the variance.

Key Concepts   Finding Variance and Standard Deviation

To find the standard deviation, σ, follow these five steps:

1. Find the mean, $\bar{x}$, of the n values in a data set.
2. Find the difference, $x - \bar{x}$, between each value x and the mean.
3. Square each difference, $(x - \bar{x})^2$.
4. Find the average (mean) of these squares. This is the variance.
$$\sigma^2 = \frac{\sum (x - \bar{x})^2}{n}$$
5. Take the square root of the variance. This is the standard deviation.
$$\sigma = \sqrt{\frac{\sum (x - \bar{x})^2}{n}}$$

11-6 Preparing to Teach

BIG idea Probability   UbD

ESSENTIAL UNDERSTANDING
Standard deviation is a measure of how far the numbers in a data set deviate from the mean.

Math Background
Measures of variation describe how data in a data set are spread out.

Variance is calculated by finding the average squared deviation of each value from the mean of the data. Because of this, it takes all of the data values into account.

Standard deviation is the positive square root of the variance. It is a measure of spread.

Calculating variance and standard deviation is sometimes difficult for students. Suggest that they write a checklist and use it for each problem until they are fully comfortable with the process. For example:
- Find the mean of the data set.

- Find the difference between each data value and the above mean. Write them in a list.
- Find and write down the square of each number on the list.
- Find the mean of the list of squares. This is the variance.

Take the square root of the variance to calculate the standard deviation.

Support Student Learning
Use the **Algebra 2 Companion** to engage and support students during instruction. See Lesson Resources at the end of this lesson for details.

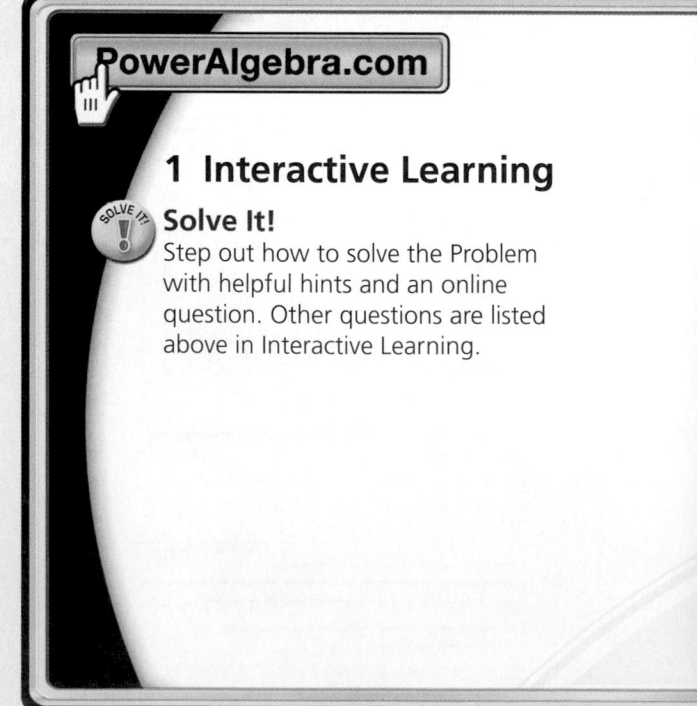

PowerAlgebra.com

1 Interactive Learning

Solve It!
Step out how to solve the Problem with helpful hints and an online question. Other questions are listed above in Interactive Learning.

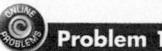 **Problem 1** Finding Variance and Standard Deviation

What are the mean, variance, and standard deviation of these values?
6.9 8.7 7.6 4.8 9.0

Step 1 Find the mean.

Use the formula and simplify. $\bar{x} = \dfrac{6.9 + 8.7 + 7.6 + 4.8 + 9.0}{5} = 7.4$

 Think

How can you organize your work?
Use a table to record the values.

Step 2 Find the variance.

Make a table. Use the columns shown.

x	$\bar{x}$	$x - \bar{x}$	$(x - \bar{x})^2$
6.9	7.4	−0.5	0.25
8.7	7.4	1.3	1.69
7.6	7.4	0.2	0.04
4.8	7.4	−2.6	6.76
9.0	7.4	1.6	2.56
			Sum: 11.30

Find the difference between each value and the mean. Square the differences.

Add the squares of the differences.

Write the formula for variance. $\sigma^2 = \dfrac{\sum (x - \bar{x})^2}{n}$

Subtitute and simplify. $= \dfrac{11.30}{5} = 2.26$

Step 3 Find the standard deviation.

Use the formula. Substitute and simplify. $\sigma = \sqrt{\sigma^2} = \sqrt{2.26} \approx 1.5$

The mean is 7.4. The variance is 2.26. The standard deviation is about 1.5.

✓ **Got It?** **1.** What are the mean, variance, and standard deviation of these values?
52 63 65 77 80 82

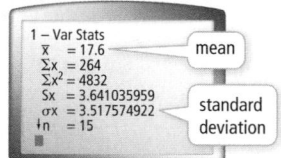 **Problem 2** Using a Calculator to Find Standard Deviation

Meteorology The table displays the number of U.S. hurricane strikes by decade from the years 1851 to 2000. What are the mean and standard deviation for this data set?

Decade	1	2	3	4	5	6	7	8	9	10	11	12	13	14	15
Strikes	19	15	20	22	21	18	21	13	19	24	17	14	12	15	14

Source: National Hurricane Center

Think

How do you know you are entering all the data values?
The calculator value for n should match the number of table values.

Use **STAT EDIT** to enter the data in list **L1**.

In **STAT CALC** select the **1– Var Stats** option.

The mean is 17.6, and the standard deviation is about 3.5.

```
1 - Var Stats
 x̄   = 17.6          ← mean
 Σx  = 264
 Σx² = 4832
 Sx  = 3.641035959
 σx  = 3.517574922   ← standard deviation
↓n   = 15
```

PowerAlgebra.com   Lesson 11-6   Standard Deviation   733

Problem 1 — EXTENSION

When calculating variance, squaring each value's difference from the mean serves two purposes:
- It makes each term positive, so values above the mean do not cancel values below.
- It amplifies larger deviations in the data set.

Q What is the sum of the differences from the mean in the third column of the table? **[0]**

Q Why is the sum of the differences from the mean of a data set always 0? **[The mean lies at the center of a distribution where the sum of data values above it equals the sum of the data values below it.]**

Q Can the variance of a data set be negative? Explain. **[No; the variance is the quotient of two positive numbers—the sum of the squares and the number of data values.]**

Finding the square root of the variance serves two purposes:
- It converts the measurement's unit back to the unit of the data values in the set.
- It reduces the size of the measurement so it is easier to use for data analysis.

Got It? — ELL SUPPORT

Students can add labels to their tables to help them understand the terms and symbols used: Left to right; "Data Value," "Mean of Data Set," "Difference from Mean," and "Square of Difference."

Problem 2 — EXTENSION

Q Does the VAR STATS screen give the variance of the data set? **[no]**

Q How can you use the information on the screen to find the variance? **[Square the standard deviation.]**

---

2 Guided Instruction

 Each Problem is worked out and supported online.

Problem 1
Finding Variance and Standard Deviation
Animated

Problem 2
Using a Calculator to Find Standard Deviation
Animated

Problem 3
Using Standard Deviation to Describe Data
Animated

Support in Algebra 2 Companion
- Vocabulary
- Key Concepts
- Got It?

Answers

Solve It!

$\sum\limits_{i=1}^{3} x_i$ is the sum of 3 values x_1, x_2, and x_3.

$\sqrt{\sum\limits_{i=1}^{3} (x_i)^2}$ is the square root of the sum of the square of three values i.e. $\sqrt{(x_1)^2 + (x_2)^2 + (x_3)^2}$.

Got It?

1. $\bar{x} = 69.8\overline{3}$, $\sigma^2 \approx 115.1389$, $\sigma \approx 10.7303$

Got It?   ERROR PREVENTION

Most scientific calculators save entered data sets. To avoid reusing older data sets, students can choose ClrStat to clear the previously used data.

Problem 3   ELL SUPPORT

Explain to students that in general about 95% of all data fall within two standard deviations of the mean.

> **Q** Does this result mean that the U.S. will never have more than 24.6 hurricane strikes in a decade? Explain. **[No; it is only a prediction. It means that more than 25 hurricanes is unlikely, but still possible.]**
>
> **Q** Do decimals like 10.6 and 24.6 for the data make sense in this problem? Explain. **[No; hurricanes are counted in whole numbers. You do not have 10.6 hurricane strikes in a decade; you have 10 or 11 strikes.]**

Got It?   VISUAL LEARNERS

A bell curve diagram can help students better understand normal distribution of data in a population.

Use a sketch of a bell curve to explain that in a normal distribution:

• about 68% of data values are within 1 standard deviation of the mean.
• about 95% are within 2 standard deviations.
• about 99% are within 3 standard deviations.

 Got It? 2. **Meteorology** The table displays the number of hurricanes in the Atlantic Ocean from 1992 to 2006. What are the mean and standard deviation?

Year	1	2	3	4	5	6	7	8	9	10	11	12	13	14	15
Number	4	4	3	11	10	3	10	8	8	9	4	7	9	14	5

SOURCE: National Hurricane Center

In a data list, every value falls within some number of standard deviations of the mean. For example, if the mean is 50 and the standard deviation is 10, then a value x, where $40 \leq x \leq 60$, is within one standard deviation of the mean.

 Problem 3 Using Standard Deviation to Describe Data

Meteorology Use the U.S. hurricane-strike data from Problem 2. Within how many standard deviations from the mean do all of the values fall?

Know	Need	Plan
The data values, their mean, and their standard deviation	The number of standard deviations from the mean that include all the data	• Draw a number line. • Plot the data values and the mean. • Mark off intervals of 3.5 on either side of the mean.

 **Think**
What is a good way to tell which values lie within each σ interval?
Plotting the values on a number line makes it easy to see the σ intervals.

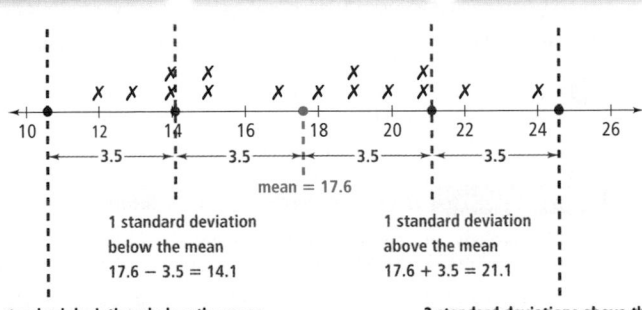

1 standard deviation below the mean
$17.6 - 3.5 = 14.1$

1 standard deviation above the mean
$17.6 + 3.5 = 21.1$

2 standard deviations below the mean
$17.6 - 2(3.5) = 10.6$

2 standard deviations above the mean
$17.6 + 2(3.5) = 24.6$

All of the values fall within two standard deviations of the mean. Hurricane watchers can expect that the number of U.S. hurricane strikes in a decade will probably fall within two standard deviations of the 15-decade mean.

 Got It? 3. **Meteorology** Use the Atlantic Ocean hurricane data from Got It 2.
a. Within how many standard deviations of the mean do all of the values fall?
b. **Reasoning** How might the U.S. Federal Emergency Management Agency (FEMA) use this information?

Additional Problems

1. What are the mean, variance, and standard deviation of these values?
6.5 5.8 3.9 5.7 4.2

ANSWER mean = 5.22; variance: 0.9976; standard deviation ≈ 0.999

2. The table displays the number of sales a salesperson made each month during the past 15 months. What are the mean and standard deviation?

ANSWER mean = 4.4; standard deviation ≈ 1.82

Month	Sales
1	4
2	3
3	5
4	4
5	6
6	8
7	1
8	3
9	2
10	5
11	6
12	4
13	7
14	5
15	3

3. Use the sales data from Exercise 2. Within how many standard deviations of the mean do all of the values fall?

ANSWER All of the data values fall within two standard deviations of the mean.

Answers

Got It? (continued)
2. $\bar{x} = 7.2\overline{6}$, $\sigma \approx 3.214$
3. a. within 3 standard deviations of the mean
b. FEMA can expect that the no. of hurricanes for a 15-year period will fall within 3 standard deviations of the mean.

Focus Question What are standard deviation and variance?

Answer Standard deviation and variance are measures of how the data values of a data set vary from the mean. The standard deviation is the square root of the variance. Use variance to describe how spread out a set of data is.

Lesson Check

Do you know HOW?

1. Find the mean, variance, and standard deviation for the data set.

5, 15, 9, 3, 12, 8, 13, 6, 18, 11

2. Within how many standard deviations of the mean do all of the data values fall?

12, 17, 15, 13, 9, 10, 12, 10, 15, 17

Do you UNDERSTAND?

3. Vocabulary Explain the difference between *measures of central tendency* and *measures of variation*.

4. Compare and Contrast Three data sets each have a mean of 70. Set A has a standard deviation of 10. Set B has a standard deviation of 5. Set C has a standard deviation of 20. Compare and contrast these 3 sets.

Practice and Problem-Solving Exercises

 **Practice**

Find the mean, variance, and standard deviation for each data set. ◀ **See Problem 1.**

Guided Practice

To start, find the mean of the data.

5. 78 90 456 673 111 381 21

$$\bar{x} = \frac{78 + 90 + 456 + 673 + 111 + 381 + 21}{7}$$

$$\approx 258.57$$

6. 13 15 17 18 12 21 10   **7.** 12 3 2 4 5 7   **8.** 60 40 35 45 39

Graphing Calculator Find the mean and the standard deviation. ◀ **See Problem 2.**

9. The Dow Jones Industrial average for the first 12 weeks of 1988:

| 1911.31 | 1956.07 | 1903.51 | 1958.22 | 1910.48 | 1983.26 |
| 2014.59 | 2023.21 | 2057.86 | 2034.98 | 2087.37 | 2067.14 |

10. The Dow Jones Industrial average for the first 12 weeks of 2008:

| 12800.18 | 12606.30 | 12099.3 | 12207.17 | 12743.19 | 12182.13 |
| 12348.21 | 12381.02 | 12266.39 | 11893.69 | 11951.09 | 11972.25 |

3 Lesson Check

Do you know HOW?

- For Exercise 1, suggest using a table to organize the computations as shown in Problem 1.
- For Exercises 1 and 2, students can use a calculator to verify their answers.

Do you UNDERSTAND?

- For Exercise 3, if necessary, remind students that mean, median, and mode are measures of central tendency. Range, interquartile range, variance, and standard deviation are measures of variation.
- For Exercise 4, students can use graphs to help compare and contrast the data sets. The mean is the peak of each graph's curve, which changes to concave-up at approximately one standard deviation greater than and less than the mean.

Close

Q What is standard deviation and how is it used? **[Answers may vary. Sample: Standard deviation is a measure of how the values of a data set vary from the mean. It is used to analyze data and to make predictions.]**

Lesson Check

1. $\bar{x} = 10$, $\sigma^2 = 19.8$, $\sigma \approx 4.45$

2. within two standard deviations of the mean

3. Measures of central tendency are specific data pts. which give a summary of the middle of the data set, whereas the measures of variation give a summary of the variation of the data set within the range of distribution.

4. Standard deviation measures how widely spread the data values are. If the data pts. are close to the mean, the standard deviation is small; if the data pts. are far from the mean, the standard deviation is large. The data pts. of Set B are closer to the mean of 70 than the data pts. of Sets A and C; likewise, the data pts. of Set A are closer to 70 than the data pts. of Set C.

Practice and Problem-Solving Exercises

5. $\bar{x} \approx 258.6$, $\sigma^2 \approx 52,136.81$, $\sigma \approx 228.3$

6. $\bar{x} \approx 15.1$, $\sigma^2 \approx 12.34$, $\sigma \approx 3.5$

7. $\bar{x} \approx 5.5$, $\sigma^2 \approx 10.9$, $\sigma \approx 3.3$

8. $\bar{x} \approx 43.8$, $\sigma^2 \approx 75.76$, $\sigma \approx 8.7$

9. $\bar{x} \approx 1992.\overline{3}$, $\sigma \approx 61.85$

10. $\bar{x} \approx 12,287.58$, $\sigma \approx 289.49$

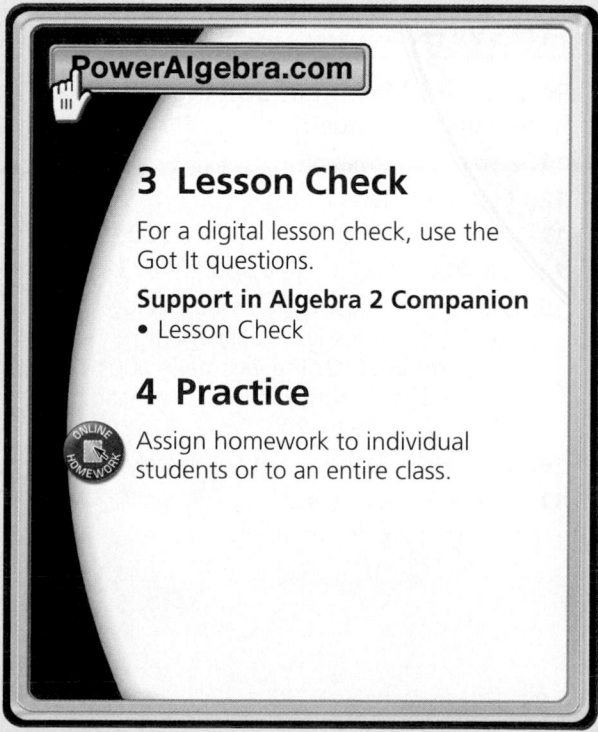

PowerAlgebra.com

3 Lesson Check

For a digital lesson check, use the Got It questions.

Support in Algebra 2 Companion
- Lesson Check

4 Practice

Assign homework to individual students or to an entire class.

4 Practice

ASSIGNMENT GUIDE

Basic: 5–13, 17, 18

Average: 5–18

Standardized Test Prep: 5–18

Mixed Review: 19–22

Reasoning exercises have blue headings.

Applications exercises have red headings.

EXERCISE 17: Use the Think About a Plan worksheet in the **Student Companion** (also available in the Teaching Resources in print and online) to further support students' development in becoming independent learners.

HOMEWORK QUICK CHECK

To check students' understanding of key skills and concepts, go over Exercises 7, 9, 12, 17, and 23.

Determine the whole number of standard deviations from the mean that include all data values.   ◀ See Problem 3.

11. The mean price of the nonfiction books on a best-sellers list is $25.07; the standard deviation is $2.62.
$26.95, $22.95, $24.00, $24.95, $29.95, $19.95, $24.95, $24.00, $27.95, $25.00

12. The mean length of Beethoven's nine symphonies is 37 minutes; the standard deviation is 12 minutes.
27 min, 30 min, 47 min, 35 min, 30 min, 40 min, 35 min, 22 min, 65 min

Ⓑ Apply

13. **Think About a Plan** Use the data for daily energy usage of a small town during ten days in June. Find the mean and the standard deviation of the data. How many values in the data set fall within one standard deviation from the mean? Within two standard deviations? Within three standard deviations?

| 51.8 MWh | 53.6 MWh | 54.7 MWh | 51.9 MWh | 49.3 MWh |
| 52.0 MWh | 53.5 MWh | 51.2 MWh | 60.7 MWh | 59.3 MWh |

- How is the mean of the data set used in the formula for standard deviation?
- How can a table help you find the standard deviation?
- How can a graph help you decide how many standard deviations a data value is from the mean?

Income Use the chart at the right for Exercises 14–16.

14. Find the mean income for each year.

15. **Writing** Use the standard deviation for each year to describe how farm income varied from 2001 to 2002.

16. For 2001, the farm incomes of which states are not within one standard deviation of the mean?

17. **Energy** The data for daily energy usage of a small town during ten days in January is shown.

83.8 MWh   87.1 MWh   92.5 MWh   80.6 MWh   82.4 MWh
77.6 MWh   78.9 MWh   78.2 MWh   81.8 MWh   80.1 MWh

a. Find the mean and the standard deviation of the data.
b. How many values in the data set fall within one standard deviation from the mean? Within two standard deviations? Within three standard deviations?

Farm Income in Midwestern States (millions of dollars)

State	2001	2002
Iowa	10,653	10,834
Kansas	7979	7862
Minnesota	7537	7478
Missouri	4723	4402
Nebraska	9221	9589
North Dakota	2938	3223
South Dakota	3897	3779

Source: U.S. Department of Agriculture

Answers

Practice and Problem-Solving Exercises (continued)

11. 2 standard deviations

12. 3 standard deviations

13. $\bar{x} = 53.8$, $\sigma \approx 3.4$; 1σ: 7; 2σ: 9; 3σ: 10

14. year 2001: ≈6707; year 2002: ≈6738

15. Overall farm income increased slightly, but there was less variability among the states in 2002. The income in 2001 clustered more tightly around the mean. (2001: $\sigma_x \approx 2679$, 2002: $\sigma_x \approx 2758$)

16. Iowa, North Dakota, and South Dakota

17. a. $\bar{x} = 82.3$, $\sigma \approx 4.3$
    b. 1σ: 7; 2σ: 9; 3σ: 10

18. Error Analysis One of your friends says that the data below fall within three standard deviations from the mean. Your other friend disagrees, saying that the data fall within six standard deviations from the mean. With whom do you agree? Explain.

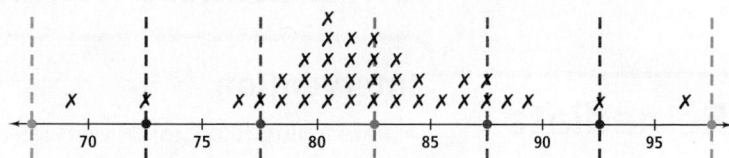

mean = 82.5

Standardized Test Prep

GRIDDED RESPONSE

SAT/ACT

For Exercises 19–20, use the following bowling scores for six members of a bowling team: 175, 210, 180, 195, 208, 196.

19. What is the mean of the scores?

20. What is the standard deviation of the scores?

21. The 30th term of a finite arithmetic series is 4.4. The sum of the first 30 terms is 78. What is the value of the first term of the series?

22. What is the probability of NOT getting a five when rolling a number cube? Write your answer as a fraction reduced to lowest terms.

Mixed Review

Make a box-and-whisker plot for each set of values.   ◀ See Lesson 11-5.

23. 25, 25, 30, 35, 45, 45, 50, 55, 60, 60   **24.** 20, 23, 25, 36, 37, 38, 39, 50, 52, 55

Find the center and the radius of each circle.   ◀ See Lesson 10-3.

25. $(x - 2)^2 + (y + 1)^2 = 36$ **26.** $(x - 1)^2 + (y - 1)^2 = 4$

Get Ready! To prepare for Lesson 11-7, do Exercises 27–29.

Simplify each radical expression.   ◀ See Lesson 6-1.

27. $\dfrac{1}{\sqrt{4}}$ **28.** $-\dfrac{1}{\sqrt{9}}$ **29.** $\dfrac{1}{\sqrt{36}}$

18. Your first friend; one standard deviation encompasses all values within one standard deviation above and below the mean. The graph shows that all values are within 3 standard deviations of the mean.

25. center (2, −1); radius 6

26. center (1, 1); radius 2

27. $\dfrac{1}{2}$

28. $-\dfrac{1}{3}$

Standardized Test Prep

19. 194

20. 13

21. 0.8

22. $\dfrac{5}{6}$

29. $\dfrac{1}{6}$

Mixed Review

23.

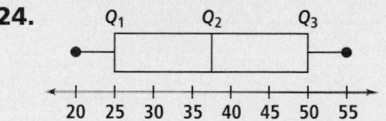

24.

Additional Instructional Support

Algebra 2 Companion

Students can use the **Algebra 2 Companion** worktext (4 pages) as you teach the lesson. Use the Companion to support

- New Vocabulary
- Key Concepts
- Got It for each Problem
- Lesson Check

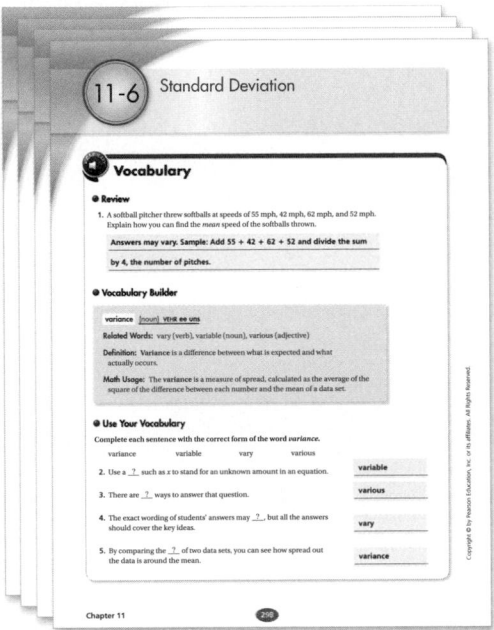

ELL Support

Focus on Language Write *vary, variance,* and *variation* on the board. Underline *vary* and explain that it is a verb meaning "to change or to make different." Use a group of different-sized objects to illustrate the meaning. (They vary in size: some are large; some are small.)

Now circle *variance* and underline its root *vari.* Explain that *variance* is a noun form of *vary* that means "the quality, state, or fact of changing or being different." Repeat the process for *variation* (the act or process of changing or being different). Use both nouns in sentences that show their meanings.

Finally, write *variable* on the board and remind students that a variable is a letter used to stand for an unknown value in an equation. Underline *vari* in *variable* and challenge students to explain how the meaning of *variable* relates to the meaning of its root *vary.*

5 Assess & Remediate

Lesson Quiz

1. What are the mean, variance, and standard deviation of these values?

   3.5   4.7   6.4   5.8   4.2

2. **Do you UNDERSTAND?** The table at right displays the number of points a basketball player scored in each game last season. What are the mean and standard deviation?

Game	Points
1	11
2	14
3	10
4	8
5	12
6	13
7	12
8	18
9	9
10	12
11	16
12	15
13	11
14	9
15	10

3. Use the basketball points data from Exercise 2. Within how many standard deviations of the mean do all of the values fall?

ANSWERS TO LESSON QUIZ

1. mean = 4.92; variance = 1.1096; standard deviation ≈ 1.05

2. mean = 12; standard deviation ≈ 2.71

3. All the values fall within three standard deviations of the mean.

PRESCRIPTION FOR REMEDIATION

Use the student work on the Lesson Quiz to prescribe a differentiated review assignment:

Points	Differentiated Remediation
0–1	Intervention
2	On-level
3	Extension

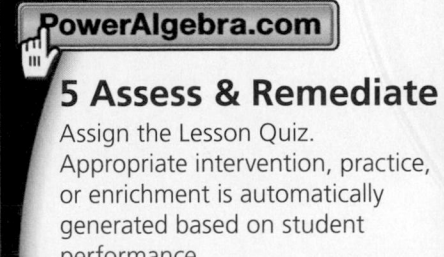

5 Assess & Remediate

Assign the Lesson Quiz. Appropriate intervention, practice, or enrichment is automatically generated based on student performance.

Intervention

- **Reteaching** (2 pages) Provides reteaching and practice exercises for the key lesson concepts. Use with struggling students or absent students.

- **English Language Learner Support** Helps students develop and reinforce mathematical vocabulary and key concepts.

All-in-One Resources/Online
Reteaching

11-6 Reteaching
Standard Deviation

The mean tells you what the center of a set of data values looks like. But two very different data sets can have the same mean. For example, each of these data sets has a mean of 25.

Set A: {23 24 25 26 27}   Set B: {1 5 25 45 49}

Notice that the data values on the number line for set B are much more spread out from the mean than the data values for set A. *Variance* and *standard deviation* are measures of how widely data values differ from the mean.

The lowercase Greek letter sigma, σ, is the symbol for standard deviation. Variance is the square of the standard deviation, and is written as σ². For a set of n data values:

$$\sigma^2 = \frac{\sum (x - \bar{x})^2}{n} \qquad \sigma = \sqrt{\frac{\sum (x - \bar{x})^2}{n}}$$

Problem

What are the variance and standard deviation for the data set {100 158 170 192}?

Step 1 Find the mean of the values.

$$\bar{x} = \frac{100 + 158 + 170 + 192}{4} = 155.$$

Step 2 Subtract the mean from each value in the data set. Then square each difference.

$(100 - 155)^2 = 3025$ $(158 - 155)^2 = 9$
$(170 - 155)^2 = 225$ $(192 - 155)^2 = 1369$

Step 3 Find the mean of the squared differences. This is the variance.

$$\sigma^2 = \frac{3025 + 9 + 225 + 1369}{4} = 1157$$

Step 4 Find the square root of the variance. This is the standard deviation.

$$\sigma = \sqrt{1157} \approx 34$$

The variance for the data set is 1157 and the standard deviation is about 34.

Exercises

Find the variance and standard deviation for each data set.

1. 6.5 7.0 9.0 8.0 7.5 **0.74; about 0.86**   2. 5.6 5.8 5.9 6.1 **0.0325; about 0.18**
3. 201 203 208 210 211 **15.44; about 3.93**   4. 12 14 15 17 19 **5.84; about 2.42**

All-in-One Resources/Online
English Language Learner Support

11-6 ELL Support
Standard Deviation

Rita was studying for a quiz on standard deviation. She wrote the steps to find standard deviation on a set of note cards, but the cards got mixed up.

Calculate the variance by finding the mean of these squares. $\sigma^2 = \frac{\sum (x - \bar{x})^2}{n}$

Find the mean, $\bar{x}$, of the n values in the data set.

Square each difference, $(x_i - \bar{x})^2$.

Take the square root of the variance. $\sigma = \sqrt{\frac{\sum (x - \bar{x})^2}{n}}$

Find the difference, $x_1 - \bar{x}$, between each value x_1 and the mean.

Use the note cards to write the steps in order.

1. First, **find the mean, $\bar{x}$, of the n values in the data set**

2. Second, **find the difference, $x_1 - \bar{x}$, between each value x_1 and the mean**

3. Next, **square each difference, $(x_i - \bar{x})^2$**

4. Then, **calculate the variance by finding the mean of these squares.** $\sigma^2 = \frac{\sum (x - \bar{x})^2}{n}$

5. Finally, **take the square root of the variance.** $\sigma = \frac{\sum (x - \bar{x})^2}{n}$

Differentiated Remediation *continued*

On-Level

- **Practice** (2 pages) Provides extra practice for each lesson. For more challenging practice exercises, use the Form G Practice pages found in the All-in-One Teaching Resources and online.

- **Think About a Plan** Helps students develop specific problem-solving skills and strategies by providing scaffolded guiding questions.

- **Standardized Test Prep** Focuses on all major exercises, all major question types, and helps students prepare for the high-stakes assessments.

Extension

- **Enrichment** Provides students with interesting problems and activities that extend the concepts of the lesson.

- **Activities, Games, and Puzzles** Worksheets that can be used for concepts development, enrichment, and for fun!

Student Companion/ All-in-One Resources/Online
Practice page 1

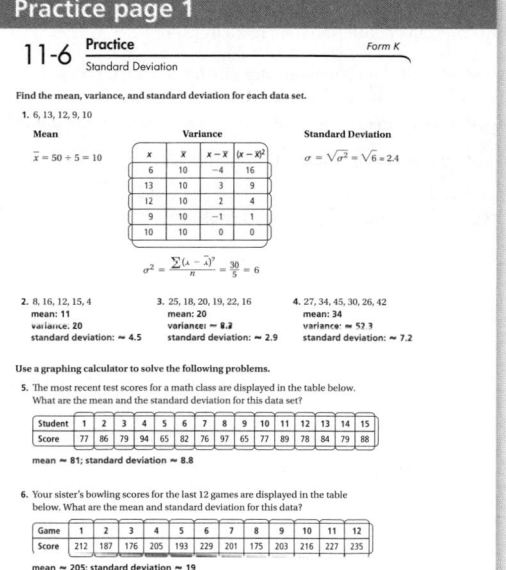

Student Companion/ All-in-One Resources/Online
Practice page 2

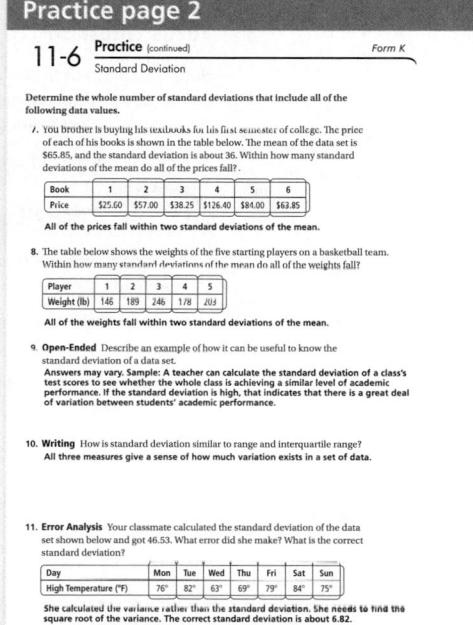

All-in-One Resources/Online
Enrichment

Student Companion/ All-in-One Resources/Online
Think About a Plan

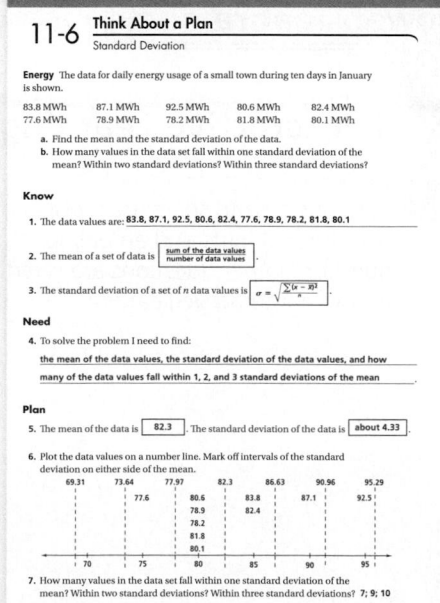

Student Companion/ All-in-One Resources/Online
Standardized Test Prep

Online Teacher Resource Center
Activities, Games, and Puzzles

1 Interactive Learning

Solve It!

PURPOSE To determine information about a population from a sample

PROCESS Students may consider the minimum number, total number, or possible range of the number of fish.

FACILITATE

Q What is the minimum number of fish that there could be in the pond? How do you know? **[There must be at least 197 fish in the pond, the 97 caught the first day, the three caught twice, and the 97 untagged fish caught the second day.]**

Q Suppose the catch from the second day represents any catch of one hundred fish. What is the ratio of untagged fish to tagged fish in the pond? **[97 to 3]**

ANSWER See Solve It in Answers on next page.
CONNECT THE MATH In the Solve It, students evaluate a random sample to reach conclusions about a population. In the lesson, students will analyze sampling methods and study methods for validity and bias.

2 Guided Instruction

Take Note

Q Are any of the sampling types and methods random? If a sample is not random, does that mean the conclusions drawn based on the sample are false? Explain. **[The samples are not random because not all members of the population have the same chance of being chosen as part of the sample. The conclusions drawn from such samples may be true, but will likely be biased.]**

Objectives To identify sampling methods
To recognize bias in samples and surveys

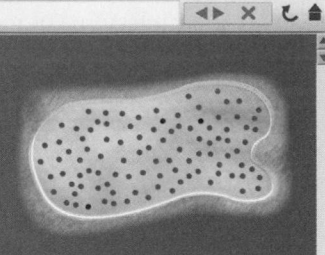

> **Getting Ready!**
>
> One day, you catch 100 fish at random from a lake. You tag the fish and then release them back into the lake. The next day you again catch 100 fish at random, as shown on the map. The red dots indicate the fish that have your tags. What can you conclude? Justify your conclusion.

This is a good sample problem!

Lesson Vocabulary
- population
- sample
- convenience sample
- self-selected sample
- systematic sample
- random sample
- bias
- observational study
- controlled experiment
- survey

A **population** is all the members of a set. A **sample** is part of a population. If you determine a sample carefully, it can give a good estimate of the total population.

Focus Question How can you collect unbiased data in a sample?

Suppose you want to know what percent of all voters in your city favor a tax increase to pay for school improvements. It would be too difficult to ask an opinion of every voter. Instead, you select a sample of the voters to estimate the percentage who favor the idea.

You can define different types of samples by the methods used to select them.

take note
Key Concepts   Sampling Types and Methods

For a **convenience sample**, select any members of the population who are conveniently and readily available.

For a **self-selected sample**, select only members of the population who volunteer for the sample.

For a **systematic sample**, order the population in some way, and then select from it at regular intervals.

In a **random sample**, all members of the population are equally likely to be chosen.

BIG idea Probability   UbD

ESSENTIAL UNDERSTANDING
You can get good statistical information about a population by studying a sample of the population.

Math Background
The statistical information you get about a population depends on the methods you use to sample the population. These methods may cause bias and influence the results of the studies. Understanding these can help you interpret the information more accurately.

SAMPLE METHODS
- Convenience sample: this may have bias when the members of the population who are conveniently and readily available do not represent all groups evenly.
- Self-selected sample: this may have bias when certain groups of people choose not to volunteer.
- Systematic sample: this may have bias when the method used to sample the population does not include everyone.

STUDY METHODS
- Observational study: this may introduce bias or inaccuracy depending on the measuring tools and human error.
- Controlled experiment: a double-blind study can help reduce bias.
- Survey: poorly written survey questions may introduce bias.

Support Student Learning
Use the **Algebra 2 Companion** to engage and support students during instruction. See Lesson Resources at the end of this lesson for details.

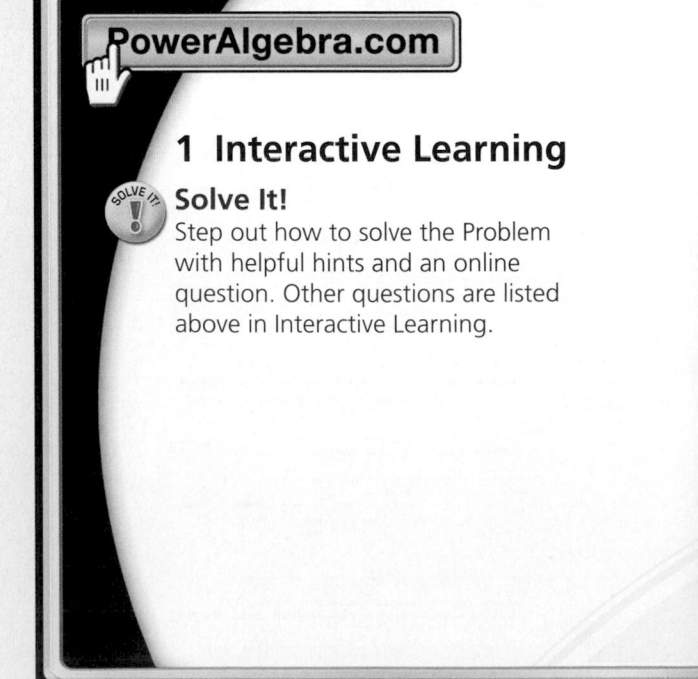

PowerAlgebra.com

1 Interactive Learning

Solve It!
Step out how to solve the Problem with helpful hints and an online question. Other questions are listed above in Interactive Learning.

A sample has a *bias* when a part of a population is overrepresented or underrepresented. A **bias** is a systematic error introduced by the sampling method.

 Problem 1 Analyzing Sampling Methods

Public Opinion A newspaper wants to find out what percent of the city population favors a property tax increase to raise money for local parks. What is the sampling method used for each situation? Does the sample have a bias? Explain.

A A newspaper article on the tax increase invites readers to call the paper and express their opinions.

This is a self-selected sample. It might have a bias, depending on who calls the newspaper. The people who call may overrepresent or underrepresent some views. For example, some property owners who are against the tax might organize a campaign to get friends and neighbors to call in.

B A reporter interviews people leaving the city's largest park.

This is a convenience sample, since it is convenient for the reporter to stay in one place. Because the location is near a park, the sample may overrepresent park supporters and the results will have a bias.

C A survey service calls every 50th listing from the local phone book.

This is a systematic sample because the phone listing is ordered alphabetically. The regular sampling interval is every 50 listings. This sample may have a bias if there is some link between people who are listed (or not listed) in a phone book and people who pay property taxes.

 **Got It?** **1. a.** To survey the eating habits of the community, employees of a local television station interview people visiting a food court in the mall. What sampling method are they using? Does the sample have a bias? Explain.

b. Reasoning A poll of every person in the population is a *census*. What is a situation that requires a census instead of a sample?

Think

Who are the people in the sample? The people in the sample are only those who might be selected. In this case, only those who call the newspaper.

One way to collect sample information is to perform a study.

 take note **Key Concepts** **Study Methods**

In an **observational study**, you measure or observe members of a sample in such a way that they are not affected by the study.

In a **controlled experiment**, you divide the sample into two groups. You impose a treatment on one group but not on the other "control" group. Then you compare the effect on the treated group to the control group.

In a **survey**, you ask every member of the sample a set of questions.

Problem 1

Q In 1A, what other concerns might you have about how the sample is collected? [Sample: Not everyone takes a newspaper.]

Q What is an example of a location that the reporter could have used in 1B that might have reduced the likeliness of bias? [Sample: a grocery store]

EXTENSION

Q Suppose the newspaper drew a conclusion about the public's opinion of a future proposed property tax. Why might you want to know what sampling method was used? [If the sample is random, then the conclusions reached by the newspaper are more reliable than if the sample is not random.]

Got It?

Q What question could be answered by the survey sample described in 1a? [Sample: What food do people choose to eat in the mall food court?]

Q For 1b, why would someone choose to use a sample instead of a census? [Sample: It might be too expensive or too time consuming to poll every member of a population.]

Take Note

Q Which study method would be the best to use to test the effectiveness of a new migraine headache pain reliever? Explain. [Controlled experiment; administer the new drug to one group of migraine sufferers and another drug to a control group of migraine sufferers, and then compare the effectiveness.]

---

2 Guided Instruction

Each Problem is worked out and supported online.

Problem 1
Analyzing Sampling Methods
Animated

Problem 2
Analyzing Survey Questions
Animated

Problem 3
Designing a Survey
Animated

Support in Algebra 2 Companion
- Vocabulary
- Key Concepts
- Got It?

Answers

Solve It!

There are about 3333 fish in the lake. You can estimate that for every 3 fish you tagged, there are 97 additional fish. $\frac{100}{3} = 33.\overline{3}$ and $33.\overline{3} \times 100 = 3333$.

Got It?

1. a. convenience sample; yes; since the location is at the food court in the mall, the sample may over represent food court or fast food supporters.

b. Answers may vary. Sample: population data for the US census

2. a. Yes; the question asks about two issues, nutrition and taste.

b. Yes; the question is "loaded," suggesting the student council is "highly effective" and that you want a particular answer.

Problem 2

A loaded question is similar to loaded or weighted number cubes in that it produces somewhat predictable results.

> **Q** How could you reword the questions in 2A, 2B and 2C to eliminate the listed bias? **[For 2A ask: Should farmers use pesticide to control insects on crops? For 2B ask: Are most childcare workers underpaid? For 2C ask two questions: one about teacher/student and one about teacher/parent communication.]**

Got It?

> **Q** How can you reword the question in 2b to remove the bias? **[Remove "highly effective."]**

Problem 3

> **Q** What do you need to be concerned about as you think of a sampling method? **[whether populations are underrepresented or over-represented and whether all members of the population have an equal opportunity to be chosen]**
>
> **Q** What conditions in your school would require you to revise the sampling method to avoid bias? **[Sample: Some students do not arrive at school in the morning.]**
>
> **Q** What should the photograph not depict? **[Sample: a swimming pool, medals, the Olympic symbol]**

Got It?

> **Q** Would mailing a survey to neighbors be a good sampling method? Explain. **[No; residents who do not recognize the name may be less interested and therefore less likely to respond.]**

Hint
A survey question should be clear, precise, and fair so that everyone hears the same question.

Plan
How do you tell whether a survey question is biased? Look for unclear wording, strong words, suggestive wording, and combined questions.

Think
How do you think of a survey question that has no bias? Keep it simple. The simplest question is likely to be the least biased.

A poorly written survey question can introduce bias. An unbiased survey question *avoids*:

- combining two or more issues
- using double negatives
- overlapping answer choices
- words that cause strong reactions (a *loaded* question)
- suggesting that you want a particular answer (a *leading* question)

 **Problem 2** Analyzing Survey Questions

Is the survey question biased? Explain.

A Do you think farmers should use poison to control insects on crops?

There is bias because the question is loaded. Using the term "poison" instead of "pesticide" could cause a strong reaction from respondents.

B Don't you agree that most childcare workers are underpaid?

There is bias because the question is leading. It suggests that you want a certain answer, that childcare workers are underpaid.

C Do you think teachers should communicate frequently with students and their parents about class grades?

There is bias because the question asks about two issues: teachers communicating with students and teachers communicating with parents.

 Got It? 2. Is the survey question biased? Explain.
   a. Do you think the cafeteria food is nutritional and tasty?
   b. How would you rate the performance of the highly effective student council?

 **Problem 3** Designing a Survey

Sports During the 2008 Olympic Games, a U.S. swimmer won more gold medals than any Olympic swimmer before. What sampling method could you use to find the percent of students in your school who recognize that swimmer from a photograph? What is a survey question that is likely to yield unbiased information?

A possible sampling method is to question every 10th student entering school in the morning. This is a systematic sampling. It usually contains the least bias. A possible unbiased survey question is, "Who is pictured in this photograph?".

Got It? 3. **a.** What sampling method could you use to find the percent of residents in your neighborhood who recognize the governor of your state by name? What is a survey question that is likely to yield unbiased information?
   b. For the scenario described in Problem 3, suppose you asked members of your school's swim team the survey question "Who is this world-famous swimmer?". Why are this sampling method and question not appropriate?

Additional Problems

1. For each situation, what sampling method is used? Identify the bias in the sample, if any.

  a. A political candidate wants to know what percent of his voting public supports Referendum A. His staff asks everyone who comes in their office this week if they support Referendum A.

  b. A grocery store manager wants to determine the percent of shoppers that are using the store coupons from the local newspaper. He has an employee ask every tenth shopper for the next week if they intend on using a coupon during their visit.

ANSWERS

  a. convenience sample; visitors to the candidate's office may share the candidate's opinions more than the population as a whole

  b. systematic sample; this sample avoids bias

2. Identify the bias in the survey question, if any.

  a. Should already-high movie ticket prices be raised by fifty cents per person?

  b. Do you think the dress code is too strict and the punishments for violating the dress code too harsh?

  c. Should cell phone usage while driving be outlawed?

ANSWERS

  a. leading question; "already high" indicates prices are too high

  b. combining two issues; strictness and punishments are two separate issues

  c. no bias is present

3. The city planning commission is considering widening Main Street to relieve traffic jams. What sampling method could you use to find the percent of city drivers who would favor a change to Main Street? What survey question would you ask to avoid bias?

ANSWER From an alphabetical list of licensed drivers in your city, call every twentieth driver. A good survey question would be "Would you favor widening Main Street?"

Answers

Got It? (continued)

3. a. Answers may vary. Sample: Use a systematic sample. Go to every fifth house in your neighborhood. State the first and last names of the governor and ask a household member to identify the named person. A possible unbiased survey question is, "Who is this person?"

  b. Sample: The sampling method is not appropriate because the members of a swim team are more likely than a person not on a swim team to know the name of a famous swimmer. Also, the question is not appropriate as it identifies the person in the photo as a swimmer.

Focus Question How can you collect unbiased data in a sample?
Answer Choose your sampling method carefully. Systematic samples and random samples are more likely to produce results that represent the entire population. Avoid biased survey questions by using simple, clear language.

Lesson Check

Do you know HOW?

1. To investigate a community's reading habits, a newspaper conducts a poll from a table near the exit of a history museum.
   a. What is the sampling method?
   b. Does the sampling method have any bias? Explain.

2. A survey asks, "Aren't handmade gifts always better than tacky purchased gifts?" Does this survey question have any bias? Explain.

Do you UNDERSTAND?

3. **Vocabulary** What is the difference between a population and a sample? Give an example of each.

4. **Writing** What does it mean to have an unbiased sample? Why does it matter?

5. **Reasoning** Would a large or small sample tend to give a better estimate of how the total population feels about a topic? Explain.

Practice and Problem-Solving Exercises

 **Practice**

Identify the sampling method. Then identify any bias in each method. ◀ **See Problem 1.**

Guided Practice →

6. A supermarket wants to find the percent of shoppers who use coupons. A manager interviews every shopper entering the greeting card aisle.

   To start, identify the type of sample.   This is a convenience sample.

7. A maintenance crew wants to estimate how many of 3000 air filters in an office building need replacing. The crew examines five filters chosen at random on each floor of the building.

8. The student government wants to find out how many students have after-school jobs. A pollster interviews students selected at random as they board buses at the end of the school day.

Identify any bias in each survey question. ◀ **See Problem 2.**

9. Do you feel that you spend too much time each week doing academic homework and household chores?

10. Do you prefer reading exciting historical novels or dull autobiographies?

11. Don't you agree that the wrestling team doesn't get enough coverage in the school newspaper?

3 Lesson Check

Do you know HOW?

- If students cannot identify the bias in Exercise 1b, ask them why people might sit near the exit.
- If students have difficulty identifying the bias of the survey question in Exercise 2, ask them to identify the adjectives in the question.

Do you UNDERSTAND?

- In Exercise 3, if students do not understand the difference between a population and a sample, use the class as an example of a population and a student as an example of a sample.
- For Exercise 4, if students are unsure what makes a sample unbiased, ask them what makes a sample biased.
- If students have difficulty with the reasoning in Exercise 5, pose questions about the fish pond in the Solve It: If you only caught one fish on the second day, and it was tagged, could you conclude that all the fish in the pond were tagged?

Close

Q What things should you consider when determining if a given sample is reliable? **[the sampling type, the sampling method, the survey question or questions asked, and the size of the sample]**

Lesson Check

1. a. convenience sample
   b. Yes; since the location is near the exit of a history museum, the sample may overrepresent people who enjoy learning history and the results will have a bias.

2. Yes; the question is leading and loaded. It suggests the person wants a particular answer.

3. All members of the set are the population. A sample is a subset of the population. Answers may vary. Sample: population: students in a high school; sample: students who like to snowboard.

4. It is important to have as little error as possible in a sample, thus giving an unbiased sample. An unbiased sample is more representative of an entire population.

5. A large sample size would give a better estimate. The size of the sample is important to the reliability of the sample

Practice and Problem-Solving Exercises

6. Convenience sampling; this sampling method overrepresents shoppers that buy greeting cards.

7. systematic sampling; no

8. convenience sampling; if students walk or drive to school, or are involved in after school activities, they are underrepresented by this sampling method.

9. The question asks about two issues, academic homework and household chores.

10. The question is loaded and suggests you want a particular answer by using the adjectives "exciting" and "dull."

11. The question is leading. It suggests you want a certain answer, that the wrestling team doesn't get enough coverage in the school newspaper.

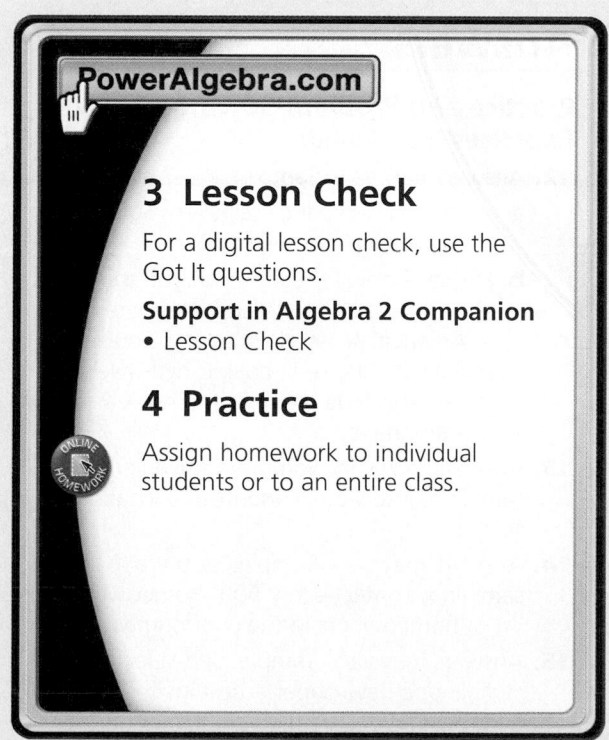

PowerAlgebra.com

3 Lesson Check

For a digital lesson check, use the Got It questions.

Support in Algebra 2 Companion
- Lesson Check

4 Practice

Assign homework to individual students or to an entire class.

4 Practice

ASSIGNMENT GUIDE

Basic: 6–12, 17, 23

Average: 6–12, 13–25 odd

Standardized Test Prep: 26–29

Mixed Review: 30–37

Reasoning exercises have blue headings.

Applications exercises have red headings.

EXERCISE 23: Use the Think About a Plan worksheet in the **Student Companion** (also available in the Teaching Resources in print and online) to further support students' development in becoming independent learners.

HOMEWORK QUICK CHECK

To check students' understanding of key skills and concepts, go over Exercises 7, 9, 12, 17, and 23.

---

12. a. Energy What sampling method could you use to find the percent of adults in your community who support building more nuclear power plants?
  b. What is an example of a survey question that is likely to yield unbiased information?

 See Problem 3.

Ⓑ Apply A university researcher is studying the effect of watching television on residents of the city. Describe a sampling method that can be used for each population.

13. all teenagers

14. all homeowners

15. all women over the age of 21

16. all children under the age of 13

17. Think About a Plan An online advertisement asks you to participate in a survey. The survey asks how much time you spend online each week. What sampling method is the survey using? Identify any bias in the sampling method.
  • What population is likely to see the survey?
  • What population is likely to respond to the survey?

Suppose you are conducting a survey about careers. Write a survey question using each of the following biases.

18. leads people to a particular response

19. does not provide enough information

20. combines two or more issues

21. is too wordy or confusing

22. a. Data Collection Write a survey question to find out the number of students at your school who plan to continue their education after high school.
  b. Describe the sampling method you would use.
  c. Conduct your survey.

23. Entertainment A magazine publisher mails a survey to every tenth person on a subscriber list that is alphabetized by last name. The survey asks for three favorite leisure-time activities. What sampling method is the survey using? Identify any bias in the sampling method.

Margin of Error When you take a random sample of size n from a large population, the sample has a *margin of error* of approximately $\pm\frac{1}{\sqrt{n}}$. Approximate the margin of error for each sample.

24. In 2007, the U.S. Mint began issuing one-dollar coins featuring the images of the nation's Presidents. In a survey, 76% of 2431 U.S. adults opposed using one-dollar coins. (Source: *The Harris Poll #41, April 14, 2008.* Copyright © 2008 Harris Interactive, Inc.)

25. In 2008, tax rebate checks were sent to many American tax payers. In a poll, 45% of 2529 U.S. adults said they felt the rebate program would help stimulate the U.S. economy. (Source: Rebate Checks: No Economic Stimulus, September 10, 2008. Copyright © 2008 Harris Interactive, Inc.)

Answers

Practice and Problem-Solving Exercises (continued)

12. Answers may vary. Sample:
  a. systematic sampling: call every 50th listing from the local phonebook
  b. Please circle all the methods you think should be used to expand energy resources in America. A. wind, B. solar, C. nuclear power, D. oil/gas, E. coal, F. hydroelectric; Rotate the order equally among A–F for the questionnaire.

13. Answers may vary. Sample: Convenience sampling; interview students at a local high school.

14. Answers may vary. Sample: Systematic sampling; contact every 50th homeowner on a list of homeowners in the community.

15. Answers may vary. Sample: Self-selected sampling; a newspaper article invites females over the age of 21 to call the paper and express their opinions.

16. Answers may vary. Sample: Convenience sampling; contact pediatricians in the community to ask them to have parents of all children under the age of 13 complete a questionnaire.

17. self-selected sampling; biased because only those who spend time online will respond.

18. Answers may vary. Sample: Given the increased unemployment and decreased number of students pursuing higher education, don't you think Congress should change the education system?

19. Answers may vary. Sample: Do you think career opportunities will decrease if Congress considers additional unemployment control laws?

20. Answers may vary. Sample: Do you think additional career opportunities for illegal immigrants and educated citizens will be effective?

21. Answers may vary. Sampling: Do you think opening more colleges and encouraging students to complete their education will help provide careers to financially challenged people?

22. a–c. Check students' work.

23. systematic sampling; This sample may have a bias since people with no strong interest in any leisure-time activity may choose not to respond.

24. $\approx \pm 0.0203$, or $\pm 2.03\%$

25. $\approx \pm 0.01988$, or $\pm 1.99\%$

Standardized Test Prep

26. To determine the most popular brands of tea consumed by Americans, a survey is conducted in a busy downtown location at lunchtime. Which of the following is NOT a potential bias in the sampling method?

Ⓐ Urban office employees are not representative of the general population.

Ⓑ The results could be influenced by national brand teas available in the area.

Ⓒ A lunchtime survey does not reflect peoples' tastes at other times of the day.

Ⓓ The survey must include call-in and online responses.

27. Which is the equation for the graph of the circle at the right?

Ⓕ $x^2 + (y - 5)^2 = 16$

Ⓖ $x^2 + (y + 5)^2 = 16$

Ⓗ $(x - 5)^2 + y^2 = 16$

Ⓘ $(x + 5)^2 + y^2 = 16$

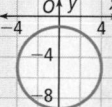

28. A bag contains 5 red marbles, 1 blue marble, 3 yellow marbles, and 2 green marbles. One marble is drawn from the bag, the color is noted, and then the marble is replaced. The experiment is repeated. What is the probability that the first marble drawn is red and the second marble drawn is not red?

Ⓐ 1

Ⓑ $\frac{1}{2}$

Ⓒ $\frac{30}{121}$

Ⓓ $\frac{1}{11}$

29. What is the sum of the infinite geometric sequence? Show your work.

$$\frac{2}{5}, \frac{4}{25}, \frac{8}{125}, \cdots$$

Mixed Review

Find the mean and the standard deviation for each data set.   ◆ See Lesson 11-6.

30. 0, 1, 1, 1, 2, 2, 2, 3, 3, 4, 5, 10

31. 1, 1, 2, 2, 3, 4, 5, 6, 8, 9, 10, 10, 12

Find the inverse of each function. Is the inverse a function?   ◆ See Lesson 6-7.

32. $f(x) = 2x + 5$

33. $f(x) = x^2$

34. $f(x) = 3\sqrt{x}$

Get Ready!   To prepare for Lesson 11-8, do Exercises 35–37.

Evaluate each expression.   ◆ See Lesson 11-1.

35. $_4C_2$

36. $_3C_3$

37. $_5C_2$

Standardized Test Prep

26. D

27. G

28. C

29. [2] $a = \frac{2}{5}$ and $r = \frac{2}{5}$, Sum $= \dfrac{\frac{2}{5}}{1 - \frac{2}{5}} = \frac{2}{3}$

  [1] appropriate method, with one computational error

Mixed Review

30. $\bar{x} \approx 2.83$, $\sigma \approx 2.54$

31. $\bar{x} \approx 5.62$, $\sigma \approx 3.67$

32. $y = \frac{1}{2}(x - 5)$; yes

33. $y = \pm\sqrt{x}$; no

34. $y = \frac{x^2}{9}$; $x \geq 0$; yes

35. 6

36. 1

37. 10

Additional Instructional Support

Algebra 2 Companion

Students can use the **Algebra 2 Companion** worktext (4 pages) as you teach the lesson. Use the Companion to support

- New Vocabulary
- Key Concepts
- Got It for each Problem
- Lesson Check

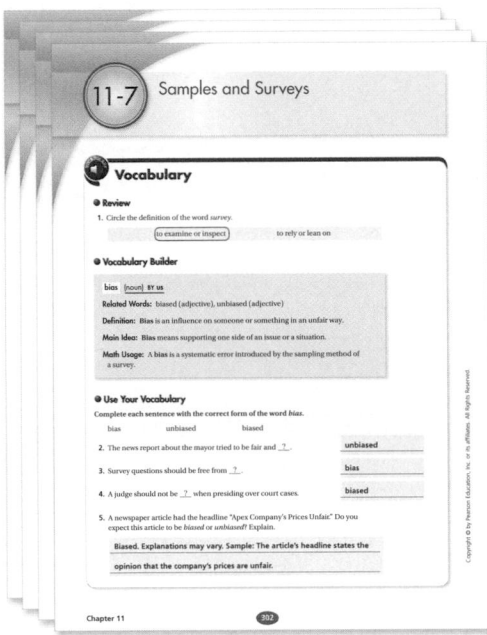

ELL Support

Assess Understanding Have students each write a survey question. In a small group, ask students to revise the questions to remove any bias. Then, have students devise sampling methods for their questions and discuss possible sources of bias.

5 Assess & Remediate

Lesson Quiz

1. Identify the sampling method used and any bias the sample might have: A survey is taken by the student council of the first twenty students buying lunch in the cafeteria to see whether students think the cafeteria lunch is a good value.

2. What, if any, bias is in this survey question: Don't you think that not taking the bus is irresponsible?

3. **Do you UNDERSTAND?** The student council is considering petitioning the school board for permission to change the school colors. What sampling method could you use to find the percent of students who would favor a change of school colors? What survey question would you ask to avoid bias?

ANSWERS TO LESSON QUIZ

1. convenience sample; people who are eager for lunch may be overrepresented

2. Samples: double negative, this may cause confusion; leading, suggests not taking the bus is irresponsible

3. Ask every tenth student in the alphabetical directory for a systematic sample. A good survey question would be, "Would you favor a change in school colors?"

PRESCRIPTION FOR REMEDIATION

Use the student work on the Lesson Quiz to prescribe a differentiated review assignment:

Points	Differentiated Remediation
0–1	Intervention
2	On-level
3	Extension

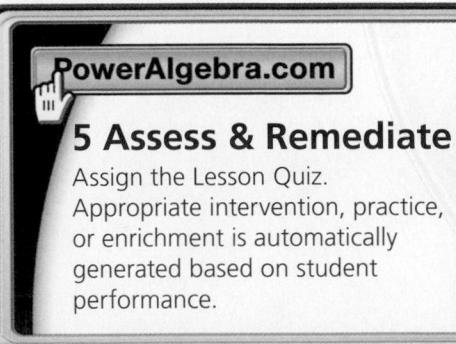

PowerAlgebra.com

5 Assess & Remediate

Assign the Lesson Quiz. Appropriate intervention, practice, or enrichment is automatically generated based on student performance.

Intervention

- **Reteaching** (2 pages) Provides reteaching and practice exercises for the key lesson concepts. Use with struggling students or absent students.

- **English Language Learner Support** Helps students develop and reinforce mathematical vocabulary and key concepts.

All-in-One Resources/Online
Reteaching

11-7 **Reteaching**
Samples and Surveys

When doing a survey, it usually is not practical to get the opinion of every member of a population. You can get a fairly accurate picture of the opinion of a population by surveying a *sample* of the population. A sample is a smaller group that represents the whole population. There are several ways to choose a sample:

Convenience	choosing any people easily available
Self-selection	having people volunteer to participate in the survey
Systematic	ordering the population and choosing participants at regular intervals (such as choosing every fifth person from the telephone book)
Random	all members of the population have an equal chance of being asked to participate

The way you choose the sample can introduce *bias*, or systematic error, into the survey. When a survey is biased, the results are inaccurate.

Problem

An athletic shoe company wants to learn which brand of athletic shoes is worn most often by local high-school students. The company sets up a booth in a local mall and offers a coupon for a free pair of their athletic shoes to anyone who answers the question, "What is your favorite brand of athletic shoes?"

a. What is the sampling method used? There may be more than one.
b. Is there any bias in the company's sampling method?

a. People in the mall are readily available to the booth. Also, people must volunteer to participate. The sample is a convenience sample and is self-selected.
b. The survey is biased in several ways:
- People who do not shop at the mall are excluded.
- Only people who choose to walk up to the booth participate in the survey.
- People who are not high-school students may participate in the survey.
- People may be more likely to say this company makes their favorite shoes when they are offered a free pair.

Exercises

A politician wants to know what issues are most important to the voters in his district. Identify the sampling method and any bias in the method.

1. The politician spends 9:00 A.M. to 4:00 P.M. on Tuesday talking to people as they enter a grocery store. **convenience; excludes people who don't shop during that day**

2. The politician sets up a questionnaire on his website. **self-selected; excludes people without Internet access**

All-in-One Resources/Online
English Language Learner Support

11-7 **ELL Support**
Samples and Surveys

Choose the word from the list that best matches each sentence.

bias	controlled experiment	observational study
population	self-selected sample	

1. The members of a set. **population**

2. A study method that involves observing members of a sample without affecting them. **observational study**

3. Systematic error caused by the sampling method. **bias**

4. A sample that includes only volunteers. **self-selected sample**

5. A study method that involves a control group and a treated group. **controlled experiment**

Choose the word from the list that best completes each sentence.

convenience sample	random sample	sample
survey	systematic sample	

6. When conducting a **survey**, you ask members of a sample a set of questions.

7. All members of the population are equally likely to be chosen in a **random sample**.

8. A **convenience sample** includes members of the population who are readily available.

9. A **sample** is a part of the population.

10. To create a **systematic sample**, you must order the population and then select from it at regular intervals.

Differentiated Remediation *continued*

On-Level

- **Practice** (2 pages) Provides extra practice for each lesson. For more challenging practice exercises, use the Form G Practice pages found in the All-in-One Teaching Resources and online.
- **Think About a Plan** Helps students develop specific problem-solving skills and strategies by providing scaffolded guiding questions.
- **Standardized Test Prep** Focuses on all major exercises, all major question types, and helps students prepare for the high-stakes assessments.

Extension

- **Enrichment** Provides students with interesting problems and activities that extend the concepts of the lesson.
- **Activities, Games, and Puzzles** Worksheets that can be used for concepts development, enrichment, and for fun!

Student Companion/ All-in-One Resources/Online
Practice page 1

11-7 Practice — *Form K*
Samples and Surveys

Identify the sampling methods used in each of the following situations. Then state whether the sampling method has any bias.

1. A television station invites viewers to call in and name their favorite game show.
   This is a self-selected sample. All of the sample members will be viewers, so the entire population will not be accurately represented.
2. A school principal gathers an alphabetical list of all the students at her school. Then she selects every 15th student to take a survey about the cafeteria's lunch menu.
   This is a systematic sample. There is most likely no bias in this sample.
3. A reporter asks people leaving a movie theater to take a survey about their television viewing habits.
   This is a convenience sample. Because the members of the sample are leaving a movie theater, they may have different television viewing habits than most other members of the population.
4. A psychologist uses a computer program to randomly select names from a list of students at a university. The members of the sample will take a survey about student housing at the university.
   This is a random sample. There is most likely no bias in this sample.
5. **Writing** A group of television producers plans to survey 10-year-olds to determine their opinions about a new cartoon. Describe a sampling method that could be used to gather a biased sample in this situation. Then describe a method to gather an unbiased sample. **Answers may vary. Sample: In order to gather a biased sample, the producers could stand outside of a toy store and give the survey to the children entering and exiting. To gather an unbiased sample, the producers could randomly select children from elementary schools across the country.**
6. **Multiple Choice** A school psychologist sits in a school cafeteria and takes notes on students' behavior while they eat lunch. Which of the following types of studies is the researcher conducting? **B**
   Ⓐ controlled experiment Ⓑ observational study Ⓒ survey
7. **Open-Ended** Your classmate is randomly selecting a sample of students at his high school to take a survey. You say that your classmate's sample is biased because it only contains high school students. In what case might you be wrong?
   Answers may vary. Sample: Your classmate's sample is not biased if the survey deals only with issues pertaining to the high school.

Student Companion/ All-in-One Resources/Online
Practice page 2

11-7 Practice (continued) — *Form K*
Samples and Surveys

Identify and describe the bias in the following survey questions.

8. Isn't summer a much more pleasant season than winter?
   This is a leading question. The question suggests that summer is more pleasant than winter.
9. Are college students better off studying useful subjects such as math or impractical subjects such as art history?
   This is a loaded question. Positive terms are used to describe one option and negative terms are used to describe the other option.
10. Do you believe that this year's class field trip was fun and educational?
    This question combines two issues. Whether or not the field trip was fun and whether or not it was educational are two separate issues.
11. Do you agree that Mrs. Regis's class is more interesting than Mr. Wright's class?
    This is a leading question. The question suggests that Mrs. Regis's class is more interesting than Mr. Wright's class.

Rewrite the following survey questions so that they are no longer biased.

12. Do you prefer the excitement of rock and roll or the tediousness of classical music?
    Answers may vary. Sample: Do you prefer rock and roll or classical music?
13. Would you agree that dogs make better pets than cats?
    Answers may vary. Sample: Which pet would you prefer, a dog or a cat?
14. Do you believe that Mayor Johnson is friendly and effective?
    Answers may vary. Sample: Do you believe that Mayor Johnson is effective?
15. **Writing** A supervisor wants to determine what percent of people in his office building believe it is important to have an Internet connection at home. What sampling method can he use to gather an unbiased sample? What is an example of a survey question that is likely to yield unbiased information?
    He could ask every eighth person leaving the building at the end of the day whether or not he or she believes it is important to have an Internet connection at home; "Do you believe that it is important to have an Internet connection at home?"

All-in-One Resources/Online
Enrichment

11-7 Enrichment
Samples and Surveys

By choosing a random sample and avoiding bias in survey questions, you can get results that accurately reflect a larger population. However, it is important that the survey be reliable. Reliability is the extent to which a survey will produce the same results on repeated trials. There are three key types of reliability:

Test-retest reliability	the extent to which two items measure the same concept at the same level of difficulty
Internal consistency	how well items measure the same characteristics
Interrater reliability	the extent to which two people conducting a survey get the same results

State which type of reliability is illustrated in each situation.

1. A researcher wants to determine how prepared high school students are for a mathematics class. Several questions in the survey measure the same mathematical concept. **internal consistency reliability**
2. A group of students were given an IQ test. Each student was given the test twice two weeks apart. **test-retest reliability**
3. A certain level of communication skills is needed for a telemarketing position. When hiring, an employer gives a communication skills test to each applicant. The interviewer rates the candidate on a scale of 1 to 10. The test is given during the first round of interviews and then again by a second interviewer to all candidates invited back for a second interview. **interrater reliability**
4. A researcher is designing a survey to find out how satisfied readers are with a particular newspaper. Certain questions are analyzed to make sure that they indicate that the person is satisfied with the newspaper. **internal consistency reliability**
5. Two researchers are observing an English classroom. The class is discussing a movie the class recently watched as a group. The researchers separately rate each student's level of discussion on a scale of 1 to 5. **interrater reliability**
6. Before each Olympic wrestling match, each wrestler is weighed twice during the sign-in process. **test-retest reliability**

Student Companion/ All-in-One Resources/Online
Think About a Plan

11-7 Think About a Plan
Samples and Surveys

Entertainment A magazine publisher mails a survey to every tenth person on a subscriber list that is alphabetized by last name. The survey asks for three favorite leisure-time activities. What sampling method is the survey using? Identify any bias in the sampling method.

Know

1. The company sending out the survey is a **magazine publisher**.
2. The surveys are mailed to **every tenth person on a subscriber list, alphabetized by last name**.
3. The survey asks for **three favorite leisure-time activities**.

Need

4. To solve the problem I need to find:
   the sampling method used by the survey and any bias in the sampling method.

Plan

5. What sampling method is the survey using? **systematic sampling**
6. Do the people who receive the survey represent the general population? Explain.
   Answers may vary. Sample: No; only people who already subscribe to the publisher's magazines receive the survey.
7. Do the people who return the survey represent the general population? Explain.
   Answers may vary. Sample: No; only people who choose to return the survey are represented.
8. Is there any bias in the sampling method? Explain.
   Answers may vary. Sample: Yes; the people who receive the survey subscribe to magazines, so they are likely to list reading magazines as a favorite leisure-time activity. The sample is also self-selected, depending on who returns the survey. These people may overrepresent or underrepresent some choices of activities.

Student Companion/ All-in-One Resources/Online
Standardized Test Prep

11-7 Standardized Test Prep
Samples and Surveys

Multiple Choice

For Exercises 1–4, choose the correct letter.

1. The School Dance Committee conducts a survey to find what type of music students would like to hear at the next dance. Which is an example of a random sample? **B**
   Ⓐ Call 20% of the people in the senior class directory.
   Ⓑ Interview every 10th student as they enter the school.
   Ⓒ Ask every 5th person leaving a school orchestra concert.
   Ⓓ Set up a jazz website where students can list their 3 favorite songs.
2. Which is a characteristic of a biased survey question? **H**
   Ⓕ It is about a controversial issue. Ⓗ It produces inaccurate results.
   Ⓖ It is about a well-known person. Ⓘ It is about a very unpopular person.
3. In a survey, 36% of 1600 students said they spent at least 5 h online during the past week. What is the approximate margin of error for this sample? **B**
   Ⓐ ± 0.6% Ⓑ ±2.5% Ⓒ ± 6% Ⓓ ± 25%
4. A newspaper surveys a sample of 2500 people and finds that 64% agree with a certain political position. What interval is most likely to contain the percentage of the total population who agree with the position? **F**
   Ⓕ 62–66% Ⓖ 62–64% Ⓗ 63–65% Ⓘ 64–66%

Short Response

5. A city council surveys a sample of citizens about a new law. The survey finds that 38% of citizens think the law should be repealed. The survey has a margin of error of about 8%. About how many people did the council survey? Show your work.
   [2] $ME = \frac{1}{\sqrt{n}}$
   $\sqrt{n} = \frac{1}{ME}$
   $n = \left(\frac{1}{ME}\right)^2 = \left(\frac{1}{0.08}\right)^2 \approx 156$
   The council surveyed about 156 people.
   [1] incorrect or incomplete work shown
   [0] incorrect answer and no work shown OR no answer given

Online Teacher Resource Center
Activities, Games, and Puzzles

11-7 Activity: Proportions and Samples
Samples and Surveys

This activity is best for groups of three or four students.

Step 1

Decide as a group on a proportion you would like to estimate using sampling. Here are some ideas.

- What proportion of students prefers sweet-tasting food to sour-tasting food?
- What proportion of students drives his or her own car to school?
- What proportion of students has a cell phone at school?

Step 2

Split your group and poll every student in class. Be sure to include yourselves.

Step 3

Analyze the data your group collected. Use your results to answer the following questions.

1. Which proportion are you estimating?
   Check students' work.
2. Which question did your group ask the other students?
   Check students' work.
3. From which population does your sample come?
   Answers will vary. Sample: all students in school; all juniors in school; all seniors in school
4. What is your sample proportion?
   Check students' work.
5. What is your margin of error?
   Check students' work.
6. How many students would you have to poll to get a margin of error of ±5%?
   400
7. Can you identify any bias in your sampling method?
   Answers will vary. Samples: convenience sample; group members did not use the same question.

Guided Instruction

PURPOSE To randomly sample from a population and compare the results of the sample in terms of mean, range, standard deviation, and data analysis

PROCESS Students will

- use random sampling to obtain data about the number of letters in last names in a phone book.
- use tables and graphs to analyze and interpret the sample data.

DISCUSS Students may intuitively know that the more names they sample, the less varied the sample means will be. It may be useful to have students make graphs of what they think the data might show before they do the activity.

Activity 1

Q How many samples will you collect in Step 6? How many total names will you examine for Data Set A and for Data Set B? **[You still collect twenty samples, but since the samples have a different number of names for Data Sets A and B, you examine 40 names for Data Set A and 200 for B.]**

Q In Exercise 1, why do you expect Data Set B to have less variation? **[Names with very few or very many letters (outliers) are less likely to affect the mean of a large sample.]**

Q In Exercise 3, how do you know which data set has a greater standard deviation? **[The sample mean values are more spread out on the graph.]**

If students have difficulty with Exercise 6, ask them to open the phone book to a common name, such as Smith.

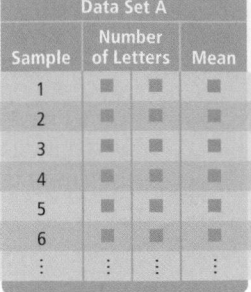

Concept Byte   Describing Data
For Use With Lesson 11-7

ACTIVITY

Suppose you want to know the mean number of letters in the last names of everyone listed in your local phone book. You could count the letters in every last name, but that is not very practical. Instead, you could approximate this mean by taking a *sample* of last names and finding the mean number of letters in only those names.

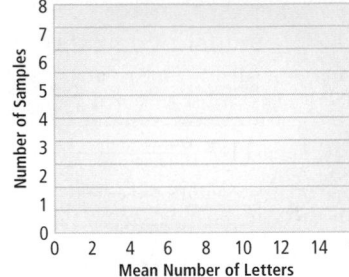

Data Set A		
Sample	Number of Letters	Mean
1	■	■	■
2	■	■	■
3	■	■	■
4	■	■	■
5	■	■	■
6	■	■	■
⋮	⋮	⋮	⋮

Activity 1

Step 1 Copy the table at the right. Extend the table to go to Sample 20.

Step 2 Without looking, open a phone book to a random page. Place your index finger on the page, still without looking. Then, count the number of letters in the name closest to the tip of your finger. Record this number in the table in the first blank space for Sample 1. Close the phone book.

Step 3 Repeat Step 2 and record this number in the table in the second blank space for Sample 1. These two numbers make up one sample. Find the mean and record it in the table.

Step 4 Collect a total of 20 samples by repeating Steps 2 and 3.

Step 5 Copy the grid at the right and use the means from Data Set A to make a bar graph.

Step 6 Make a second table with space for 10 numbers in each of the 20 samples. Label this table Data Set B.

Step 7 Repeat Steps 2 and 3, but now select 10 names for each sample. Record the data in the second table.

Step 8 Copy the grid again and use the means in Data Set B to make a bar graph.

1. Does the graph of Data Set A or the graph of Data Set B show more variation?

2. Which data set has a greater range?

3. Which data set has a greater standard deviation?

4. The *Law of Large Numbers* states that the variation in the means of repeated samples decreases as the sample size increases. Do your results support this law?

5. **Compare and Contrast** Compare your results with those of another student in the class. How are they the same? How are they different?

6. **Reasoning** Suppose you conduct this experiment by collecting all of the samples from one page of the phone book. Predict how this sampling technique might affect your results.

Answers

Activity 1

Check students' work.

1–4. Answers may vary. Most likely answers are given.

1. Data Set A

2. Data Set B

3. Data Set A

4. yes

5. Check students' work.

6. Answers may vary. Sample: The phone book is ordered alphabetically. The data of one page will be isolated to one letter, or within one letter of the initial letter, of the alphabet.

11-8 Binomial Distributions

Objective To find binomial probabilities and to use binomial distributions

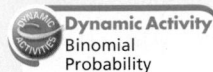

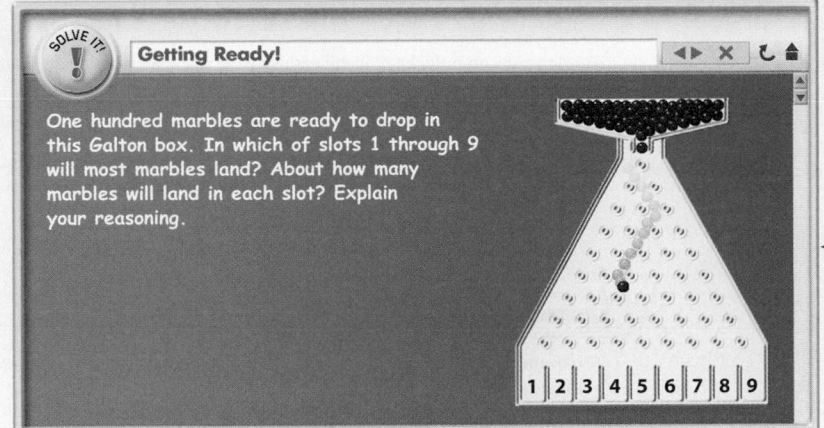

Getting Ready!

One hundred marbles are ready to drop in this Galton box. In which of slots 1 through 9 will most marbles land? About how many marbles will land in each slot? Explain your reasoning.

1 2 3 4 5 6 7 8 9

At each level of a Galton box, a marble can take one of two possible paths.

Focus Question What is binomial probability?

Key Concept Binomial Experiment

A **binomial experiment** has these important features:

• There are a fixed number of trials.
• Each trial has two possible outcomes.
• The trials are independent.
• The probability of each outcome is constant throughout the trials.

The tree diagram on the following page shows different outcomes and probabilities for a basketball player shooting two free throws. It is known that this player is a good shooter, having hit (*H*) about 90% of the free throws so far this season.

1 Interactive Learning

Solve It!

PURPOSE To analyze an experiment that results in a binomial distribution

PROCESS Students may

• use a Galton box with fewer rows (4 or 5) to understand the probabilities involved.
• make a tree diagram to identify the possible outcomes of each marble's fall and determine the theoretical probabilities of each outcome.

FACILITATE

Q Is each marble's fall an independent event? Explain. **[Yes; the result of a marble's fall does not affect the fall of any other marble.]**

Q When each marble hits any peg, what are the possible outcomes? What is the probability of each outcome? [The marble goes left or right; $\frac{1}{2}$.]**

ANSWER See Solve It in Answers on next page.
CONNECT THE MATH In the Solve It, students analyzed the theoretical results of binomial experiments. In this lesson, students will calculate and apply binomial probabilities to analyze binomial distributions.

2 Guided Instruction

Take Note

Q How does the Galton box problem illustrate the features of a binomial experiment? **[It has a fixed number of trials—the ball will always hit exactly nine pegs. Each trial has two possible outcomes—left or right. The trials are independent—one trial's outcome cannot affect the probabilities of other trials. The probabilities do not change from trial to trial.]**

11-8 Preparing to Teach

BIG ideas Probability
Data Collection and Analysis

UbD

ESSENTIAL UNDERSTANDING

Binomial probabilities can be used to model situations in which there are two possible outcomes.

Math Background

A *binomial experiment* is a series of independent trials, each of which has one of two possible outcomes. One example is flipping a fair coin a number of times. Each flip is either heads or tails, and the probability of heads or tails on any given flip is independent of all other flips.

A *binomial probability*, *P*(*x*), is a function that gives the probability of *x* successes in *n* trials of a binomial experiment. For example, if you define success as a coin landing heads and *n* = 10, then *P*(3) gives the probability

that a coin lands heads three times in ten flips of the coin.

Recall that a binomial is a polynomial with two terms. The Binomial Theorem gives a formula for raising a binomial to a power using combinations.

$$(a + b)^n = {}_nC_0a^n + {}_nC_1a^{n-1}b + {}_nC_2a^{n-2}b^2 + \ldots + {}_nC_{n-1}ab^{n-1} + {}_nC_nb^n$$

Notice in each expansion:

• The powers of *a* decrease by 1 in successive terms and the powers of *b* increase by 1.
• The sum of powers in each term is *n*.
• The coefficients increase and then decrease in a symmetrical pattern.

The coefficients of the expansion are called binomial coefficients and when arranged in a triangular pattern form Pascal's Triangle.

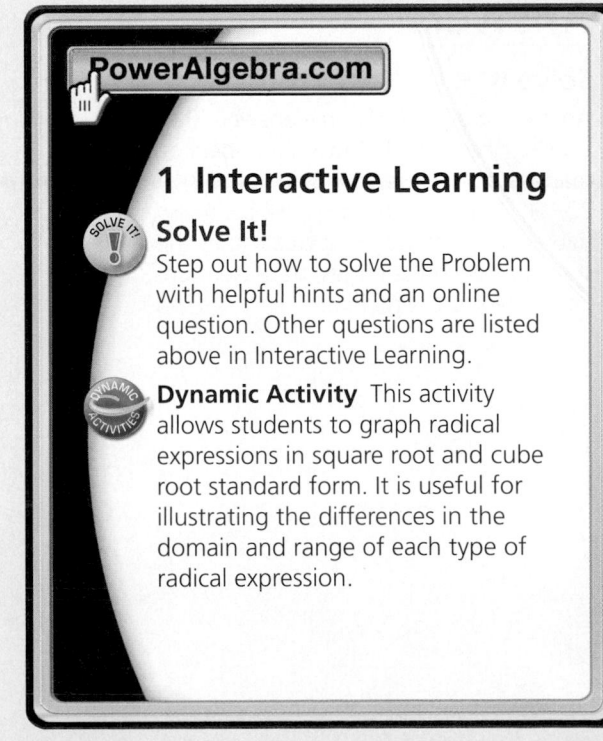

1 Interactive Learning

Solve It!
Step out how to solve the Problem with helpful hints and an online question. Other questions are listed above in Interactive Learning.

Dynamic Activity This activity allows students to graph radical expressions in square root and cube root standard form. It is useful for illustrating the differences in the domain and range of each type of radical expression.

Take Note

Students may benefit from a review of the variables used in the binomial formula:

$_nC_x$ = the number of possible combinations of x items from a set of n items (the combination formula)

n = the number of trials

x = the number of successes among n trials

p = the probability of success in one trial

q = the probability of failure in one trial

($q = 1 - p$, the *complement* of the event)

Q For any binomial experiment, what must be the sum of $p + q$? **[1]**

Problem 1   ELL SUPPORT

Since the text in this problem might be difficult for English learners, rephrase the information in shorter sentences that are easier to understand.

A store is giving away scratch-off cards. 40% of the cards have prizes. You have five cards. What is the probability that exactly four of the cards have prizes?

Q Why is the word *exactly* used in this problem's question? **[The number of successes is four, not four *or* five.]**

Q What does $_5C_4$ mean in this problem? **[the number of ways four students can be selected (or combined) out of a group of five students]**

Q How can you find the value of $_5C_4$ without using a calculator or the combination formula? **[Make a tree diagram to find all the possible combinations.]**

Hint

The basketball player shoots 2 free throws—each independent of the other (ignoring pressure). The player will succeed on 0, 1, or 2 of them.

H: Hits (makes) a shot	M: Misses a shot

HH $P(2\ hits) = 0.9^2 = 0.81$

HM $P(1\ hit) = 0.9\,(0.1) + 0.1(0.9)$
MH $= 0.18$

MM $P(0\ hits) = 0.1^2 = 0.01$

You can also compute the probabilities using the formula for *binomial probability*.

Hint

A tree diagram is only useful when n is small.

Key Concept   Binomial Probability

Suppose you have n repeated independent trials, each with a probability of success p and a probability of failure q (with $p + q = 1$). Then the **binomial probability** of x successes in the n trials can be found using the following formula.

$$P(x) = {_nC_x}\,p^x q^{n-x}$$

 Problem 1   Using a Formula to Find Probabilities

Merchandising As part of a promotion, a store is giving away scratch-off cards. Each card has a 40% chance of awarding a prize. Suppose you have five cards. Find the probability that exactly four of the five cards will reveal a prize.

Know
• The number of trials n
• The number of successes x
• The probability of success p

Need
• The probability of failure q
• The probability of picking exactly 4 winning cards

Plan
• Determine that this is binomial probability.
• Find the probability of failure q.
• Use the formula for binomial probability.

Determine if this a binomial experiment:
• The situation involves 5 repeated trials—5 cards selected at random.
• Each trial has two possible outcomes: A card is a winner or it is not.
• The probability of success is constant, 0.4, throughout the trials.
• The trials are independent. The outcome of scratching one card does not affect the probability of any of the other cards revealing a prize.

Think

How can you find $_nC_x$ using your calculator?

$$_nC_x = \frac{n!}{x!(n-x)!}$$

On a graphing calculator, use **MATH** and $_nC_r$ in the **PRB** menu.

This is a binomial experiment with $n = 5$, $x = 4$, $p = 0.4$, and $q = 1 - p = 0.6$.

Write the formula for binomial probability. $P(x) = {_nC_x}\,p^x q^{n-x}$

Substitute. $P(4) = {_5C_4}(0.4)^4(0.6)^1$

Evaluate $_5C_4$ and simplify. $= 5(0.4)^4(0.6)^1 \approx 0.08$

The probability is about 8% that exactly 4 of the five cards will reveal a prize.

Answers

Solve It!

Answers may vary. Sample answer: The slots will have the following numbers of marbles, respectively: 0, 3, 11, 22, 28, 22, 11, 3, 0; more marbles will be in the middle slots, gradually decreasing as the slots approach the edges, because more paths lead to the middle.

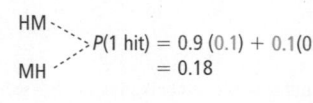

2 Guided Instruction

Each Problem is worked out and supported online.

Support in Algebra 2 Companion
• Vocabulary
• Key Concepts
• Got It?

Problem 1
Using a Formula to Find Probabilities
Animated

Problem 2
Expanding Binomials
Animated

Problem 3
Applying Binomial Probability
Animated

The Binomial Theorem (Lesson 5-7) says that for every positive integer n,

$$(a + b)^n = P_0a^n + P_1a^{n-1}b + P_2a^{n-2}b^2 + \cdots + P_{n-1}ab^{n-1} + P_nb^n$$

where $P_0, P_1, \ldots, P_n$ are the numbers in the nth row of Pascal's Triangle.

For that row, it is possible to show that $P_i = {}_nC_i$.

```
         1                              0C0
       1   1                          1C0   1C1
     1   2   1          ───────►    2C0   2C1   2C2
   1   3   3   1                   3C0   3C1   3C2   3C3
 1   4   6   4   1              4C0   4C1   4C2   4C3   4C4
```

So, you can restate the **Binomial Theorem** using combinations.

> **Key Concept** **Binomial Theorem**
>
> For every positive integer n,
>
> $$(a + b)^n = {}_nC_0a^n + {}_nC_1a^{n-1}b + {}_nC_2a^{n-2}b^2 + \cdots + {}_nC_{n-1}ab^{n-1} + {}_nC_nb^n$$

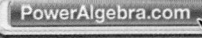 **Problem 2** **Expanding Binomials**

Use the Binomial Theorem to solve.

A What is the binomial expansion of $(x + y)^5$?

Use the Binomial Theorem with $a = x$, $b = y$, and $n = 5$.

Write the expansion. $(x + y)^5 = {}_5C_0x^5 + {}_5C_1x^4y + {}_5C_2x^3y^2 + {}_5C_3x^2y^3 + {}_5C_4xy^4 + {}_5C_5y^5$

Substitute for the $_nC_i$. $= x^5 + 5x^4y + 10x^3y^2 + 10x^2y^3 + 5xy^4 + y^5$

B What is the third term of $(2x - 3y)^4$?

The third term of the binomial expansion is $_4C_2a^{4-2}b^2$.

Think
Which $_4C_i$ do you use in the third term?
You use $_4C_0$, not $_4C_1$, for the first term. Therefore, use $_4C_2$ in the third term.

Substitute $a = 2x$ and $b = -3y$. $_4C_2a^{4-2}b^2 = {}_4C_2(2x)^2(-3y)^2$

Evaluate $_4C_2$. $= 6(4x^2)(9y^2)$

Simplify. $= 216x^2y^2$

 Got It? **2.** What is the binomial expansion of $(3x + y)^4$?

Got It? EXTENSION
In a binomial distribution, only n and p are needed to determine the mean, variance, and standard deviation.
mean $= np$
variance $= np(1 - p)$ or npq
standard deviation $= \sqrt{np(1 - p)}$ or $\sqrt{npq}$
Challenge students to use these formulas to analyze the binomial experiment in Problem 1.

Take Note

Q Why is 1 the coefficient of the first term in every binomial expansions? **[For the first term n equals 1, so $_nC_0$ refers to the number of ways 1 item can be arranged, which is 1.]**

Q What pattern do you see in all the sums of the powers in each term? **[They all equal 5, the binomial's power.]**

Q How can you use this pattern to verify that you expanded the binomial correctly? **[If the sum of the powers in one of the expansion's terms does not equal the number of the binomial's power, a mistake was made.]**

Got It? ERROR PREVENTION
Students sometimes forget to account for a coefficient in binomials like $(3x + y)^4$. Suggest they first write the expansion using a and b:
$(a + b)^4 = {}_4C_0a^4 + {}_4C_1a^3b + {}_4C_2a^2b^2 + {}_4C_3ab^3 + {}_4C_4b^4$. Then substitute $3x$ for a and y for b.

Additional Problems

1. In a tennis league, 80% of the players are right-handed. The league president is randomly selecting seven players to demonstrate serves. What is the probability that exactly three of the selected players will be right-handed?

ANSWER about 0.029

2. a. What is the binomial expansion of $(4x + 2y)^3$?

b. What is the fifth term of $(2x - 3y)^7$?

ANSWERS

a. $(4x + 2y)^3 = 64x^3 + 96x^2y + 48xy^2 + 8y^3$

b. $22{,}680x^3y^4$

3. A spinner has five equal sections. Each section is a different color; red, blue, green, yellow, and orange. You spin the spinner four times. What is the probability that at least two of the spins will land on the red section?

ANSWER 18.08%

Answers

Got It?

1. $P(0) = 0.07776$; $P(1) = 0.2592$; $P(2) = 0.3456$; $P(3) = 0.2304$; $P(5) = 0.01024$

2. $81x^4 + 108x^3y + 54x^2y^2 + 12xy^3 + y^4$

A **probability distribution** is a function that gives the probability of each outcome in a sample space. To find the full probability distribution for a binomial experiment, use the Binomial Theorem to expand the binomial $(p + q)^n$. For example, suppose you guess on four questions of a five-choice multiple-choice test. For four questions, $n = 4$, $P(\text{guessing correctly}) = \frac{1}{5}$, so $p = 0.2$, and $q = 0.8$.

Hint
The full probability distribution for a binomial experiment must sum to 1, or 100%.

	4 correct	3 correct	2 correct	1 correct	0 correct
$(p + q)^4 =$	$1p^4$	$4p^3q$	$6p^2q^2$	$4pq^3$	$1q^4$
$=$	$(0.2)^4$	$4(0.2)^3(0.8)$	$6(0.2)^2(0.8)^2$	$4(0.2)(0.8)^3$	$(0.8)^4$
$=$	0.0016	0.0256	0.1536	0.4096	0.4096

You can display the distribution of binomial probabilities as a graph.

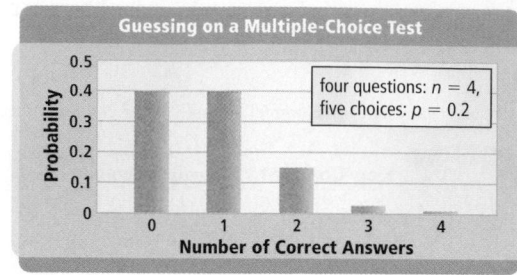

Guessing on a Multiple-Choice Test

four questions: $n = 4$, five choices: $p = 0.2$

Number of Correct Answers

 Problem 3 Applying Binomial Probability

Manufacturing Each hour at a cell phone factory, Quality Control (QC) tests the durability of four randomly selected phones. If more than one fails, QC rejects the entire production for that hour. If in one hour, 95% of the phones made are acceptable, what is the probability that QC rejects that hour's phone production?

Think
What is a "success" in one trial of this binomial experiment?
Success in this experiment means that a phone fails the test.

Write the binomial expansion of $(p + q)^n$ with $n = 4$, $p = 0.05$, and $q = 0.95$.

	4 fail	3 fail	2 fail	1 fail	0 fail

$(p + q)^4 = p^4q^0 + 4p^3q^1 + 6p^2q^2 + 4p^1q^3 + p^0q^4$

$= (0.05)^4 + 4(0.05)^3(0.95)^1 + 6(0.05)^2(0.95)^2 + 4(0.05)^1(0.95)^3 + (0.95)^4$

$\approx 0.000006 + 0.000475 + 0.013538 + 0.171475 + 0.814506$

Probability (4, 3, or 2 phones fail) $\approx 0.000006 + 0.000475 + 0.013538$

≈ 0.014019

There is about a 1.4% chance that QC will reject the phones produced in the last hour.

Got It? 3. A multiple-choice quiz has five questions. Each question has four answer choices. If you guess every answer, what is the probability of getting at least three correct?

Problem 3   ELL SUPPORT

English learners might be confused by the terms *success* and *fail* in this problem. Emphasize that in this lesson, *success* means the result you want to test for in a probability. Use a simple example, such as a coin toss, to explain.

> **Q** Why does $p = 0.05$ in this problem? **[p equals the probability that a phone will *not* be durable enough, so 95% of them, or 95, *are* durable enough.]**
>
> **Q** Why do you find the probability of 4, 3, or 2 phones failing, but not 1? **[The QC only rejects an hour's production if *more than one* phone fails the test.]**

Got It?

You may want to remind students that for this problem, p is the probability of guessing the correct answer on one question, and q is the probability of guessing the wrong answer.

> **Q** Since there are four answer choices for each question, what is p? What is q? **[$\frac{1}{4}$; $\frac{3}{4}$]**
>
> **Q** How does the phrase "at least three correct" affect the way this problem is solved? **[You must find the probability of guessing 3, 4, or 5 correct.]**

Answers

Got It? (continued)

3. ≈ 0.1035, or about 10.4%

Focus Question What is binomial probability?

Answer For n independent trials, each with a probability of success p and probability of failure q, the binomial probability of x successes is $P(x) = {}_nC_x p^x q^{n-x}$. Use binomial probability to model situations with two possible outcomes.

Lesson Check

Do you know HOW?

Find the probability of x successes in n trials for the given probability of success p on each trial.

1. $x = 2, n = 6, p = 0.4$ **2.** $x = 6, n = 9, p = 0.5$

Find the indicated term of each binomial expansion.

3. fourth term of $(c + d)^6$ **4.** second term of $(x - 2y)^5$

5. What is the probability of 2 successes in 4 trials of an experiment if the probability of success of one trial is 0.3?

Do you UNDERSTAND?

6. Vocabulary Explain how flipping a coin 10 times meets all of the conditions for a binomial experiment.

7. Error Analysis A student finds the fifth term of the binomial expansion $(j - k)^7$. Describe and correct the error the student made.

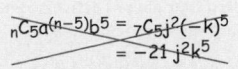

$${}_nC_5 a^{(n-5)} b^5 = {}_7C_5 j^2(-k)^5$$
$$= -21 j^2 k^5$$

Practice and Problem-Solving Exercises

A Practice   Find the probability of x successes in n trials for the given probability of success p on each trial.   **See Problem 1.**

Guided Practice

To start, identify the probability of failure q.

8. $x = 3, n = 8, p = 0.3$
$q = 1 - p$
$= 1 - 0.3 = 0.7$

9. $x = 5, n = 10, p = 0.5$ **10.** $x = 5, n = 10, p = 0.1$

11. Battery Life A calculator contains four batteries. With normal use, each battery has a 90% chance of lasting for one year. What is the probability that all four batteries will last a year?

Expand each binomial.   **See Problem 2.**

12. $(m + 5n)^3$ **13.** $(4c - d)^4$

Find the indicated term of each binomial expansion.

Guided Practice

To start, write the second term of the binomial expansion of $(a + b)^7$.

14. second term of $(2g + 2h)^7$
${}_7C_1 a^{(7-1)} b^1 = {}_7C_1 a^6 b$

15. fifth term of $(x - y)^5$ **16.** eighth term of $(3x - y)^8$

Lesson Check

1. ≈ 0.3110, or $\approx 31.10\%$
2. ≈ 0.1641, or $\approx 16.41\%$
3. $20c^3 d^3$ **4.** $-10x^4 y$
5. 0.2646, or 26.46%
6. Answers may vary. Sample: A binomial experiment has three important features:
a. The situation involves repeated trials; flipping a coin 10 times has 10 trials.
b. Each trial has two possible outcomes; in this case, heads or tails.
c. The probability of success is constant throughout the trials; the trials of flipping a coin, are independent.
7. The student wrote "5" instead of "4". It should be:
$${}_nC_{(5-1)} a^{n-4} b^4 = {}_7C_4 j^3 (-k)^4$$
$$= 35 j^3 k^4$$

Practice and Problem-Solving Exercises

8. ≈ 0.2541, or $\approx 25.41\%$
9. ≈ 0.2461, or $\approx 24.61\%$
10. ≈ 0.0015, or $\approx 0.15\%$
11. ≈ 0.6561, or $\approx 65.61\%$
12. $m^3 + 15m^2 n + 75mn^2 + 125n^3$
13. $256c^4 - 256c^3 d + 96c^2 d^2 - 16cd^3 + d^4$
14. $896g^6 h$
15. $5xy^4$
16. $-24xy^7$

3 Lesson Check

Do you know HOW?

- For Exercises 1 and 2, remind students that $q = 1 - p$.
- For Exercises 3 and 4, suggest that students first determine the number of terms that will be in each binomial expansion. Encourage students to completely expand each binomial up to the desired term to verify their answers.

Do you UNDERSTAND?

- For Exercise 6, suggest that students ask themselves these questions: *Is there a fixed number of trials? Does each trial have two possible outcomes? Is each trial independent? Is the probability of success constant for each trial?*
- For Exercise 7, some students may find it easier to identify and explain the error by first solving the problem and then comparing steps.

Close

Q What information is needed when using binomial probability in an experiment? **[Answers may vary. Sample: First, it must be determined that the experiment is binomial. Then the following information is needed: the number of trials, the number of successes among that number of trials, and the probability of success on each trial.]**

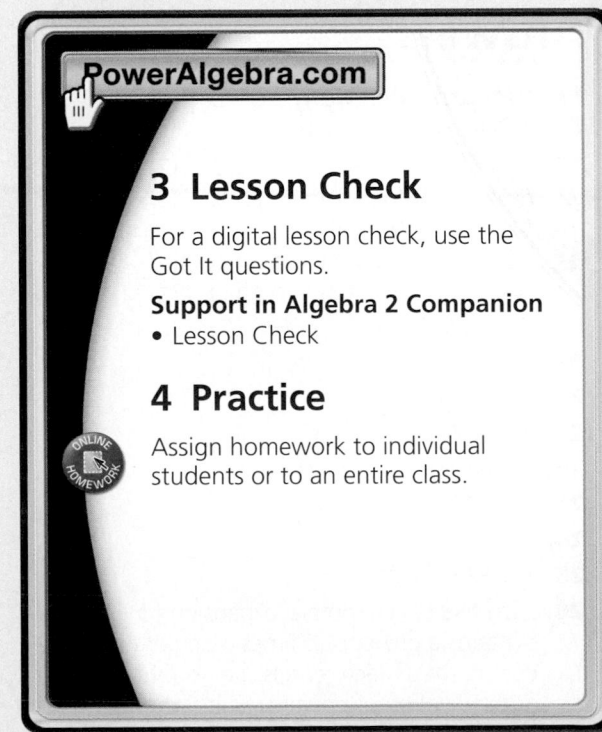

PowerAlgebra.com

3 Lesson Check

For a digital lesson check, use the Got It questions.

Support in Algebra 2 Companion
- Lesson Check

4 Practice

Assign homework to individual students or to an entire class.

4 Practice

ASSIGNMENT GUIDE

Basic: 8–20

Average: 8–18 even, 19–28

Standardized Test Prep: 31–35

Mixed Review: 36–47

Reasoning exercises have blue headings.

Applications exercises have red headings.

EXERCISE 20: Use the Think About a Plan worksheet in the **Student Companion** (also available in the Teaching Resources in print and online) to further support students' development in becoming independent learners.

HOMEWORK QUICK CHECK

To check students' understanding of key skills and concepts, go over Exercises 10, 12, 18, 19, and 20.

Use the binomial expansion of $(p + q)^n$ to calculate each binomial distribution.   ◆ See Problem 3.

17. $n = 6, p = 0.3$

18. $n = 6, p = 0.5$

Ⓑ Apply

19. Think About a Plan One survey found that 80% of respondents eat corn on the cob in circles rather than from side to side. Assume that this sample accurately represents the population. What is the probability that, out of five people you know, at least two of them eat corn on the cob in circles?
   • How can you find the probability that one person eats corn on the cob in circles?
   • How does a probability distribution help you solve the problem?

20. Weather A scientist hopes to launch a weather balloon on one of the next three mornings. For each morning, there is a 40% chance of suitable weather. What is the probability that there will be at least one morning with suitable weather?

Marketing A fruit company guarantees that 90% of the pineapples it ships will ripen within four days of delivery. Find each probability for a case containing 12 pineapples.

21. All 12 are ripe within four days.

22. At least 10 are ripe within four days.

Sociology A study shows that 50% of people in a community watch television during dinner. Suppose you select 10 people at random from this population. Find each probability.

23. P(exactly 5 of the 10 people watch television during dinner)

24. P(exactly 6 of the 10 people watch television during dinner)

25. P(at least 5 of the 10 people watch television during dinner)

26. Writing Explain how a binomial experiment is related to a binomial expansion.

27. Quality Control A company claims that 99% of its cereal boxes have at least as much cereal by weight as the amount stated on the box.
   a. At a quality control checkpoint, one box out of a random sample of ten boxes falls short of its stated weight. What is the probability of this happening due to chance variation in box weights?
   b. Reasoning Suppose three of ten boxes fail to have the claimed weight. What would you conclude? Explain.

28. Genetics About 11% of the general population is left-handed. At a school with an average class size of 30, each classroom contains four left-handed desks. Does this seem adequate? Justify your answer.

29. Open-Ended Describe a binomial experiment that can be solved using the expression ${}_7C_2(0.6)^2(0.4)^5$.

30. Graph each probability distribution for $(p + q)^3$.
   a. $p = 0.9, q = 0.1$
   b. $p = 0.45, q = 0.55$
   c. Compare and Contrast How are the graphs in parts (a) and (b) similar? How are they different?

Answers

Practice and Problem-Solving Exercises (continued)

17. $P(0) \approx 0.1176$, $P(1) \approx 0.3025$, $P(2) \approx 0.3241$, $P(3) \approx 0.1852$, $P(4) \approx 0.0595$, $P(5) \approx 0.0102$, $P(6) \approx 0.0007$

18. $P(0) \approx 0.0156$, $P(1) \approx 0.0938$, $P(2) \approx 0.2344$, $P(3) \approx 0.3125$, $P(4) \approx 0.2344$, $P(5) \approx 0.0938$, $P(6) \approx 0.0156$

19. 0.99328

20. 0.784, or 78.4%

21. ≈0.2824

22. ≈0.8891

23. ≈0.2461

24. ≈0.2051

25. ≈0.6230

26. Each term of a binomial expansion $(p + q)^n$ contains a power of p times a power of q. The coefficient of each term is the no. of times that a combination of powers results when $(p + q)^n$

is expanded. In a binomial experiment of n trials, each trial results in success or failure, with probabilities p and q. The probability of each outcome contains n factors, each of which is either p or q. The coefficient of each term is the no. of ways that outcome can be achieved.

27. a. 0.0914

   b. The probability that three boxes would be underweight is 0.0001. You can conclude that there might be a malfunction in the machinery or that the company's claim may be false.

28. The probability of a group of 30 students having 4 or fewer left-handed students is about 77.05%. This means that more than three quarters of the classes will have enough left-handed desks; 4 is an adequate no.

29. Answers may vary. Sample: 60% of the summer days in Eastport are sunny. What is the probability of a week containing exactly two sunny days?

30. a. $P(0) = 0.001$, $P(1) = 0.027$, $P(2) = 0.243$, $P(3) = 0.729$

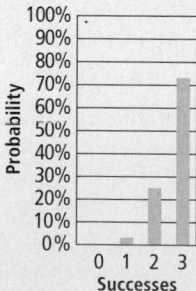

b. $P(0) = 0.166375$, $P(1) = 0.408375$, $P(2) = 0.334125$, $P(3) = 0.091125$

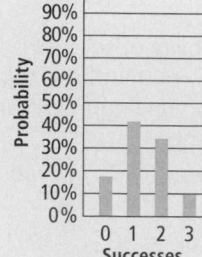

Standardized Test Prep

SAT/ACT

31. A survey shows that 60% of adults floss their teeth every day. In a random sample of ten adults, what is the probability that exactly six adults floss every day?

    Ⓐ 11%   Ⓑ 25%   Ⓒ 60%   Ⓓ 100%

32. Which of the statements about the following equation is correct?

$$\frac{b^2 - 4b + 3}{b - 3} = b - 1$$

    Ⓕ The equation is always true.

    Ⓖ The equation is true, except when $b = 3$.

    Ⓗ The equation is never true.

    Ⓘ The equation is true when $b = 3$.

33. Which is the inverse of $f(x) = (x - 3)^2$?

    Ⓐ $f^{-1}(x) = \dfrac{x^2}{(3x - 1)^2}$ Ⓒ $f^{-1}(x) = \dfrac{1}{(3x - 1)^2}$

    Ⓑ $f^{-1}(x) = \pm\sqrt{x} + 3$ Ⓓ $f^{-1}(x) = \pm\sqrt{x - 3}$

34. If $\log 4 \approx 0.60206$ and $\log 5 \approx 0.69897$, what is the approximate value of $\log 80$?

    Ⓕ 0.2534   Ⓖ 0.2914   Ⓗ 1.903   Ⓘ 11.1835

Extended Response

35. In a geometric sequence, $a_1 = 3$ and $a_4 = 192$. Explain how to find a_2 and a_3.

Mixed Review

Identify any bias in each survey question.   🔊 **See Lesson 11-7.**

36. Do you agree that replacing that dog park with a beautiful new library would be better for our town?

37. Do you agree with the amendments to Proposition 39?

Find the vertices, foci, and asymptotes of each hyperbola.   🔊 **See Lesson 10-5.**

38. $\dfrac{y^2}{49} - \dfrac{x^2}{25} = 1$ **39.** $4y^2 - 9x^2 = 36$ **40.** $64y^2 - 36x^2 = 576$

A standard number cube is tossed. Find each probability.   🔊 **See Lesson 11-3.**

41. $P(2 \text{ or greater than } 3)$ **42.** $P(6 \text{ or even})$ **43.** $P(\text{prime or } 1)$

Get Ready! To prepare for Lesson 11-9, do Exercises 44–47.

Find the mean and standard deviation for each data set.   🔊 **See Lessons 11-5 and 11-6.**

44. 16, 20, 28, 25, 26, 33, 27, 22, 29, 18   **45.** 81, 78, 79, 80, 76, 88, 83, 90, 87, 76

46. 8.5, 7.9, 8.2, 9.0, 8.3, 9.1, 9.2   **47.** 23.5, 22.4, 25.6, 26.8, 28.1, 22.3, 24.5

---

42. $\dfrac{1}{2}$

43. $\dfrac{2}{3}$

44. $\bar{x} = 24.4$, $\sigma \approx 5.04$

45. $\bar{x} = 81.8$, $\sigma \approx 4.77$

46. $\bar{x} = 8.6$, $\sigma \approx 0.47$

47. $\bar{x} \approx 24.74$, $\sigma \approx 2.046$

---

c. The probabilities of each graph sum to 1; $P(0) + P(1) + P(2) + P(3) = 1$. The probabilities of part (a) increase with increasing success numbers; the maximum probability occurring at $P(3)$. The probabilities of part (b) peak with a maximum at $P(1)$ and then decrease with increasing success numbers.

Standardized Test Prep

31. B

32. G

33. B

34. H

35. [4] $a_n = a_1 r^{n-1}$. Use $a_1 = 3$ and $a_4 = 192$ to find r.

    $192 = (3)r^{(4-1)}$

        $4 = r$

    Use a_1 and r to find $a_2 = 12$ and $a_3 = 48$.

[3] appropriate method, with one computational error

[2] only a_2 is found correctly OR only a_3 is found correctly

[1] a_2 and a_3 are correct, without work shown

Mixed Review

36. loaded and leading question by the use of the words "beautiful" and "Do you agree"

37. not enough information about the amendments to make a decision

38. vertices: $(0, \pm 7)$; foci: $(0, \pm\sqrt{74})$; asymptotes: $y = \pm\dfrac{7}{5}x$

39. vertices: $(0, \pm 3)$; foci: $(0, \pm\sqrt{13})$; asymptotes: $y = \pm\dfrac{3}{2}x$

40. vertices: $(0, \pm 3)$; foci: $(0, \pm 5)$; asymptotes: $y = \pm\dfrac{3}{4}x$

41. $\dfrac{2}{3}$

Additional Instructional Support

Algebra 2 Companion

Students can use the **Algebra 2 Companion** worktext (4 pages) as you teach the lesson. Use the Companion to support

- New Vocabulary
- Key Concepts
- Got It for each Problem
- Lesson Check

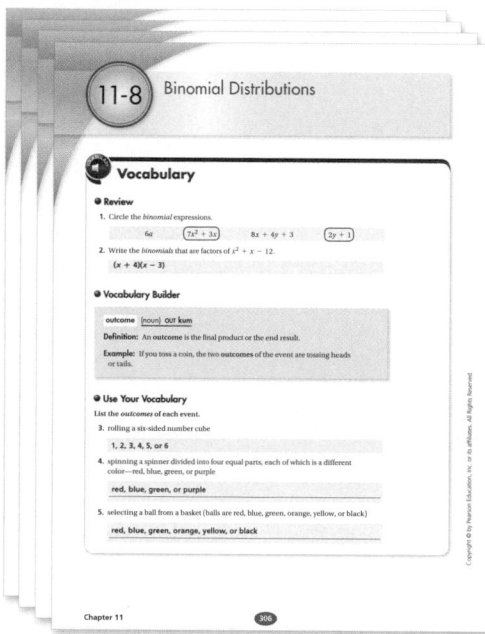

ELL Support

Use Role Playing Have students work in pairs.

Tell students that they are going to do an *experiment* with a coin. Instruct pairs to take turns flipping a coin 10 times and recording the results. Explain that each time they flip the coin it is a *trial* in their experiment. They are "trying" something to see what happens. They are flipping a coin 10 times to see how many times it lands heads up or tails up.

Emphasize that each flip has only two *possible outcomes*—heads or tails. Have one student in each pair flip while the other chooses heads or tails. Explain that the student's choice is *a success*. If the student chooses heads, then heads is a success and tails is a *failure*.

Point out that the chances that a coin will land heads up does not change—*the probability is constant*. For each flip/trial, the probability of success is $\frac{1}{2}$ or 50%.

5 Assess & Remediate

Lesson Quiz

1. **Do you UNDERSTAND?** In a high school, 70% of the 2000 students have cellular phones. The principal is randomly selecting six students to help plan rules for using cell phones in the school. What is the probability that exactly four of the selected students have cellular phones?

2. What is the binomial expansion of $(x + 2y)^4$?

3. What is the fourth term of $(3x - y)^5$?

4. A multiple-choice quiz has four questions. Each question has four answer choices. If you guess every answer, what is the probability of getting at least two correct?

ANSWERS TO LESSON QUIZ

1. about 0.32
2. $(x + 2y)^4 = x^4 + 8x^3y + 24x^2y^2 + 32xy^3 + 16y^4$
3. $-90x^2y^3$
4. about 26.2%

PRESCRIPTION FOR REMEDIATION

Use the student work on the Lesson Quiz to prescribe a differentiated review assignment:

Points	Differentiated Remediation
0–1	Intervention
2	On-level
3	Extension

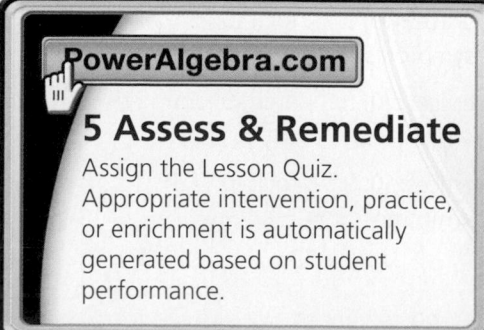

PowerAlgebra.com

5 Assess & Remediate

Assign the Lesson Quiz. Appropriate intervention, practice, or enrichment is automatically generated based on student performance.

Intervention

- **Reteaching** (2 pages) Provides reteaching and practice exercises for the key lesson concepts. Use with struggling students or absent students.

- **English Language Learner Support** Helps students develop and reinforce mathematical vocabulary and key concepts.

All-in-One Resources/Online
Reteaching

11-8 Reteaching
Binomial Distributions

Suppose you repeat an experiment n times, and each time you run the experiment it has a probability of success p and a probability of failure q. Then, the probability of x successes in n trials is:

$$_nC_x \, p^x q^{n-x}, \text{ where } q = 1 - p$$

Problem

What is the probability of two successes in five trials, where the probability of success for each trial is 0.2?

$_nC_x = {}_5C_2$ Find $_nC_r$

$\quad = \dfrac{5!}{2!(5-2)!}$

$\quad = 10$

$q = 1 - p$ Find q.

$\quad = 1 - .2$

$\quad = 0.8$

$P(2 \text{ successes}) = {}_5C_2 (0.2)^2 (0.8)^{5-2}$ Substitute for n, x, p, and q in the formula.

$\quad = 10(0.2)^2(0.8)^3$ Simplify.

$\quad = 10(0.04)(0.512)$

$\quad = 0.2048$

The probability of two successes in five trials is about 20%.

Exercises

Find the probability of x successes in n trials for the given probability of success p on each trial. Round to the nearest tenth of a percent.

1. $x = 3$, $n = 4$, $p = 0.3$ **7.6%**
2. $x = 4$, $n = 6$, $p = 0.1$ **0.1%**
3. $x = 7$, $n = 9$, $p = 0.4$ **2.1%**
4. $x = 5$, $n = 6$, $p = 0.3$ **1.0%**

5. A light fixture contains six light bulbs. With normal use, each bulb has a 95% chance of lasting for 2 yr. What is the probability that all six bulbs last for 2 yr? **about 73.5%**

6. Use the information from Exercise 5. What is the probability that five of the six bulbs will last for 2 yr? **about 23.2%**

7. Suppose the bulbs have an 80% chance of lasting for 2 yr. Find the probability that three of the six bulbs will last for 2 yr. **0.8%**

All-in-One Resources/Online
English Language Learner Support

11-8 ELL Support
Binomial Distributions

In the town of Rainesville, 15% of the 10,000 houses are made of brick. If 7 houses are randomly selected, what is the probability that 4 of them will be made of brick?

There are two sets of cards below that show how to solve the above problem. The set on the left explains the thinking. The set on the right shows the steps in the correct order.

Think Cards	Write Cards
Simplify the exponents.	$P(4) = 35(0.0005)(0.6141)$
Evaluate $_7C_4$.	$P(x) = {}_nC_x \, p^x q^{n-x}$
Multiply.	$P(4) \approx 0.01$
Write the Binomial Probability formula.	$P(4) = {}_7C_4(0.15)^4(0.85)^3$
Substitute values from the problem into the formula.	$P(4) = 35(0.15)^4(0.85)^3$

Think	Write
First, write the Binomial Probability formula.	Step 1 $P(x) = {}_nC_x \, p^x q^{n-x}$
Second, substitute values from the problem into the formula.	Step 2 $P(4) = {}_7C_4(0.15)^4(0.85)^3$
Next, evaluate $_7C_4$.	Step 3 $P(4) = 35(0.15)^4(0.85)^3$
Then, simplify the exponents.	Step 4 $P(4) = 35(0.0005)(0.6141)$
Finally, multiply.	Step 4 $P(4) \approx 0.01$

Differentiated Remediation *continued*

On-Level

- **Practice** (2 pages) Provides extra practice for each lesson. For more challenging practice exercises, use the Form G Practice pages found in the All-in-One Teaching Resources and online.

- **Think About a Plan** Helps students develop specific problem-solving skills and strategies by providing scaffolded guiding questions.

- **Standardized Test Prep** Focuses on all major exercises, all major question types, and helps students prepare for the high-stakes assessments.

Extension

- **Enrichment** Provides students with interesting problems and activities that extend the concepts of the lesson.

- **Activities, Games, and Puzzles** Worksheets that can be used for concepts development, enrichment, and for fun!

Student Companion/All-in-One Resources/Online
Practice page 1

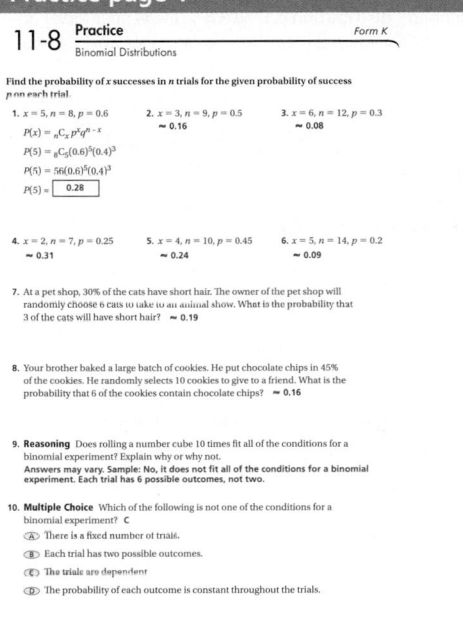

Student Companion/All-in-One Resources/Online
Practice page 2

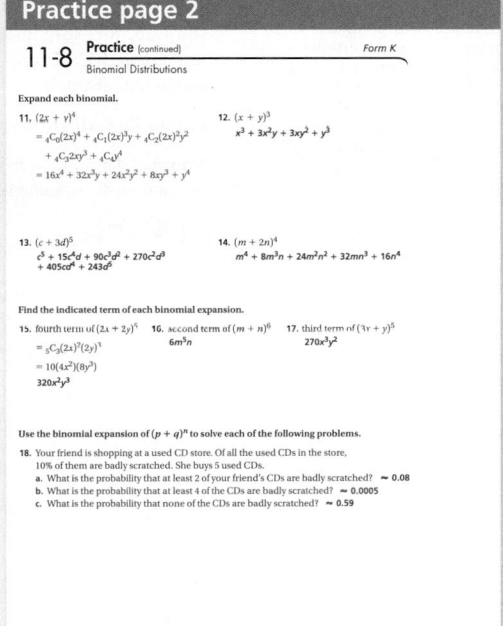

All-in-One Resources/Online
Enrichment

Student Companion/All-in-One Resources/Online
Think About a Plan

Student Companion/All-in-One Resources/Online
Standardized Test Prep

Online Teacher Resource Center
Activities, Games, and Puzzles

1 Interactive Learning

Solve It!

PURPOSE To distinguish between the graphs of even and odd functions using the definitions

PROCESS Students may

- test ordered pairs from the graphs to see whether the graph satisfies the definitions.
- consider how each definition affects the ordered pair given by $(x, f(x))$.

FACILITATE

Q In an even function, when the sign of the *x*-value of an ordered pair changes, what happens to the *y*-value? **[It stays the same.]**

Q In an odd function, when the sign of the *x*-value of an ordered pair changes, what happens to the *y*-value? **[It changes sign.]**

Q How are even functions symmetric? Odd functions? **[Even functions are symmetric about the y-axis. Odd functions are symmetric about the origin.]**

ANSWER See Solve It in Answers on next page.

CONNECT THE MATH In the Solve It students explore the definitions and symmetry of graphs of even and odd functions. In the lesson, students will explore the graphs of normal distributions that are symmetric about the mean.

2 Guided Instruction

Take Note

Q Suppose a normal distribution has a mean of 50 and a standard deviation of 11. Between which two point values would 68 percent of the data points fall? **[39 and 61]**

Objective To use a normal distribution

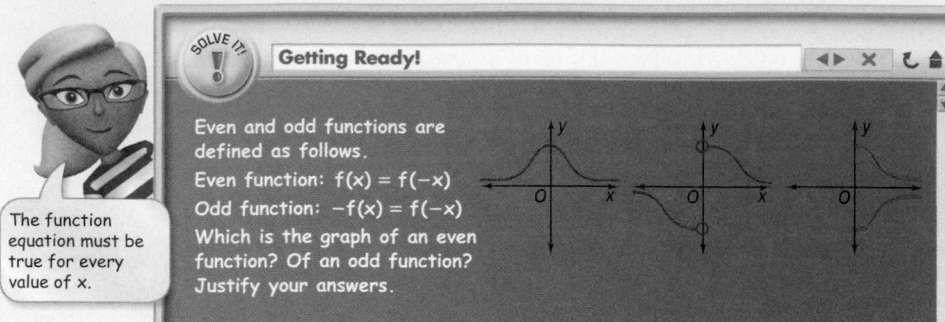

Getting Ready!

Even and odd functions are defined as follows.
Even function: $f(x) = f(-x)$
Odd function: $-f(x) = f(-x)$
Which is the graph of an even function? Of an odd function? Justify your answers.

The function equation must be true for every value of *x*.

Lesson Vocabulary
- discrete probability distribution
- continuous probability distribution
- normal distribution

A **discrete probability distribution** has a finite number of possible events, or values. The binomial probability distribution you studied in the preceding lesson is a discrete probability distribution.

The events for a **continuous probability distribution** can be any value in an interval of real numbers. If a data set is large, the distribution of its discrete values approximates a continuous distribution.

Focus Question What is a normal distribution?

A **normal distribution** has data that vary randomly from the mean. The graph of a normal distribution is called a normal curve.

take note

Key Concept   Normal Distribution

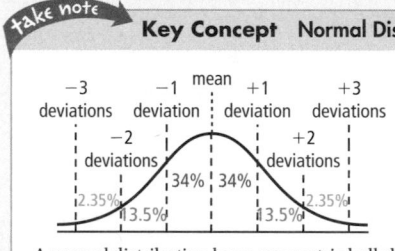

In a normal distribution,
- 68% of data fall within one standard deviation of the mean
- 95% of data fall within two standard deviations of the mean
- 99.7% of data fall within three standard deviations of the mean

A normal distribution has a symmetric bell shape centered on the mean.

11-9 Preparing to Teach

BIG idea Probability   **UbD**

ESSENTIAL UNDERSTANDING

Normal distributions model many common natural phenomena, such as human height, weight, and blood pressure.

Math Background

Normal distributions occur often in real life such as standardized test scores and heights of adults. The normal distribution curve has the following characteristics:

- The graph has its maximum at the center.
- The graph is symmetric about the mean.
- The mean, mode, and median are equal.
- About 68% of the values fall within one standard deviation of the mean, 34% fall within one standard deviation to the right of the mean, and 34% fall within one standard deviation to the left of the mean.

- About 95% of the values fall within two standard deviations of the mean, 47.5% fall within two standard deviations to the right of the mean, and 47.5% fall within two standard deviations to the left of the mean.
- About 99.7% of the values fall within three standard deviations of the mean, 49.85% fall within three standard deviations to the right of the mean, and 49.85% fall within three standard deviations to the left of the mean.

Support Student Learning

Use the **Algebra 2 Companion** to engage and support students during instruction. See Lesson Resources at the end of this lesson for details.

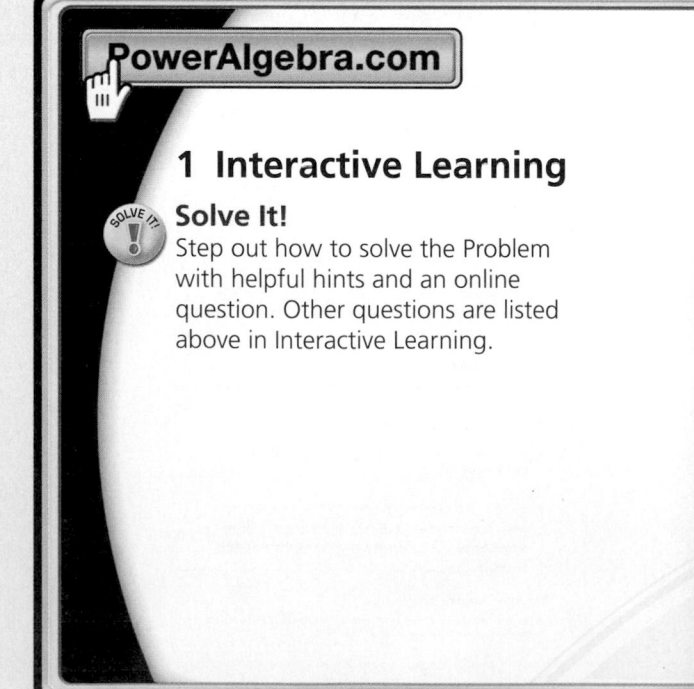

PowerAlgebra.com

1 Interactive Learning

Solve It!

Step out how to solve the Problem with helpful hints and an online question. Other questions are listed above in Interactive Learning.

Sometimes an extraordinary factor affects data that would otherwise be normally distributed. A coin, for example, may be somehow weighted unevenly so that heads tends to come up more frequently than tails. In such a case, the data set could have a distribution that is *skewed*, an asymmetric curve where one end stretches out further than the other end.

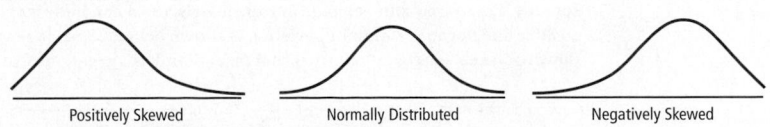

Positively Skewed   Normally Distributed   Negatively Skewed

Problem 1 Analyzing Normally Distributed Data

Zoology The bar graph gives the weights of a population of female brown bears. The red curve shows how the weights are normally distributed about the mean, 115 kg. Approximately what percent of female brown bears weigh between 100 and 129 kg?

Female Brown Bear Weights

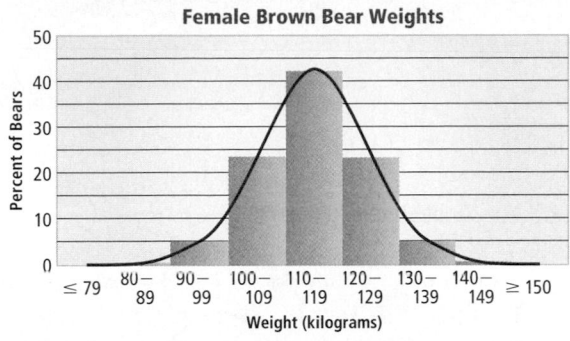

Estimate and add the percents for the intervals 100–109, 110–119, and 120–129.

$$23 + 42 + 23 = 88$$

About 88% of female brown bears weigh between 100 and 129 kg.

Plan
How do you find this percent?
The percents for each bar are based on the same sample population of bears. You can add the percents.

 Got It? 1. a. Approximately what percent of female brown bears in Problem 1 weigh less than 120 kg?
  b. The standard deviation in the weights of female brown bears is about 10 kg. Approximately what percent of female brown bears have weights that are within 1.5 standard deviations of the mean?

Problem 1

Q Why do you expect the weights of the female brown bear to be normally distributed? **[Although there may be a few heavy or light bears, most bears are similar in size, so the weights of most of the bears should be close to the average weight of the female brown bears.]**

Q About what percent of the female brown bears weigh less than 100 kg or more than 129 kg? Describe a way to find this value. **[Samples: Since 88% of the bears weigh between 100 kg and 129 kg, 100 − 88 = 12% of the bears weigh less than 100 kg or more than 129 kg. You could also add the percentages for the bars for 80–89, 90–99, 130–139, and 140–149 to get 1 + 5 + 5 + 1 = 12%]**

Q What percent of female brown bears should weigh less than 115 kg? Explain. **[Since the weight is normally distributed, half of the bears, or 50%, should weigh less than the mean and half should weigh more than the mean.]**

Got It?

Q Which intervals on the graph will you need to find the percent for 1a? **[80–89, 90–99, 100–109, and 110–119]**

Q What weight values are 1.5 standard deviations from the mean? How do you find these values? **[130 kg and 100 kg; because 115 + 1.5(10) = 130 and 115 − 1.5(10) = 100]**

---

2 Guided Instruction

Each Problem is worked out and supported online.

Support in Algebra 2 Companion
• Vocabulary
• Key Concepts
• Got It?

Problem 1
Analyzing Normally Distributed Data
Animated

Problem 2
Sketching a Normal Curve
Animated

Problem 3
Analyzing a Normal Distribution
Animated

Answers

Solve It!
The first graph is of an even function because the *y*-values are the same for *x* and −*x*. The second graph is of an odd function because the *y*-value for −*x* is equal to the opposite of the *y*-value for *x*. The third graph is not of a function.

Got It?
1. a. 71%   **b.** 88%

Problem 2

Q Do you have to sketch the graph very far beyond three standard deviations? Explain. **[No; less than 0.3 percent of the data points fall outside three standard deviations.]**

Q What effect does the standard deviation have on the shape of the bell curve? **[no effect]**

Q Compare the height of the bell curve at ±1 standard deviation from the mean to the height of the bell curve at the mean. **[The height of the bell curve at ±1 standard deviation from the mean is a little more than half as tall as the height of the bell curve at the mean.]**

Q About how tall should the bell curve be at ±1 standard deviation from the mean compared to the height of the bell curve at the mean? **[a little more than half as tall]**

Q What should the height of the bell curve be at ±3 standard deviations from the mean? **[close to zero]**

EXTENSION

Q Why are the intervals between the vertical lines spaced the same distance apart? **[The distances between the lines represent the same value of one standard deviation.]**

Got It?

Q What will be the values along the bottom of your graph? **[7, 11.7, 16.4, 21.1, 25.8, 30.5, and 35.2]**

Q How high should your graph be? **[The vertical axis is not scaled, so the height does not matter.]**

Q Around what value should the graph be symmetric? **[the mean of 21.1 in]**

When data are normally distributed, you can sketch the graph of the distribution because a normal curve has a symmetric bell shape.

Problem 2 Sketching a Normal Curve

Zoology For a population of male European eels, the mean body length and one positive and negative standard deviation is shown below. Sketch a normal curve showing the eel lengths at one, two, and three standard deviations from the mean.

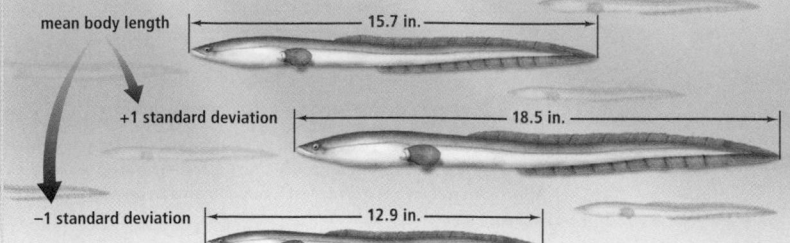

Know	Need	Plan
The mean and the standard deviation of the population	Lengths that are one, two, and three standard deviations from the mean	• Multiply the standard deviation by 1, 2, and 3. • Draw vertical lines at the mean ± these values. • Sketch the normal curve.

Think
How high do you draw the curve?
Unless you actually label the vertical scale, the height of the curve doesn't matter.

Distribution of Body Lengths for Male European Eels

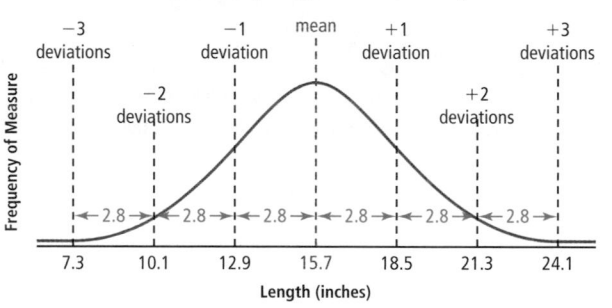

✓ **Got It?** **2.** For a population of female European eels, the mean body length is 21.1 in. The standard deviation is 4.7 in. Sketch a normal curve showing eel lengths at one, two, and three standard deviations from the mean.

Additional Problems

1. You track the number of letters in your text messages for a month and create the bar graph shown. The number of letters is normally distributed about a mean of 10. About what percent of your text messages are between 9 and 11 letters long?

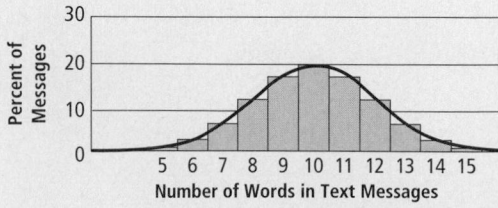

ANSWER 56%

2. For an English class, the average score on a research project was 82 and the standard deviation of the normally distributed scores was 5. Sketch a normal curve showing the project scores and three standard deviations from the mean.

ANSWER

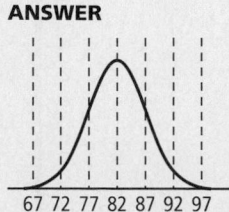

3. Using the normal curve from Additional Problem 2, what percent of students scored between 72 and 82 points?

ANSWER 47.5%

When you show a probability distribution as a bar graph, the height of the bar indicates probability. For a normal distribution, however, the area between the curve and an interval on the x-axis represents probability.

 Problem 3 Analyzing a Normal Distribution

The heights of adult American males are approximately normally distributed with mean 69.5 in. and standard deviation 2.5 in.

Ⓐ What percent of adult American males are between 67 in. and 74.5 in. tall?

Step 1 Draw a normal curve.

Step 2 Label the mean, 69.5.

Step 3 Divide the graph into sections that are one standard-deviation, or 2.5 in., wide.

Step 4 Label the percentages for each section.

Because the graph is a normal distribution, each section within one standard deviation has a probability of 34%. Similarly, each section from one standard deviation to two standard deviations has a probability of 13.5%. Each outermost section has a probability of 2.35%.

Distribution of Heights—Adult American Males

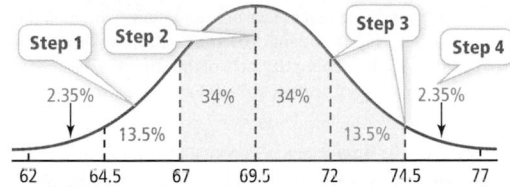

Step 5 Find the probability between 67 and 74.5.

Use the percentages to calculate probability.

$$P(67 < \text{height} < 74.5) = 0.34 + 0.34 + 0.135$$

Simplify. $= 0.815$

About 82% of adult American males are between 67 in. and 74.5 in. tall.

Think

How do you divide the graph of the distribution?
Draw vertical lines at intervals that are one standard deviation wide, on both sides of the mean.

Problem 3

Q Is there another way to find out what percent of males you would expect to be taller than 72 in? **[You could add 13.5 + 2.35 + 0.15 to get 16%.]**

EXTENSION

Q The area between the curve and the x-axis represents probability for a normal distribution. What is the area under the entire curve? Explain. **[The area under the entire normal curve is one. One hundred percent of the data is represented by the entire curve.]**

Answers

Got It? (continued)

2.

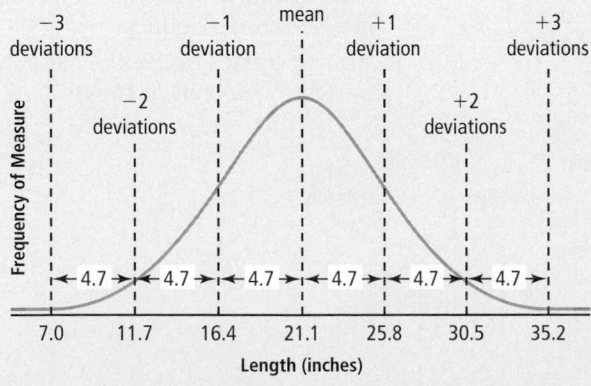

Distribution of Female European Eels

Got It?

Q What percent of the scores are below 150? **[Since the graph is symmetric, 50% lie above the mean, and 50% lie below.]**

Q For 3b, what is the most convenient way to divide the graph of the normal curve to find the percent of students scoring above 135? **[Divide the graph into the 34% between 135 and 150 and the 50% scoring above the mean of 150.]**

3 Lesson Check

Do you know HOW?

- If students have difficulty finding the percentage in Exercise 1, ask them which bars of the graph are included by the condition "at least 100 kg."
- If students cannot draw the curve in Exercise 2, remind them that the curve is symmetric about the mean and covers ±3 standard deviations.
- If students have difficulty solving Exercise 3, ask them to draw and label the normal curve that fits the conditions.

Do you UNDERSTAND?

- If students have difficulty comparing the mean and median of a normal distribution for Exercise 5, ask them what percent of the data falls above and below each of the median and mean. Point out that the normal distribution is symmetric about the mean.
- If students have difficulty understanding the graph change for an increase in the mean for Exercise 6, then ask what kinds of values increase the mean and where those values occur in a graph.

Close

Q How can the graph of a normal distribution of data help you understand the data? **[A normal distribution allows you to calculate what percentage of data falls within various standard deviations of the mean.]**

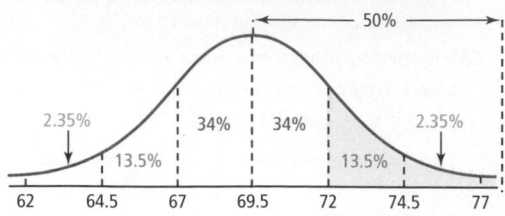

What information do you need?
You need the percentage of adult American males taller than 6 ft.

B In a group of 2000 adult American males, about how many would you expect to be taller than 6 ft (or 72 in.)?

Because the graph is symmetric about the mean, the right half of the distribution contains 50% of the data. If you subtract everything between 69.5 in. and 72 in. from the right half, only the part of the distribution that is greater than 72 in. remains.

Distribution of Heights—Adult American Males

$$P(\text{height} > 72) = 0.50 - 0.34 = 0.16$$

You would expect about 16% of the 2000 adult American males to be taller than 72 in. You would expect about $0.16 \cdot 2000 = 320$ to be over 6 ft tall.

Got It? 3. The scores on the Algebra 2 final are approximately normally distributed with a mean of 150 and a standard deviation of 15.
  a. What percentage of the students who took the test scored above 180?
  b. If 250 students took the final, approximately how many scored above 135?
  c. Reasoning If 13.6% of the students received a B on the final, how can you describe their scores? Explain.

Focus Question What is a normal distribution?

Answer A normal distribution is a continuous distribution whose data vary randomly from the mean. The graph of a normal distribution is a symmetric bell-shaped curve centered on the mean. Use the percentage for each interval to calculate probability.

Lesson Check

Do you know HOW?

1. Use the graph from Problem 1. What is the approximate percent of female brown bears weighing at least 100 kg?

2. Draw a curve to represent a normally distributed experiment that has a mean of 180 and a standard deviation of 15. Label the x-axis and indicate the probabilities.

3. The scores on an exam are normally distributed, with a mean of 85 and a standard deviation of 5. What percent of the scores are from 85 to 95?

Do you UNDERSTAND?

4. **Vocabulary** Why is a normal distribution "normal"?

5. **Compare and Contrast** How do the mean and median compare in a normal distribution?

6. **Reasoning** What is the effect on a normal distribution if each data value increases by 10? Justify your answer.

Answers

Got It? (continued)

3. a. 2.5%
  b. 210 students
  c. The students that received a B had scores between 165 and 180.

Lesson Check

1. 94%

2.

3. 47.5%

4. Normal distribution means that most of the examples in a data set are close to the mean; the distribution of the data is within 1, 2, or 3 standard deviations of the mean.

5. The mean and median are equivalent in a normal distribution.

6. mean increases by 10: the bell curve is translated 10 units to the rt.

Practice and Problem-Solving Exercises

A Practice   **Biology** The heights of men in a survey are distributed normally about the mean. Use the graph to the right for Exercises 7–10.   ◆ See Problem 1.

7. About what percent of men aged 25 to 34 are 69–71 in. tall?

8. About what percent of men aged 25 to 34 are less than 70 in. tall?

9. Suppose the survey included data on 100 men. About how many would you expect to be 69–71 in. tall?

10. The mean of the data is 70, and the standard deviation is 2.5. Approximately what percent of men are within one standard deviation of the mean height?

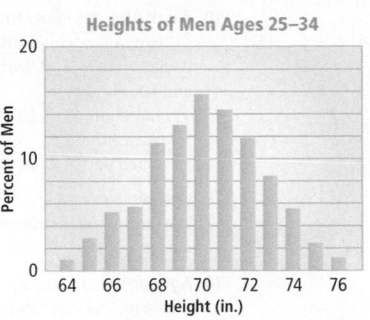

Heights of Men Ages 25–34

Sketch a normal curve for each distribution. Label the *x*-axis values at one, two, and three standard deviations from the mean.   ◆ See Problem 2.

Guided Practice

11. mean = 45, standard deviation = 5

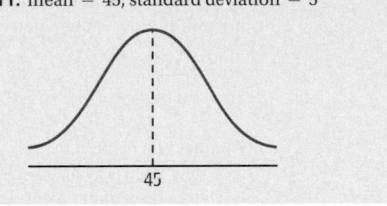

To start, sketch a normal curve and label the mean.

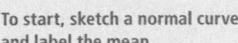

12. mean = 45, standard deviation = 2   **13.** mean = 45, standard deviation = 3.5

A set of data has a normal distribution with a mean of 50 and a standard deviation of 8. Find the percent of data within each interval.   ◆ See Problem 3.

14. from 42 to 58   **15.** greater than 34   **16.** less than 50

ASSIGNMENT GUIDE

Basic: 7–16, 18, 20, 26

Average: 7–15 odd, 16–26

Standardized Test Prep: 28–31

Mixed Review: 32–40

Reasoning exercises have blue headings.

Applications exercises have red headings.

EXERCISE 20: Use the Think About a Plan worksheet in the **Student Companion** (also available in the Teaching Resources in print and online) to further support students' development in becoming independent learners.

HOMEWORK QUICK CHECK

To check students' understanding of key skills and concepts, go over Exercises 7, 12, 18, 20, and 26.

Practice and Problem-Solving Exercises

7. ≈43%

8. ≈39%

9. ≈43 men

10. ≈66%

11.

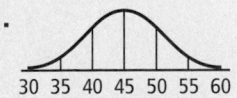

30 35 40 45 50 55 60

12.

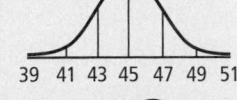

39 41 43 45 47 49 51

13.

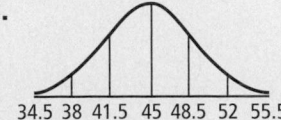

34.5 38 41.5 45 48.5 52 55.5

14. 68%

15. 97.5%

16. 50%

Answers

Practice and Problem-Solving Exercises (continued)

17. a. Set 2

b–c.

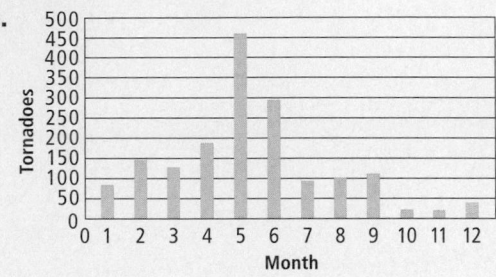

4 5 6 7 8 9 10 11

18. 32%

19. yes; 99% of all grades are expected to be within 3 standard deviations of the mean, and this score is 4.4 standard deviations above the mean.

20. 2.5%

21. 47.5%

22. 81.5%

23. 84%

24. 97.5%

25. a.

Tornadoes	(histogram with y-axis 0–500 in steps of 50, x-axis Month 0–12)

b. Yes; the curve is skewed to the left.

26. No; the mean could be 206 with standard deviation of 42, or the mean could be 269 with a standard deviation of 21.

27. Yes; Elena scored within the top 10% of her group. Her score is 2.75 standard deviations above the mean, which places her in the top 1%. Jake did not score in the top 10%. His score is 1.16 standard deviations above the mean, or at the 88th percentile.

 Apply

17. a. From the table at the right, select the set of values that appears to be distributed normally.
   b. Using the set you chose in part (a), make a histogram of the values.
   c. Sketch a normal curve over your graph.

18. Think About a Plan The numbers of paper clips per box in a truckload of boxes are normally distributed, with a mean of 100 and a standard deviation of 5. Find the probability that a box will *not* contain between 95 and 105 clips.
   • How should you label the vertical lines on the graph of the normal distribution?
   • Which parts of the graph are *not* between 95 and 105 clips?

19. Writing In a class of 25, one student receives a score of 100 on a test. The grades are distributed normally, with a mean of 78 and a standard deviation of 5. Do you think the student's score is an outlier? Explain.

20. Agriculture To win a prize, the diameter of a tomato must be greater than 4 in. The diameters of a crop of tomatoes grown in a special soil are normally distributed, with a mean of 3.2 in. and a standard deviation of 0.4 in. What is the probability that a tomato grown in the special soil will be a winner?

Set 1	Set 2	Set 3
1	5	5
10	7	6
5	7	9
19	7	1
2	4	1
7	11	5
1	7	11
7	7	1
2	7	10
10	9	4
6	7	2
9	7	8

A normal distribution has a mean of 100 and a standard deviation of 10. Find the probability that a value selected at random is in the given interval.

21. from 80 to 100

22. from 90 to 120

23. at most 110

24. at least 80

25. Weather The table at the right shows the number of tornadoes that were recorded in the U.S. in 2008.
   a. Draw a histogram to represent the data.
   b. Does the histogram approximate a normal curve? Explain.

26. Error Analysis In a set of data, the value 332 is 3 standard deviations from the mean and the value 248 is 1 standard deviation from the mean. A classmate claims that there is only one possible mean and standard deviation for this data set. Do you agree? Explain.

27. Reasoning Jake and Elena took the same standardized test, but with different groups of students. They both received a score of 87. In Jake's group, the mean was 80 and the standard deviation was 6. In Elena's group, the mean was 76 and the standard deviation was 4. Did either student score in the top 10% of his or her group? Explain.

Month	Tornadoes
1	84
2	147
3	129
4	189
5	461
6	294
7	93
8	101
9	111
10	21
11	20
12	40

SAT/ACT

28. For a daily airline flight between two cities, the number of pieces of checked luggage has a mean of 380 and a standard deviation of 20. On what percent of the flights would you expect from 340 to 420 pieces of checked luggage?

   Ⓐ 34%   Ⓑ 47.5%   Ⓒ 68%   Ⓓ 95%

29. A jar contains 37 pennies, 53 nickels, 29 dimes, and 21 quarters. A coin is drawn at random from the jar. What is the probability that the coin drawn is NOT a quarter?

   Ⓕ $\frac{56,869}{2,744,000}$ Ⓖ $\frac{3}{20}$ Ⓗ $\frac{3}{17}$ Ⓘ $\frac{17}{20}$

30. A multiple-choice quiz contains five questions, each with three answer choices. You select all five answer choices at random. What is the best estimate of the probability that you will get at least four answers correct?

   Ⓐ 4.1%   Ⓑ 4.5%   Ⓒ 13.2%   Ⓓ 46.1%

Short Response

31. Distribution A has 50 data values with mean 40 and standard deviation 2.4. Distribution B has 30 data values with mean 40 and standard deviation 2.8. Which distribution has more data values at or below 40? Show your work.

Mixed Review

Find the probability of x successes in n trials for the given probability of success p on each trial.   ◀ **See Lesson 11-8.**

32. $x = 4, n = 7, p = 0.2$ **33.** $x = 2, n = 9, p = 0.4$ **34.** $x = 6, n = 10, p = 0.3$

Graph each equation. Identify the conic section and describe the graph and its lines of symmetry. Then find the domain and range.   ◀ **See Lesson 10-1.**

35. $x^2 + y^2 = 64$ **36.** $x^2 - y^2 = 9$ **37.** $9x^2 + 25y^2 = 225$

Get Ready!   To prepare for Lesson 12-1, do Exercises 38–40.

Write an equation for each horizontal translation of $y = x - 2$. Then graph each translation.   ◀ **See Lesson 2-6.**

38. 1 unit right   **39.** 2 units left   **40.** $\frac{3}{4}$ unit left

38. $y = x - 3$;
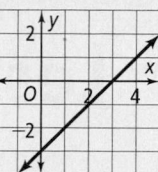

39. $y = x$;
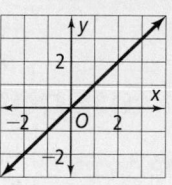

40. $y = x - \frac{5}{4}$;
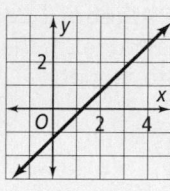

Standardized Test Prep

28. D

29. I

30. B

31. **[2]** For Distribution A with 50 data values, 25 values are at or below 40, which is the mean. For Distribution B with 30 data values, 15 values are at or below the mean 40. So Distribution A has more values at or below 40.

   [1] correct distribution, without explanation or work shown

Mixed Review

32. 0.02867

33. 0.1612

34. 0.03676

35.
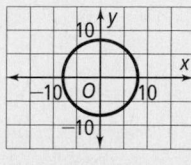

circle; center: (0, 0), radius: 8; lines of sym.: all lines through the center; domain: $-8 \le x \le 8$, range: $-8 \le y \le 8$

36.
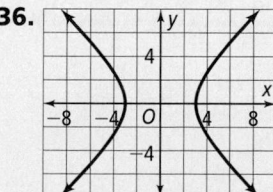

hyperbola; center: (0, 0), foci: $(\pm 3\sqrt{2}, 0)$; lines of sym.: $x = 0$, $y = 0$; domain: $x \le -3$ or $x \ge 3$; range: all real numbers

37.
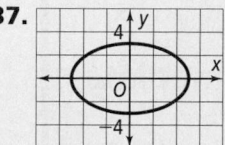

ellipse; center: (0, 0), foci: $(\pm 4, 0)$; lines of sym.: $x = 0$, $y = 0$; domain: $-5 \le x \le 5$, range: $-3 \le y \le 3$

Additional Instructional Support

Algebra 2 Companion

Students can use the **Algebra 2 Companion** worktext (4 pages) as you teach the lesson. Use the Companion to support

- New Vocabulary
- Key Concepts
- Got It for each Problem
- Lesson Check

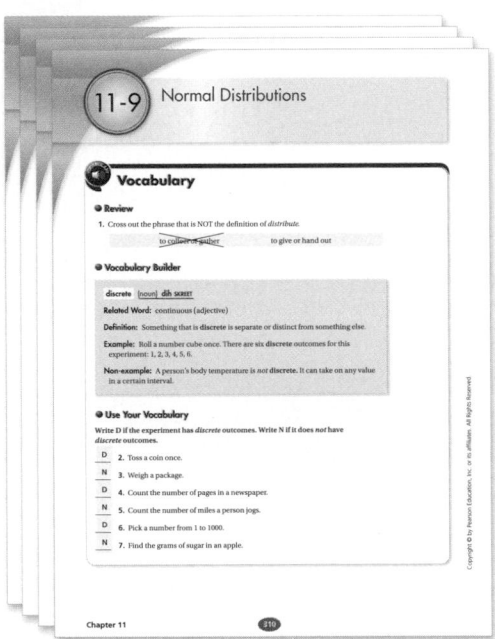

ELL Support

Assess Understanding This section contains several word problems. In small groups, have each student prepare the normal curve graph that would accompany a word problem. Check them, and then have each student read the word problem aloud to the group and share the graph with the other group members to aid them in completing the exercises.

Focus on Communication Sketch a normal distribution on the board and draw a line down the middle and the lines representing three standard deviations. Point to each line and ask students to identify what each line represents.

5 Assess & Remediate

Lesson Quiz

1. The bar graph shows the number of minutes that people spent browsing a web site for one week. The curve shows how the time spent is normally distributed about a mean of 4.5 minutes. About what percentage of people spent between 3 and 6 minutes browsing the site?

2. The wait times on a computer help line average 4.2 minutes. The standard deviation is 1.3 minutes. Sketch the normal curve showing the wait times at one, two, and three standard deviations from the mean.

3. **Do you UNDERSTAND?** Using the normal curve from Question 2, about what percent of people wait longer than 5.5 minutes?

ANSWERS TO LESSON QUIZ

1. about 76%

2.

```
        0.3  2.9  5.5  8.1
```

3. about 16%

PRESCRIPTION FOR REMEDIATION
Use the student work on the Lesson Quiz to prescribe a differentiated review assignment:

Points	Differentiated Remediation
0–1	Intervention
2	On-level
3	Extension

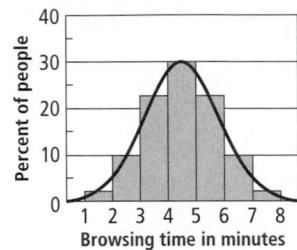

5 Assess & Remediate

Assign the Lesson Quiz. Appropriate intervention, practice, or enrichment is automatically generated based on student performance.

Intervention

- **Reteaching** (2 pages) Provides reteaching and practice exercises for the key lesson concepts. Use with struggling students or absent students.

- **English Language Learner Support** Helps students develop and reinforce mathematical vocabulary and key concepts.

All-in-One Resources/Online
Reteaching

11-9 Reteaching
Normal Distributions

If a data set has a *normal distribution*:
- 2.35% of the values will be between 2 and 3 standard deviations below the mean.
- 13.5% of the values will be between 1 and 2 standard deviations below the mean.
- 34% of the values will be within 1 standard deviation below the mean.
- 34% of the values will be within 1 standard deviation above the mean.
- 13.5% of the values will be between 1 and 2 standard deviations above the mean.
- 2.35% of the values will be between 2 and 3 standard deviations above the mean.

The graph of a normal distribution is a *normal curve*.
- A normal curve is shaped like a bell, with the highest point at the mean and tapering down evenly on either side of the bell.

Problem

The weight in pounds of newborn calves on a farm is distributed normally, with a mean of 85 and a standard deviation of 4. What percent of newborn calves on the farm weigh between 77 lb and 89 lb?

Step 1 Draw a normal curve. Label the mean.

Step 2 Divide the graph into 6 equal sections. Each section should be one standard deviation wide, which is 4 lb in this problem. Label each section with the appropriate percent for a normal distribution.

Step 3 Add the percents for the sections with weights 77 lb–81 lb, 81 lb–85 lb, and 85 lb–89 lb.
13.5 + 34 + 34 = 81.5

About 82% of newborn calves will weigh 77 lb–89 lb.

Exercises

Use the graph above to find the percent of calf weights within each interval.

1. from 73 lb to 81 lb **about 16%**
2. greater than 81 lb **about 84%**
3. from 77 lb to 97 lb **about 97%**
4. less than 85 lb **about 50%**
5. at most 89 lb **about 84%**
6. at least 93 lb **about 2.5%**

All-in-One Resources/Online
English Language Learner Support

11-9 ELL Support
Normal Distributions

Choose the word from the list that best completes each sentence.

| continuous probability distribution | discrete probability distribution |
| normal distribution | normal curve | scatter plot |

1. The data vary randomly from the mean in a _____ **normal distribution**

2. The graph of a discrete probability distribution is a _____ **scatter plot**

3. In a _____ **continuous probability distribution**, the events can be any value in an interval of real numbers.

4. The graph of a normal distribution is a _____ **normal curve**

5. There are a finite number of possible values in a _____ **discrete probability distribution**

Identify each of the following graphs as *positively skewed*, *normally distributed*, or *negatively skewed*.

6. normally distributed
7. positively skewed
8. negatively skewed

Multiple Choice

9. In a normal distribution, about what percent of the data are within one standard deviation of the mean? **C**
   Ⓐ 16%   Ⓑ 34%   Ⓒ 68%   Ⓓ 95%

10. A normal curve is shaped like a symmetric bell centered around the _____. **G**
    Ⓕ mode   Ⓖ mean   Ⓗ median   Ⓘ range

Differentiated Remediation *continued*

On-Level

- **Practice** (2 pages) Provides extra practice for each lesson. For more challenging practice exercises, use the Form G Practice pages found in the All-in-One Teaching Resources and online.

- **Think About a Plan** Helps students develop specific problem-solving skills and strategies by providing scaffolded guiding questions.

- **Standardized Test Prep** Focuses on all major exercises, all major question types, and helps students prepare for the high-stakes assessments.

Extension

- **Enrichment** Provides students with interesting problems and activities that extend the concepts of the lesson.

- **Activities, Games, and Puzzles** Worksheets that can be used for concepts development, enrichment, and for fun!

Student Companion/All-in-One Resources/Online
Practice page 1

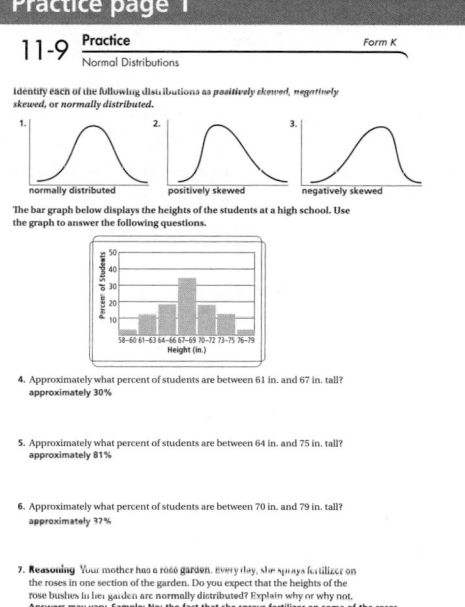

11-9 Practice   Form K
Normal Distributions

Identify each of the following distributions as *positively skewed*, *negatively skewed*, or *normally distributed*.

1. normally distributed
2. positively skewed
3. negatively skewed

The bar graph below displays the heights of the students at a high school. Use the graph to answer the following questions.

4. Approximately what percent of students are between 61 in. and 67 in. tall?
approximately 30%

5. Approximately what percent of students are between 64 in. and 75 in. tall?
approximately 81%

6. Approximately what percent of students are between 70 in. and 79 in. tall?
approximately 37%

7. **Reasoning** Your mother has a rose garden. Every day, she sprays fertilizer on the roses in one section of the garden. Do you expect that the heights of the rose bushes in her garden are normally distributed? Explain why or why not.
Answers may vary. Sample: No; the fact that she sprays fertilizer on some of the roses will most likely skew the data.

Student Companion/All-in-One Resources/Online
Practice page 2

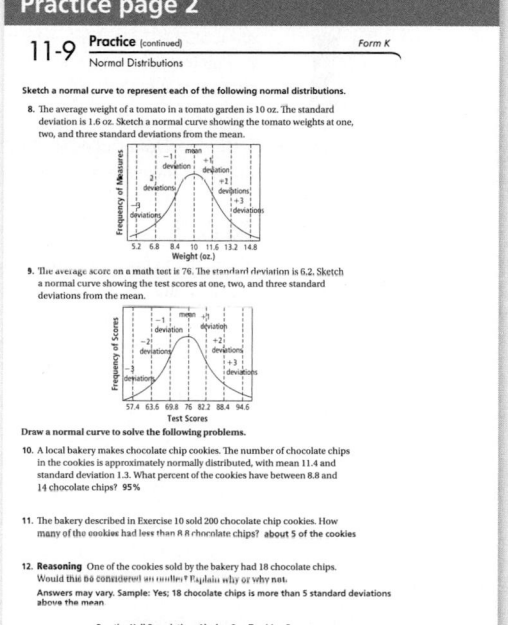

11-9 Practice (continued)   Form K
Normal Distributions

Sketch a normal curve to represent each of the following normal distributions.

8. The average weight of a tomato in a tomato garden is 10 oz. The standard deviation is 1.6 oz. Sketch a normal curve showing the tomato weights at one, two, and three standard deviations from the mean.

9. The average score on a math test is 76. The standard deviation is 6.2. Sketch a normal curve showing the test scores at one, two, and three standard deviations from the mean.

Draw a normal curve to solve the following problems.

10. A local bakery makes chocolate chip cookies. The number of chocolate chips in the cookies is approximately normally distributed, with mean 11.4 and standard deviation 1.3. What percent of the cookies have between 8.8 and 14 chocolate chips? **95%**

11. The bakery described in Exercise 10 sold 200 chocolate chip cookies. How many of the cookies had less than 8.8 chocolate chips? **about 5 of the cookies**

12. **Reasoning** One of the cookies sold by the bakery had 18 chocolate chips. Would this be considered an outlier? Explain why or why not.
Answers may vary. Sample: Yes; 18 chocolate chips is more than 5 standard deviations above the mean.

Prentice Hall Foundations Algebra 2 • Teaching Resources
Copyright © by Pearson Education, Inc. or its affiliates. All Rights Reserved.

All-in-One Resources/Online
Enrichment

11-9 Enrichment
Normal Distributions

Tchebycheff's Theorem

Tchebycheff's Theorem states that given a number k greater than or equal to 1 and a set of n measurements, at least $\left(1 - \frac{1}{k^2}\right)$ of the measurements will lie within k standard deviations of the mean. Note that the theorem is true for any number you wish to choose for k as long as it is greater than or equal to 1.

The mean and standard deviation of a sample of $n = 25$ measurements are 75 and 10, respectively.

1. Using Tchebycheff's Theorem and $k = 2$, what can you assume?
that $\frac{3}{4}$ of data lie within 55 and 95

2. What is the least number of measurements in the sample that will lie in the interval for $k = 2$? **19**

3. Using Tchebycheff's Theorem and $k = 3$, what can you assume?
that $\frac{8}{9}$ of data lie within 45 and 105

4. What is the least number of measurements in the sample that will lie in the interval for $k = 3$? **23**

5. If $k = 1$, do you learn anything about the data? No; it says that at least 0 measurements lie within 65–85.

Consider the following data:

23 45 12 56 34 37 85 26 77 74
15 80 65 47 37 55 26 44 73 86
85 16 37 85 74 57 43 63 37 34
72 65 37 75 77 34

6. Calculate the mean and standard deviation. Round to the nearest whole number. **52; 22**

7. Using Tchebycheff's Theorem and $k = 2$, what is the least number of measurements in the sample that will lie within 2 standard deviations of the mean? What interval corresponds to within 2 standard deviations of the mean? **27; between 8 and 96**

8. How many measurements in the sample actually lie in that interval? **36**

9. Using Tchebycheff's Theorem and $k = 3$, what is the least number of measurements in the sample that will lie within 3 standard deviations of the mean? What interval corresponds to within 3 standard deviations of the mean? **32; between 0 and 118**

10. How many measurements in the sample actually lie in that interval? **36**

Student Companion/All-in-One Resources/Online
Think About a Plan

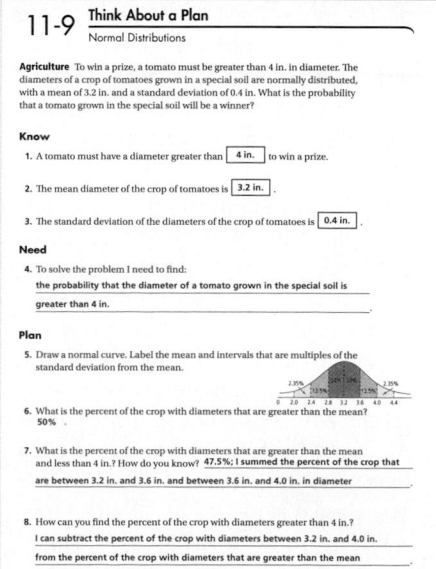

11-9 Think About a Plan
Normal Distributions

Agriculture To win a prize, a tomato must be greater than 4 in. in diameter. The diameters of a crop of tomatoes grown in a special soil are normally distributed, with a mean of 3.2 in. and a standard deviation of 0.4 in. What is the probability that a tomato grown in the special soil will be a winner?

Know

1. A tomato must have a diameter greater than [4 in.] to win a prize.

2. The mean diameter of the crop of tomatoes is [3.2 in.].

3. The standard deviation of the diameters of the crop of tomatoes is [0.4 in.].

Need

4. To solve the problem I need to find:
the probability that the diameter of a tomato grown in the special soil is greater than 4 in.

Plan

5. Draw a normal curve. Label the mean and intervals that are multiples of the standard deviation from the mean.

6. What is the percent of the crop with diameters that are greater than the mean? **50%**

7. What is the percent of the crop with diameters that are greater than the mean and less than 4 in.? How do you know? **47.5%; I summed the percent of the crop that are between 3.2 and 3.6 in. and between 3.6 and 4.0 in. in diameter**

8. How can you find the percent of the crop with diameters greater than 4 in.?
I can subtract the percent of the crop with diameters between 3.2 in. and 4.0 in. from the percent of the crop with diameters that are greater than the mean

9. What is the probability that a tomato grown in the special soil will be a winner? **2.5%**

Student Companion/All-in-One Resources/Online
Standardized Test Prep

11-9 Standardized Test Prep
Normal Distributions

Multiple Choice

For Exercises 1–5, choose the correct letter.

1. The mean number of pairs of shoes sold daily by a shoe store is 36, with a standard deviation of 3. On what percent of days would you expect the store to sell from 33 to 42 pairs of shoes? **D**
   - Ⓐ 13.5%
   - Ⓑ 50%
   - Ⓒ 68%
   - Ⓓ 81.5%

2. What is the standard deviation for the normal distribution shown at the right? **F**
   496 556 616 676 736 796 856
   - Ⓕ 60
   - Ⓖ 360
   - Ⓗ 120
   - Ⓘ 676

3. A normal distribution has a mean of 700 and a standard deviation of 35. What is the probability that a value selected at random is at most 630? **B**
   - Ⓐ 0.0235
   - Ⓑ 0.025
   - Ⓒ 0.700
   - Ⓓ 0.975

4. Scores on an exam are distributed normally with a mean of 76 and a standard deviation of 10. Out of 230 tests, about how many students score above 96? **H**
   - Ⓕ 2
   - Ⓖ 3
   - Ⓗ 6
   - Ⓘ 5

5. A hardware store sells bags of mixed nails. The number of nails of a given length is distributed normally with a mean length of 5 in. and a standard deviation of 0.03 in. About how many nails in a bag of 120 are between 4.97 in. and 5.03 in. long? **D**
   - Ⓐ 34
   - Ⓑ 41
   - Ⓒ 68
   - Ⓓ 82

Short Response

6. The heights of the girls in a school choir are distributed normally, with a mean of 64 and a standard deviation of 1.75. If 38 girls are between 60.5 in. and 67.5 in. tall, how many girls are in the choir? Show your work.
[2] 64 − 1.75 = 60.5; 64 + 1.75 = 67.5
The range 60.5 − 67.5 is within two standard deviations of the mean.
13.5 + 34 + 34 + 13.5 = 95%; 95% of the data is within the range 60.5 − 67.5.
38 = 0.95x
x = 40; there are 40 girls in the choir.
[1] incorrect or incomplete work shown
[0] incorrect answer and no work shown OR no answer given

Online Teacher Resource Center
Activities, Games, and Puzzles

11-9 Game: Risk and Reward
Normal Distributions

Provide the host with the following questions and answers.

	Vocabulary (Define)	What's the z-score?	What's the SAT Score?	How Many Students Scored:	Review
10 pts	mean	Math: 515	Writing: 0	between 399 and 515 on Math?	Find ₄P₂ and ₄C₂
20 pts	standard deviation	Reading: 390	Math: −1	between 384 and 604 on Writing?	Add: 2 + 6 + 10 + ⋯ + 38
30 pts	z-score	Writing: 659	Math: 1.5	between 278 and 614 on Reading?	Solve: $3^{2x + 1} = 81$
40 pts	normally distributed	Math: 370	Reading: −2.25	greater than 747 on Math?	Find the center and radius of $x^2 + y^2 - 4x + 2y = 4$.
50 pts	standard normal curve	Reading: 698	Writing: 2.7	greater than 384 on Writing?	Solve: $2x + y = 5$ $-3x + 4y = 31$

The middle three categories are based on the results of the 2008 SAT scores. About 1,500,000 college-bound students took this test and their normally distributed results are summarized below. Copy the table for each team before starting the game.

2008 SAT Results	Subject	Mean	Standard Deviation
1,500,000 testers	Reading	502	112
	Math	515	116
	Writing	494	110

Source: www.collegeboard.com

Answers to Questions

	Vocabulary	z-score?	SAT Score?	Number of Students	Review
10 pts	1. See below.	0	494	510,000	56, 28
20 pts	2. See below.	−1	399	1,020,000	200
30 pts	3. See below.	1.5	689	1,222,500	1.5
40 pts	4. See below.	−1.25	250	37,500	$(2, -1), r = 3$
50 pts	5. See below.	1.75	791	1,260,000	$(-1, 7)$

1. the numerical average
2. a measure of how much the values in a data set vary, $\sigma = \sqrt{\frac{\sum (x - \bar{x})^2}{n}}$
3. a number that tells how many standard deviations away from the mean a particular score is
4. about 68% of data fall within one standard deviation of the mean; about 95% of data fall within two standard deviations of the mean
5. a normal distribution with mean 0 and standard deviation 1

Performance Task    UbD

Pull It All Together

The concepts and skills required to solve these problems are from several lessons within this chapter and from earlier chapters. As students solve these problems, they will demonstrate their reasoning strategies and their growth as independent problem solvers.

Task 1

Explain the relationship between permutations and combinations.

- How many ways can you arrange n items chosen r at a time?

Task 2

Solve a counting problem by breaking the problem into simpler parts.

- How many ways can you stack three number cubes so that all four sides show all the same number?
- Is it possible for two adjacent sides of the stack to show the same numbers without the other two sides also showing the same two numbers?
- How many ways can you stack the dice so that only one pair of opposite sides show the same numbers on the sides of the stack?

Task 3

Demonstrate how outliers can affect the standard deviation without affecting the mean.

- To have the same mean as two standard number cubes, the sum of the numbers on the new number cube would have to total to what number?
- Which numbers in a set of data increase the value of standard deviation?

To solve these problems, you will pull together concepts and skills related to probability and statistics.

BIG idea Probability

Various counting methods (such as permutations and combinations) can help you analyze situations and develop theoretical probabilities.

Task 1

Suppose you have n items from which you choose r at a time. Explain why you must divide the number of permutations $\frac{n!}{(n-r)!}$ by $r!$ to find the number of combinations $\frac{n!}{r!(n-r)!}$.

Task 2

Suppose you stack three identical number cubes. It is possible to have no sides, two sides, or all four sides of the stack showing all the same number. (Note that if one side of a stack shows all the same number, then the opposite side must as well.)

How many ways are there to stack three standard number cubes so that at least two sides of the stack show all the same number? If you can rotate a stack so that it is the same as another, count them as the same arrangement.

0 sides   2 sides   4 sides

BIG idea Data Collection and Analysis

Standard measures that describe data from a real-world situation can help you make estimates or decisions about the situation, or predictions about future occurrences.

Task 3

Show all of your work and explain your steps.

a. Find the mean and standard deviation of the sums you should get when you roll two standard number cubes.

b. Suppose you can replace one number cube with a nonstandard number cube, where any of the numbers 1 through 6 can appear on multiple faces. How can you arrange the numbers on the nonstandard cube so that the mean of the rolls is the same as that of two standard number cubes, but the standard deviation is as large as possible? What is this value?

Assess
Performance    UbD

Pull It All Together

See p. 53 for a holistic scoring rubric to gauge a student's progress on Understanding the Problem, Planning a Solution, Getting an Answer, and Assessing Autonomy.

SOLUTION OUTLINES

1. When counting permutations, order is important so you must count every arrangement of n items taken r at a time. But with combinations, order is not important so you don't need to count every arrangement of r out of n items ($r!$). Using $\frac{n!}{(n-r)!}$ over counts the combinations by a factor of $r!$. Dividing this expression by $r!$ leaves you with the number of combinations of n items taken r at a time.

2. Possible Plan: One strategy would be to count all stacks showing all 6's on one side and all 1's on the opposite side, then to count stacks with all 5's on one side and all 2's on the opposite side, then finally to count stacks with all 4's on one side and all 3's on the opposite side. You must keep track of duplicate stacks and subtract them from the total count.

First Step: Suppose the front of a stack shows all 6's and the back shows all 1's. You can find another arrangement by rotating the top cube so that the 6 stays in the front and the 1 stays in the back. There are four ways to do this. Next, rotate the middle cube and the bottom cube each four ways to generate a new stack with all 6's in the fronts and 1's in the back. There are 4^3 stacks with 6's in the front and 1's in the back.

Second Step: Repeat the first step but with all 5's in the front and all 2's in the back. However, one of these stacks will have all 6's on the left and all 1's on the right. Another will have all 1's on the right and all 6's on the left. There are $4^3 - 2$ stacks with all 5's in the front and all 2's in the back that have not already been counted in Step 1.

Third Step: Repeat the first step but with all 4's in the front and all 3's in the back. Two of these stacks have all 6's and all 1's on the other two sides of the stack, and two stacks have all 5's and all 2's on the other two sides of the stack. So, there are $4^3 - 4$ stacks with all 4's in the front and all 3's in the back that have not already been counted in Steps 1 or 2.

The total will be
$4^3 + (4^3 - 2) + (4^3 - 4) = 186.$

Connecting **BIG** ideas and Answering the Essential Questions

1 Probability
A combination is a collection. A permutation is an ordered collection.

Permutations and Combinations (Lesson 11-1)
For n items chosen r at a time, $0 \leq r \leq n$,
- $_nP_r = \dfrac{n!}{(n-r)!}$
- $_nC_r = \dfrac{n!}{r!(n-r)!}$

Probability of Multiple Events and Conditional Probability (Lessons 11-3 and 11-4)
If A and B are independent events,
- $P(A \text{ and } B) = P(A) \cdot P(B)$
- $P(A \text{ or } B) = P(A) + P(B)$
The probability of event B, given event A is $P(B \mid A) = \dfrac{P(A \text{ and } B)}{P(A)}$.

2 Probability
You base experimental probability on *past*—and theoretical probability on *possible*—occurrences.

Probability (Lesson 11-2)
Experimental probability:
$$P(\text{event}) = \frac{\text{number of times the event occurs}}{\text{number of trials}}$$
Theoretical probability: For n equally likely outcomes, if event A occurs in m of these outcomes, then $P(A) = \dfrac{m}{n}$.

3 Data Collection and Analysis
Standard deviation describes how spread out data is from the mean of the data.

Analyzing Data and Standard Deviation (Lessons 11-5 and 11-6)
- $\bar{x}$, the mean, $= \dfrac{\sum x}{n}$
- σ, standard deviation, $= \sqrt{\dfrac{\sum(x - \bar{x})^2}{n}}$

Binomial Distributions and Normal Distributions (Lessons 11-8 and 11-9)
In a normal distribution, about 68% (95%) of data are within one (two) standard deviation(s) of the mean.

Chapter Vocabulary

- bias (p. 739)
- bimodal (p. 724)
- binomial experiment (p. 745)
- binomial probability (p. 746)
- Binomial Theorem (p. 747)
- box-and-whisker plot (p. 725)
- continuous probability distribution (p. 752)
- controlled experiment (p. 739)
- convenience sample (p. 738)
- discrete probability distribution (p. 752)
- interquartile range (p. 725)
- mean (p. 723)
- measure of central tendency (p. 723)
- measure of variation (p. 732)
- median (p. 723)
- mode (p. 723)
- normal distribution (p. 752)
- observational study (p. 739)
- outlier (p. 724)
- percentile (p. 728)
- population (p. 738)
- probability distribution (p. 748)
- quartile (p. 725)
- random sample (p. 738)
- range of a set of data (p. 725)
- sample (p. 738)
- self-selected sample (p. 738)
- standard deviation (p. 732)
- survey (p. 739)
- systematic sample (p. 738)
- variance (p. 732)

Fill in the blanks.

1. A(n) __?__ is part of a population.

2. A(n) __?__ has a value substantially different from other data in the set.

3. A function that gives the probability of each event in a sample space is a(n) __?__ .

4. The __?__ is the simplest measure of variation.

3. a. First Step: Make a table to find all the possible sums.
(There 36 possible sums.)
Second Step: Find the mean of all the sums. (mean = 7)
Third Step: Find the standard deviation. ($s = 2.415$)

b. Possible Plan: To increase the standard deviation, you want to increase the number of 6's. You need the sum of opposite sides of the nonstandard cube to be 7. So, the nonstandard cube should have sides, 1, 1, 1, 6, 6, and 6. The mean will be 7 and the standard deviation will be about 3.54.

Answers

Chapter Review for Part B
1. sample
2. outlier
3. probability distribution
4. range of a set of data

Essential Questions **UbD**

BIG idea   Probability
ESSENTIAL QUESTION What is the difference between a permutation and a combination?
ANSWER A permutation is an arrangement of items in a particular order. A combination is an arrangement where order does not matter.

BIG idea   Probability
ESSENTIAL QUESTION What is the difference between experimental and theoretical probability?
ANSWER You can compute an experimental probability from collected data. You find theoretical probability by considering the likelihood of every possible outcome.

BIG idea   Data Collection and Analysis
ESSENTIAL QUESTION How are measures of central tendency different from standard deviation?
ANSWER Measures of central tendency are ways to describe a "middle" value of a data set. Standard deviation describes how data are spread out from a particular middle value.

Summative Questions **UbD**

Use the following prompts as you review this chapter with your students. The prompts are designed to help you assess your students' understanding of the BIG ideas they have studied.

- How can sample and study methods influence the results of a study?
- What is the difference between a discrete probability distribution and a continuous probability distribution? Give an example of each.

Answers

Chapter Review for Part B (continued)

5. 9

6. mean: 6, median: 6, mode: 9

7. mean: $10.\overline{6}$, median: 7, modes: 3 and 7

8. mean: 15, median: 15, mode: 18

9. mean: 9.5, median: 9.5, mode: none

10. range: 35; $Q_1 = 30$; $Q_3 = 55$

11. range: 35; $Q_1 = 25$; $Q_3 = 50$

12. range: 65; $Q_1 = 42$; $Q_3 = 87$

13. heights of 3 ppl.

14. ages of thirty college students

15. gas mileage of 18 automobiles of various types

16. $\bar{x} \approx 6.64$, $\sigma \approx 5.12$

17. $\bar{x} \approx 17.14$, $\sigma \approx 3.52$

18. $\bar{x} = 7.5$, $\sigma \approx 2.67$

11-5 Analyzing Data

Quick Review

You can use **measures of central tendency** to analyze data. The **mean**, $\bar{x}$, equals the sum of the values divided by the number of values. The **median** is the middle value of a data set in numerical order. The **mode** is the most frequently occurring value. A data value substantially different from the rest of the data is an **outlier**. A **box-and-whisker plot** summarizes information about the **range**, the median, and the first and third **quartiles** of a data set.

Example

Find the mean, median, mode, and range of the following set of numbers, and identify any outliers.

3, 3, 4, 6, 19

The mean is $\frac{3 + 3 + 4 + 6 + 19}{5} = 7$.

The median is the middle data value, which is 4.

The mode is 3, which occurs twice.

The range is $19 - 3 = 16$.

The value 19 is very different from the others and is an outlier.

Exercises

5. Identify the outlier of this set of values.

17, 15, 16, 15, 9, 18, 16

Find the mean, median, and mode for each set of values.

6. 1, 1, 3, 3, 5, 5, 6, 7, 9, 9, 9, 10, 10

7. 0, 3, 3, 7, 7, 8, 21, 22, 25

8. 8, 9, 11, 12, 13, 15, 16, 18, 18, 18, 27

9. 11, 6, 9, 4, 19, 10, 15, 2

Find the range, Q_1, and Q_3 for each set of values.

10. 25, 25, 30, 35, 45, 45, 50, 55, 60, 60

11. 20, 23, 25, 36, 37, 38, 39, 50, 52, 55

12. 36, 36, 48, 65, 75, 82, 92, 101

11-6 Standard Deviation

Quick Review

The range of a data set is one **measure of variation**, used to describe the spread of data. Another measure of variation is the **standard deviation**, defined as

$$\sigma = \sqrt{\frac{\sum(x - \bar{x})^2}{n}}$$

where $\bar{x}$ is the mean of the data set and n is the number of values. The **variance** is σ^2.

Example

Find the mean, variance, and standard deviation for the following data values: 1, 3, 4, 6, 8, 11, 23.

The mean is $\bar{x} = \frac{1 + 3 + 4 + 6 + 8 + 11 + 23}{7} = 8$.

The sum of the squares of the differences is

$(-7)^2 + (-5)^2 + (-4)^2 + (-2)^2 + 0^2 + 3^2 + 15^2 = 328$.

So the variance is $\sigma^2 = \frac{328}{7} \approx 46.9$, and the standard deviation is $\sigma \approx \sqrt{46.9} \approx 6.8$.

Exercises

For each pair of data sets, which is likely to have the greater standard deviation?

13. heights of three people
heights of twenty people

14. ages of thirty college students
ages of thirty high school students

15. gas mileages of eighteen sport utility vehicles
gas mileages of eighteen automobiles of various types

Find the mean and the standard deviation for each set of values.

16. 1, 1, 2, 2, 3, 4, 5, 6, 8, 9, 10, 10, 12, 20

17. 15, 17, 19, 20, 14, 23, 12

18. 3.1, 4.5, 7.8, 7.9, 8.0, 9.6, 11.6

11-7 Samples and Surveys

Quick Review

A **sample** is part of a **population**. For a **random sample**, all members of the population are equally likely to be chosen. A **bias** is a systematic error introduced by the sampling method.

Example

Identify any bias in the survey question "Do you think the school day should be extended even longer than it already is?". Explain.

There is bias because the question is leading. It implies that the school day is already too long and should not be extended.

Exercises

Determine if each of the following is a random sample. Explain your answer.

19. The first 50 names in the telephone directory

20. Twelve jurors chosen through examination by opposing lawyers

21. Two class representatives chosen by drawing names from a hat

22. Five newspapers picked on the basis of circulation size

23. The city council is trying to determine if the city's residents support the building of a new parking garage. They poll 200 people at the local bus station. Identify any bias in the sampling method.

11-8 Binomial Distributions

Quick Review

A **binomial experiment** has repeated independent trials with each trial having two possible outcomes. In a binomial experiment with probability of success p and of failure q (so $p + q = 1$), the probability of exactly x successes in n trials is $_nC_x p^x q^{n-x}$. This value is the **binomial probability**. The **Binomial Theorem** says that for every positive integer n, $(a + b)^n = {_nC_0}a^n + {_nC_1}a^{n-1}b + {_nC_2}a^{n-2}b^2 + \cdots + {_nC_{n-1}}ab^{n-1} + {_nC_n}b^n$.

Example

In a binomial experiment, the probability of success is 0.8 for each trial. Find the probability of exactly 4 successes in 7 trials.

$p = 0.8$, $q = 0.2$, $x = 4$, and $n = 7$

$P(4) = {_7C_4}(0.8)^4(0.2)^3$

$\quad\quad = \frac{7!}{3!4!}(0.8)^4(0.2)^3$

$\quad\quad \approx 0.115$

The probability of 4 successes in 7 trials is about 0.115.

Exercises

For each of the following binomial experiments, state the value of p, the probability of success.

24. A series of coin flips, where success is "heads."

25. A series of number cube rolls, where success is "2 or 4."

In a binomial trial, the probability of success is 0.6 for each trial. Find the probability of each of the following.

26. 13 successes in 24 trials

27. 9 successes in 20 trials

28. 9 successes in 15 trials

29. 6 failures in 12 trials

Use the Binomial Theorem to write each of the following.

30. the third term in the expansion of $(a + b)^7$

31. the sixth term in the expansion of $(a + b)^8$

19. not a random sample; they will all begin with the letter "a"

20. not a random sample; the lawyers will choose jurors that are likely to support their side

21. random sample; all students have an equal chance to be chosen

22. not a random sample; the five with the largest (or smallest) circulation size will be picked

23. not a random sample; people at the bus station may be less likely to own a car and therefore less likely to be in favor of a new garage

24. $\frac{1}{2}$

25. $\frac{1}{3}$

26. ≈ 0.14

27. ≈ 0.0710

28. ≈ 0.2066

29. ≈ 0.1766

30. $21a^5b^2$

31. $56a^3b^5$

Answers

Chapter Review for Part B (continued)

32. continuous
33. discrete
34. discrete
35. continuous
36. 16%; 2.5%

Quick Review

A **discrete probability distribution** has a finite number of possible values, while the values for a **continuous probability distribution** are all the values on some interval of real numbers. A **normal distribution** shows data that vary from the mean in a random, continuous manner. The pattern they form is a bell-shaped curve called a normal curve. When a data set follows the normal curve, about 68% of the data fall within one standard deviation of the mean, about 95% fall within two standard deviations, and about 99.7% fall within three standard deviations.

Example

Sketch a curve for a normal distribution with mean 10 and standard deviation 4. Label the *x*-axis at one, two, and three standard deviations from the mean.

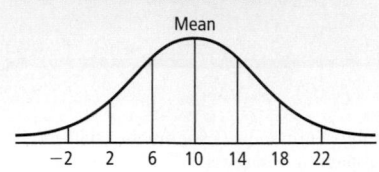

Mean

$-2 \quad 2 \quad 6 \quad 10 \quad 14 \quad 18 \quad 22$

Exercises

For each of the following, state whether the probability distribution would be *discrete* or *continuous*.

32. distance from an arrow's impact point to the center of the bullseye

33. shoe sizes on a softball team

34. price of a gallon of premium unleaded gasoline at a randomly selected gas station

35. time a customer spends on hold during a call to a computer manufacturer's tech support

36. Auto Maintenance Suppose the time required for an auto shop to do a tune-up is normally distributed, with a mean of 102 minutes and a standard deviation of 18 minutes. What is the probability that a tune-up will take more than two hours? Under 66 minutes?

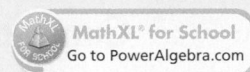
MathXL® for School
Go to PowerAlgebra.com

Do you know HOW?

Evaluate each expression.

1. $6!$ **2.** $_7C_3$ **3.** $_{11}P_9$

Q and R are independent events. Find $P(Q \text{ and } R)$.

4. $P(Q) = 0.5, P(R) = 0.4$

5. $P(Q) = \frac{1}{3}, P(R) = \frac{3}{8}$

Use the table below for Exercises 6–8.

Age of Respondent	Number of Groups	
	0–4	5 or more
< 30	7	18
≥ 30	12	12

6. Find $P(5 \text{ or more})$.

7. Find $P(5 \text{ or more} \mid \text{age} < 30)$.

8. Find $P(\text{age} \geq 30 \mid 0-4)$.

Two standard number cubes are tossed. State whether the events are mutually exclusive.

9. One of the numbers is 1 less than the other. The sum is odd.

10. The sum is greater than 10. Six is one of the numbers.

11. Find Q_1 and Q_3 for this set of values: 36, 38, 42, 47, 51, 56, 62, 69, 70, 74.

12. Open-Ended Write a set of values that has a range of 10, a mean of 86, and a mode of 85.

A set of data has a normal distribution with a mean of 29 and a standard deviation of 4. Find the percent of data within each interval.

13. from 25 to 33   **14.** greater than 29

A newspaper wants to take a poll about which candidate voters prefer for President. Identify any bias in each sampling method.

15. The newspaper interviews people at a political debate.

16. The newspaper calls people selected at random from the local telephone book.

17. At a high school, 30% of the students buy class rings. You select five students at random. Find $P(\text{exactly two buy rings})$ and $P(\text{at least two buy rings})$.

Do you UNDERSTAND?

18. Indicate whether each situation involves a combination or a permutation.
   a. A team of 6 chosen from a class of 36
   b. An 8-digit code chosen for a lock

19. A data set is normally distributed with a mean of 37 and a standard deviation of 8.1. Sketch a normal curve for the distribution. Label the x-axis values at one, two, and three standard deviations from the mean.

20. Open-Ended A student guesses the answers to three questions on a true-false test. Design and describe a simulation to find the probability that the student guesses at least one of the questions correctly.

21. Writing Describe how a situation can have more than one sample space. Include an example.

22. Airline Ticket Pricing The table contains information from a study of the prices of comparable airline tickets. Which sample most likely was greater in size, A or B? Explain.

Sample	Standard deviation
A	$10.81
B	$3.97

Answers

Chapter Test for Part B

1. 720

2. 35

3. 19,958,400

4. 0.2

5. $\frac{1}{8}$

6. $\frac{30}{49}$

7. $\frac{18}{25}$

8. $\frac{12}{19}$

9. not mutually exclusive

10. not mutually exclusive

11. $Q_1 = 42, Q_3 = 69$

12. Answers may vary. Sample: 82, 85, 85, 92

13. 68%

14. 50%

15. bias toward active voters

16. bias toward voters with listed numbers

17. 0.309; 0.472

18. a. combination
   b. permutation

19.

12.7 20.8 28.9 37 45.1 53.2 61.3

20. Check students' work.

21. Sample: Suppose two hybrid Aa parent plants are crossed. The offspring can be described by the sample space {AA, Aa, aa} or by the sample space {dominant, recessive}.

22. Sample B

Item Number	Lesson
1	11-3
2	7-2
3	2-1
4	4-2
5	4-5
6	10-3
7	11-6
8	9-2
9	4-7
10	4-5
11	6-6
12	6-6
13	9-4
14	4-7
15	11-4
16	6-2
17	11-8
18	3-4
19	4-7
20	4-5
21	7-5
22	9-5
23	11-3
24	10-3
25	8-1
26	11-1
27	8-6
28	7-4
29	8-3
30	10-5
31	9-5
32	11-5

11 Cumulative Test Prep

TIPS FOR SUCCESS

Some questions on standardized tests ask you to use data analysis concepts like mean, outlier, and percentile. Read the question at the right. Then follow the tips to answer the sample question.

TIP 1

If necessary, rewrite the data values in order, from least to greatest.

Find the third quartile for the data set.

2 6 8 5 9 3 5 7 1 8 4 4 5

Ⓐ 6.5

Ⓑ 7

Ⓒ 7.5

Ⓓ 8

TIP 2

Make sure you clearly understand the definition of the concept you are applying. The third quartile is the median of the upper half of the data, not including the median.

Think It Through

In order, the data values are as follows.

1 2 3 4 4 5 5 5 6 7 8 8 9

The upper half of the data contains the values 5 6 7 8 8 9

The median of the upper half is $\frac{7+8}{2} = 7.5$.

The correct answer is C.

Vocabulary Review

As you solve test items, you must understand the meanings of mathematical terms. Match each term with its mathematical meaning.

A. normal distribution

B. standard deviation

C. quartile

D. median

E. mutually exclusive events

I. one of three values that separate a finite data set into 4 equal parts

II. a measure of how much the values in a data set vary from the mean

III. the middle value of an ordered data set

IV. shows data that vary randomly from the mean in a bell-shaped curve

V. events that cannot happen at the same time

Multiple Choice

Read each question. Then write the letter of the correct answer on your paper.

1. A and B are mutually exclusive events. $P(A) = \frac{1}{3}$ and $P(B) = \frac{1}{2}$. What is $P(A \text{ or } B)$?

Ⓐ $\frac{1}{6}$

Ⓑ $\frac{2}{3}$

Ⓒ $\frac{5}{6}$

Ⓓ 1

2. Which of the following relationships is best represented by the graph at the right?

Ⓕ $y = -2^x$

Ⓖ $y = 2(3)^{-x}$

Ⓗ $y = -2(3)^x$

Ⓘ $y = (-6)^x$

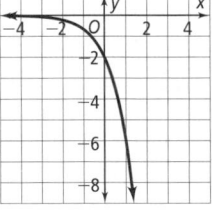

Answers

Cumulative Test Prep

A. IV

B. II

C. I

D. III

E. V

1. C

2. H

3. Which relation is *not* a function?

  (A) $\{(-1, 2), (-2, 2), (-3, 2), (-4, 2)\}$

  (B) $\{(2, 1), (3, 2), (4, 3), (3, 1)\}$

  (C) $\{(0, 1), (2, 1), (3, -1), (-1, 2)\}$

  (D) $\{(4, 2), (-3, 2), (-2, 1), (-4, 1)\}$

4. What is the vertex of the graph of $y = 2x^2 - 4x + 5$?

  (F) $(1, 5)$ (H) $(1, 3)$

  (G) $(3, 1)$ (I) $(5, 0)$

5. Which equation has $2 - \sqrt{3}$ as one of its solutions?

  (A) $x^2 + 4x + 1 = 0$

  (B) $x^2 - 4x + 1 = 0$

  (C) $x^2 + 4x - 1 = 0$

  (D) $x^2 - 4x - 1 = 0$

6. The equation for the circle below is $x^2 + y^2 = 9$. If the graph is translated one unit up and two units to the left, what is the new equation?

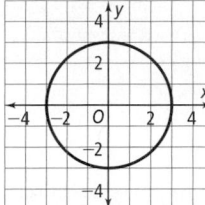

  (F) $(x - 1)^2 + (y + 2)^2 = 9$

  (G) $(x + 1)^2 + (y - 2)^2 = 9$

  (H) $(x - 2)^2 + (y + 1)^2 = 9$

  (I) $(x + 2)^2 + (y - 1)^2 = 9$

7. In six basketball games, you scored the following points per game. What is the approximate standard deviation of points scored?

  8 11 14 7 12 18

  (A) 1.0   (C) 4.0

  (B) 2.0   (D) 5.0

8. Which sequence has a common difference of 3?

  I. $a_n = a_{n-1} - 3, a_1 = 2$

  II. $a_n = 3$

  III. $a_n = a_{n-1} + 3, a_1 = -7$

  IV. $a_n = n^2 + 3$

  (F) I only   (H) II only

  (G) III only   (I) II and IV

9. Which number completes the square for $x^2 - 3x$?

  (A) 9   (C) $-\frac{9}{2}$

  (B) $-\frac{3}{2}$ (D) $\frac{9}{4}$

10. What are the solutions to $9x^2 + 4 = 0$?

  (F) ± 2 (H) $\pm\frac{2}{3}$

  (G) $\pm\frac{2}{3}i$ (I) $\pm\sqrt{\frac{2}{3}}$

11. If $f(x) = x^2 - 1$ and $g(x) = |2x + 3|$, which has the greatest value?

  (A) $f(g(3))$ (C) $g(f(-1))$

  (B) $g(f(2))$ (D) $f(g(10))$

12. If $f(x) = 2x^2$ and $g(x) = 3(x + 1)$, what is $f(x) + g(x)$?

  (F) $2x^2 + 3x + 1$

  (G) $2x^2 + 3x + 3$

  (H) $2x^2 + 3x - 3$

  (I) $5x^3 + 3$

13. The first term of an arithmetic series is 123. The common difference is 12 and the sum is 1113. How many terms are in the series?

  (A) 7   (C) 9

  (B) 8   (D) 10

14. In the equation $y = 2x^2 - x - 21$, which is a value of x when $y = 0$?

  (F) -21 (H) 3

  (G) $1\frac{1}{2}$ (I) $3\frac{1}{2}$

3. B

4. H

5. B

6. I

7. C

8. G

9. D

10. G

11. D

12. G

13. A

14. I

Answers

Cumulative Test Prep (continued)

15. A

16. I

17. D

18. 16

19. 1

20. 2

21. 59.1

22. 54

23. $\frac{5}{22}$

24. 5

25. 3

26. [2] a. combination; order is not important; the employer can select four employees in any order

    b. 27,405 selections

    [1] only part(a) or part(b) is correct

27. [2] $\frac{x}{6} = \frac{x+4}{9}$

$$9x = 6x + 24$$
$$3x = 24$$
$$x = 8$$

Check: $\frac{8}{6} = \frac{8+4}{9} = \frac{12}{9}$

$$\frac{4}{3} = \frac{4}{3}$$

    [1] correct solution; without work shown

28. [2] Power Prop. and Quotient Prop.

    [1] only one prop. stated correctly

29. [2] vertical asymptotes when $x^2 + 2x - 3 = 0$.
$(x + 3)(x - 1) = 0$, $x = -3$ and $x = 1$, horizontal asymptote at $y = 3$

    [1] correct horizontal asymptote, but incorrect vert. asymptote

30. [4] vertices: $(\pm 4, 0)$, intercepts: $(\pm 4, 0)$, asymptotes: $y = \pm\frac{3}{4}x$, foci: $(\pm 5, 0)$

    [3] three correctly found, but one incorrect

    [2] two correctly found, but two incorrect

    [1] one correctly found, but three incorrect

31. [4] geometric;

$$S_n = \frac{a_1(1 - r^n)}{1 - r} = \frac{10{,}000\left(1 - \left(\frac{1}{10}\right)^8\right)}{1 - \frac{1}{10}}$$

$$= 11{,}111.111$$

    [3] appropriate method, but with one computational error

    [2] correct sum, but the series is not identified as geometric

    [1] correct sum, without work shown

---

15. Students were asked in a survey whether they had been to a movie theater in the last month. The table below shows the results.

	Yes	No
Male	35	17
Female	28	20

What is the probability that a student did not go to a movie in the last month, given that the student is a male?

Ⓐ $\frac{17}{52}$ Ⓒ $\frac{52}{37}$

Ⓑ $\frac{37}{52}$ Ⓓ $\frac{17}{37}$

16. Which expression simplifies to 15?

Ⓕ $(5 + \sqrt{3})(5 - \sqrt{3})$

Ⓖ $(2\sqrt{3} - 1)(2\sqrt{3} + 1)$

Ⓗ $(6 + 3\sqrt{2})(6 - 3\sqrt{2})$

Ⓘ $(2\sqrt{6} - 3)(2\sqrt{6} + 3)$

17. What is the coefficient of $x^2 y^4$ in the expansion of $(x + 2y)^6$?

Ⓐ 15   Ⓒ 160

Ⓑ 60   Ⓓ 240

GRIDDED RESPONSE

18. What is the maximum value of the objective function $P = 3x + 4y$ within the feasible region described by the constraints at the right?

$$\begin{cases} x \geq 0, \, y \geq 0 \\ x + y \leq 4 \\ 2x + y \leq 5 \end{cases}$$

19. What is the discriminant of $2x^2 - 5x + 3 = 0$?

20. What is the sum of the solutions to the equation $x^2 = 2x + 15$?

21. Solve $\log_7 x = \log_3 10$. Round your answer to the nearest tenth.

22. Evaluate $\sum_{n=1}^{8} \frac{3n}{2}$.

---

23. For a school play, six 9th graders and six 10th graders volunteer to be ushers. If two ushers are chosen at random by drawing names from a bowl, what is the probability that both ushers will be 10th graders? Write your answer as a fraction.

24. What is the radius of the circle with equation $x^2 - 6x + y^2 - 4y - 12 = 0$? If necessary, round your answer to the nearest hundredth.

25. Suppose x and y vary inversely and $x = 4$ when $y = 9$. What is x when $y = 12$?

Short Response

26. An employer is selecting 4 out of 30 workers as employees of the month.
    a. Does this situation involve a combination or a permutation? Explain.
    b. How many different selections are possible?

27. Solve the equation $\frac{x}{6} = \frac{x+4}{9}$. Check your solution. Show your work.

28. State the property or properties used to justify the identity $9 \log 3 - 3 \log 9 = \log 27$.

29. Find all asymptotes of the graph of $y = \frac{3x^2 + 1}{x^2 + 2x - 3}$.

Extended Response

30. Find the vertices, intercepts, asymptotes, and foci of the hyperbola $\frac{x^2}{16} - \frac{y^2}{9} = 1$.

31. Is the series $10{,}000 + 1000 + 100 + 10 + \ldots$ *arithmetic* or *geometric*? Find the sum of the first eight terms.

32. Find the mean, median, and mode for the following set of values.

13 12 15 18 14 16 18 12 13 14 14 17 15 8 17 16
12 16 14 15 13 13 17 15 14 18 16 12 12 13

Then make a box-and-whisker plot.

---

32. [4] mean: 14.4; median: 14; modes: 12, 13 and 14;

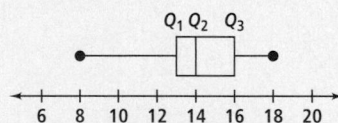

    [3] incorrect mean or median or mode, correct box-and-whisker plot given previous results

    [2] only one correct out of the mean, median, and mode, correct box-and-whisker plot given previous results OR correct mean, median, and mode, with one error in the box-and-whisker plot

    [1] correct mean, median and mode, but no box-and-whisker plot made and no work shown

Get Ready!

Lesson 1-3 ◆ **Evaluating Expressions**

Evaluate $ad - bc$ for the given values of the variables.

1. $a = -1, b = -2, c = 5, d = 4$ **2.** $a = \frac{1}{2}, b = -1, c = -\frac{2}{3}, d = 2$

3. $a = 2, b = \frac{1}{2}, c = \frac{1}{4}, d = -\frac{1}{8}$ **4.** $a = -\frac{1}{3}, b = \frac{1}{2}, c = \frac{1}{4}, d = -\frac{2}{3}$

Lesson 3-6 ◆ **Identifying Matrix Elements**

Identify the indicated element.

$$A = \begin{bmatrix} 2 & -1 & 3 \\ 5 & 7 & -9 \\ 4 & 11 & 21 \end{bmatrix}$$

5. a_{23} **6.** a_{32} **7.** a_{13}

Lessons 3-2 and 3-6 ◆ **Solving Systems of Equations**

Solve each system.

8. $\begin{cases} -2x + y = -5 \\ 4x + y = -2 \end{cases}$ **9.** $\begin{cases} 4x - y = -2 \\ -\frac{1}{2}x - y = 1 \end{cases}$

10. $\begin{cases} 3x + y = 5 \\ -x + y = 2 \end{cases}$ **11.** $\begin{cases} x + y + z = 10 \\ 2x - y = 5 \\ y - z = 15 \end{cases}$

12. $\begin{cases} -x + y + 2z = 16 \\ 2x - 2y - 2z = -16 \\ x + y = 0 \end{cases}$ **13.** $\begin{cases} -2x + 3y + z = 1 \\ x - 3z = 7 \\ -y + z = -5 \end{cases}$

 Looking Ahead Vocabulary

14. The local museum store sells books, postcards, and gifts. There are different prices for museum members and nonmembers. At the end of each month, the numbers of items sold in each category are recorded in a table, or *matrix*. Make a sketch of what one of these might look like for one month.

15. Suppose you have the twelve tables, one for each month, of the museum's sales in the previous problem. These can be combined using *matrix addition* to determine the total number of items sold in each category during the year. Describe how this is done. Use several examples like the one you made in the previous problem to see if your method works.

Get Ready!

Assign this diagnostic assessment to determine if students have the prerequisite skills for Chapter 12.

Lesson	Skill
1-3	Evaluate Expressions
3-6	Identify Matrix Elements
3-2 and 3-6	Solve Systems of Equations

To remediate students, select from these resources (available for every lesson).
• Online Problems (PowerAlgebra.com)
• Reteaching (All-in-One Teaching Resources)
• Practice (All-in-One Teaching Resources)

Why Students Need These Skills
EVALUATING EXPRESSIONS
Evaluating expressions is essential to finding determinants and inverse matrices.
IDENTIFYING MATRIX ELEMENTS
Identifying matrix elements is essential to performing operations on them.
SOLVING SYSTEMS OF EQUATIONS
Students will extend solving systems of linear equations with matrix row operations to matrix equations.

Looking Ahead Vocabulary
MATRIX Like a table, a matrix is divided into rows and columns and can be used to organize, store, and display data.
MATRIX ADDITION Ask students to consider whether the sum of two matrices is another matrix or a number.

Answers

Get Ready!
1. 6

2. $\frac{1}{3}$

3. $-\frac{3}{8}$

4. $\frac{7}{72}$

5. -9

6. 11

7. 3

8. $\left(\frac{1}{2}, -4\right)$

9. $\left(-\frac{2}{3}, -\frac{2}{3}\right)$

10. $\left(\frac{3}{4}, \frac{11}{4}\right)$

11. $(7, 9, -6)$
12. $(0, 0, 8)$
13. $(7, 5, 0)$
14. Check students' work.
15. Check students' work.

Chapter 12 Overview

UbD Understanding by Design

Chapter 12 expands on students' understandings and skills related to matrices and systems of equations. In this chapter, students will develop the answers to the Essential Questions posed on the student page as they learn the concepts and skills bulleted below.

BIG idea Data Representation

ESSENTIAL QUESTION How can you use a matrix to organize data?

• Students will use matrices to compare data.

BIG idea Modeling

ESSENTIAL QUESTION How can you use a matrix equation to model a real-world situation?

• Students will solve systems of equations with matrix equations.

CHAPTER 12 Matrices

PowerAlgebra.com
Your place to get all things digital

VIDEO Download videos connecting math to your world.

VOCABULARY Math definitions in English and Spanish

SOLVE IT! The online Solve It will get you in gear for each lesson.

DYNAMIC ACTIVITIES Interactive! Vary numbers, graphs, and figures to explore math concepts.

ONLINE PROBLEMS Download Step-by-Step Problems with Instant Replay.

ONLINE HOMEWORK Get and view your assignments online.

MathXL FOR SCHOOL Extra practice and review online

Matrices are used to do encryption. The sculpture <u>Kryptos</u> pictured on the next page contains encrypted messages.

How can you add, subtract, and multiply arrays of numbers? How can you use a matrix to represent and solve systems of equations? And how can you use matrices to find areas of geometric figures? You will learn how in this chapter.

Vocabulary

English/Spanish Vocabulary Audio Online:

English	Spanish
coefficient matrix, *p. 801*	matriz de coeficientes
determinant, *p. 790*	determinante
equal matrices, *p. 775*	matrices equivalentes
matrix equation, *p. 773*	ecuación matricial
scalar multiplication, *p. 781*	multiplicación escalar
square matrix, *p. 789*	matriz cuadrada
variable matrix, *p. 801*	matriz variable
zero matrix, *p. 775*	matriz cero

PowerAlgebra.com

Chapter 12 Overview

Use these online assets to engage your students. These include support for the Solve It and step-by-step solutions for Problems.

 VIDEO Show the student-produced video demonstrating relevant and engaging applications of the new concepts in the chapter.

 VOCABULARY Find online definitions for new terms in English and Spanish.

 SOLVE IT! Start each lesson with an attention-getting Problem. View the Problem online with helpful hints.

My Math Video

My Math Video

Use this photo to introduce the concept of using math for encryption. The Kryptos sculpture contains four different messages that have been encrypted with polyalphabetic substitution and transposition ciphers.

Q What are some codes or ciphers you are familiar with? **[Samples: pig latin, Morse code, text-messaging lingo, or acronyms such as NASA, IRS, USA]**

Q What must a person on the receiving end of a code or cipher be able to do? How? **[Sample: Decode or decipher the message to understand it; use a key or work backwards.]**

Q How might you use math to encrypt a message? **[Sample: Assign numerical values to letters and perform specific operations on the values.]**

EXTENSION

Have students invent their own codes or ciphers using mathematical operations.

BIG ideas

1 **Data Representation**
Essential Question How can you use a matrix to organize data?

2 **Modeling**
Essential Question How can you use a matrix equation to model a real-world situation?

Chapter Preview

 Increase students' depth of knowledge with interactive online activities.

 Show problems from each lesson solved step by step. Instant replay allows students to go at their own pace when studying online.

 Prepare students for the Chapter Test with online practice and review.

UbD

Data Representation

BIG idea The most appropriate data representations depend on the type of data—quantitative or qualitative, and univariate or bivariate. Line plots, box plots, and histograms are different ways to show distribution of data over a possible range of values.

ESSENTIAL UNDERSTANDINGS

12-1 You can extend the addition and subtraction of numbers to matrices.

12-2 The product of two matrices is a matrix. To find an element in the product matrix, you multiply the elements of a row from the first matrix to the corresponding elements of a column from the second matrix. Then add the products.

Modeling

BIG idea Many real-world mathematical problems can be represented algebraically. These representations can lead to algebraic solutions. A function that models a real-world situation can then be used to make estimates or predictions about future occurrences.

ESSENTIAL UNDERSTANDINGS

12-3 The product of a matrix and its inverse matrix is the multiplicative identity matrix. Not all matrices have inverse matrices.

12-4 You can solve some matrix equations $AX = B$ by multiplying each side of the equation by A^{-1}, the inverse of matrix A.

Operations with Matrices

Operations that are defined for matrices include addition, subtraction, scalar multiplication, and matrix multiplication.

Addition, Subtraction, and Scalar Multiplication

The properties of equality for real numbers hold for these operations since all operations occur between two elements that are real numbers.

- **Matrix addition** is performed by adding corresponding elements in two or more matrices of the same dimensions:

$$\begin{bmatrix} a & b \\ c & d \end{bmatrix} + \begin{bmatrix} e & f \\ g & h \end{bmatrix} = \begin{bmatrix} a+e & b+f \\ c+g & d+h \end{bmatrix}$$

- **Matrix subtraction** is performed by subtracting corresponding elements in two matrices of the same dimensions.

- **Matrix scalar multiplication** is performed by multiplying each element in the matrix by the scalar. Scalar multiplication can be performed on matrices of any dimensions.

$$k\begin{bmatrix} a & b \\ c & d \end{bmatrix} = \begin{bmatrix} ka & kb \\ kc & kd \end{bmatrix}$$

Matrix Multiplication

The properties of equality for real numbers do not all hold for matrix multiplication, though some properties do hold for square matrix multiplication. One matrix can be multiplied by a second matrix only if the number of columns of the first matrix equals the number of rows of the second.

Common Errors With Matrix Operations

Errors in dimensions occur when students try to add or subtract matrices of different dimensions, or multiply matrices that cannot be multiplied under defined matrix multiplication.

Properties of equality may be taken for granted even though matrices are not real numbers. Make sure students understand that matrix multiplication is not commutative, and show some examples.

Errors in matrix multiplication may occur when students multiply columns by rows instead or rows by columns. Suggest students sketch lines as a reminder:

$$\begin{bmatrix} a_{11} & a_{12} \\ a_{21} & a_{22} \\ a_{31} & a_{32} \end{bmatrix} \times \begin{bmatrix} b_{11} & b_{12} & b_{13} \\ b_{21} & b_{22} & b_{23} \end{bmatrix}$$

Determinants and Inverse Matrices

Inverse matrices are used to analyze the existence of solutions for systems of linear equations.

Identity and Inverse Matrices

Every square matrix has an identity matrix I that contains 1's along the main diagonal and 0's elsewhere. The multiplicative inverse of a square matrix A can be expressed as $AA^{-1} = A^{-1}A = I$. Not all matrices have multiplicative inverses.

Determinant

The concept and notation of a determinant will be new for most students. The determinant is only defined for square matrices. Students should understand that a determinant is a number rather than a matrix. The determinant of a 2×2 matrix is:

$$\det \begin{bmatrix} a & b \\ c & d \end{bmatrix} = ad - bc$$

The determinant of a 3×3 matrix $\begin{bmatrix} a_1 & b_1 & c_1 \\ a_2 & b_2 & c_2 \\ a_3 & b_3 & c_3 \end{bmatrix}$ is

$$a_1b_2c_3 + b_1c_2a_3 + c_1a_2b_3 - (a_3b_2c_1 + b_3c_2a_1 + c_3a_2b_1)$$

A matrix whose determinant is zero has no multiplicative inverse. If the determinant of a matrix is nonzero, use the determinant to obtain the inverse matrix.

$$A^{-1} = \frac{1}{\det A} \begin{bmatrix} d & -b \\ -c & a \end{bmatrix}$$

Common Errors With Determinants and Inverse Matrices

Errors in finding determinants may occur when students forget that subtraction of a negative product is addition.

Errors in finding inverse matrices may occur when students incorrectly write the matrix that is to be multiplied by the reciprocal of the determinant.

Applications of Matrices

Besides organizing and comparing data, matrices are used for several other purposes.

Finding the Area of Polygons

The area of any triangle with vertices (x_1, y_1), (x_2, y_2), and (x_3, y_3) equals $\frac{1}{2} \det \begin{bmatrix} x_1 & y_1 & 1 \\ x_2 & y_2 & 1 \\ x_3 & y_3 & 1 \end{bmatrix}$. The determinant may be negative, and area can only be nonnegative, so any negative sign must be dropped.

Because any polygon can be divided into two or more triangles, this formula can be used to find the area of any polygon.

Solving Systems of Equations

Previously, students used matrix row operations to solve systems of linear equations. Another method uses inverse matrices and matrix multiplication to apply the following relationship:

For matrices A and B, A invertible, if $AX = B$, then $X = A^{-1}B$.

For example, for the system $\begin{cases} ax + by = c \\ dx - ey = f \end{cases}$, the matrix equation is $\begin{bmatrix} a & b \\ d & -e \end{bmatrix}\begin{bmatrix} x \\ y \end{bmatrix} = \begin{bmatrix} c \\ f \end{bmatrix}$ and is solved using the equivalent matrix equation: $\begin{bmatrix} x \\ y \end{bmatrix} = \begin{bmatrix} a & b \\ d & -e \end{bmatrix}^{-1}\begin{bmatrix} c \\ f \end{bmatrix}$. Note that if the coefficient matrix is not invertible, there will not be a unique solution.

Common Errors With Matrix Applications

Errors in solving systems occur when students forget that matrix multiplication is not commutative, or fail to find the inverse of the first matrix.

MATRICES
Pacing and Assignment Guide

		TRADITIONAL		BLOCK
Lesson	**Teaching Day(s)**	**Basic**	**Average**	**Block**
12-1	1	Problems 1–4 Exs. 6–14, 19, 23, 25–36	Problems 1–4 Exs. 6–18, 19–23 odd, 25–36	**Day 1** Problems 1–4 Exs. 6–18, 19–23 odd, 25–36
12-2	1	Problems 1–5 Exs. 7–25, 28, 29, 37–45	Problems 1–5 Exs. 7–27 odd, 28–34, 37–45	Problems 1–5 Exs. 7–27 odd, 28–34, 37–45
12-3	1	Problems 1–2 Exs. 4–15, 19	Problems 1–2 Exs. 4–18 even, 19	**Day 2** Part 1 Problems 1–2 Exs. 4–18 even, 19 Part 2 Problems 3–5 Exs. 4–38
		Problems 3–5 Exs. 4–14, 27–38	Problems 3–5 Exs. 4–38	
12-4	1	Problems 1–2 Exs. 4–11	Problems 1–2 Exs. 4–13	**Day 3** Part 1 Problems 1–2 Exs. 4–13 Part 2 Problems 3–4 Exs. 4–10 even, 11–25, 29–42
		Problems 3–4 Exs. 4–13, 29–42	Problems 3–4 Exs. 4–10 even, 11–25, 29–42	
Review	1	Chapter 12 Review	Chapter 12 Review	**Day 4** Chapter 12 Review Chapter 12 Test
Assess	1	Chapter 12 Test	Chapter 12 Test	
Total		**8 Days**	**8 Days**	**4 Days**

Note: Pacing does not include Concept Bytes and other feature pages.

Resources

	For the Chapter	12-1	12-2	12-3	12-4
Planning					
Teacher Center Online Planner & Grade Book	I	I	I	I	I
Interactive Learning & Guided Instruction					
My Math Video	I				
Solve It!		I TM	I TM	I TM	I TM
Student Companion (SP)*		P M	P M	P M	P M
Vocabulary Support		I P M	I P M	I P M	I P M
Got It? Support		I P	I P	I P	I P
Dynamic Activity					
Online Problems		I	I	I	I
Additional Problems		M	M	M	M
English Language Learner Support (TR)		E P M	E P M	E P M	E P M
Activities, Games, and Puzzles		E M	E M	E M	E M
Teaching With TI Technology With CD-ROM					
TI-Nspire™ Support CD-ROM		✓	✓	✓	✓
Lesson Check & Practice					
Student Companion (SP)*		P M	P M	P M	P M
Lesson Check Support		I P	I P	I P	I P
Think About a Plan (TR)*		E P M	E P M	E P M	E P M
Practice Form K (TR)*		E P M	E P M	E P M	E P M
Standardized Test Prep (TR)*		P M	P M	P M	P M
Practice Form G (TR)*		E P M	E P M	E P M	E P M
Extra Practice	E M				
Find the Errors!	M				
Enrichment (TR)		E P M	E P M	E P M	E P M
Answers and Solutions CD-ROM	✓	✓	✓	✓	✓
Assess & Remediate					
ExamView CD-ROM	✓	✓	✓	✓	✓
Lesson Quiz		I TM	I TM	I TM	I TM
Quizzes and Tests Form K (TR)*	E P M				E P M
Quizzes and Tests Form G (TR)*	E P M				E P M
Reteaching (TR)		E P M	E P M	E P M	E P M
Performance Tasks (TR)*	P M				
Cumulative Review (TR)*	P M				
Progress Monitoring Assessments	I P M				

(TR) Available in All-In-One Teaching Resources   * Spanish available

1 Interactive Learning

Solve It!

PURPOSE To find and complete a pattern among square arrays of numbers

PROCESS Students may

- compare numbers within an array to determine a pattern.
- compare numbers in the same position of different arrays to find a pattern.

FACILITATE

Q Is each array identical? Explain. **[No; notice the center terms.]**

Q What number goes in the center of the first square? **[5]**

Q What is the pattern of the center squares? **[Sample: multiples of 5]**

Q What could be the pattern for the numbers in the first row third column? **[Sample: multiples of 3]**

ANSWER See Solve It in Answers on next page.

CONNECT THE MATH In the Solve It, students compare ordered arrays of numbers, or matrices. In the lesson, students will add and subtract matrices and use them to compare data.

2 Guided Instruction

Take Note

Q How do you know which are the corresponding elements in two matrices? **[Samples: they have the same position of rows and columns; they have the same subscript.]**

Objectives To add and subtract matrices
To solve matrix equations

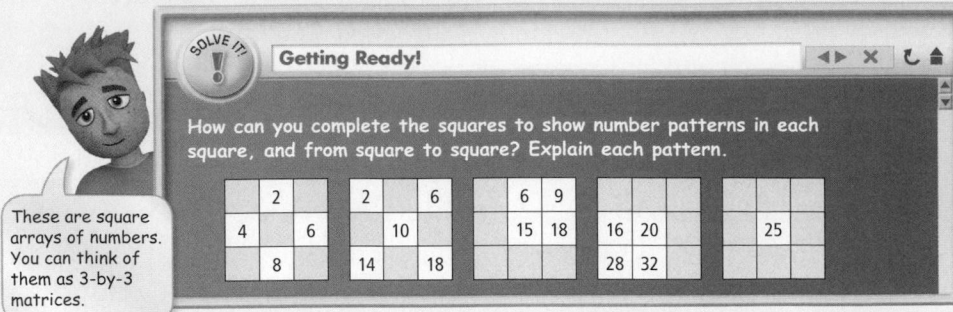

These are square arrays of numbers. You can think of them as 3-by-3 matrices.

Lesson Vocabulary
- corresponding elements
- matrix equation
- zero matrix
- equal matrices

In Lesson 3-6, you solved a system of equations by expressing it as a single matrix. Now you will learn how to work with more than one matrix at a time.

Focus Question When can you add and subtract matrices?

Recall that the *dimensions* of a matrix are the numbers of rows and columns. A matrix with 2 rows and 3 columns is a 2×3 matrix. Each number in a matrix is a *matrix element*. In matrix A, a_{12} is the element in row 1 and column 2.

Sometimes you want to combine matrices to get new information. You can combine two matrices with equal dimensions by adding or subtracting the *corresponding elements*. **Corresponding elements** are elements in the same position in each matrix.

Key Concept **Matrix Addition and Subtraction**

To add matrices A and B with the same dimensions, add corresponding elements. Similarly, to subtract matrices A and B with the same dimensions, subtract corresponding elements.

$$A = \begin{bmatrix} a_{11} & a_{12} \\ a_{21} & a_{22} \end{bmatrix} \qquad B = \begin{bmatrix} b_{11} & b_{12} \\ b_{21} & b_{22} \end{bmatrix}$$

$$A + B = \begin{bmatrix} a_{11} + b_{11} & a_{12} + b_{12} \\ a_{21} + b_{21} & a_{22} + b_{22} \end{bmatrix} \qquad A - B = \begin{bmatrix} a_{11} - b_{11} & a_{12} - b_{12} \\ a_{21} - b_{21} & a_{22} - b_{22} \end{bmatrix}$$

BIG idea Data Representation   **UbD**
ESSENTIAL UNDERSTANDINGS
- The addition and subtraction of numbers can be extended to matrices.
- Matrices can be added or subtracted by adding or subtracting corresponding elements.

Math Background

To add or subtract two matrices, you add or subtract the corresponding elements of each matrix. Therefore, it is only possible to add or subtract matrices of the same dimensions.

The definition of matrix addition and subtraction allows you to extend the properties of addition and subtraction of real numbers to matrices.

It follows that, like any real number, each matrix has an additive inverse, which is a matrix with each element the opposite of the corresponding matrix element. Like real numbers, the sum of a matrix

and its additive inverse is the additive identity. For addition and subtraction, the additive identity matrix for a given matrix is a matrix of the same dimensions with all elements equal to zero.

Two other properties include the following:
- Closure: Adding or subtracting matrices results in a matrix.
- Commutative: Like real numbers, matrix addition is commutative, while matrix subtraction is not.

Support Student Learning

Use the **Algebra 2 Companion** to engage and support students during instruction. See Lesson Resources at the end of this lesson for details.

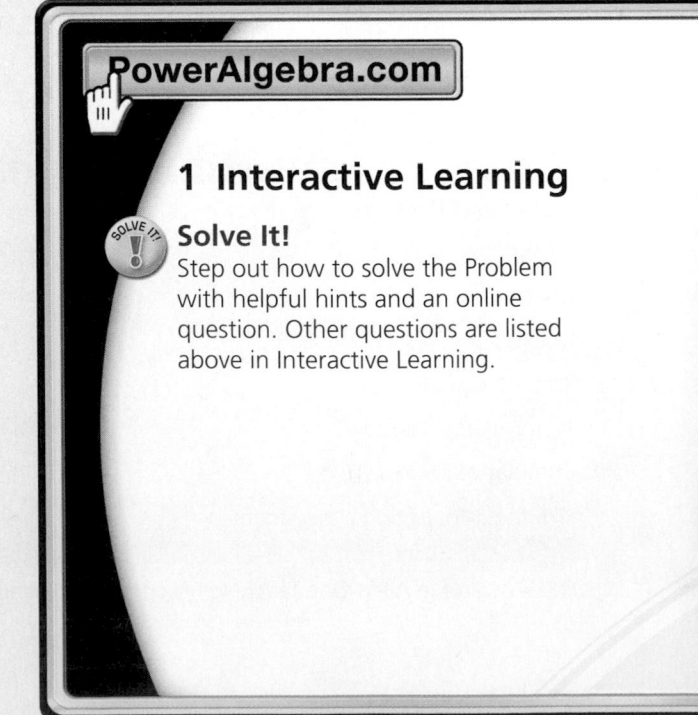

PowerAlgebra.com

1 Interactive Learning

Solve It!
Step out how to solve the Problem with helpful hints and an online question. Other questions are listed above in Interactive Learning.

Problem 1 Adding and Subtracting Matrices

Given $C = \begin{bmatrix} 3 & 2 & 4 \\ -1 & 4 & 0 \end{bmatrix}$ and $D = \begin{bmatrix} 1 & 4 & 3 \\ -2 & 2 & 4 \end{bmatrix}$, what are the following?

A $C + D$

Write the matrix addition. $\quad \begin{bmatrix} 3 & 2 & 4 \\ -1 & 4 & 0 \end{bmatrix} + \begin{bmatrix} 1 & 4 & 3 \\ -2 & 2 & 4 \end{bmatrix}$

Add corresponding elements. $\quad = \begin{bmatrix} 3+1 & 2+4 & 4+3 \\ -1+(-2) & 4+2 & 0+4 \end{bmatrix}$

Simplify each sum. $\quad = \begin{bmatrix} 4 & 6 & 7 \\ -3 & 6 & 4 \end{bmatrix}$

B $C - D$

Write the matrix subtraction. $\quad \begin{bmatrix} 3 & 2 & 4 \\ -1 & 4 & 0 \end{bmatrix} - \begin{bmatrix} 1 & 4 & 3 \\ -2 & 2 & 4 \end{bmatrix}$

Subtract corresponding elements. $\quad = \begin{bmatrix} 3-1 & 2-4 & 4-3 \\ -1-(-2) & 4-2 & 0-4 \end{bmatrix}$

Simplify each difference. $\quad = \begin{bmatrix} 2 & -2 & 1 \\ 1 & 2 & -4 \end{bmatrix}$

Got It? **1.** Given $A = \begin{bmatrix} -12 & 24 \\ -3 & 5 \\ -1 & 10 \end{bmatrix}$ and $B = \begin{bmatrix} -3 & 1 \\ 2 & -4 \\ -1 & 5 \end{bmatrix}$, what are the following?

    a. $A + B$

    b. $A - B$

    c. Reasoning Is matrix addition commutative? Explain.

A **matrix equation** is an equation in which the variable is a matrix. You can use the addition and subtraction properties of equality to solve a matrix equation. An example of a matrix equation is shown below.

$$\begin{bmatrix} 1 & 0 & 12 \\ 3 & 5 & 9 \\ 7 & 8 & -2 \end{bmatrix} + A = \begin{bmatrix} 8 & 11 & 9 \\ -5 & 5 & 2 \\ 10 & 7 & 8 \end{bmatrix}$$

Problem 1

Q Which number in matrix D corresponds to the element with value 3 in matrix C? **[The element with value 3 in row one corresponds to the 1 in matrix D.]**

Q Which value in matrix C corresponds to d_{21}? **[c_{21} has a value of -1.]**

EXTENSION

Q If the elements in matrix C are input values and the elements in matrix D are output values, do the matrices show a function with one-to-one correspondence? Why or why not? **[No; the input value of 4 would map to two different output values.]**

Got It?

Q Your answers to 1a and 1b will be matrices of what size? **[3 × 2]**

Q What is the value of the element in row 1 column 1 of the solution matrix for 1a? Explain. **[-15; a_{11} is -12 and b_{11} is -3. So $a_{11} + b_{11}$ is -15.]**

Q Does $A - B$ equal $B - A$? Explain. **[No; Because subtraction is not a commutative operation, matrix subtraction is not commutative either.]**

2 Guided Instruction

 Each Problem is worked out and supported online.

Problem 1
Adding and Subtracting Matrices
Animated

Problem 2
Solving a Matrix Equation
Animated

Problem 3
Using Identity and Opposite Matrices

Problem 4
Finding Unknown Matrix Values
Animated

Support in Algebra 2 Companion
• Vocabulary
• Key Concepts
• Got It?

Answers

Solve It!

Answers may vary. Sample:

1	2	3		2	4	6		3	6	9
4	5	6,		8	10	12,		12	15	18,
7	8	9		14	16	18		21	24	27

4	8	12		5	10	15
16	20	24,		20	25	30
28	32	36		35	40	45

Each 3-by-3 square has 9 elements. The first square contains the first 9 multiples of 1, the second contains the first 9 multiples of 2, and so on. Within each square, the top row contains the first 3 multiples, the middle row contains the fourth through the sixth multiples, and the bottom row contains the seventh through the ninth multiples.

Got It?

1. a. $\begin{bmatrix} -15 & 25 \\ -1 & 1 \\ -2 & 15 \end{bmatrix}$ **b.** $\begin{bmatrix} -9 & 23 \\ -5 & 9 \\ 0 & 5 \end{bmatrix}$

    c. Yes; it does not matter in which order you add matrices.

Problem 2   ERROR PREVENTION

Q How many rows and columns do the tables contain? If you made a matrix for the tables, how many rows and columns would the matrices contain? Explain. **[The tables each have 5 rows and 3 columns. A matrix for each table would have 4 rows and 2 columns because matrices contain values, not names and descriptions.]**

Q Did all four teams play the same number of games during the second half? How can you find out? **[Yes; the first column of each matrix shows games won, and the second column shows games lost, so totaling each row in a single matrix gives total games.]**

Q Would matrix *F* change if the Wins and Losses columns in both tables were reversed? Will this affect the answer? Explain. **[The columns in matrix *F* will be reversed. However, the answer will remain the same because Team 2 will show 3 losses and 38 wins.]**

Got It?

Q How do you solve the literal equation? **[Add *B* to both sides: *A* = *C* + *B*.]**

Q What other equation will also give the correct answer? Why? **[*A* = *B* + *C*, because matrix addition is commutative.]**

 **Problem 2** Solving a Matrix Equation

Sports The first table shows the teams with the four best records halfway through their season. The second table shows the full season records for the same four teams. Which team had the best record during the second half of the season?

Records for the First Half of the Season

Team	Wins	Losses
Team 1	30	11
Team 2	29	12
Team 3	25	16
Team 4	24	17

Records for Season

Team	Wins	Losses
Team 1	53	29
Team 2	67	15
Team 3	58	24
Team 4	61	21

Know
- Records for the first half of the season
- Records for the full season

Need
- Records for the second half of the season

Plan
- Use the equation first half records + second half records = season records.
- Solve the matrix equation.

Step 1 Write 4 × 2 matrices to show the information from the two tables. The rows should represent the teams. The columns should represent the wins and losses.

Let *A* = the first half records.
Let *B* = the second half records.
Let *F* = the final records.

$$A = \begin{bmatrix} 30 & 11 \\ 29 & 12 \\ 25 & 16 \\ 24 & 17 \end{bmatrix} \quad F = \begin{bmatrix} 53 & 29 \\ 67 & 15 \\ 58 & 24 \\ 61 & 21 \end{bmatrix}$$

Think

What are the dimensions of matrix *B*?
Matrix *B* will have 4 rows and 2 columns. It is a 4 × 2 matrix.

Step 2 Solve *A* + *B* = *F* for *B* and substitute.

$B = F - A$

$$B = \begin{bmatrix} 53 & 29 \\ 67 & 15 \\ 58 & 24 \\ 61 & 21 \end{bmatrix} - \begin{bmatrix} 30 & 11 \\ 29 & 12 \\ 25 & 16 \\ 24 & 17 \end{bmatrix} = \begin{bmatrix} 53-30 & 29-11 \\ 67-29 & 15-12 \\ 58-25 & 24-16 \\ 61-24 & 21-17 \end{bmatrix} = \begin{bmatrix} 23 & 18 \\ 38 & 3 \\ 33 & 8 \\ 37 & 4 \end{bmatrix}$$

Team 2 had the best record (38 wins and 3 losses) during the second half of the season.

✔ **Got It? 2.** If $B = \begin{bmatrix} 1 & 6 & -1 \\ 2 & 6 & 1 \\ -1 & -2 & 4 \end{bmatrix}$, $C = \begin{bmatrix} 2 & 0 & 0 \\ -1 & -3 & 6 \\ 2 & 3 & -1 \end{bmatrix}$, and $A - B = C$, what is *A*?

Additional Problems

1. Given $A = \begin{bmatrix} -9 & -3 \\ 9 & 0 \\ 4 & 3 \end{bmatrix}$ and $B = \begin{bmatrix} -7 & -2 \\ 4 & 6 \\ 9 & -3 \end{bmatrix}$, what is $B + A$?

ANSWER $\begin{bmatrix} -16 & -5 \\ 13 & 6 \\ 13 & 0 \end{bmatrix}$

2. The tables show the number of hours two students spent on homework in Math and Science classes.

Fall Semester Hours

	Math	Science
Student A	166	133
Student B	140	120

Fall and Spring Semester Hours

	Math	Science
Student A	300	227
Student B	282	231

Which student spent more hours on homework in the Spring Semester?

ANSWER Student B

3. What is the sum of the matrices $[-6 \ \ 7 \ \ 0]$ and $[6 \ \ -7 \ \ 0]$?

ANSWER $[0 \ \ 0 \ \ 0]$

4. What values of *x* and *y* make the equation true?

$$\begin{bmatrix} 8 & -2x \\ 3 & 7 \end{bmatrix} + \begin{bmatrix} 0 & -7 \\ 8 & 2 \end{bmatrix} = \begin{bmatrix} 8 & -5 \\ 11 & 3y \end{bmatrix}$$

ANSWER $x = -1; y = 3$

Answers

Got It? (continued)

2. $A = \begin{bmatrix} 3 & 6 & -1 \\ 1 & 3 & 7 \\ 1 & 1 & 3 \end{bmatrix}$

For $m \times n$ matrices, the additive identity matrix is the **zero matrix** O, or $O_{m \times n}$, with all elements zero. The *opposite*, or *additive inverse*, of an $m \times n$ matrix A is $-A$. Each element of $-A$ is the opposite of the corresponding element of A.

 Problem 3 Using Identity and Opposite Matrices

What are the following sums?

A $\begin{bmatrix} 1 & 2 \\ 5 & -7 \end{bmatrix} + \begin{bmatrix} 0 & 0 \\ 0 & 0 \end{bmatrix}$

Add corresponding elements. $\begin{bmatrix} 1 & 2 \\ 5 & -7 \end{bmatrix} + \begin{bmatrix} 0 & 0 \\ 0 & 0 \end{bmatrix} = \begin{bmatrix} 1+0 & 2+0 \\ 5+0 & -7+0 \end{bmatrix}$

Simplify. $= \begin{bmatrix} 1 & 2 \\ 5 & -7 \end{bmatrix}$

B $\begin{bmatrix} 2 & 8 \\ -3 & 0 \end{bmatrix} + \begin{bmatrix} -2 & -8 \\ 3 & 0 \end{bmatrix}$

Add corresponding elements. $\begin{bmatrix} 2 & 8 \\ -3 & 0 \end{bmatrix} + \begin{bmatrix} -2 & -8 \\ 3 & 0 \end{bmatrix} = \begin{bmatrix} 2+(-2) & 8+(-8) \\ -3+3 & 0+0 \end{bmatrix}$

Simplify. $= \begin{bmatrix} 0 & 0 \\ 0 & 0 \end{bmatrix}$

Think

How is this like adding real numbers?
Adding the zero matrix results in the original matrix. Adding opposite matrices gives you the zero matrix.

 Got It? 3. What are the following sums?

a. $\begin{bmatrix} 14 & 5 \\ 0 & -2 \end{bmatrix} + \begin{bmatrix} -14 & -5 \\ 0 & 2 \end{bmatrix}$

b. $\begin{bmatrix} 0 & 0 & 0 \\ 0 & 0 & 0 \end{bmatrix} + \begin{bmatrix} -1 & 10 & -5 \\ 0 & 2 & -3 \end{bmatrix}$

 **Properties** Properties of Matrix Addition

If A, B, and C are $m \times n$ matrices, then

Example	Property
$A + B$ is an $m \times n$ matrix	**Closure Property of Addition**
$A + B = B + A$	**Commutative Property of Addition**
$(A + B) + C = A + (B + C)$	**Associative Property of Addition**
There is a unique $m \times n$ matrix O such that $O + A = A + O = A$	**Additive Identity Property**
For each A, there is a unique opposite, $-A$, such that $A + (-A) = O$	**Additive Inverse Property**

Hint

You can use the definition of equal matrices to find unknown values in a matrix equation.

Equal matrices have the same dimensions and equal corresponding elements.

For example, $\begin{bmatrix} 0.25 & 1.5 \\ -3 & \frac{4}{5} \end{bmatrix}$ and $\begin{bmatrix} \frac{1}{4} & 1\frac{1}{2} \\ -3 & 0.8 \end{bmatrix}$ are equal matrices.

PowerAlgebra.com   Lesson 12-1   Adding and Subtracting Matrices   775

Problem 3

Q What do you think a subtractive identity matrix might look like? Explain. **[A subtractive identity matrix would be the same as an additive identity matrix. Neither adding zero to a number nor subtracting zero from a number changes a value.]**

Got It?

Q In 3a, name the left-hand matrix A and name the right-hand matrix B. Which matrix is the additive inverse of the other? Explain. **[$-A = B$ and $-B = A$, so each matrix is the additive inverse of the other.]**

Take Note

Q What does $m \times n$ mean in the Take Note box? Does it have anything to do with multiplication? **[$m \times n$ is the generic size of a matrix, with m rows and n columns. This does not mean multiplication inside the matrix, but the product mn is the total number of elements in the matrix; for example, a 2×2 matrix has 4 elements in it.]**

Q What do you think the Closure Property means? Does this property also apply to matrix subtraction? **[The Closure Property means that the sum of two equal-sized matrices is a matrix. This property does apply to matrix subtraction.]**

---

3. **a.** $\begin{bmatrix} 0 & 0 \\ 0 & 0 \end{bmatrix}$

b. $\begin{bmatrix} -1 & 10 & -5 \\ 0 & 2 & -3 \end{bmatrix}$

Problem 4

> Q If you replaced each matrix with a variable, what could the equation look like? [**A = B**]
>
> Q How could you rewrite the left-hand matrix as the sum of two matrices to isolate the variable terms in a single matrix? How would this help you solve the problem? [**Answers may vary. Sample: Write a sum of two 2 × 2 matrices with elements 3x, 0, 0, 2y and 1, 9, 10, and −1. The matrix that does not contain variables can be subtracted from both sides.**]

Got It?

> Q In 4b, what two equations did you write to solve for the variables? [**Sample: 3x − x = 8; 0 − (2y + 6) = 4y + 12**]

3 Lesson Check

Do you know HOW?

- To solve Exercises 1–3, students must understand that the sum of two matrices of the same size is another matrix of the same size. The solution to Exercises 1 and 3 is a 2 × 2 matrix; the solution to Exercise 2 is a 2 × 3 matrix.

Do you UNDERSTAND?

- To start on Exercise 4, students should convert all elements to either fractional or decimal number form.

Close

> Q How does matrix addition compare with real-number addition? [**Matrix addition and real-number addition involve the same basic operations. Matrix addition is a way of performing many real-number additions at once.**]

PowerAlgebra.com

3 Lesson Check

For a digital lesson check, use the Got It questions.

Support in Algebra 2 Companion
- Lesson Check

4 Practice

Assign homework to individual students or to an entire class.

You can use the definition of equal matrices to find unknown values in matrix elements.

 Problem 4 Finding Unknown Matrix Values

Multiple Choice What values of x and y make the equation true?

$$\begin{bmatrix} 3x+1 & 9 \\ 10 & 2y-1 \end{bmatrix} = \begin{bmatrix} 16 & 9 \\ 10 & -5 \end{bmatrix}$$

  Ⓐ $x = 3, y = 5$ Ⓒ $x = 5, y = -2$

  Ⓑ $x = \frac{17}{3}, y = 5$ Ⓓ $x = 5, y = -3$

Plan

How can you solve the equation?
For the two matrices to be equal, the corresponding elements must be equal.

Identify corresponding elements that contain unknowns.

$$\begin{bmatrix} 3x+1 & 9 \\ 10 & 2y-1 \end{bmatrix} = \begin{bmatrix} 16 & 9 \\ 10 & -5 \end{bmatrix}$$

Set corresponding elements equal. $3x + 1 = 16$ $2y - 1 = -5$

Isolate the variable term. $3x + 1 - 1 = 16 - 1$ $2y - 1 + 1 = -5 + 1$

Simplify. $3x = 15$ $2y = -4$

Solve for x and y. $x = 5$ $y = -2$

The correct answer is C.

 Got It? 4. What values of x and y make the following equations true?

  a. $\begin{bmatrix} x+3 & -2 \\ y-1 & x+1 \end{bmatrix} = \begin{bmatrix} 9 & -2 \\ 2y+5 & 7 \end{bmatrix}$

  b. $\begin{bmatrix} 12 & -3 \\ 3x & 0 \end{bmatrix} - \begin{bmatrix} 10 & -4 \\ x & 2y+6 \end{bmatrix} = \begin{bmatrix} 2 & 1 \\ 8 & 4y+12 \end{bmatrix}$

Focus Question When can you add or subtract matrices?
Answer You can only add or subtract matrices that have the same dimensions. To add two matrices, add corresponding elements. To subtract two matrices, subtract corresponding elements.

 Lesson Check

Do you know HOW?

Find each sum or difference.

1. $\begin{bmatrix} 1 & -1 \\ 2 & 3 \end{bmatrix} + \begin{bmatrix} 0 & 2 \\ -4 & 5 \end{bmatrix}$

2. $\begin{bmatrix} 5 & -3 & 7 \\ -1 & 0 & 8 \end{bmatrix} - \begin{bmatrix} 4 & 6 & -1 \\ 2 & 1 & 0 \end{bmatrix}$

3. What is the solution of this matrix equation?

$\begin{bmatrix} 6 & 1 \\ 4 & -2 \end{bmatrix} + X = \begin{bmatrix} 3 & 5 \\ -1 & 9 \end{bmatrix}$

Do you UNDERSTAND?

4. Vocabulary Are the two matrices equal? Explain.

$\begin{bmatrix} \frac{1}{2} & \frac{3}{8} \\ 0.2 & \sqrt[3]{27} \end{bmatrix}$ and $\begin{bmatrix} 0.5 & 0.375 \\ \frac{1}{5} & 3 \end{bmatrix}$

5. Error Analysis Describe and correct the error made in subtracting the two matrices.

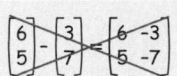

Answers

Got It? (continued)

4. a. $x = 6, y = -6$

   b. $x = 4, y = -3$

Lesson Check

1. $\begin{bmatrix} 1 & 1 \\ -2 & 8 \end{bmatrix}$

2. $\begin{bmatrix} 1 & -9 & 8 \\ -3 & -1 & 8 \end{bmatrix}$

3. $\begin{bmatrix} -3 & 4 \\ -5 & 11 \end{bmatrix}$

4. Yes; the elements in each of the corresponding positions are equal.

5. The elements were not subtracted. The correct answer is

$\begin{bmatrix} 6 \\ 5 \end{bmatrix} - \begin{bmatrix} 3 \\ 7 \end{bmatrix} = \begin{bmatrix} 3 \\ -2 \end{bmatrix}$

Practice and Problem-Solving Exercises

Ⓐ Practice

Find each sum or difference. ◆ See Problem 1.

Guided Practice

To start, subtract corresponding elements.

6. $\begin{bmatrix} 2 & 1 & 2 \\ 1 & 2 & 1 \end{bmatrix} - \begin{bmatrix} 2 & 3 & 2 \\ 3 & 2 & 3 \end{bmatrix}$

$\begin{bmatrix} 2-2 & 1-3 & 2-2 \\ 1-3 & 2-2 & 1-3 \end{bmatrix}$

7. $\begin{bmatrix} 6.4 & -1.9 \\ -6.4 & 0.8 \end{bmatrix} + \begin{bmatrix} -2.5 & -0.4 \\ 5.8 & 8.3 \end{bmatrix}$

8. $\begin{bmatrix} 1.5 & -1.9 \\ 0 & 4.6 \end{bmatrix} - \begin{bmatrix} 8.3 & -3.2 \\ 2.1 & 5.6 \end{bmatrix}$

Solve each matrix equation. ◆ See Problem 2.

Guided Practice

To start, use the Addition Property of Equality to isolate the variable matrix.

9. $X - \begin{bmatrix} 1 & 4 \\ -2 & 3 \end{bmatrix} = \begin{bmatrix} 5 & -2 \\ 1 & 0 \end{bmatrix}$

$X = \begin{bmatrix} 5 & -2 \\ 1 & 0 \end{bmatrix} + \begin{bmatrix} 1 & 4 \\ -2 & 3 \end{bmatrix}$

10. $X + \begin{bmatrix} 6 & 1 \\ -2 & 3 \end{bmatrix} = \begin{bmatrix} 2 & 0 \\ -3 & 1 \end{bmatrix}$

11. $\begin{bmatrix} 2 & 1 & -1 \\ 0 & 2 & 1 \end{bmatrix} - X = \begin{bmatrix} 11 & 3 & -13 \\ 15 & -9 & 8 \end{bmatrix}$

Find each sum. ◆ See Problem 3.

12. $\begin{bmatrix} 2 & -3 & 4 \\ 5 & 6 & -7 \end{bmatrix} + \begin{bmatrix} 0 & 0 & 0 \\ 0 & 0 & 0 \end{bmatrix}$

13. $\begin{bmatrix} 6 & -3 \\ -7 & 2 \end{bmatrix} + \begin{bmatrix} -6 & 3 \\ 7 & -2 \end{bmatrix}$

Find the value of each variable. ◆ See Problem 4.

14. $\begin{bmatrix} 2 & 2 \\ -1 & 6 \end{bmatrix} - \begin{bmatrix} 4 & -1 \\ 0 & 5 \end{bmatrix} = \begin{bmatrix} r & y \\ -1 & z \end{bmatrix}$

15. $\begin{bmatrix} 2 & 4 \\ 8 & 4.5 \end{bmatrix} = \begin{bmatrix} 4x - 6 & -10t + 5 \\ 4x & 15t + 1.5x \end{bmatrix}$

Ⓑ Apply

Find each matrix sum or difference if possible. If not possible, explain why.

$A = \begin{bmatrix} 3 & 4 \\ 6 & -2 \\ 1 & 0 \end{bmatrix}$ $B = \begin{bmatrix} -3 & 1 \\ 2 & -4 \\ -1 & 5 \end{bmatrix}$ $C = \begin{bmatrix} 1 & 2 \\ -3 & 1 \end{bmatrix}$ $D = \begin{bmatrix} 5 & 1 \\ 0 & 2 \end{bmatrix}$

16. $A + B$

17. $B + D$

18. $C - D$

Practice and Problem-Solving Exercises

6. $\begin{bmatrix} 0 & -2 & 0 \\ -2 & 0 & -2 \end{bmatrix}$

7. $\begin{bmatrix} 3.9 & -2.3 \\ -0.6 & 9.1 \end{bmatrix}$

8. $\begin{bmatrix} -6.8 & 1.3 \\ -2.1 & -1 \end{bmatrix}$

9. $\begin{bmatrix} 6 & 2 \\ -1 & 3 \end{bmatrix}$

10. $\begin{bmatrix} -4 & -1 \\ -1 & -2 \end{bmatrix}$

11. $\begin{bmatrix} -9 & -2 & 12 \\ -15 & 11 & -7 \end{bmatrix}$

12. $\begin{bmatrix} 2 & -3 & 4 \\ 5 & 6 & -7 \end{bmatrix}$

13. $\begin{bmatrix} 0 & 0 \\ 0 & 0 \end{bmatrix}$

14. $(-2, 3, 1)$

15. $x = 2, t = \frac{1}{10}$

16. $\begin{bmatrix} 0 & 5 \\ 8 & -6 \\ 0 & 5 \end{bmatrix}$

17. B and D cannot be added because they do not have the same dimensions.

18. $\begin{bmatrix} -4 & 1 \\ -3 & -1 \end{bmatrix}$

4 Practice

ASSIGNMENT GUIDE

Basic: 6–14, 19, 23

Average: 6–18, 19–23 odd

Standardized Test Prep: 25–28

Mixed Review: 29–36

Reasoning exercises have blue headings.

Applications exercises have red headings.

EXERCISE 23: Use the Think About a Plan worksheet in the **Student Companion** (also available in the Teaching Resources in print and online) to further support students' development in becoming independent learners.

HOMEWORK QUICK CHECK

To check students' understanding of key skills and concepts, go over Exercises 7, 10, 12, 19, and 23.

Lesson 12-1   777

Answers

Practice and Problem-Solving Exercises (continued)

19.

Plant 1

	Plastic	Rubber
1-color	1000	1400
3-color	2600	3800

$$\begin{array}{cc} & \begin{array}{cc}\text{Plastic} & \text{Rubber}\end{array} \\ \begin{array}{c}\text{1-color}\\ \text{3-color}\end{array} & \begin{bmatrix}1000 & 1400\\ 2600 & 3800\end{bmatrix}\end{array}$$

Plant 2

$$\begin{array}{cc} & \begin{array}{cc}\text{Plastic} & \text{Rubber}\end{array} \\ \begin{array}{c}\text{1-color}\\ \text{3-color}\end{array} & \begin{bmatrix}1200 & 3600\\ 1800 & 4800\end{bmatrix}\end{array};$$

Plant 1 − Plant 2 $= \begin{bmatrix} -200 & -2200 \\ 800 & -1000 \end{bmatrix}$, where the top row represents 1-color balls and the bottom represents 3-color balls.

20. $a = 2$, $b = \frac{9}{4}$, $c = -1$, $d = 0$, $f = \frac{1}{2}$, $g = -4$

21. $c = \frac{5}{2}$, $d = \frac{2}{5}$, $f = 7$, $g = 5$, $h = -1$

22. a. $\begin{bmatrix} 952 \\ 720 \\ 1108 \\ 1172 \\ 1044 \end{bmatrix}$; $\begin{bmatrix} 760 \\ 832 \\ 1252 \\ 1144 \\ 1064 \end{bmatrix}$

b. Allen: 4996; Iagorashvili: 5052

23. a. $\begin{bmatrix} 124.6 \\ 113.3 \\ 71.6 \\ 87.2 \end{bmatrix}$

b. $\begin{bmatrix} -6.2 \\ -4.7 \\ 9.4 \\ 3.6 \end{bmatrix}$

c. Yes; order matters because subtraction is not comm.

24. Matrix *B* would have the same dimensions as *A*. Its elements would be the opposites of the corresponding elements in *A*.

---

19. Think About a Plan The table shows the number of beach balls produced during one shift at two manufacturing plants. Plant 1 has two shifts per day and Plant 2 has three shifts per day. Write matrices to represent one day's total output at the two plants. Then find the difference between daily production totals at the two plants.
- How can you use the number of shifts to find the total daily production totals at each plant?
- What matrix equation can you use to solve this problem?

Beach Ball Production Per Shift

	1-color		3-color	
	Plastic	Rubber	Plastic	Rubber
Plant 1	500	700	1300	1900
Plant 2	400	1200	600	1600

Solve each equation for each variable.

20. $\begin{bmatrix} 4b + 2 & -3 & 4d \\ -4a & 2 & 3 \\ 2f - 1 & -14 & 1 \end{bmatrix} = \begin{bmatrix} 11 & 2c - 1 & 0 \\ -8 & 2 & 3 \\ 0 & 3g - 2 & 1 \end{bmatrix}$

21. $\begin{bmatrix} 4c & 2 - d & 5 \\ -3 & -1 & 2 \\ 0 & -10 & 15 \end{bmatrix} = \begin{bmatrix} 2c + 5 & 4d & g \\ -3 & h & f - g \\ 0 & -4c & 15 \end{bmatrix}$

22. Sports The modern pentathlon is a grueling all-day competition. Each member of a team competes in five events: target shooting, fencing, swimming, horseback riding, and cross-country running. Here are scores for the U.S. women at the 2004 Olympic Games.
a. Write two 5×1 matrices to represent each woman's scores for each event.
b. Find the total score for each athlete.

U.S. Women's Pentathlon Scores, 2004 Olympics

Event	Anita Allen	Mary Beth Iagorashvili
Shooting	952	760
Fencing	720	832
Swimming	1108	1252
Riding	1172	1144
Running	1044	1064

Source: Athens 2004 Olympic Games

23. Data Analysis Refer to the table.
a. Add two matrices to find the total number of people participating in each activity.
b. Subtract two matrices to find the difference between the numbers of males and females in each activity.
c. Reasoning In part (b), does the order of the matrices matter? Explain.

24. Writing Given a matrix *A*, explain how to find a matrix *B* such that $A + B = 0$.

U.S. Participation (millions) in Selected Leisure Activities

Activity	Male	Female
Movies	59.2	65.4
Exercise Programs	54.3	59.0
Sports Events	40.5	31.1
Home Improvement	45.4	41.8

Source: U.S. National Endowment for the Arts

SAT/ACT

25. What is the sum $\begin{bmatrix} 5 & 7 & 3 \\ -1 & 0 & -4 \end{bmatrix} + \begin{bmatrix} -7 & 4 & 2 \\ 1 & -2 & -3 \end{bmatrix}$?

Ⓐ The matrices cannot be added.

Ⓒ $\begin{bmatrix} 12 & 3 & 1 \\ -2 & 2 & -1 \end{bmatrix}$

Ⓑ $\begin{bmatrix} -2 & 11 & 5 \\ 0 & -2 & -7 \end{bmatrix}$

Ⓓ $\begin{bmatrix} -35 & 28 & 6 \\ -1 & 0 & 12 \end{bmatrix}$

26. Which arithmetic sequence includes the term 27?

I. $a_1 = 7, a_n = a_{n-1} + 5$ II. $a_n = 3 + 4(n - 1)$ III. $a_n = 57 - 6n$

Ⓕ I only   Ⓖ I and II only   Ⓗ II and III only   Ⓘ I, II, and III

27. Which equation is graphed at the right?

Ⓐ $(x + 3)^2 + (y - 2)^2 = 25$

Ⓑ $(x - 2)^2 + (y + 3)^2 = 25$

Ⓒ $(x + 2)^2 + (y - 3)^2 = 25$

Ⓓ $(x - 3)^2 + (y + 2)^2 = 25$

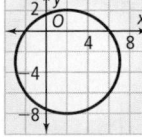

Short Response

28. For a daily airline flight to Denver, the numbers of checked pieces of luggage are normally distributed with a mean of 380 and a standard deviation of 20. What number of checked pieces of luggage is 3 standard deviations above the mean?

Mixed Review

A set of data with a mean of 62 and a standard deviation of 5 is normally distributed. Find the percent of data within each interval.   ← **See Lesson 11-9.**

29. from 57 to 67   **30.** greater than 52   **31.** from 62 to 72

Find the slope and y-intercept of each line.   ← **See Lesson 2-3.**

32. $y = 2x - 6$ **33.** $3y = 6 + 2x$ **34.** $y = 5x$

Get Ready!   To prepare for Lesson 12-2, do Exercises 35 and 36.

Find each sum.   ← **See Lesson 12-1.**

35. $\begin{bmatrix} 3 & 5 \\ 2 & 8 \end{bmatrix} + \begin{bmatrix} 3 & 5 \\ 2 & 8 \end{bmatrix} + \begin{bmatrix} 3 & 5 \\ 2 & 8 \end{bmatrix}$

36. $\begin{bmatrix} 4 \\ 7 \end{bmatrix} + \begin{bmatrix} -4 \\ 7 \end{bmatrix} + \begin{bmatrix} -4 \\ 7 \end{bmatrix} + \begin{bmatrix} -4 \\ 7 \end{bmatrix} + \begin{bmatrix} -4 \\ 7 \end{bmatrix}$

Standardized Test Prep

25. B

26. I

27. B

35. $\begin{bmatrix} 9 & 15 \\ 6 & 24 \end{bmatrix}$

36. $\begin{bmatrix} -20 \\ 35 \end{bmatrix}$

28. [2] 440 pieces of luggage; since 3 standard deviations is $3 \cdot 20 = 60$ pieces of luggage, 3 standard deviations above the mean is $380 + 60 = 440$ pieces of luggage.

[1] incomplete explanation OR one computational error

Mixed Review

29. 68%

30. 97.5%

31. 47.5%

32. 2, −6

33. $\frac{2}{3}$, 2

34. 5, 0

Additional Instructional Support

Algebra 2 Companion

Students can use the **Algebra 2 Companion** worktext (4 pages) as you teach the lesson. Use the Companion to support

- New Vocabulary
- Key Concepts
- Got It for each Problem
- Lesson Check

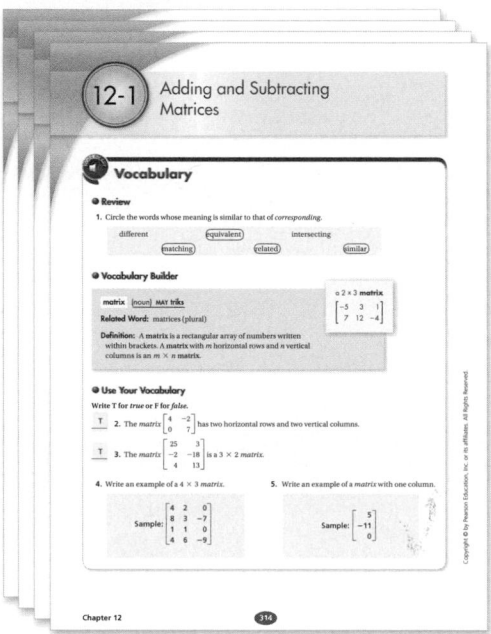

ELL Support

Focus on Communication Although few ideas are simple for every student to learn, the concepts presented in this lesson are fairly elementary.

Explain that rows go across and columns go up and down. Ask: How many rows of desks are in the classroom? How many columns of desks are in the classroom?

Have students draw a rectangular matrix of seating positions in the classroom and label it with position numbers similar to the matrix in the Take Note box on p. 772. Make sure the positions are labeled with numbers in the order row-column.

Have students ask each other (or the whole group) questions about the positions on their matrix, such as,

- How many rows are in the matrix?
- Which student sits at position 23? (Note: say "23" as "two three" not "twenty-three.")
- At which position is [student's name] sitting?
- What are the dimensions of the matrix?

5 Assess & Remediate

Lesson Quiz

1. Given $A = \begin{bmatrix} 2 & -4 \\ 0 & 3 \end{bmatrix}$ and $B = \begin{bmatrix} 5 & 6 \\ 7 & 8 \end{bmatrix}$, what is $B - A$?

2. What is the sum of the matrices $\begin{bmatrix} 0 & 0 \\ 0 & 0 \end{bmatrix}$ and $\begin{bmatrix} 2 & -4 \\ -4 & 8 \end{bmatrix}$?

3. Do you UNDERSTAND? What values of x and y make the equation true?

$$\begin{bmatrix} 2x - 1 & 0 \\ -3y & 4 \end{bmatrix} = \begin{bmatrix} 1 & 0 \\ y + 2 & 4 \end{bmatrix}$$

ANSWERS TO LESSON QUIZ

1. $\begin{bmatrix} 3 & 10 \\ 7 & 5 \end{bmatrix}$

2. $\begin{bmatrix} 2 & -4 \\ -4 & 8 \end{bmatrix}$

3. $x = 1$; $y = -0.5$

PRESCRIPTION FOR REMEDIATION

Use the student work on the Lesson Quiz to prescribe a differentiated review assignment:

Points	Differentiated Remediation
0–2	Intervention
3	On-level
4	Extension

PowerAlgebra.com

5 Assess & Remediate

Assign the Lesson Quiz. Appropriate intervention, practice, or enrichment is automatically generated based on student performance.

Intervention

- **Reteaching** (2 pages) Provides reteaching and practice exercises for the key lesson concepts. Use with struggling students or absent students.

- **English Language Learner Support** Helps students develop and reinforce mathematical vocabulary and key concepts.

All-in-One Resources/Online
Reteaching

12-1 Reteaching
Adding and Subtracting Matrices

All-in-One Resources/Online
English Language Learner Support

12-1 ELL Support
Adding and Subtracting Matrices

Differentiated Remediation *continued*

On-Level

- **Practice** (2 pages) Provides extra practice for each lesson. For more challenging practice exercises, use the Form G Practice pages found in the All-in-One Teaching Resources and online.

- **Think About a Plan** Helps students develop specific problem-solving skills and strategies by providing scaffolded guiding questions.

- **Standardized Test Prep** Focuses on all major exercises, all major question types, and helps students prepare for the high-stakes assessments.

Extension

- **Enrichment** Provides students with interesting problems and activities that extend the concepts of the lesson.

- **Activities, Games, and Puzzles** Worksheets that can be used for concepts development, enrichment, and for fun!

Student Companion/All-in-One Resources/Online
Practice page 1

12-1 Practice — Form K
Adding and Subtracting Matrices

Find each sum or difference.
To start, add or subtract corresponding elements.

(worksheet exercises 1–10)

10. **Error Analysis** Maria added $\begin{bmatrix} 5 & 9 \\ 1 & -3 \end{bmatrix} + \begin{bmatrix} -2 & -5 \\ 6 & 3 \end{bmatrix}$ and found a sum of $\begin{bmatrix} 0 & 7 \\ 4 & 3 \end{bmatrix}$. What error did Maria make, and what is the correct sum? Maria added corresponding elements in the two matrices but did not put them in the correct place in the sum; $\begin{bmatrix} 3 & 4 \\ 7 & 0 \end{bmatrix}$.

Student Companion/All-in-One Resources/Online
Practice page 2

12-1 Practice (continued) — Form K
Adding and Subtracting Matrices

Find each sum.
(exercises 11–13)

Find the value of each variable.
(exercises 14–17)

18. **Writing** Describe the Commutative and Associative Properties of Matrix Addition. How are these properties similar to the Commutative and Associative Properties of Real-Number Addition? The Commutative Property of Matrix Addition states that matrices can be added in any order and the sum will remain the same. The Associative Property of Matrix Addition states that matrices can be grouped in any way and the sum will remain the same. The properties of matrix addition are the same as those of real numbers, except the properties apply to the elements of a matrix.

19. **Reasoning** Is it possible to find the value of x in the following equation? Why or why not? $\begin{bmatrix} 2x & -1 \\ 4 & -5 \end{bmatrix} = \begin{bmatrix} 5x - 4 & -1 \\ 4 & -5 \end{bmatrix}$ Yes; the variable appears in the same pair of corresponding elements. Solving the equation $2x = 5x - 4$ gives the answer $x = \frac{4}{3}$.

All-in-One Resources/Online
Enrichment

12-1 Enrichment
Adding and Subtracting Matrices

Transpose is another operation that you can apply to a matrix. You form the transpose of a matrix by switching the rows for columns. For example, matrix A^T below is the transpose of matrix A.

$A = \begin{bmatrix} -1 & 3 & 0 \\ 5 & -6 & 2 \\ 3 & -3 & 1 \end{bmatrix}$ $A^T = \begin{bmatrix} -1 & 5 & 3 \\ 3 & -6 & -3 \\ 0 & 2 & 1 \end{bmatrix}$

1. Write the transpose of matrix $R = \begin{bmatrix} 5 & 11 \\ -4 & 1 \end{bmatrix}$. $R^T = \begin{bmatrix} 5 & -4 \\ 11 & 1 \end{bmatrix}$

In 1934, an Indian student named S. P. Sundaram constructed an interesting matrix. The first row in his matrix was 4, 7, 10, 13, 16, and so on. He then created the first column by transposing this row.

2. What is the pattern used to generate each number in the first row? add 3 to the element to the left

3. Each successive row increases by the next odd number, so the numbers in row two grow by adding 5, the numbers in row three grow by adding 7, and so on. Fill in the remaining elements of this matrix.

$\begin{bmatrix} 4 & 7 & 10 & 13 \\ 7 & 12 & 17 & 22 \\ 10 & 17 & 24 & 31 \\ 13 & 22 & 31 & 40 \end{bmatrix}$

This matrix is called the sieve of Sundaram and is used to find all of the prime numbers up to a certain integer.

4. Choose a number in the sieve of Sundaram. Double it and add one. Is your final number prime? Try several more numbers. Answers may vary. Sample: 7, 2(7) + 1 = 15; for the chosen number, the final number is not prime.

5. Choose a number that is not in the sieve of Sundaram. Double it and add one. Try several numbers. Are your final numbers prime? Answers may vary. Sample: 11, 2(11) + 1 = 23; yes, the final numbers are all prime for the chosen numbers.

6. Explain how the sieve of Sundaram helps determine if a number will be prime or not. Answers may vary. Sample: If a number n does not appear in the sieve of Sundaram, then $2n + 1$ is prime.

Student Companion/All-in-One Resources/Online
Think About a Plan

12-1 Think About a Plan
Adding and Subtracting Matrices

Data Analysis Refer to the table.
a. Find the total number of people participating in each activity.
b. Find the difference between the numbers of males and females in each activity.
c. **Reasoning** In part (b), does the order of the matrices matter? Explain.

U.S. Participation in Selected Leisure Activities (millions)

Activity	Male	Female
Movies	59.2	65.4
Exercise Programs	54.3	59.0
Sports Events	40.5	31.1
Home Improvement	45.4	41.8

Source: U.S. National Endowment for the Arts

1. Write matrices to show the information from the table.
$M = \begin{bmatrix} 59.2 \\ 54.3 \\ 40.5 \\ 45.4 \end{bmatrix}$ $F = \begin{bmatrix} 65.4 \\ 59.0 \\ 31.1 \\ 41.8 \end{bmatrix}$

2. Write a matrix equation to find the number of people, in millions, participating in each activity. $T = M + F$

3. Solve the matrix equation. How many million people participate in each activity?
$T = \begin{bmatrix} 124.6 \\ 113.3 \\ 71.6 \\ 87.2 \end{bmatrix}$ Movies 124.6 Exercise Programs 113.3 Sports Events 71.6 Home Improvement 87.2

4. Write a matrix equation to find the difference, in millions, between the number of males and females in each activity. $T = M - F$

5. Solve the matrix equation. What is the difference, in millions, between the number of males and females in each activity?
$T = \begin{bmatrix} -6.2 \\ -4.7 \\ 9.4 \\ 3.6 \end{bmatrix}$ Movies -6.2 Exercise Programs -4.7 Sports Events 9.4 Home Improvement 3.6

6. Does the order of the matrices matter? Explain. Yes. Answers may vary. Sample: If you subtract matrix M from matrix F, then you will get the difference, in millions, between the number of females and males in each activity, which will change the signs of all elements in the matrix.

Student Companion/All-in-One Resources/Online
Standardized Test Prep

12-1 Standardized Test Prep
Adding and Subtracting Matrices

Multiple Choice
For Exercises 1–4, choose the correct letter.

1. What matrix is equal to the difference $\begin{bmatrix} 5 & 9 & -3 \\ 6 & -2 & 1 \end{bmatrix} - \begin{bmatrix} 6 & 4 & 2 \\ 0 & 3 & 5 \end{bmatrix}$? C

2. Which matrix is equivalent to X in the equation $\begin{bmatrix} 4 & 0 \\ 1 & -2 \end{bmatrix} + X = \begin{bmatrix} -2 & 0 \\ 1 & 4 \end{bmatrix}$? F

3. Which matrix is equivalent to P in the equation $\begin{bmatrix} 7 & 8 \\ 9 & 10 \\ 11 & 12 \end{bmatrix} - P = \begin{bmatrix} 0 & 0 \\ 0 & 0 \\ 0 & 0 \end{bmatrix}$? D

4. Let $R + S = \begin{bmatrix} 0 & 0 & 0 & 0 \\ 0 & 0 & 0 & 0 \end{bmatrix}$. If $R = \begin{bmatrix} -3 & 2 & 9 \\ 7 & 6 & -4 \end{bmatrix}$, which matrix is equivalent to S? H

Short Response

5. If $\begin{bmatrix} 8 & 2x - 1 \\ 2y + 1 & 3 \end{bmatrix} = \begin{bmatrix} 8 & -7 \\ y & -x \end{bmatrix}$, what values of x and y make the equation true? Show your work.
[2] $2x - 1 = -7$ $2y + 1 = y$ $3 = -x$
  $2x = -6$ $y = -1$ $-3 = x$
  $x = -3$
  The solution is $x = -3, y = -1$.
[1] partially incorrect or incomplete work shown
[0] incorrect answers and no work shown OR no answers given

Online Teacher Resource Center
Activities, Games, and Puzzles

12-1 Activity: Board With Matrices
Adding and Subtracting Matrices

For this activity, you will need some markers and highlighters in different colors, and a large poster board or sheet of paper. Your teacher may also provide colored cellophane, glitter, stencils, paste, and other art supplies.

- On your poster board, make a large and clear presentation of how to add and subtract two matrices. Use an example from the textbook or write one of your own.
- Be inventive in your use of artistic devices. For example, in your addition of two matrices, you could draw boxes and other shapes around corresponding matrix elements.

$\begin{bmatrix} 3 & 2 \\ -1 & 4 \end{bmatrix} + \begin{bmatrix} 1 & 0 \\ 2 & 5 \end{bmatrix} = \begin{bmatrix} 4 & 2 \\ 1 & 9 \end{bmatrix}$

- Or you could choose a color scheme. This means that in your presentation of adding two matrices, you could highlight corresponding pairs of addends in the same color. Or you could write an explanation of each matrix operation in your own words and color-code each step.
- These are only a few suggestions. The use of different colors is only one artistic device; the use of different lettering is another. Choose an artistic device that will help classmates follow the math and see patterns they might otherwise miss. Use whatever artistic device works best for you.

Your teacher can display all of the posters when everyone has finished. Select the poster that is your favorite. If there is enough time left in class, your teacher can start a discussion by calling on students. Be prepared to discuss and explain why you chose your favorite poster. Comment not only on the artistic elements, but also on mathematical accuracy and any other element you think is important. Check students' work.

Guided Instruction

PURPOSE To use a graphing calculator to work with matrices

PROCESS Students will

- enter and edit matrices in their graphing calculators.
- perform simple operations on matrices using a graphing calculator.

DISCUSS To enter the matrix correctly in Example 1, point out that on some graphing calculators the negative sign key is different from the subtraction key. This is the key used when entering numbers in the matrix.

The keystrokes to move from screen to screen and within a screen are not always apparent. Encourage students to try several times. If they get stuck, they can use the QUIT feature to return to the start screen and try again.

Make sure students enter [B] in the EDIT matrix menu when entering B in Example 2. They should not re-edit the matrix they entered in Example 1, although they should use similar steps.

Example 1

> **Q** What do you think will happen if you add A and A?
> [**Answers will vary. Sample: A + A will be a matrix of the same size but with each element doubled.**]

Example 2

> **Q** What do you think $A - B + (B - A)$ will equal? Check your answer on your calculator.
> [$A - B + (B - A)$ **should equal the zero matrix with 3 rows and 2 columns of zeros.**]

Concept Byte

For Use With Lesson 12-1

TECHNOLOGY

Working with Matrices

You can use a graphing calculator to work with matrices. First you need to know how to enter a matrix into the calculator.

Example 1

Enter matrix $A = \begin{bmatrix} -3 & 4 \\ 7 & -5 \\ 0 & -2 \end{bmatrix}$ into your graphing calculator.

Select the **EDIT** option of the (matrix) feature to edit matrix **[A]**. Specify a 3×2 matrix by pressing ③ ⟨enter⟩ ② ⟨enter⟩. Enter the matrix elements one row at a time, pressing ⟨enter⟩ after each element. Then use the ⟨quit⟩ feature to return to the main screen.

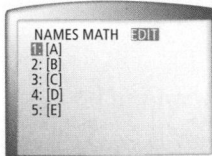 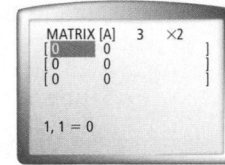 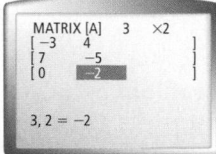

Example 2

Given $A = \begin{bmatrix} -3 & 4 \\ 7 & -5 \\ 0 & -2 \end{bmatrix}$ and $B = \begin{bmatrix} 10 & -7 \\ 4 & -3 \\ -12 & 11 \end{bmatrix}$, find $A + B$ and $A - B$.

Enter both matrices in the calculator. Use the **NAMES** option of the (matrix) feature to select each matrix. Press ⟨enter⟩ to see the sum. Repeat the corresponding steps to find the difference $A - B$.

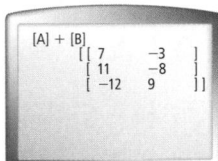

Exercises

Find each sum or difference.

1. $\begin{bmatrix} 0 & -3 \\ 5 & -7 \end{bmatrix} - \begin{bmatrix} -5 & 3 \\ 4 & 10 \end{bmatrix}$

2. $\begin{bmatrix} 3 & 5 & -7 \\ 0 & -2 & 0 \end{bmatrix} - \begin{bmatrix} -1 & 6 & 2 \\ -9 & 4 & 0 \end{bmatrix}$

3. $\begin{bmatrix} 3 \\ 5 \end{bmatrix} - \begin{bmatrix} -6 \\ 7 \end{bmatrix}$

4. $\begin{bmatrix} 3 & 5 & -8 \end{bmatrix} + \begin{bmatrix} -6 & 4 & 1 \end{bmatrix}$

5. $\begin{bmatrix} 17 & 8 & 0 \\ 3 & -5 & 2 \end{bmatrix} - \begin{bmatrix} 4 & 6 & 5 \\ 2 & -2 & 9 \end{bmatrix}$

6. $\begin{bmatrix} -9 & 6 & 4 \end{bmatrix} + \begin{bmatrix} -3 & 8 & 4 \end{bmatrix}$

Answers

Exercises

1. $\begin{bmatrix} 5 & -6 \\ 1 & -17 \end{bmatrix}$

2. $\begin{bmatrix} 4 & -1 & -9 \\ 9 & -6 & 0 \end{bmatrix}$

3. $\begin{bmatrix} 9 \\ -2 \end{bmatrix}$

4. $\begin{bmatrix} -3 & 9 & -7 \end{bmatrix}$

5. $\begin{bmatrix} 13 & 2 & -5 \\ 1 & -3 & -7 \end{bmatrix}$

6. $\begin{bmatrix} -12 & 14 & 8 \end{bmatrix}$

12-2 Matrix Multiplication

Objective To multiply matrices using scalar and matrix multiplication

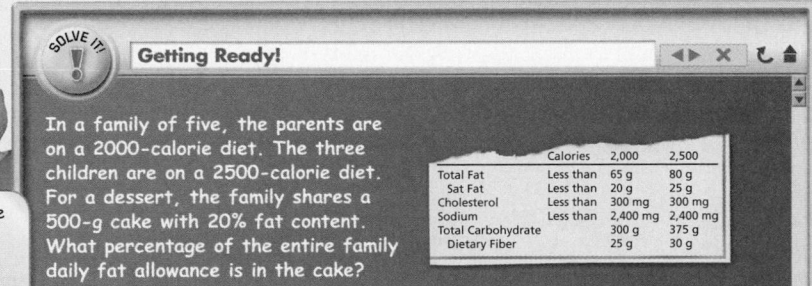

SOLVE IT

Getting Ready!

In a family of five, the parents are on a 2000-calorie diet. The three children are on a 2500-calorie diet. For a dessert, the family shares a 500-g cake with 20% fat content. What percentage of the entire family daily fat allowance is in the cake?

The values in the chart are the recommended 100% daily allowances.

		Calories	2,000	2,500
Total Fat		Less than	65 g	80 g
Sat Fat		Less than	20 g	25 g
Cholesterol		Less than	300 mg	300 mg
Sodium		Less than	2,400 mg	2,400 mg
Total Carbohydrate			300 g	375 g
Dietary Fiber			25 g	30 g

Lesson Vocabulary
• scalar
• scalar multiplication

In the Solve It, you may have found the sum of products. Finding the sum of products is essential to matrix multiplication.

Focus Question How do you find the product of two matrices?

Before you learn how to multiply two matrices, you should learn a simpler type of multiplication. This type of multiplication allows you to *scale*, or resize, the elements of a matrix.

$$3\begin{bmatrix} 5 & -1 \\ 3 & 7 \end{bmatrix} = \begin{bmatrix} 3(5) & 3(-1) \\ 3(3) & 3(7) \end{bmatrix} = \begin{bmatrix} 15 & -3 \\ 9 & 21 \end{bmatrix}$$

The real number factor (such as 3 in the example above) is a **scalar**. Multiplication of a matrix A by a scalar c is **scalar multiplication**. To find the resulting matrix cA, you multiply each element of A by c.

Hint
This process is similar to the Distributive Property of Real Numbers.

take note

Key Concept Scalar Multiplication

To multiply a matrix by a scalar c, multiply each element of the matrix by c.

$$A = \begin{bmatrix} a_{11} & a_{12} & a_{13} \\ a_{21} & a_{22} & a_{23} \end{bmatrix} \quad cA = \begin{bmatrix} ca_{11} & ca_{12} & ca_{13} \\ ca_{21} & ca_{22} & ca_{23} \end{bmatrix}$$

---

1 Interactive Learning

Solve It!
PURPOSE To use information from a table to solve a percentage problem
PROCESS Students may calculate the entire fat allowance for the family and the fat content of the cake and then divide the fat content of the cake by the total fat allowance to find the percentage.

FACILITATE

Q Do you need to know how much cake each person had? Explain. **[No; even if the pieces were not the same size, the total grams of fat of the consumed 500 g cake will remain the same.]**

Q What expression will calculate the total grams of fat in the cake? **[500 × 0.2]**

Q What expression will calculate the total grams of fat the family is allowed to consume? Explain. **[2 · 65 + 3 · 80; there are two parents who are each allowed 65g and three children who each are allowed 80g.]**

ANSWER See Solve It in Answers on next page.
CONNECT THE MATH In the Solve It, students multiply elements of the table by a number as a step to solve the problem. In the lesson, students will multiply elements of a matrix by a scalar.

2 Guided Instruction

Take Note

Q How is scalar multiplication different from the Distributive Property of Real Numbers? **[Scalar multiplication involves only multiplication. The Distributive Property involves multiplication and addition.]**

12-2 Preparing to Teach

BIG idea Data Representation   **UbD**

ESSENTIAL UNDERSTANDINGS
• To multiply a matrix by a scalar, multiply each element of the matrix by the scalar.
• If A is an $m \times n$ matrix, and B is an $n \times p$ matrix, then AB is an $m \times p$ matrix.

Math Background
It is important to clearly differentiate between the two different kinds of multiplication with matrices.

Scalar multiplication is the product of a constant (called a scalar) and a matrix. Each element of the matrix is multiplied by the scalar. It can be thought of as changing the scale of the matrix.
• Scalar multiplication does not change the dimensions of the matrix. The product of a scalar and an $m \times n$ matrix is an $m \times n$ matrix.
• The product of a matrix and a scalar always exists.
• Scalar multiplication is commutative.

Matrix multiplication is the product of two matrices. To find element c_{ij}, each element in the ith row of the first matrix is multiplied by the corresponding element in the jth row of the second matrix. The sum of the products is c_{ij}.
• Matrix multiplication changes the dimensions of non-square matrices. The product of an $m \times n$ matrix by an $n \times p$ matrix is an $m \times p$ matrix.
• The product only exists if the number of columns of the first matrix equals the number of rows of the second.
• Therefore, matrix multiplication is not commutative.

Support Student Learning
Use the **Algebra 2 Companion** to engage and support students during instruction. See Lesson Resources at the end of this lesson for details.

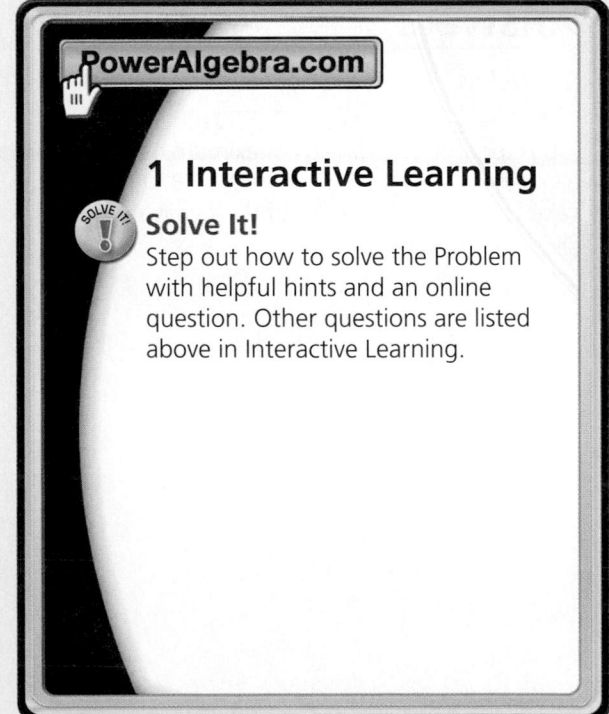

PowerAlgebra.com

1 Interactive Learning

SOLVE IT

Solve It!
Step out how to solve the Problem with helpful hints and an online question. Other questions are listed above in Interactive Learning.

Problem 1

Q Do you have to follow the order of operations with matrices? Explain using Problem 1. **[Yes; in Problem 1, you have to multiply before adding.]**

Got It?

Q Does it matter whether you multiply B by 2 or -2? Explain. **[No; but if you multiply B by 2, you will have to subtract B from A, and if you multiply B by -2, you will have to add A and B.]**

Take Note

EXTENSION

Q Does the Commutative Property hold for scalar multiplication? Explain. **[Yes; multiplication is commutative, and for scalar multiplication, you are simply multiplying many elements by a number, so order does not matter.]**

Problem 2

Q Are the steps you use to solve for matrix X any different than the steps you used when solving simple equations of one variable? Explain. **[No; you still use inverse operations, addition, subtraction, multiplication, division, and simplification to solve for the unknown variable.]**

Got It?

Q What steps should you take and in what order to solve the equation? **[Sample: Multiply the matrix by the scalar and then use the additive inverse operation to isolate 3X. Finally, multiply each side by $\frac{1}{3}$ to solve for matrix X.]**

Q What will be the dimensions of the solution for matrix X? **[2 × 2]**

Problem 1 Using Scalar Products

If $A = \begin{bmatrix} 2 & 8 & -3 \\ -1 & 5 & 2 \end{bmatrix}$ and $B = \begin{bmatrix} -1 & 0 & 5 \\ 0 & 3 & -2 \end{bmatrix}$, what is $4A + 3B$?

Substitute matrices A and B.
$$4A + 3B = 4\begin{bmatrix} 2 & 8 & -3 \\ -1 & 5 & 2 \end{bmatrix} + 3\begin{bmatrix} -1 & 0 & 5 \\ 0 & 3 & -2 \end{bmatrix}$$

Multiply each element of A by 4.
Multiply each element of B by 3.
$$= \begin{bmatrix} 8 & 32 & -12 \\ -4 & 20 & 8 \end{bmatrix} + \begin{bmatrix} -3 & 0 & 15 \\ 0 & 9 & -6 \end{bmatrix}$$

Add corresponding elements.
$$= \begin{bmatrix} 5 & 32 & 3 \\ -4 & 29 & 2 \end{bmatrix}$$

Think
What operation should you do first?
You should first multiply by the scalars, 4 and 3.

✓ **Got It? 1.** Using matrices A and B from Problem 1, what is $3A - 2B$?

 Properties **Scalar Multiplication**

If A and B are $m \times n$ matrices, c and d are scalars, and O is the $m \times n$ zero matrix, then

Example	Property
cA is an $m \times n$ matrix	**Closure Property**
$(cd)A = c(dA)$	**Associative Property of Multiplication**
$c(A + B) = cA + cB$ $(c + d)A = cA + dA$	**Distributive Properties**
$1 \cdot A = A$	**Multiplicative Identity Property**
$0 \cdot A = O$ and $cO = O$	**Multiplicative Properties of Zero**

Problem 2 Solving a Matrix Equation With Scalars

What is the solution of $2X + 3\begin{bmatrix} 2 & -1 \\ 3 & 4 \end{bmatrix} = \begin{bmatrix} 8 & 5 \\ 11 & 0 \end{bmatrix}$?

Multiply by the scalar 3.
$$2X + \begin{bmatrix} 6 & -3 \\ 9 & 12 \end{bmatrix} = \begin{bmatrix} 8 & 5 \\ 11 & 0 \end{bmatrix}$$

Use the Subtraction Property of Equality to isolate the variable matrix.
$$2X = \begin{bmatrix} 8 & 5 \\ 11 & 0 \end{bmatrix} - \begin{bmatrix} 6 & -3 \\ 9 & 12 \end{bmatrix}$$

Subtract corresponding elements.
$$2X = \begin{bmatrix} 2 & 8 \\ 2 & -12 \end{bmatrix}$$

Multiply each side by $\frac{1}{2}$ and simplify.
$$X = \frac{1}{2}\begin{bmatrix} 2 & 8 \\ 2 & -12 \end{bmatrix} = \begin{bmatrix} 1 & 4 \\ 1 & -6 \end{bmatrix}$$

Think
Where have you seen problems that look like this before?
You saw problems like this when you solved one variable equations like $2x + 3(5) = 20$.

✓ **Got It? 2.** What is the solution of $3X - 2\begin{bmatrix} -1 & 5 \\ 7 & 0 \end{bmatrix} = \begin{bmatrix} 17 & -13 \\ -7 & 0 \end{bmatrix}$?

Answers

Solve It!

27%; the cake contains $(0.2)(500 \text{ g}) = 100$ g of fat. Altogether, the family's maximum daily allowance of fat is $2(65) + 3(80) = 370$ g. The cake contains $\frac{100}{370} = 27\%$ of the family's daily allowance of fat.

Got It?

1. $\begin{bmatrix} 8 & 24 & -19 \\ -3 & 9 & 10 \end{bmatrix}$

2. $\begin{bmatrix} 5 & -1 \\ \frac{7}{3} & 0 \end{bmatrix}$

PowerAlgebra.com

2 Guided Instruction

 Each Problem is worked out and supported online.

Problem 1
Using Scalar Products

Problem 2
Solving a Matrix Equation With Scalars
Animated

Problem 3
Multiplying Matrices
Animated

Problem 4
Applying Matrix Multiplication
Animated

Problem 5
Determining Whether Product Matrices Exist

Support in Algebra 2 Companion
• Vocabulary
• Key Concepts
• Got It?

Not all pairs of matrices can be multiplied to obtain a product. If you *can* multiply a pair of matrices, the product is also a matrix.

 **Key Concept** Matrix Multiplication

To find element c_{ij} of the product matrix AB, multiply each element in the ith row of A by the corresponding element in the jth column of B. Then add the products.

$$AB = \begin{bmatrix} a_{11} & a_{12} \\ a_{21} & a_{22} \end{bmatrix}\begin{bmatrix} b_{11} & b_{12} \\ b_{21} & b_{22} \end{bmatrix} = \begin{bmatrix} a_{11}b_{11} + a_{12}b_{21} & a_{11}b_{12} + a_{12}b_{22} \\ a_{21}b_{11} + a_{22}b_{21} & a_{21}b_{12} + a_{22}b_{22} \end{bmatrix}$$

 Problem 3 Multiplying Matrices

If $A = \begin{bmatrix} 2 & 1 \\ -3 & 0 \end{bmatrix}$ and $B = \begin{bmatrix} -1 & 3 \\ 0 & 4 \end{bmatrix}$, what is AB?

Think
What relationship must exist between the numbers of elements in a row of A and a column of B?
They must be equal.

Step 1 Multiply the elements in the first row of A by the elements in the first column of B. Add the products, and place the sum in the first row, first column of AB.

$$\begin{bmatrix} 2 & 1 \\ -3 & 0 \end{bmatrix}\begin{bmatrix} -1 & 3 \\ 0 & 4 \end{bmatrix} = \begin{bmatrix} -2 & \\ & \end{bmatrix}$$ $2(-1) + 1(0) = -2$

Step 2 Multiply the elements in the first row of A by the elements in the second column of B. Add the products, and place the sum in the first row, second column of AB.

$$\begin{bmatrix} 2 & 1 \\ -3 & 0 \end{bmatrix}\begin{bmatrix} -1 & 3 \\ 0 & 4 \end{bmatrix} = \begin{bmatrix} -2 & 10 \\ & \end{bmatrix}.$$ $2(3) + 1(4) = 10$

Step 3 Multiply the elements in the second row of A by the elements in the first column of B. Add the products, and place the sum in the second row, first column of AB.

$$\begin{bmatrix} 2 & 1 \\ -3 & 0 \end{bmatrix}\begin{bmatrix} -1 & 3 \\ 0 & 4 \end{bmatrix} = \begin{bmatrix} -2 & 10 \\ 3 & \end{bmatrix}$$ $(-3)(-1) + 0(0) = 3$

Step 4 Multiply the elements in the second row of A by the elements in the second column of B. Add the products, and place the sum in the second row, second column of AB.

$$\begin{bmatrix} 2 & 1 \\ -3 & 0 \end{bmatrix}\begin{bmatrix} -1 & 3 \\ 0 & 4 \end{bmatrix} = \begin{bmatrix} -2 & 10 \\ 3 & -9 \end{bmatrix}$$ $(-3)(3) + 0(4) = -9$

The product $\begin{bmatrix} 2 & 1 \\ -3 & 0 \end{bmatrix}\begin{bmatrix} -1 & 3 \\ 0 & 4 \end{bmatrix}$ is $\begin{bmatrix} -2 & 10 \\ 3 & -9 \end{bmatrix}$.

Got It? **3.** If $A = \begin{bmatrix} 2 & -1 \\ 3 & 4 \end{bmatrix}$ and $B = \begin{bmatrix} -3 & 1 \\ 0 & 2 \end{bmatrix}$, what are the following products?

a. AB **b.** BA
c. Reasoning Is matrix multiplication commutative? Explain.

Take Note

Q In the final product of two matrices, where would the result of multiplying row two by column one be located? **[in row two, column one]**

Problem 3

Q Why do the number of elements in each row of the first matrix have to equal the number of elements in each column of the second matrix in order to multiply the two matrices? **[each row element of the first matrix must be multiplied by a corresponding element in each column of the second matrix.]**

Q Is it possible for two matrices A and B to exist so that AB has an answer and BA does not? Explain. **[Yes; if the number of elements in each row of matrix A equals the number of elements in each column of matrix B, but the number of elements in each row of matrix B does not equal the number of elements in each column of matrix A. For example, A is 2×3 and B is 3×3.]**

Got It?

Q What would have to be true about AB and BA for multiplication of A and B to be commutative? **[AB would have to equal BA.]**

EXTENSION

Q If matrices A and B were exactly the same and could be multiplied, would $AB = BA$? Explain. **[Yes; the dimensions would allow for multiplication, and the elements would be identical in both products.]**

Additional Problems

1. If $A = \begin{bmatrix} 4 & -3 \\ 1 & 2 \end{bmatrix}$ and $B = \begin{bmatrix} 7 & 3 \\ -2 & -4 \end{bmatrix}$, what is $3A - B$?

ANSWER $\begin{bmatrix} 5 & -12 \\ 5 & 10 \end{bmatrix}$

2. What is the solution of $-2\begin{bmatrix} 2 & 3 \\ 1 & 0 \end{bmatrix} + 2T = \begin{bmatrix} -2 & -14 \\ -2 & 6 \end{bmatrix}$?

ANSWER $\begin{bmatrix} 1 & -4 \\ 0 & 3 \end{bmatrix}$

3. If $V = \begin{bmatrix} -4 & 0 \\ 3 & 5 \end{bmatrix}$ and $W = \begin{bmatrix} 2 & 2 \\ -1 & 3 \end{bmatrix}$, what is VW?

ANSWER $\begin{bmatrix} -8 & -8 \\ 1 & 21 \end{bmatrix}$

4. A library has three printers. The cost of printing from printer A is 3 cents per page, from printer B is 6 cents per page, and from printer C is 14 cents per page. During October and November, the librarian recorded the number of pages printed on each printer, as shown in the table. Using matrix multiplication, what was the monthly cost of operating the printers for October and November?

	Oct	Nov
Printer A	584	598
Printer B	549	610
Printer C	159	185

ANSWER October: $72.72
November: $80.44

5. Does either product AB or BA exist?

$A = \begin{bmatrix} -5 & 0 \\ 3 & -2 \end{bmatrix}$

$B = \begin{bmatrix} -2 & 1 & -1 \\ 4 & 2 & 5 \end{bmatrix}$

ANSWER AB is a 2×3 matrix; BA does not exist.

Answers

Got It? (continued)

3. a. $\begin{bmatrix} -6 & 0 \\ -9 & 11 \end{bmatrix}$

b. $\begin{bmatrix} -3 & 7 \\ 6 & 8 \end{bmatrix}$

c. No; explanations may vary. Sample: For the matrices in parts (a) and (b), $AB = \begin{bmatrix} -6 & 0 \\ -9 & 11 \end{bmatrix}$ and $BA = \begin{bmatrix} -3 & 7 \\ 6 & 8 \end{bmatrix}$, so $AB \neq BA$.

Problem 4

Q In matrix S, how would you label each row? How would you label each row of the product matrix? **[Both would be labeled with the team names.]**

Q In matrix P, how would you label the column? How would you label the column of the product matrix? **[Both would be labeled with point values.]**

Q How would you label the columns of matrix S and the rows of matrix P? **[Both would be labeled with score type.]**

Got It?

Q What matrix would represent the total count of types of scores for the 1994 and 2006 players?
$$\begin{bmatrix} 0 & 36 & 28 \\ 7 & 21 & 18 \end{bmatrix}$$

Q What matrix would represent the point values for each type of score? $\begin{bmatrix} 3 \\ 2 \\ 1 \end{bmatrix}$

Q What will be the dimensions of the matrix product? **[2 × 1]**

 Problem 4 Applying Matrix Multiplication

Sports In 1966, Washington and New York (Giants) played the highest scoring game in National Football League history. The table summarizes the scoring. A touchdown (TD) is worth 6 points, a field goal (FG) is worth 3 points, a safety (S) is worth 2 points, and a point after touchdown (PAT) is worth 1 point. Using matrix multiplication, what was the final score?

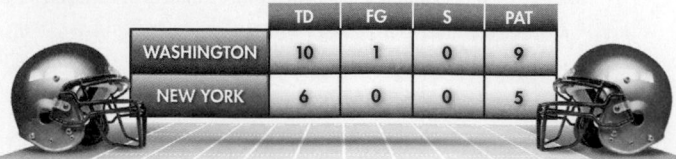

	TD	FG	S	PAT
WASHINGTON	10	1	0	9
NEW YORK	6	0	0	5

Know
- The number of each type of score
- The point value of each score

Need
The scoring summary and point values as matrices

Plan
Multiply the matrices to find each team's final score.

Think

What is the meaning of each number in matrix P?
They are the point values for each type of score.

Step 1 Enter the information in matrices.

$$S = \begin{bmatrix} 10 & 1 & 0 & 9 \\ 6 & 0 & 0 & 5 \end{bmatrix} \qquad P = \begin{bmatrix} 6 \\ 3 \\ 2 \\ 1 \end{bmatrix}$$

Step 2 Use matrix multiplication. The final score is the product SP.

Write the matrix multiplication.
$$SP = \begin{bmatrix} 10 & 1 & 0 & 9 \\ 6 & 0 & 0 & 5 \end{bmatrix} \begin{bmatrix} 6 \\ 3 \\ 2 \\ 1 \end{bmatrix}$$

Multiply and simplify.
$$= \begin{bmatrix} 10(6) + 1(3) + 0(2) + 9(1) \\ 6(6) + 0(3) + 0(2) + 5(1) \end{bmatrix} = \begin{bmatrix} 72 \\ 41 \end{bmatrix}$$

Step 3 Interpret the product matrix.

The first row of SP shows scoring for Washington, so the final score was Washington 72, New York 41.

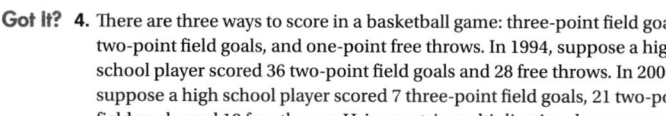 **Got It?** **4.** There are three ways to score in a basketball game: three-point field goals, two-point field goals, and one-point free throws. In 1994, suppose a high school player scored 36 two-point field goals and 28 free throws. In 2006, suppose a high school player scored 7 three-point field goals, 21 two-point field goals, and 18 free throws. Using matrix multiplication, how many points did each player score?

You can multiply two matrices A and B only if the number of columns of A is equal to the number of rows of B.

Answers

Got It? (continued)

4. player from 1994: 100 pts., player from 2006: 81 pts.

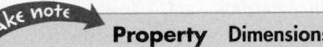

Property Dimensions of a Product Matrix

If A is an $m \times n$ matrix and B is an $n \times p$ matrix,
then the product matrix AB is an $m \times p$ matrix.

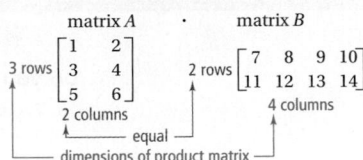

$$\text{matrix } A \qquad \cdot \qquad \text{matrix } B$$

3 rows $\begin{bmatrix} 1 & 2 \\ 3 & 4 \\ 5 & 6 \end{bmatrix}$
2 columns

2 rows $\begin{bmatrix} 7 & 8 & 9 & 10 \\ 11 & 12 & 13 & 14 \end{bmatrix}$
4 columns

equal

dimensions of product matrix

The product matrix AB is a 3×4 matrix.

 **Problem 5** Determining Whether Product Matrices Exist

Does either product AB or BA exist?

$$A = \begin{bmatrix} -2 & 1 \\ 3 & -2 \\ 0 & 1 \end{bmatrix} \qquad B = \begin{bmatrix} -1 & 0 & 2 & 1 \\ 2 & 0 & 0 & 3 \end{bmatrix}$$

Think

How can you tell if a product matrix exists without computing it?
Compare the dimensions of the matrices.

$$AB \qquad\qquad\qquad\qquad BA$$

$(3 \times 2)(2 \times 4) \;\rightarrow\; 3 \times 4$ product matrix $\qquad (2 \times 4)(3 \times 2) \;\rightarrow\;$ no product

equal $\qquad\qquad\qquad\qquad\qquad\qquad$ not equal

Product AB exists.

Got It? 5. Do the following products exist?
$$A = \begin{bmatrix} 1 & 4 \\ -3 & 5 \end{bmatrix} \qquad B = \begin{bmatrix} -1 & 1 \end{bmatrix} \qquad C = \begin{bmatrix} 4 & 2 & 0 \\ 1 & 3 & 5 \end{bmatrix}$$

a. AB **b.** BA **c.** AC **d.** CA **e.** BC

Hint

Matrix multiplication of square ($n \times n$) matrices shares some properties of real number multiplication.

  Properties **Matrix Multiplication**

If A, B, and C are $n \times n$ matrices, and O is the $n \times n$ zero matrix, then

Example	Property
AB is an $n \times n$ matrix	**Closure Property**
$(AB)C = A(BC)$	**Associative Property of Multiplication**
$A(B + C) = AB + AC$ $(B + C)A = BA + CA$	**Distributive Property**
$OA = AO = O$	**Multiplicative Property of Zero**

Take Note

Q Can all matrices be squared? Explain. **[No; only square matrices can be squared, because for the inside dimensions to match, the number of rows must equal the number of columns.]**

Problem 5

Q If the dimensions of two matrices are 2×4 and 4×3, can they be multiplied? In what order? What would the dimensions of the product matrix be? **[Yes; you can only multiply the 2×4 matrix times the 4×3 matrix to get a 2×3 matrix.]**

Q Is it possible for two matrices A and B of different dimensions to be multiplied to get products for AB and BA? What would their dimensions be? **[yes; $n \times m$ and $m \times n$]**

Got It?

Q What are the dimensions of matrices A, B, and C? **[Matrix A: 2×2; matrix B: 1×2; matrix C: 2×3]**

Q Where the product exists, what would be the dimensions of the product matrix? **[5b: 1×2; 5c: 2×3; 5e: 1×3]**

Take Note

Q Why must the matrices be $n \times n$ for these properties to be true? **[so that multiplication is defined for the three matrices no matter what order you multiply them and so that addition is defined no matter how you add the matrices or products]**

5. **a.** no
   b. yes
   c. yes
   d. no
   e. yes

3 Lesson Check

Do you know HOW?
- If students have difficulty evaluating Exercises 1 and 2, remind them that scalar multiplication means they have to multiply every element of the matrix by the scalar.
- If students think that Exercises 3 and 4 are the same problem, remind them that multiplication of matrices is not commutative.

Do you UNDERSTAND?
- In Exercise 5, if students have difficulty determining which is more appropriate to do repeated matrix addition, ask them what expression they would use to add five 3's.
- If students have difficulty explaining the error in Exercise 6, ask them to write out both possibilities and compare the inside dimensions.

Close

> **Q** How do you multiply a matrix by a scalar?
> **[Multiply each element of the matrix by the scalar.]**
>
> **Q** When can you multiply two matrices, and how?
> **[If the number of columns of the first matrix equals the number of rows of the second matrix, multiply the elements of each row of the first matrix by the corresponding elements of each of the columns of the second matrix, add the results, and place the new element in the corresponding row and column of the product matrix.]**

Focus Question How do you find the product of two matrices?

Answer The product of two matrices A and B is the matrix AB. To find element c_{ij} of AB, multiply each element in the ith row of A by the corresponding element of the jth column of B. Then add the products. Not all pairs of matrices can be multiplied.

 Lesson Check

Do you know HOW?

Let $A = \begin{bmatrix} 3 & -1 \\ 2 & 0 \end{bmatrix}$ and $B = \begin{bmatrix} 1 & 3 \\ -2 & 2 \end{bmatrix}$.

Find each of the following.

1. $2A$

2. $3B - 2A$

3. AB

4. BA

Do you UNDERSTAND?

5. **Vocabulary** Which type of multiplication, *scalar* or *matrix*, can help you with a repeated matrix addition problem? Explain.

6. **Error Analysis** Your friend says there is a right order and a wrong order when multiplying A (a 2×4 matrix) and B (a 3×6 matrix). Explain your friend's error.

 Practice and Problem-Solving Exercises

 **Practice** Use matrices A, B, C, and D. Find each product, sum, or difference. ◆ See Problem 1.

$$A = \begin{bmatrix} 3 & 4 \\ 6 & -2 \\ 1 & 0 \end{bmatrix} \quad B = \begin{bmatrix} -3 & 1 \\ 2 & -4 \\ -1 & 5 \end{bmatrix} \quad C = \begin{bmatrix} 1 & 2 \\ -3 & 1 \end{bmatrix} \quad D = \begin{bmatrix} 5 & 1 \\ 0 & 2 \end{bmatrix}$$

7. $3A$

8. $-3C$

9. $-D$

10. $A - 2B$

11. $4C + 3D$

12. $2A - 5B$

Solve each matrix equation. Check your answers. ◆ See Problem 2.

Guided Practice →

13. $4X + \begin{bmatrix} 1 & 3 \\ -7 & 9 \end{bmatrix} = \begin{bmatrix} -3 & 11 \\ 5 & -7 \end{bmatrix}$

To start, use the subtraction property of equality to isolate the variable matrix.

$$4X = \begin{bmatrix} -3 & 11 \\ 5 & -7 \end{bmatrix} - \begin{bmatrix} 1 & 3 \\ -7 & 9 \end{bmatrix}$$

14. $3\begin{bmatrix} 2 & 0 \\ -1 & 5 \end{bmatrix} - 2X = \begin{bmatrix} -10 & 5 \\ 0 & 17 \end{bmatrix}$

15. $\frac{1}{2}X + \begin{bmatrix} 4 & -3 \\ 12 & 1 \end{bmatrix} = \begin{bmatrix} 2 & 1 \\ 1 & 2 \end{bmatrix}$

3 Lesson Check

For a digital lesson check, use the Got It questions.

Support in Algebra 2 Companion
- Lesson Check

4 Practice

Assign homework to individual students or to an entire class.

Answers

Lesson Check

1. $\begin{bmatrix} 6 & -2 \\ 4 & 0 \end{bmatrix}$

2. $\begin{bmatrix} -3 & 11 \\ -10 & 6 \end{bmatrix}$

3. $\begin{bmatrix} 5 & 7 \\ 2 & 6 \end{bmatrix}$

4. $\begin{bmatrix} 9 & -1 \\ -2 & 2 \end{bmatrix}$

5. Scalar; repeated matrix addition is repeated addition of each element of the matrix, which is the same as scalar multiplication of the matrix.

6. The product of two matrices A and B exists only if the number of columns of A is equal to the number of rows of B. Since A is a 2×4 matrix with 4 columns and B is a 3×6 matrix with 3 rows and $4 \neq 3$, the product AB does not exist. Likewise, since $6 \neq 2$, the product BA does not exist.

Practice and Problem-Solving Exercises

7. $\begin{bmatrix} 9 & 12 \\ 18 & -6 \\ 3 & 0 \end{bmatrix}$

8. $\begin{bmatrix} -3 & -6 \\ 9 & -3 \end{bmatrix}$

9. $\begin{bmatrix} -5 & -1 \\ 0 & -2 \end{bmatrix}$

10. $\begin{bmatrix} 9 & 2 \\ 2 & 6 \\ 3 & -10 \end{bmatrix}$

11. $\begin{bmatrix} 19 & 11 \\ -12 & 10 \end{bmatrix}$

12. $\begin{bmatrix} 21 & 3 \\ 2 & 16 \\ 7 & -25 \end{bmatrix}$

13. $\begin{bmatrix} -1 & 2 \\ 3 & -4 \end{bmatrix}$

14. $\begin{bmatrix} 8 & -2.5 \\ -1.5 & -1 \end{bmatrix}$

15. $\begin{bmatrix} -4 & 8 \\ -22 & 2 \end{bmatrix}$

Find each product.

◀ See Problem 3.

Guided Practice

16. $\begin{bmatrix} -3 & 4 \\ 5 & 2 \end{bmatrix} \begin{bmatrix} 1 & 0 \\ 2 & -3 \end{bmatrix}$

To start, find the element in the first row, first column of the product matrix.

$\begin{bmatrix} -3 & 4 \\ 5 & 2 \end{bmatrix} \begin{bmatrix} 1 & 0 \\ 2 & -3 \end{bmatrix} \rightarrow (-3)(1) + (4)(2) = 5$

17. $\begin{bmatrix} 1 & 0 \\ 2 & -3 \end{bmatrix} \begin{bmatrix} -3 & 4 \\ 5 & 2 \end{bmatrix}$

18. $\begin{bmatrix} 0 & 2 \\ -4 & 0 \end{bmatrix} \begin{bmatrix} 0 & 2 \\ -4 & 0 \end{bmatrix}$

19. $\begin{bmatrix} -3 & 5 \end{bmatrix} \begin{bmatrix} -3 \\ 5 \end{bmatrix}$

20. $\begin{bmatrix} -3 & 5 \end{bmatrix} \begin{bmatrix} -3 & 0 \\ 5 & 0 \end{bmatrix}$

21. $\begin{bmatrix} -3 & 5 \end{bmatrix} \begin{bmatrix} 0 & -3 \\ 0 & 5 \end{bmatrix}$

22. $\begin{bmatrix} 0 & -3 \\ 0 & 5 \end{bmatrix} \begin{bmatrix} -3 & 0 \\ 5 & 0 \end{bmatrix}$

23. Business A florist makes three special floral arrangements. One uses three lilies. The second uses three lilies and four carnations. The third uses four daisies and three carnations. Lilies cost $2.15 each, carnations cost $.90 each, and daisies cost $1.30 each. ◀ See Problem 4.
  a. Write a matrix to show the number of each type of flower in each arrangement.
  b. Write a matrix to show the cost of each type of flower.
  c. Find the matrix showing the cost of each floral arrangement.

Determine whether the product exists. ◀ See Problem 5.

$F = \begin{bmatrix} 2 & 3 \\ 6 & 9 \end{bmatrix}$ $G = \begin{bmatrix} -3 & 6 \\ 2 & -4 \end{bmatrix}$ $H = \begin{bmatrix} -5 \\ 6 \end{bmatrix}$ $J = \begin{bmatrix} 0 & 7 \end{bmatrix}$

24. FG **25.** GF **26.** HG **27.** JH

 **Apply**

28. Think About a Plan A hardware store chain sells hammers for $3, flashlights for $5, and lanterns for $7. The store manager tracks the daily purchases at three of the chain's stores in a 3 × 3 matrix. What is the total gross revenue from the flashlights sold at all three stores?
  • How can you use matrix multiplication to solve this problem?
  • What does the product matrix represent?

Number of Items Sold

	Store A	Store B	Store C
Hammers	10	9	8
Flashlights	3	14	6
Lanterns	2	5	7

29. Sports Two teams are competing in a two-team track meet. Points for individual events are awarded as follows: 5 points for first place, 3 points for second place, and 1 point for third place. Points for team relays are awarded as follows: 5 points for first place and no points for second place.
  a. Use matrix operations to determine the score in the track meet.
  b. Who would win if the scoring was changed to 5 points for first place, 2 points for second place, and 1 point for third place in each individual event and 5 points for first place and 0 points for second place in a relay?

	Individual Events			Relays	
Team	First	Second	Third	First	Second
West River	8	5	2	8	5
River's Edge	6	9	12	6	9

30. Writing Suppose A is a 2 × 3 matrix and B is a 3 × 2 matrix with elements not all being equal. Are AB and BA equal? Explain your reasoning. Include examples.

16. $\begin{bmatrix} 5 & -12 \\ 9 & -6 \end{bmatrix}$

17. $\begin{bmatrix} -3 & 4 \\ -21 & 2 \end{bmatrix}$

18. $\begin{bmatrix} -8 & 0 \\ 0 & -8 \end{bmatrix}$

19. $\begin{bmatrix} 34 \end{bmatrix}$

20. $\begin{bmatrix} 34 & 0 \end{bmatrix}$

21. $\begin{bmatrix} 0 & 34 \end{bmatrix}$

22. $\begin{bmatrix} -15 & 0 \\ 25 & 0 \end{bmatrix}$

23. a.

	Lilies	Carnations	Daisies
Arrangement 1	3	0	0
Arrangement 2	3	4	4
Arrangement 3	0	3	4

b.

	Cost
Lilies	$2.15
Carnations	$0.90
Daisies	$1.30

c.

	Cost
Arrangement 1	$6.45
Arrangement 2	$10.05
Arrangement 3	$7.90

24. yes   **25.** yes   **26.** no   **27.** yes

28. $115

29. a. River's Edge: 99 pts.; West River: 97 pts.
  b. West River

30. No; AB will be a 2 × 2 matrix, BA will be a 3 × 3 matrix, and equal matrices must have the same dimensions. Answers may vary. Sample:

Let A be the matrix $\begin{bmatrix} 0 & 1 & 2 \\ 3 & 0 & 0 \end{bmatrix}$,

and let B be the matrix $\begin{bmatrix} 1 & 0 \\ 2 & 4 \\ 3 & 1 \end{bmatrix}$. Then

$AB = \begin{bmatrix} 8 & 6 \\ 3 & 0 \end{bmatrix}$ and $BA = \begin{bmatrix} 0 & 1 & 2 \\ 12 & 2 & 4 \\ 3 & 3 & 6 \end{bmatrix}$.

4 Practice

ASSIGNMENT GUIDE
Basic: 7–25, 28, 29
Average: 7–27 odd, 28–34
Standardized Test Prep: 37–41
Mixed Review: 42–45

Reasoning exercises have blue headings.

Applications exercises have red headings.

EXERCISE 29: Use the Think About a Plan worksheet in the **Student Companion** (also available in the Teaching Resources in print and online) to further support students' development in becoming independent learners.

HOMEWORK QUICK CHECK
To check students' understanding of key skills and concepts, go over Exercises 14, 17, 24, 28, and 29.

Answers

Practice and Problem-Solving Exercises (continued)

31. $\begin{bmatrix} 1 & -6 & -5 \\ 6 & 1 & -5 \\ -3 & -12 & 0 \end{bmatrix}$

32. $\begin{bmatrix} 9 & -6 \\ 15 & -3 \\ -6 & -12 \end{bmatrix}$

33. $\begin{bmatrix} 17 & -24 \\ -33 & -7 \\ 69 & -18 \end{bmatrix}$

34. $\begin{bmatrix} 17 & -24 \\ -33 & -7 \\ 69 & -18 \end{bmatrix}$

35. $\begin{bmatrix} 34 & -1 \\ 6 & -13 \\ -7 & 16 \end{bmatrix}$

36. $\begin{bmatrix} 16 & 8 & -15 \\ 15 & -9 & -15 \\ 2 & 11 & -5 \end{bmatrix}$

Standardized Test Prep

37. B
38. F
39. C
40. F
41. **[2]** Since the center is at the origin, the vertices are $\left(\pm\frac{50}{2}, 0 \right)$ and the co-vertices are $\left(0, \pm\frac{40}{2} \right)$. Using $\frac{x^2}{a^2} + \frac{y^2}{b^2} = 1$,

$a = \pm25$ and $b = \pm20$, so $\frac{x^2}{625} + \frac{y^2}{400} = 1$.

[1] correct vertices and co-vertices, but incorrect eq. OR incomplete explanation

Mixed Review

42. $\begin{bmatrix} -33 & -12 \\ -6 & 27 \end{bmatrix}$

43. $\begin{bmatrix} 9 & -6 & 12 \\ 2 & 20 & 12 \end{bmatrix}$

44. a. 12
b. 12
c. 0

45. a. −12
b. −12
c. 0

Use matrices D, E, and F. Perform the indicated operations if they are defined. If an operation is not defined, label it *undefined*.

$$D = \begin{bmatrix} 1 & 2 & -1 \\ 0 & 3 & 1 \\ 2 & -1 & -2 \end{bmatrix} \qquad E = \begin{bmatrix} 2 & -5 & 0 \\ 1 & 0 & -2 \\ 3 & 1 & 1 \end{bmatrix} \qquad F = \begin{bmatrix} -3 & 2 \\ -5 & 1 \\ 2 & 4 \end{bmatrix}$$

31. DE **32.** $-3F$ **33.** $(DE)F$

34. $D(EF)$ **35.** $(E - D)F$ **36.** $(DD)E$

Standardized Test Prep

SAT/ACT

37. Which product is NOT defined?

Ⓐ $\begin{bmatrix} -1 \\ 2 \end{bmatrix}\begin{bmatrix} -1 & 2 \end{bmatrix}$ Ⓑ $\begin{bmatrix} -1 & 2 \\ -1 & 2 \end{bmatrix}\begin{bmatrix} -1 & 2 \end{bmatrix}$ Ⓒ $\begin{bmatrix} -1 & 2 \\ -1 & 2 \end{bmatrix}\begin{bmatrix} 2 & -1 \\ 2 & -1 \end{bmatrix}$ Ⓓ $\begin{bmatrix} -1 & 2 \end{bmatrix}\begin{bmatrix} -1 \\ 2 \end{bmatrix}$

38. What is the geometric mean of 8 and 18?

Ⓕ 12   Ⓖ 13   Ⓗ 26   Ⓘ 36

39. The random number table simulates an experiment where you toss a coin 90 times. Even digits represent heads and odd digits represent tails. What is the experimental probability, to the nearest percent, of the coin coming up heads?

Ⓐ 45%   Ⓑ 50%   Ⓒ 54%   Ⓓ 56%

Random Number Table		
31504	51648	40613
79321	80927	42404
15594	84675	68591
34178	00460	31754
49676	58733	00884
85400	72294	22551

40. Four percent of the tenants in an apartment building live alone. Suppose five tenants are selected randomly. Which expression represents $P(\text{all live alone})$?

Ⓕ $(0.04)^5$ Ⓖ $(0.4)^5$ Ⓗ $(0.96)^5$ Ⓘ $(5)^{0.04}$

Short Response

41. Explain how to find an equation for the ellipse, centered at the origin, that is 50 units wide and 40 units high.

Mixed Review

Add or subtract.   ◀ See Lesson 12-1.

42. $\begin{bmatrix} -1 & 2 \\ 0 & 17 \end{bmatrix} - \begin{bmatrix} 32 & 14 \\ 6 & -10 \end{bmatrix}$ **43.** $\begin{bmatrix} 0 & -1 & 5 \\ 6 & 10 & 12 \end{bmatrix} + \begin{bmatrix} 9 & -5 & 7 \\ -4 & 10 & 0 \end{bmatrix}$

Get Ready! To prepare for Lesson 12-3, do Exercises 44 and 45.

Simplify each group of expressions.   ◀ See p. 868.

44. a. 3(4)   **b.** 2(6)   **c.** 3(4) − 2(6)

45. a. 3(−4)   **b.** 2(−6)   **c.** 3(−4) − 2(−6)

Lesson Resources

Additional Instructional Support

Algebra 2 Companion

Students can use the **Algebra 2 Companion** worktext (4 pages) as you teach the lesson. Use the Companion to support

- Solve It!
- New Vocabulary
- Key Concepts
- Got It for each Problem
- Lesson Check

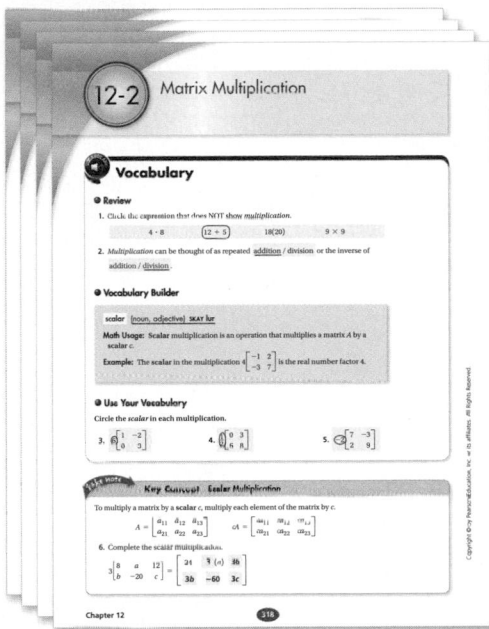

ELL Support

Graphic Organizers To help students understand the process of multiplying two matrices, put on the board two matrices: a 2×2 and a 2×3. Label the elements a, b, c, d in the first matrix and the elements e, f, g, h, j, k in the second matrix. Model the thinking for multiplying rows times columns, and work out a few together. Then ask students to multiply the remainder and record their results on paper and on the board. The resulting matrix shows clearly the pattern of elements being multiplied. Point out to students that the elements in the row of the first matrix do not appear in any of the expressions outside of that row in the product matrix and that the elements of the first column of the second matrix do not appear outside the first column of the product matrix. This will provide a visual graphic for the students to refer to as they multiply matrices in the exercises.

5 Assess & Remediate

Lesson Quiz

1. If $A = \begin{bmatrix} 3 & 6 \\ -1 & 0 \\ 2 & -7 \end{bmatrix}$ and $B = \begin{bmatrix} 0 & -3 \\ 8 & 2 \\ 1 & -4 \end{bmatrix}$, what is $A - 3B$?

2. Solve $\begin{bmatrix} -2 & 1 \\ 4 & 3 \end{bmatrix} - 4X = \begin{bmatrix} -6 & -7 \\ 0 & 3 \end{bmatrix}$.

3. If $G = \begin{bmatrix} -1 & 2 & -3 \\ 2 & 0 & 1 \end{bmatrix}$ and $H = \begin{bmatrix} -1 & -2 \\ 0 & 2 \\ 3 & 1 \end{bmatrix}$, what is GH?

4. **Do you UNDERSTAND?** Can you multiply $\begin{bmatrix} -1 & 3 \\ 2 & 0 \end{bmatrix} \begin{bmatrix} -3 \\ 5 \end{bmatrix}$? Explain.

ANSWERS TO LESSON QUIZ

1. $\begin{bmatrix} 3 & 15 \\ -25 & -6 \\ -1 & 5 \end{bmatrix}$ 2. $\begin{bmatrix} 1 & 2 \\ 1 & 0 \end{bmatrix}$

3. $\begin{bmatrix} -8 & 3 \\ 1 & -3 \end{bmatrix}$

4. yes; sample: A 2×2 matrix times a 2×1 matrix is a 2×1 matrix.

PRESCRIPTION FOR REMEDIATION

Use the student work on the Lesson Quiz to prescribe a differentiated review assignment:

Points	Differentiated Remediation
0–1	Intervention
2–3	On-level
4–5	Extension

PowerAlgebra.com

5 Assess & Remediate

Assign the Lesson Quiz. Appropriate intervention, practice, or enrichment is automatically generated based on student performance.

Intervention

- **Reteaching** (2 pages) Provides reteaching and practice exercises for the key lesson concepts. Use with struggling students or absent students.

- **English Language Learner Support** Helps students develop and reinforce mathematical vocabulary and key concepts.

All-in-One Resources/Online

Reteaching

12-2 Reteaching
Matrix Multiplication

- To multiply a matrix by a real number, multiply each element in the matrix by the real number. This is *scalar multiplication*. The real number is the *scalar*.
- Solving matrix equations with scalars is like solving other kinds of equations. Isolate the variable on one side of the equal sign and simplify the other side.

Problem

What is the solution of $-3\begin{bmatrix} 1 & 3 \\ 6 & 4 \end{bmatrix} + 2X = \begin{bmatrix} -3 & 1 \\ -20 & 6 \end{bmatrix}$?

$\begin{bmatrix} -3 \cdot 1 & -3 \cdot 3 \\ -3 \cdot 6 & -3 \cdot 4 \end{bmatrix} + 2X = \begin{bmatrix} -3 & 1 \\ -20 & 6 \end{bmatrix}$ Multiply $\begin{bmatrix} 1 & 3 \\ 6 & 4 \end{bmatrix}$ by the scalar -3.

$\begin{bmatrix} -3 & -9 \\ -18 & -12 \end{bmatrix} + 2X = \begin{bmatrix} -3 & 1 \\ -20 & 6 \end{bmatrix}$ Simplify.

$2X = \begin{bmatrix} -3 & 1 \\ -20 & 6 \end{bmatrix} - \begin{bmatrix} -3 & -9 \\ -18 & -12 \end{bmatrix}$ Subtract $\begin{bmatrix} -3 & -9 \\ -18 & -12 \end{bmatrix}$ from each side.

$2X = \begin{bmatrix} 0 & 10 \\ -2 & 6 \end{bmatrix}$ Simplify.

$\frac{1}{2}(2X) = \frac{1}{2}\begin{bmatrix} 0 & 10 \\ -2 & 6 \end{bmatrix}$ Multiply each side by $\frac{1}{2}$ to isolate X.

$X = \begin{bmatrix} \frac{1}{2} \cdot 0 & \frac{1}{2} \cdot 10 \\ \frac{1}{2} \cdot (-2) & \frac{1}{2} \cdot 6 \end{bmatrix}$ Multiply $\begin{bmatrix} 0 & 10 \\ -2 & 6 \end{bmatrix}$ by the scalar $\frac{1}{2}$.

$X = \begin{bmatrix} 0 & 5 \\ -1 & 3 \end{bmatrix}$ Simplify.

Exercises

Solve each matrix equation.

1. $\begin{bmatrix} 5 & -1 \\ 0 & 3 \end{bmatrix} + X = 2\begin{bmatrix} 3 & 4 \\ 4 & 3 \end{bmatrix}$ $\begin{bmatrix} 11 & 9 \\ 8 & 3 \end{bmatrix}$ 2. $\frac{2}{3}\begin{bmatrix} 9 & 12 \\ 3 & -6 \end{bmatrix} = 4X + \begin{bmatrix} -6 & 0 \\ 0 & -3 \end{bmatrix}$ $\begin{bmatrix} 3 & 2 \\ \frac{1}{2} & -\frac{1}{4} \end{bmatrix}$

3. $\begin{bmatrix} 1 & 2 & 0 \\ 0 & 0 & 3 \end{bmatrix} - 3X = \begin{bmatrix} -2 & -7 & 6 \\ 3 & -3 & 9 \end{bmatrix}$ $\begin{bmatrix} 1 & 3 & -2 \\ -1 & 1 & -2 \end{bmatrix}$ 4. $2\begin{bmatrix} 3 \\ 8 \end{bmatrix} = \begin{bmatrix} 14 \\ 20 \end{bmatrix} - 4X$ $\begin{bmatrix} 2 \\ 1 \end{bmatrix}$

All-in-One Resources/Online

English Language Learner Support

12-2 ELL Support
Matrix Multiplication

Kerri is learning how to multiply matrices. She wrote the steps to multiply $A = \begin{bmatrix} 3 & 7 \\ 1 & -2 \end{bmatrix}$ by $B = \begin{bmatrix} 0 & 2 \\ 3 & 4 \end{bmatrix}$ on note cards, but the cards got mixed up.

Multiply the elements in the first row of A by the elements in the second column of B. Place the sum in the first row, second column of AB.

Multiply the elements in the second row of A by the elements in the second column of B. Place the sum in the second row, second column of AB.

Multiply the elements in the second row of A by the elements in the first column of B. Place the sum in the second row, first column of AB.

Multiply the elements in the first row of A by the elements in the first column of B. Place the sum in the first row, first column of AB.

Use the note cards to write the steps in order.

1. First, multiply the elements in the first row of A by the elements in the first column of B. Place the sum in the first row, first column of AB

2. Second, multiply the elements in the first row of A by the elements in the second column of B. Place the sum in the first row, second column of AB

3. Then, multiply the elements in the second row of A by the elements in the first column of B. Place the sum in the second row, first column of AB

4. Finally, multiply the elements in the second row of A by the elements in the second column of AB

On-Level

- **Practice** (2 pages) Provides extra practice for each lesson. For more challenging practice exercises, use the Form G Practice pages found in the All-in-One Teaching Resources and online.
- **Think About a Plan** Helps students develop specific problem-solving skills and strategies by providing scaffolded guiding questions.
- **Standardized Test Prep** Focuses on all major exercises, all major question types, and helps students prepare for the high-stakes assessments.

Extension

- **Enrichment** Provides students with interesting problems and activities that extend the concepts of the lesson.
- **Activities, Games, and Puzzles** Worksheets that can be used for concepts development, enrichment, and for fun!

Student Companion/ All-in-One Resources/Online
Practice page 1

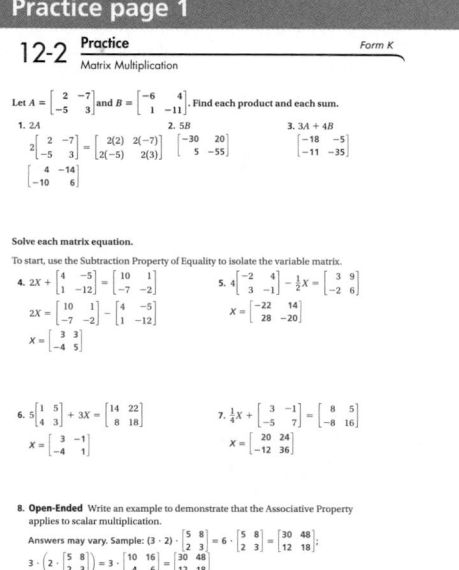

12-2 Practice Form K
Matrix Multiplication

Let $A = \begin{bmatrix} 2 & -7 \\ -5 & 3 \end{bmatrix}$ and $B = \begin{bmatrix} -6 & 4 \\ 1 & -11 \end{bmatrix}$. Find each product and each sum.

1. $2A$ $\quad 2\begin{bmatrix} 2 & -7 \\ -5 & 3 \end{bmatrix} = \begin{bmatrix} 2(2) & 2(-7) \\ 2(-5) & 2(3) \end{bmatrix}$ $\quad \begin{bmatrix} 4 & -14 \\ -10 & 6 \end{bmatrix}$
2. $5B$ $\quad \begin{bmatrix} -30 & 20 \\ 5 & -55 \end{bmatrix}$
3. $3A + 4B$ $\quad \begin{bmatrix} -18 & -5 \\ -11 & -35 \end{bmatrix}$

Solve each matrix equation.

To start, use the Subtraction Property of Equality to isolate the variable matrix.

4. $2X + \begin{bmatrix} 4 & -5 \\ 1 & -12 \end{bmatrix} = \begin{bmatrix} 10 & 1 \\ -7 & -2 \end{bmatrix}$ $\quad 2X = \begin{bmatrix} 10 & 1 \\ -7 & -2 \end{bmatrix} - \begin{bmatrix} 4 & -5 \\ 1 & -12 \end{bmatrix}$ $\quad X = \begin{bmatrix} 3 & 3 \\ -4 & 5 \end{bmatrix}$
5. $4\begin{bmatrix} -2 & 4 \\ 3 & -1 \end{bmatrix} - \frac{1}{2}X = \begin{bmatrix} 3 & 9 \\ -2 & 6 \end{bmatrix}$ $\quad X = \begin{bmatrix} -22 & 14 \\ 28 & -20 \end{bmatrix}$
6. $5\begin{bmatrix} 1 & 5 \\ 4 & 3 \end{bmatrix} + 3X = \begin{bmatrix} 14 & 22 \\ 8 & 18 \end{bmatrix}$ $\quad X = \begin{bmatrix} 3 & -1 \\ -4 & 1 \end{bmatrix}$
7. $\frac{1}{4}X + \begin{bmatrix} 3 & -1 \\ -5 & 7 \end{bmatrix} = \begin{bmatrix} 8 & 5 \\ -8 & 16 \end{bmatrix}$ $\quad X = \begin{bmatrix} 20 & 24 \\ -12 & 36 \end{bmatrix}$
8. **Open-Ended** Write an example to demonstrate that the Associative Property applies to scalar multiplication.
Answers may vary. Sample: $(3 \cdot 2) \cdot \begin{bmatrix} 5 & 8 \\ 2 & 3 \end{bmatrix} = 6 \cdot \begin{bmatrix} 5 & 8 \\ 2 & 3 \end{bmatrix} = \begin{bmatrix} 30 & 48 \\ 12 & 18 \end{bmatrix}$; $3 \cdot \left(2 \cdot \begin{bmatrix} 5 & 8 \\ 2 & 3 \end{bmatrix}\right) = 3 \cdot \begin{bmatrix} 10 & 16 \\ 4 & 6 \end{bmatrix} = \begin{bmatrix} 30 & 48 \\ 12 & 18 \end{bmatrix}$

Student Companion/ All-in-One Resources/Online
Practice page 2

12-2 Practice (continued) Form K
Matrix Multiplication

Find each product.

To start, find the element in the first row and first column of the product matrix.

9. $\begin{bmatrix} 4 & -2 \\ -3 & 7 \end{bmatrix}\begin{bmatrix} 3 & 6 \\ 1 & -5 \end{bmatrix}$
$4(3) + (-2)(1) = 10 \rightarrow \begin{bmatrix} 10 & \\ & \end{bmatrix}$
$4(6) + (-2)(-5) = 34 \rightarrow \begin{bmatrix} 10 & 34 \\ & \end{bmatrix}$
$(-3)(3) + 7(1) = -2 \rightarrow \begin{bmatrix} 10 & 34 \\ -2 & \end{bmatrix}$
$(-3)(6) + 7(-5) = -53 \rightarrow \begin{bmatrix} 10 & 34 \\ -2 & -53 \end{bmatrix}$
10. $\begin{bmatrix} 5 & 3 \\ -2 & 0 \end{bmatrix}\begin{bmatrix} 2 & -3 \\ -1 & 4 \end{bmatrix}$ $\quad \begin{bmatrix} 7 & -3 \\ -4 & 6 \end{bmatrix}$
11. $\begin{bmatrix} 2 & 5 \end{bmatrix}\begin{bmatrix} -1 & 3 \\ 4 & 7 \end{bmatrix}$ $\quad \begin{bmatrix} 18 & 41 \end{bmatrix}$
12. $\begin{bmatrix} 6 & -2 \\ -3 & 0 \end{bmatrix}\begin{bmatrix} 1 & 5 \\ 8 & 3 \end{bmatrix}$ $\quad \begin{bmatrix} -10 & 24 \\ -3 & -15 \end{bmatrix}$

Determine whether the product exists.

$A = \begin{bmatrix} 2 & 0 \\ -6 & 9 \end{bmatrix}$ $\quad B = \begin{bmatrix} -2 \\ 6 \end{bmatrix}$ $\quad C = \begin{bmatrix} 1 & -3 \\ 13 & -5 \end{bmatrix}$ $\quad D = \begin{bmatrix} -7 & 5 \end{bmatrix}$

13. AC yes
14. BA no
15. DC yes
16. BD yes

17. The table below shows the number of small, medium, large, and extra-large drinks sold at two snack stands in an hour. The small drinks cost \$1.00, the medium drinks cost \$1.50, the large drinks cost \$2.00, and the extra-large drinks cost \$2.50. Using matrix multiplication, what was the sales total for each snack stand? Stand 1: \$70.50; Stand 2: \$87.00

	Small	Medium	Large	Extra Large
Stand 1	16	8	10	9
Stand 2	6	12	9	18

All-in-One Resources/Online
Enrichment

12-2 Enrichment
Matrix Multiplication

Nilpotent Matrices

A matrix A is said to be nilpotent if there is an integer n such that $A^n = 0$, the zero matrix.

1. What can you say about the dimensions of a nilpotent matrix? Why? The number of rows must be the same as the number of columns, so it can be multiplied by itself.
If $A = \begin{bmatrix} 0 & 1 \\ 0 & 0 \end{bmatrix}$, find A^2 and A^3. What can you conclude? $\begin{bmatrix} 0 & 0 \\ 0 & 0 \end{bmatrix}$; $\begin{bmatrix} 0 & 0 \\ 0 & 0 \end{bmatrix}$; A nonzero matrix may be nilpotent.
The *order* of a nilpotent matrix A is the least integer n such that $A^n = 0$. In the example above, although both $A^2 = 0$ and $A^3 = 0$, the order of matrix A is 2.
2. Examine the conditions under which a nonzero 2×2 matrix of order 2 is nilpotent. Suppose $A = \begin{bmatrix} a & b \\ c & d \end{bmatrix}$. Find A^2. $\begin{bmatrix} a^2 + bc & ab + bd \\ ac + cd & bc + d^2 \end{bmatrix}$
If A is nilpotent of order 2, then $A^2 = 0$. Therefore, each element of the matrix A^2 must be equal to zero.
3. Write four equations that show that the elements in the corresponding rows and columns are zero. $a^2 + bc = 0$; $ab + bd = 0$; $ac + cd = 0$; $bc + d^2 = 0$
Equation (1, 1): Equation (1, 2):
Equation (2, 1): Equation (2, 2):
4. Factor equation (1, 2). $b(a + d) = 0$
5. Find two possible solutions. $b = 0$; $a + d = 0$
6. If $b = 0$, what can you conclude from equation (1, 1)? From equation (2, 2)? $a^2 = 0$, so $a = 0$; $d^2 = 0$, so $d = 0$
7. Use this information to write matrix A. Verify that this matrix is nilpotent of order 2. $A = \begin{bmatrix} 0 & 0 \\ c & 0 \end{bmatrix}$; $A^2 = \begin{bmatrix} 0 & 0 \\ 0 & 0 \end{bmatrix}$
8. Using equations (2, 1), (1, 1), and (2, 2), and substituting in matrix A, find another nilpotent matrix of order 2. $\begin{bmatrix} 0 & b \\ 0 & 0 \end{bmatrix}$

Student Companion/ All-in-One Resources/Online
Think About a Plan

12-2 Think About a Plan
Matrix Multiplication

Sport Two teams are competing in a track meet. Points for individual events are awarded as follows: 5 points for first place, 3 points for second place, and 1 point for third place. Points for team relays are awarded as follows: 5 points for first place and no points for second place.

a. Use matrix operations to determine the score in the track meet.
b. Who would win if the scoring was changed to 5 points for first place, 2 points for second place, and 1 point for third place in each individual event with relay scoring remaining 5 points for first place?

Team	Individual Events: First	Second	Third	Relays: First	Second
West River	8	5	2	8	5
River's Edge	6	9	12	6	9

Know

1. The number of each place for each school and the point value of each place

Need

2. To solve the problem I need to: write the number of wins and the point values as matrices, then multiply the matrices

Plan

3. Write the number of wins as a 2×5 matrix and the original and alternate point values as 5×1 matrices. $\begin{bmatrix} 8 & 5 & 2 & 8 & 5 \\ 6 & 9 & 12 & 6 & 9 \end{bmatrix}$; $\begin{bmatrix} 5 \\ 3 \\ 1 \\ 5 \\ 0 \end{bmatrix}$; $\begin{bmatrix} 5 \\ 2 \\ 1 \\ 5 \\ 0 \end{bmatrix}$
4. Use matrix multiplication to find the original total team scores and the alternate total team scores for the track meet.
$\begin{bmatrix} 8 & 5 & 2 & 8 & 5 \\ 6 & 9 & 12 & 6 & 9 \end{bmatrix}\begin{bmatrix} 5 \\ 3 \\ 1 \\ 5 \\ 0 \end{bmatrix} = \begin{bmatrix} 97 \\ 99 \end{bmatrix}$ $\quad \begin{bmatrix} 8 & 5 & 2 & 8 & 5 \\ 6 & 9 & 12 & 6 & 9 \end{bmatrix}\begin{bmatrix} 5 \\ 2 \\ 1 \\ 5 \\ 0 \end{bmatrix} = \begin{bmatrix} 92 \\ 90 \end{bmatrix}$
5. What was the score in the track meet? West River: 97, River's Edge: 99
6. Who would win if the scoring were changed? West River

Student Companion/ All-in-One Resources/Online
Standardized Test Prep

12-2 Standardized Test Prep
Matrix Multiplication

Multiple Choice

For Exercises 1–3, choose the correct letter.

1. Which matrix is equivalent to $-2\begin{bmatrix} 1 & 5 & -3 \\ 0 & 2 & 4 \\ 7 & -2 & 0 \end{bmatrix}$? A
Ⓐ $\begin{bmatrix} -2 & -10 & 6 \\ 0 & -4 & -8 \\ -14 & 4 & 0 \end{bmatrix}$ Ⓒ $\begin{bmatrix} -2 & -10 & 6 \\ 0 & 2 & 4 \\ 7 & -2 & 0 \end{bmatrix}$
Ⓑ $\begin{bmatrix} 1 & 5 & -3 \\ 0 & -4 & -8 \\ 7 & -2 & 0 \end{bmatrix}$ Ⓓ $\begin{bmatrix} -1 & 3 & -5 \\ -2 & 0 & 2 \\ 5 & -4 & -2 \end{bmatrix}$
2. What is the product $\begin{bmatrix} 6 & -1 \\ 3 & 9 \end{bmatrix}\begin{bmatrix} 3 \\ -6 \end{bmatrix}$? H
Ⓕ $\begin{bmatrix} 18 & -3 \\ -18 & -54 \end{bmatrix}$ Ⓖ $\begin{bmatrix} 24 & -45 \end{bmatrix}$ Ⓗ $\begin{bmatrix} 24 \\ -45 \end{bmatrix}$ Ⓘ $\begin{bmatrix} 15 & 36 \\ -30 & -72 \end{bmatrix}$
3. Which matrix is the solution of $\begin{bmatrix} 1 & -1 & 2 \\ 2 & 0 & -1 \end{bmatrix} - 2X = \begin{bmatrix} 4 & 5 & 6 \\ 6 & 5 & 4 \end{bmatrix}$? D
Ⓐ $\begin{bmatrix} 3 & 6 & 4 \\ 4 & 5 & 5 \end{bmatrix}$ Ⓒ $\begin{bmatrix} \frac{3}{2} & 3 & 2 \\ 2 & \frac{5}{2} & \frac{5}{2} \end{bmatrix}$
Ⓑ $\begin{bmatrix} -6 & -12 & -8 \\ -8 & -10 & -10 \end{bmatrix}$ Ⓓ $\begin{bmatrix} -\frac{3}{2} & -3 & -2 \\ -2 & -\frac{5}{2} & -\frac{5}{2} \end{bmatrix}$

Extended Response \$107 for Bath 1, \$67 for Bath 2, \$220 for the kitchen, so \$394 total.

4. The table shows the number of tiles used in a house. Blue tiles cost \$1.20 each, white cost \$1.50 each, and green cost \$.80 each. Write and solve a matrix equation to find the total cost of the tile. Show your work.

Tiles Used

	Blue	White	Green
Bath #1	20	50	10
Bath #2	15	30	5
Kitchen	25	100	50

$\begin{bmatrix} 20 & 50 & 10 \\ 15 & 30 & 5 \\ 25 & 100 & 50 \end{bmatrix}\begin{bmatrix} 1.20 \\ 1.50 \\ 0.80 \end{bmatrix} = \begin{bmatrix} 20(1.20) + 50(1.50) + 10(0.80) \\ 15(1.20) + 30(1.50) + 5(0.80) \\ 25(1.20) + 100(1.50) + 50(0.80) \end{bmatrix} = \begin{bmatrix} 107 \\ 67 \\ 220 \end{bmatrix}$

[3] appropriate solution strategy with a minor computational or copying error
[2] correct equation solved incorrectly OR incorrect equation solved correctly; total cost correct based on previous work
[1] correct total cost with no work shown
[0] incorrect answers and no work shown OR no answers given

Online Teacher Resource Center
Activities, Games, and Puzzles

12-2 Activity: Matrix "Eggsperiment"
Matrix Multiplication

For this activity you will need some empty egg cartons, pennies, dimes, and tape.

- Use scissors to divide the cartons into 2-by-1, 2-by-2, and 2-by-3 sections.
- Decide each section's orientation to obtain a matrix. For instance, a 2-by-3 section can give you a 2×3 matrix or 3×2 matrix.
- Place anywhere from 0 to 5 coins in each space for every matrix. Use dimes to represent negative numbers. Leave some of the spaces empty.

Activity Directions

The number of pennies minus the number of dimes in each position of the carton represents the value of that entry in the matrix. Pick a partner and compare your matrices to your classmates' matrices. Decide whether or not you can add your matrix to another matrix or multiply your matrix with another matrix.

Add or multiply your matrix with your partner's to make a new resulting matrix. Decide whether or not a different size matrix or additional coins are required. You can use tape to put smaller matrices together and create larger ones. If time permits, change partners and repeat the activity.

1. Which size matrices could be added to your matrix? matrices with the same dimension as your matrix
2. Which size matrices could be multiplied with your matrix? Does the way the carton was oriented make a difference? To multiply two matrices, the number of columns in the first matrix must equal the number of rows in the second matrix. Orientation makes a difference; a 2×3 matrix is different from a 3×2 matrix.
3. How do you find the size of a matrix resulting from the multiplication of two matrices? Explain by giving an example. An $n \times m$ matrix multiplied by an $m \times p$ matrix gives an $n \times p$ matrix.
4. Is the size of the product of two matrices always different from the original matrices? Explain by giving an example. Not necessarily; multiplying two square matrices gives a square matrix of the same size.
5. Is the size of the sum of two matrices always the same as the original matrices? yes

12-3
PART 1
Determinants and Inverses

Objective To find the determinant of a matrix

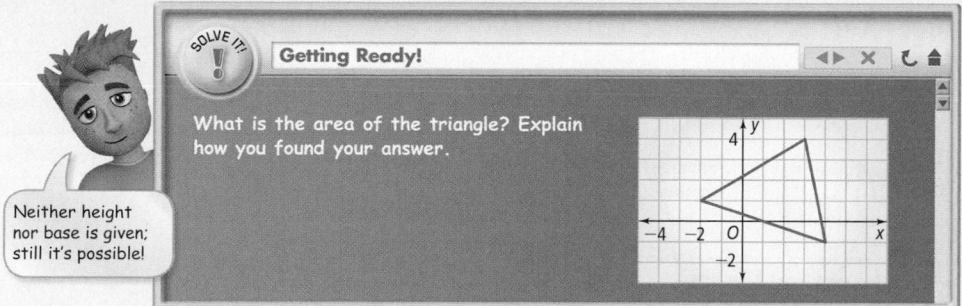

Getting Ready!

What is the area of the triangle? Explain how you found your answer.

Neither height nor base is given; still it's possible!

Lesson Vocabulary
• square matrix
• multiplicative identity matrix
• multiplicative inverse matrix
• determinant

This lesson will prepare you to use matrices to solve problems, including how to find the area of a triangle with vertices anywhere in the coordinate plane.

Focus Question What are multiplicative identity matrices and multiplicative inverse matrices?

A **square matrix** is a matrix with the same number of rows and columns. While there is a multiplicative identity matrix for any square matrix, not all square matrices have multiplicative inverses.

Hint

main diagonal
The main diagonal of a square matrix are the entries that run from the top left corner to the bottom right corner.

take note
Key Concepts Identity and Multiplicative Inverse Matrices

For an $n \times n$ matrix, the **multiplicative identity matrix** is an $n \times n$ matrix I, or I_n with 1's along the main diagonal and 0's elsewhere.

$$I_2 = \begin{bmatrix} 1 & 0 \\ 0 & 1 \end{bmatrix}, \quad I_3 = \begin{bmatrix} 1 & 0 & 0 \\ 0 & 1 & 0 \\ 0 & 0 & 1 \end{bmatrix}, \quad \text{and so forth.}$$

If A and B are square matrices and $AB = BA = I$, then B is the **multiplicative inverse matrix** of A, written A^{-1}.

1 Interactive Learning

Solve It!
PURPOSE To find the area of a triangle using the vertices of the triangle
PROCESS Students may
• find the area of the rectangle containing the triangle and subtract the areas of the right triangles formed between the given triangle and the sides of the rectangles.
• find the lengths of the sides using the distance formula and then use Heron's formula to find the area.

FACILITATE
Q What are the coordinates of the vertices of the triangle? **[(−2, 1), (3, 4), and (4, −1)]**
Q What are the dimensions of the smallest rectangle that has sides parallel to the axes and contains the triangle? **[6 by 5 units]**
Q How many triangles are in your rectangle? Which can you find the area of? **[four, the given triangle and the three that contain the area between the sides of the rectangle and the given triangle; all four]**

ANSWER See Solve It in Answers on next page.
CONNECT THE MATH In the Solve It, students find the area of a triangle by comparing surrounding areas. In the lesson, students will use a formula using this same idea to calculate area of a triangle from the coordinates of the vertices.

2 Guided Instruction
Take Note

Q Why must A and B be square matrices? **[so that AB and BA are defined]**

12-3
Preparing to Teach

PART 1

BIG idea Modeling **UbD**
ESSENTIAL UNDERSTANDINGS
• The product of a matrix and its inverse matrix is the multiplicative identity matrix. Not all matrices have inverse matrices.
• A matrix has an inverse if and only if its determinant does not equal 0.

Math Background
All square matrices have a multiplicative identity matrix. It contains 1's along the main diagonal and 0's elsewhere. Students might expect the multiplicative identity matrix to have all elements equal to one, since the multiplicative identity of real numbers is 1. You may wish to have them multiply such a matrix by another matrix to see what happens.

Unlike real numbers, not all matrices have multiplicative inverses. One way

to determine whether a matrix has a multiplicative inverse is to calculate its determinant. If the determinant is 0, the matrix does not have an inverse. The determinant is only defined for square matrices.

Students may be confused by the concept of the determinant. It is a number, not a matrix. It has many uses beyond determining whether a matrix has a multiplicative inverse. It can also be used to determine the inverse and to find areas of polygons. It has applications in calculus, linear algebra, and elsewhere.

Support Student Learning
Use the **Algebra 2 Companion** to engage and support students during instruction. See Lesson Resources at the end of this lesson for details.

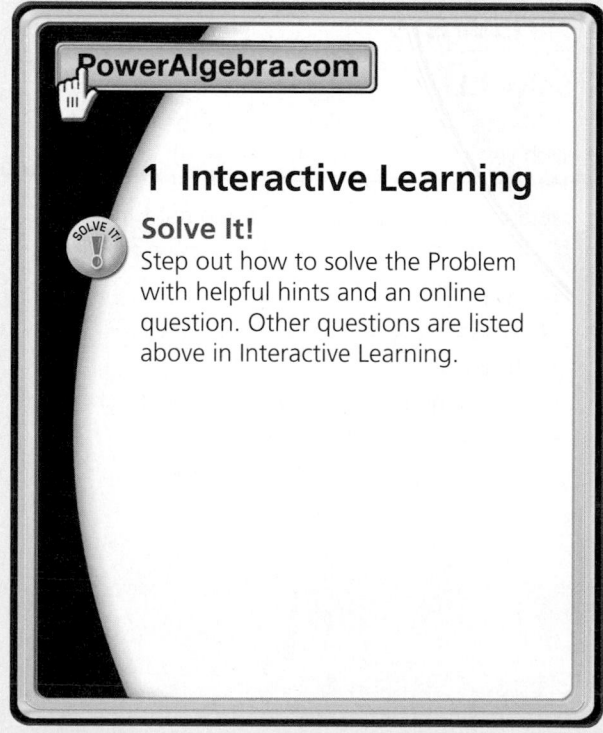

PowerAlgebra.com

1 Interactive Learning

Solve It!
Step out how to solve the Problem with helpful hints and an online question. Other questions are listed above in Interactive Learning.

Problem 1

Q Could A and B be square matrices with $AB = BA$, but not be inverses? Explain using an example. **[Yes; samples: if A and B are the same matrix;**

$$\begin{bmatrix} 2 & 4 \\ 4 & 2 \end{bmatrix} \text{ and } \begin{bmatrix} 3 & -1 \\ -1 & 3 \end{bmatrix}, \text{ whose product is}$$

$$\begin{bmatrix} 2 & 10 \\ 10 & 2 \end{bmatrix} \text{ for } AB \text{ or } BA]$$

Q If $AB \neq I$, do you have to check BA to see whether A and B are inverses? Explain. **[No; if any part of the conditions that must be satisfied for B to be a multiplicative inverse of A fail, then B is not the multiplicative inverse of A. You still might want to check BA in case you made an error in calculation for BA.]**

Got It?

Q What conditions must be met for A and B to be multiplicative inverses? **[A and B must be square matrices, and $AB = BA = I$.]**

Q What is the result if you multiply any square matrix by the same size zero matrix? Explain. **[The resulting matrix will be the zero matrix; each element of the square matrix will equal zero when multiplied by zero.]**

Take Note

Q What is another equivalent formula for finding the determinant of any 2×2 matrix? Explain. **[Sample: $da - cb$, because multiplication of each term is commutative.]**

Problem 1 Determining Whether Matrices are Inverses

Think

How do you determine whether A and B are inverses? Find AB and BA. Both products must equal I for the matrices to be inverses.

Hint

Once you find that $AB \neq I$ (or $BA \neq I$) you can conclude that the matrices are not inverses, without having to find the other product.

For each of the following, are matrices A and B inverses?

A $A = \begin{bmatrix} 1 & 0 & 2 \\ -2 & 1 & 1 \\ -1 & 1 & 2 \end{bmatrix}$ $B = \begin{bmatrix} -1 & -2 & 2 \\ -3 & -4 & 5 \\ 1 & 1 & -1 \end{bmatrix}$

Since $AB = I$ and $BA = I$, matrices A and B are inverses.

B $A = \begin{bmatrix} 2 & 4 \\ 2 & 2 \end{bmatrix}$ $B = \begin{bmatrix} 2 & 5 \\ -1 & -3 \end{bmatrix}$

Since $AB \neq I$ (and $BA \neq I$), matrices A and B are not inverses.

Got It? **1.** For each of the following, are matrices A and B inverses?

a. $A = \begin{bmatrix} 1 & 1 \\ 5 & 4 \end{bmatrix}$ $B = \begin{bmatrix} -4 & 1 \\ 5 & -1 \end{bmatrix}$ **b.** $A = \begin{bmatrix} 3 & 2 \\ 5 & 4 \end{bmatrix}$ $B = \begin{bmatrix} 2 & -1 \\ -\frac{5}{2} & \frac{3}{2} \end{bmatrix}$

c. Reasoning Does the matrix $\begin{bmatrix} 0 & 0 \\ 0 & 0 \end{bmatrix}$ have an inverse? Explain.

Every square matrix with real-number elements has a certain number associated with it. The number is called its *determinant*. Given $A = \begin{bmatrix} a & b \\ c & d \end{bmatrix}$,

Write	Read	Evaluate
↓	↓	↓
$\det A$	the determinant of A	$\det\begin{bmatrix} a & b \\ c & d \end{bmatrix} = ad - bc$

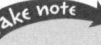 **Key Concept** **Determinant of a 2×2 Matrix**

The **determinant** of a 2×2 matrix $\begin{bmatrix} a & b \\ c & d \end{bmatrix}$ is $\det\begin{bmatrix} a & b \\ c & d \end{bmatrix} = ad - bc$.

Answers

Solve It!

≈ 14 unit^2; enclose the triangle in the rectangle with vertices $(-2, -1)$, $(4, -1)$, $(4, 4)$, and $(-2, 4)$. The area of the triangle is the area of the rectangle minus the areas of three right triangles; $6 \cdot 5 - \frac{1}{2} \cdot 6 \cdot 2 - \frac{1}{2} \cdot 5 \cdot 1 - \frac{1}{2} \cdot 5 \cdot 3 = 14$.

Got It?

1. a. yes

   b. yes

   c. No; no matrix that is multiplied by the zero matrix will give an identity matrix.

 PowerAlgebra.com

2 Guided Instruction

Each Problem is worked out and supported online.

Support in Algebra 2 Companion
- Vocabulary
- Key Concepts
- Got It?

Problem 1
Determining Whether Matrices are Inverses *Animated*

Problem 2
Evaluating the Determinants of Matrices *Animated*

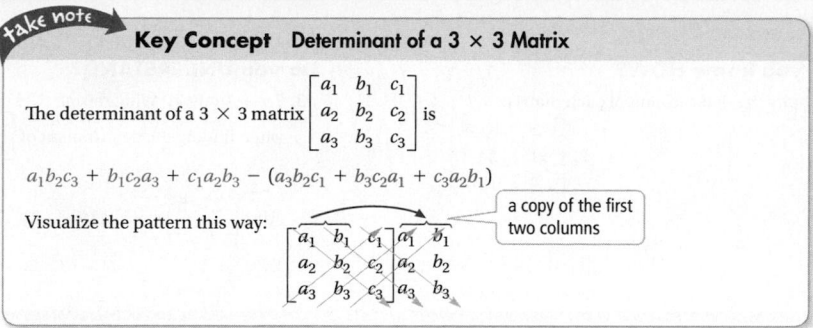

Key Concept Determinant of a 3 × 3 Matrix

The determinant of a 3 × 3 matrix $\begin{bmatrix} a_1 & b_1 & c_1 \\ a_2 & b_2 & c_2 \\ a_3 & b_3 & c_3 \end{bmatrix}$ is

$$a_1 b_2 c_3 + b_1 c_2 a_3 + c_1 a_2 b_3 - (a_3 b_2 c_1 + b_3 c_2 a_1 + c_3 a_2 b_1)$$

Visualize the pattern this way:

a copy of the first two columns

$\begin{bmatrix} a_1 & b_1 & c_1 \\ a_2 & b_2 & c_2 \\ a_3 & b_3 & c_3 \end{bmatrix} \begin{matrix} a_1 & b_1 \\ a_2 & b_2 \\ a_3 & b_3 \end{matrix}$

Problem 2 Evaluating the Determinants of Matrices

What are the following determinants?

A det$\begin{bmatrix} 3 & -1 \\ 2 & 5 \end{bmatrix}$

Use the formula.   det$\begin{bmatrix} 3 & -1 \\ 2 & 5 \end{bmatrix} = (3)(5) - (-1)(2)$

Simplify. $= 15 - (-2) = 17$

Think
What can you do first to evaluate a 3 × 3 determinant?
Copy the first two columns to the right of the matrix.

$\begin{bmatrix} 1 & 0 & -2 \\ 0 & 4 & -1 \\ 3 & 5 & 2 \end{bmatrix} \begin{matrix} 1 & 0 \\ 0 & 4 \\ 3 & 5 \end{matrix}$

B det$\begin{bmatrix} 1 & 0 & -2 \\ 0 & 4 & -1 \\ 3 & 5 & 2 \end{bmatrix}$

Use the formula. $= [(1)(4)(2) + (0)(-1)(3) + (-2)(0)(5)] - [(3)(4)(-2) + (5)(-1)(1) + (2)(0)(0)]$

Multiply. $= 8 + 0 + 0 - (-24 - 5 + 0)$

Simplify. $= 8 - (-29) = 37$

Check Use a graphing calculator.

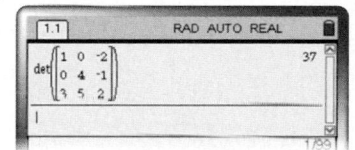

Got It? 2. What are the following determinants?

a. $\begin{bmatrix} 3 & 6 \\ 2 & 5 \end{bmatrix}$ b. $\begin{vmatrix} 1 & 0 & 3 \\ 2 & 4 & 6 \\ 5 & -1 & 3 \end{vmatrix}$

Focus Question What are multiplicative identity matrices and multiplicative inverse matrices?

Answer Multiplicative identity matrices are square matrices with 1's along the main diagonal and 0's elsewhere. The product of a square matrix and its multiplicative inverse matrix is a multiplicative identity matrix.

PowerAlgebra.com   Lesson 12-3 Determinants and Inverses   791

Take Note   EXTENSION

Q Gather together terms that contain a_1 and factor out a_1. Do the same for $-b_1$ and c_1. What is the result? **[$a_1(b_2 c_3 - b_3 c_2) - b_1(a_2 c_3 - a_3 c_2) + c_1(a_2 b_3 - a_3 b_2)$]**

Q Does the pattern for finding the determinant of a 3 × 3 matrix work for finding the determinant of a 4 × 4 matrix? Use your calculator to check if this is true. **[no]**

Problem 2

Q What would be different about the value of the determinant if you subtracted the down diagonal products from the up diagonal products? **[If the determinant equals n, you would end up with $-n$.]**

Got It?

Q What are the expanded expressions that will give the value of the determinants for 2a and 2b? **[(3)(5) − (6)(2); and (1)(4)(3) + (0)(6)(5) + (3)(2)(−1) − ((5)(4)(3) + (−1)(6)(1) + (3)(2)(0))]**

Additional Problems

1. If $A = \begin{bmatrix} 2 & 0 & 1 \\ 1 & 3 & -1 \\ 2 & 1 & 1 \end{bmatrix}$ and

$B = \begin{bmatrix} \frac{4}{3} & \frac{1}{3} & -1 \\ -1 & 0 & 1 \\ -\frac{5}{3} & -\frac{2}{3} & 2 \end{bmatrix}$, are

A and B inverses?

ANSWER yes

2. What is the determinant

of $\begin{bmatrix} 3 & 5 & -1 \\ 1 & 0 & -2 \\ 2 & 3 & 1 \end{bmatrix}$?

ANSWER −10

Answers

Got It? (continued)
   2. a. 3
      b. −48

3 Lesson Check

Do you know HOW?
• If students have difficulty finding the determinants for Exercises 1 and 2, refer them to Problem 2. Encourage them to use the formula and then a graphing calculator to check their answers.

Do you UNDERSTAND?
• For Exercise 3, have students review the formula for finding the determinant of a 2 × 2 matrix in the Take Note box labeled Determinants of 2 × 2 Matrices.

Close

Q For matrix A, what is the meaning of A^{-1}?
[A^{-1} is the multiplicative inverse of matrix A.]

Q What does it mean if two matrices are multiplicative inverses of each other? [Multiplying the matrices in any order yields the identity matrix.]

4 Practice

ASSIGNMENT GUIDE
Basic: 4–14, 19.

Average: 4–18 even, 19.

Reasoning exercises have blue headings.

Applications exercises have red headings.

HOMEWORK QUICK CHECK
To check students' understanding of key skills and concepts, go over Exercises 4, 6, 10, 14, and 19.

 Lesson Check

Do you know HOW?

Evaluate the determinant of each matrix.

1. $\begin{bmatrix} 4 & -1 \\ 8 & 2 \end{bmatrix}$

2. $\begin{bmatrix} 1 & 0 & 0 \\ -1 & 2 & 3 \\ 4 & -1 & 2 \end{bmatrix}$

Do you UNDERSTAND?

3. **Error Analysis** What mistake did the student make when finding the determinant of $\begin{bmatrix} 2 & 5 \\ -3 & 1 \end{bmatrix}$?

$$\det \begin{bmatrix} 2 & 5 \\ -3 & 1 \end{bmatrix} = (2)(1) + (-3)(5) = 2 - 15 = -13$$

Practice and Problem-Solving Exercises

Ⓐ Practice

Determine whether the matrices are multiplicative inverses. ◆ See Problem 1.

4. $\begin{bmatrix} 3 & 2 \\ 4 & 3 \end{bmatrix}, \begin{bmatrix} 3 & -2 \\ -4 & 3 \end{bmatrix}$

5. $\begin{bmatrix} -3 & 7 \\ -2 & 5 \end{bmatrix}, \begin{bmatrix} -5 & 7 \\ -2 & 3 \end{bmatrix}$

6. $\begin{bmatrix} 1 & 2 & -1 \\ -1.5 & -3 & 1.75 \\ 0 & -1 & 0.5 \end{bmatrix}, \begin{bmatrix} 1 & 0 & 2 \\ 3 & 2 & -1 \\ 6 & 4 & 0 \end{bmatrix}$

7. $\begin{bmatrix} 2 & 2 & 2 \\ -2 & 2 & -2 \\ -2 & -2 & -2 \end{bmatrix}, \begin{bmatrix} 2 & 2 & 2 \\ -2 & 2 & -2 \\ -2 & -2 & -2 \end{bmatrix}$

Evaluate the determinant of each matrix. ◆ See Problem 2.

Guided Practice

8. $\begin{bmatrix} 7 & 2 \\ 0 & -3 \end{bmatrix}$

To start, write the formula for the determinant of a 2 × 2 matrix.

$\det \begin{bmatrix} a & b \\ c & d \end{bmatrix} = ad - bc$

9. $\begin{bmatrix} 6 & 2 \\ -6 & -2 \end{bmatrix}$

10. $\begin{bmatrix} -1 & 3 \\ 5 & 2 \end{bmatrix}$

11. $\begin{bmatrix} 5 & 3 \\ -2 & 1 \end{bmatrix}$

12. $\begin{bmatrix} 1 & 2 & 5 \\ 3 & 1 & 0 \\ 1 & 2 & 1 \end{bmatrix}$

13. $\begin{bmatrix} 1 & 4 & 0 \\ 2 & 3 & 5 \\ 0 & 1 & 0 \end{bmatrix}$

14. $\begin{bmatrix} -2 & 4 & 1 \\ 3 & 0 & -1 \\ 1 & 2 & 1 \end{bmatrix}$

Ⓑ Apply

Evaluate each determinant.

15. $\begin{bmatrix} 4 & 5 \\ -4 & 4 \end{bmatrix}$

16. $\begin{bmatrix} -3 & 10 \\ 6 & 20 \end{bmatrix}$

17. $\begin{bmatrix} 4 & 6 & -1 \\ 2 & 3 & 2 \\ 1 & -1 & 1 \end{bmatrix}$

18. $\begin{bmatrix} -3 & 2 & -1 \\ 2 & 5 & 2 \\ 1 & -2 & 0 \end{bmatrix}$

19. **Writing** Evaluate the determinant of each matrix. Describe any patterns.

a. $\begin{bmatrix} 1 & 2 & 3 \\ 1 & 2 & 3 \\ 1 & 2 & 3 \end{bmatrix}$

b. $\begin{bmatrix} -1 & -2 & -3 \\ -3 & -2 & -1 \\ -1 & -2 & -3 \end{bmatrix}$

c. $\begin{bmatrix} 1 & 2 & 3 \\ 2 & 3 & 1 \\ 1 & 2 & 3 \end{bmatrix}$

d. $\begin{bmatrix} -1 & 2 & -3 \\ 2 & -3 & -1 \\ -1 & 2 & -3 \end{bmatrix}$

 PowerAlgebra.com

3 Lesson Check

For a digital lesson check, use the Got It questions.

Support in Algebra 2 Companion
• Lesson Check

4 Practice

Assign homework to individual students or to an entire class.

Answers

Lesson Check
1. 16
2. 7
3. The student added $ad + bc$ instead of subtracting $ad - bc$;

$$\det \begin{bmatrix} 2 & 5 \\ -3 & 1 \end{bmatrix} = (2)(1) - (-3)(5)$$
$$= 2 - (-15)$$
$$= 2 + 15 = 17$$

Practice and Problem-Solving Exercises
4. yes
5. yes
6. yes
7. no
8. −21
9. 0
10. −17
11. 11
12. 20
13. −5
14. −14
15. 36
16. −120
17. 25
18. 1
19. a. 0
   b. 0
   c. 0
   d. 0

Answers may vary. Sample: When the top row and bottom row are identical and the middle row has the same numbers as both rows, then the determinant is zero.

Determinants and Inverses

Objective To find the inverse of a matrix

In Part 1 of the lesson, you learned when two matrices are inverses and how to find a determinant.

Connect to What You Know

Here you will relate determinants to inverse matrices and explore real-world applications.

Focus Question Why is the determinant of a matrix useful?

It is sometimes easy to calculate the area of a triangle in the coordinate plane by using the formula $A = \frac{1}{2}bh$.

For the triangle shown here, the length of the base is the difference in the x-coordinates: $6 - 2 = 4$. The height is the difference in the y-coordinates: $4 - 1 = 3$. The area of the triangle is $\frac{1}{2}(4)(3) = 6$ square units.

For other triangles, the lengths of the base and height are not obvious from its graph. You can use determinants to help you find the area of a triangle given only its vertices.

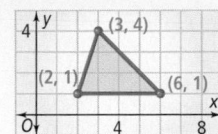

Hint
Since all polygons can be divided into triangles, you can use this method to find the area of any polygon.

Key Concept Area of a Triangle

The area of a triangle with vertices (x_1, y_1), (x_2, y_2), and (x_3, y_3) is

$$\text{Area} = \frac{1}{2} \cdot \det A, \text{ where } A = \begin{bmatrix} x_1 & y_1 & 1 \\ x_2 & y_2 & 1 \\ x_3 & y_3 & 1 \end{bmatrix}$$

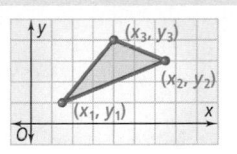

1 Launch

CONNECT THE MATH In Part 2, students will learn how determinants and inverse matrices can be used in real-life situations. First, determinants will be used to find the area of a triangle given its vertices. Next, students will learn how to determine whether matrices are inverses and apply these inverse matrices to encoding and decoding data.

FOCUS QUESTION
Can determinants be positive, negative or 0?

Q How is the determinant of $A = \begin{bmatrix} 2 & 5 \\ 3 & 12 \end{bmatrix}$ different from determinant of $B = \begin{bmatrix} 2 & 8 \\ 3 & 12 \end{bmatrix}$?

[det A = 9; det B = 0]

Q For what value of x in the matrix $\begin{bmatrix} 3 & x \\ 1 & 2 \end{bmatrix}$ is the determinant 0? a negative number? Explain. **[For det = 0, you must have $(3)(2) - 1x = 0$. so $x = 6$. For a negative number, $1x$ must be greater than 6, so $x = 10$ will result in a negative determinant.]**

2 Guided Instruction

Take Note

Q What expression can be used to find det A? $[x_1 y_2(1) + y_1(1)x_3 + (1)x_2 y_3 - (x_3 y_2(1) + y_3(1)x_1 + (1)x_2 y_1)]$

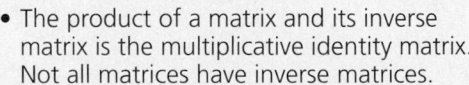

12-3 Preparing to Teach

PART 2

BIG idea Modeling   **UbD**

ESSENTIAL UNDERSTANDINGS

• The product of a matrix and its inverse matrix is the multiplicative identity matrix. Not all matrices have inverse matrices.

• A matrix has an inverse if and only if its determinant does not equal 0.

Math Background

Thus far, students have seen that the value of the determinant can verify whether a matrix has an inverse or not. Determinants can also be used by themselves to find areas of polygons. Using the coordinates of the triangle vertices to write a 3 × 3 matrix, the area of the triangle is half the absolute value of the determinant.

Inverse matrices can be used for encoding and decoding information. Coding is

used when it is necessary to classify information such as in banking or online sales. The process of encoding requires that information be entered into a matrix and then multiplied by a coded matrix to yield coded numbers. To decode the information, the coded matrix must be multiplied by the inverse matrix. Because the coded matrix must have an inverse, remind students this matrix must have the same number of rows and columns and its determinant must not equal 0.

Support Student Learning

Use the **Algebra 2 Companion** to engage and support students during instruction. See Lesson Resources at the end of this lesson for details.

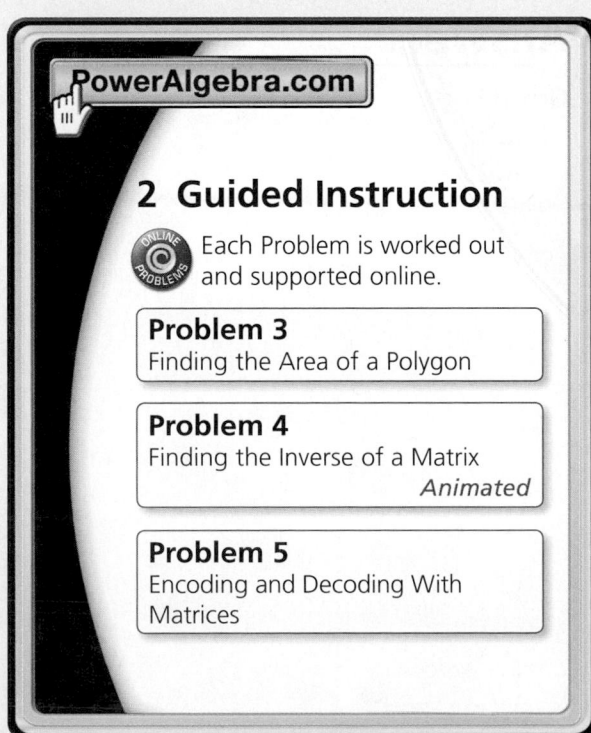

PowerAlgebra.com

2 Guided Instruction

Each Problem is worked out and supported online.

Problem 3
Finding the Area of a Polygon

Problem 4
Finding the Inverse of a Matrix
Animated

Problem 5
Encoding and Decoding With Matrices

Problem 3

Q Does it matter in which order you list the points? Explain. **[No, as long as you list the coordinates of each point in their own row. The naming of the vertices as (x_1, y_1), (x_2, y_2), and (x_3, y_3) is arbitrary.]**

Q How would you check for reasonableness if none of the vertices were located at $(0, 0)$? **[Use half of the area of the rectangle with dimensions of (greatest x-coordinate − least x-coordinate) and (greatest y-coordinate − least y-coordinate).]**

Got It?

Q What matrices would you use to find the area of the triangles in 3a and 3b?

$$\begin{bmatrix} 1 & 3 & 1 \\ -3 & 0 & 1 \\ 5 & 0 & 1 \end{bmatrix} ; \begin{bmatrix} 1 & 3 & 1 \\ 5 & 8 & 1 \\ 9 & -1 & 1 \end{bmatrix}$$

Q What values for reasonableness would you use to check the areas you find for 3a and 3b? What expressions would you use to find these values? **[half of the area of the rectangle formed by the difference of the greatest and least x and y coordinates; 3a: $(5 - (-3)) \cdot (3 - 0) \cdot 0.5 = 12$; 3b: $(9 - 1) \cdot (8 - (-1)) \cdot 0.5 = 36$]**

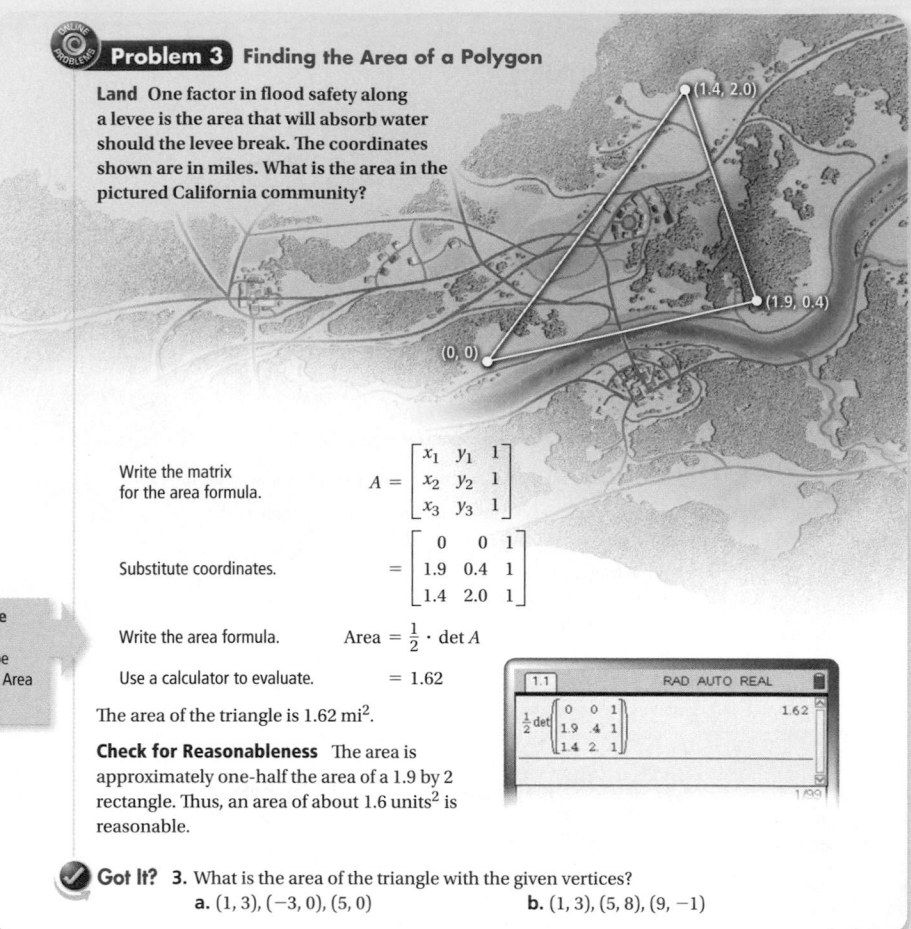

Problem 3 Finding the Area of a Polygon

Land One factor in flood safety along a levee is the area that will absorb water should the levee break. The coordinates shown are in miles. What is the area in the pictured California community?

Write the matrix for the area formula.

$$A = \begin{bmatrix} x_1 & y_1 & 1 \\ x_2 & y_2 & 1 \\ x_3 & y_3 & 1 \end{bmatrix}$$

Substitute coordinates.

$$= \begin{bmatrix} 0 & 0 & 1 \\ 1.9 & 0.4 & 1 \\ 1.4 & 2.0 & 1 \end{bmatrix}$$

Think

Why must you use absolute value? A determinant can be positive or negative. Area must be positive.

Write the area formula.　Area $= \frac{1}{2} \cdot \det A$

Use a calculator to evaluate.　$= 1.62$

The area of the triangle is 1.62 mi^2.

Check for Reasonableness The area is approximately one-half the area of a 1.9 by 2 rectangle. Thus, an area of about 1.6 units^2 is reasonable.

Got It? **3.** What is the area of the triangle with the given vertices?
a. $(1, 3), (-3, 0), (5, 0)$　　　　**b.** $(1, 3), (5, 8), (9, -1)$

The determinant of a matrix can help you determine whether the matrix has an inverse. If an inverse matrix exists, you can use the determinant to find the inverse.

Answers

Got It?

3. a. 12 units^2
　　b. 28 units^2

Key Concept   Inverse of a 2 × 2 Matrix

Let $A = \begin{bmatrix} a & b \\ c & d \end{bmatrix}$.

If det $A = 0$, then A is a **singular matrix** and has no inverse.

If det $A \neq 0$, then the inverse of A, written A^{-1}, is

$$A^{-1} = \frac{1}{\det A}\begin{bmatrix} d & -b \\ -c & a \end{bmatrix} = \frac{1}{ad - bc}\begin{bmatrix} d & -b \\ -c & a \end{bmatrix}.$$

Hint
You switch the elements on the main diagonal. You change the sign on the other diagonal.

Problem 4   Finding the Inverse of a Matrix

Does the matrix $A = \begin{bmatrix} -3 & 6 \\ -1 & 3 \end{bmatrix}$ have an inverse? If it does, what is A^{-1}?

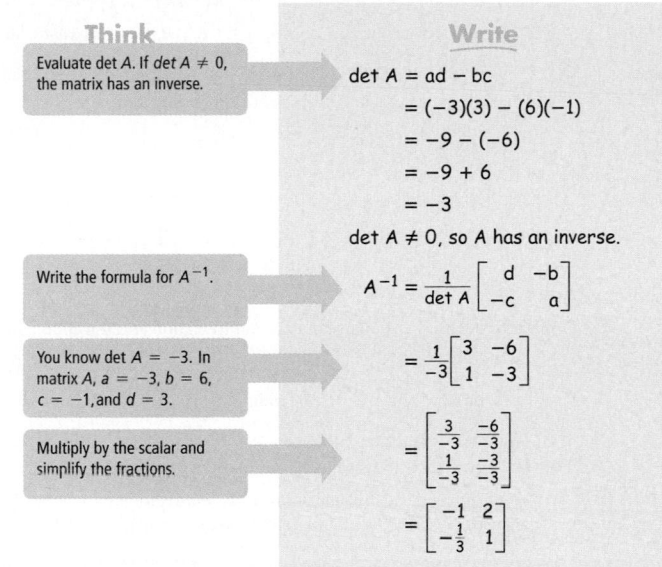

Think

Evaluate det A. If det $A \neq 0$, the matrix has an inverse.

Write

det $A = ad - bc$
$= (-3)(3) - (6)(-1)$
$= -9 - (-6)$
$= -9 + 6$
$= -3$
det $A \neq 0$, so A has an inverse.

Write the formula for A^{-1}.

$A^{-1} = \frac{1}{\det A}\begin{bmatrix} d & -b \\ -c & a \end{bmatrix}$

You know det $A = -3$. In matrix A, $a = -3$, $b = 6$, $c = -1$, and $d = 3$.

$= \frac{1}{-3}\begin{bmatrix} 3 & -6 \\ 1 & -3 \end{bmatrix}$

Multiply by the scalar and simplify the fractions.

$= \begin{bmatrix} \frac{3}{-3} & \frac{-6}{-3} \\ \frac{1}{-3} & \frac{-3}{-3} \end{bmatrix}$

$= \begin{bmatrix} -1 & 2 \\ -\frac{1}{3} & 1 \end{bmatrix}$

Hint
You can check your answer using a graphing calculator. Either verify that $AA^{-1} = I$ or evaluate A^{-1} directly.

✓ **Got It?**   4. Does the matrix have an inverse? If so, what is it?

a. $A = \begin{bmatrix} 4 & 2 \\ 3 & 2 \end{bmatrix}$ b. $B = \begin{bmatrix} 2 & 5 \\ -4 & -10 \end{bmatrix}$ c. $C = \begin{bmatrix} 7 & 4 \\ 5 & 3 \end{bmatrix}$

Take Note

Q Why does a matrix not have an inverse if its determinant is zero? [**A determinant of zero would cause division by zero when you tried to find the inverse, and division by zero is not defined.**]

Problem 4   ERROR PREVENTION

Q When you check the inverse, you find that your matrix is not the correct matrix. What are the possible errors you might have made? [**Samples: You may have calculated the determinant incorrectly; one or more signs may have been changed incorrectly; you may have forgotten to switch the numbers on the diagonal; you may have forgotten to multiply by the scalar; the inverse matrix may have been simplified incorrectly.**]

Q If you do not have access to a graphing calculator, what would you have to do to check if the matrix you found is the inverse? [**Multiply the original matrix by the matrix you found to see if you get the identity matrix, *I*.**]

EXTENSION

Q If you forget to change the diagonals of the matrix when calculating the determinant, how will the matrix you find be different from the inverse matrix? [**The elements on the main diagonal will be in the wrong corners and the signs of the elements on the other diagonal will be wrong.**]

Got It?

Q What are the determinants of 4a, 4b, and 4c? [**2, 0 and 1**]

Q How do you find the inverse if it exists for 4a, 4b, and 4c? [**You multiply by the scalar $\frac{1}{\det A}$;**
$\begin{bmatrix} 2 & -2 \\ -3 & 4 \end{bmatrix}$; $\begin{bmatrix} -10 & -5 \\ 4 & 2 \end{bmatrix}$; and $\begin{bmatrix} 3 & -4 \\ -5 & 7 \end{bmatrix}$]

Additional Problems

3. As part of a remodeling project, you want to paint a triangular area on a cement floor that is marked along the wall with decorative stones every meter. Using the stones as a reference, you determine the coordinates of the vertices of the area you want to paint are (4, 6), (12, 9), and (7, 11). What is the area of the triangle?

ANSWER 15.5 sq m

4. Does the matrix
$A = \begin{bmatrix} 4 & -4 \\ -3 & 6 \end{bmatrix}$ have an inverse? If it does, what is A^{-1}?

ANSWER yes; $\begin{bmatrix} \frac{1}{2} & \frac{1}{3} \\ \frac{1}{4} & \frac{1}{3} \end{bmatrix}$

5. You stored your credit card numbers in a file after they were coded by the matrix
$\begin{bmatrix} -5 & 3 \\ 3 & -7 \end{bmatrix}$. One of the numbers in the file is −1, −14, −16, −22, 10, 10, −31, −29, −15, −2, −6, 8, −32, −32, 3, 7. What is the original credit card number?

ANSWER 2455 1187 3231 5532

Answers

Got It? (continued)

4. a. yes; $\begin{bmatrix} 1 & -1 \\ -\frac{3}{2} & 2 \end{bmatrix}$

b. no

c. yes; $\begin{bmatrix} 3 & -4 \\ -5 & 7 \end{bmatrix}$

Problem 5

Q Could you use a coding matrix with three columns? Explain. **[No; the credit card has sixteen digits, which cannot be divided evenly into three rows.]**

Got It?

Q Would you change matrix *A* in any way to code the credit card number using the new coding matrix? Explain. **[No; since the coding matrix still has two columns, matrix *A* does not have to be altered to allow multiplication.]**

3 Lesson Check

Do you know HOW?

• If students are unsure whether the matrix they found for Exercise 2 is the inverse, remind them that they can check the answer by multiplying the matrix by the inverse.

Do you UNDERSTAND?

• For Exercise 3, if students cannot figure out why a 2 × 3 matrix does not have a multiplicative inverse, ask them what kinds of matrices have determinants.

Close

Q What steps do you take to find the inverse of a 2 × 2 matrix *A*? **[Find the determinant, if it exists. Switch the elements of the main diagonal of the matrix, and switch the signs of the elements of the other diagonal. Multiply the new matrix by the scalar $\frac{1}{\det A}$, and simplify the resulting matrix. Check.]**

PowerAlgebra.com

3 Lesson Check

For a digital lesson check, use the Got It questions.

Support in Algebra 2 Companion
• Lesson Check

4 Practice

Assign homework to individual students or to an entire class.

 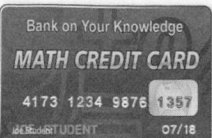

Problem 5 Encoding and Decoding With Matrices

A How can you use matrix multiplication with matrix *C* to encode the account number from the credit card?

$$C = \begin{bmatrix} 2 & -1 \\ 3 & 5 \end{bmatrix}$$

Step 1 Place the card information in a matrix with appropriate dimensions for multiplication by the coding matrix.

$$A = \begin{bmatrix} 4 & 1 & 7 & 3 & 1 & 2 & 3 & 4 \\ 9 & 8 & 7 & 6 & 1 & 3 & 5 & 7 \end{bmatrix}$$

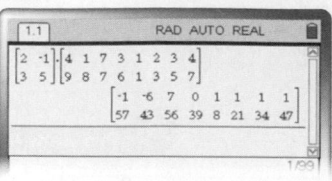

Step 2 Multiply the coding matrix and the information matrix to encode the information. Use a calculator.

$$CA = \begin{bmatrix} 2 & -1 \\ 3 & 5 \end{bmatrix}\begin{bmatrix} 4 & 1 & 7 & 3 & 1 & 2 & 3 & 4 \\ 9 & 8 & 7 & 6 & 1 & 3 & 5 & 7 \end{bmatrix}$$

$$= \begin{bmatrix} -1 & -6 & 7 & 0 & 1 & 1 & 1 & 1 \\ 57 & 43 & 56 & 39 & 8 & 21 & 34 & 47 \end{bmatrix}$$

Step 3 The coded account number is $-1, -6, 7, 0, 1, 1, 1, 1, 57, 43, 56, 39, 8, 21, 34, 47$.

B How do you use a decoding matrix to recover the account number?

The decoding matrix is the inverse of the encoding matrix *C*. Use a calculator to find C^{-1}.

$$C^{-1} = \begin{bmatrix} \frac{5}{13} & \frac{1}{13} \\ -\frac{3}{13} & \frac{2}{13} \end{bmatrix}$$

Multiply the coded information by C^{-1}. Use a calculator.

$$\begin{bmatrix} \frac{5}{13} & \frac{1}{13} \\ -\frac{3}{13} & \frac{2}{13} \end{bmatrix}\begin{bmatrix} -1 & -6 & 7 & 0 & 1 & 1 & 1 & 1 \\ 57 & 43 & 56 & 39 & 8 & 21 & 34 & 47 \end{bmatrix} = \begin{bmatrix} 4 & 1 & 7 & 3 & 1 & 2 & 3 & 4 \\ 9 & 8 & 7 & 6 & 1 & 3 & 5 & 7 \end{bmatrix}$$

 Got It? 5. a. How can you use matrix multiplication and the coding matrix $\begin{bmatrix} 4 & 8 \\ -2 & 4 \end{bmatrix}$ to encode the credit card account number in Problem 5?

b. How can you use a decoding matrix to recover the credit card number?

Focus Question Why is the determinant of a matrix useful?

Answer You can use the determinant of a matrix to find the area of a triangle. You can also use the determinant to find the inverse of a matrix, if one exists.

Lesson Check

Do you know HOW?

Find the inverse of each matrix, if it exists.

1. $\begin{bmatrix} 4 & 2 \\ 10 & 5 \end{bmatrix}$

2. $\begin{bmatrix} 5 & 2 \\ 7 & 3 \end{bmatrix}$

Do you UNDERSTAND?

3. **Reasoning** Explain why a 2 × 3 matrix does not have a multiplicative inverse.

Answers

Got It? (continued)

5. a. 88, 68, 84, 60, 12, 32, 52, 72, 28, 30, 14, 18, 2, 8, 14, 20

b. Multiply the coded information by the inverse of the coding matrix and get the following:

$$\begin{bmatrix} 4 & 1 & 7 & 3 & 1 & 2 & 3 & 4 \\ 9 & 8 & 7 & 6 & 1 & 3 & 5 & 7 \end{bmatrix}$$

Lesson Check

1. does not exist

2. $\begin{bmatrix} 3 & -2 \\ -7 & 5 \end{bmatrix}$

3. Answers may vary. Sample: A 2 × 3 matrix does not have a multiplicative inverse because the set of 2 × 3 matrices has no multiplicative identity.

Practice and Problem-Solving Exercises

See Problem 3.

A Practice

4. Use the map to determine the approximate area of the Bermuda Triangle.

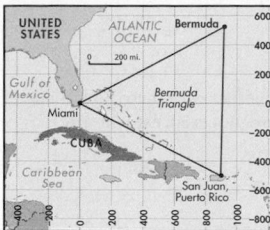

Determine whether each matrix has an inverse. If an inverse matrix exists, find it.

See Problem 4.

Guided Practice

5. $\begin{bmatrix} 2 & -1 \\ 1 & 0 \end{bmatrix}$

To start, find the determinant of the matrix.

$\det\begin{bmatrix} 2 & -1 \\ 1 & 0 \end{bmatrix} = (2)(0) - (-1)(1) = 1$

6. $\begin{bmatrix} 2 & 3 \\ 1 & 1 \end{bmatrix}$ **7.** $\begin{bmatrix} 2 & 3 \\ 2 & 4 \end{bmatrix}$ **8.** $\begin{bmatrix} 1 & 3 \\ 2 & 0 \end{bmatrix}$ **9.** $\begin{bmatrix} 6 & -8 \\ -3 & 4 \end{bmatrix}$

10. Use the coding matrix $C = \begin{bmatrix} 2 & -1 \\ 3 & 5 \end{bmatrix}$ to encode the phone number (555) 358-0001.

See Problem 5.

B Apply

11. Think About a Plan Use matrices to find the area of the figure.
• What shapes do you know how to find the area of?
• Can the polygon be broken into these shapes?
• How many shapes will you need to break the polygon into?

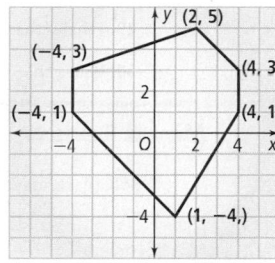

12. Writing Suppose $A = \begin{bmatrix} a & b \\ c & d \end{bmatrix}$ has an inverse. In your own words, describe how to switch or change the elements of A to write A^{-1}.

13. Geometry Use matrices to find the area of the figure at the right. Check your result by using standard area formulas.

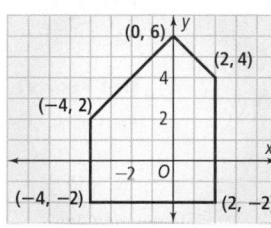

14. Error Analysis A student wrote $\begin{bmatrix} 1 & \frac{1}{2} \\ \frac{1}{3} & \frac{1}{4} \end{bmatrix}$ as the inverse of $\begin{bmatrix} 1 & 2 \\ 3 & 4 \end{bmatrix}$.
What mistake did the student make? Explain your reasoning.

---

4 Practice

ASSIGNMENT GUIDE
Basic: 4–14
Average: 4–26
Standardized Test Prep: 27–30
Mixed Review: 31–38
Reasoning exercises have blue headings.
Applications exercises have red headings.

EXERCISE 13: Use the Think About a Plan worksheet in the **Student Companion** (also available in the Teaching Resources in print and online) to further support students' development in becoming independent learners.

HOMEWORK QUICK CHECK
To check students' understanding of key skills and concepts, go over Exercises 4, 6, 11, 13, and 14.

Practice and Problem-Solving Exercises

4. 466,250 mi^2

5. yes; $\begin{bmatrix} 0 & 1 \\ -1 & 2 \end{bmatrix}$

6. yes; $\begin{bmatrix} -1 & 3 \\ 1 & -2 \end{bmatrix}$

7. yes; $\begin{bmatrix} 2 & -1.5 \\ -1 & 1 \end{bmatrix}$

8. yes; $\begin{bmatrix} 0 & \frac{1}{2} \\ \frac{1}{3} & -\frac{1}{6} \end{bmatrix}$

9. no

10. 2, 10, 10, 6, 9, 55, 15, 15, 9, 20

11. 44 units^2

12. Answers may vary. Sample: Form a new matrix by switching the element in row 1, column 1 with the element in row 2, column 2. Then replace the other two elements with their opposites. Finally, divide each element by the determinant of the original matrix.

13. 38 units^2

14. The student found the inverse of each individual element of the matrix and NOT the inverse of the entire matrix.
The inverse of $\begin{bmatrix} 1 & 2 \\ 3 & 4 \end{bmatrix}$ is $\begin{bmatrix} -2 & 1 \\ \frac{3}{2} & -\frac{1}{2} \end{bmatrix}$.

Answers

Practice and Problem-Solving
Exercises (continued)

15. 0

16. 9

17. −30

18. −3

19. yes; $\begin{bmatrix} -3 & 4 \\ 1 & -1 \end{bmatrix}$

20. yes; $\begin{bmatrix} 7 & 11 \\ 2 & 3 \end{bmatrix}$

21. yes; $\begin{bmatrix} 0.5 & 0 \\ 0 & 0.5 \end{bmatrix}$

22. $\begin{bmatrix} -4 & -3.5 & 2 \\ -5 & -5 & 3 \\ 2 & 2 & -1 \end{bmatrix}$

23. yes; $\begin{bmatrix} 0.4 & 0.4 & 0.2 \\ -0.6 & -0.6 & 0.2 \\ -0.2 & 0.8 & 0.4 \end{bmatrix}$

24. $\begin{bmatrix} 0 & \frac{1}{7} & \frac{2}{7} \\ \frac{1}{4} & \frac{3}{14} & -\frac{1}{14} \\ \frac{1}{2} & 0 & 0 \end{bmatrix}$

25. 6

26. Check students' work.

Standardized Test Prep

27. 15

28. $\frac{1}{2}$

29. $\frac{1}{56}$

30. 15

Mixed Review

31. $\begin{bmatrix} 2 & 5 \\ 1 & 1 \end{bmatrix}$

32. $\begin{bmatrix} -10 & 19 \\ -20 & 7 \end{bmatrix}$

33. 720

34. 362,880

35. $1.08972864 \times 10^{10}$

36. 110,880

37. no solution

38. $(6, 0, -3)$

Evaluate each determinant.

15. $\begin{bmatrix} -\frac{1}{2} & 2 \\ -2 & 8 \end{bmatrix}$

16. $\begin{bmatrix} 6 & 9 \\ 3 & 6 \end{bmatrix}$

17. $\begin{bmatrix} 0 & 2 & -3 \\ 1 & 2 & 4 \\ -2 & 0 & 1 \end{bmatrix}$

18. $\begin{bmatrix} 5 & 1 & 0 \\ 0 & 2 & -1 \\ -2 & -3 & 1 \end{bmatrix}$

Determine whether each matrix has an inverse. If an inverse matrix exists, find it. If it does not exist, explain why.

19. $\begin{bmatrix} 1 & 4 \\ 1 & 3 \end{bmatrix}$

20. $\begin{bmatrix} -3 & 11 \\ 2 & -7 \end{bmatrix}$

21. $\begin{bmatrix} 2 & 0 \\ 0 & 2 \end{bmatrix}$

22. $\begin{bmatrix} -2 & 1 & -1 \\ 2 & 0 & 4 \\ 0 & 2 & 5 \end{bmatrix}$

23. $\begin{bmatrix} 2 & 0 & -1 \\ -1 & -1 & 1 \\ 3 & 2 & 0 \end{bmatrix}$

24. $\begin{bmatrix} 0 & 0 & 2 \\ 1 & 4 & -2 \\ 3 & -2 & 1 \end{bmatrix}$

> **Hint** Use the formula to find the inverses of the 2 × 2 matrices. Use a calculator to find the inverses of the 3 × 3 matrices.

25. Reasoning For what value of x will matrix A have no inverse? $A = \begin{bmatrix} 1 & 2 \\ 3 & x \end{bmatrix}$

26. Open Ended Write a 2 × 2 matrix that has an inverse. Use the matrix to encode your telephone number (including the area-code).

Standardized Test Prep

GRIDDED RESPONSE

SAT/ACT

27. What is the determinant of $\begin{bmatrix} -2 & -3 \\ 5 & 0 \end{bmatrix}$?

28. If $A = \begin{bmatrix} 4 & 2 \\ -3 & -1 \end{bmatrix}$, and the inverse of A is $x \begin{bmatrix} -1 & -2 \\ 3 & 4 \end{bmatrix}$, what is the value of x? Enter your answer as a fraction.

29. What is the value of $\frac{6!}{8!}$? Give your answer as a fraction in simplest terms.

30. If $\log(7y - 5) = 2$, what is the value of y?

Mixed Review

Solve each matrix equation. ◀ See Lesson 12-2.

31. $2\begin{bmatrix} -1 & 3 \\ -2 & 0 \end{bmatrix} - 3X = \begin{bmatrix} -8 & -9 \\ -7 & -3 \end{bmatrix}$

32. $2X + 3\begin{bmatrix} 4 & -6 \\ 8 & -3 \end{bmatrix} = \begin{bmatrix} -8 & 20 \\ -16 & 5 \end{bmatrix}$

Evaluate each expression. ◀ See Lesson 11-1.

33. $6!$

34. $9!$

35. $\frac{15!}{5!}$

36. $\frac{12!}{6!3!}$

Get Ready! To prepare for Lesson 12-4, do Exercises 37 and 38.

Solve each system. ◀ See Lesson 3-5.

37. $\begin{cases} x = 5 \\ x - y + z = 5 \\ x + y - z = -5 \end{cases}$

38. $\begin{cases} x - y - z = 9 \\ 3x + 2z = 12 \\ x = y - 2z \end{cases}$

Additional Instructional Support

Algebra 2 Companion

Students can use the **Algebra 2 Companion** worktext (4 pages) as you teach the lesson. Use the Companion to support

- New Vocabulary
- Key Concepts
- Got It for each Problem
- Lesson Check

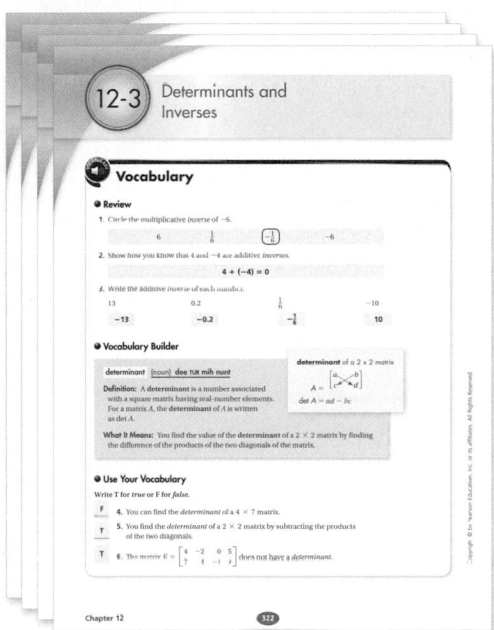

ELL Support

Use Graphic Organizers To aid student understanding of the process of finding the determinant, refer to the diagonal multiplications by their physical directions as you use the board in instruction. Draw the arrows indicating the directions of multiplication, and use real numbers instead of the notation for the elements. In addition, as you draw the arrows through the diagonals whose values are being multiplied, place the product value at the end of each arrow tip. Show the sums of the product results above and below the matrix for a 3×3 matrix to indicate the source of the values.

5 Assess & Remediate

Lesson Quiz

1. If $A = \begin{bmatrix} 1 & 3 \\ -1 & 4 \end{bmatrix}$ and $B = \begin{bmatrix} 4 & -3 \\ 1 & 1 \end{bmatrix}$, are A and B inverses?

2. What is the determinant of $\begin{bmatrix} -4 & 3 \\ 1 & 2 \end{bmatrix}$?

3. **Do you UNDERSTAND?** You want to buy a corner lot shaped like a triangle. You use the scale of a map to measure the coordinates of the lot in feet. They are (0, 0), (50, 45), and (−25, 90). What is the area of the lot?

4. Find the inverse of the matrix $\begin{bmatrix} -3 & -6 \\ 1 & 3 \end{bmatrix}$ if it exists.

5. What would the credit card number 3087 2377 1988 3579 be coded by the matrix $\begin{bmatrix} -1 & 4 \\ 2 & 1 \end{bmatrix}$?

ANSWERS TO LESSON QUIZ

1. no
2. −11
3. 2812.5 sq ft
4. $\begin{bmatrix} -1 & -2 \\ \frac{1}{3} & 1 \end{bmatrix}$
5. 1, 36, 24, 25, 10, 17, 21, 29, 7, 9, 24, 22, 7, 11, 21, 23

PRESCRIPTION FOR REMEDIATION

Use the student work on the Lesson Quiz to prescribe a differentiated review assignment:

Points	Differentiated Remediation
0–2	Intervention
3–4	On-level
5	Extension

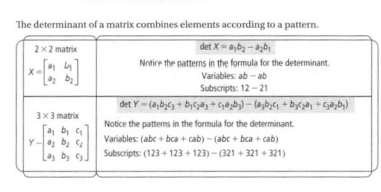

5 Assess & Remediate

Assign the Lesson Quiz. Appropriate intervention, practice, or enrichment is automatically generated based on student performance.

Intervention

- **Reteaching** (2 pages) Provides reteaching and practice exercises for the key lesson concepts. Use with struggling students or absent students.
- **English Language Learner Support** Helps students develop and reinforce mathematical vocabulary and key concepts.

All-in-One Resources/Online
Reteaching

12-3 Reteaching
Determinants and Inverses

The determinant of a matrix combines elements according to a pattern.

2×2 matrix $X = \begin{bmatrix} a_1 & b_1 \\ a_2 & b_2 \end{bmatrix}$	$\det X = a_1b_2 - a_2b_1$ Notice the patterns in the formula for the determinant. Variables: $ab - ab$ Subscripts: $12 - 21$
3×3 matrix $Y = \begin{bmatrix} a_1 & b_1 & c_1 \\ a_2 & b_2 & c_2 \\ a_3 & b_3 & c_3 \end{bmatrix}$	$\det Y = (a_1b_2c_3 + b_1c_2a_3 + c_1a_2b_3) - (a_3b_2c_1 + b_3c_2a_1 + c_3a_2b_1)$ Notice the patterns in the formula for the determinant. Variables: $(abc + bca + cab) - (abc + bca + cab)$ Subscripts: $(123 + 123 + 123) - (321 + 321 + 321)$

Problem

Let $B = \begin{bmatrix} 1 & 2 & 3 \\ 4 & 5 & 6 \\ 7 & 8 & 9 \end{bmatrix}$. What is the determinant of B?

Step 1 Name the matrix elements.
$a_1 = 1, b_1 = 2, c_1 = 3, a_2 = 4, b_2 = 5, c_2 = 6, a_3 = 7, b_3 = 8, c_3 = 9$

Step 2 Substitute in the determinant formula and simplify.
$\det B = (a_1b_2c_3 + b_1c_2a_3 + c_1a_2b_3) - (a_3b_2c_1 + b_3c_2a_1 + c_3a_2b_1)$
$= (1 \cdot 5 \cdot 9 + 2 \cdot 6 \cdot 7 + 3 \cdot 4 \cdot 8) - (7 \cdot 5 \cdot 3 + 8 \cdot 6 \cdot 1 + 9 \cdot 4 \cdot 2)$
$= (45 + 84 + 96) - (105 + 48 + 72)$
$= 0$

Exercises

Evaluate the determinant of each matrix.

1. $\begin{bmatrix} 3 & 3 \\ 8 & 1 \end{bmatrix}$ 21
2. $\begin{bmatrix} -3 & -2 \\ -5 & -1 \end{bmatrix}$ −7
3. $\begin{bmatrix} 4 & -7 \\ 2 & 9 \end{bmatrix}$ 50

4. $\begin{bmatrix} 6 & 2 & -3 \\ -1 & 8 & 0 \\ 3 & -7 & 4 \end{bmatrix}$ 266
5. $\begin{bmatrix} 7 & 0 & 3 \\ 0 & 8 & 2 \\ 0 & 2 & 1 \end{bmatrix}$ 28
6. $\begin{bmatrix} -3 & 3 & 9 \\ 1 & -2 & 5 \\ 5 & 1 & -6 \end{bmatrix}$ 171

All-in-One Resources/Online
English Language Learner Support

12-3 ELL Support
Determinants and Inverses

Choose the word from the list that best matches each sentence.

determinant	multiplicative identity matrix	multiplicative inverse matrix
	singular matrix	square matrix

1. The ___determinant___ of $\begin{bmatrix} 4 & 1 \\ 3 & 2 \end{bmatrix}$ is $8 - 3 = 5$.
2. A ___square matrix___ has the same number of rows and columns.
3. The ___multiplicative inverse matrix___ of matrix A can be written as A^{-1}.
4. A matrix with a determinant of zero is called a ___singular matrix___.
5. A matrix multiplied by its inverse produces the ___multiplicative identity matrix___.

Circle the determinant of the following matrices.

6. $\begin{bmatrix} 6 & 5 \\ 1 & 2 \end{bmatrix}$ Ⓐ7 Ⓑ12 Ⓒ28
7. $\begin{bmatrix} 3 & 6 \\ 2 & 4 \end{bmatrix}$ Ⓐ18 Ⓑ10 Ⓒ0
8. $\begin{bmatrix} 2 & 1 & -2 \\ -1 & -4 & 3 \\ 4 & 6 & 5 \end{bmatrix}$ Ⓐ−79 Ⓑ47 Ⓒ79

Determine whether the following matrices are inverses.

9. $A = \begin{bmatrix} 2 & -5 \\ -1 & 4 \end{bmatrix}$ $B = \begin{bmatrix} \frac{4}{3} & \frac{5}{3} \\ \frac{1}{3} & \frac{2}{3} \end{bmatrix}$ ___inverses___
10. $A = \begin{bmatrix} 3 & 6 \\ 1 & 4 \end{bmatrix}$ $B = \begin{bmatrix} \frac{2}{3} & 1 \\ \frac{1}{6} & 1 \end{bmatrix}$ ___not inverses___

Differentiated Remediation *continued*

On-Level

- **Practice** (2 pages) Provides extra practice for each lesson. For more challenging practice exercises, use the Form G Practice pages found in the All-in-One Teaching Resources and online.

- **Think About a Plan** Helps students develop specific problem-solving skills and strategies by providing scaffolded guiding questions.
- **Standardized Test Prep** Focuses on all major exercises, all major question types, and helps students prepare for the high-stakes assessments.

Extension

- **Enrichment** Provides students with interesting problems and activities that extend the concepts of the lesson.
- **Activities, Games, and Puzzles** Worksheets that can be used for concepts development, enrichment, and for fun!

Student Companion/ All-in-One Resources/Online
Practice page 1

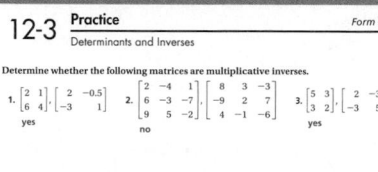

12-3 Practice *Form K*
Determinants and Inverses

Determine whether the following matrices are multiplicative inverses.

1. yes 2. no 3. yes

Evaluate the determinant of each matrix.
To start, write the formula for the determinant of a 2 × 2 matrix.

4. 17   5. 16   6. 2

7. 0   8. 1   9. 120

10. **Error Analysis** Your friend evaluated the determinant of the matrix $\begin{bmatrix} -6 & -7 \\ 3 & 2 \end{bmatrix}$ and got −9. What error did your friend make, and what is the correct determinant?
Your friend subtracted the product of *ad* from the product of *bc* rather than subtracting *bc* from *ad*. The correct determinant is 9.

11. **Open-Ended** Write a 2 × 2 matrix with a determinant of zero.
Answers may vary. Sample: $\begin{bmatrix} 6 & 4 \\ 3 & 2 \end{bmatrix}$

Student Companion/ All-in-One Resources/Online
Practice page 2

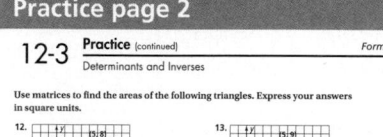

12-3 Practice (continued) *Form K*
Determinants and Inverses

Use matrices to find the areas of the following triangles. Express your answers in square units.

12. 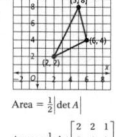   13. 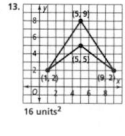 16 units²

Area = $\frac{1}{2}$ |det *A*|

Area = $\frac{1}{2}$ det $\begin{bmatrix} 2 & 2 & 1 \\ 6 & 4 & 1 \\ 5 & 8 & 1 \end{bmatrix}$

Area = 9 units²

Find the inverse of each matrix, if one exists.
To start, find the determinant of the matrix.

14. $A = \begin{bmatrix} 6 & 2 \\ 2 & 1 \end{bmatrix}$ 15. $A = \begin{bmatrix} 5 & 8 \\ 3 & 5 \end{bmatrix}$ 16. $A = \begin{bmatrix} 10 & 5 \\ 4 & 2 \end{bmatrix}$

det A = 6(1) − 2(2) = 2 $A^{-1} = \begin{bmatrix} 5 & -8 \\ -3 & 5 \end{bmatrix}$ A has no inverse.

$A^{-1} = \frac{1}{2}\begin{bmatrix} 1 & -2 \\ -2 & 6 \end{bmatrix}$

$A^{-1} = \begin{bmatrix} \frac{1}{2} & -1 \\ -1 & 3 \end{bmatrix}$

17. Your aunt's checking account number is 6143-0571-2943-3072. Use the coding matrix $C = \begin{bmatrix} -2 & 1 \\ -1 & 3 \end{bmatrix}$ to encode the account number.

$\begin{bmatrix} -10 & 7 & -4 & -3 & 3 & -10 & -7 & 0 \\ 0 & 26 & 8 & 6 & 9 & -5 & 14 & 5 \end{bmatrix}$

All-in-One Resources/Online
Enrichment

12-3 Enrichment
Determinants and Inverses

Suppose *A* and *B* are 2 × 2 matrices as follows:
$A = \begin{bmatrix} a & b \\ c & d \end{bmatrix}$, $B = \begin{bmatrix} e & f \\ g & h \end{bmatrix}$

1. What is the value of the determinant of *A*, det *A*? *ad* − *bc*

2. Evaluate det *B*. *eh* − *fg*

3. Evaluate det *A* · det *B*. *adeh* + *bcfg* − *bceh* − *adfg*

4. Compute matrix *AB*. $\begin{bmatrix} ae + bg & af + bh \\ ce + dg & cf + dh \end{bmatrix}$

5. Evaluate det(*AB*). (*ae* + *bg*)(*cf* + *dh*) − (*af* + *bh*)(*ce* + *dg*) = *adeh* + *bcfg* − *bceh* − *adfg*

6. What can you conclude? det(*AB*) = det *A* · det *B*

7. Explain your results.
The determinant of the product of two matrices is equal to the product of the determinants.

8. Suppose that a 2 × 2 matrix *A* has an inverse A^{-1}. Use the product rule to investigate how the determinant of A^{-1} is related to the determinant of *A*. det *I*; 1; $\frac{1}{\det A}$

det($A \cdot A^{-1}$) = det *A* · det A^{-1}
_____ = det *A* · det A^{-1}
_____ = det *A* · det A^{-1}
_____ = det A^{-1}

9. Explain your results.
The determinant of the inverse of a matrix is equal to the reciprocal (inverse) of the determinant of the original matrix.

Student Companion/ All-in-One Resources/Online
Think About a Plan

12-3 Think About a Plan
Determinants and Inverses

Geometry Find the area of the figure to the right.

Understanding the Problem

1. You know how to find the area of what shape using matrices? triangle

2. Can you divide the figure into these shapes? Explain.
Answers may vary. Sample: Yes; by picking a vertex and drawing two segments from it to the other two nonadjacent vertices, I can divide the figure into 3 triangles

3. What is the problem asking you to find?
the area of the figure by dividing it into triangles and adding the areas of the triangles

Planning the Solution

4. Divide the figure into these shapes. List the vertices of the shapes.
Answers may vary. Sample: (0, 6), (2, 4), (−4, 2); (2, 4), (2, −2), (−4, 2); (2, −2), (−4, −2), (−4, 2)

5. Write an expression to find the area of the figure. Answers may vary. Sample:
$\frac{1}{2}$ det $\begin{bmatrix} 0 & 6 & 1 \\ 2 & 4 & 1 \\ -4 & 2 & 1 \end{bmatrix}$ + $\frac{1}{2}$ det $\begin{bmatrix} 2 & 4 & 1 \\ 2 & -2 & 1 \\ -4 & 2 & 1 \end{bmatrix}$ + $\frac{1}{2}$ det $\begin{bmatrix} 2 & -2 & 1 \\ -4 & -2 & 1 \\ -4 & 2 & 1 \end{bmatrix}$

Getting an Answer
6. Simplify your expression to find the area of the figure. 3B units²

7. Is your answer reasonable? Explain.
Answers may vary. Sample: Yes; the figure fits within a rectangle that is 6 units wide and 8 units high, so an area somewhat less than 48 units² is reasonable

Student Companion/ All-in-One Resources/Online
Standardized Test Prep

12-3 Standardized Test Prep
Determinants and Inverses

Gridded Response

Solve each exercise and enter your answer in the grid provided.

1. What is the determinant of $\begin{bmatrix} 4 & -2 \\ 5 & -3 \end{bmatrix}$?

2. If $A = \begin{bmatrix} 2 & 1 \\ -9 & 3 \end{bmatrix}$ and the inverse of *A* is *x* · $\begin{bmatrix} 3 & -1 \\ 9 & 2 \end{bmatrix}$ what is the value of *x*?

3. If $\begin{bmatrix} 6 & 2 \\ 4 & 1 \end{bmatrix}$ and $A^{-1} = \begin{bmatrix} x & 1 \\ 2 & -3 \end{bmatrix}$ what is the value of *x*?

4. What is the determinant of $\begin{bmatrix} 1 & 0 & 2 \\ -1 & 2 & 3 \\ 0 & 3 & 2 \end{bmatrix}$?

5. What is the area of a triangle with vertices at (−5, 0), (3, −1), and (2, 6)?

Answers

Online Teacher Resource Center
Activities, Games, and Puzzles

12-3 Puzzle: That's Sum Matrix!
Determinants and Inverses

Match each exercise to its answer. Write the exercise number of the corresponding letter into the empty puzzle grid at the bottom of the page. All of your grid entries are correct if the sum of each column, row, and diagonal is 34.

1. Find the inverse of $\begin{bmatrix} 2 & 3 \\ 1 & 4 \end{bmatrix}$. H   A. −2

2. Evaluate $\begin{bmatrix} 3 & 4 \\ 1 & 5 \end{bmatrix}$. B   B. 11

3. Evaluate the determinant of $\begin{bmatrix} 6 & 7 \\ 8 & 9 \end{bmatrix}$. A   C. 0

4. Find $\begin{bmatrix} 3 & 5 \\ 1 & 2 \end{bmatrix}^{-1}$. G   D. −9

5. Evaluate det $\begin{bmatrix} 3 & 4 \\ 6 & 8 \end{bmatrix}$. C   E. $\begin{bmatrix} 5 & -11 \\ -4 & 9 \end{bmatrix}$

6. If $M = \begin{bmatrix} 9 & 11 \\ 4 & 5 \end{bmatrix}$, find M^{-1}. E   F. $\begin{bmatrix} 0.3 & -0.7 \\ -0.2 & 0.8 \end{bmatrix}$

7. Find the inverse of $\begin{bmatrix} 8 & 7 \\ 2 & 3 \end{bmatrix}$. F   G. $\begin{bmatrix} 2 & -5 \\ -1 & 3 \end{bmatrix}$

8. Evaluate $\begin{bmatrix} -1 & 4 \\ 0 & 9 \end{bmatrix}$. D   H. $\begin{bmatrix} 0.8 & -0.6 \\ -0.2 & 0.4 \end{bmatrix}$

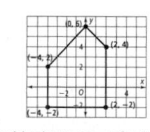

16	A. 3	B. 2	13
C. 5	10	11	D. 8
9	E. 6	F. 7	12
G. 4	15	14	H. 1

12-4
PART 1

Inverse Matrices and Systems

Objective To solve matrix equations using matrix inverses and multiplication

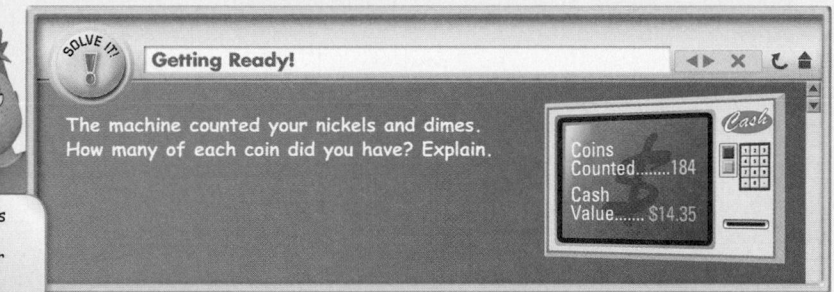

Getting Ready!

The machine counted your nickels and dimes. How many of each coin did you have? Explain.

Coins Counted........184
Cash Value....... $14.35

Some machines charge a percentage for counting your coins.

In Chapter 3, you used row operations on a matrix to solve a system of equations. Now you will solve systems by solving a matrix equation.

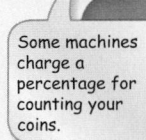

Lesson Vocabulary
• coefficient matrix
• variable matrix
• constant matrix

Focus Question How can you solve a matrix equation of the form $AX = B$?

If matrix A has an inverse, you can use it to solve the matrix equation $AX = B$. Multiply each side of the equation by A^{-1} *on the left* to find X.

Write the matrix equation. $\qquad AX = B$

Multiply each side by A^{-1}. $\qquad A^{-1}AX = A^{-1}B$

$A^{-1}A = I$, the identity matrix. $\qquad IX = A^{-1}B$

$IX = X$ $\qquad X = A^{-1}B$

Hint
Remember that matrix multiplication is not commutative.

Notice that you cannot multiply AX by A^{-1} on the *left* and multiply B by A^{-1} on the *right*.

Suppose $A = \begin{bmatrix} 2 & 5 \\ 1 & 3 \end{bmatrix}$, $A^{-1} = \begin{bmatrix} 3 & -5 \\ -1 & 2 \end{bmatrix}$, and $B = \begin{bmatrix} 2 & 2 \\ 1 & 1 \end{bmatrix}$. Solve $AX = B$ for X.

Correct

$A^{-1}AX = A^{-1}B$

$X = \begin{bmatrix} 3 & -5 \\ -1 & 2 \end{bmatrix}\begin{bmatrix} 2 & 2 \\ 1 & 1 \end{bmatrix} = \begin{bmatrix} 1 & 1 \\ 0 & 0 \end{bmatrix}$

Check

$AX = \begin{bmatrix} 2 & 5 \\ 1 & 3 \end{bmatrix}\begin{bmatrix} 1 & 1 \\ 0 & 0 \end{bmatrix} = \begin{bmatrix} 2 & 2 \\ 1 & 1 \end{bmatrix} = B$ ✔

Incorrect

$A^{-1}AX = BA^{-1}$

$X = \begin{bmatrix} 2 & 2 \\ 1 & 1 \end{bmatrix}\begin{bmatrix} 3 & -5 \\ -1 & 2 \end{bmatrix} = \begin{bmatrix} 4 & -6 \\ 2 & -3 \end{bmatrix}$

Check

$AX = \begin{bmatrix} 2 & 5 \\ 1 & 3 \end{bmatrix}\begin{bmatrix} 4 & -6 \\ 2 & -3 \end{bmatrix} = \begin{bmatrix} 18 & -27 \\ 10 & -15 \end{bmatrix}$ ✘

---

1 Interactive Learning

Solve It!

PURPOSE To write and solve a system of linear equations in two variables

PROCESS Students may

• choose two variables to represent the number of each type of coin and write and solve a system of linear equations.

• guess and check.

FACILITATE

Q What system of equations can you write to represent the unknown number of nickels and dimes in the machine? **[If *n* and *d* represent the number of nickels and dimes respectively, then two equations are $0.05n + 0.10d = 14.35$ and $n + d = 184$]**

Q What two methods can you use to solve this system of equations algebraically? **[substitution and elimination]**

ANSWER See Solve It in Answers on next page.

CONNECT THE MATH In the Solve It, students solve a system of linear equations in two variables algebraically. In this lesson, students will solve systems of linear equations in two or three variables by writing equivalent matrix equations and using matrix operations and properties.

12-4 Preparing to Teach

PART 1

BIG idea Modeling

UbD

ESSENTIAL UNDERSTANDINGS

• Systems of linear equations can be modeled by matrix equations.

• Some matrix equations of the form $AX = B$ can be solved by multiplying each side of the equation on the left by A^{-1}, the inverse of matrix A.

Math Background

Students have seen that matrices can be added, subtracted, and multiplied. Students are also able to find the inverse of the matrix and a matrix determinant. These skills are necessary to solve matrix equations. It might be helpful to compare solving matrices with solving an equation in one variable. For example, students often learn to solve the equation $5x = 50$ by performing the "inverse" operation.

Because 5 is multiplied by the variable, the equation can be solved by dividing each side by 5. The same concept is used to solve matrix equations. By multiplying each side by the inverse of a matrix, it is possible to find a solution matrix.

Both solving matrix equations and writing linear systems as matrices prepare students for solving systems of linear equations. Emphasize the importance of matrices as students learn they can solve linear systems of 2 equations and 2 unknowns, 3 equations and 3 unknowns, etc. Matrices are used in numerous real-life situations and are a powerful tool in both mathematical theory and practice.

Support Student Learning

Use the **Algebra 2 Companion** to engage and support students during instruction. See Lesson Resources at the end of this lesson for details.

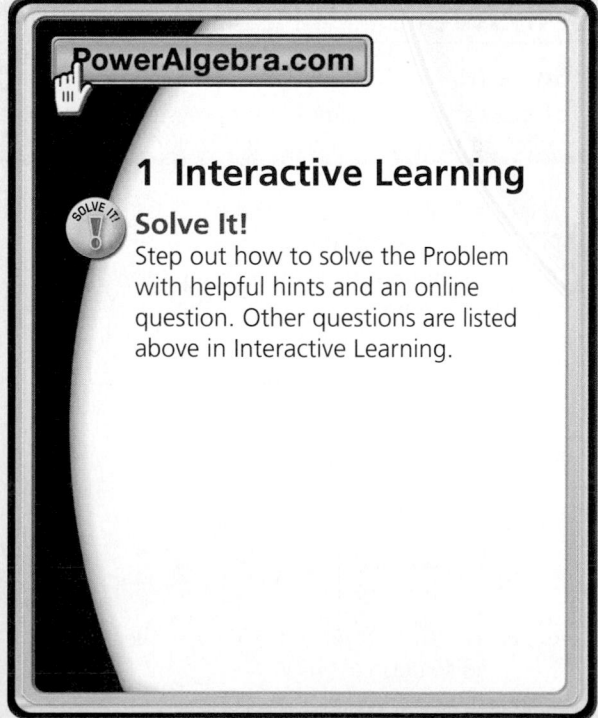

PowerAlgebra.com

1 Interactive Learning

Solve It!

Step out how to solve the Problem with helpful hints and an online question. Other questions are listed above in Interactive Learning.

2 Guided Instruction

Problem 1

> **Q** In 1A, how do the elements in matrix A compare with the elements in matrix A^{-1}? **[The elements on the main diagonal are switched, and the elements on the other diagonal have opposite signs.]**
>
> **Q** In Step 2 of 1A, can you write the matrix product on the right side of the equation as $\begin{bmatrix} 1 \\ -3 \end{bmatrix}\begin{bmatrix} 2 & -3 \\ -3 & 5 \end{bmatrix}$ instead of $\begin{bmatrix} 2 & -3 \\ -3 & 5 \end{bmatrix}\begin{bmatrix} 1 \\ -3 \end{bmatrix}$? Why or why not? **[No, because matrix multiplication is not commutative: $A^{-1}B \neq BA^{-1}$.]**
>
> **Q** In 1B, why does a value of 0 for the determinant of A mean that there is no solution for this equation? **[The formula to calculate A^{-1} includes the scalar $\frac{1}{ab - cd}$, where $ab - cd$ is the determinant of A. If it is 0, then the factor becomes $\frac{1}{0}$, which is undefined.]**

Got It?   SYNTHESIZING

The first step in solving a matrix equation is to evaluate $ab - cd$, the determinant of A in the equation $AX = B$. Since a, b, c, and d are real numbers, by the Law of Trichotomy, the determinant is either equal to 0, which means that there is no unique solution to the equation, or it is less than or greater than 0, which means that there is a unique solution to the equation.

> **Q** What does it mean when there is no unique solution? **[Sample: Either the lines that represent the system are parallel (no solution) or coinciding (infinitely many solutions).]**

Problem 1 Solving Matrix Equations Using an Inverse Matrix

What is the solution of each matrix equation?

Think
How do you know the equation has a solution?
Check det A. If det $A \neq 0$, you can solve the equation.

A $\begin{bmatrix} 5 & 3 \\ 3 & 2 \end{bmatrix} X = \begin{bmatrix} 1 \\ -3 \end{bmatrix}$

Step 1 Evaluate det A and find A^{-1}.

$$\det A = ad - bc = (5)(2) - (3)(3) = 1$$

$$A^{-1} = \frac{1}{\det A}\begin{bmatrix} d & -b \\ -c & a \end{bmatrix} = \frac{1}{1}\begin{bmatrix} 2 & -3 \\ -3 & 5 \end{bmatrix} = \begin{bmatrix} 2 & -3 \\ -3 & 5 \end{bmatrix}$$

Think
Does it matter if you multiply by A^{-1} on the left or right side of A?
Even though $A^{-1}A = AA^{-1} = I$, you must multiply each side of the equation by A^{-1} on the left.

Step 2 Multiply each side of the equation by A^{-1}.

$$\begin{bmatrix} 2 & -3 \\ -3 & 5 \end{bmatrix}\begin{bmatrix} 5 & 3 \\ 3 & 2 \end{bmatrix} X = \begin{bmatrix} 2 & -3 \\ -3 & 5 \end{bmatrix}\begin{bmatrix} 1 \\ -3 \end{bmatrix}$$

$$\begin{bmatrix} (2)(5) + (-3)(3) & (2)(3) + (-3)(2) \\ (-3)(5) + (5)(3) & (-3)(3) + (5)(2) \end{bmatrix} X = \begin{bmatrix} (2)(1) + (-3)(-3) \\ (-3)(1) + (5)(-3) \end{bmatrix}$$

$$\begin{bmatrix} 1 & 0 \\ 0 & 1 \end{bmatrix} X = \begin{bmatrix} 11 \\ -18 \end{bmatrix}$$

$$X = \begin{bmatrix} 11 \\ -18 \end{bmatrix}$$

Check

Method 1 Use paper and pencil.

$$\begin{bmatrix} 5 & 3 \\ 3 & 2 \end{bmatrix} X \stackrel{?}{=} \begin{bmatrix} 1 \\ -3 \end{bmatrix}$$

$$\begin{bmatrix} 5 & 3 \\ 3 & 2 \end{bmatrix}\begin{bmatrix} 11 \\ -18 \end{bmatrix} \stackrel{?}{=} \begin{bmatrix} 1 \\ -3 \end{bmatrix}$$

$$\begin{bmatrix} (5)(11) + (3)(-18) \\ (3)(11) + (2)(-18) \end{bmatrix} \stackrel{?}{=} \begin{bmatrix} 1 \\ -3 \end{bmatrix}$$

$$\begin{bmatrix} 1 \\ -3 \end{bmatrix} = \begin{bmatrix} 1 \\ -3 \end{bmatrix} ✔$$

Method 2 Use a calculator.

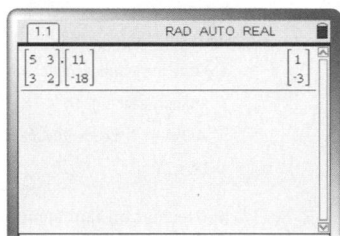

B $\begin{bmatrix} 3 & -9 \\ -2 & 6 \end{bmatrix} X = \begin{bmatrix} 2 \\ 5 \end{bmatrix}$

Evaluate det A.

$$\det A = (3)(6) - (-2)(-9) = 18 - 18 = 0$$

Since det $A = 0$, matrix A does not have an inverse. The equation has no solution.

 Got It? **1.** What is the solution of each matrix equation?

a. $\begin{bmatrix} 4 & 3 \\ 2 & 2 \end{bmatrix} X = \begin{bmatrix} -5 \\ 2 \end{bmatrix}$ **b.** $\begin{bmatrix} 7 & 5 \\ 4 & 3 \end{bmatrix} X = \begin{bmatrix} -3 & 0 \\ 1 & 4 \end{bmatrix}$ **c.** $\begin{bmatrix} 2 & 3 \\ 4 & 6 \end{bmatrix} X = \begin{bmatrix} 3 \\ -7 \end{bmatrix}$

Answers

Solve It!

81 nickels and 103 dimes; write a system of eqs. to represent the problem and then solve the system using either substitution or elimination.

$$n + d = 184$$
$$0.05n + 0.1d = 14.35$$

Using substitution, solve the first eq. for n and plug it into the second.

$$0.05(184 - d) + 0.1d = 14.35$$

Solving for d, we get $d = 103$. Since $n + d = 184$, $n = 81$.

Got It?

1. a. $\begin{bmatrix} -8 \\ 9 \end{bmatrix}$

b. $\begin{bmatrix} -14 & -20 \\ 19 & 28 \end{bmatrix}$

c. Since matrix A has no inverse, the eq. has no solution.

 PowerAlgebra.com

2 Guided Instruction

Each Problem is worked out and supported online.

Problem 1
Solving Matrix Equations Using an Inverse Matrix
Animated

Problem 2
Writing Systems as Matrix Equations
Animated

Support in Algebra 2 Companion
• Vocabulary
• Key Concepts
• Got It?

You can write a system of equations as a matrix equation $AX = B$, using a **coefficient matrix**, a **variable matrix**, and a **constant matrix**.

Hint

In Chapter 3, you represented a system of equations using only one matrix.

System of Equations	Matrix Equation

$$\begin{cases} 2x + 3y = 1 \\ 5x - 2y = 13 \end{cases}$$

$$\begin{bmatrix} 2 & 3 \\ 5 & -2 \end{bmatrix} \begin{bmatrix} x \\ y \end{bmatrix} = \begin{bmatrix} 1 \\ 13 \end{bmatrix}$$

coefficient matrix, A — variable matrix, X — constant matrix, B

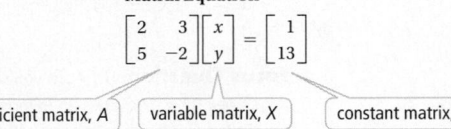

Problem 2 Writing Systems as Matrix Equations

What is the matrix equation that corresponds to each system?

A $\begin{cases} 4x + 7y = 6 \\ -5x + 3y = 1 \end{cases}$

Step 1 Identify the coefficient, variable, and constant matrices.

coefficient matrix, A variable matrix, X constant matrix, B

$$\begin{bmatrix} 4 & 7 \\ -5 & 3 \end{bmatrix} \qquad \begin{bmatrix} x \\ y \end{bmatrix} \qquad \begin{bmatrix} 6 \\ 1 \end{bmatrix}$$

Step 2 Write the matrix equation.

$$\begin{bmatrix} 4 & 7 \\ -5 & 3 \end{bmatrix} \begin{bmatrix} x \\ y \end{bmatrix} = \begin{bmatrix} 6 \\ 1 \end{bmatrix}$$

B $\begin{cases} 3a + 5b - 12c = 6 \\ 7b + 2c = 8 \\ 5a = 3c + 1 \end{cases}$

Plan

How is this system different from the one in part A?
There are three variables. Some terms have coefficients of 0 and the third equation has a variable on the right side of the = sign.

Step 1 Rewrite the system so the variables are in the same order in each equation. Leave spaces for variables with coefficients of 0.

$$\begin{cases} 3a + 5b - 12c = 6 \\ 7b + 2c = 8 \\ 5a = 3c + 1 \end{cases} \rightarrow \begin{cases} 3a + 5b - 12c = 6 \\ 7b + 2c = 8 \\ 5a \quad - 3c = 1 \end{cases}$$

Step 2 Identify the coefficient, variable, and constant matrices.

coefficient matrix, A variable matrix, X constant matrix, B

$$\begin{bmatrix} 3 & 5 & -12 \\ 0 & 7 & 2 \\ 5 & 0 & -3 \end{bmatrix} \qquad \begin{bmatrix} a \\ b \\ c \end{bmatrix} \qquad \begin{bmatrix} 6 \\ 8 \\ 1 \end{bmatrix}$$

Step 3 Write the matrix equation.

$$\begin{bmatrix} 3 & 5 & -12 \\ 0 & 7 & 2 \\ 5 & 0 & -3 \end{bmatrix} \begin{bmatrix} a \\ b \\ c \end{bmatrix} = \begin{bmatrix} 6 \\ 8 \\ 1 \end{bmatrix}$$

Problem 2

To write a system of two (or three) linear equations as a matrix equation, each equation should be in standard form: $Ax + By = C$, where A, B, and C are real numbers.

Q In Step 1 of 2A, what is the relationship between the elements in each row of the coefficient matrix and each equation of the system? **[The elements in each row are the coefficients of the variables x and y in each equation written in standard form.]**

Q In Step 1 of 2B, can matrix A be written as
$$\begin{bmatrix} 5 & 0 & -3 \\ 0 & 7 & 2 \\ 3 & 5 & -12 \end{bmatrix} \begin{bmatrix} a \\ b \\ c \end{bmatrix} = \begin{bmatrix} 1 \\ 8 \\ 6 \end{bmatrix}$$; that is can the rows in A and B be rearranged? Explain. **[Yes; rows in a matrix can be switched without changing the value of the matrix.]**

Q In Step 2 of 2B, can the matrix equation be written as $\begin{bmatrix} 6 \\ 8 \\ 1 \end{bmatrix} = \begin{bmatrix} 3 & 5 & -12 \\ 0 & 7 & 2 \\ 5 & 0 & -3 \end{bmatrix} \begin{bmatrix} a \\ b \\ c \end{bmatrix}$? Explain.
[Yes, because matrix equations are symmetric; $AX = B \Leftrightarrow B = AX$. When solving $B = AX$, both sides would still be multiplied on the left by A^{-1}.]

Additional Problems

1. What is the solution of this matrix equation?

$$\begin{bmatrix} 2 & 1 \\ 1 & -1 \end{bmatrix} X = \begin{bmatrix} 6 \\ 3 \end{bmatrix}$$

ANSWER $\begin{bmatrix} 3 \\ 0 \end{bmatrix}$

2. What is a matrix equation that corresponds to each system?

a. $\begin{cases} 2x - y = -1 \\ x + 3y = 17 \end{cases}$

b. $\begin{cases} 3a + 2b = 5 \\ 4a = 3c + 7 \\ 6b - 6c = -5 \end{cases}$

ANSWERS

a. $\begin{bmatrix} 2 & -1 \\ 1 & 3 \end{bmatrix} \begin{bmatrix} x \\ y \end{bmatrix} = \begin{bmatrix} -1 \\ 17 \end{bmatrix}$

b. $\begin{bmatrix} 3 & 2 & 0 \\ 4 & 0 & -3 \\ 0 & 6 & -6 \end{bmatrix} \begin{bmatrix} a \\ b \\ c \end{bmatrix} = \begin{bmatrix} 5 \\ 7 \\ -5 \end{bmatrix}$

Got It?

ERROR PREVENTION

Students should know that the number of variables in a coefficient matrix is the same as the number of elements in each row. They should also know that if a variable term is missing from an equation of the system, then 0 is the implied coefficient and is inserted in the matrix to represent the missing term in the equation.

3 Lesson Check

Do you know HOW?

- In Exercise 2, check that students insert a 0 in two of the three rows of the coefficient matrix, representing the missing variable terms.

Do you UNDERSTAND?

- For Exercise 3, encourage students to perform multiplication using the coefficient matrix and the variable matrix to help write the linear system.

Close

> **Q** When does the matrix equation $AX = B$ have no unique solution? **[when the determinant of A, the coefficient matrix, is 0]**
>
> **Q** How do you solve a matrix equation of the form $AX = B$? **[Multiply both sides of the equation on the left by A^{-1}, the inverse of the coefficient matrix.]**

4 Practice

ASSIGNMENT GUIDE

Basic: 4–11
Average: 4–13

Reasoning exercises have blue headings.

Applications exercises have red headings.

HOMEWORK QUICK CHECK

To check students' understanding of key skills and concepts, go over Exercises 5, 6, 8, 10, and 11.

Chapter 12

 Got It? 2. What is the matrix equation that corresponds to each system?

a. $\begin{cases} 3x - 7y = 8 \\ 5x + y = -2 \end{cases}$ b. $\begin{cases} x + 3y + 5z = 12 \\ -2x + y - 4z = -2 \\ 7x - 2y = 7 \end{cases}$ c. $\begin{cases} 2x + 3 = 8y \\ -x + y = -4 \end{cases}$

Focus Question How can you solve a matrix equation of the form $AX = B$?

Answer If matrix A has an inverse, you can solve the matrix equation $AX = B$ by multiplying both sides of the equation (in the same order) by A^{-1}. So, $X = A^{-1}B$.

 Lesson Check

Do you know HOW?

Write each system as a matrix equation.

1. $\begin{cases} -6x + 3y = 8 \\ 4x - 2y = 10 \end{cases}$ 2. $\begin{cases} 2x + 3y = 12 \\ x - 2y + z = 9 \\ 6y - 4z = 8 \end{cases}$

Do you UNDERSTAND?

3. **Reasoning** Explain how to write the matrix equation $\begin{bmatrix} -2 & 3 \\ 4 & 1 \end{bmatrix}\begin{bmatrix} p \\ q \end{bmatrix} = \begin{bmatrix} 2 \\ -5 \end{bmatrix}$ as a system of linear equations.

 Practice and Problem-Solving Exercises

 **Practice** Solve each matrix equation. If an equation cannot be solved, explain why.   ◀ See Problem 1.

4. $\begin{bmatrix} 12 & 7 \\ 5 & 3 \end{bmatrix} X = \begin{bmatrix} 2 & -1 \\ 3 & 2 \end{bmatrix}$

Guided Practice To start, find the determinant of the coefficient matrix. $\det \begin{bmatrix} 12 & 7 \\ 5 & 3 \end{bmatrix} = (12)(3) - (7)(5) = 1$

5. $\begin{bmatrix} 5 & 1 & 4 \\ 2 & -3 & -5 \\ 7 & 2 & -6 \end{bmatrix} X = \begin{bmatrix} 5 \\ 2 \\ 5 \end{bmatrix}$ 6. $\begin{bmatrix} 0 & -4 \\ 0 & -1 \end{bmatrix} X = \begin{bmatrix} 0 \\ 4 \end{bmatrix}$ 7. $\begin{bmatrix} 6 & 10 & 13 \\ 4 & -2 & 7 \\ 0 & 9 & -8 \end{bmatrix} X = \begin{bmatrix} 84 \\ 18 \\ 56 \end{bmatrix}$

Write each system as a matrix equation. Identify the coefficient matrix, the variable matrix, and the constant matrix.   ◀ See Problem 2.

8. $\begin{cases} x + y = 5 \\ x - 2y = -4 \end{cases}$ 9. $\begin{cases} y = 3x - 7 \\ x = 2 \end{cases}$ 10. $\begin{cases} x + 3y - z = 2 \\ x + 2z = 8 \\ 2y - z = 1 \end{cases}$

 Apply Solve each matrix equation. If the coefficient matrix has no inverse, write *no unique solution.*

11. $\begin{bmatrix} 1 & 1 \\ 1 & 2 \end{bmatrix}\begin{bmatrix} x \\ y \end{bmatrix} = \begin{bmatrix} 8 \\ 10 \end{bmatrix}$ 12. $\begin{bmatrix} 2 & -3 \\ -4 & 6 \end{bmatrix}\begin{bmatrix} a \\ b \end{bmatrix} = \begin{bmatrix} 1 \\ -2 \end{bmatrix}$ 13. $\begin{bmatrix} 2 & 1 \\ 4 & 3 \end{bmatrix}\begin{bmatrix} x \\ y \end{bmatrix} = \begin{bmatrix} 10 \\ -2 \end{bmatrix}$

Chapter 12   Matrices

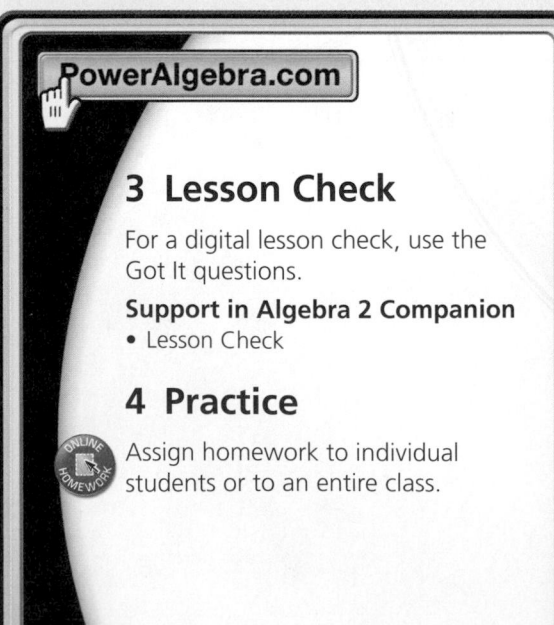

Chapter 12

3 Lesson Check

For a digital lesson check, use the Got It questions.

Support in Algebra 2 Companion
- Lesson Check

4 Practice

Assign homework to individual students or to an entire class.

Answers

Got It? (continued)

2. a. $\begin{bmatrix} 3 & -7 \\ 5 & 1 \end{bmatrix}\begin{bmatrix} x \\ y \end{bmatrix} = \begin{bmatrix} 8 \\ -2 \end{bmatrix}$

b. $\begin{bmatrix} 1 & 3 & 5 \\ -2 & 1 & -4 \\ 7 & -2 & 0 \end{bmatrix}\begin{bmatrix} x \\ y \\ z \end{bmatrix} = \begin{bmatrix} 12 \\ -2 \\ 7 \end{bmatrix}$

c. $\begin{bmatrix} 2 & -8 \\ -1 & 1 \end{bmatrix}\begin{bmatrix} x \\ y \end{bmatrix} = \begin{bmatrix} -3 \\ -4 \end{bmatrix}$

Lesson Check

1. $\begin{bmatrix} -6 & 3 \\ 4 & -2 \end{bmatrix}\begin{bmatrix} x \\ y \end{bmatrix} = \begin{bmatrix} 8 \\ 10 \end{bmatrix}$

2. $\begin{bmatrix} 2 & 3 & 0 \\ 1 & -2 & 1 \\ 0 & 6 & -4 \end{bmatrix}\begin{bmatrix} x \\ y \\ z \end{bmatrix} = \begin{bmatrix} 12 \\ 9 \\ 8 \end{bmatrix}$

3. Use matrix multiplication to combine the coefficient matrix and the variable matrix into a product matrix. Then set the first element in the product matrix equal to the first element in the

constant matrix and set the second element in the product matrix equal to the second element in the constant matrix. The result will be a system of equations:

$-2p + 3q = 2$
$4p + q = -5$

Practice and Problem-Solving Exercises

4. $\begin{bmatrix} -15 & -17 \\ 26 & 29 \end{bmatrix}$ 5. $-\begin{bmatrix} \frac{29}{31} \\ \frac{66}{217} \\ \frac{34}{217} \end{bmatrix}$

6. No solution; the determinant of A is 0.

7. $\begin{bmatrix} \frac{2487}{253} \\ \frac{1192}{253} \\ -\frac{430}{253} \end{bmatrix}$

8–13. See back of book.

12-4 PART 2 — Inverse Matrices and Systems

Objective To solve systems of equations using matrix inverses and multiplication

In Part 1 of the lesson, you learned how to represent a system of equations using a matrix equation.

Connect to What You Know

Here you will learn to solve a system of equations using a matrix equation and inverse matrices.

Focus Question How can you solve a system of equations using a related matrix equation?

If the coefficient matrix has an inverse, you can use it to find a unique solution to a system of equations.

In Part 1 of the lesson, you wrote the system of equations $\begin{cases} 2x + 3y = 1 \\ 5x - 2y = 13 \end{cases}$ as the matrix equation $AX = B$, or $\begin{bmatrix} 2 & 3 \\ 5 & -2 \end{bmatrix}\begin{bmatrix} x \\ y \end{bmatrix} = \begin{bmatrix} 1 \\ 13 \end{bmatrix}$. The determinant of the coefficient matrix, A, is $(2)(-2) - (3)(5) = -19 \neq 0$, so the system has a unique solution, $A^{-1}B$. To find it, first find A^{-1}.

$$A^{-1} = \frac{1}{\det A}\begin{bmatrix} -2 & -3 \\ -5 & 2 \end{bmatrix} = -\frac{1}{19}\begin{bmatrix} -2 & -3 \\ -5 & 2 \end{bmatrix} - \begin{bmatrix} \frac{2}{19} & \frac{3}{19} \\ \frac{5}{19} & -\frac{2}{19} \end{bmatrix}$$

Now find $A^{-1}B$.

$$X = A^{-1}B$$

$$\begin{bmatrix} x \\ y \end{bmatrix} = \begin{bmatrix} \frac{2}{19} & \frac{3}{19} \\ \frac{5}{19} & -\frac{2}{19} \end{bmatrix}\begin{bmatrix} 1 \\ 13 \end{bmatrix} = \begin{bmatrix} \frac{41}{19} \\ -\frac{21}{19} \end{bmatrix}$$

Hint
Always check your solutions in the original system of equations.

Check

Write the original equations.	$2x + 3y = 1$	$5x - 2y = 13$
Substitute.	$2\left(\frac{41}{19}\right) + 3\left(-\frac{21}{19}\right) \stackrel{?}{=} 1$	$5\left(\frac{41}{19}\right) - 2\left(-\frac{21}{19}\right) \stackrel{?}{=} 13$
Multiply.	$\frac{82}{19} - \frac{63}{19} \stackrel{?}{=} 1$	$\frac{205}{19} + \frac{42}{19} \stackrel{?}{=} 13$
Simplify.	$\frac{19}{19} = 1$ ✔	$\frac{247}{19} = 13$ ✔

So, the solution is $x = \frac{41}{19}$ and $y = -\frac{21}{19}$.

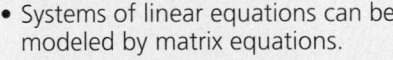

Lesson 12-4 Inverse Matrices and Systems   803

12-4 Preparing to Teach

PART 2

BIG idea Modeling   UbD

ESSENTIAL UNDERSTANDINGS
- Systems of linear equations can be modeled by matrix equations.
- Some matrix equations of the form $AX = B$ can be solved by multiplying each side of the equation on the left by A^{-1}, the inverse of matrix A.

Math Background

In 3-6, students solved systems of linear equations using matrix row operations. In this lesson, they apply what they know about inverse matrices and determinants to solve systems of linear equations.

If you write a system of linear equations as a matrix equation with a coefficient matrix, variable matrix, and constant matrix, you can solve for the variables by multiplying both sides of the equation on the left by the inverse coefficient matrix.

If the determinant is zero, the inverse coefficient matrix does not exist, and the associated system of linear equations does not have a unique solution.

Support Student Learning

Use the **Algebra 2 Companion** to engage and support students during instruction. See Lesson Resources at the end of this lesson for details.

1 Launch

CONNECT THE MATH In Part 2, students will use the skills they learned in Part 1 to first write a system of linear equations in matrix form, then use inverse matrices to find a solution for the system. Students will use determinants to find the inverse matrix of a system of 2 linear equations and a calculator to find the inverse matrix of a system of 3 linear equations.

FOCUS QUESTION
How does a linear system correspond to a matrix equation?

Q What is a linear system for the matrix equation $\begin{bmatrix} 2 & -6 \\ 4 & 0 \end{bmatrix}\begin{bmatrix} x \\ y \end{bmatrix} = \begin{bmatrix} -2 \\ 8 \end{bmatrix}$? [$\begin{cases} 2x - 6y = -2 \\ 4x = 8 \end{cases}$]

Q How can the system above be solved without using matrices? What is the solution? **[Sample: Substitution; $4x = 8$ so $x = 2$. Substituting $x = 2$ into the first equation yields $y = 1$.]**

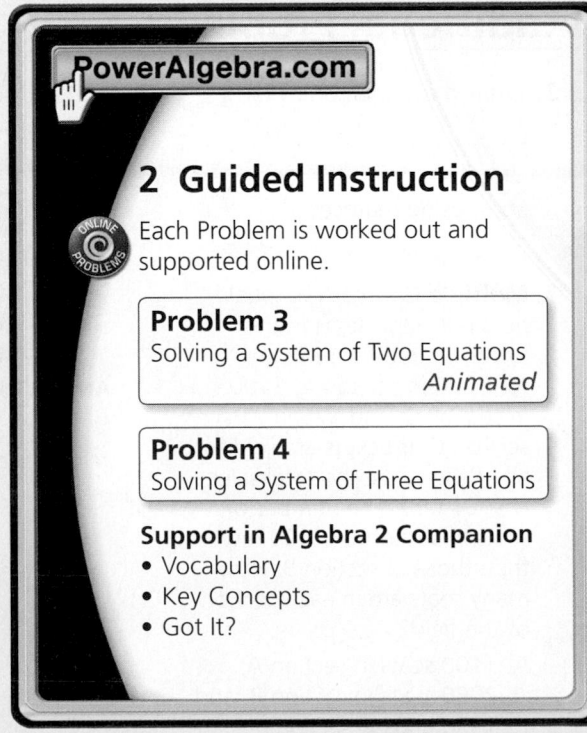

PowerAlgebra.com

2 Guided Instruction

Each Problem is worked out and supported online.

Problem 3
Solving a System of Two Equations
Animated

Problem 4
Solving a System of Three Equations

Support in Algebra 2 Companion
- Vocabulary
- Key Concepts
- Got It?

Lesson 12-4   803

Problem 3

Q What would be the matrix equation if the system of equations were written as $\begin{cases} 3x - 2y = 3 \\ 5x - 4y = 4 \end{cases}$?

$[\begin{bmatrix} 3 & -2 \\ 5 & -4 \end{bmatrix} \begin{bmatrix} x \\ y \end{bmatrix} = \begin{bmatrix} 3 \\ 4 \end{bmatrix}]$

Q What matrix is equivalent to A^{-1}? $[\begin{bmatrix} -1 & 2 \\ -1.5 & 2.5 \end{bmatrix}]$

Q What do the solution of this matrix equation and system of linear equations represent in the rectangular coordinate plane? **[Each equation represents a linear function, and the values of x and y represent the coordinates of the point of intersection of the two lines.]**

Got It?   SYNTHESIZING

Q How could writing the equations in slope-intercept form help you anticipate whether a system of two linear equations has a solution? **[If the resulting equations have the same slope, you can determine whether the lines are parallel or coincident by comparing the y-intercepts of both lines and whether the system has no solution or an infinite number of solutions.]**

To see whether the matrix solution of the system in 3a is reasonable, have students graph the lines and determine the coordinates of the point of intersection of the two lines.

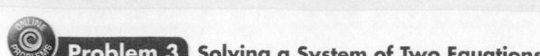

Problem 3 Solving a System of Two Equations

What is the solution of the system $\begin{cases} 5x - 4y = 4 \\ 3x - 2y = 3 \end{cases}$? Solve using matrices.

Think

Write the system as a matrix equation. Write the coefficient, variable, and constant matrices.

First, find A^{-1}.

Since det $A = 2$, A^{-1} exists.

Multiply each side of the matrix equation by A^{-1} on the left.

Solve for $\begin{bmatrix} x \\ y \end{bmatrix}$ and check.

Write

$$\underset{A}{\begin{bmatrix} 5 & -4 \\ 3 & -2 \end{bmatrix}} \underset{X}{\begin{bmatrix} x \\ y \end{bmatrix}} = \underset{B}{\begin{bmatrix} 4 \\ 3 \end{bmatrix}}$$

$$A^{-1} = \frac{1}{\det A} \begin{bmatrix} -2 & 4 \\ -3 & 5 \end{bmatrix}$$

$$= \frac{1}{(5)(-2) - (3)(-4)} \begin{bmatrix} -2 & 4 \\ -3 & 5 \end{bmatrix}$$

$$= \frac{1}{2} \begin{bmatrix} -2 & 4 \\ -3 & 5 \end{bmatrix}$$

$$= \begin{bmatrix} -1 & 2 \\ -\frac{3}{2} & \frac{5}{2} \end{bmatrix}$$

$$\begin{bmatrix} -1 & 2 \\ -\frac{3}{2} & \frac{5}{2} \end{bmatrix} \begin{bmatrix} 5 & -4 \\ 3 & -2 \end{bmatrix} \begin{bmatrix} x \\ y \end{bmatrix} = \begin{bmatrix} -1 & 2 \\ -\frac{3}{2} & \frac{5}{2} \end{bmatrix} \begin{bmatrix} 4 \\ 3 \end{bmatrix}$$

$$\begin{bmatrix} x \\ y \end{bmatrix} = \begin{bmatrix} (-1)(4) + (2)(3) \\ (-\frac{3}{2})(4) + (\frac{5}{2})(3) \end{bmatrix} = \begin{bmatrix} 2 \\ \frac{3}{2} \end{bmatrix}$$

The solution is $x = 2$, $y = \frac{3}{2}$.

$5(2) - 4(\frac{3}{2}) = 4$ ✔

$3(2) - 2(\frac{3}{2}) = 3$ ✔

✅ **Got It? 3.** What is the solution of each system of equations? Solve using matrices.

a. $\begin{cases} 9x + 2y = 3 \\ 3x + y = -6 \end{cases}$ **b.** $\begin{cases} 4x - 6y = 9 \\ -10x + 15y = 8 \end{cases}$

Hint

The lines represented by this system are parallel.

The system $\begin{cases} -6x + 3y = 8 \\ 4x - 2y = 10 \end{cases}$ has coefficient matrix A with det $A = 0$. There is no inverse matrix and the system has no unique solution. Recall that this means the system either has no solutions (graphs represent parallel lines in the 2×2 case) or infinitely many solutions (graphs represent coinciding lines in the 2×2 case).

Additional Problems

3. What is the solution of the system $\begin{cases} 4x + 5y = -8 \\ x + \frac{3}{4}y = 2 \end{cases}$?

Solve using matrices.

ANSWER $(8, -8)$

4. Multiple Choice A baseball field has 6200 seats in the lower three tiers. Seats sell for $120 in section A, $100 in section B, and $75 in section C. If tickets are sold for all of the seats, the total sales is $604,000. The number of seats in section C is 500 fewer than those in section B. How many seats are in each section of the field?

A. 1100 seats in section A, 2050 seats in section B, and 1550 seats in section C

B. 1200 seats in section A, 1500 seats in section B, and 2000 seats in section C

C. 1500 seats in section A, 1850 seats in section B, and 1350 seats in section C

D. 1700 seats in section A, 2500 seats in section B, and 2000 seats in section C

ANSWER D

Answers

Got It?

3. a. $(5, -21)$

b. no solution

You can use a graphing calculator to solve a system of three equations.

 Problem 4 Solving a System of Three Equations

Multiple Choice On a new exercise program, your friend plans to do a run-jog-walk routine every other day for 40 min. She would like to burn 310 calories during each session. The table shows how many calories a person your friend's age and weight burns per minute of each type of exercise.

Calories Burned

Running (8 mi/h)	Jogging (5 mi/h)	Walking (3.5 mi/h)
12.5 cal/min	7.5 cal/min	3.5 cal/min

If your friend plans on jogging twice as long as she runs, how many minutes should she exercise at each rate?

Ⓐ run 10, jog 5, walk 25   Ⓒ run 5, jog 10, walk 25
Ⓑ run 30, jog 15, walk 5   Ⓓ run 10, jog 20, walk 10

Step 1 Define the variables.

Let x = number of minutes running.
Let y = number of minutes jogging.
Let z = number of minutes walking.

Think

How many equations do you need to solve this problem? Since there are three variables you need three equations.

Step 2 Write a system of equations for the problem.

$$\begin{cases} 12.5x + 7.5y + 3.5z = 310 \\ x + y + z = 40 \\ 2x = y \end{cases} \rightarrow \begin{cases} 12.5x + 7.5y + 3.5z = 310 \\ x + y + z = 40 \\ 2x - y + 0z = 0 \end{cases}$$

Step 3 Write the system as a matrix equation.

$$\begin{bmatrix} 12.5 & 7.5 & 3.5 \\ 1 & 1 & 1 \\ 2 & -1 & 0 \end{bmatrix}\begin{bmatrix} x \\ y \\ z \end{bmatrix} = \begin{bmatrix} 310 \\ 40 \\ 0 \end{bmatrix}$$

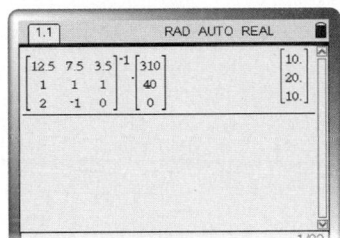

Step 4 Use a calculator. Solve for the variable matrix.

Step 5 Interpret the solution.

Your friend should run for 10 min, jog for 20 min, and walk for 10 min.

The correct answer is D.

 Got It? 4. After following her exercise program from Problem 4 for a month, your friend plans to increase the calories she burns with each session. She still wants to exercise for 40 min every other day, but now she wants to burn 460 calories during each session. If she only runs and jogs, how many minutes of each exercise type should she do now?

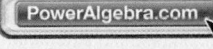

4. run: 32 min; jog: 8 min

Problem 4

Students should recognize that there are three variables and three relationships among them: the total number of calories expended every other day, the number of minutes to be spent exercising every other day, and the relationship between the time spent running versus jogging. Expressing these relationships in words may help students translate them into equations.

Q What does the equation $2x = y$ represent in terms of the variables x and y? **[The time spent jogging y is twice that spent running x.]**

Q What units correspond to each constant in the constant matrix? **[310 is the number of calories burned each session; 40 is the total time in minutes spent exercising every other day; 0 is the difference in minutes between twice the time spent running and the time spent jogging every other day.]**

Q How would you check this solution? **[Samples: Find the matrix product of the coefficient matrix and the matrix solution to see if they equal the constant matrix; substitute the values 10, 20, and 10 for the variables x, y, and z in each equation of the system.]**

Got It?   ERROR PREVENTION

Q In 4b, how many variables need to be represented in writing a system of equations that represents this situation and why? **[Two: x represents the time spent running, and y represents the time spent jogging.]**

Q What are the dimensions of the constant matrix for this situation? **[2 × 1]**

3 Lesson Check

Do you know HOW?
- In Exercises 1 and 2, suggest that students first check to be sure that the determinant of each coefficient matrix is not 0. Then they can use matrix operations to solve the equation. The solution represents the coordinates of the points of intersection of each pair of lines represented by each system.

Do you UNDERSTAND?
- For Exercise 3, suggest students write what they think was the original system and then use it to write the matrix equation. They should recognize that the variables should be removed.

Close

> **Q** What are the dimensions of the coefficient matrix when solving a system of 3 linear equations in 3 variables? the variable matrix? the constant matrix? **[3 × 3; 3 × 1; 3 × 1]**
>
> **Q** Is the determinant needed when solving a linear system? Explain. **[The determinant is needed to find the inverse using pencil and paper. If using a calculator, the inverse is displayed without showing the determinant.]**

Focus Question How can you solve a system of equations using a related matrix equation?

Answer You can solve a system of equations by first writing it as a matrix equation $AX = B$, where A is the coefficient matrix, X is the variable matrix, and B is the constant matrix. Then, find A^{-1} (if it exists) and compute $A^{-1}B$ to get the solution.

Lesson Check

Do you know HOW?
Solve each system using a matrix equation. Check your answer.

1. $\begin{cases} x + 2y = 11 \\ x + 4y = 17 \end{cases}$

2. $\begin{cases} 2x - 3y = 6 \\ x + y = -12 \end{cases}$

Do you UNDERSTAND?
3. **Error Analysis** A student is trying to use the matrix equation below to solve a system of equations. What error did the student make? What matrix equation should the student use?

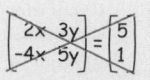

Practice and Problem-Solving Exercises

A Practice Solve each system of equations using a matrix equation. Check your answers.   ◀ See Problem 3.

Guided Practice → To start, write the system as a matrix equation.

4. $\begin{cases} x + 3y = 5 \\ x + 4y = 6 \end{cases}$

$\begin{bmatrix} 1 & 3 \\ 1 & 4 \end{bmatrix}\begin{bmatrix} x \\ y \end{bmatrix} = \begin{bmatrix} 5 \\ 6 \end{bmatrix}$

5. $\begin{cases} 300x - y = 130 \\ 200x + y = 120 \end{cases}$

6. $\begin{cases} x + 5y = -4 \\ x + 6y = -5 \end{cases}$

7. $\begin{cases} 2x + 3y = 12 \\ x + 2y = 7 \end{cases}$

8. $\begin{cases} 2x + 3y = 5 \\ x + 2y = 6 \end{cases}$

9. $\begin{cases} x + y + z = 4 \\ 4x + 5y = 3 \\ y - 3z = -10 \end{cases}$

10. $\begin{cases} 9y + 2z = 18 \\ 3x + 2y + z = 5 \\ x - y = -1 \end{cases}$

11. **Fitness** Your classmate is starting a new fitness program. He is planning to ride his bicycle 60 minutes every day. He burns 7 Calories per minute bicycling at 11 mph and 11.75 Calories per minute bicycling at 15 mph. How long should he bicycle at each speed to burn 600 calories per hour?   ◀ See Problem 4.

Answers

11. about 22 min at 11 mph and about 38 min at 15 mph

Lesson Check
1. $(5, 3)$
2. $(-6, -6)$
3. The student did not separate the coefficient matrix and the variable matrix. The matrix eq. should be written as $\begin{bmatrix} 2 & 3 \\ -4 & 5 \end{bmatrix}\begin{bmatrix} x \\ y \end{bmatrix} = \begin{bmatrix} 5 \\ 1 \end{bmatrix}$.

Practice and Problem-Solving Exercises
4. $(2, 1)$
5. $\left(\frac{1}{2}, 20\right)$
6. $(1, -1)$
7. $(3, 2)$
8. $(-8, 7)$
9. $(2, -1, 3)$
10. $(-3, -2, 18)$

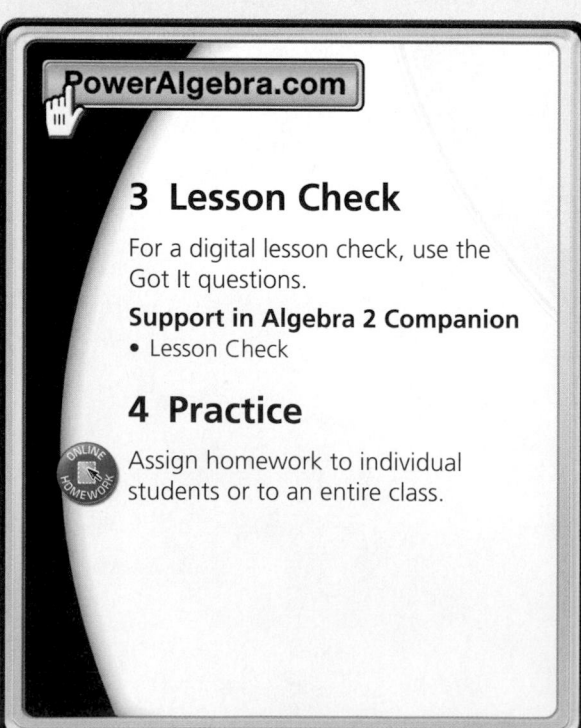

PowerAlgebra.com

3 Lesson Check
For a digital lesson check, use the Got It questions.

Support in Algebra 2 Companion
- Lesson Check

4 Practice
Assign homework to individual students or to an entire class.

 **Apply**

12. Think About a Plan Suppose you want to fill nine 1-lb tins with a snack mix. You plan to buy almonds for $2.45/lb, peanuts for $1.85/lb, and raisins for $.80/lb. You want the mix to contain twice as much nuts as raisins by weight. If you spend exactly $15, how much of each ingredient should you buy?
- How many equations do you need to represent this situation?
- How can you represent this system using a matrix equation?

13. Nutrition Suppose you are making a trail mix for your friends and want to fill three 1-lb bags. Almonds cost $2.25/lb, peanuts cost $1.30/lb, and raisins cost $.90/lb. You want each bag to contain twice as much nuts as raisins by weight. If you spent $4.45, how much of each ingredient did you buy?

Solve each system.

14. $\begin{cases} -3x + 4y = 2 \\ x - y = -1 \end{cases}$

15. $\begin{cases} x + 2y = 10 \\ 3x + 5y = 26 \end{cases}$

 **16.** $\begin{cases} x = 5 - y \\ 3y = z \\ x + z = 7 \end{cases}$

17. $\begin{cases} -x = -4 - z \\ 2y = z - 1 \\ x = 6 - y - z \end{cases}$

18. $\begin{cases} x + y + z = 4 \\ 4x + 5y = 4 \\ y - 3z = -9 \end{cases}$

19. $\begin{cases} x + y + z = 4 \\ 4x + 5y = 3 \\ y - 3z = -10 \end{cases}$

20. Coordinate Geometry The coordinates (x, y) of a point in a plane are the solution of the system $\begin{cases} 2x + 3y = 13 \\ 5x + 7y = 31 \end{cases}$. Find the coordinates of the point.

21. Geometry A rectangle is twice as long as it is wide. The perimeter is 840 ft. Find the dimensions of the rectangle.

22. Reasoning Substitute each point, $(-3, 5)$ and $(2, -1)$, into the slope-intercept form of a linear equation to write a system of equations. Then use the system to find the equation of the line containing the two points. Explain your reasoning.

Solve each system using matrices. If the coefficient matrix has no inverse, write *no unique solution.*

23. $\begin{cases} 20x + 5y = 240 \\ y = 20x \end{cases}$

24. $\begin{cases} 20x + 5y = 145 \\ 30x - 5y = 125 \end{cases}$

25. $\begin{cases} y = 2000 - 65x \\ y = 500 + 55x \end{cases}$

26. $\begin{cases} y = \frac{2}{3}x - 3 \\ y = -x + 7 \end{cases}$

27. $\begin{cases} 3x + 2y = 10 \\ 6x + 4y = 16 \end{cases}$

28. $\begin{cases} x + 2y + z = 4 \\ y = x - 3 \\ z = 2x \end{cases}$

ASSIGNMENT GUIDE

Basic: 4–13

Average: 4–10 even, 11–25

Standardized Test Prep: 29–32

Mixed Review: 33–42

Reasoning exercises have blue headings.

Applications exercises have red headings.

EXERCISE 13: Use the Think About a Plan worksheet in the **Student Companion** (also available in the Teaching Resources in print and online) to further support students' development in becoming independent learners.

HOMEWORK QUICK CHECK

To check students' understanding of key skills and concepts, go over Exercises 5, 9, 11, 12, and 13.

12. 2.5 lb of almonds, 3.5 lb of peanuts, and 3 lb of raisins

13. 1 lb of almonds, 1 lb of peanuts, and 1 lb of raisins

14. $(-2, -1)$

15. $(2, 4)$

16. $(4, 1, 3)$

17. $(5, 0, 1)$

18. $(1, 0, 3)$

19. $(2, -1, 3)$

20. $(2, 3)$

21. length = 280 ft, width = 140 ft

22. $6x + 5y = 7$; There are 2 eqs. in the system: $5 = -3m + b$ and $-1 = 2m + b$, where m = slope and b = y-intercept Solving the system, the eq. of the line is $y = -1.2x + 1.4$ or, in standard form, $6x + 5y = 7$.

23. $(2, 40)$

24. $(5.4, 7.4)$

25. $(12.5, 1187.5)$

26. $(6, 1)$

27. no unique solution

28. $(2, -1, 4)$

Answers

Standardized Test Prep

29. B

30. H

31. A

32. [2] First, write each eq. in standard form. Then place the coefficients in a matrix with the coefficients of x in the first column, the coefficients of y in the second column, and the coefficients of z in the third column:

$\begin{bmatrix} 2 & -3 & 1 \\ 1 & 4 & -2 \\ -3 & -2 & 3 \end{bmatrix}$. Finally, put this in an eq. with the variable matrix $\begin{bmatrix} x \\ y \\ z \end{bmatrix}$ and the constant matrix

$\begin{bmatrix} -10 \\ 11 \\ -7 \end{bmatrix}$, to get $\begin{bmatrix} 2 & -3 & 1 \\ 1 & 4 & -2 \\ -3 & -2 & 3 \end{bmatrix}$ $\begin{bmatrix} x \\ y \\ z \end{bmatrix} = \begin{bmatrix} -10 \\ 11 \\ -7 \end{bmatrix}$.

[1] incomplete explanation OR mistake in arrangement of coefficient matrix.

Mixed Review

33. -44

34. 4913

35. -218

36. $34.\overline{4}$; 30.9; 5.56

37. 4.17; 1.32; 1.15

38. $19.\overline{6}$ m; $22.\overline{2}$ m; 4.7 m

39. 57.4 mi; 345.44 mi^2; 18.6 mi

40. 4

41. 21

42. 52.5

Standardized Test Prep

SAT/ACT

29. Which matrix equation represents the system $\begin{cases} 2x - 3y = -3 \\ -5x + y = 14 \end{cases}$?

(A) $\begin{bmatrix} x \\ y \end{bmatrix} \begin{bmatrix} 2 & -3 \\ -5 & 1 \end{bmatrix} = \begin{bmatrix} -3 \\ 14 \end{bmatrix}$

(C) $\begin{bmatrix} 2 & -3 \\ -5 & 1 \end{bmatrix} \begin{bmatrix} -3 \\ 14 \end{bmatrix} = \begin{bmatrix} x \\ y \end{bmatrix}$

(B) $\begin{bmatrix} 2 & -3 \\ -5 & 1 \end{bmatrix} \begin{bmatrix} x \\ y \end{bmatrix} = \begin{bmatrix} -3 \\ 14 \end{bmatrix}$

(D) $\begin{bmatrix} -3 \\ 14 \end{bmatrix} [x \ y] = \begin{bmatrix} 2 & -3 \\ -5 & 1 \end{bmatrix}$

30. What is the value of x if $17 \cdot 10^{4x} = 85$?

(F) $\frac{5}{4}$

(G) $\frac{\log 85}{17 \cdot \log 4}$

(H) $\frac{\log 5}{4}$

(I) $\frac{\log 85 - \log 17}{\log 4}$

31. A set of data is normally distributed with a mean of 44 and a standard deviation of 3.2. Which statements are NOT true?

  I. 68% of the values are between 37.6 and 50.4
  II. 13.5% of the values are less than 40.8
  III. 5% of the values are lower than 37.6 or higher than 50.4

(A) I and II only

(C) II and III only

(B) I and III only

(D) I, II, and III

Short Response

32. How can you write the three equations below as a matrix equation for a system? Explain your steps.

$2x - 3y + z + 10 = 0$
$x + 4y = 2z + 11$
$-2y + 3z + 7 = 3x$

Mixed Review

Evaluate the determinant of each matrix. ◀ See Lesson 12-3.

33. $\begin{bmatrix} -1 & 3 & 7 \\ 5 & -4 & -2 \\ 0 & 2 & 10 \end{bmatrix}$

34. $\begin{bmatrix} 17 & 0 & 0 \\ 0 & 17 & 0 \\ 0 & 0 & 17 \end{bmatrix}$

35. $\begin{bmatrix} -3 & 0 & 5 \\ 5 & -3 & 2 \\ -3 & -5 & -2 \end{bmatrix}$

Find the mean, variance, and standard deviation for each data set. ◀ See Lesson 11-6.

36. 29, 35, 44, 25, 36, 30, 40, 33, 38

37. 5.2, 6.0, 3.5, 4.4, 2.5, 3.0, 4.6

38. 14 m, 18 m, 22 m, 28 m, 15 m, 21 m

39. 71 mi, 60 mi, 82 mi, 30 mi, 44 mi

Get Ready! To prepare for Lesson T-1, do Exercises 40–42.

Solve each proportion. ◀ See p. 867.

40. $\frac{x}{7} = \frac{28}{49}$

41. $\frac{10}{14} = \frac{15}{x}$

42. $\frac{21}{10} = \frac{x}{25}$

Additional Instructional Support

Algebra 2 Companion

Students can use the **Algebra 2 Companion** worktext (4 pages) as you teach the lesson. Use the Companion to support

- New Vocabulary
- Key Concepts
- Got It for each Problem
- Lesson Check

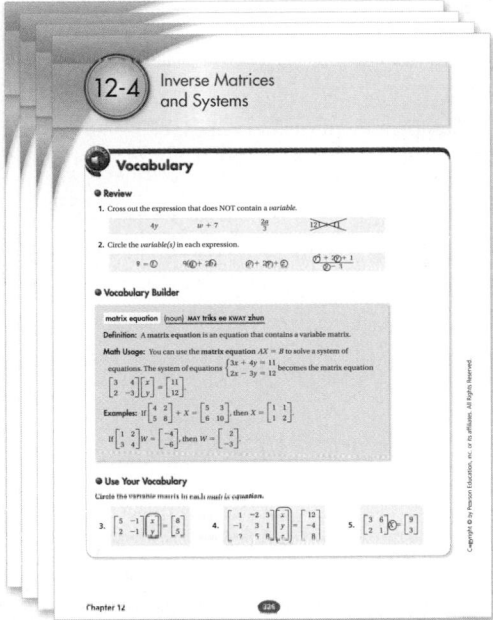

ELL Support

Assess Understanding Have students compare the solution of simple linear equations like $ax = b$ and the solution of matrix equations $AX = B$. In the first case, a is a non-zero real number, and x can be found by multiplying both sides of the equation by a^{-1}, or $\frac{1}{a}$. If $a = 2$, $a^{-1} = \frac{1}{2}$. However, in the second case, A^{-1} is the scalar product:

$$\frac{1}{ab - cd}\begin{bmatrix} d & -b \\ -c & a \end{bmatrix}$$, so to solve $A^{-1}B$

without using a calculator, students must follow three steps:

(1) determine the value of the non-zero determinant of the coefficient matrix;
(2) write its (multiplicative) inverse; and
(3) find the corresponding scalar product described above.

5 Assess & Remediate

Lesson Quiz

1. What is the solution of this matrix equation?

$$\begin{bmatrix} 2 & -3 \\ 1 & 1 \end{bmatrix} X = \begin{bmatrix} 6 \\ -12 \end{bmatrix}$$

2. What is a matrix equation that corresponds to the system

$$\begin{cases} 5p - 3q + r = 5 \\ 4p - 3r = 1 \\ 2q = 3r - 2 \end{cases} ?$$

3. What is the solution of the system

$$\begin{cases} 4x + 3y = 4 \\ 2x - y = 7 \end{cases} ?$$ Solve using matrices.

4. **Do you UNDERSTAND?** There are 34 coins in your friend's piggy bank made up of nickels, dimes, and quarters. The total value of the coins in the bank is $3. If the number of nickels is 6 more than the number of dimes and the number of quarters put together, how many coins of each type are in the bank?

ANSWERS TO LESSON QUIZ

1. $$\begin{bmatrix} -6 \\ -6 \end{bmatrix}$$

2. $$\begin{bmatrix} 5 & -3 & 1 \\ 4 & 0 & -3 \\ 0 & 2 & -3 \end{bmatrix}\begin{bmatrix} p \\ q \\ r \end{bmatrix} = \begin{bmatrix} 5 \\ 1 \\ -2 \end{bmatrix}$$

3. $(2.5, -2)$

4. 20 nickels, 10 dimes, 4 quarters

PRESCRIPTION FOR REMEDIATION

Use the student work on the Lesson Quiz to prescribe a differentiated review assignment:

Points	Differentiated Remediation
0–2	Intervention
3	On-level
4	Extension

PowerAlgebra.com

5 Assess & Remediate

Assign the Lesson Quiz. Appropriate intervention, practice, or enrichment is automatically generated based on student performance.

Intervention

- **Reteaching** (2 pages) Provides reteaching and practice exercises for the key lesson concepts. Use with struggling students or absent students.

- **English Language Learner Support** Helps students develop and reinforce mathematical vocabulary and key concepts.

All-in-One Resources/Online
Reteaching

12-4 Reteaching
Inverse Matrices and Systems

All-in-One Resources/Online
English Language Learner Support

12-4 ELL Support
Inverse Matrices and Systems

Differentiated Remediation *continued*

On-Level

- **Practice** (2 pages) Provides extra practice for each lesson. For more challenging practice exercises, use the Form G Practice pages found in the All-in-One Teaching Resources and online.

- **Think About a Plan** Helps students develop specific problem-solving skills and strategies by providing scaffolded guiding questions.

- **Standardized Test Prep** Focuses on all major exercises, all major question types, and helps students prepare for the high-stakes assessments.

Extension

- **Enrichment** Provides students with interesting problems and activities that extend the concepts of the lesson.

- **Activities, Games, and Puzzles** Worksheets that can be used for concepts development, enrichment, and for fun!

Student Companion/ All-in-One Resources/Online
Practice page 1

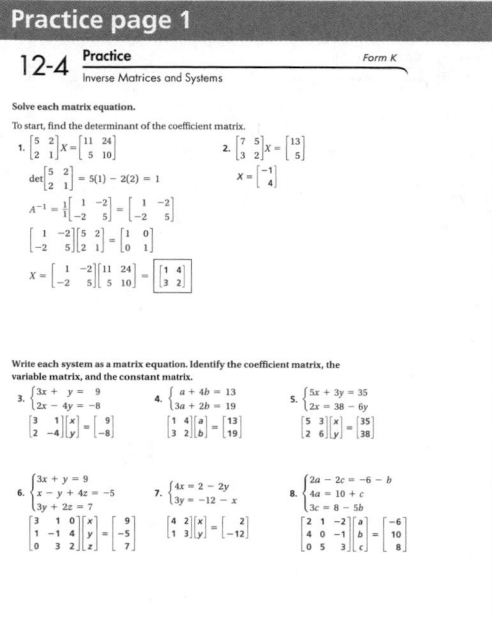

Student Companion/ All-in-One Resources/Online
Think About a Plan

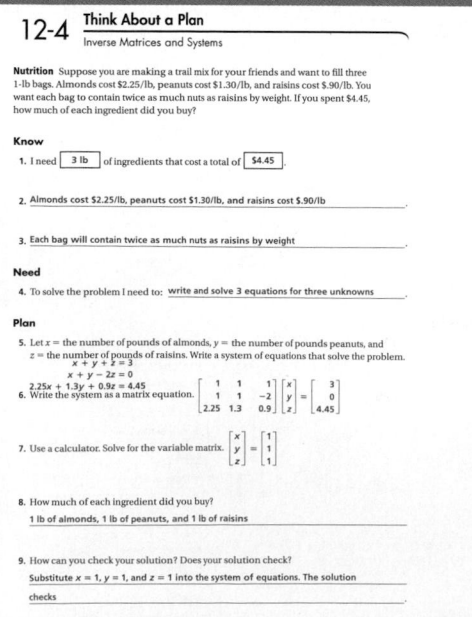

Student Companion/ All-in-One Resources/Online
Practice page 2

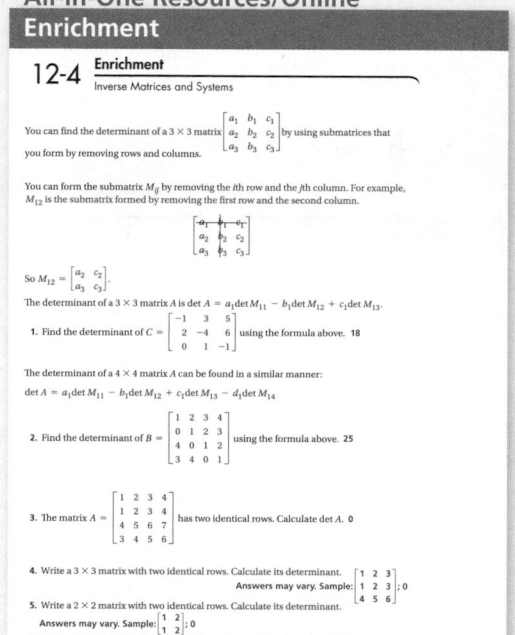

Student Companion/ All-in-One Resources/Online
Standardized Test Prep

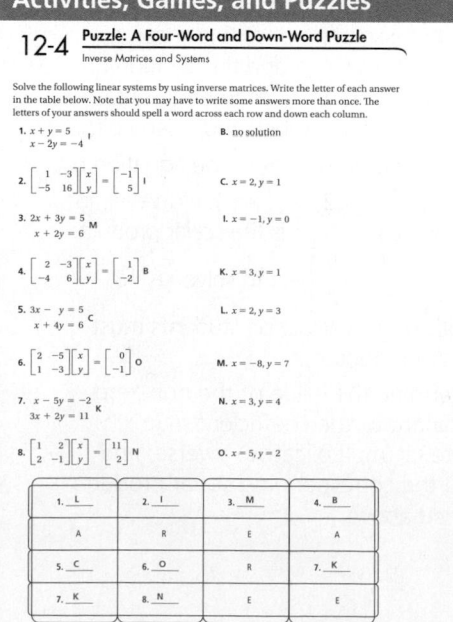

All-in-One Resources/Online
Enrichment

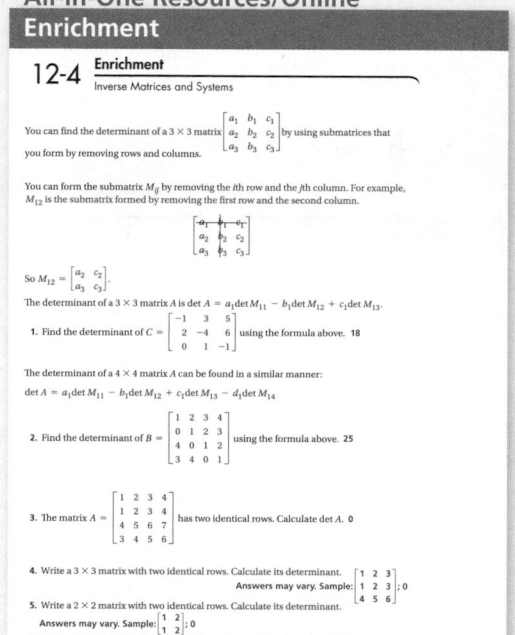

Online Teacher Resource Center
Activities, Games, and Puzzles

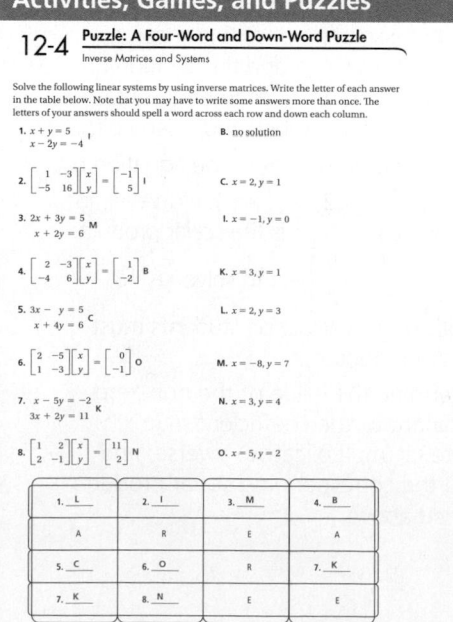

12

Pull It **All Together**

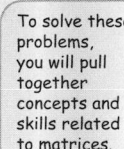

To solve these problems, you will pull together concepts and skills related to matrices.

BIG idea Data Representation
You can represent data in a variety of ways.

TASK 1

The first matrix represents inventory (how many there are) of four types of objects. The second matrix is a price matrix. The third matrix is the product of the first two matrices. Give an example of real inventory and real prices for which the product matrix makes sense. Explain the meaning of the product.

$$\begin{bmatrix} a_1 & a_2 \\ b_1 & b_2 \end{bmatrix} \begin{bmatrix} p_1 \\ p_2 \end{bmatrix} = \begin{bmatrix} r_1 \\ r_2 \end{bmatrix}$$

BIG idea Modeling
You can represent many real-world mathematical problems algebraically. These representations can lead to algebraic solutions.

TASK 2

Suppose the matrix equation $AX = B$ represents the system $\begin{cases} a_1x + a_2y = b_1 \\ a_3x + a_4y = b_2 \end{cases}$ and det $A = 0$. Show that the system has either infinitely many solutions or no solutions. (*Hint:* First show that a_3 and a_4 are proportional to a_1 and a_2.)

Performance Task UbD

Pull It All Together

The concepts and skills required to solve these problems are from several lessons within this chapter and from earlier chapters. As students solve these problems, they will demonstrate their reasoning strategies and their growth as independent problem solvers.

Task 1

Assign values under specific conditions to undefined elements in a matrix equation and then explain the matrix equation.
• What do r_1 and r_2 represent?
• What products are usually bought in sets but priced separately?

Task 2

Use the determinant of a matrix to show that a system of equations must either have no solutions or many solutions.
• What matrix represents A?
• What is the determinant of A? What value can you set the determinant equal to?
• Once you show the proportionality of a_3 and a_4 to a_1 and a_2, how do the expressions $a_1x + a_2y$ and $a_3x + a_4y$ compare?

Assess
Performance UbD

Pull It All Together

See p. 53 for a holistic scoring rubric to gauge a student's progress on Understanding the Problem, Planning a Solution, Getting an Answer, and Assessing Autonomy.

PARTIAL SOLUTION OUTLINES

1. Possible Plan: You are buying supplies for two art classes. For each class you will need markers and drawing tablets. The first matrix will be the number of items needed. The second matrix will be the cost of each item. The product matrix will be the total cost of the supplies.

2. First step: Write a matrix equation to represent the system.

$$\left(\begin{bmatrix} a_1 & a_2 \\ a_3 & a_4 \end{bmatrix} \begin{bmatrix} x \\ y \end{bmatrix} = \begin{bmatrix} b_1 \\ b_2 \end{bmatrix} \right)$$

Second step: The determinant is equal to 0. So,
$$a_1a_4 - a_2a_3 = 0$$
$$a_1a_4 = a_2a_3$$
$$\frac{a_1}{a_2} = \frac{a_3}{a_4}$$

Third step: Since a_1 and a_2 are proportional to a_3 and a_4, there is no inverse matrix and the system has no unique solution. Depending on the values of b_1 and b_2 the graphs will be either parallel lines (no solutions) or the same line (infinitely many solutions).

Essential Questions

BIG idea **Data Representation**

ESSENTIAL QUESTION How can you use a matrix to organize data?

ANSWER You can organize data in a matrix in exactly the same way that you organize data in a rectangular table.

BIG idea **Modeling**

ESSENTIAL QUESTION How can you use a matrix equation to model a real-world situation?

ANSWER If you can model a real situation with a system of equations, you can represent the system with a matrix equation.

---

12 Chapter Review

Connecting **BIG** ideas and Answering the Essential Questions

1 Data Representation
You can organize data in a matrix in exactly the same way that you organize data in a rectangular table.

Adding, Subtracting, and Multiplying Matrices (Lessons 12-1 and 12-2)
To add or subtract matrices, add or subtract corresponding elements.
To multiply two matrices:
$$\begin{bmatrix} a & b \\ c & d \end{bmatrix}\begin{bmatrix} e & f \\ g & h \end{bmatrix} = \begin{bmatrix} ae + bg & af + bh \\ ce + dg & cf + dh \end{bmatrix}$$

2 Modeling
If you can model a real-world situation with a system of equations, you can represent the system with a matrix equation.

Determinants and Inverses (Lesson 12-3)
Let A be an $n \times n$ matrix. If det $A \neq 0$, then A^{-1} exists and $AA^{-1} = A^{-1}A = I_n$ (the $n \times n$ identity matrix).

Inverse Matrices and Systems (Lesson 12-4)
The matrix equation $AX = B$ represents a system of linear equations.

A is the coefficient matrix,
X is the variable matrix,
B is the constant matrix.

If det $A \neq 0$, then multiply each side by A^{-1} to find X.
$$A^{-1}AX = A^{-1}B$$
$$X = A^{-1}B$$

 ## Chapter Vocabulary

- coefficient matrix (p. 801)
- constant matrix (p. 801)
- corresponding elements (p. 772)
- determinant (p. 790)
- equal matrices (p. 775)
- matrix equation (p. 773)
- multiplicative identity matrix (p. 789)
- multiplicative inverse matrix (p. 789)
- scalar (p. 781)
- scalar multiplication (p. 781)
- singular matrix (p. 795)
- square matrix (p. 789)
- variable matrix (p. 801)
- zero matrix (p. 775)

Choose the correct term to complete each sentence.

1. If corresponding elements of matrices are equal, the matrices are _?_ .

2. The additive identity of a matrix is the _?_ .

3. A(n) _?_ consists of a coefficient matrix, a variable matrix, and a constant matrix.

4. An $n \times n$ matrix is called a(n) _?_ .

Summative Questions

Use the following prompts as you review this chapter with your students. The prompts are designed to help you assess your students' understanding of the BIG ideas they have studied.

- Could you add an $m \times n$ matrix and an $m \times p$ matrix? Could you multiply them?
- Compare and contrast matrix multiplication and scalar multiplication. Can they both change the dimensions of a matrix?
- Why is matrix multiplication not commutative?
- How can you use a determinant to analyze a system of linear equations?

Answers

Chapter Review

1. equal matrices

2. zero matrix

3. matrix equation

4. square matrix

12-1 Adding and Subtracting Matrices

Quick Review

To perform matrix addition or subtraction, add or subtract the **corresponding elements** in the matrices.

Two matrices are **equal matrices** when they have the same dimensions and corresponding elements are equal. This principle is used to solve a **matrix equation**.

Example

If $A = \begin{bmatrix} 2 & 1 & -2 \\ 1 & 4 & 3 \\ -2 & -1 & 5 \end{bmatrix}$ and $B = \begin{bmatrix} 1 & -2 & 4 \\ -3 & -2 & 1 \\ 0 & 0 & 5 \end{bmatrix}$,

what is $A + B$?

$A + B = \begin{bmatrix} 2+1 & 1+(-2) & -2+4 \\ 1+(-3) & 4+(-2) & 3+1 \\ -2+0 & -1+0 & 5+5 \end{bmatrix}$

$= \begin{bmatrix} 3 & -1 & 2 \\ -2 & 2 & 4 \\ -2 & -1 & 10 \end{bmatrix}$

Exercises

Find each sum or difference.

5. $\begin{bmatrix} 1 & 2 & -5 \\ 3 & -2 & 1 \end{bmatrix} + \begin{bmatrix} -2 & 7 & -3 \\ 1 & 2 & 5 \end{bmatrix}$

6. $\begin{bmatrix} 0 & 2 \\ -4 & -1 \end{bmatrix} - \begin{bmatrix} -5 & 6 \\ -9 & -1 \end{bmatrix}$

Solve each matrix equation.

7. $\begin{bmatrix} 2 & -6 & 8 \end{bmatrix} + \begin{bmatrix} -1 & -2 & 4 \end{bmatrix} = X$

8. $\begin{bmatrix} 7 & -1 \\ 0 & 8 \end{bmatrix} + X = \begin{bmatrix} 4 & 9 \\ -3 & 11 \end{bmatrix}$

Find the value of each variable.

9. $\begin{bmatrix} x-5 & 9 \\ 4 & t+2 \end{bmatrix} = \begin{bmatrix} -7 & w+1 \\ 8-r & 1 \end{bmatrix}$

10. $\begin{bmatrix} -4+t & 2y \\ r & w+5 \end{bmatrix} = \begin{bmatrix} 2t & 11 \\ -2r+12 & 9 \end{bmatrix}$

12-2 Matrix Multiplication

Quick Review

To obtain the product of a matrix and a **scalar**, multiply each matrix element by the scalar. Matrix multiplication uses both multiplication and addition. The element in the ith row and the jth column of the product of two matrices is the sum of the products of each element of the ith row of the first matrix and the corresponding element of the jth column of the second matrix. The first matrix must have the same number of columns as the second matrix has rows.

Example

If $A = \begin{bmatrix} 1 & -3 \\ -2 & 0 \end{bmatrix}$ and $B = \begin{bmatrix} 1 & 4 \\ 0 & 2 \end{bmatrix}$, what is AB?

$AB = \begin{bmatrix} (1)(1)+(-3)(0) & (1)(4)+(-3)(2) \\ (-2)(1)+(0)(0) & (-2)(4)+(0)(2) \end{bmatrix}$

$= \begin{bmatrix} 1 & -2 \\ -2 & -8 \end{bmatrix}$

Exercises

Use matrices A, B, C, and D to find each product, sum, or difference, if possible. If an operation is not defined, label it *undefined*.

$A = \begin{bmatrix} 6 & 1 & 0 & 8 \\ -4 & 3 & 7 & 11 \end{bmatrix}$ $B = \begin{bmatrix} 1 & 3 \\ -2 & 4 \end{bmatrix}$

$C = \begin{bmatrix} -2 & 1 \\ 4 & 0 \\ 2 & 2 \\ 1 & 1 \end{bmatrix}$ $D = \begin{bmatrix} 5 & -2 \\ 3 & 6 \end{bmatrix}$

11. $3A$

12. $B - 2A$

13. AB

14. BA

15. $AC - BD$

16. $4B - 3D$

5. $\begin{bmatrix} -1 & 9 & -8 \\ 4 & 0 & 6 \end{bmatrix}$

6. $\begin{bmatrix} 5 & -4 \\ 5 & 0 \end{bmatrix}$

7. $\begin{bmatrix} 1 & -8 & 12 \end{bmatrix}$

8. $\begin{bmatrix} -3 & 10 \\ -3 & 3 \end{bmatrix}$

9. $x = -2, w = 8, r = 4, t = -1$

10. $t = -4, y = \frac{11}{2}, r = 4, w = 4$

11. $\begin{bmatrix} 18 & 3 & 0 & 24 \\ -12 & 9 & 21 & 33 \end{bmatrix}$

12. undefined

13. undefined

14. $\begin{bmatrix} -6 & 10 & 21 & 41 \\ -28 & 10 & 28 & 28 \end{bmatrix}$

15. $\begin{bmatrix} -14 & -2 \\ 43 & -7 \end{bmatrix}$

16. $\begin{bmatrix} -11 & 18 \\ -17 & -2 \end{bmatrix}$

Answers

Chapter Review (continued)

17. $24;$ $\begin{bmatrix} \frac{1}{6} & -\frac{1}{24} \\ 0 & \frac{1}{4} \end{bmatrix}$

18. $0;$ does not exist

19. $42;$ $\begin{bmatrix} \frac{5}{42} & -\frac{1}{42} \\ -\frac{4}{21} & \frac{5}{21} \end{bmatrix}$

20. $6;$ $\begin{bmatrix} \frac{1}{3} & -\frac{2}{3} & 0 \\ -\frac{1}{6} & \frac{1}{3} & -\frac{1}{2} \\ \frac{1}{3} & \frac{1}{3} & 0 \end{bmatrix}$

21. $\begin{bmatrix} 1 & 2 \\ -1 & 0 \end{bmatrix}$

22. $(-4, -7)$

23. $\begin{bmatrix} 2 \\ 2 \end{bmatrix}$

24. $\begin{bmatrix} 2 & 1 \\ 3 & 2 \end{bmatrix}$

25. no unique solution

26. no unique solution

12-3 Determinants and Inverses

Quick Review

A **square matrix** with 1's along its main diagonal and 0's elsewhere is the **multiplicative identity matrix**, I. If A and X are square matrices such that $AX = I$, then X is the **multiplicative identity matrix** of A, A^{-1}.

You can use a calculator to find the inverse of a matrix. You can find the inverse of a 2×2 matrix

$A = \begin{bmatrix} a & b \\ c & d \end{bmatrix}$ by using its **determinant**.

$$A^{-1} = \frac{1}{\det A}\begin{bmatrix} d & -b \\ -c & a \end{bmatrix} = \frac{1}{ad - bc}\begin{bmatrix} d & -b \\ -c & a \end{bmatrix}$$

Example

What is the determinant of $\begin{bmatrix} 2 & -3 \\ 3 & -4 \end{bmatrix}$?

$$\det\begin{bmatrix} 2 & -3 \\ 3 & -4 \end{bmatrix} = (2)(-4) - (-3)(3)$$
$$= -8 - (-9) = 1$$

Exercises

Evaluate the determinant of each matrix and find the inverse, if possible.

17. $\begin{bmatrix} 6 & 1 \\ 0 & 4 \end{bmatrix}$

18. $\begin{bmatrix} 5 & -2 \\ 10 & -4 \end{bmatrix}$

19. $\begin{bmatrix} 10 & 1 \\ 8 & 5 \end{bmatrix}$

20. $\begin{bmatrix} 1 & 0 & 2 \\ -1 & 0 & 1 \\ -1 & -2 & 0 \end{bmatrix}$

12-4 Inverse Matrices and Systems

Quick Review

You can use inverse matrices to solve some matrix equations and systems of equations. When equations in a system are in standard form, the product of the **coefficient matrix** and the **variable matrix** equals the **constant matrix**. You solve the equation by multiplying both sides of the equation by the inverse of the coefficient matrix. If that inverse does not exist, the system does not have a unique solution.

Example

What is the matrix equation that corresponds to the following system? $\begin{cases} 2x - y = 12 \\ x + 4y = 15 \end{cases}$

Identify $A = \begin{bmatrix} 2 & -1 \\ 1 & 4 \end{bmatrix}$, $X = \begin{bmatrix} x \\ y \end{bmatrix}$, and $B = \begin{bmatrix} 12 \\ 15 \end{bmatrix}$.

The matrix equation is $AX = B$ or $\begin{bmatrix} 2 & -1 \\ 1 & 4 \end{bmatrix}\begin{bmatrix} x \\ y \end{bmatrix} = \begin{bmatrix} 12 \\ 15 \end{bmatrix}$.

Exercises

Use an inverse matrix to solve each equation or system.

21. $\begin{bmatrix} 3 & 5 \\ 6 & 2 \end{bmatrix}X = \begin{bmatrix} -2 & 6 \\ 4 & 12 \end{bmatrix}$

22. $\begin{cases} x - y = 3 \\ 2x - y = -1 \end{cases}$

23. $\begin{bmatrix} 4 & 1 \\ 2 & 1 \end{bmatrix}\begin{bmatrix} x \\ y \end{bmatrix} = \begin{bmatrix} 10 \\ 6 \end{bmatrix}$

24. $\begin{bmatrix} -6 & 0 \\ 7 & 1 \end{bmatrix}X = \begin{bmatrix} -12 & -6 \\ 17 & 9 \end{bmatrix}$

25. $\begin{cases} x + 2y = 15 \\ 2x + 4y = 30 \end{cases}$

26. $\begin{cases} a + 2b + c = 14 \\ b = c + 1 \\ a = -3c + 6 \end{cases}$

MathXL® for School
Go to PowerAlgebra.com

Do you know HOW?

Find each sum or difference.

1. $\begin{bmatrix} 4 & 7 \\ -2 & 1 \end{bmatrix} - \begin{bmatrix} -9 & 3 \\ 6 & 0 \end{bmatrix}$

2. $\begin{bmatrix} 4 & -5 & 1 \\ 10 & 7 & 4 \\ 21 & -9 & -6 \end{bmatrix} + \begin{bmatrix} -7 & -10 & 4 \\ 17 & 0 & 3 \\ -2 & -6 & 1 \end{bmatrix}$

Find each product.

3. $\begin{bmatrix} 2 & 6 \\ 1 & 0 \end{bmatrix}\begin{bmatrix} -1 & 5 \\ 3 & 1 \end{bmatrix}$ 4. $2\begin{bmatrix} -8 & 5 & -1 \\ 0 & 9 & 7 \end{bmatrix}$

5. $\begin{bmatrix} 0 & 3 \\ -4 & 9 \end{bmatrix}\begin{bmatrix} -4 & 6 & 1 & 3 \\ 9 & -8 & 10 & 7 \end{bmatrix}$

Solve each equation for x and y.

6. $\begin{bmatrix} -3+2x & 2 \\ 4 & -7y \end{bmatrix} = \begin{bmatrix} x-4 & 2 \\ 4 & -35 \end{bmatrix}$

7. $\begin{bmatrix} 2x & 3 \\ -3 & -7x+y \end{bmatrix} = \begin{bmatrix} 3x+2 & 3 \\ -3 & -4x \end{bmatrix}$

Find the determinant of each matrix.

8. $\begin{bmatrix} 1 & 0 & 0 \\ 0 & 1 & 0 \\ 0 & 0 & 1 \end{bmatrix}$ 9. $\begin{bmatrix} 2 & 3 & 0 \\ -1 & 1 & 0 \\ 4 & 2 & 1 \end{bmatrix}$

10. $\begin{bmatrix} 8 & -3 \\ 2 & 9 \end{bmatrix}$ 11. $\begin{bmatrix} \frac{1}{2} & -3 \\ 1 & 0 \end{bmatrix}$

Find the inverse of each matrix, if it exists.

12. $\begin{bmatrix} 3 & 8 \\ -7 & 10 \end{bmatrix}$ 13. $\begin{bmatrix} 0 & -5 \\ 9 & 6 \end{bmatrix}$

14. $\begin{bmatrix} 3 & 1 & 0 \\ 1 & -1 & 2 \\ 1 & 1 & 1 \end{bmatrix}$ 15. $\begin{bmatrix} 1 & 1 & 2 \\ 2 & 1 & 3 \\ 2 & 1 & 1 \end{bmatrix}$

Solve each matrix equation.

16. $\begin{bmatrix} 3 & -8 \\ 10 & 5 \end{bmatrix} - X = \begin{bmatrix} 2 & 8 \\ -1 & 12 \end{bmatrix}$

17. $\begin{bmatrix} 3 & 2 \\ -1 & 5 \end{bmatrix}X = \begin{bmatrix} -10 & -11 \\ 26 & -36 \end{bmatrix}$

18. $2X - \begin{bmatrix} -2 & 0 \\ 1 & 4 \end{bmatrix} = \begin{bmatrix} 5 & 10 \\ -15 & 9 \end{bmatrix}$

Find the area of each triangle with the given vertices.

19. vertices at $(2, 3), (-3, -1), (0, 4)$

20. vertices at $(-2, -3), (5, 0), (-1, 4)$

Do you UNDERSTAND?

21. **Open-Ended** Write a matrix that has no inverse.

22. **Writing** Explain how to determine whether two matrices can be multiplied and what the dimensions of the product matrix will be.

23. **Reasoning** Suppose the product of two matrices has dimensions 4×3. If one of the matrices in the multiplication has dimensions 4×5, what are the dimensions of the other matrix?

24. **Sales** A store sells three kinds of pencils and the first matrix below shows the prices, in dollars, for each type. The second matrix shows the quantity sold for each type. Explain how you can find the total sales using the two matrices.

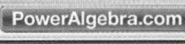
$$\text{Type } A \ B \ C \qquad \begin{array}{c} A \\ B \\ C \end{array}\begin{bmatrix} 20 \\ 10 \\ 15 \end{bmatrix}$$
$$\begin{bmatrix} 3 & 4 & 2 \end{bmatrix}$$

25. **Shopping** A local store is having a special promotion where all movies sell at the same price and all video games sell at another. Suppose you buy 5 movies and 4 video games for $97.50 and your friend buys 3 movies and 6 video games for $103.50. Write a matrix equation to describe the purchases. Then solve the matrix equation to find the price of a movie and the price of a video game.

18. $\begin{bmatrix} \frac{3}{2} & 5 \\ -7 & \frac{13}{2} \end{bmatrix}$

19. $\frac{13}{2}$ units², or 6.5 units²

20. 23 units²

21. Answers may vary. Sample: $\begin{bmatrix} 1 & 2 \\ 1 & 2 \end{bmatrix}$

22. Answers may vary. Sample: Two matrices can be multiplied if and only if the number of columns of the first matrix equals the number of rows of the second matrix. The product matrix will have the same number of rows as the first matrix and the same number of columns as the second matrix.

23. 5×3

24. Multiply the first matrix (price for each type of pencil) by the second matrix (quantity solve for each type of pencil) to find the total sales. $3(20) + 4(10) + 2(15) = 130.$

25. $\begin{bmatrix} 5 & 4 \\ 3 & 6 \end{bmatrix}\begin{bmatrix} m \\ v \end{bmatrix} = \begin{bmatrix} 97.50 \\ 103.50 \end{bmatrix}$; movie: $9.50; video game: $12.50

Answers

Chapter Test

1. $\begin{bmatrix} 13 & 4 \\ -8 & 1 \end{bmatrix}$

2. $\begin{bmatrix} -3 & -15 & 5 \\ 27 & 7 & 7 \\ 19 & -15 & -5 \end{bmatrix}$

3. $\begin{bmatrix} 16 & 16 \\ -1 & 5 \end{bmatrix}$

4. $\begin{bmatrix} -16 & 10 & -2 \\ 0 & 18 & 14 \end{bmatrix}$

5. $\begin{bmatrix} 27 & -24 & 30 & 21 \\ 97 & -96 & 86 & 51 \end{bmatrix}$

6. $x = -1, y = 5$

7. $x = -2, y = -6$

8. 1

9. 5

10. 78

11. 3

12. $\begin{bmatrix} \frac{5}{43} & -\frac{4}{43} \\ \frac{7}{86} & \frac{3}{86} \end{bmatrix}$

13. $\begin{bmatrix} \frac{2}{15} & \frac{1}{9} \\ -\frac{1}{5} & 0 \end{bmatrix}$

14. $\begin{bmatrix} \frac{3}{8} & \frac{1}{8} & \frac{2}{8} \\ -\frac{1}{8} & \frac{3}{8} & \frac{6}{8} \\ \frac{2}{8} & \frac{2}{8} & \frac{4}{8} \end{bmatrix}$

15. $\begin{bmatrix} -1 & 0.5 & 0.5 \\ 2 & -1.5 & 0.5 \\ 0 & 0.5 & -0.5 \end{bmatrix}$

16. $\begin{bmatrix} 1 & -16 \\ 11 & -7 \end{bmatrix}$

17. $\begin{bmatrix} -6 & 1 \\ 4 & -7 \end{bmatrix}$

PowerAlgebra.com

MathXL for School

Prepare students for the Chapter Test with online practice and review.

Item Number	Lesson	ADP Standard
1	p.257	E2.b
2	1-4	E2.e
3	6-6	F1.a
4	6-6	F1.b
5	6-7	F2.b
6	6-3	O1.b
7	6-2	O1.c
8	4-8	O2.b
9	8-4	O3.e
10	8-5	O3.e
11	4-5	P1.a
12	4-1	P1.a
13	5-2	P2.c
14	8-2	P2.d
15	5-5	E2.a
16	7-2	X1.b
17	p. 90	F3.b
18	8-2	P2.e
19	7-2	X1.a
20	6-7	F2.a
21	8-6	E2.a
22	6-5	E2.a
23	6-4	O3.a
24	4-2	P1.a
25	8-3	P2.d
26	2-7	F3.b
27	4-1	P1.c
28	7-2	X1.c
29	6-7	F1.b, F2.b
30	6-4	O1.c
31	1-6	E1.a
32	3-2	E1.d
33	4-8	E2.b
34	p. 91	F3.c
35	6-4	O3.c
36	4-3	P1.a
37	5-1	P2.b
38	7-6	X1.d
39	7-2	X1.c
40	8-3	P2.f
41	7-2	X1.d
42	7-5	E2.a
43	7-2	X1.b
44	7-2	X1.a
45	5-9	P2.a
46	3-2	E1.d
47	3-5	E1.b
48	4-7	E2.c
49	6-6	F1.a
50	5-1	P2.f
51	4-3	P1.d
52	3-5	E1.b
53	7-5	E2.a

End-of-Course Assessment to Prepare for the ADP Algebra 2 Test

This practice test is designed to help you prepare for the American Diploma Project (ADP) Algebra 2 Test.

Complete the following items *without* a calculator. For multiple choice items, write the letter of the correct response on your paper. For all other items, show or explain your work.

1. The graph of a quadratic function $f(x)$ is shown below.

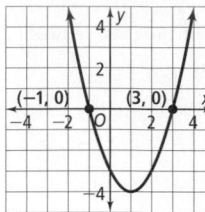

Use the graph to solve $f(x) < 0$.

  Ⓐ $-1 < x < 3$
  Ⓒ $x < -1$ or $x > 3$
  Ⓑ $-1 \le x \le 3$
  Ⓓ $x \le -1$ or $x > 3$

2. Newton's Law of Universal Gravitation is $F = \frac{Gm_1m_2}{r^2}$. Solve this equation for r.

  Ⓕ $r = \sqrt{\frac{F}{Gm_1m_2}}$
  Ⓗ $r = \frac{F}{2Gm_1m_2}$
  Ⓖ $r = \sqrt{\frac{Gm_1m_2}{F}}$
  Ⓘ $r = \frac{Gm_1m_2}{2F}$

3. Let $f(x) = x^3 - 4x^2 + 9x$ and let $g(x) = 6x^3 + x^2 - 5x - 12$. What is $f(x) - g(x)$?

  Ⓐ $-5x^3 - 5x^2 + 14x + 12$
  Ⓑ $-5x^3 - 3x^2 + 4x - 12$
  Ⓒ $7x^3 - 3x^2 + 4x - 12$
  Ⓓ $-5x^4 - 5x^3 + 14x^2 + 12x$

4. Let $f(x) = x - 3$ and let $g(x) = 2x^2 - 6$. What is $g(f(x))$?

  Ⓕ $2x^2 - 9$
  Ⓗ $2x^2 - 12x + 12$
  Ⓖ $2x^2 - 12$
  Ⓘ $2x^3 - 6x^2 - 6x + 18$

5. Let $f^{-1}(x) = 2x + 3$. What is the solution of $f(x) = f^{-1}(x)$?

  Ⓐ $x = -1$ or $x = -2$
  Ⓒ $(x, y) = (-1, -2)$
  Ⓑ $x = -3$
  Ⓓ $(x, y) = (-3, -3)$

6. Which is a simpler form of $\frac{\sqrt{5}}{3 - \sqrt{2}}$?

  Ⓕ $\frac{\sqrt{10}}{3\sqrt{2} - 2}$
  Ⓗ $\frac{3\sqrt{5} - \sqrt{10}}{7}$
  Ⓖ $\frac{5}{3\sqrt{5} - 10}$
  Ⓘ $\frac{3\sqrt{5} + \sqrt{10}}{7}$

7. Suppose that $\sqrt[4]{n} = 2$. What is $n^{-\frac{1}{2}}$?

  Ⓐ -8
  Ⓒ $\frac{1}{8}$
  Ⓑ -4
  Ⓓ $\frac{1}{4}$

8. What is the quotient $\frac{2 + 5i}{4 + 3i}$ written in standard form?

  Ⓕ $\frac{1}{2} + \frac{5}{3}i$
  Ⓗ $-\frac{7}{7} + \frac{26}{7}i$
  Ⓖ $\frac{8}{25} - \frac{12}{25}i$
  Ⓘ $\frac{23}{25} + \frac{14}{25}i$

9. Multiply $\frac{x^3}{x^2 - 4} \cdot \frac{5x + 10}{10x}$.

  Ⓐ $\frac{5x}{4}$
  Ⓒ $\frac{x^2}{2(x + 2)}$
  Ⓑ $\frac{x^2}{2(x - 2)}$
  Ⓓ $\frac{5^3}{10(x - 2)}$

10. Which is a simpler form of the complex fraction $\frac{\frac{1}{b} + c}{b + \frac{1}{c}}$?

  Ⓕ 1
  Ⓗ $\left(\frac{1}{b} + c\right)^2$
  Ⓖ $\frac{c}{b}$
  Ⓘ $(1 + c)(b + 1)$

11. What is the sum of the x-intercepts of the graph of the quadratic function $y = x^2 - 4x - 12$?

  Ⓐ 6
  Ⓒ -1
  Ⓑ 4
  Ⓓ -4

Item Number	Lesson	ADP Standard
54	7-2	X1.d
55	3-3	E1.c
56	6-1	O3.d
57	2-7	F3.a
58	4-9	E2.d
59	3-4	E1.d
60	8-3	P2.d
61	9-2	I1.d
62	10-4	C1.d
63	11-7	S2.d
64	11-9	R2.b
65	13-2	T1.b
66	10-4	C1.a
67	12-3	M2.a
68	7-4	L1.a
69	11-4	R1.c
70	10-6	C1.c
71	11-5	S2.b

Item Number	Lesson	ADP Standard
72	13-3	T1.c
73	2-5	S2.a
74	11-3	R1.d
75	9-3	I1.a
76	7-4	L1.a
77	12-3	M2.b
78	11-8	R1.b
79	7-3	L2.d
80	11-5	S1.b
81	11-1	R1.a
82	13-6	T1.b
83	12-2	M1.b
84	12-6	M4.b
85	7-6	L1.b
86	9-5	I1.f
87	10-6	C1.b
88	12-4	M2.c
89	13-7	T1.f

12. What is an equation of a parabola with the following characteristics?

Axis of symmetry: $x = -3$

Range: all real numbers less than or equal to 4

F $y = -(x - 4)^2 - 3$

G $y = (x - 4)^2 - 3$

H $y = -(x + 3)^2 + 4$

I $y = (x + 3)^2 + 4$

13. The graph of a degree 4 polynomial function with integer zeros is shown below.

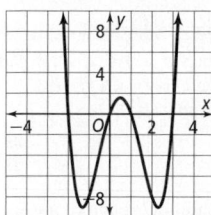

What is the equation of the polynomial function?

A $y = x^4 - 6x^3 + 11x^2 - 6x$

B $y = x^4 - 2x^3 - 5x^2 + 6x$

C $y = x^4 - 2x^3 + x^2 + 3x$

D $y = x^4 + 2x^3 - 5x^2 - 6x$

14. Which function is best represented by the graph below?

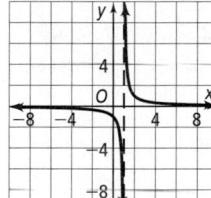

F $y = \frac{1}{x - 1}$

H $y = \frac{x}{x - 1}$

G $y = \frac{1}{x + 1}$

I $y = \frac{x}{x + 1}$

15. How many distinct real roots does the equation $x^4 + 3x^3 - 4x = 0$ have?

A 1

C 3

B 2

D 4

16. Which function best represents the graph?

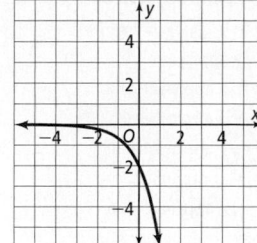

F $f(x) = 2 \cdot 3^{-x}$

G $f(x) = -2 \cdot 3^x$

H $f(x) = 2 \cdot 3^x$

I $f(x) = -2 \cdot 3^{-x}$

17. Which system is represented by the graph below?

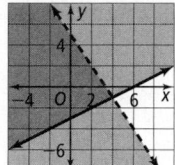

A $\begin{cases} 2y + 6 \geq x \\ y < -\frac{3}{2}x + 5 \end{cases}$

C $\begin{cases} 2y - 6 \geq x \\ y < -\frac{3}{2}x + 5 \end{cases}$

B $\begin{cases} 2y + 6 \geq x \\ y > -\frac{3}{2}x + 5 \end{cases}$

D $\begin{cases} 2y + 6 \geq x \\ -y < \frac{3}{2}x + 5 \end{cases}$

18. The graph of a rational function is shown below.

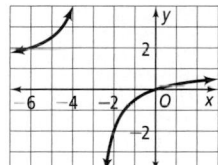

Which function best represents the graph?

F $f(x) = \frac{3}{x - 1}$

H $f(x) = \frac{3x}{x - 1}$

G $f(x) = \frac{1}{x + 3}$

I $f(x) = \frac{x}{x + 3}$

Answers

1. A

2. G

3. A

4. H

5. B

6. I

7. D

8. I

9. B

10. G

11. B

12. H

13. B

14. F

15. C

16. G

17. A

18. I

Answers

19. A

20. F

21. D

22. G

23. A

24. G

25. B

26.

Scoring Rubric

Score	Description
2	Student earns 2 points.
1	Student earns 1 point.
0	Response is incorrect or irrelevant to the skill or concept being measured.

Scoring Notes:

- 1 point for a correct graph with a vertex at $(-3, -1)$ and going through the points $(-5, 3)$, $(-4, 1)$, $(-2, 1)$ and $(-1, 3)$
- 1 point for V-shaped graph opening up with two legs that have slopes with the same absolute value but one is positive and one is negative

Sample graph:

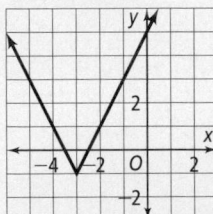

27.

Scoring Rubric

Score	Description
2	Student earns 2 points.
1	Student earns 1 point.
0	Response is incorrect or irrelevant to the skill or concept being measured.

Scoring Notes:

- 1 point for a parabola opening down to show the vertical reflection
- 1 point for a parabola that is moved down 3 units so that the vertex is at $(0, -3)$
- -1 point if the above are listed in incorrect order

Sample Graph:

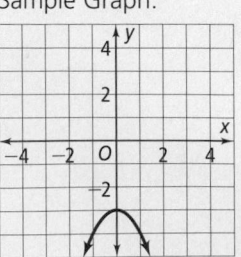

---

19. Consider the exponential function $f(x) = ab^x$. If $a < 0$ and $0 < b < 1$, what is the end behavior of the graph?

- (A) as x approaches $-\infty$, y approaches $-\infty$
  as x approaches ∞, y approaches 0
- (B) as x approaches $-\infty$, y approaches ∞
  as x approaches ∞, y approaches 0
- (C) as x approaches $-\infty$, y approaches 0
  as x approaches ∞, y approaches $-\infty$
- (D) as x approaches $-\infty$, y approaches 0
  as x approaches ∞, y approaches ∞

20. If $f(x) = (x + 2)^2 - 1$, restrict the domain of f so that its inverse is also a function.

- (F) $x \geq -2$
- (G) $x \geq -1$
- (H) $x \geq 0$
- (I) $x \geq 2$

21. Solve $\frac{3}{2x + 10} + \frac{5}{4} = \frac{7}{x + 5}$ for x.

- (A) $-\frac{50}{11}$
- (B) $-\frac{34}{10}$
- (C) $-\frac{9}{5}$
- (D) $-\frac{3}{5}$

22. Solve $\sqrt{x - 2} - 7 = -4$ for x.

- (F) 5
- (G) 11
- (H) 18
- (I) 25

23. What is the value of x if $\sqrt[5]{b^3} = b^x$?

- (A) $\frac{3}{5}$
- (B) $\frac{5}{3}$
- (C) 3
- (D) 15

24. What is the x-coordinate of the vertex of the graph of $f(x) = 2x^2 + 4x - 6$?

- (F) -6
- (G) -1
- (H) 1
- (I) 4

25. The horizontal asymptote of the graph of $y = \frac{4x - 4}{2x - 6}$ is $y = t$ for a real number t. What is the value of t?

- (A) 1
- (B) 2
- (C) 3
- (D) 4

26. Graph $f(x) = |2x + 6| - 1$.

27. The graph of $y = x^2$ is shown below.

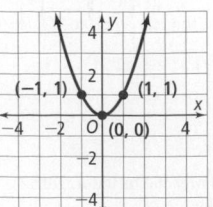

Use transformations to graph $y = -x^2 - 3$.

28. Consider the graph of the function $f(x) = 2(4)^x$. Explain how the graph of the function $g(x) = -2(4)^x + 3$ can be obtained from the graph of $f(x)$.

29. Let $f(x) = \frac{4}{x - 1}$.

Part A: Determine $f^{-1}(x)$. Show or explain your work.

Part B: Find $f(f^{-1}(x))$ and $f^{-1}(f(x))$. Show your work.

Part C: How are the domain and range of f and f^{-1} related?

30. Consider this expression: $\left(\frac{r^{3m}}{r^{-m}t^{4n}}\right)^{\frac{1}{n}} \cdot \left(\frac{r^{\frac{1}{n}}}{t^{\frac{2}{m}}}\right)^{-m}$

Part A: Simplify the expression so that r and t are only written once. Show your work.

Part B: Using your answer from Part A, evaluate the expression when $m = 1$, $n = 2$, and $t = -3i$. Show your work.

Part C: For what values of r will the expression you found in Part B be a real number? Explain your answer.

28.

Scoring Rubric

Score	Description
2	Student earns 2 points.
1	Student earns 1 point.
0	Response is incorrect or irrelevant to the skill or concept being measured.

Scoring Notes:
2 points

- 1 point for explanation that the graph of $f(x)$ is reflected across the x-axis
- 1 point for explanation that the reflection of $f(x)$ is moved up 3 units

29.

Scoring Rubric

Score	Description
4	Student earns 5 points.
3	Student earns 3 or 4 points.
2	Student earns 2 points.
1	Student earns 1 point.
0	Response is incorrect or irrelevant to the skill or concept being measured.
Blank	Student fails to respond.

Scoring Notes:
Part A: 2 points

- 1 point for a correct strategy:

$$\begin{bmatrix} y = \frac{4}{x - 1} \\ yx - y = 4 \\ x = \frac{4 + y}{y} \end{bmatrix}$$

- 1 point for a correct answer:

$$\left[f^{-1}(x) = \frac{4}{x} + 1 \right]$$

You may use a calculator with the following items. For multiple choice items, write the letter of the correct response on your paper. For all other items, show or explain your work.

31. Solve $|x + 2| \geq 5$.

  (A) $x \geq 3$ (C) $x \leq 3$ or $x \geq 7$

  (B) $-7 \leq x \leq 3$ (D) $x \leq -7$ or $x \geq 3$

32. Which equation shows an inverse variation?

  (F) $y = 5x$ (H) $6 = \frac{x}{y}$

  (G) $xy - 4 = 0$ (I) $y = -4$

33. What are all the complex solutions of $x^2 - 4x = -5$?

  (A) $-1, 5$

  (B) $1, 3$

  (C) $2 + i, 2 - i$

  (D) $2 + 3i, 2 - 3i$

34. The length of a rectangle is $2x^2 - 4x + 1$. The width is $3x - 5$. Which polynomial represents the area of the rectangle?

  (F) $6x^3 + 22x^2 + 23x + 5$

  (G) $6x^3 - 22x^2 + 23x - 5$

  (H) $3x^3 - 11x^2 + 11.5x - 2.5$

  (I) $2x^2 - x - 4$

35. Simplify $\dfrac{r^{\frac{1}{2}}}{r^{-\frac{1}{4}}}$.

  (A) $r^{\frac{1}{4}}$ (C) $r^{\frac{1}{8}}$

  (B) $-r^2$ (D) $r^{\frac{3}{4}}$

36. The graph of a quadratic function, $y = ax^2 + bx + c$ passes through the points shown. What is the axis of symmetry of the parabola?

  (F) $x = -2$

  (G) $x = -1$

  (H) $x = 1$

  (I) $x = 2$

37. What is the end behavior of the graph of the polynomial function $f(x) = -2x^5 + x^4 + 3x^3 - x + 1$?

  (A) down and down

  (B) down and up

  (C) up and down

  (D) up and up

38. $500 is invested in an account with 1.5% interest compounded continuously. The equation $A(x) = 500(1.015)^x$ can be used to find the balance in the account after x years. To the nearest year, in how many years will the account have a balance of $817?

  (F) 2 years   (H) 72 years

  (G) 33 years   (I) 109 years

39. The graph of the exponential equation $y = 2^x$ is reflected in the x-axis and translated down 1 unit. What is the equation of the resulting graph?

  (A) $y = 2^{-x-1}$

  (B) $y = -2^{x-1}$

  (C) $y = 2^{-x} - 1$

  (D) $y = -2^x - 1$

40. The function $C(x) = \frac{10}{2x^2 + 1}$ can be used to find the concentration $C(x)$ in mg/L of a certain drug in the bloodstream of a patient x hours after an injection. In approximately how many hours after an injection will the concentration of the drug be 1.3 mg/L?

  (F) 0.5 h   (H) 1.8 h

  (G) 0.7 h   (I) 2.3 h

41. The half-life of radium-226 is about 1600 years. After 4000 years what percentage of a sample of radium-226 remains?

  (A) 2.5%   (C) 40.0%

  (B) 17.7%   (D) 75.8%

42. Solve $8.2(3^{2x-4}) - 11 = 557.1$. Round your answer to the nearest tenth.

  (F) 1.8   (H) 3.5

  (G) 2.9   (I) 3.9

Scoring Notes:
Part A: 2 points
• 1 point for a correct strategy:

$$\left[\left(\frac{r^{4m}}{t^{4n}}\right)^{\frac{1}{n}} \cdot \left(\frac{t^{\frac{2}{m}}}{r^{\frac{1}{n}}}\right)^m\right]$$

$$\left[\frac{r^{\frac{4m}{n}}}{t^4} \cdot \frac{t^2}{r^{\frac{m}{n}}}\right]$$

• 1 point for a correct answer: $\left[\dfrac{r^{\frac{3m}{n}}}{t^2}\right]$

Part B: 2 points

• 1 point for a correct strategy: $\left[\dfrac{\frac{r^{\frac{3 \cdot 1}{2}}}{(-3i)^2}}{\frac{r^{\frac{3}{2}}}{9i^2}}\right]$

• 1 point for a correct answer: $\left[-\dfrac{r^{\frac{3}{2}}}{9}\right]$

Part C: 1 point
• 1 point for a correct explanation [$r \geq 0$ because the exponent of $\frac{3}{2}$ means the same thing as taking a square root of r and then cubing the result. A square root of a negative number results in an imaginary number.]

31. D

32. G

33. C

34. G

35. D

36. H

37. C

38. G

39. D

40. H

41. B

42. I

Part B: 2 points
• 1 point for a correct strategy showing $f(f^{-1}(x)) = x$:

$$f\left(\frac{4}{x} + 1\right) = \frac{4}{\frac{4}{x} + 1 - 1} = \frac{4}{\frac{4}{x}}$$

$$= 4 \cdot \frac{x}{4} = x$$

• 1 point for a correct strategy showing $f^{-1}(f(x)) = x$:

$$f^{-1}\left(\frac{4}{x - 1}\right) = \frac{4}{\frac{4}{x - 1}} + 1$$

$$= 4 \cdot \frac{x - 1}{4} + 1$$

$$= x - 1 + 1 = x$$

Part C: 1 point
• 1 point for a correct explanation [The domain of f is equal to the range of f^{-1}, and the range of f is equal to the domain of f^{-1}.]

30.

Scoring Rubric

Score	Description
4	Student earns 5 points.
3	Student earns 4 points.
2	Student earns 2 or 3 points.
1	Student earns 1 point.
0	Response is incorrect or irrelevant to the skill or concept being measured.
Blank	Student fails to respond.

Answers

43. A   **44.** F
45. A   **46.** G
47. C   **48.** I
49. B   **50.** F
51. A   **52.** F
53. C   **54.** G

55.

Scoring Rubric

Score	Description
2	Student earns 2 points.
1	Student earns 1 point.
0	Response is incorrect or irrelevant to the skill or concept being measured.

Scoring Notes:
2 points
- 1 point for a solid line for $x - 3y = 6$ and a dashed line for $2x + y = 5$
- 1 point for correct shading above the solid line and above the dashed line

Sample graph:

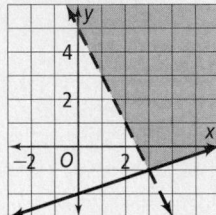

56.

Scoring Rubric

Score	Description
2	Student earns 2 points.
1	Student earns 1 point.
0	Response is incorrect or irrelevant to the skill or concept being measured.

Scoring Notes:
2 points
- 1 point for correct strategy

$$\left[\begin{array}{l} \sqrt{4(4x^2 + 12x + 9)} \\ \sqrt{4(2x + 3)^2} \end{array}\right]$$

- 1 point for a correct answer $[2|2x + 3|]$

---

43. An exponential function is represented in the table below.

x	f(x)
−2	12
−1	6
0	3
1	1.5

Which equation best represents the function?

   (A) $f(x) = 3(2^{-x})$ (C) $f(x) = 2^{-x} + 3$
   (B) $f(x) = 3(2^x)$ (D) $f(x) = 2^x + 3$

44. What is the range of the graph of $f(x) = -ab^x$ if $a > 0$ and $b > 1$?

   (F) $f(x) \leq 0$ (H) $f(x) \geq a$
   (G) $f(x) \leq a$ (I) All real numbers

45. The characteristics of function $f(x) = ax^n$ are shown below.

Domain: All real numbers

Range: $f(x) \leq 0$

Symmetric with respect to the y-axis

What must be true about the values of a and n?

   (A) $a < 0$ and n is even   (C) $a > 0$ and n is even
   (B) $a < 0$ and n is odd   (D) $a > 0$ and n is odd

46. A train leaves a city traveling due north. A car leaves the city at the same time traveling due west. The car is traveling 15 mi/h faster than the train. After 2 h they are approximately 150 mi apart. What is the speed of the train?

   (F) 30 mi/h   (H) 60 mi/h
   (G) 45 mi/h   (I) 75 mi/h

47. A high school sold 800 tickets for a soccer game. Three types of tickets were sold: adult, student, and child. There were four times as many adult tickets sold as child tickets, and there were 62 more student tickets sold than adult tickets. How many adult tickets were sold?

   (A) 82   (C) 328
   (B) 123   (D) 384

48. The equation $x^2 - 0.8x + c = 0$ has one real solution. Use the discriminant to find the value of c.

   (F) 0.4   (G) 0.8   (H) 0.12   (I) 0.16

49. Let $f(x) = 3x + 5$ and let $g(x) = x^2 + 2x$. What is $f(-3) \cdot g(-3)$?

   (A) −32   (B) −12   (C) 9   (D) 60

50. The volume of a square pyramid with a height equal to four less than the length of a side of the base is given by $V(x) = \frac{1}{3}(x^3 + 8x^2 + 16x)$ where x is the height in cm. If the length of a side of the base is 9 cm, what is the volume of the pyramid?

   (F) 135 cm^3 (H) 507 cm^3
   (G) 405 cm^3 (I) 1521 cm^3

51. A quadratic function is represented in the table below.

x	f(x)
1	−13
2	−3
3	3
4	5
5	3

Which equation best represents the function?

   (A) $f(x) = -2(x - 4)^2 + 5$
   (B) $f(x) = -2(x - 3)^2 + 3$
   (C) $f(x) = 2(x - 4)^2 + 5$
   (D) $f(x) = 2(x - 3)^2 + 3$

52. Find the x-value of the solution to the following system of equations.

$$\begin{cases} 3x + y = -3 \\ 2y - z = 6 \\ x + y - 2z = 1 \end{cases}$$

   (F) −2   (H) $\frac{3}{5}$
   (G) −1   (I) 3

53. Solve: $4(3^x) = 26$. Round your answer to the nearest tenth.

   (A) 0.3   (C) 1.7
   (B) 1.3   (D) 2.2

57.

Scoring Rubric

Score	Description
2	Student earns 2 points.
1	Student earns 1 point.
0	Response is incorrect or irrelevant to the skill or concept being measured.

Scoring Notes:
2 points

- 1 point for correct answer $\left[\left(\frac{1}{b}, c\right)\right]$

- 1 point for a correct explanation [The x-value of the vertex makes the expression inside the absolute value zero. The solution to $bx - 1 = 0$ is $\frac{1}{b}$. The y-value of the vertex is $f\left(\frac{1}{b}\right) = c$.]

58.

Scoring Rubric

Score	Description
2	Student earns 2 points.
1	Student earns 1 point.
0	Response is incorrect or irrelevant to the skill or concept being measured.

Scoring Notes:
2 points

- 1 point for correct strategy

$$\left[\begin{array}{l} (x - 2)(x + 2) > 0 \\ x - 2 > 0 \text{ and } x + 2 > 0 \text{ or} \\ x - 2 < 0 \text{ and } x + 2 < 0 \\ x > 2 \text{ and } x > -2 \text{ or} \\ x < 2 \text{ and } x < -2 \end{array}\right]$$

- 1 point for correct answer $[x > 2 \text{ or } x < -2]$

54. The amount of cesium-137 remaining after x years in an initial sample of 200 milligrams can be found using the equation $C(x) = 200e^{-0.02295x}$. In approximately how many years will the sample contain 120 milligrams of cesium-137?

   Ⓕ 13   Ⓖ 22   Ⓗ 26   Ⓘ 39

55. Graph the solution set of the following system of inequalities.
$$\begin{cases} x - 3y \le 6 \\ 2x + y > 5 \end{cases}$$

56. Simplify the expression below. Show your work.
$$\sqrt{16x^2 + 48x + 36}$$

57. What is the vertex of the graph of $f(x) = a|bx - 1| + c$? Explain your answer.

58. Find the solution set for $x^2 - 4 > 0$.

59. A company produces two types of doghouses, regular and deluxe. A regular doghouse requires 7 hours to build and 3 hours to paint. A deluxe doghouse requires 11 hours to build and 4 hours to paint. The company employs 5 builders and 2 painters. Each employee can work a maximum of 40 hours.

Part A: Write a system of inequalities that can be used to find the number of each type of doghouse built in a week. Define the variables you use in your system.

Part B: Graph the solution set of your system of inequalities from Part A. Label each line in your graph.

Part C: How many of each type of doghouse can be built in one week if each employee works exactly 40 hours? Show your work.

60. Consider the function $f(x) = \frac{1}{x}$.

Part A: Graph $f(x)$.

Part B: Explain how the graph of $g(x) = \frac{4}{x + 2}$ compares to the graph of $f(x)$.

Part C: What is the horizontal asymptote (if any) of the graph of $g(x)$?

Part D: What is the vertical asymptote of the graph of $g(x)$? Explain how this relates to the domain of $g(x)$.

The following items cover topics from the ADP modules: Data and Statistics, Probability, Logarithmic Functions, Matrices, Conic Sections, and Sequences and Series.

You may use a calculator with these items.

61. Consider the recursive model shown below.
$$\begin{cases} a_1 = 5 \\ a_{n+1} = a_n - 7 \end{cases}$$

What is an explicit formula for this sequence?

  Ⓐ $a_n = 5 + 7(n - 1)$
  Ⓑ $a_n = 5n - 7(n - 1)$
  Ⓒ $a_n = -7 + 5(n - 1)$
  Ⓓ $a_n = 5 - 7(n - 1)$

62. An arch in the shape of the upper half of an ellipse supports a bridge that spans a distance of 80 ft. The maximum height of the arch is 30 ft. To the nearest tenth of a foot, what is the height of the arch 28 ft from the center of the ellipse?

  Ⓕ 14.4 ft   Ⓗ 28.1 ft
  Ⓖ 21.4 ft   Ⓘ 29.7 ft

63. A scientist wants to study the effects of a new medication on acne. Which type of study would give the most reliable results?

  Ⓐ Controlled experiment
  Ⓑ Observational study
  Ⓒ Survey
  Ⓓ Random sample

64. Suppose scores on an entry exam are normally distributed. The exam has a mean score of 140 and a standard deviation of 20. What is the probability that a person who takes the test will score between 120 and 160?

  Ⓕ 14%   Ⓗ 68%
  Ⓖ 40%   Ⓘ 95%

65. If $\log_b 4 \approx 1.2$ and $\log_b 5 \approx 1.4$, what is the approximate value of $\log_b 80$?

  Ⓐ 2.3   Ⓒ 3.8
  Ⓑ 2.6   Ⓓ 4.0

59.

Scoring Rubric

Score	Description
4	Student earns 8 points.
3	Student earns 6 or 7 points.
2	Student earns 3, 4 or 5 points.
1	Student earns 1 or 2 points.
0	Response is incorrect or irrelevant to the skill or concept being measured.
Blank	Student fails to respond.

Scoring Notes:
Part A: 3 points
- 1 point for correctly defined variables [x = number of regular doghouses, y = number of deluxe doghouses]
- 1 point for the following two correct inequalities:
$$\begin{bmatrix} 7x + 11y \le 200 \\ 3x + 4y \le 80 \end{bmatrix}$$

- 1 point for the correct constraints
$$\begin{bmatrix} 7x + 11y \le 200 \\ 3x + 4y \le 80 \\ x \ge 0 \\ y \ge 0 \end{bmatrix}$$

Part B: 3 points
- 1 point for solid line for $7x + 11y = 200$
- 1 point for solid line for $3x + 4y = 80$
- 1 point for correct shading below both lines and within the first quadrant.

Sample graph:

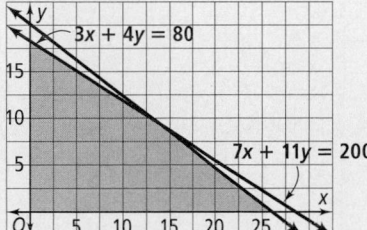

Part C: 2 points
- 1 point for a correct strategy
$$\begin{bmatrix} 3(7x + 11y = 200) \\ -7(3x + 4y = 80) \\ \overline{21x + 33y = 600} \\ \underline{-21x - 28y = -560} \\ 5y = 40 \\ y = 8 \\ 3x + 4(8) = 80 \end{bmatrix}$$

- 1 point for a correct answer [16 regular doghouses, 8 deluxe doghouses]

60.

Scoring Rubric

Score	Description
4	Student earns 6 points.
3	Student earns 4 or 5 points.
2	Student earns 2 or 3 points.
1	Student earns 1 point.
0	Response is incorrect or irrelevant to the skill or concept being measured.
Blank	Student fails to respond.

Scoring Notes:
Part A: 1 point
- 1 point for a correct graph
Sample graph:

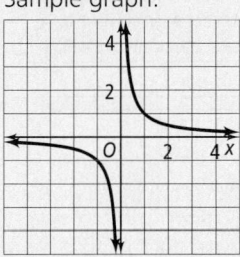

Part B: 2 points
- 1 point for explanation that the factor 4 multiplies the y-values of $f(x)$ by 4 and stretches the graph vertically.
- 1 point for explanation that the "+ 2" shifts the graph 2 units to the left

Part C: 1 point
- 1 point for a correct answer [$y = 0$]

Part D: 2 points
- 1 point for a correct vertical asymptote [$x = -2$]
- 1 point for a correct explanation [The vertical asymptote occurs at the x-value omitted from the domain.]

61. D

62. G

63. A

64. H

65. C

Answers

66. G
67. D
68. F
69. C
70. H
71. D
72. G
73. D
74. H
75. C
76. H
77. B
78. G
79. D
80. I
81. B
82. H
83. D
84.

Scoring Rubic

Score	Description
4	Student earns 6 points.
3	Student earns 4 or 5 points.
2	Student earns 2 or 3 points.
1	Student earns 1 point.
0	Response is incorrect or irrelevant to the skill or concept being measured.
Blank	Student fails to respond.

Scoring Notes:
Part A: 3 points
• 1 point for a correct mean [35]
• 1 point for a correct median [25]
• 1 point for a correct mode [25]
Part B: 2 points
• 1 point for a correct range [50]
• 1 point for a correct interquartile range [40]
Part C: 1 point
• 1 point for a correct box-and-whisker plot

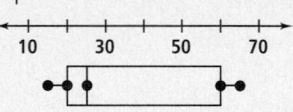

---

66. Which parabola has focus $(3, 0)$ and directrix $x = -3$?

   Ⓕ $y = \frac{1}{12}x^2$ Ⓗ $y = -\frac{1}{3}x^2$

   Ⓖ $x = \frac{1}{12}y^2$ Ⓘ $x = \frac{1}{3}y^2$

67. What is the determinant of the matrix below?

$$\begin{bmatrix} 1 & 3 & -1 \\ 1 & 2 & 1 \\ -2 & -5 & -4 \end{bmatrix}$$

   Ⓐ -8 Ⓒ 0

   Ⓑ -4 Ⓓ 4

68. Write the expression below as a single logarithm.
$4 \log_3 x + \log_3 y - 2 \log_3 z$

   Ⓕ $\log_3 \frac{x^4 y}{z^2}$ Ⓗ $\log_3 (4x + y - 2z)$

   Ⓖ $\frac{\log_3 x^4 y}{\log_3 z^2}$ Ⓘ $\log_3 (x^4 + y - z^2)$

69. A computer manufacturing company sampled two different parts and tested for defects. The results are shown in the table below.

	Part A	Part B
Defective	14	33
Not defective	266	312

What is the probability that if a Part B is randomly chosen, it is defective?

   Ⓐ 5.28%   Ⓒ 9.57%

   Ⓑ 5.71%   Ⓓ 10.58%

70. Which equation represents a circle with center $(-3, 8)$ and radius 12?

   Ⓕ $(x - 8)^2 + (y + 3)^2 = 144$

   Ⓖ $(x - 8)^2 - (y + 3)^2 = 144$

   Ⓗ $(x + 3)^2 + (y - 8)^2 = 144$

   Ⓘ $(x - 3)^2 - (y - 8)^2 = 144$

71. Which of the following numbers is an outlier for the given data set?

3, 7, 19, 2, 6, 8, 5, 8

   Ⓐ 6.5   Ⓑ 8   Ⓒ 16   Ⓓ 19

72. What is the 30th term of the sequence
7, 16, 25, 34, . . . ?

   Ⓕ 261   Ⓗ 270

   Ⓖ 268   Ⓘ 277

73. Which is the best indicator of the accuracy of a line of best fit?

   Ⓐ The y-intercept of the line of best fit

   Ⓑ The number of points below the line of best fit

   Ⓒ The distance of the points from the line of best fit

   Ⓓ The absolute value of the slope of the line of best fit

74. A fair coin is tossed 4 times. What is the probability that it lands heads up at least 3 times?

   Ⓕ 18.75%   Ⓖ 25%   Ⓗ 31.25%   Ⓘ 75%

75. An employee's initial salary is $30,000. The person receives a 5% raise at the end of each year. What is the formula for the term s_n which represents the salary at the beginning of the nth year?

   Ⓐ $s_n = 30{,}000 + 1.05n$

   Ⓑ $s_n = 30{,}000 + 5(n - 1)$

   Ⓒ $s_n = 30{,}000(1.05)^{n-1}$

   Ⓓ $s_n = 30{,}000(1.05)^n$

76. Use the Change of Base Formula to approximate the value of $\log_2 3.2$ to the nearest tenth.

   Ⓕ 0.2   Ⓖ 0.8   Ⓗ 1.7   Ⓘ 9.2

77. If $B = \begin{bmatrix} -2 & 1 \\ 4 & -1 \end{bmatrix}$, what is B^{-1}?

   Ⓐ $\begin{bmatrix} -0.5 & 1 \\ 0.25 & -1 \end{bmatrix}$ Ⓒ $\begin{bmatrix} 2 & -1 \\ -4 & 1 \end{bmatrix}$

   Ⓑ $\begin{bmatrix} 0.5 & 0.5 \\ 2 & 1 \end{bmatrix}$ Ⓓ $\begin{bmatrix} 4 & -1 \\ -2 & 1 \end{bmatrix}$

78. A multiple choice test has 8 questions with 4 options per question. What is the probability of getting exactly 3 answers correct by guessing?

   Ⓕ 0.00371   Ⓗ 0.21875

   Ⓖ 0.20764   Ⓘ 0.37500

85.

Scoring Rubric

Score	Description
2	Student earns 2 points.
1	Student earns 1 point.
0	Response is incorrect or irrelevant to the skill or concept being measured.

Scoring Notes:
• 1 point for a correct strategy

$$\begin{bmatrix} 2 \log 4x = 3 \\ \log 4x = \frac{3}{2} \\ 4x = 10^{\frac{3}{2}} \\ x = \frac{10^{\frac{3}{2}}}{4} \end{bmatrix}$$

• 1 point for a correct answer

$$\begin{bmatrix} \frac{10^{\frac{3}{2}}}{4}, \text{ or } \approx 7.91 \end{bmatrix}$$

86.

Scoring Rubric

Score	Description
4	Student earns 6 points.
3	Student earns 4 or 5 points.
2	Student earns 2 or 3 points.
1	Student earns 1 point.
0	Response is incorrect or irrelevant to the skill or concept being measured.
Blank	Student fails to respond.

79. The magnitude M of an earthquake can be found using the equation $M(x) = \log\left(\frac{x}{0.001}\right)$ where x represents the seismograph reading of the earthquake in mm. An earthquake has a magnitude of 6.2. What is the seismograph reading of the earthquake in mm?

(A) 0.0062   (B) 0.0008   (C) 1.014   (D) 1584.9

80. A teacher's grading scale is shown below:

Item	Percent of Total Grade
Homework	5%
Quizzes	10%
Tests 1, 2, 3	20% each
Final Exam	25%

Sally's grade in the class was an 88. She earned a 97 on homework, 95 on quizzes, 85 on Test 1, 79 on Test 2 and 93 on Test 3. What was Sally's Final Exam grade?

(F) 22   (G) 66   (H) 79   (I) 89

81. There are 15 runners in a semifinal race where the top three runners advance to the finals. In how many ways can three runners advance?

(A) 6   (B) 455   (C) 910   (D) 2730

82. The first term of a finite arithmetic series is 123. The common difference is 12 and the sum is 1539. How many terms are in the series?

(F) 7   (G) 8   (H) 9   (I) 10

83. Multiply $\begin{bmatrix} 4 & -1 \\ 0 & 5 \end{bmatrix} \cdot \begin{bmatrix} 1 & 3 \\ -6 & 1 \end{bmatrix}$

(A) $\begin{bmatrix} 4 & 14 \\ -24 & 11 \end{bmatrix}$ (C) $\begin{bmatrix} 10 & -30 \\ 11 & 5 \end{bmatrix}$

(B) $\begin{bmatrix} 4 & -3 \\ 0 & 5 \end{bmatrix}$ (D) $\begin{bmatrix} 10 & 11 \\ -30 & 5 \end{bmatrix}$

84. Consider the data set: 15, 20, 25, 25, 35, 60, 65.
Part A: Find the mean, median, and mode.
Part B: Find the range and interquartile range.
Part C: Make a box-and-whisker plot for the data.

85. Solve for x to the nearest hundredth. Show or explain your work.
$2 \log 4x + 5 = 8$

86. A pendulum initially swings through an arc that is 20 inches long. On each swing, the length of the arc is 0.85 of the previous swing.
Part A: Write a recursive model of geometric decay to represent the sequence of lengths of the arc of each swing. Let $p_1 = 20$.
Part B: Rewrite your model from Part A using an explicit formula.
Part C: What is the approximate total distance the pendulum swings after 11 swings? Show your work.
Part D: What is the total distance, approximately, that the pendulum has swung when it stops? Show your work.

87. A dietician wants to prepare a meal with 24 g of protein, 27 g of fat, and 20 g of carbohydrates using the three foods shown in the table.

Food	Protein	Fat	Carbohydrates
A	2 g/oz	3 g/oz	4 g/oz
B	3 g/oz	3 g/oz	1 g/oz
C	3 g/oz	3 g/oz	2 g/oz

Part A: Set up a matrix equation for the data.
Part B: Solve the matrix equation.
Part C: How many ounces of each food are needed? Show your work or explain your answer.

88. Consider the following system of equations.
$$\begin{cases} x + 2z = -1 \\ y - 2z = 2 \\ 2x + y + z = 1 \end{cases}$$
Part A: Represent the system of equations using the matrix equation $AX = B$.
Part B: Find the determinant of the matrix A.
Part C: Solve the equation from Part A. If it cannot be solved, use your result from Part B to explain why.

89. An ellipse centered at the origin has a horizontal major axis of length 4 and a vertical minor axis of length 2.
Part A: What is the equation of the ellipse in standard form?
Part B: Identify the foci of the ellipse.
Part C: Explain how to use your work from Parts A and B to find the equation and foci of the ellipse centered at the origin with a vertical major axis of length 4 and horizontal minor axis of length 2.

Part C: 1 point
• 1 point for a correct interpretation [3 oz of Food A, 4 oz of Food B, 2 oz of Food C]

88.

Score	Description
4	Student earns 5 or 4 points.
3	Student earns 3 points.
2	Student earns 2 points.
1	Student earns 1 point.
0	Response is incorrect or irrelevant to the skill or concept being measured.
Blank	Student fails to respond.

Scoring Rubric

Scoring Notes:
Part A: 1 point
• 1 point for a correct equation:
$$\begin{bmatrix} 1 & 0 & 2 \\ 0 & 1 & -2 \\ 2 & 1 & 1 \end{bmatrix} \cdot \begin{bmatrix} x \\ y \\ z \end{bmatrix} = \begin{bmatrix} -1 \\ 2 \\ 1 \end{bmatrix}$$

Part B: 2 points
• 1 point for a correct strategy
$$\begin{bmatrix} 1 & 0 & 2 & 1 & 0 \\ 0 & 1 & -2 & 0 & 1 \\ 2 & 1 & 1 & 2 & 1 \end{bmatrix}$$
$(1 \cdot 1 \cdot 1) + (0 \cdot -2 \cdot 2) + (2 \cdot 0 \cdot 1) - [(2 \cdot 1 \cdot 2) + (1 \cdot -2 \cdot 1) + (0 \cdot 0 \cdot 1)]$
• 1 point for a correct answer: $[-1]$

Part C: 2 points
• 1 point for a correct strategy
$[A^{-1}AX = A^{-1}B, \text{ so } X = A^{-1}B.]$
• 1 point for a correct answer
$[x = 1, y = 0, z = -1]$

89.

Score	Description
4	Student earns 6 points.
3	Student earns 4 or 5 points.
2	Student earns 2 or 3 points.
1	Student earns 1 point.
0	Response is incorrect or irrelevant to the skill or concept being measured.
Blank	Student fails to respond.

Scoring Rubic

Scoring Notes:
Part A: 2 points
• 2 points for a correct equation
$\left[\frac{x^2}{4} + y^2 = 1\right]$

Part B: 2 points
• 2 points for correct foci $[(\pm\sqrt{3}, 0)]$

Part C: 2 points
• 2 points for a correct explanation [Interchange the x- and y-components. The equation is $x^2 + \frac{y^2}{4} = 1$ and the foci are $(0, \pm\sqrt{3})$.]

Scoring Notes:
Part A: 1 point
• 1 point for a correct recursive model:
$\begin{bmatrix} p_1 = 20 \\ p_n = 0.85p_{n-1}, n > 1 \end{bmatrix}$

Part B: 1 point
• 1 point for a correct exponential model: $\left[p_n = 20(0.85)^{n-1}\right]$

Part C: 2 points
• 1 point for a correct strategy:
$\left[S_{11} = 20 \cdot \dfrac{1 - (0.85)^{11}}{1 - 0.85}\right]$
• 1 point for a correct answer [111 in.]

Part D: 2 points
• 1 point for a correct strategy:
$\left[\dfrac{20}{1 - 0.85}\right]$
• 1 point for a correct answer [133 in.]

87.

Score	Description
4	Student earns 6 points.
3	Student earns 4 or 5 points.
2	Student earns 2 or 3 points.
1	Student earns 1 point.
0	Response is incorrect or irrelevant to the skill or concept being measured.
Blank	Student fails to respond.

Scoring Rubic

Scoring Notes:
Part A: 2 points
• 2 points for a correct matrix equation
$$\begin{bmatrix} 2 & 3 & 3 \\ 3 & 3 & 3 \\ 4 & 1 & 2 \end{bmatrix}\begin{bmatrix} A \\ B \\ C \end{bmatrix} = \begin{bmatrix} 24 \\ 27 \\ 20 \end{bmatrix}$$

Part B: 3 points
• 3 points for a correct solution [(3, 4, 2)]

Chapter T Overview

UbD **Understanding by Design**

Chapter T expands on students' understandings and skills related to trigonometry and periodic functions. In this chapter, students will develop the answers to the Essential Questions posed on the student page as they learn the concepts and skills bulleted below.

BIG idea **Function**

ESSENTIAL QUESTION If you know the value of sin θ, how can you find the values of the other trigonometric ratios?
- Students will use right triangles to find trigonometric ratios.

BIG idea **Modeling**

ESSENTIAL QUESTION How can you model periodic behavior?
- Students will use the sine and cosine functions to model periodic behavior.

BIG idea **Equivalence**

ESSENTIAL QUESTION How do you verify that a trigonometric equation is an identity?
- Students will apply Properties of Equality to verify trigonometric identities.

CHAPTER

T

Trigonometry Concepts

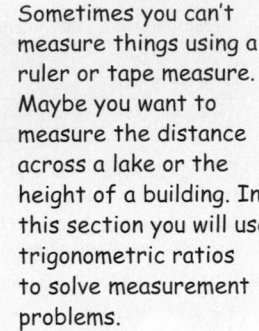

Sometimes you can't measure things using a ruler or tape measure. Maybe you want to measure the distance across a lake or the height of a building. In this section you will use trigonometric ratios to solve measurement problems.

Table of Contents

BIG ideas

1 **Function**
Essential Question If you know the value of sin θ, how can you find the values of the other trigonometric ratios?

2 **Modeling**
Essential Question How can you model periodic behavior?

3 **Equivalence**
Essential Question How do you verify that a trigonometric equation is an identity?

T-1 Right Triangles and Trigonometric Ratios

Objective To find lengths of sides in a right triangle
To find measures of angles in a right triangle

Lesson Vocabulary
• trigonometric ratios

You can use *trigonometric ratios* to relate angle measures to the lengths of certain line segments. You can then use these relationships to solve algebraic equations.

Focus Question What are the trigonometric ratios of a right triangle?

The **trigonometric ratios** for a right triangle are the six different ratios of the sides of a right triangle. These ratios do not depend on the size of the right triangle. They depend only on the measures of the acute angles in the triangle.

take note

Key Concept Trigonometric Ratios for a Right Triangle

If θ is an acute angle of a right triangle, x is the length of the adjacent leg, y is the length of the opposite leg, and r is the length of the hypotenuse, then the trigonometric ratios of θ are as follows.

$$\text{sine } \theta = \frac{\text{opposite}}{\text{hypotenuse}} \qquad \text{cosecant } \theta = \frac{\text{hypotenuse}}{\text{opposite}}$$

$$\text{cosine } \theta = \frac{\text{adjacent}}{\text{hypotenuse}} \qquad \text{secant } \theta = \frac{\text{hypotenuse}}{\text{adjacent}}$$

$$\text{tangent } \theta = \frac{\text{opposite}}{\text{adjacent}} \qquad \text{cotangent } \theta = \frac{\text{adjacent}}{\text{opposite}}$$

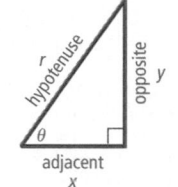

Hint
Notice that the ratios in the second column are the reciprocals of the ratios in the first column.

Using the side lengths from the right triangle above, you can write the trigonometric ratios as follows. (The abbreviation of each ratio is given.)

$$\text{sine } \theta \rightarrow \sin \theta = \frac{y}{r} \qquad \text{cosecant } \theta \rightarrow \csc \theta = \frac{r}{y}$$

$$\text{cosine } \theta \rightarrow \cos \theta = \frac{x}{r} \qquad \text{secant } \theta \rightarrow \sec \theta = \frac{r}{x}$$

$$\text{tangent } \theta \rightarrow \tan \theta = \frac{y}{x} \qquad \text{cotangent } \theta \rightarrow \cot \theta = \frac{x}{y}$$

Hint
For a right triangle, these ratios are defined for <u>both</u> acute angles, in terms of their respective opposite and adjacent sides.

Guided Instruction

Take Note
The hypotenuse is *always* the side opposite the right angle. The adjacent and opposite sides will change, depending on the acute angle referenced.

Q How are the lengths x, y, and r related? **[they are all sides of a right triangle; according to the Pythagorean Theorem and their positions on the triangle, $x^2 + y^2 = r^2$]**

Q What will the measure of the angle opposite r always be? **[90°]**

Q What can you say about the sine and cosine values of the angle complementary to θ $(90° - \theta)$? Explain. **[sin θ equals cos $(90° - \theta)$ and cos θ equals sin $(90° - \theta)$, because if you consider the angle complementary to θ, the labels adjacent and opposite are reversed, but the length of the hypotenuse is unchanged.]**

T-1 Preparing to Teach

BIG idea Function   **UbD**

ESSENTIAL UNDERSTANDINGS
• If the domains of the trigonometric functions are restricted to angle measures between 0° and 90°, the function values are the trigonometric ratios associated with the acute angles of a right triangle.
• In right triangle trigonometry, the value of one trigonometric ratio determines the values of the others.

Math Background
Since the measure of one angle of a right triangle is 90°, the sum of the measures of the other two angles is 180° − 90° = 90°. Thus the domain of 0° < θ < 90° includes all possible acute angles for a right triangle.

You can use the trigonometric ratios for right triangles to find unknown lengths of sides of right triangles.

To minimize mistakes, make sure students draw diagrams each time they solve a problem involving the trigonometric ratios for a right triangle.

Problem 1

Q How is finding sin X similar to finding sin Y? How is it different? **[The hypotenuse for sin X and sin Y is the same; the length opposite ∠X is 4, and the length opposite ∠Y is 3.]**

Q Which trigonometric ratios do not require the hypotenuse? **[Tangent and cotangent]**

Got It?

Q Which lengths do you need to find the value of cos Y? **[adjacent and hypotenuse]**

EXTENSION

Q Can knowing only cos Y help you find sec Y? Explain. **[Yes, because secant is the reciprocal of cosine.]**

Problem 2

Q What does it mean for a side of a triangle to be opposite an angle? **[Sample: A side opposite an angle does not include the vertex of the angle as one of its endpoints.]**

Got It?

Q If the sides of the triangle are labeled d, e, and f, what equation will relate the side lengths? **[$e^2 + f^2 = d^2$]**

Q Which variables do you know values for in the given information? **[None; you know only the ratio of e to f.]**

Think

How is the leg adjacent to ∠Y related to ∠X?
The leg adjacent to ∠Y is the same as the leg opposite ∠X.

Think

What additional information do you need to calculate the trigonometric ratios?
You need the length of the third side.

Problem 1 Identifying Trigonometric Ratios

Right triangle XYZ is shown.
What is the value of each trigonometric ratio?

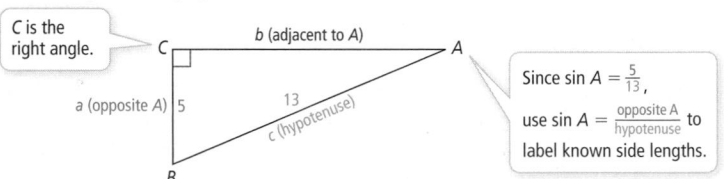

A sin X

Look at the relationships in the diagram.

Use the definition of sin X and substitute.

$$\sin X = \frac{\text{length of leg opposite } \angle X}{\text{length of hypotenuse}} = \frac{4}{5}$$

B sec Y

$$\sec Y = \frac{\text{length of hypotenuse}}{\text{length of leg adjacent to } \angle Y} = \frac{5}{4}$$

C cot Y

$$\cot Y = \frac{\text{length of leg adjacent to } \angle Y}{\text{length of leg opposite } \angle Y} = \frac{4}{3}$$

✓ **Got It?** **1.** For right triangle XYZ from Problem 1, what is the value of each trigonometric ratio?

    a. cos Y   **b.** csc Y   **c.** tan X

In right triangle trigonometry, the value of one trigonometric ratio determines the values of the others.

Problem 2 Finding Trigonometric Ratios

In △ABC, ∠C is a right angle and $\sin A = \frac{5}{13}$. What are cos A, cot A, and sin B?

Step 1 Draw a diagram to display the known information.

C is the right angle.

b (adjacent to A)

a (opposite A) 5

13 c (hypotenuse)

Since $\sin A = \frac{5}{13}$, use $\sin A = \frac{\text{opposite } A}{\text{hypotenuse}}$ to label known side lengths.

Step 2 Find the missing side length.

Write the Pythagorean Theorem.	$c^2 = a^2 + b^2$
Substitute.	$13^2 = 5^2 + b^2$
Simplify.	$169 = 25 + b^2$
Subtract.	$144 = b^2$
Solve for b.	$12 = b$

Step 3 Write the ratios.

$$\cos A = \frac{\text{adjacent } A}{\text{hypotenuse}} = \frac{12}{13}$$

$$\cot A = \frac{\text{adjacent } A}{\text{opposite } A} = \frac{12}{5}$$

$$\sin B = \frac{\text{opposite } B}{\text{hypotenuse}} = \frac{12}{13}$$

The side opposite ∠B is the same as the side adjacent to ∠A.

✓ **Got It?** **2.** In △DEF, ∠D is a right angle and $\tan E = \frac{3}{4}$. What are sin E and sec F?

824   **Chapter T** Trigonometry Concepts

Answers

Got It?

1. a. $\frac{4}{5}$

   b. $\frac{5}{3}$

   c. $\frac{4}{3}$

2. $\sin E = \frac{3}{5}$, $\sec F = \frac{5}{3}$

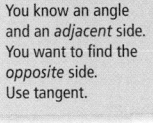
There are many applications of right-triangle trigonometry. Most involve degree measure and require the use of a calculator.

Problem 3 Finding Distance

The large glass pyramid at the Louvre in Paris has a square base. The angle formed by each face and the ground is 49.7°. How high is the pyramid?

Plan
Which trigonometric ratio do you use?
You know an angle and an *adjacent* side. You want to find the *opposite* side. Use tangent.

Look at the photograph. The distance from the midpoint of a side of the square base to the "center" of the base (directly below the top of the pyramid) is half the length of a side of the base, or $\frac{1}{2}(35) = 17.5$ m.

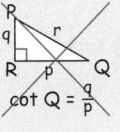

Use tan $\theta = \frac{\text{opposite}}{\text{adjacent}}$.	$\tan 49.7° = \frac{x}{17.5}$
Solve for x.	$x = 17.5 \cdot \tan 49.7°$
Use a calculator.	$x \approx 20.6$

The pyramid is about 20.6 m high.

Hint
A lateral face of a square pyramid is any one of the triangular faces.

Got It? **3.** What is each distance for the Louvre pyramid?
  a. from the midpoint of a side of the base to the top, along a lateral face
  b. from a corner of the base to the top

Focus Question What are the trigonometric ratios of a right triangle?

Answer There are six trigonometric ratios of an acute angle of a right triangle. These ratios are relationships between different side lengths of the triangle. You can use trigonometric ratios to find missing side lengths of a right triangle.

Lesson Check

Do you know HOW?

Use the diagram for Exercises 1–3.

1. Write ratios for sin 57°, cos 57°, and tan 57°.

2. If $a = 10$, what is b?

3. Find the values of sin 33°, cos 33°, and tan 33° as fractions and as decimals. Round to the nearest tenth.

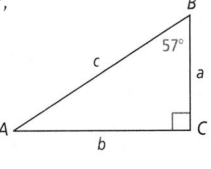

Do you UNDERSTAND?

4. **Error Analysis** Your friend drew a diagram and made the conclusion shown. What is his error?

5. **Writing** In a right triangle, the length of the shortest side is 6.3 m. The sine of the angle opposite that side is $\frac{3}{5}$. Explain how to find the tangent of the angle opposite the shortest side.

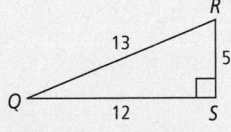

$\cot Q = \frac{q}{p}$

Problem 3

Q Why do you use 17.5 instead of 35 in the equation? **[The base of the right triangle is half the length of a side of the square base.]**

Got It?

Q What part of the diagram represents the distance in 3a? **[the hypotenuse of the right triangle]**

Q How could you find the length described by 3b? **[Sample: Use the Pythagorean Theorem.]**

Q What trigonometric function could you use to find the length described by 3a? Explain. **[Sample: Sine; sin 49.7 = $\frac{x}{r}$, and x was found in Problem 3.]**

Lesson Check

Do you know HOW?

- For Exercise 1, suggest students label the sides of the triangle in relation to $\angle B$ as opposite, adjacent, and hypotenuse.
- For Exercise 2, ask which trigonometric ratio relates a and b to $\angle B$.

Do you UNDERSTAND?

- For Exercise 5, have students draw and label the right triangle that models the given information.

Close

Q How are the side lengths in a right triangle related to a given acute angle of the triangle? **[The sine of the angle equals the ratio of the lengths of the opposite leg and the hypotenuse. The cosine of the angle equals the ratio of the lengths of the adjacent leg and the hypotenuse. The tangent of the angle equals the ratio of the lengths of the opposite and adjacent legs.]**

Additional Problems

1. Right triangle *QRS* is shown. What is the value of each trigonometric ratio?

   a. cot *Q*

   b. sin *R*

   c. sec *Q*

   ANSWERS

   a. $\frac{12}{5}$ **b.** $\frac{12}{13}$ **c.** $\frac{13}{5}$

2. In $\triangle TUW$, $\angle U$ is a right angle and $\cos T = \frac{24}{25}$. What are tan *T* and sin *T*?

   ANSWER $\tan T = \frac{7}{24}$, $\sin T = \frac{7}{25}$

3. Part of a circle of paper with a diameter of 10 in. is cut and taped together to form a cone and then is set upright on a table. The angle that the cone makes with the table is measured and found to be 50°. What is the height of the cone?

   ANSWER 3.8 in.

Answers

Got It? (continued)
3. **a.** 27.1 m
   b. 32.2 m

Lesson Check
1. $\sin 57° = \frac{b}{c}$, $\cos 57° = \frac{a}{c}$, $\tan 57° = \frac{b}{a}$

2. 15.4

3. $\sin 33° = \frac{a}{c} = 0.5$, $\cos 33° = \frac{b}{c} = 0.8$, $\tan 33° = \frac{a}{b} = 0.6$

4. The cotangent is $\frac{\text{adjacent}}{\text{opposite}}$ and he used $\frac{\text{opposite}}{\text{adjacent}}$. So $\cot Q = \frac{p}{q}$.

5. Answers may vary. Sample: Use the inverse of sine to find the measure of the angle opposite the shortest side, $\theta = \sin^{-1}\frac{3}{5} \approx 36.9°$. Then find the tangent of the angle opposite the shortest side, $\tan 36.9° \approx 0.75$.

Practice

ASSIGNMENT GUIDE

Basic: 6–19, 26, 27

Average: 6–28

Standardized Test Prep: 31–33

Mixed Review: 34–39

Reasoning exercises have blue headings.

Applications exercises have red headings.

HOMEWORK QUICK CHECK

To check students' understanding of key skills and concepts, go over Exercises 7, 12, 19, 26, and 27.

Practice and Problem-Solving Exercises

Ⓐ Practice   In △ABC, find each value.

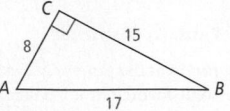

◆ See Problem 1.

Guided Practice

To start, write the formula for the sine of angle A.

6. sin A

$$\sin A = \frac{\text{leg opposite } \angle A}{\text{hypotenuse}}$$

7. sec A   **8.** cot A   **9.** csc B   **10.** sec B   **11.** tan B

In △GHI, ∠H is a right angle, GH = 40, and cos G = $\frac{40}{41}$. Draw a diagram and find each value.

◆ See Problem 2.

12. sin G   **13.** sin I   **14.** cot G

15. csc G   **16.** cos I   **17.** sec H

Use trigonometric ratios to solve each problem.

◆ See Problem 3.

18. You want to build a bicycle ramp that is 10 ft long and makes a 30° angle with the ground. What would be the height of the ramp?

Guided Practice

To start, draw a diagram to represent this situation.

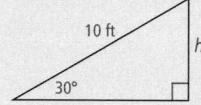

19. Indirect Measurement In 1915, the tallest flagpole in the world stood in San Francisco.

  a. When the sun was 55° above the ground, the length of the shadow cast by this flagpole was 210 ft. Find the height of the flagpole to the nearest foot.

  b. What was the length of the shadow when the sun was 34° above the ground?

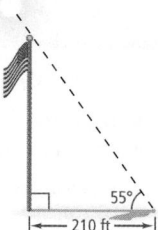

Ⓑ Apply   Sketch a right triangle with θ as the measure of one acute angle. Find the other five trigonometric ratios of θ.

20. sin θ = $\frac{3}{8}$ **21.** cos θ = $\frac{7}{20}$ **22.** cos θ = $\frac{1}{5}$

23. tan θ = $\frac{24}{7}$ **24.** sec θ = $\frac{16}{9}$ **25.** sin θ = 0.35

Answers

Practice and Problem-Solving Exercises

6. $\frac{15}{17} \approx 0.88$ **7.** $\frac{17}{8} \approx 2.13$

8. $\frac{8}{15} \approx 0.53$ **9.** $\frac{17}{8} \approx 2.13$

10. $\frac{17}{15} \approx 1.13$

11. $\frac{8}{15} \approx 0.53$

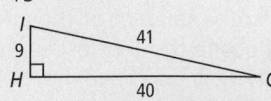

12. $\frac{9}{41} \approx 0.22$ **13.** $\frac{40}{41} \approx 0.98$

14. $\frac{40}{9} \approx 4.44$ **15.** $\frac{41}{9} \approx 4.56$

16. $\frac{9}{41} \approx 0.22$ **17.** not defined

18. height = 10 sin 30° = 5 ft

19. a. 300 ft   **b.** 445 ft

20.

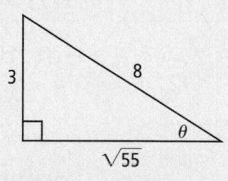

$\cos θ = \frac{\sqrt{55}}{8}$, $\tan θ = \frac{3\sqrt{55}}{55}$,

$\csc θ = \frac{8}{3}$, $\sec θ = \frac{8\sqrt{55}}{55}$,

$\cot θ = \frac{\sqrt{55}}{3}$

21.

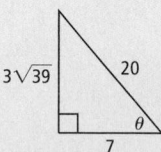

$\sin θ = \frac{3\sqrt{39}}{20}$, $\tan θ = \frac{3\sqrt{39}}{7}$,

$\csc θ = \frac{20\sqrt{39}}{117}$, $\sec θ = \frac{20}{7}$,

$\cot θ = \frac{7\sqrt{39}}{117}$

22.

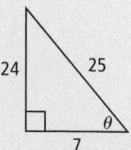

$\sin θ = \frac{2\sqrt{6}}{5}$, $\tan θ = 2\sqrt{6}$,

$\csc θ = \frac{5\sqrt{6}}{12}$, $\sec θ = 5$, $\cot θ = \frac{\sqrt{6}}{12}$

23.

$\sin θ = \frac{24}{25}$, $\cos θ = \frac{7}{25}$, $\csc θ = \frac{25}{24}$,

$\sec θ = \frac{25}{7}$, $\cot θ = \frac{7}{24}$

26. Construction A radio tower has supporting cables attached to it at points 100 ft above the ground. Write a model for the length d of each supporting cable as a function of the angle θ that it makes with the ground. Then find d when $\theta = 60°$ and when $\theta = 50°$.

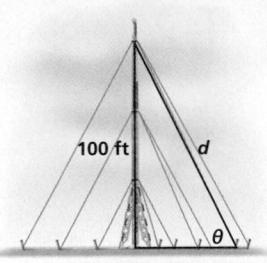
100 ft d

θ

27. Geometry An altitude inside a triangle is 5 m long and forms 36° and 42° angles with two of the sides. Find the area of the triangle.

28. Indirect Measurement You are 330 ft from the base of a building. The angles of elevation to the top and bottom of a flagpole on top of the building are 55° and 53°. Find the height of the flagpole.

In $\triangle ABC$, $\angle C$ is a right angle. Two measures are given. Find the remaining sides and angles. Round your answers to the nearest tenth.

29. $a = 7, b = 10$ **30.** $m\angle A = 52°, c = 10$

> **Hint** The <u>angle of elevation</u> is the angle between a horizontal line (usually the ground) and a person's line of sight, looking up or down at an object.

Standardized Test Prep

31. In $\triangle XYZ$, $\angle Z$ is a right angle and $\tan X = \frac{8}{15}$. What is $\sin Y$?

   Ⓐ $\frac{8}{17}$ Ⓑ $\frac{15}{17}$ Ⓒ $\frac{17}{15}$ Ⓓ $\frac{15}{8}$

32. What is the center of the circle with equation $(x + 3)^2 + (y - 2)^2 = 49$?

   Ⓕ $(3, -2)$ Ⓖ $(-3, 2)$ Ⓗ $(3, 2)$ Ⓘ $(-3, -2)$

Short Response

33. Find the measures of the acute angles of a right triangle, to the nearest tenth, if the legs are 135 cm and 95 cm.

Mixed Review

Solve each system of equations. Check your answers.

◀ **See Lesson 12-4.**

34. $\begin{cases} 3x + 2y = 5 \\ -x + y = -5 \end{cases}$ **35.** $\begin{cases} x + 4y + 3z = 3 \\ 2x - 5y - z = 5 \\ 3x + 2y - 2z = -3 \end{cases}$ **36.** $\begin{cases} x + y + z = -1 \\ y + 3z = -5 \\ x + z = -2 \end{cases}$

Get Ready! To prepare for Lesson T-2, do Exercises 37–39.

◀ **See p. 874.**

Find the missing length in each right triangle.

37.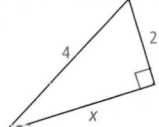

38.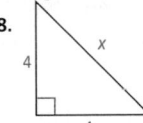

39.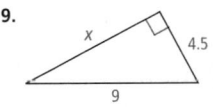

PowerAlgebra.com

37. $2\sqrt{3} \approx 3.464$

38. $4\sqrt{2} \approx 5.657$

39. $\frac{9\sqrt{3}}{2} \approx 7.794$

Lesson Quiz

1. What is the value of each trig function for the angle θ as shown?

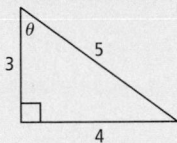
θ 5
3
4

2. In $\triangle PQR$, $\angle P$ is a right angle and $\cos Q = \frac{8}{17}$. What are $\sin Q$ and $\tan Q$?

3. Do you UNDERSTAND? An airplane climbs at an angle of 2.7° from an altitude of 4500 ft to an altitude of 5600 ft. Draw a diagram to show the situation. How far does the airplane travel as it climbs as measured along the horizontal?

4. In $\triangle XYZ$, $\angle Z$ is a right angle, $x = 6$ and $m\angle X = 56.3°$. What is the length of y?

ANSWERS TO LESSON QUIZ

1. $\sin \theta = \frac{4}{5}$, $\cos \theta = \frac{3}{5}$, $\tan \theta = \frac{4}{3}$,

$\csc \theta = \frac{5}{4}$, $\sec \theta = \frac{5}{3}$, $\cot \theta = \frac{3}{4}$

2. $\sin Q = \frac{15}{17}$; $\tan Q = \frac{15}{8}$

3.
?   2.7°   1100 ft

23,325 ft or 4.4 mi

4. $y = 4$

24.

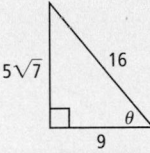
$5\sqrt{7}$ 16
θ
9

$\sin \theta = \frac{5\sqrt{7}}{16}$, $\cos \theta = \frac{9}{16}$, $\tan \theta = \frac{5\sqrt{7}}{9}$,

$\csc \theta = \frac{16\sqrt{7}}{35}$, $\cot \theta = \frac{9\sqrt{7}}{35}$

25.

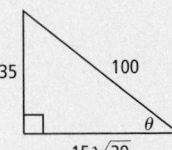
35   100
θ
$15\sqrt{39}$

$\cos \theta = \frac{3\sqrt{39}}{20}$, $\tan \theta = \frac{7\sqrt{39}}{117}$,

$\csc \theta = \frac{20}{7}$, $\sec \theta = \frac{20\sqrt{39}}{117}$,

$\cot \theta = \frac{3\sqrt{39}}{7}$

26. $d = \frac{100}{\sin \theta}$; 115.5 ft; 130.5 ft

27. 20.3 m²

28. 33.4 ft

29. $c \approx 12.2$, $m\angle A \approx 35.0°$, $m\angle B \approx 55.0°$

30. $a \approx 7.9$, $b \approx 6.2$, $m\angle B = 38°$

Standardized Test Prep

31. B

32. G

33. [2] $\tan \angle A = \frac{135}{95}$

$m\angle A = \tan^{-1} \frac{135}{95}$

$m\angle A \approx 54.9°$

$\tan \angle B = \frac{95}{135}$

$m\angle B = \tan^{-1} \frac{95}{135}$

$m\angle B \approx 35.1°$

[1] only one measure correctly calculated OR correct answers, but with less efficient method

Mixed Review

34. $(3, -2)$

35. $(1, -1, 2)$

36. $(0, 1, -2)$

Guided Instruction

Take Note

Explain that a 45°-45°-90° triangle is an isosceles triangle because the base angles are congruent. If each leg has length s and the hypotenuse has length y, you can solve for y in terms of s.

$$s^2 + s^2 = y^2$$
$$2s^2 = y^2$$
$$s\sqrt{2} = y$$

Problem 1

> **Q** Which sides are the legs? Explain. **[The legs are shorter than the hypotenuse, so they are opposite the 45° angles.]**
>
> **Q** How can you use the Pythagorean Theorem to show the special relationship in any 45°-45°-90° triangle? **[The legs are congruent, so in the equation $a^2 + b^2 = c^2$, $a = b$; you can show that $a^2 + a^2 = c^2$ or $c = \sqrt{2a^2} = a\sqrt{2}$.]**
>
> **Q** How can you check that the answer is reasonable? Explain. **[The hypotenuse should be longer than either side. The sides measure 5 units and the hypotenuse is about 7.07 units.]**
>
> **Q** Does the figure need both legs marked? Explain. **[No; for a 45°-45°-90° triangle, both legs have the same measure.]**

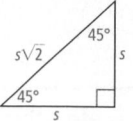
Objectives To use the properties of 45°-45°-90° and 30°-60°-90° triangles
To find the trigonometric ratios of 30°, 45°, and 60° angles

In Geometry, you learned about two special types of right triangles: 45°-45°-90° and 30°-60°-90° triangles.

Focus Question What are the properties of special right triangles?

take note Key Concepts   Special Right Triangles

45°-45°-90° triangles
In a 45°-45°-90° triangle, both legs are congruent and the length of the hypotenuse is $\sqrt{2}$ times the length of a leg.

$$\text{hypotenuse} = \sqrt{2} \cdot \text{leg}$$

30°-60°-90° triangles
In a 30°-60°-90° triangle, the length of the hypotenuse is twice the length of the shorter leg. The length of the longer leg is $\sqrt{3}$ times the length of the shorter leg.

$$\text{hypotenuse} = 2 \cdot \text{shorter leg}$$
$$\text{longer leg} = \sqrt{3} \cdot \text{shorter leg}$$

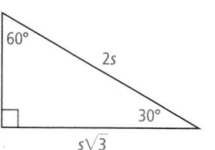

You can use these properties to find missing side lengths in special right triangles.

Hint
The relationships between sides of special right triangles are related to the Pythagorean Theorem.

Problem 1 Finding Side Lengths in 45°-45°-90° Triangles

What is the value of each variable?

A

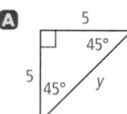

Think
How is length of the hypotenuse related to the length of a leg?
The length of the hypotenuse is $\sqrt{2}$ times the length of a leg.

Relate the side lengths.	$\text{hypotenuse} = \sqrt{2} \cdot \text{leg}$
Substitute.	$y = \sqrt{2} \cdot 5$
Simplify.	$y = 5\sqrt{2}$

T-2 Preparing to Teach

BIG idea Function   **UbD**

ESSENTIAL UNDERSTANDINGS

- If the domains of the trigonometric functions are restricted to angle measures between 0° and 90°, the function values are the trigonometric ratios associated with the acute angles of a right triangle.
- In right triangle trigonometry, the value of one trigonometric ratio determines the values of the others.

Math Background

In this lesson, students will focus on 45°-45°-90° and 30°-60°-90° triangles. These special right triangles occur often in mathematics and engineering. Although the Pythagorean Theorem can be used to derive the relationship between the legs and hypotenuse of these triangles, it is worthwhile to remember these special relationships. In the 45°-45°-90° triangle, the length of the hypotenuse equals $\sqrt{2}$ times the length of a leg. In the 30°-60°-90° triangle, the

hypotenuse is twice the length of the short leg and the longer leg is $\sqrt{3}$ times the shorter leg.

At the end of the lesson students are introduced to the trigonometric ratios of these special angles. Using a hypotenuse of length 1 unit, the six basic trigonometric functions are found for 30°, 45°, and 60° angles. These important ratios will be used in the next lesson as students explore the unit circle as well as sine and cosine of angles.

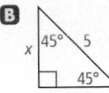

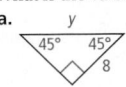

Relate the side lengths. $\text{hypotenuse} = \sqrt{2} \cdot \text{leg}$

Substitute. $5 = \sqrt{2} \cdot x$

Multiplying by 1 does not change the value of an expression.

Divide each side by $\sqrt{2}$. $x = \dfrac{5}{\sqrt{2}}$

Rationalize the denominator and simplify. $= \dfrac{5}{\sqrt{2}} \cdot \dfrac{\sqrt{2}}{\sqrt{2}} = \dfrac{5\sqrt{2}}{2}$

 Got It? **1.** What is the value of each variable?

a.
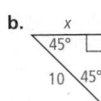

b.

Hint

The length of a leg is the length of the hypotenuse <u>divided</u> by $\sqrt{2}$.

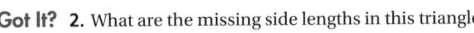

Problem 2 Finding Side Lengths in 30°-60°-90° Triangles

What are the missing side lengths in this triangle?

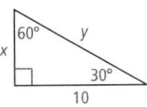

Step 1 Find the length of the shorter leg.

Relate the side lengths. $\text{longer leg} = \sqrt{3} \cdot \text{shorter leg}$

Substitute. $4 = \sqrt{3} \cdot z$

Solve for z. $z = \dfrac{4}{\sqrt{3}}$

Simplify. $z = \dfrac{4}{\sqrt{3}} \cdot \dfrac{\sqrt{3}}{\sqrt{3}} = \dfrac{4\sqrt{3}}{3}$

The length of the shorter leg is $\dfrac{4\sqrt{3}}{3}$ units.

Step 2 Find the length of the hypotenuse.

Relate the side lengths. $\text{hypotenuse} = 2 \cdot \text{shorter leg}$

Substitute. $w = 2 \cdot z$

Substitute for z. $= 2 \cdot \dfrac{4\sqrt{3}}{3}$

Simplify. $= \dfrac{2 \cdot 4\sqrt{3}}{3} = \dfrac{8\sqrt{3}}{3}$

The length of the hypotenuse is $\dfrac{8\sqrt{3}}{3}$ units.

 Got It? **2.** What are the missing side lengths in this triangle?

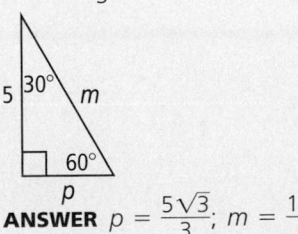

Plan

Which is the known side length?
You know the length of the longer leg.

Q What is the value of x if the length of the hypotenuse is 8? If the hypotenuse is h? $\left[\dfrac{8\sqrt{2}}{2} = 4\sqrt{2};\ \dfrac{h\sqrt{2}}{2}\right]$

Got It?

Q How could you find the missing side length of the triangle in 1a? Explain. **[Because the two base angles are congruent, the sides opposite them are congruent. The missing side length is 8.]**

Problem 2

Q If only the longer leg of a 30°-60°-90° triangle is marked, how do you determine the angle measures in the triangle? **[The longest side of any triangle will always be opposite the greatest angle. The hypotenuse is opposite the 90° angle and the longer leg is opposite the 60° angle.]**

EXTENSION

Q What is an equation for the length of the shorter leg z if the length of the hypotenuse is w and length of the longer leg is x? $\left[z = \dfrac{x\sqrt{3}}{3}\right]$

Q What is the approximate length of the shorter leg? Is this reasonable? Explain. **[About 2.3 units; yes, because the length of the shorter leg should be less than the length of the longer leg.]**

Got It?

Q Is the value of x going to be greater than or less than 10? Explain. **[The side with length 10 is opposite the larger 60° angle, so the side opposite the 30° angle will be less than 10.]**

Additional Problems

1. What is the value of each variable?

a.
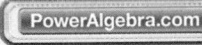

ANSWER $y = 7\sqrt{2}$

b.
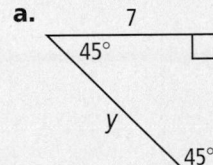

ANSWER $x = 6\sqrt{2}$

2. What are the missing side lengths in this triangle?

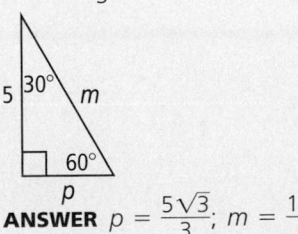

ANSWER $p = \dfrac{5\sqrt{3}}{3};\ m = \dfrac{10\sqrt{3}}{3}$

3. What are the values of a and b for this right triangle?

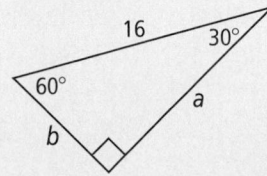

ANSWER $b = 8;\ a = 8\sqrt{3}$

Answers

Got It?

1. a. $y = 8\sqrt{2}$
   b. $x = 5\sqrt{2}$

2. shorter leg: $\dfrac{10\sqrt{3}}{3}$ units;
   hypotenuse: $\dfrac{20\sqrt{3}}{3}$ units

Problem 3 EXTENSION

Q How can an equation for the length of the hypotenuse be written in terms of the length of the longer leg? Explain. **[If a is the length of the longer leg, and b is the length of the shorter leg, then $a = b\sqrt{3}$ and $b = \frac{a\sqrt{3}}{3}$. The length of the hypotenuse is $2b$, so substitution yields $\frac{2a\sqrt{3}}{3}$.]**

Q How can you find the length of the other sides if only the length of the shorter leg is given? **[Double the length of the shorter leg to get the hypotenuse. Find the length of the longer leg by multiplying the shorter leg by $\sqrt{3}$.]**

Q Why is the length of the shorter leg half the length of the hypotenuse? Use an equilateral triangle to explain. **[An equilateral triangle has 60° angles, and the altitude divides the equilateral triangle into two congruent 30°-60°-90° triangles. Since the altitude divides one side into two equal lengths, the length of the shorter leg is half the length of the original side, or hypotenuse.]**

Got It?

Q Which missing side length should you find first? Explain. **[Samples: Find b or the shorter leg; the length of the shorter leg is half of the length of the hypotenuse.]**

Q How can you check your answer? **[Use the Pythagorean Theorem to confirm that the sum of the squares of the lengths of the legs equals the length of the hypotenuse squared.]**

Think

Which leg should you find first?
The hypotenuse is given in terms of the shorter leg, and so is the longer leg. Find the length of leg a first.

Problem 3 Finding Missing Legs Given the Hypotenuse

What are the values of a and b?

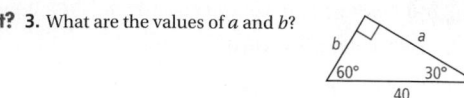

Find the length of the shorter leg, a.

Relate the side lengths.	hypotenuse $= 2 \cdot$ shorter leg
Substitute.	$24 = 2 \cdot a$
Solve for a.	$a = 12$

The length of the shorter leg is 12 units, so $a = 12$.

Find the length of the longer leg, b.

Relate the side lengths.	longer leg $= \sqrt{3} \cdot$ shorter leg.
Substitute.	$b = \sqrt{3} \cdot 12$
Simplify.	$= 12\sqrt{3}$

The length of the longer leg is $12\sqrt{3}$ units, so $b = 12\sqrt{3}$.

Got It? **3.** What are the values of a and b?

You can extend the relationships explored in Problems 1–3 to find the trigonometric ratios for the special angles 30°, 45°, and 60°. For each type of special right triangle, let the hypotenuse have a length of 1 unit. Then find the lengths of the legs as shown below.

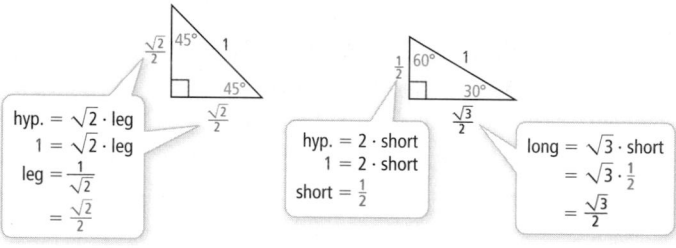

hyp. $= \sqrt{2} \cdot$ leg
$1 = \sqrt{2} \cdot$ leg
leg $= \frac{1}{\sqrt{2}}$
$= \frac{\sqrt{2}}{2}$

hyp. $= 2 \cdot$ short
$1 = 2 \cdot$ short
short $= \frac{1}{2}$

long $= \sqrt{3} \cdot$ short
$= \sqrt{3} \cdot \frac{1}{2}$
$= \frac{\sqrt{3}}{2}$

Answers

Got It? (continued)

3. $a = 20\sqrt{3}$; $b = 20$

Using the diagrams on the previous page, you can apply the definitions of each trigonometric ratio.

 take note

Key Concepts   Trigonometric Ratios of Special Angles

θ	30°	45°	60°
$\sin\theta$	$\frac{1}{2}$	$\frac{\sqrt{2}}{2}$	$\frac{\sqrt{3}}{2}$
$\cos\theta$	$\frac{\sqrt{3}}{2}$	$\frac{\sqrt{2}}{2}$	$\frac{1}{2}$
$\tan\theta$	$\frac{\sqrt{3}}{3}$	1	$\sqrt{3}$
$\csc\theta$	2	$\sqrt{2}$	$\frac{2\sqrt{3}}{3}$
$\sec\theta$	$\frac{2\sqrt{3}}{3}$	$\sqrt{2}$	2
$\cot\theta$	$\sqrt{3}$	1	$\frac{\sqrt{3}}{3}$

Hint

Recall the six trigonometric ratios:

$\sin\theta = \frac{OPP}{HYP}$

$\cos\theta = \frac{ADJ}{HYP}$

$\tan\theta = \frac{OPP}{ADJ}$

$\csc\theta = \frac{HYP}{OPP}$

$\sec\theta = \frac{HYP}{ADJ}$

$\cot\theta = \frac{ADJ}{OPP}$

Focus Question What are the properties of special right triangles?

Answer In a 45°-45°-90° triangle, both legs are congruent and the length of the hypotenuse is $\sqrt{2}$ times the length of a leg. In a 30°-60°-90° triangle, the length of the hypotenuse is twice the length of the shorter leg. The length of the longer leg is $\sqrt{3}$ times the length of the shorter leg. Use the properties of special right triangles as a shortcut to determine side lengths without using the Pythagorean Theorem.

✓ Lesson Check

Do you know HOW?

Find each value of *x*.

1.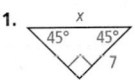

2.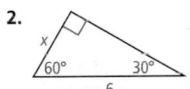

Do you UNDERSTAND?

3. **Error Analysis** A classmate drew a 30°-60°-90° triangle with a hypotenuse of 5 in. She concluded that the length of the shorter leg of the triangle is $\frac{5\sqrt{2}}{2}$ in. Do you agree? Explain.

Take Note

Remind students that csc θ, sec θ, and cot θ are reciprocals of sin θ, cos θ, and tan θ, so it is not necessary to memorize every value.

Q How can you check that the reciprocal of sin 45° is equal to csc 45°? Explain. **[sin 45° = $\frac{\sqrt{2}}{2}$, so $\frac{1}{\sin 45°} = \left(\frac{2}{\sqrt{2}}\right)\left(\frac{\sqrt{2}}{\sqrt{2}}\right) = \frac{2\sqrt{2}}{2} = \sqrt{2}$. This is equal to csc 45°.]**

Lesson Check

Do you know HOW?   ERROR INTERVENTION

• If students have difficulty solving Exercises 1–2, ask them to first identify the type of special triangle. Then suggest they review Problems 1 and 2.

Do you UNDERSTAND?

• If students have trouble with Problem 3, suggest they sketch a triangle with the appropriate labels. Have them review Exercise 3 to determine the correct length of the shorter leg.

Close

Q How can you find the length of the hypotenuse when given the length of a leg of a 45°-45°-90° triangle? **[Multiply the length of the leg by $\sqrt{2}$.]**

Q Given the length of the shorter leg of a 30°-30°-90° triangle, how can you find the length of the longer leg? the hypotenuse? **[Multiply the length of the shorter leg by $\sqrt{3}$; multiply the length of the shorter leg by 2.]**

Lesson Check

1. $x = 7\sqrt{2}$

2. $x = 3$

3. No; in a 30°-60°-90° triangle, the length of the shorter leg is half the length of the hypotenuse, so the length is half of 5, or 2.5.

Practice

ASSIGNMENT GUIDE

Basic: 4–12, 16

Average: 4–15, 16–26 even

Standardized Test Prep: 27–29

Mixed Review: 30–35

Reasoning exercises have blue headings.

Applications exercises have red headings.

HOMEWORK QUICK CHECK

To check students' understanding of key skills and concepts, go over Exercises 4, 8, 11, 12, and 16.

 Practice and Problem-Solving Exercises

A Practice Find the value of each variable.   ◀ See Problem 1.

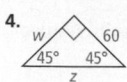

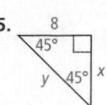

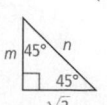

Find the value of each variable.   ◀ See Problems 2 and 3.

Guided Practice

7.

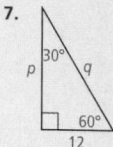

To start, write the relationship between the hypotenuse and the shorter leg.

hypotenuse = 2 · shorter leg

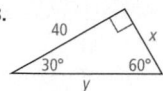

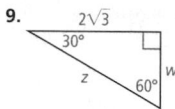

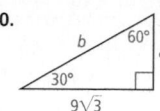

B Apply

11. Air Travel A conveyor belt moves luggage from the ground outside the airport up to an entrance into the baggage claim area. The conveyor belt moves at a rate of 100 ft/min. How many seconds does it take for a suitcase to go from the ground to the entrance?

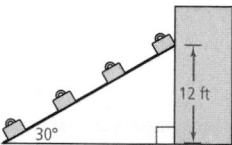

Geometry Find the value of each variable.

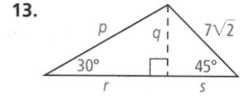

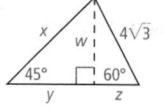

15. Recreation A city park is in the shape of a square. Each side of the park is 300 ft in length, and sidewalks across the park join opposite corners. To the nearest foot, how long is each diagonal sidewalk?

> **Hint** An isosceles right triangle is always a 45°-45°-90° triangle.

Use the given information to find the missing side length(s) in each 45°-45°-90° triangle. Rationalize any denominators.

16. leg 2 cm   **17.** hypotenuse $\sqrt{3}$ ft   **18.** leg $2\sqrt{5}$ m

---

Answers

Practice and Problem-Solving Exercises

4. $w = 60$; $z = 60\sqrt{2}$

5. $x = 8$; $y = 8\sqrt{2}$

6. $m = \sqrt{2}$; $n = 2$

7. $p = 12\sqrt{3}$; $q = 24$

8. $x = \frac{40\sqrt{3}}{3}$; $y = \frac{80\sqrt{3}}{3}$

9. $w = 2$; $z = 4$

10. $a = 9$; $b = 18$

11. 0.24 min, or 14.4 s

12. $a = 5\sqrt{3}$; $b = 10\sqrt{3}$; $c = 5$; $d = 15$

13. $p = 14$; $q = 7$; $r = 7\sqrt{3}$; $s = 7$

14. $w = 6$; $x = 6\sqrt{2}$; $y = 6$; $z = 2\sqrt{3}$

15. about 424 ft

16. hypotenuse: $2\sqrt{2}$ cm

17. leg: $\frac{\sqrt{6}}{2}$ ft

18. hypotenuse: $2\sqrt{10}$ m

Use the given information to find the missing side lengths in each 30°-60°-90° triangle. Rationalize any denominators.

19. shorter leg 3 in. **20.** longer leg 1 cm **21.** hypotenuse $2\sqrt{2}$ ft

22. longer leg $\sqrt{5}$ cm **23.** hypotenuse $3\sqrt{2}$ m **24.** shorter leg $\sqrt{3}$ cm

25. Tree Planting To ensure that a young tree stays upright in a windy area, a gardener placed a 3 m brace against the tree at a 45° angle. Then, at the same spot on the ground, she placed a second, longer brace to make a 30° angle with the trunk of the tree.
 a. How long is the longer brace? Round to the nearest tenth of a meter.
 b. About how much higher does the longer brace reach than the shorter brace?

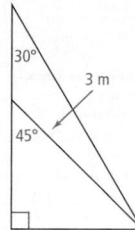

26. Open Ended Write a real-world problem that you can solve using a 30°-60°-90° triangle with a 15-ft hypotenuse. Show your solution.

Standardized Test Prep

27. A right isosceles triangle has a hypotenuse of length 36 mm. What is the length of each leg?
 Ⓐ $36\sqrt{2}$ mm Ⓑ $24\sqrt{3}$ mm Ⓒ $18\sqrt{2}$ mm Ⓓ $12\sqrt{3}$ mm

28. A ladder rests against a building. The ladder is 14 ft long and forms an angle of 76.5° with the ground. Which statement is NOT true?
 Ⓕ The bottom of the ladder is 13.6 ft from the base of the building.
 Ⓖ The bottom of the ladder is 3.3 ft from the base of the building.
 Ⓗ The top of the ladder touches the building 13.6 ft from the ground.
 Ⓘ The ladder forms an angle of 13.5° with the building.

Short Response

29. How can you use the arithmetic mean to find the missing terms in the arithmetic sequence 15, ■, ■, ■, 47, . . . ?

Mixed Review

In $\triangle ABC$, $\angle C$ is a right angle. Two measures are given. Find the remaining sides and angles. Round answers to the nearest tenth. ◀ See Lesson T-1.

30. $m\angle A = 34.2°, b = 5.7$ **31.** $m\angle B = 17.2°, b - 8.3$ **32.** $m\angle B - 8.3°, c = 20$

Get Ready! To prepare for Lesson T-3, do Exercises 33–35.

Write an equation of the circle that passes through the given point and has its center at the origin. (*Hint:* Use the distance formula to find the radius.) ◀ See Lesson 10-3.

33. $(0, 1)$ **34.** $\left(\frac{\sqrt{3}}{2}, \frac{1}{2}\right)$ **35.** $\left(\frac{\sqrt{2}}{2}, \frac{\sqrt{2}}{2}\right)$

---

1. What is the value of y?

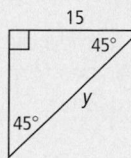

2. Find the missing side lengths in a 45°-45°-90° triangle for the following lengths:
 a. leg = 3 inches
 b. hypotenuse = 1 foot

3. Find the missing side lengths in a 30°-60°-90° triangle for the following lengths:
 a. shorter leg = 4 cm
 b. hypotenuse = 20 inches

4. Do you UNDERSTAND? Explain how to find the length of the longer leg of a 30°-60°-90° triangle if you are given the length of the hypotenuse.

ANSWERS TO LESSON QUIZ

1. $15\sqrt{2}$

2. a. hypotenuse = $3\sqrt{2}$ inches
 b. legs = $\frac{\sqrt{2}}{2}$ feet

3. a. hypotenuse = 8 cm; longer leg = $4\sqrt{3}$ cm
 b. Shorter leg = 10 inches; longer leg = $10\sqrt{3}$

4. Divide the length of the hypotenuse by 2 to find the length of the shorter leg. Then multiply the length of the shorter leg by $\sqrt{3}$.

---

19. hypotenuse: 6 in.; longer leg: $3\sqrt{3}$ in.

20. shorter leg: $\frac{\sqrt{3}}{3}$ cm;
 hypotenuse: $\frac{2\sqrt{3}}{3}$ cm

21. shorter leg: $\sqrt{2}$ ft;
 longer leg: $\sqrt{6}$ ft

22. shorter leg: $\frac{\sqrt{15}}{3}$ cm;
 hypotenuse: $\frac{2\sqrt{15}}{3}$ cm

23. shorter leg: $\frac{3\sqrt{2}}{2}$ m;
 longer leg: $\frac{3\sqrt{6}}{2}$ m

24. hypotenuse: $2\sqrt{3}$ cm;
 longer leg: 3 cm

25. a. about 4.2 m
 b. about 1.6 m

26. Check students' work.

Standardized Test Prep

27. C

28. F

29. [2] Let a_1, a_2, and a_3 represent the missing terms in the arithmetic sequence: 15, a_1, a_2, a_3, 47. a_2 is the arithmetic mean of 15 and 47, so $a_2 = \frac{15 + 47}{2} = 31$. Likewise,
$$a_1 = \frac{15 + a_2}{2} = \frac{15 + 31}{2} = 23$$
and
$$a_3 = \frac{a_2 + 47}{2} = \frac{31 + 47}{2} = 39.$$
The missing terms are 23, 31, and 39.

[1] incomplete explanation OR correct explanation with one computational error

Mixed Review

30. $a \approx 3.9, c \approx 6.9, m\angle B = 55.8°$

31. $a \approx 26.8, c \approx 28.1, m\angle A = 72.8°$

32. $a \approx 19.8, c \approx 2.9, m\angle A = 81.7°$

33. $x^2 + y^2 = 1$

34. $x^2 + y^2 = 1$

35. $x^2 + y^2 = 1$

Guided Instruction

Problem 1

Point out that in a unit circle, angles formed by clockwise movements are negative. Angles formed by counterclockwise movements are positive.

Q What is the terminal side of an angle measuring −90°? **[The terminal side is along the negative part of the y-axis.]**

Q For 1B, in which quadrant does the terminal side of the angle lie? What do you know about ordered pairs in this quadrant? **[Quadrant III; both x- and y-coordinates are negative.]**

Objectives To work with angles in standard position
To find coordinates of points on the unit circle

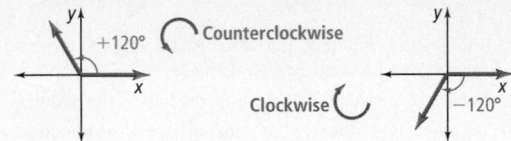

Standard Position

Lesson Vocabulary
• standard position
• initial side
• terminal side
• reference angle
• unit circle

An angle in the coordinate plane is in **standard position** when the vertex is at the origin and one ray is on the positive x-axis. The ray on the x-axis is the **initial side** of the angle. The other ray is the **terminal side** of the angle.

The measure of an angle in standard position is the amount of rotation from the initial side to the terminal side.

Focus Question How is the unit circle related to trigonometric ratios?

The measure of an angle is positive when the rotation from the initial side to the terminal side is in the counterclockwise direction. The measure is negative when the rotation is clockwise.

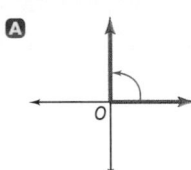

Counterclockwise

Clockwise

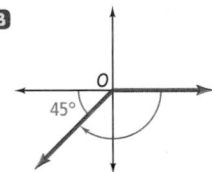

Problem 1 Measuring Angles in Standard Position

What is the measure of each angle?

Think
How many degrees are in a circle?
There are 360° in a circle, 180° in half of a circle, and 90° in a quarter of a circle.

A

This angle is a counterclockwise rotation that makes a right angle, so its measure is 90°.

B

This angle is a clockwise rotation that goes 45° beyond a right angle, so its measure is −135°.

T-3 Preparing to Teach

BIG ideas Modeling
Function

UbD

ESSENTIAL UNDERSTANDING

• The measure of an angle in standard position is the input for two important functions. The outputs, cosine and sine, are the coordinates of the point on the terminal side of the angle, 1 unit from the origin.

Math Background

Many students are not familiar with the idea of angles being greater than 180 degrees or less than 0 degrees.

This lesson prepares students for trigonometry, where it is more helpful to relate angle measure to the concept of rotations and to allow for angles of any measure, positive or negative.

For angles in standard position, a counterclockwise rotation is positive, and a clockwise rotation is negative.

The acute angle formed by an angle's terminal side and the x-axis is called a *reference angle*. Reference angles will be used to find values of trigonometric functions for angles with measures greater than 90 degrees.

The unit circle definitions of the sine and cosine functions reveal that these are periodic functions. These definitions are new to students who associate trigonometric functions only with triangles.

Hint

Use your results from part B to help you solve the Got It.

Got It? 1. What is the measure of the angle shown?

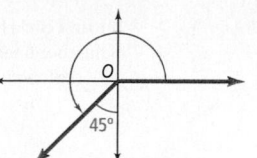

Got It?

Q How can you check your answer? **[Since the angle is a counterclockwise rotation and its terminal side is in Quadrant III, the measure of the angle must be between 180° and 270°.]**

Hint

Quadrantal angles (0°, 90°, 180°, 270°, and 360° angles) do not have reference angles.

An angle in standard position with a terminal side not on an axis has an associated *reference angle*. The **reference angle** is the acute angle formed by the terminal side of an angle in standard position and the *x*-axis. A reference angle corresponds to a right triangle, as shown in the diagram at the right.

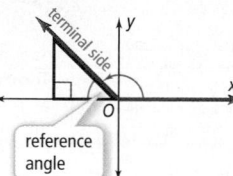

reference angle

Problem 2 Sketching Angles in Standard Position

Think

What is the initial side of the angle?
In standard position, the initial side is always the positive *x*-axis.

What is a sketch of each angle in standard position? Identify the reference angle?

A 36°

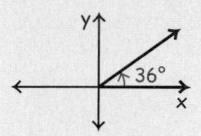

36° Counterclockwise

The reference angle is the angle itself: 36°.

B 315°

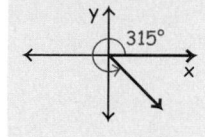

315° Counterclockwise

The reference angle is 360° − 315° = 45°.

C −150°

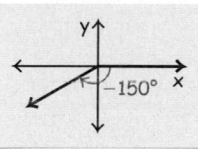

150° Clockwise

The reference angle is 180° − 150° = 30°.

Problem 2

Q Can a reference angle be negative? Explain. **[No; a reference angle is an acute angle so it must be nonnegative and have a measure between 0° and 90°.]**

EXTENSION

Q What is a negative angle whose terminal side is the same as that of 45°? Explain. **[Sample: −315°; an angle with measure −315° has a terminal side in Quadrant I and has a reference angle of 45°, so the terminal side is the same.]**

Got It? 2. What is a sketch of each angle in standard position? Identify the reference angle.

a. 85°   b. −320°   c. 140°

Got It?

Q In what quadrant is the terminal side for 2a? for 2b? for 2c? **[I, I, II]**

Answers

Got It?

1. 225°

2. a.

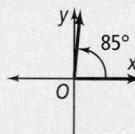

b. 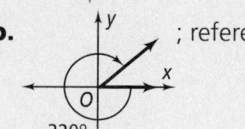 ; reference angle: 40°

c. 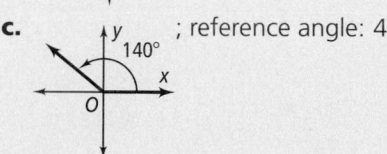 ; reference angle: 40°

Take Note

Encourage students to sketch the unit circle as shown on a piece of paper. Have them draw a line down from point P perpendicular to the x-axis. Explain that this value on the x-axis will be cos θ. Repeat using a line from P that is perpendicular to the y-axis. This value is sin θ.

> **Q** What is the greatest value of sine for any angle on the unit circle? What is the greatest value for cosine? Explain. **[As point P moves along the unit circle, the greatest value of x or y is 1. Therefore, the greatest value of sine or cosine is 1.]**
>
> **Q** For what values of θ is the sine increasing? decreasing? Explain. **[The sine will increase as θ goes from 0° to 90° because the y-values are increasing. It will decrease from 90° to 270°, then increase from 270° to 360°.]**

Problem 3   EXTENSION

> **Q** What negative angle will have the same sine and cosine as 90°? Explain. **[−270°; because 90° − 360° = −270°, so the angles have the same terminal side.]**

Got It?

> **Q** What angle between 0° and 360° has the same terminal side as 540°? Explain. **[180°; because 540° − 360° = 180°, so the angles have the same terminal side.]**

The **unit circle** has a radius of 1 unit and its center at the origin of the coordinate plane. Points on the unit circle are related to periodic functions.

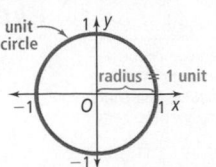

Key Concepts   Cosine and Sine of an Angle

Suppose an angle in standard position has measure θ. The cosine of θ (cos θ) is the x-coordinate of the point at which the terminal side of the angle intersects the unit circle. The sine of θ (sin θ) is the y-coordinate.

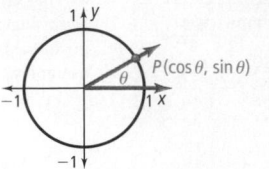

Hint
You can use the symbol θ for the measure of an angle in standard position.

Problem 3   Finding Cosines and Sines of Angles

What are cos θ and sin θ for each angle?

A θ = 60°

Sketch the angle in standard position. The cosine of 60° is the length of the shorter leg of the triangle. The sine of 60° is the length of the longer leg.

$$x = \cos 60° \qquad\qquad y = \sin 60°$$
$$= \text{length of shorter leg} \qquad = \text{length of longer leg}$$
$$= \frac{1}{2} \qquad\qquad\qquad = \frac{\sqrt{3}}{2}$$

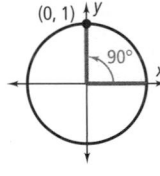

Hint
In a 30°-60°-90° triangle, the shorter leg is half the hypotenuse. The longer leg is √3 times the shorter leg.

B θ = 90°

Since a 90° angle in standard position has no reference angle, use the coordinates of the point at the intersection of the unit circle and the terminal side.

$$x = \cos 90° \qquad\qquad y = \sin 90°$$
$$= 0 \qquad\qquad\qquad = 1$$

Think
Does every angle have a reference angle?
No; an angle whose terminal side is on an axis does not have a reference angle.

✓ **Got It? 3.** What are cos θ and sin θ for each angle?
     a. θ = 30°   **b.** θ = 360°   **c.** θ = 540°

Additional Problems

1. What is the measure of each angle?

a.

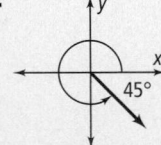

b.
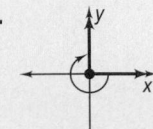

ANSWERS
a. 315°   **b.** −270°

2. What is a sketch of each angle in standard position?
a. 100°   **b.** −215°

ANSWERS

a.
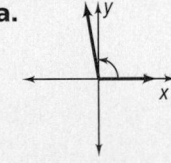

b.
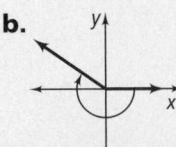

3. What are the cosine and sine of each angle?
a. θ = −180°   **b.** θ = 45°

ANSWERS
a. −1, 0   **b.** $\frac{\sqrt{2}}{2}, \frac{\sqrt{2}}{2}$

4. What are the cosine and sine of the angle?
a. 135°   **b.** 300°

ANSWERS
a. $\cos 135° = -\frac{\sqrt{2}}{2}$,
$\sin 135° = \frac{\sqrt{2}}{2}$

b. $\cos 300° = \frac{1}{2}$,
$\sin 300° = -\frac{\sqrt{3}}{2}$

Answers

Got It? (continued)

3. a. $\frac{\sqrt{3}}{2}, \frac{1}{2}$

    b. 1, 0

    c. −1, 0

Hint

Refer to the chart of trigonometric ratios for 30°, 45°, and 60° angles from Lesson T-2.

You can find the exact value of sine and cosine for angles that are multiples of 30° or 45° using their corresponding reference angles.

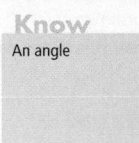 **Problem 4** **Finding Exact Values of Cosine and Sine**

What are the cosine and sine of each angle?

A $\theta = -120°$

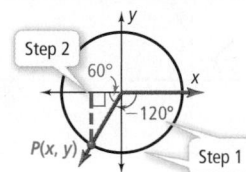

Know	Need	Plan
An angle	The x- and y-coordinates of the point where the angle intersects the unit circle	• Sketch the angle on the unit circle. • Use the angle to draw a right triangle with one leg on the x-axis. • Find the lengths of the legs. • Identify the coordinates.

Step 1 Sketch an angle of $-120°$ in standard position. Also sketch a unit circle and the point of intersection with the terminal side of the angle.

Step 2 Use the reference angle to sketch the associated 30°-60°-90° triangle.

Step 3 Find the lengths of the legs of the triangle.

The hypotenuse is the radius of the unit circle.	hypotenuse $= 1$
The shorter leg is half the hypotenuse.	shorter leg $= \frac{1}{2}$
The longer leg is $\sqrt{3}$ times the shorter leg.	longer leg $= \sqrt{3} \cdot \frac{1}{2} = \frac{\sqrt{3}}{2}$

Step 4 Identify the coordinates.

Since the point lies in Quadrant III, both the x- and y-coordinates are negative. The shorter leg lies along the x-axis, so $\cos(-120°) = -\frac{1}{2}$, and $\sin(-120°) = -\frac{\sqrt{3}}{2}$.

B $\theta = 135°$

Sketch a 135° angle in standard position to determine the point $P(x, y)$ on the unit circle. Find the reference angle and sketch the associated right triangle.

The hypotenuse of the triangle has length 1, so the legs have length $\frac{\sqrt{2}}{2}$. Since point P is in Quadrant II, the x-coordinate is negative and the y-coordinate is positive.

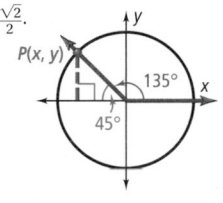

$x = \cos 135°$ $y = \sin 135°$

$\quad = -(\text{length of leg}) \quad = \text{length of leg}$

$\quad = -\frac{\sqrt{2}}{2} \qquad\qquad\quad = \frac{\sqrt{2}}{2}$

Hint

Refer to Lesson T-2 for the side relationships in special right triangles.

Think

How are the side lengths related in a 45°-45°-90° triangle?

The length of a leg is $\frac{\sqrt{2}}{2}$ times the length of the hypotenuse.

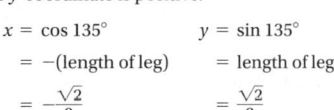

Problem 4

Q How do you know the measure of the hypotenuse is 1? **[The circle is a unit circle, which by definition has a radius of 1 unit. Therefore, the hypotenuse is 1 unit.]**

Q How can the information from 4A be used to find the cosine and sine of an angle with measure 120°? Explain. **[An angle with measure 120° has the same reference angle as an angle with measure −120°. The values of sine and cosine are the same for 120° and −120°, except for the signs. Because the terminal side of a 120° angle is in the second quadrant, the sine is positive, and the cosine is negative.]**

Q What is the reference angle in 4B? Explain. **[The reference angle must be an acute angle formed by the terminal side and the x-axis. 135° is in Quadrant II, so 180° − 135° = 45°.]**

Q How can you check that the answer in 4B is reasonable? [Using a calculator, $\frac{\sqrt{2}}{2} \approx 0.707$, so the approximate value of $P(x, y)$ is $(-0.707, 0.707)$ which is in Quadrant II so the answer is reasonable.]

Q For 4b, does the negative angle indicate negative values for sine and cosine? Explain. **[No; the negative angle indicates a clockwise direction. An angle of −30° is in Quadrant IV, so the cosine is positive and sine is negative.]**

Q What is the reference angle for 4a? for 4b? **[60°; 30°]**

Lesson Check

Do you know HOW?　　ERROR INTERVENTION
• For Exercises 1 and 2, suggest that students copy the sketch and label the axes with 90°, 180°, 270° and 360°.

Do you UNDERSTAND?
• If students have difficulty with Exercise 4, suggest that they sketch the angle of 50° and the angle of 310° to determine in which quadrants they reside. Then use this information to explain and correct any error.

Close

Q What are the meanings of positive and negative angle measures? **[A positive angle measure means the rotation from the initial side to the terminal side is counterclockwise. A negative angle measure means the rotation is clockwise.]**

Q What are the meanings of sine and cosine? **[Sine is the *y*-coordinate where the terminal side of an angle intersects the unit circle. The cosine is the *x*-coordinate.]**

 Got It? **4.** What are the cosine and sine of the angle?
　　a. $\theta = 330°$　　　　　　　　　**b.** $\theta = -30°$
　　c. Reasoning For an angle θ, can $\cos \theta$ equal $\sin \theta$? Explain.

Focus Question How is the unit circle related to trigonometric ratios?
Answer The sine and cosine ratios are related to the point where the terminal side of an angle in standard position intersects the unit circle. If θ represents the angle, then $\sin \theta$ is the *y*-coordinate of the point and $\cos \theta$ is the *x*-coordinate.

 Lesson Check

Do you know HOW?
Find the measure of each angle in standard position.

1. 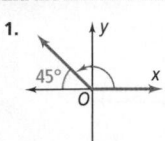　　**2.**

Do you UNDERSTAND?
3. Open-Ended Find a reference angle for $\theta = 1485°$.

4. Error Analysis On a test, a student wrote that a 310° angle in standard position has the same terminal side as a 50° angle. Describe and correct the student's error.

 Practice and Problem-Solving Exercises

 **Practice**　Find the measure of each angle in standard position.　　　◀ **See Problem 1.**

5.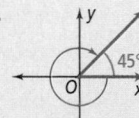

Guided Practice　To start, identify whether the measure of the angle is positive or negative.　　The rotation is clockwise, so the angle measure is negative.

6. 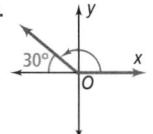　　**7.**　　**8.**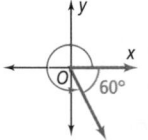

Sketch each angle in standard position. Then determine the reference angle.　　◀ **See Problem 2.**

9. 40°　　**10.** −130°　　**11.** −270°　　**12.** 120°

Answers

Got It? (continued)

4. a. $\frac{\sqrt{3}}{2}, -\frac{1}{2}$

　b. $\frac{\sqrt{3}}{2}, -\frac{1}{2}$

　c. Yes; for example, when $\theta = 45°$, $\cos \theta = \sin \theta$.

Lesson Check

1. 135°

2. 240°

3. 45°

4. A 310° angle in standard position does not have the same terminal side as a 50° angle in standard position; it has the same terminal side as a −50° angle.

Practice and Problem-Solving Exercises

5. −315°

6. 150°

7. −90°

8. 300°

9. 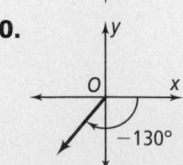　; reference angle: 40°

10. 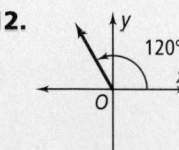　; reference angle: 50°

11. ; reference angle: 90°

12. ; reference angle: 60°

Find the cosine and sine of each angle.

See Problem 3.

13. 45°   **14.** 30°   **15.** 180°

Find the exact values of the cosine and sine of each angle.

See Problem 4.

16.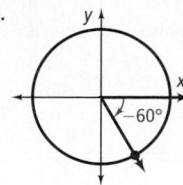

17.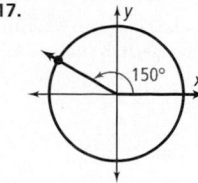

18.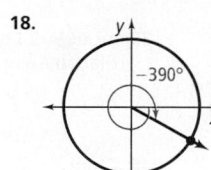

19. −240°   **20.** 315°   **21.** −30°

B Apply  **Graphing Calculator** For each angle θ, find the values of cos θ and sin θ. Round your answers to the nearest hundredth.

22. −95°   **23.** −10°   **24.** 154°   **25.** 210°

26. Time On an analog clock, the minute hand has moved 128° from 12 o'clock. What number will it pass next?

Determine the quadrant or axis where the terminal side of each angle lies.

27. 150°   **28.** 210°   **29.** 540°   **30.** −60°

31. Time The time is 2:46 P.M. What is the measure of the angle that the minute hand swept through since 2:00 P.M.?

32. a. Copy and complete the chart at the right.
  b. Suppose you know that cos θ is negative and sin θ is positive. In which quadrant does the terminal side of the angle lie?
  c. Writing Summarize how the quadrant in which the terminal side of an angle lies affects the sign of the sine and cosine of that angle.

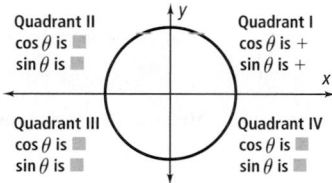

Quadrant II
cos θ is ▩
sin θ is ▩

Quadrant I
cos θ is +
sin θ is +

Quadrant III
cos θ is ▩
sin θ is ▩

Quadrant IV
cos θ is ▩
sin θ is ▩

33. a. Graphing Calculator Use a calculator to find the value of each expression: cos 40°, cos 400°, and cos (−320°).
  b. Reasoning What do you notice about the values you found in part (a)? Explain.

13. $\frac{\sqrt{2}}{2}, \frac{\sqrt{2}}{2}$

14. $\frac{\sqrt{3}}{2}, \frac{1}{2}$

15. −1, 0

16. $\frac{1}{2}, -\frac{\sqrt{3}}{2}$

17. $-\frac{\sqrt{3}}{2}, \frac{1}{2}$

18. $\frac{\sqrt{3}}{2}, -\frac{1}{2}$

19. $-\frac{1}{2}, \frac{\sqrt{3}}{2}$

20. $\frac{\sqrt{2}}{2}, -\frac{\sqrt{2}}{2}$

21. $\frac{\sqrt{3}}{2}, -\frac{1}{2}$

22. −0.09, −1.00

23. 0.98, −0.17

24. −0.90, 0.44

25. −0.87, −0.5

26. 5

27. II

28. III

29. negative *x*-axis

30. IV

31. −276°

32. a. Quadrant II
      cos θ is −
      sin θ is +

      Quadrant I
      cos θ is +
      sin θ is +

      Quadrant III
      cos θ is −
      sin θ is −

      Quadrant IV
      cos θ is +
      sin θ is −

  b. II

  c. If the terminal side of an angle is in Quadrants I or II, then the sine of the angle is positive. If the terminal side of an angle is in Quadrants I or IV, then the cosine of the angle is positive.

33. a. 0.77, 0.77, 0.77

  b. The cosines of the three angles are equal because the angles are coterminal.

Practice

ASSIGNMENT GUIDE
Basic: 5–22, 26, 31
Average: 5–12, 13–25 odd, 26–33
Standardized Test Prep: 34–37
Mixed Review: 38–49
Reasoning exercises have blue headings.
Applications exercises have red headings.

HOMEWORK QUICK CHECK
To check students' understanding of key skills and concepts, go over Exercises 6, 17, 23, 26, and 31.

Answers

Standardized Test Prep

34. C

35. I

36. C

37. [2]

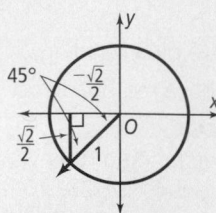

The terminal side forms an angle
of 45° with the negative x-axis,
so: $\sin(-135°) = -\frac{\sqrt{2}}{2}$ and
$\cos(-135°) = -\frac{\sqrt{2}}{2}$. Then
$[\sin(-135°)]^2 + [\cos(-135°)]^2 =$
$\left(-\frac{\sqrt{2}}{2}\right)^2 + \left(-\frac{\sqrt{2}}{2}\right)^2 = \frac{2}{4} + \frac{2}{4} = \frac{4}{4} = 1.$

[1] no diagram OR incorrect explanation

Mixed Review

38. $x = 7\sqrt{2}$; $y = 7\sqrt{2}$

39. $a = 6\sqrt{3}$; $b = 3\sqrt{3}$

40. $m = 23$; $n = 23\sqrt{3}$

41. $(0, 2\sqrt{5})$, $(0, -2\sqrt{5})$;

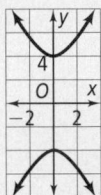

42. $(0, 5\sqrt{5})$, $(0, -5\sqrt{5})$;

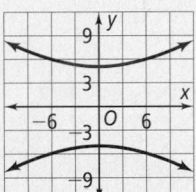

43. $(\sqrt{85}, 0)$, $(-\sqrt{85}, 0)$;

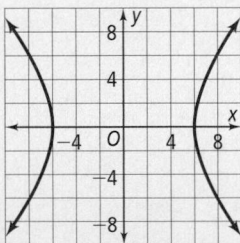

44. $y - 1 = -3x$ or $y + 5 = -3(x - 2)$

45. $y + 4 = -\frac{7}{5}(x + 4)$ or $y - 3 = -\frac{7}{5}(x + 9)$

46. $y - 2 = -(x - 7)$ or $y - 8 = -(x - 1)$

47. 50.24 in.²

48. 200.96 mi²

49. 9.0746 ft²

SAT/ACT

34. An angle drawn in standard position has a terminal side that passes through the
point $(\sqrt{2}, -\sqrt{2})$. What is one possible measure of the angle?

(A) 45°   (B) 225°   (C) 315°   (D) 330°

35. An angle of 120° is in standard position. What are the coordinates of the point at
which the terminal side intersects the unit circle?

(F) $\left(\frac{1}{2}, \frac{\sqrt{3}}{2}\right)$ (G) $\left(-\frac{1}{2}, \frac{\sqrt{3}}{-2}\right)$ (H) $\left(\frac{-\sqrt{3}}{2}, \frac{1}{2}\right)$ (I) $\left(-\frac{1}{2}, \frac{\sqrt{3}}{2}\right)$

36. Given $P = \begin{bmatrix} 4 & 3 & -2 \\ -1 & 0 & 5 \end{bmatrix}$ and $Q = \begin{bmatrix} 3 & -2 & -5 \\ -1 & -2 & -1 \end{bmatrix}$, what is $2P - 3Q$?

(A) $\begin{bmatrix} 1 & -5 & 3 \\ 0 & -2 & 6 \end{bmatrix}$ (B) $\begin{bmatrix} 17 & 0 & 19 \\ -5 & 6 & 7 \end{bmatrix}$ (C) $\begin{bmatrix} -1 & 12 & 11 \\ 1 & 6 & 13 \end{bmatrix}$ (D) $\begin{bmatrix} 1 & 5 & 3 \\ 0 & 2 & 6 \end{bmatrix}$

Short Response

37. Use an angle in standard position to find the exact value of
$[\sin(-135°)]^2 + [\cos(-135°)]^2$. Show your work.

Mixed Review

Find the value of each variable.   ◀ See Lesson T-2.

38.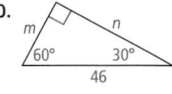

39.

40.

Find the foci of each hyperbola. Draw the graph.   ◀ See Lesson 10-5.

41. $\frac{y^2}{16} - \frac{x^2}{4} = 1$ **42.** $\frac{y^2}{25} - \frac{x^2}{100} = 1$ **43.** $\frac{x^2}{36} - \frac{y^2}{49} = 1$

Write in point-slope form an equation of the line through each pair of points.   ◀ See Lesson 2-4.

44. $(0, 1)$ and $(2, -5)$ **45.** $(-9, 3)$ and $(-4, -4)$ **46.** $(1, 8)$ and $(7, 2)$

Get Ready!   To prepare for Lesson T-4, do Exercises 47–49.

Find the area of a circle with the given radius or diameter. Use 3.14 for π.   ◀ See p. 869.

47. radius 4 in.   **48.** radius 8 mi   **49.** diameter 3.4 ft

---

Lesson Quiz

1. What is a sketch of each angle in
standard position?

 a. 225°   **b.** −90°

2. Do you UNDERSTAND? What is
the reference angle for a 570° angle?
Explain.

3. What are the sine and cosine of −270°?

4. What are the sine and cosine of −150°?

ANSWERS TO LESSON QUIZ

1. a.

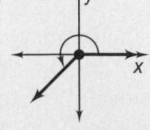

 b.

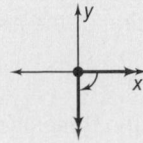

2. 30°; First find an angle between 0°
and 360° with the same terminal side.
570° − 360° = 210°. The reference
angle is an acute angle formed by
the terminal side and the x-axis.
210° is in the third quadrant. So
210° − 180° = 30°.

3. $\sin(-270°) = 1$, $\cos(-270°) = 0$

4. $\sin(-150°) = -\frac{1}{2}$; $\cos(-150°)$
$= -\frac{\sqrt{3}}{2}$

Degrees and Radian Measure

Objectives To use radian measure for angles
To find the length of an arc of a circle

In the past, you have used degrees to measure angles. In certain functions, angles are often measured in larger units called *radians*.

Focus Question What is a radian?

A **central angle** of a circle is an angle with a vertex at the center of a circle. An **intercepted arc** is the portion of the circle with endpoints on the sides of the central angle.

A **radian** is the measure of a central angle that intercepts an arc with length equal to the radius of the circle. Radians, like degrees, measure the amount of rotation from the initial side to the terminal side of an angle.

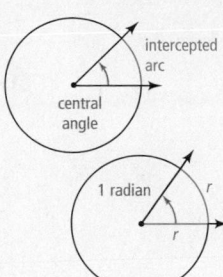

take note

Key Concept **Proportion Relating Radians and Degrees**

You can use the proportion $\frac{d°}{180°} = \frac{r\ \text{radians}}{\pi\ \text{radians}}$ to convert between radians and degrees.

Here's Why It Works Suppose you continued marking intercepted arcs of length r around a circle. Because the circumference of a circle is $2\pi r$, a circle can be divided into $\frac{2\pi r}{r} = 2\pi$ arcs of length r. Therefore, there are 2π radians in any circle, including the unit circle, the top half of which is shown here. Since 2π radians = 360°, it follows that π radians = 180°. This equality leads to the following *conversion factors* for radian measure and degree measure.

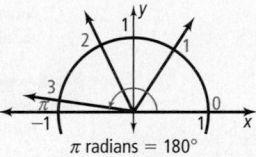

π radians = 180°

take note

Key Concept **Converting Between Radians and Degrees**

To convert degrees to radians, multiply by $\frac{\pi\ \text{radians}}{180°}$.

To convert radians to degrees, multiply by $\frac{180°}{\pi\ \text{radians}}$.

Guided Instruction

Take Note
When converting between radians and degrees, make sure the units cancel when multiplying.

Q In the proportion, the denominator on the left were 360°, what would be the denominator on the right? **[2π radians]**

Take Note

Q How many radians are in a circle? in a line? in a right angle? in any angle of x degrees?
$[\frac{360}{180}\pi = 2\pi;\ \frac{180}{180}\pi = \pi;\ \frac{90}{180}\pi = \frac{\pi}{2};\ \frac{x}{180}\pi]$

T-4 Preparing to Teach

BIG ideas Modeling
Function

UbD

ESSENTIAL UNDERSTANDINGS

• An angle with a full circle rotation measures 2π radians. An angle with a semicircle rotation measures π radians.
• To convert degrees to radians, multiply by $\frac{\pi\ \text{radians}}{180°}$.
• To convert radians to degrees, multiply by $\frac{180°}{\pi\ \text{radians}}$.
• For a circle of radius r and a central angle of measure θ (in radians), the length of the intercepted arc is $s = r\theta$.

Math Background
Students may not be aware of the advantages radian measure has over degree measure. It is actually a more convenient unit and simplifies calculations in trigonometry, calculus, and other higher-level mathematics and engineering.

The radian measure of an angle is the ratio of the arc length to the radius of the circle. The conversion factor follows directly from this definition; the circumference of a circle is $2\pi r$, so 2π radians is 360 degrees.

The relationship between the angle measure in radians and its arc length s determined by a central angle θ in a circle, $s = r\theta$.

Problem 1

Q Look at the negative angle measure in 1A. What are the degree and radian measurements of this angle expressed in positive terms? Describe your method. **[Sample: A full circle has 2π radians or 360°, so an angle with the same terminal side is $2\pi - \frac{3\pi}{4} = \frac{5\pi}{4}$ and $360° - 135° = 225°$.]**

Q If the radius of the circle in 1B was equal to 1, what would be the length of the arc intercepted by the angle? **[Samples: 0.47; $\frac{3\pi}{20}$]**

Got It?

Before calculating the degree measure of 1c, ask students to estimate a reasonable answer. The thought process should go like this:
π radians = 180°; $\frac{\pi}{2}$ radians = 90°; $\pi \approx 3.14$, so $\frac{\pi}{2} \approx 1.07$. 2 radians must be between 90° and 180° and closer to 90°. A good estimate would be between 100° and 120°.

Problem 2

Q How many angles have a sine and a cosine that are equal in absolute value? What are the angles? **[An infinite number; from 0 radians to 2π radians, there are four angles: $\frac{\pi}{4}, \frac{3\pi}{4}, \frac{5\pi}{4}$, and $\frac{7\pi}{4}$.]**

You can use conversion factors and dimensional analysis to convert between angle measurement systems.

 Problem 1 Using Dimensional Analysis

A What is the degree measure of an angle of $-\frac{3\pi}{4}$ radians?

Think

How do you know which conversion factor to use?
Because radians are in the numerator, use the conversion factor with radians in the denominator.

Multiply by the conversion factor $\frac{180°}{\pi \text{ radians}}$.	$-\frac{3\pi}{4}$ radians $= -\frac{3\pi}{4}$ radians $\cdot \frac{180°}{\pi \text{ radians}}$
Divide out common factors and units.	$= -\frac{3\pi}{\cancel{4}^1} \text{ radians} \cdot \frac{\cancel{180}^{45}°}{\cancel{\pi} \text{ radians}}$
Simplify.	$= -3 \cdot 45° = -135°$

An angle of $-\frac{3\pi}{4}$ radians measures $-135°$.

B What is the radian measure of an angle of 27°?

Multiply by the conversion factor $\frac{\pi \text{ radians}}{180°}$.	$27° = 27° \cdot \frac{\pi \text{ radians}}{180°}$
Divide out common factors and units.	$= {}^3\cancel{27} \cdot \frac{\pi \text{ radians}}{{}_{20}\cancel{180}}$
Simplify.	$= 3 \cdot \frac{\pi \text{ radians}}{20} = \frac{3\pi}{20}$ radians

An angle of 27° measures $\frac{3\pi}{20}$ radians.

 Got It? **1.** What is the degree measure of each angle expressed in radians? What is the radian measure of each angle expressed in degrees? (Express radian measures in terms of π.)

   a. $\frac{\pi}{2}$ radians   **b.** 225°   **c.** 2 radians   **d.** 150°

Although you can find the sine and cosine of angles in radian measure by converting the radian measure to degrees, this step is unnecessary if you are able to think in radians.

 **Problem 2** Finding Cosine and Sine of a Radian Measure

Think

What kind of angle is π?
It is a straight angle.

What are the exact values of $\cos \frac{\pi}{4}$ and $\sin \frac{\pi}{4}$?

Step 1 Draw the angle on the unit circle.

$\frac{\pi}{4} = \frac{1}{4}\pi = \frac{1}{4}$ of a straight angle, or 45°

Step 2 Complete a 45°-45°-90° triangle.

Since the hypotenuse has length 1, both legs have length $\frac{\sqrt{2}}{2}$.

Step 3 Identify the sine and cosine.

The point (x, y) is in Quadrant I, so x and y are positive.

$x = \cos \frac{\pi}{4} = \frac{\sqrt{2}}{2}$ $y = \sin \frac{\pi}{4} = \frac{\sqrt{2}}{2}$

Answers

Got It?

1. a. 90°

b. $\frac{5\pi}{4}$ radians

c. $\frac{360°}{\pi} \approx 114.59°$

d. $\frac{5\pi}{6}$ radians

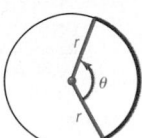 **Got It?** **2.** What are the exact values of $\cos \frac{7\pi}{6}$ and $\sin \frac{7\pi}{6}$?

If you know the radius and the measure in radians of a central angle, you can find the length of the intercepted arc.

Key Concept **Length of an Intercepted Arc**

For a circle of radius r and a central angle of measure θ (in radians), the length s of the intercepted arc is $s = r\theta$.

Here's Why It Works The length of the intercepted arc is the same fraction of the circumference of the circle as the central angle is of 2π. So, $\frac{\theta}{2\pi} = \frac{s}{C}$.

Write the proportion.	$\frac{\theta}{2\pi} = \frac{s}{C}$
Substitute $2\pi r$ for C.	$\frac{\theta}{2\pi} = \frac{s}{2\pi r}$
Write the cross products.	$2\pi r\theta = 2\pi s$
Divide out common factors.	$2\cancel{\pi} r\theta = 2\cancel{\pi} s$
Simplify.	$s = r\theta$

 Problem 3 **Finding the Length of an Arc**

Think
What units will the length of the arc have?
Because the radius is in inches, the arc length will also be in inches.

Use the circle at the right. What is length s to the nearest tenth?

Use the formula.	$s = r\theta$
Substitute 3 for r and $\frac{5\pi}{6}$ for θ.	$= 3 \cdot \frac{5\pi}{6}$
Simplify.	$= \frac{5\pi}{2}$
Use a calculator.	≈ 7.9

The arc has a length of about 7.9 in.

 **Got It?** **3. a.** What is length b in Problem 3 to the nearest tenth?
b. Reasoning If the radius of the circle doubled, how would the arc length change?

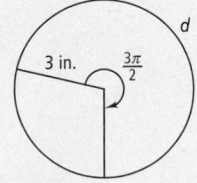

Got It?

Q From 0 radians to 2π radians, how many angles have either a sine or a cosine value with absolute value equal to $\frac{1}{2}$? What are they? **[Eight; $\frac{\pi}{6}, \frac{\pi}{3}, \frac{2\pi}{3}, \frac{5\pi}{6}, \frac{7\pi}{6}, \frac{4\pi}{3}, \frac{5\pi}{3}$, and $\frac{11\pi}{6}$.]**

Take Note

An angle in standard form can have a negative measure. When calculating the length of an intercepted arc, the result is a distance. A negative distance is never a valid solution. Use the absolute value of the angle measure in these cases.

Here's Why It Works

In a unit circle, the length of an arc has the same numerical value as the angle measure of the arc in radians. Students often confuse radians with a unit of length. Radians measure the angle, not length.

Problem 3

Q What is a radius of a circle that returns an integer arc length? **[any fraction with an integer numerator and π in the denominator]**

Got It? **EXTENSION**

Q How can you find the remaining arc length of the circle in Problem 3? **[Samples: Calculate the circumference, C, and subtract the known lengths s and b; subtract the given angles from 2π and use the arc length formula.]**

Additional Problems

1. What is the degree measure of an angle of $-\frac{7\pi}{30}$ radians?
ANSWER $-42°$

2. What are the exact measures of $\sin (\pi \text{ radians})$ and $\cos (\pi \text{ radians})$?
ANSWERS 0; -1

3. What is length d to the nearest tenth?

3 in. $\frac{3\pi}{2}$

ANSWER 14.1 in.

4. A satellite in geosynchronous orbit travels one Earth circumference in a full day. From a point on the ground, the satellite appears stationary overhead. The orbital height for a geosynchronous satellite is about 36,000 km. The radius of Earth is 6400 km. About how far does the satellite travel in 8 hours? Assume the length of an Earth day is exactly 24 hours.
ANSWER 89,000 km

Answers

Got It? (continued)

2. $-\frac{\sqrt{3}}{2}, -\frac{1}{2}$

3. a. 6.3 in.
b. Arc length would also double.

Problem 4

Q How long does it take the satellite to travel 50,000 km? Explain. **[about 1 hr 46 min; use the arc length formula: $50,000 = 9000\,\theta$. $\theta = \frac{50,000}{9000} \approx 5.56$ radians. The satellite travels 2π radians every 2 hours: 5.56 radians $\cdot \frac{2}{2\pi} \approx 1.77$ hr ≈ 1 hr 46 min.]**

Got It?

Q What is an alternate way to solve 4? **[Sample: In 1 hour, the satellite completes $\frac{1}{4}$ of a circumference. Calculate the circumference and divide by 4.]**

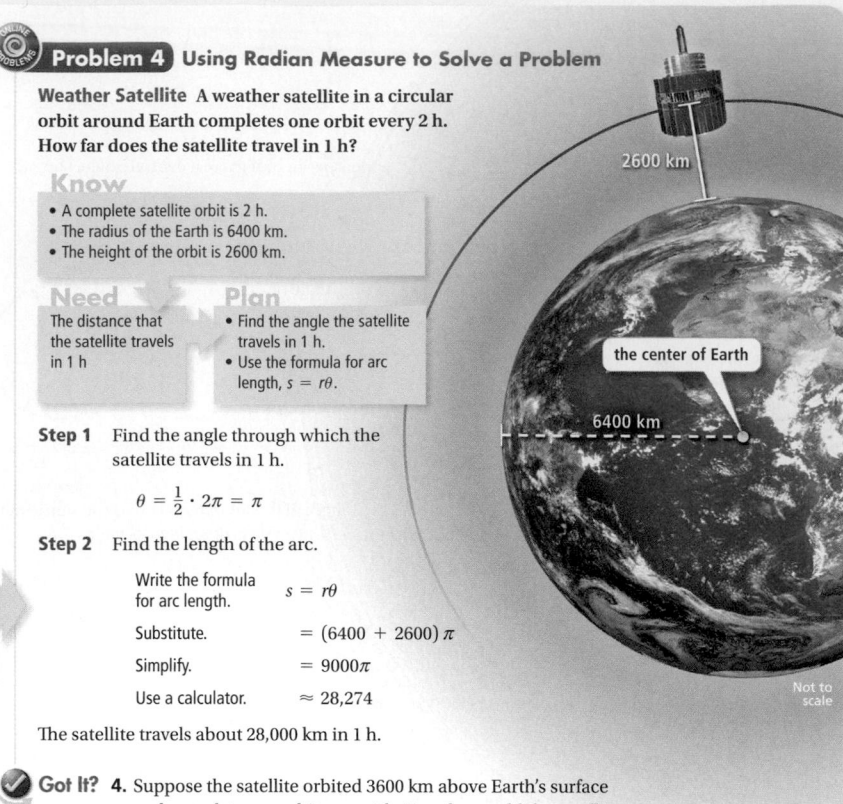

Problem 4 Using Radian Measure to Solve a Problem

Weather Satellite A weather satellite in a circular orbit around Earth completes one orbit every 2 h. How far does the satellite travel in 1 h?

2600 km

Know
- A complete satellite orbit is 2 h.
- The radius of the Earth is 6400 km.
- The height of the orbit is 2600 km.

the center of Earth

6400 km

Need
The distance that the satellite travels in 1 h

Plan
- Find the angle the satellite travels in 1 h.
- Use the formula for arc length, $s = r\theta$.

Step 1 Find the angle through which the satellite travels in 1 h.

$$\theta = \frac{1}{2} \cdot 2\pi = \pi$$

Step 2 Find the length of the arc.

Think
What value should you use for r?
Use the sum of the Earth's radius and the height of the orbit.

Write the formula for arc length.	$s = r\theta$
Substitute.	$= (6400 + 2600)\,\pi$
Simplify.	$= 9000\pi$
Use a calculator.	$\approx 28,274$

Not to scale

The satellite travels about 28,000 km in 1 h.

Got It? 4. Suppose the satellite orbited 3600 km above Earth's surface and completes an orbit every 4 h. How far would the satellite travel in 1 h?

Focus Question What is a radian?

Answer A radian is the measure of a central angle that intercepts an arc with length equal to the radius of the circle. Use the relationship $180° = \pi$ radians to convert units. Use the formula $s = r\theta$ as a shortcut to calculate arc length given the radius and the central angle.

Answers

Got It? (continued)
4. $\approx 15,708$ km

Lesson Check

Do you know HOW?

1. Find the radian measure of an angle of 300°.

2. Find the degree measure of an angle of $\frac{3\pi}{4}$ radians.

3. Find the length a.

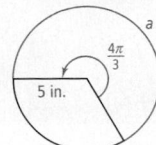

Do you UNDERSTAND?

4. **Vocabulary** The radius of a circle is 9 cm. A central angle intercepts an arc that is 9 cm. What is the measure of the central angle in radians?

5. **Reasoning** A certain baker believes that a perfect slice of pie has a central angle of 1 radian. How many "perfect" slices can he get out of one pie?

Practice and Problem-Solving Exercises

 **Practice**

Write each measure in radians. Express your answer in terms of π and as a decimal rounded to the nearest hundredth.

◆ **See Problem 1.**

6. −300°   7. 150°   8. −90°   9. 20°

Write each measure in degrees. Round your answer to the nearest degree, if necessary.

Guided Practice

10. 3π radians
To start, multiply by the conversion factor $\frac{180°}{\pi\text{ radians}}$.	3π radians $\cdot \frac{180°}{\pi\text{ radians}}$

11. $\frac{11\pi}{10}$ radians   12. $-\frac{2\pi}{3}$ radians   13. −3 radians

The measure θ of an angle in standard position is given. Find the exact values of $\cos\theta$ and $\sin\theta$ for each angle measure.

◆ **See Problem 2.**

14. $\frac{\pi}{6}$ 15. $\frac{\pi}{3}$ 16. $-\frac{\pi}{4}$

17. $\frac{2\pi}{3}$ 18. $-\frac{\pi}{2}$ 19. $\frac{7\pi}{6}$

Use each circle to find the length of the indicated arc. Round your answer to the nearest tenth.

◆ **See Problem 3.**

20.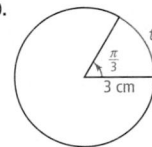

21.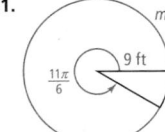

22.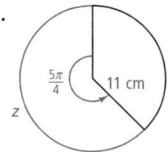

Lesson Check

Do you know HOW?   ERROR INTERVENTION

- For Exercises 1 and 2, some students may remember the conversion 360° = 2π more easily than 180° = π. Either conversion will return the correct answer.

Do you UNDERSTAND? ERROR INTERVENTION

- If students answer "9 radians" to Exercise 4, reinforce the definition of a radian by asking analogous questions, such as "What is the measure of a central angle with radius 1 that intercepts an arc with length 1?" "What is the measure of a central angle with radius 2 that intercepts an arc with length 2?"

Close

Q What advantage does radian measure have over degree measure? [**Sample: Radian measure is based on the length of the radius, so it relates to the other important measures of the circle. The "unit" of radian measure is the "unit" of a circle of radius 1.**]

Lesson Check

1. $\frac{5\pi}{3}$ radians ≈ 5.24 radians

2. 135°

3. $\frac{20\pi}{3}$ ≈ 20.94 in.

4. 1 radian

5. 6 "perfect" slices

Practice and Problem-Solving Exercises

6. $-\frac{5\pi}{3}$, −5.24

7. $\frac{5\pi}{6}$, 2.62

8. $-\frac{\pi}{2}$, −1.57

9. $\frac{\pi}{9}$, 0.35

10. 540°

11. 198°

12. −120°

13. −172°

14. $\frac{\sqrt{3}}{2}$, $\frac{1}{2}$

15. $\frac{1}{2}$, $\frac{\sqrt{3}}{2}$

16. $\frac{\sqrt{2}}{2}$, $-\frac{\sqrt{2}}{2}$

17. $-\frac{1}{2}$, $\frac{\sqrt{3}}{2}$

18. 0, −1

19. $-\frac{\sqrt{3}}{2}$, $-\frac{1}{2}$

20. 3.1 cm

21. 51.8 ft

22. 43.2 cm

Practice

ASSIGNMENT GUIDE

Basic: 6–26, 36

Average: 6–30, 35–37

Standardized Test Prep: 38–41

Mixed Review: 42–51

Reasoning exercises have blue headings.

Applications exercises have red headings.

HOMEWORK QUICK CHECK

To check students' understanding of key skills and concepts, go over Exercises 11, 14, 20, 26, and 36.

Find the length of each arc.

23.
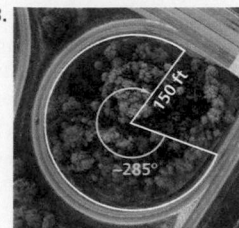

24.
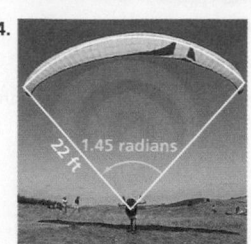

25. Space A geostationary satellite is positioned 35,800 km above Earth's surface. It takes 24 h to complete one orbit. The radius of Earth is about 6400 km. ◀ See Problem 4.
   a. What distance does the satellite travel in 1 h? 3 h? 2.5 h? 25 h?
   b. **Reasoning** After how many hours has the satellite traveled 200,000 km?

Ⓑ Apply

26. Automobiles Suppose a windshield wiper arm has a length of 22 in. and rotates through an angle of 110°. What distance does the tip of the wiper travel as it moves once across the windshield?

27. Geography The 24 lines of longitude that approximate the 24 standard time zones are equally spaced around the equator.
   a. Suppose you use 24 central angles to divide a circle into 24 equal arcs. Express the measure of each angle in degrees and in radians.
   b. The radius of the equator is about 3960 mi. About how wide is each time zone at the equator?
   c. The radius of the Arctic Circle is about 1580 mi. About how wide is each time zone at the Arctic Circle?

Determine the quadrant or axis where the terminal side of each angle lies.

28. $\frac{4\pi}{3}$ **29.** $-\frac{5\pi}{4}$ **30.** $-\pi$

Draw an angle in standard position with each given measure. Then find the values of the cosine and sine of the angle.

31. $\frac{7\pi}{4}$ **32.** $-\frac{2\pi}{3}$ **33.** $\frac{5\pi}{2}$

34. Open-Ended Draw an angle in standard position. Draw a circle with its center at the vertex of the angle. Find the measure of the angle in radians and degrees.

35. Transportation Suppose the radius of a bicycle wheel is 13 in. (measured to the outside of the tire). Find the number of radians through which a point on the tire turns when the bicycle has moved forward a distance of 12 ft.

Answers

Practice and Problem-Solving Exercises (continued)

23. ≈746 ft

24. ≈32 ft

25. a. ≈11,048 km, ≈33,144 km, ≈27,620 km, ≈276,198 km
   b. ≈18.1 h

26. ≈42.2 in.

27. a. 15°, $\frac{\pi}{12}$ radians
   b. ≈1036.7 mi
   c. ≈413.6 mi

28. III

29. II

30. negative *x*-axis

31.   0.71, −0.71
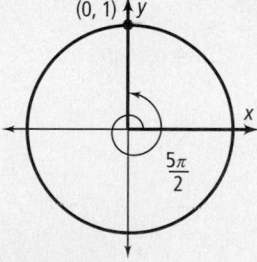

32.   −0.50, −0.87

33.   0.00, 1.00

34. Check students' work.

35. ≈11 radians

36. Error Analysis A student wanted to rewrite $\frac{9\pi}{4}$ in degrees. The screen shows her calculation. What error did the student make?

9*π/4*360/2*π
3997.189782

37. Music A CD with diameter 12 cm spins in a CD player. Calculate how much farther a point on the outside edge of the CD travels in one revolution than a point 1 cm closer to the center of the CD.

Standardized Test Prep

38. Which pairs of measurements represent the same angle measures?

   I. $240°, \frac{7\pi}{6}$ II. $135°, \frac{3\pi}{4}$ III. $150°, \frac{5\pi}{6}$

   Ⓐ I and II only   Ⓑ I and III only   Ⓒ II and III only   Ⓓ I, II, and III

39. What is the exact value of $\cos \frac{5\pi}{4}$?

   Ⓕ $-\frac{\sqrt{3}}{2}$ Ⓖ $-\frac{\sqrt{2}}{2}$ Ⓗ $-\frac{1}{2}$ Ⓘ $\frac{\sqrt{2}}{2}$

40. Two arcs have the same length. One arc is intercepted by an angle of $\frac{3\pi}{2}$ in a circle of radius 15 cm. If the radius of the other circle is 25 cm, what central angle intercepts the arc?

   Ⓐ $\frac{3\pi}{2}$ Ⓑ $\frac{9\pi}{10}$ Ⓒ $\frac{5\pi}{2}$ Ⓓ $\frac{5\pi}{3}$

41. For a central angle of one radian, describe the relationship between the radius of the circle and the length of the arc.

Mixed Review

Sketch each angle in standard position.   ◀ **See Lesson T-3.**

42. $15°$ **43.** $-75°$ **44.** $150°$ **45.** $-270°$

Find the mean and the standard deviation for each set of values.   ◀ **See Lesson 11-6.**

46. 12 13 15 9 16 5 18 16 12 11 15   **47.** 21 29 35 26 25 28 27 51 24 34

Get Ready!   **To prepare for Lesson T-5, do Exercises 48–51.**

In $\triangle PQR$, find each value.   ◀ **See Lesson T-1.**

48. $\cos P$ **49.** $\tan Q$

50. $\tan P$ **51.** $\sin Q$

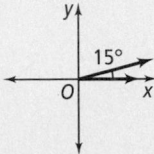

50. $\frac{15}{8}$

51. $\frac{8}{17}$

Lesson Quiz

1. What is the radian measure of an angle of 132°?

2. What are the exact values of $\sin\left(\frac{2\pi}{3}\text{ radians}\right)$ and $\cos\left(\frac{2\pi}{3}\text{ radians}\right)$?

3. What is length a to the nearest tenth?

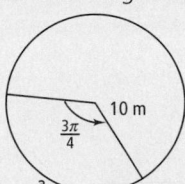

4. Do you UNDERSTAND? In a baseball field, the arc that divides the outfield from the infield has a radius of 95 feet measured from the pitching rubber. The degree measure of the arc is about 145°. What is the length of the arc to the nearest foot?

ANSWERS TO LESSON QUIZ

1. $\frac{11\pi}{15}$

2. $\frac{\sqrt{3}}{2}$; $-\frac{1}{2}$

3. 23.6 m

4. 240 ft

---

36. The student forgot to include parentheses around $2*\pi$.

37. ≈ 6.3 cm

Standardized Test Prep

38. C

39. G

40. B

41. [2] For a central angle of 1 radian, the length of the intercepted arc is the length of the radius.

   [1] correct description, but does not use the terms "intercepted arc" and "central angle"

Mixed Review

42.

43.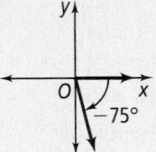

44.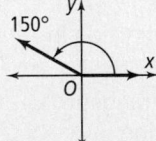

45.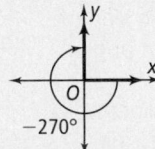

46. mean ≈ 12.9, s.d. ≈ 3.53

47. mean $= 30$, s.d. ≈ 8.09

48. $\frac{8}{17}$

49. $\frac{8}{15}$

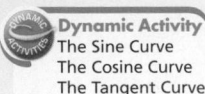

Graphs of Sine, Cosine, and Tangent Functions

Objectives To identify properties of the sine, cosine, and tangent functions
To graph sine, cosine, and tangent functions

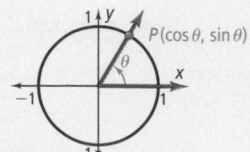

Dynamic Activity
The Sine Curve
The Cosine Curve
The Tangent Curve

Recall that for an angle in standard position with measure θ, the point at which the terminal side of the angle intersects the unit circle has coordinates ($\cos\theta$, $\sin\theta$). You can use these relationships to define and graph *sine* and *cosine functions*.

Focus Question What are the graphs of sine and cosine functions?

Lesson Vocabulary
• sine function
• cosine function
• periodic function
• cycle
• period
• amplitude
• tangent function

The **sine function**, $y = \sin\theta$, matches the measure θ of an angle in standard position with the y-coordinate of a point on the unit circle. This point is where the terminal side of the angle intersects the unit circle.

Although you can graph the sine function in radians or degrees, use radians unless degrees are specified. The graph of the sine function for $0 \le \theta \le 2\pi$ is shown below. Notice that the graph will repeat the same pattern of y-values if you continue moving around the unit circle.

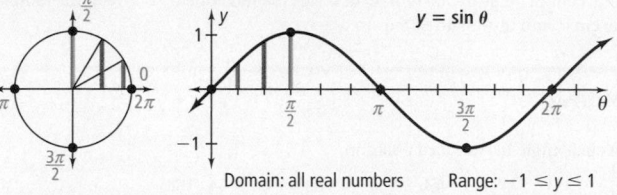

Domain: all real numbers   Range: $-1 \le y \le 1$

The **cosine function**, $y = \cos\theta$, matches θ with the x-coordinate of the point of intersection of the terminal side of angle θ and the unit circle. The symmetry of the set of points $(x, y) = (\cos\theta, \sin\theta)$ on the unit circle guarantees that the graphs of sine (above) and cosine (below) are translations of each other.

Hint

The graph of $y = \cos\theta$ is a translation of $y = \sin\theta$ either left or right $\frac{\pi}{2}$ units.

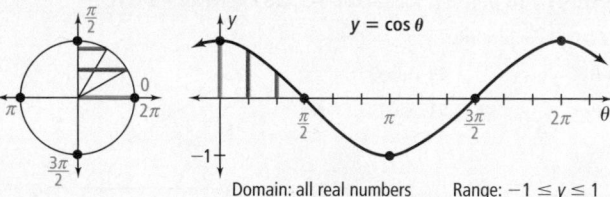

Domain: all real numbers   Range: $-1 \le y \le 1$

848   **Chapter T** Trigonometry Concepts

Preparing to Teach

BIG idea Function   **UbD**

ESSENTIAL UNDERSTANDINGS

• As the terminal side of an angle rotates about the origin (beginning at 0°), its sine value on the unit circle increases from 0 to 1, decreases from 1 to −1, and then increases back to 0.
• As the terminal side of an angle rotates about the origin (beginning at 0°), its cosine value on the unit circle decreases from 1 to −1, and then increases back to 1.
• A nontranslated function can be completely described in terms of its amplitude and period.
• The tangent function has infinitely many points of discontinuity with a vertical asymptote at each point. Its range is all real numbers. Its period is π.

Math Background

The sine and cosine functions are basic periodic functions. The parent sine function has a period of 2π and amplitude of 1. Transformations of the sine function can be represented as $y = a \sin bx$.

Transformations of the cosine function can be represented as $y = a \cos bx$.

• The period of a transformation of the sine or cosine function is equal to $\frac{2\pi}{b}$.
• The amplitude of a transformation of the sine or cosine function is equal to $|a|$.
• For $a < 0$, the graph is a reflection in the x-axis.

The relationship between the tangent function and the sine and cosine functions is that the tangent of an angle equals the ratio of the sine of that angle to the cosine of that angle. Like the graphs of sine and cosine functions, the graph of the tangent function is periodic. Unlike the sine and cosine functions, the range of the tangent function is all real numbers since it has no maximum or minimum values (no amplitude).

Because the tangent function equals the ratio of the sine function to the cosine function, the critical points for the tangent function can be easily determined.

• Where the sine is 0 the tangent is also 0. This occurs when θ equals 0, π, and 2π.
• Where the cosine is 0 the tangent is undefined. This occurs when θ equals $-\frac{\pi}{2}$, $\frac{\pi}{2}$, and $\frac{3\pi}{2}$.

Thus, the tangent function has the pattern asymptote, zero, asymptote and a period of π.

The graph of a sine function is called a sine curve. Similarly, the graph of a cosine function is called a cosine curve. Since the pattern of y-values repeat over time, sine and cosine functions are examples of *periodic functions*.

Hint
A cycle may begin at any point on the graph of the function.

A **periodic function** is a function that repeats a pattern of y-values (outputs) at regular intervals. One complete pattern is called a **cycle**. The **period** of a function is the horizontal length of one cycle. By varying the period, you can get different sine and cosine curves.

Problem 1 Finding Periods of Sine and Cosine Curves

How many cycles occur in the graph? What is the period of the function?

A
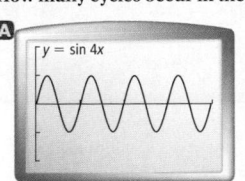

$y = \sin 4x$

Xmin = 0
Xmax = 2π
Xscl = $\pi/2$
Ymin = -2
Ymax = 2
Yscl = 1

Plan
How do you find the number of cycles?
Identify the smallest repeating section of the graph and count the number of times it occurs.

There are four complete patterns in the graph, so the graph shows 4 cycles. To find the period of the function, divide the length of the horizontal interval of the graph by the number of cycles shown on the graph.

The length of the horizontal interval shown is 2π.

$$2\pi \div 4 = \frac{\pi}{2}$$

The period of $y = \sin 4x$ is $\frac{\pi}{2}$.

B
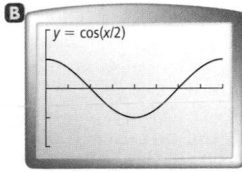

$y = \cos(x/2)$

Xmin = 0
Xmax = 4π
Xscl = $\pi/2$
Ymin = -2
Ymax = 2
Yscl = 1

There is only one complete pattern, so the graph shows only 1 cycle. Therefore, the length of the horizontal interval shown in the graph is equal to the period of the function.

The period of $y = \cos \frac{x}{2}$ is 4π.

 Got It? 1. How many cycles occur in the graph? What is the period of the function?

a.
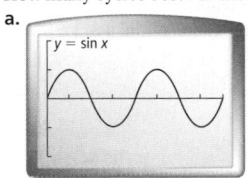

$y = \sin x$

Xmin = 0
Xmax = 4π
Xscl = $\pi/2$
Ymin = -2
Ymax = 2
Yscl = 1

b.
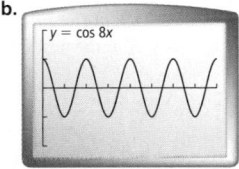

$y = \cos 8x$

Xmin = 0
Xmax = π
Xscl = $\pi/8$
Ymin = -2
Ymax = 2
Yscl = 1

PowerAlgebra.com

1 Interactive Learning

Dynamic Activity This activity has students explore the relationship between the graph of a sine function and the coordinates of the points on the unit circle. This interactive graph is a good introduction to the lesson.

Dynamic Activity This interactive graph relates the cosine curve to the unit circle. Students can manipulate the value of the central angle in either degrees or radians, and see how it relates to the cosine curve.

Dynamic Activity This activity shows how the tangent graph relates to the unit circle. Students who have difficulty understanding why the graph of the tangent function is sometimes undefined should use the Show Reference Triangle feature.

Guided Instruction

Problem 1

Q In 1A, what is the interval of x-values shown on the graph? How many cycles would you expect to see? How many are there actually? **[The interval is 0 to 2π; 1 cycle; 4 cycles.]**

Q How does $y = \sin 4x$ compare with $y = \sin x$? **[The coefficient of 4 causes a horizontal compression of $y = \sin x$, changing the period. The amplitude remains the same.]**

Got It?   ERROR PREVENTION
Students need to check the x-scale in 2a in order to find the correct solution.

Q If the graph in 1a has sine as its parent function, what do you think is the coefficient of x? **[1]**

Answers

Got It?
1. a. 2; 2π

b. 4; $\frac{\pi}{4}$

Problem 2

Q Does the coefficient *a* stretch the graphs vertically or horizontally? **[vertically]**

EXTENSION

Q The function $y = 2 \sin x$ has a range from -2 to 2. How could you modify the parent sine function so that its range is 0 to 2? **[Add 1 to the parent function: $y = \sin x + 1$]**

Got It?

Q The sine function is periodic, so you can assume it repeats in both directions. How could you write a sine function for 2a using positive 3 as the value for *a*? Assume the graph has a period of 2π. Explain. **[Answers may vary. Sample: The function $y = 3 \sin (x + \pi)$ would show the graph with a positive *a*-value. Any positive or negative *x*-shift by an odd-integer multiple of π would work.]**

Take Note

Q What happens to the cosine graph if $a < 0$? How does this affect the amplitude? **[The graph is reflected in the *x*-axis. The amplitude will not change because the difference between the maximum and minimum values remains the same.]**

Q For negative values of *a*, what pattern of five points would you use to sketch a graph? **[zero-min-zero-max-zero]**

You can also vary the *amplitude* of a sine or cosine curve. The **amplitude** of a periodic function is half the difference between the maximum and minimum values of the function. It is a way to describe the amount of variation in the function values.

$$\text{amplitude} = \tfrac{1}{2}(\text{maximum value} - \text{minimum value})$$

 Problem 2 Finding Amplitudes of Sine and Cosine Curves

The graphing calculator screens at the right show several graphs of $y = a \sin x$ and $y = a \cos x$. Each *x*-axis shows values from 0 to 2π.

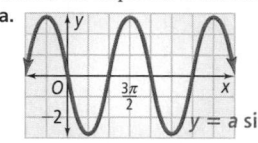
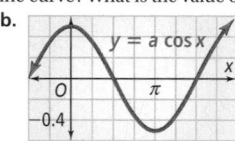

Think

What is the amplitude?
The amplitude is half the difference of the maximum and minimum values of the periodic function.

A What is the amplitude of each sine curve?

The amplitude of $y = \sin x$ is 1, and the amplitude of $y = 2 \sin x$ is 2.

B What is the amplitude of each cosine curve?

The amplitude of $y = -\cos x$ is 1, and the amplitude of $y = -2 \cos x$ is 2.

C How does the value of *a* affect the amplitude?

In each case, the amplitude of the curve is $|a|$.

Got It? **2.** What is the amplitude of each sine or cosine curve? What is the value of *a*?

a.   b.

The summary box below lists the properties of sine and cosine functions.

take note **Concept Summary Properties of Sine and Cosine Functions**

For $a \ne 0$, $b > 0$, and θ in radians, functions of the form $y = a \sin b\theta$ and $y = a \cos b\theta$ have the following properties.

- $|a|$ is the amplitude of the function.
- b is the number of cycles in the interval from 0 to 2π.
- $\frac{2\pi}{b}$ is the period of the function.

Additional Problems

1. How many cycles appear in the graph? What is the period of the graph?

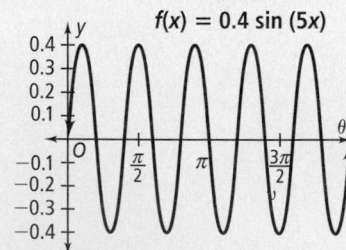

$f(x) = 0.4 \sin (5x)$

ANSWER $5; \frac{2\pi}{5}$

2. The equation of the graph for Problem 2 is of the form $y = a \sin x$. What is the amplitude of the sine curve? What is the value of *a*?

ANSWER $0.4; a = 0.4$

3. What is the graph of $y = 0.75 \cos 3\theta$ in the interval from 0 to 2π?

ANSWER

4. Sketch two cycles of the graph of $y = \tan \frac{\pi}{3}\theta$.

ANSWER
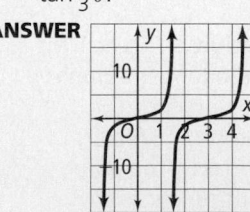

5. An architect wants to place right triangular panels on either side of the double doors of a building. The doors are each 7 ft tall. The function $y = 97 \tan \theta$ models the height of the triangles, where θ is the bottom acute angle. If the architect does not want the panels to be taller than the doors, what is the maximum angle, to the nearest whole degree, for θ?

ANSWER $4°$

Answers

Got It? (continued)
2. a. $3; -3$
   b. $0.5; 0.5$

You can use five points equally spaced through one cycle to sketch a sine or cosine curve. For $a > 0$ and $b > 0$, the five-point patterns for $y = a \sin b\theta$ and $y = a \cos b\theta$ are shown.

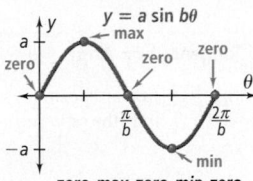

zero-max-zero-min-zero

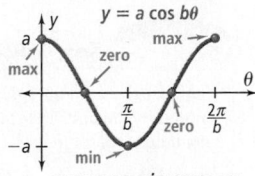

max-zero-min-zero-max

 Problem 3 Graphing From Function Rules

A What is the graph of one cycle of $y = \frac{1}{2} \sin 2\theta$?

Know	Need	Plan
An equation of the form $y = a \sin b\theta$	The graph of one cycle of the equation	• Identify the amplitude and period. • Find the critical values. • Plot the *zero-max-zero-min-zero* pattern.

Step 1 Find the amplitude and period.

$$\text{amplitude} = |a| = \left|\tfrac{1}{2}\right| = \tfrac{1}{2}$$

$$\text{period} = \tfrac{2\pi}{b} = \tfrac{2\pi}{2} = \pi$$

Step 2 Divide the period into fourths and identify the critical values.

$$\pi \div 4 = \tfrac{\pi}{4}$$

The critical values on the θ-axis are $0, \tfrac{\pi}{4}, \tfrac{\pi}{2}, \tfrac{3\pi}{4}$, and π.

Step 3 Sketch the graph.
Use $\tfrac{1}{2}$ for the maximum and $-\tfrac{1}{2}$ for the minimum.

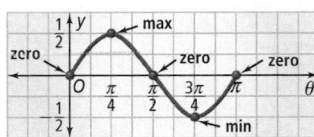

B What is the graph of one cycle of $y = 3 \cos 4\theta$?

$$\text{amplitude} = |a| = |3| = 3$$

$$\text{period} = \tfrac{2\pi}{b} = \tfrac{2\pi}{4} = \tfrac{\pi}{2}$$

Divide the period into fourths.

$\tfrac{\pi}{2} \div 4 = \tfrac{\pi}{8}$, so the critical values are $0, \tfrac{\pi}{8}, \tfrac{\pi}{4}, \tfrac{3\pi}{8}, \tfrac{\pi}{2}$.

Use the critical values to plot the five-point pattern. Use 3 for the maximum and -3 for the minimum.

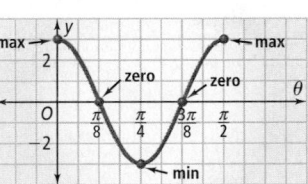

 Got It? **3.** What is the graph of one cycle of each function?
a. $y = 3 \sin \tfrac{\pi}{2}\theta$ **b.** $y = 2 \cos \tfrac{\theta}{3}$

Q In 3A, what is meant by *critical values* on the θ-axis? [**where the function has a max, min, or zero value for *y***]

Q What are the units of the θ-axis and the y-axis for the graph in 3a? [**The θ-axis has units of radians. The *y*-axis has an unspecified unit of length.**]

Got It?

Q What is the period of the cosine function in 3a? [**6π**]

Q What are the critical values on the θ axis in 3a? [**$\tfrac{3\pi}{2}, 3\pi, \tfrac{9\pi}{2}, 6\pi$**]

3. a.

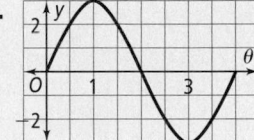

b.

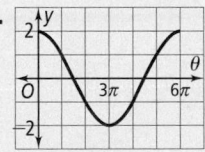

Q What is tan θ in terms of cos θ and sin θ?
[tan $\theta = \frac{\sin \theta}{\cos \theta}$]

Focus Question How is the graph of the tangent function related to the graphs of sine and cosine functions?

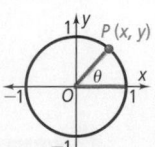

Key Concept Tangent of an Angle

Suppose the terminal side of an angle θ in standard position intersects the unit circle at the point (x, y). Then the ratio $\frac{y}{x}$ is the tangent of θ.

In this diagram, $x = \cos \theta$, $y = \sin \theta$, and $\frac{y}{x} = \tan \theta$.

Hint

There is another way to geometrically define tan θ.

The diagram shows the unit circle and the vertical line $x = 1$. The angle θ in standard position determines a point $P(x, y)$.

By similar triangles, the length of the vertical red segment divided by the length of the horizontal red segment is equal to $\frac{y}{x}$. The horizontal red segment has length 1 since it is a radius of the unit circle, so the length of the vertical red segment is $\frac{y}{x}$ or tan θ, which is also the y-coordinate of Q.

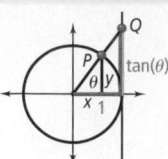

Hint

For any angle θ in standard position (except for θ = odd multiples of $\frac{\pi}{2}$), the line containing the terminal side of angle θ will intersect the line $x = 1$ at a point Q with y-coordinate tan θ.

The graph at the right shows one cycle of the **tangent function**, $y = \tan \theta$, for $-\frac{\pi}{2} < \theta < \frac{\pi}{2}$. The pattern repeats periodically with period π. At $\theta = \pm\frac{\pi}{2}$, the line through P fails to intersect the line $x = 1$, so tan θ is undefined.

$y = \tan \theta$

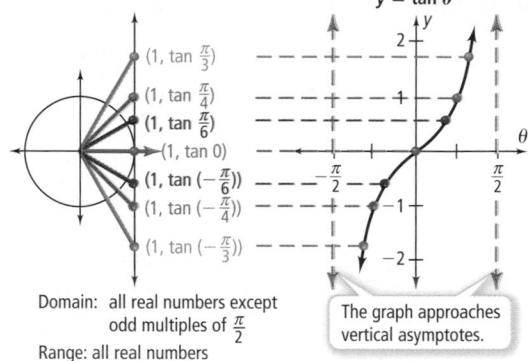

(1, tan $\frac{\pi}{3}$)
(1, tan $\frac{\pi}{4}$)
(1, tan $\frac{\pi}{6}$)
(1, tan 0)
(1, tan $(-\frac{\pi}{6})$)
(1, tan $(-\frac{\pi}{4})$)
(1, tan $(-\frac{\pi}{3})$)

Domain: all real numbers except odd multiples of $\frac{\pi}{2}$

Range: all real numbers

The graph approaches vertical asymptotes.

Take Note

Q If $y = a \tan b\theta$, how many cycles of tan θ should fit between $-\frac{\pi}{2}$ and $\frac{\pi}{2}$? [*b* cycles]

Q What effect does the value of *a* have on the graph of $y = a \tan b\theta$? [**The value of *a* will vertically stretch ($|a| > 1$) or shrink ($0 < |a| < 1$) or reflect ($a < 0$) the graph of tan θ.**]

Concept Summary Properties of Tangent Functions

Suppose $y = a \tan b\theta$, with $a \neq 0$, $b > 0$, and θ in radians.

- $\frac{\pi}{b}$ is the period of the function.
- One cycle occurs in the interval from $-\frac{\pi}{2b}$ to $\frac{\pi}{2b}$.
- There are vertical asymptotes at each end of the cycle.

Just as you did with sine and cosine, you can use five values equally spaced through one cycle to sketch a tangent curve. Two of the values are the vertical asymptotes. For $a > 0$ and $b > 0$, graph $y = a \tan b\theta$ by using the pattern asymptote-$(-a)$-zero-(a)-asymptote, as shown.

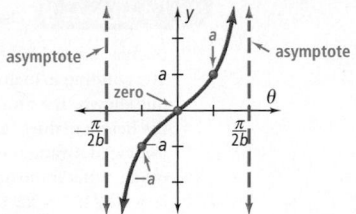

You can use the period, asymptotes, and points to graph a tangent function.

Problem 4 — Graphing a Tangent Function

Sketch two cycles of the graph of $y = \tan \pi\theta$.

Think	Write
Use the formula for the period. Substitute π for b and simplify.	$\text{period} = \frac{\pi}{b} = \frac{\pi}{\pi} = 1$
One cycle occurs in the interval from $-\frac{\pi}{2b}$ to $\frac{\pi}{2b}$.	$\frac{-\pi}{2b} = \frac{-\pi}{2\pi} = -\frac{1}{2}$ $\frac{\pi}{2b} = \frac{\pi}{2\pi} = \frac{1}{2}$ One cycle is from $-\frac{1}{2}$ to $\frac{1}{2}$.
Divide the period into fourths and identify the key θ-values for the first cycle.	$1 \div 4 = \frac{1}{4}$
Pair each θ-value with the corresponding y-feature.	$\begin{array}{ccccc} -\frac{1}{2} & -\frac{1}{4} & 0 & \frac{1}{4} & \frac{1}{2} \\ \downarrow & \downarrow & \downarrow & \downarrow & \downarrow \\ \text{asymptote} & -a & \text{zero} & a & \text{asymptote} \end{array}$
Asymptotes occur at each end of the cycle.	Asymptotes are at $\theta = -\frac{1}{2}$ and $\frac{1}{2}$.
Locate the 3 points between the asymptotes. Use 1 for a.	$\left(-\frac{1}{4}, -1\right), (0, 0), \left(\frac{1}{4}, 1\right)$
Draw the asymptotes, plot the points, and sketch the curve. Add another cycle on the right, with $\frac{3}{2}$ as an asymptote.	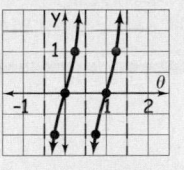

Got It? 4. Sketch the graph of each tangent curve.

  a. $y = \tan 3\theta, \ 0 < \theta \leq \pi$ **b.** $y = \tan \frac{\pi}{2}\theta, \ 0 \leq \theta < 3$

Problem 4

Q Why divide the period into fourths? [**The y-value of the function is one unit at x-values that are one-fourth of the period from the asymptotes, and the y-value in the center of the cycle is zero.**]

Q If you graphed the cycle to the left of the cycle that passes through the origin, where would the zero occur? [$x = -1$]

Got It?

Q What is the period of each tangent curve? [**4a has a period of $\frac{\pi}{3}$; 4b has a period of 2.**]

Q Suppose you graph the tangent function so that it passes through the origin. Where do the asymptotes occur for each tangent curve? [**4a has asymptotes at $x = -\frac{\pi}{6}$ and $x = \frac{\pi}{6}$. 4b has asymptotes at $x = -1$ and $x = 1$.**]

Q Now suppose you graphed the next cycle of the tangent function (the cycle to the right of the one that passes through the origin). Where would the second zero be for each curve? [**for 4a, at $x = \frac{\pi}{3}$; for 4b at $x = 2$**]

Answers

Got It? (continued)

4. a.

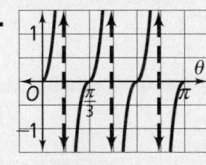

b.

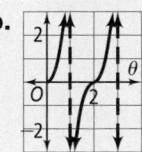

Problem 5

Q What is the domain of *x* for the front façade? Explain. [**0° < *x* < 90°; if the angle is 0° or greater than 90°, no triangle will form.**]

Q Why does $y = 100 \tan \theta$ model the height of the triangle? [**$\tan \theta = \frac{height}{100}$, so $h = 100 \cdot \tan \theta$.**]

Got It?

Q Which value in the table must be equal to 25 to find the height? [**the *x*-value**]

Lesson Check

Do you know HOW?   ERROR INTERVENTION
- If students have difficulty solving Exercises 1–2, encourage them to visualize the shape of the graph before graphing. Graph the parent function at the same time so students can see the effect of a change in amplitude and period.

Do you UNDERSTAND?
- If students have difficulty with Exercise 3, encourage them to draw the asymptotes on a graph and visualize the tangent function that would fit within those asymptotes.

Close

Q How does knowing properties of $y = \sin \theta$ help you understand the properties of $y = \cos \theta$? [**The cosine function is a translation of the sine function, so the domain, range, amplitude, and period are the same.**]

Q How is the tangent of an angle θ related to the sine and cosine of the angle θ? [**$\tan \theta = \frac{\sin \theta}{\cos \theta}$**]

Q What do you need to sketch a graph of a tangent curve? [**the period and asymptotes**]

Problem 5 Using the Tangent Function to Solve Problems

Design An architect is designing the front facade of a building to include a triangle, similar to the one shown. The function $y = 100 \tan \theta$ models the height of the triangle, where θ is the angle indicated. Graph the function using the degree mode. What is the height of the triangle if $\theta = 16°$? If $\theta = 22°$?

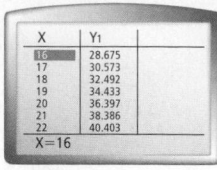

Think
How should you graph the function? "Degree mode" suggests that you use a graphing calculator. Then use TABLE to show *y* values for different θ values.

Step 1   Graph the function $y = 100 \tan \theta$.

Xmin = 0
Xmax = 470
Xscl = 50
Ymin = −300
Ymax = 300
Yscl = 90

Step 2   Use the **TABLE** feature.

X	Y₁
16	28.675
17	30.573
18	32.492
19	34.433
20	36.397
21	38.386
22	40.403

X=16

When $\theta = 16°$, the height of the triangle is about 28.7 ft. When $\theta = 22°$, the height of the triangle is about 40.4 ft.

 Got It? 5. What is the height of the triangle when $\theta = 25°$?

Focus Question   What are the graphs of sine and cosine functions?

Answer   The graphs of sine and cosine functions are periodic curves of the form $y = a \sin b\theta$ or $y = a \cos b\theta$. The value of *a* determines amplitude and reflection of the graph. The value of *b* determines the period.

Focus Question   How is the graph of the tangent function related to the graphs of sine and cosine functions?

Answer   The graph of the tangent function is related to the graphs of sine and cosine functions because, in the unit circle, $x = \cos \theta$, $y = \sin \theta$, and $\tan \theta = \frac{y}{x}$. The graph of the tangent curve is not a simple curve like sine or cosine. It has a vertical asymptote every period, the standard period is π instead of 2π, and it has no amplitude.

Lesson Check

Do you know HOW?

Sketch one cycle of the graph of each function.

1. $y = 2 \sin 6\theta$ **2.** $y = 2 \cos \frac{\pi}{3}\theta$

Do you UNDERSTAND?

3. Vocabulary Successive asymptotes of a tangent curve are $x = \frac{\pi}{3}$ and $x = -\frac{\pi}{3}$. What is the period?

4. Open-Ended Write a cosine function that has a period greater than the period for $y = 5 \cos \frac{\theta}{2}$.

Answers

Got It? (continued)
5. ≈ 46.6 ft

Lesson Check
1.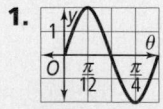

2.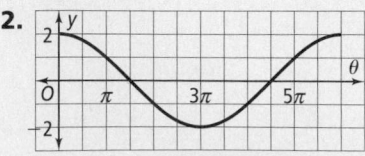

3. $\frac{2\pi}{3}$

4. Answers may vary. Sample: $y = 5 \cos \frac{\theta}{3}$

Practice and Problem-Solving Exercises

A Practice Find the period of each sine curve.

◆ See Problem 1.

5.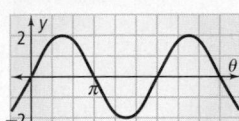

6.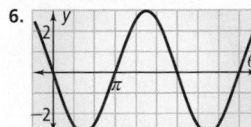

Find the period of each cosine curve.

7. 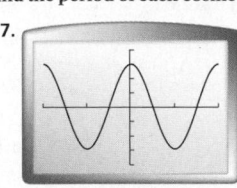
Xmin = -2π
Xmax = 2π
Xscl = π
Ymin = -4
Ymax = 4
Yscl = 1

8. 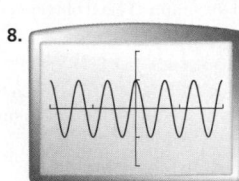
Xmin = -2π
Xmax = 2π
Xscl = π
Ymin = -2
Ymax = 2
Yscl = 1

Find the amplitude and value of a for each sine function.

◆ See Problem 2.

9.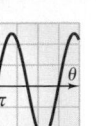

10.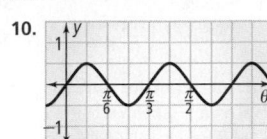

Find the amplitude and value of a for each cosine function.

11. 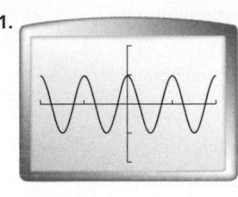
Xmin = -2π
Xmax = 2π
Xscl = π
Ymin = -2
Ymax = 2
Yscl = 1

12. 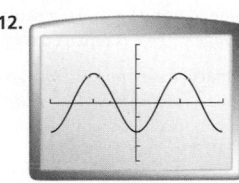
Xmin = -2π
Xmax = 2π
Xscl = π
Ymin = -4
Ymax = 4
Yscl = 1

Sketch one cycle of the graph of each function.

◆ See Problem 3.

13. $y = \sin \pi\theta$ **14.** $y = \sin 3\theta$ **15.** $y = \cos 2\theta$

16. $y = -3 \cos \theta$ **17.** $y = -\sin \frac{\pi}{2}\theta$ **18.** $y = -\cos \pi\theta$

19. $y = 2 \sin \pi\theta$ **20.** $y = \cos \frac{\pi}{2}\theta$ **21.** $y = 4 \sin \frac{1}{2}\theta$

Practice and Problem-Solving Exercises

5. 2π

6. 2π

7. 2π

8. $\frac{2\pi}{3}$

9. $\frac{5}{2}; \frac{5}{2}$

10. $\frac{1}{2}; \frac{1}{2}$

11. $1; 1$

12. $2; -2$

13.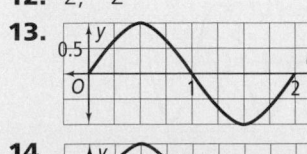

14.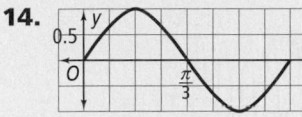

15.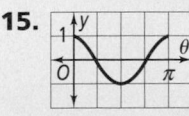

16.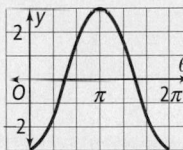

17.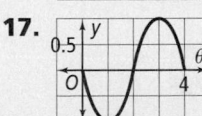

18.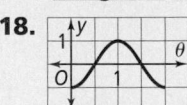

19.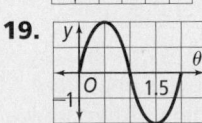

20.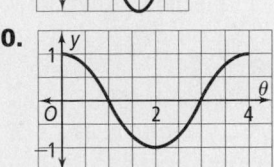

21.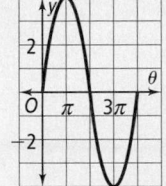

Practice

ASSIGNMENT GUIDE

Basic: 5–25, 27, 39

Average: 5–39 odd, 40–46 even

Standardized Test Prep: 50–54

Mixed Review: 55–65

Reasoning exercises have blue headings.

Applications exercises have red headings.

HOMEWORK QUICK CHECK

To check students' understanding of key skills and concepts, go over Exercises 5, 11, 22, 27, and 39.

Answers

Practice and Problem-Solving
Exercises (continued)

22. $\frac{2\pi}{3}$

23. $\frac{\pi}{2}$

24.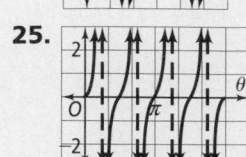

25.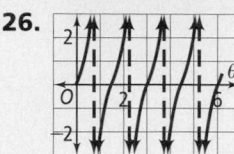

26.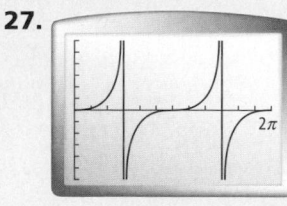

27.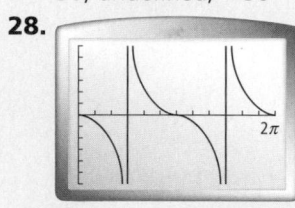

50, undefined, −50

28.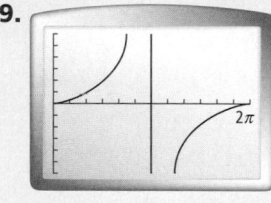

−100, undefined, 100

29.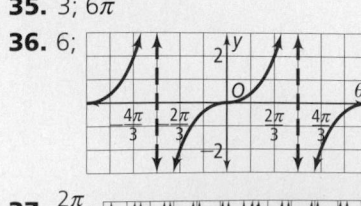

≈51.8, 125, ≈301.8

30. 1; 2

31. 5; 2π

32. 3; 2π

33. 1; π

34. 2; 4π

35. 3; 6π

36. 6;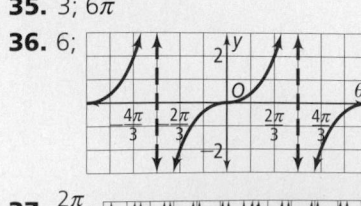

37. $\frac{2\pi}{5}$;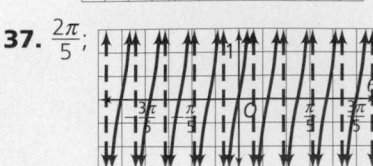

Each graphing calculator screen shows the interval 0 to 2π. What is the period of each graph?

22.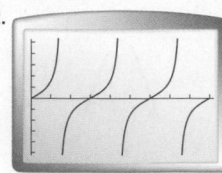

23.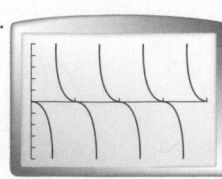

Sketch the graph of each tangent curve in the interval from 0 to 2π. ◀ See Problem 4.

24. $y = \tan \theta$　　　**25.** $y = \tan 2\theta$　　　**26.** $y = \tan \frac{2\pi}{3}\theta$

 Graphing Calculator Graph each function on the interval $0 \le x \le 2\pi$ with $-200 \le y \le 200$. Evaluate each function at $x = \frac{\pi}{4}, \frac{\pi}{2}$, and $\frac{3\pi}{4}$. ◀ See Problem 5.

27. $y = 50 \tan x$　　　**28.** $y = -100 \tan x$　　　**29.** $y = 125 \tan \left(\frac{1}{2}x\right)$

B Apply　Find the amplitude and period of each function.

30. $y = \sin \pi\theta$　　　**31.** $y = -5 \sin \theta$　　　**32.** $y = 3 \sin \theta$

33. $y = -\cos 2t$　　　**34.** $y = 2 \cos \frac{1}{2}t$　　　**35.** $y = 3 \cos \left(-\frac{\theta}{3}\right)$

Identify the period for each tangent function. Then graph each function in the interval from -2π to 2π.

36. $y = \tan \frac{\pi}{6}\theta$　　　**37.** $y = \tan 2.5\theta$　　　**38.** $y = \tan \left(-\frac{3}{2\pi}\theta\right)$

39. Graphing Calculator Graph the functions $y = 3 \sin \theta$ and $y = -3 \sin \theta$ on the same screen. How are the two graphs related? How does the graph of $y = a \sin b\theta$ change when a is replaced with its opposite?

40. Climate In Buenos Aires, Argentina, the average monthly temperature is highest in January and lowest in July, ranging from 83°F to 57°F. Write a cosine function that models the temperature according to the month of the year.

41. a. Open-Ended Write a tangent function.
　　b. Graph the function on the interval -2π to 2π.
　　c. Identify the period and the asymptotes of the function.

42. Sound Waves The sound wave for the note A above middle C can be modeled by the function $y = 0.001 \sin 880\pi\theta$. Sketch a graph of the sine curve.

Find the period and amplitude of each sine function. Then sketch each function from 0 to 2π.

43. $y = -3.5 \sin 5\theta$　　　**44.** $y = \frac{5}{2} \sin 2\theta$　　　**45.** $y = -2 \sin 2\pi\theta$

---

38. $\frac{2\pi^2}{3}$;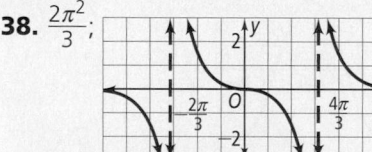

39.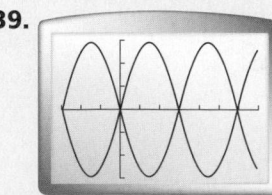

They are reflections of each other across the x-axis.

When a is replaced by its opposite, the graph is a reflection of the original graph across the x-axis.

40. $y = 70 + 13 \cos \frac{\pi}{6}(x - 1)$ where x represents the months of the year with January as 1, February as 2, March as 3, etc.

41. a–c. Check students' work.

42.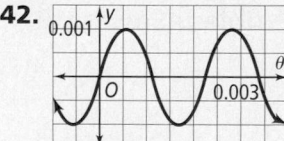

43. $\frac{2\pi}{5}$, 3.5;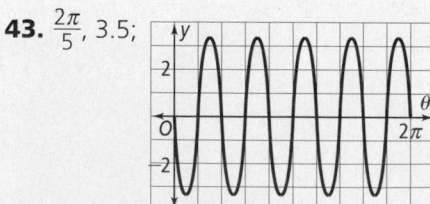

44. π, $\frac{5}{2}$;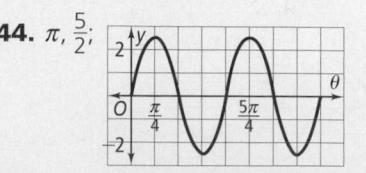

45. 1, 2;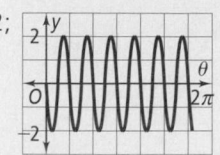

Write an equation of a tangent function for each graph.

46.
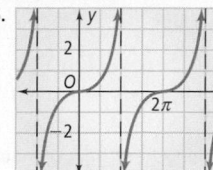

47.
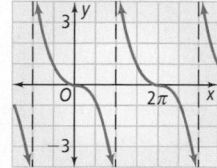

48. Open-Ended Write the equations of three sine functions with the same amplitude that have periods of 2, 3, and 4. Then sketch all three graphs.

49. Music The sound wave for a certain pitch fork can be modeled by the function $y = 0.001 \sin 1320\pi\theta$. Sketch a graph of the sine curve.

Standardized Test Prep

SAT/ACT

50. What is the amplitude of $y = 3 \sin 4\theta$?

Ⓐ $\frac{4}{3}$ Ⓑ 3   Ⓒ 4   Ⓓ 2π

51. Which equation has the same graph as $y = -\cos t$?

Ⓕ $y = \cos(-t)$ Ⓗ $y = \cos(t - \pi)$
Ⓖ $y = \sin(t - \pi)$ Ⓘ $y = -\sin t$

52. Which value is NOT defined?

Ⓐ $\tan 0$ Ⓑ $\tan \pi$ Ⓒ $\tan \frac{3\pi}{2}$ Ⓓ $\frac{1}{\tan \frac{\pi}{4}}$

53. Which function has a period of 4π and an amplitude of 8?

Ⓕ $y = -8 \sin 8\theta$ Ⓖ $y = -8 \sin \frac{1}{2}\theta$ Ⓗ $y = 8 \sin 2\theta$ Ⓘ $y = 4 \sin 8\theta$

Short Response

54. Does a tangent function have amplitude? Explain.

Mixed Review

Write each measure in radians. Express the answer in terms of π and as a decimal rounded to the nearest hundredth.

◆ See Lesson T-4.

55. $-80°$ **56.** $150°$ **57.** $-240°$ **58.** $320°$

Find the 27th term of each sequence.

◆ See Lesson 9-2.

59. $5, 8, 11, \ldots$ **60.** $59, 48, 37, \ldots$ **61.** $-11, -5, 1, \ldots$ **62.** $6, -7, -20, \ldots$

Get Ready! To prepare for Lesson T-6, do Exercises 63–65.

Determine whether each equation is true for all real numbers x. Explain your reasoning.

◆ See Lesson 1-4.

63. $2x + 3x - 5x$ **64.** $-(4x - 10) = 10 - 4x$ **65.** $3x + 15 = 5(x - 3) - 2x$

46. $y = \tan \frac{x}{2}$

47. $y = -\tan \frac{x}{2}$

48. Check students' work.

49.
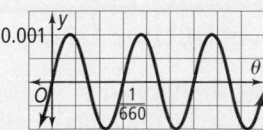

Standardized Test Prep

50. B

51. H

52. C

53. G

54. No; the tangent function has no maximum or minimum value.

Mixed Review

55. $-\frac{4\pi}{9}$, -1.40

56. $\frac{5}{6}\pi$, 2.62

57. $-\frac{4\pi}{3}$, -4.19

58. $\frac{16\pi}{9}$, 5.59

59. 83

60. -227

61. 145

62. -332

63. true; Dist. Prop.

64. true; Distr. Prop. and Comm. Prop. of Add.

65. not true; the equation simplifies to $15 = -15$, which is never true.

Lesson Quiz

1. How many cycles appear in the graph? What is the period of the cycle?

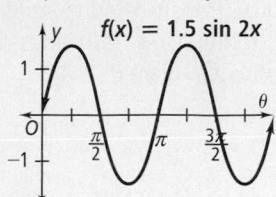

2. What is the amplitude of the cosine curve? What is the value of a?

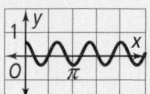

3. What is the graph of one cycle of a sine curve with amplitude 5, period π, and $a > 0$? What is an equation for the sine curve in the form $y = a \sin b\theta$?

4. Sketch two cycles of the graph of $y = \tan \frac{1}{2}\theta$.

5. Do you UNDERSTAND? A local building code requires that the angle of the pitch on a roof be between 20° and 25°. You are building a 20 ft wide shed, and the height of the roof at its center will be defined by the tangent curve $y = 10 \tan \theta$. If you wanted to put a roof that was 5 ft high measured from the top of the wall, would the roof pass the building code? What is the range of heights for the roof that will fall within the building code?

ANSWERS TO LESSON QUIZ

1. $2; \pi$

2. $\frac{1}{2}; \frac{1}{2}$

3.
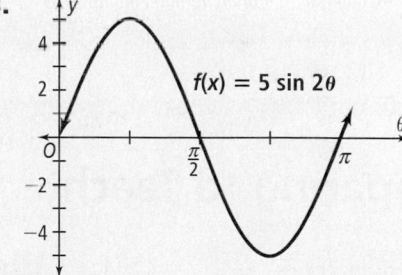

$y = 5 \sin 2\theta$

4.
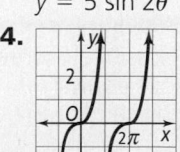

5. no; between about 3.6 and 4.6 ft

Guided Instruction

Take Note

The basic identities can be transformed to related identities. For example, multiplying both sides of $\csc \theta = \frac{1}{\sin \theta}$ by $\sin \theta$ yields $\csc \theta \sin \theta = 1$.

Problem 1

> **Q** Why is $\csc \theta$ replaced with $\frac{1}{\sin \theta}$? **[Since $\tan \theta$ includes $\sin \theta$ in the numerator, the expression can be simplified.]**
>
> **Q** What is a simplified trigonometric expression for $\frac{1 + \cot^2\theta}{\cot^2\theta}$? **[$\sec^2 \theta$]**

Got It?

ERROR PREVENTION

Simplifying an expression means each subsequent expression is equivalent to the previous one. Have students use their graphing calculator and graph each expression as a function. Each expression should result in the same graph.

T-6 Basic Identities

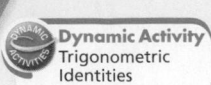
Dynamic Activity
Trigonometric Identities

Lesson Vocabulary
• trigonometric identity

Objective To verify trigonometric identities

Focus Question Why are the interrelationships among the six basic trigonometric functions useful?

A **trigonometric identity** in one variable is a trigonometric equation that is true for all values of the variable for which all expressions in the equation are defined. Some trigonometric identities are definitions or follow immediately from definitions.

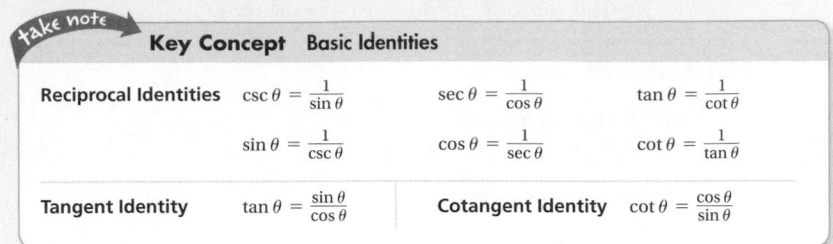

Key Concept   Basic Identities

Reciprocal Identities	$\csc \theta = \frac{1}{\sin \theta}$	$\sec \theta = \frac{1}{\cos \theta}$	$\tan \theta = \frac{1}{\cot \theta}$
	$\sin \theta = \frac{1}{\csc \theta}$	$\cos \theta = \frac{1}{\sec \theta}$	$\cot \theta = \frac{1}{\tan \theta}$
Tangent Identity	$\tan \theta = \frac{\sin \theta}{\cos \theta}$	**Cotangent Identity**	$\cot \theta = \frac{\cos \theta}{\sin \theta}$

You can use trigonometric identities to simplify trigonometric expressions.

Problem 1 Simplifying an Expression

What is a simplified trigonometric expression for $\csc \theta \tan \theta$?

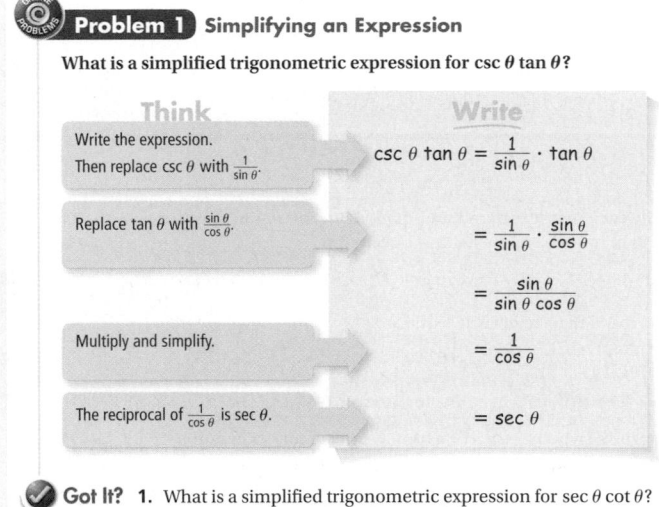

Think	Write
Write the expression. Then replace $\csc \theta$ with $\frac{1}{\sin \theta}$.	$\csc \theta \tan \theta = \frac{1}{\sin \theta} \cdot \tan \theta$
Replace $\tan \theta$ with $\frac{\sin \theta}{\cos \theta}$.	$= \frac{1}{\sin \theta} \cdot \frac{\sin \theta}{\cos \theta}$
	$= \frac{\sin \theta}{\sin \theta \cos \theta}$
Multiply and simplify.	$= \frac{1}{\cos \theta}$
The reciprocal of $\frac{1}{\cos \theta}$ is $\sec \theta$.	$= \sec \theta$

Got It? 1. What is a simplified trigonometric expression for $\sec \theta \cot \theta$?

T-6 Preparing to Teach

BIG idea Equivalence   **UbD**

ESSENTIAL UNDERSTANDINGS

• The interrelationships among the six basic trigonometric functions make it possible to write trigonometric expressions in various equivalent forms, some of which can be significantly easier to work with than others in mathematical applications.
• Known identities can be used to verify other identities.
• Trigonometric identities can be used to simplify trigonometric expressions.

Math Background

A trigonometric identity is formed by two equivalent expressions set equal to each other.

• The **Basic Identities** include the reciprocal, tangent, and cotangent identities. They follow from the definitions of the trigonometric functions.
• The **Pythagorean Identities** are derived from the Pythagorean Theorem and the unit circle.

These identities can be used to derive other trigonometric identities. Different equivalent identities make it easier to simplify when working with trigonometric equations.

It is important that students learn the Basic Identities and at least one Pythagorean Identity and use them to derive other identities as needed (rather than try to memorize a number of identities).

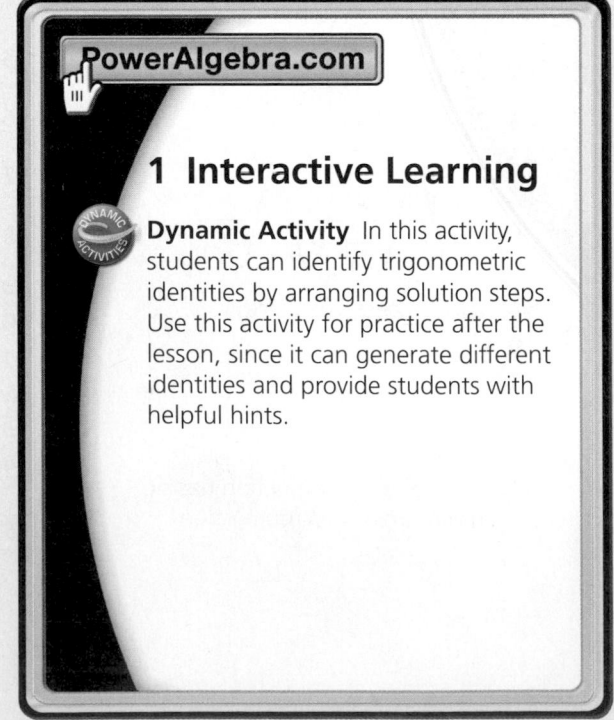

PowerAlgebra.com

1 Interactive Learning

Dynamic Activity In this activity, students can identify trigonometric identities by arranging solution steps. Use this activity for practice after the lesson, since it can generate different identities and provide students with helpful hints.

You can use known identities to verify other identities. Use previously known identities to transform one side of the equation to look like the other side.

Problem 2 Verifying an Identity Using Basic Identities

Verify each identity.

A $(\sin \theta)(\sec \theta) = \tan \theta$

To verify this identity, begin with the more complicated side of the equation. Transform the left side of the equation to look like the expression on the right side of the equation.

Use a reciprocal identity. $\quad (\sin \theta)(\sec \theta) = \sin \theta \cdot \dfrac{1}{\cos \theta}$

Simplify. $\qquad\qquad\qquad\qquad\qquad = \dfrac{\sin \theta}{\cos \theta}$

Use the tangent identity. $\qquad\qquad\quad = \tan \theta$

B $\dfrac{1}{\cot \theta} = \tan \theta$

Begin with the expression on left side of the equation. Transform it to look like the expression on the right side of the equation.

Use the definition of cotangent. $\quad \dfrac{1}{\cot \theta} = \dfrac{1}{\frac{1}{\tan \theta}}$

Simplify. $\qquad\qquad\qquad\qquad\quad = \tan \theta$

✔ **Got It?** **2.** Verify the identity $\dfrac{\csc \theta}{\sec \theta} = \cot \theta$.

Think

What identity do you know that you can use?
Look for a way to write the expression on the left in terms of $\sin \theta$ and $\cos \theta$. Use the identity $\sec \theta = \frac{1}{\cos \theta}$.

Hint

When verifying an identity, begin with the more complicated side.

Every angle θ determines a point $(x, y) = (\cos \theta, \sin \theta)$ on the unit circle. Also, every point (x, y) on the unit circle satisfies the equation $x^2 + y^2 = 1$. Therefore, for every angle θ, there are three identities related to the Pythagorean Theorem.

Hint

The expression $\cos^2 \theta$ is equivalent to $(\cos \theta)^2$. This simplified notation allows you to write the expression without using parentheses.

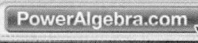

Key Concept Pythagorean Identities

$\cos^2 \theta + \sin^2 \theta = 1 \qquad\qquad 1 + \tan^2 \theta = \sec^2 \theta \qquad\qquad 1 + \cot^2 \theta = \csc^2 \theta$

You can use the basic and Pythagorean identities to verify other identities. The method of proof is always the same: transform the expression on one side of the equation to become the expression on the other side.

Problem 2
Point out to students that they are verifying that one side of the equation is equal to the other side.

Q In 2A why was the identity $\sin \theta = \frac{1}{\csc \theta}$ not used? **[Using that identity would create a fraction that could not be easily simplified.]**

Got It?   EXTENSION
Discuss with students where the fraction will be undefined. Remind them this is where the denominator of $\sec \theta = 0$. Suggest that students make a chart to help find when the trigonometric functions equal 0 or are undefined in the interval from 0 to 2π. For example,

	0	Undefined
sine	$0, \pi$	never
cosine	$\dfrac{\pi}{2}, \dfrac{3\pi}{2}$	never
tangent	$0, \pi$	$\dfrac{\pi}{2}, \dfrac{3\pi}{2}$

Take Note
Show students how to get from the first Pythagorean Identity to the second by dividing $\cos^2 \theta + \sin^2 \theta = 1$ by $\cos^2 \theta$:

$$\frac{\cos^2 \theta}{\cos^2 \theta} + \frac{\sin^2 \theta}{\cos^2 \theta} = \frac{1}{\cos^2 \theta}$$
$$1 + \tan^2 \theta = \sec^2 \theta$$

Have students find the third Pythagorean Identity by dividing the same equation by $\sin^2 \theta$.

Additional Problems

1. What is a simplified trigonometric expression for $\dfrac{1 + \cot^2 \theta}{\cot^2 \theta}$?

ANSWER $\sec^2 \theta$

2. Verify the identity.

  a. $(\sin \theta)(\cot \theta) = \cos \theta$

  b. $(\sec \theta)(\cot \theta) = \csc \theta$

ANSWERS

  a. $(\sin \theta)(\cot \theta)$

  $= (\sin \theta)\left(\dfrac{\cos \theta}{\sin \theta}\right)$

  $= \cancel{\sin \theta} \cdot \dfrac{\cos \theta}{\cancel{\sin \theta}}$

  $= \cos \theta$

  b. $(\sec \theta)(\cot \theta)$

  $= \left(\dfrac{1}{\cos \theta}\right)\left(\dfrac{\cos \theta}{\sin \theta}\right)$

  $= \left(\dfrac{1}{\cancel{\cos \theta}}\right)\left(\dfrac{\cancel{\cos \theta}}{\sin \theta}\right)$

  $= \dfrac{1}{\sin \theta}$

  $= \csc \theta$

3. Verify the identity $\dfrac{1 - \cos^2 \theta}{\sin \theta} = \sin \theta$.

ANSWER

  $\dfrac{1 - \cos^2 \theta}{\sin \theta} = \dfrac{\sin^2 \theta}{\sin \theta}$

  $\qquad\qquad = \sin \theta$

4. Verify the identity $(\sin^2 \theta)(\sec \theta) + \cos \theta = \sec \theta$.

ANSWER

  $(\sin^2 \theta)(\sec \theta) + \cos \theta$

  $= (\sin^2 \theta)\left(\dfrac{1}{\cos \theta}\right) + \cos \theta$

  $= \dfrac{\sin^2 \theta}{\cos \theta} + \cos \theta$

  $= \dfrac{\sin^2 \theta}{\cos \theta} + \dfrac{\cos^2 \theta}{\cos \theta}$

  $= \dfrac{\sin^2 \theta + \cos^2 \theta}{\cos \theta}$

  $= \dfrac{1}{\cos \theta}$

  $= \sec \theta$

Answers

Got It?

1. $\csc \theta$

2. $\dfrac{\csc \theta}{\sec \theta} = \dfrac{\left(\frac{1}{\sin \theta}\right)}{\left(\frac{1}{\cos \theta}\right)} = \dfrac{\cos \theta}{\sin \theta} = \cot \theta$

Problem 3

Remind students that it is often helpful to rewrite everything in terms of sine and cosine. Have them rewrite the problem using common denominators to help determine how the identity can be verified.

> **Q** What are $\tan \theta$ and $\sec \theta$ in terms of sine and cosine? [$\tan \theta = \frac{\sin \theta}{\cos \theta}$ and $\sec \theta = \frac{1}{\cos \theta}$]
>
> **Q** How can the identity be rewritten using only sine and cosine? [$1 + \frac{\sin^2 \theta}{\cos^2 \theta} = \frac{1}{\cos^2 \theta}$.]

Got It?

> **Q** How can the identity be rewritten using only sine and cosine? [$1 + \frac{\cos^2 \theta}{\sin^2 \theta} = \frac{1}{\sin^2 \theta}$]

Take Note

Show students how to get from the first Pythagorean Identity to the second by dividing $\cos^2 \theta + \sin^2 \theta = 1$ by $\cos^2 \theta$:

$$\frac{\cos^2 \theta}{\cos^2 \theta} + \frac{\sin^2 \theta}{\cos^2 \theta} = \frac{1}{\cos^2 \theta}$$

$$1 + \tan^2 \theta = \sec^2 \theta$$

Have students find the third Pythagorean Identity by dividing the same equation by $\sin^2 \theta$.

EXTENSION

Terms can be moved from one side to another to put identities in a form that is useful. For example,

$$\cos^2 \theta = 1 - \sin^2 \theta$$

$$\sin^2 \theta = 1 - \cos^2 \theta$$

Plan

With which side should you work?
It usually is easier to begin with the more complicated-looking side.

Hint

It often helps to write everything in terms of sines and cosines.

 Problem 3 Verifying a Pythagorean Identity

Verify the Pythagorean identity $1 + \tan^2 \theta = \sec^2 \theta$.

Begin with the expression on left side of the equation. Transform it to look like the expression on the right side.

Use the tangent identity.	$1 + \tan^2 \theta = 1 + \left(\frac{\sin \theta}{\cos \theta}\right)^2$
Simplify.	$= 1 + \frac{\sin^2 \theta}{\cos^2 \theta}$
Find a common denominator.	$= \frac{\cos^2 \theta}{\cos^2 \theta} + \frac{\sin^2 \theta}{\cos^2 \theta}$
Add.	$= \frac{\cos^2 \theta + \sin^2 \theta}{\cos^2 \theta}$
Use a Pythagorean identity.	$= \frac{1}{\cos^2 \theta}$
Use a reciprocal identity.	$= \sec^2 \theta$

You have transformed the expression on the left side of the equation to become the expression on the right side. The equation is an identity.

 Got It? 3. Verify the third Pythagorean identity, $1 + \cot^2 \theta = \csc^2 \theta$.

Focus Question Why are the interrelationships among the six basic trigonometric functions useful?

Answer The basic identities make it possible to write trigonometric expressions in various equivalent forms, some of which can be significantly easier to work with than others in mathematical applications.

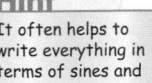 **Lesson Check**

Do you know HOW?

Verify each identity.

1. $\tan \theta \csc \theta = \sec \theta$

2. $\csc^2 \theta - \cot^2 \theta = 1$

3. $\sin \theta \tan \theta = \sec \theta - \cos \theta$

4. Simplify $\tan \theta \cot \theta - \sin^2 \theta$.

Do you UNDERSTAND?

5. **Vocabulary** How does the identity $\cos^2 \theta + \sin^2 \theta = 1$ relate to the Pythagorean Theorem?

6. **Error Analysis** A student simplified the expression $2 - \cos^2 \theta$ to $1 - \sin^2 \theta$. What error did the student make? What is the correct simplified expression?

Answers

Got It? (continued)

3. $1 + \cot^2 \theta = 1 + \left(\frac{\cos \theta}{\sin \theta}\right)^2$

$= 1 + \frac{\cos^2 \theta}{\sin^2 \theta}$

$= 1 + \frac{1 - \sin^2 \theta}{\sin^2 \theta}$

$= 1 + \frac{1}{\sin^2 \theta} - \frac{\sin^2 \theta}{\sin^2 \theta}$

$= 1 + \csc^2 \theta - 1$

$= \csc^2 \theta$

Lesson Check

1. $\tan \theta \csc \theta$

$= \frac{\sin \theta}{\cos \theta} \cdot \frac{1}{\sin \theta}$

$= \frac{1}{\cos \theta}$

$= \sec \theta$

2. $\csc^2 \theta - \cot^2 \theta$

$= \left(\frac{1}{\sin \theta}\right)^2 - \left(\frac{\cos \theta}{\sin \theta}\right)^2$

$= \frac{1}{\sin^2 \theta} - \frac{\cos^2 \theta}{\sin^2 \theta}$

$= \frac{1 - \cos^2 \theta}{\sin^2 \theta}$

$= \frac{\sin^2 \theta}{\sin^2 \theta}$

$= 1$

3. $\sin \theta \tan \theta$

$= \sin \theta \cdot \frac{\sin \theta}{\cos \theta}$

$= \frac{\sin^2 \theta}{\cos \theta}$

$= \frac{1 - \cos^2 \theta}{\cos \theta}$

$= \frac{1}{\cos \theta} - \frac{\cos^2 \theta}{\cos \theta}$

$= \sec \theta - \cos \theta$

4. $\tan \theta \cot \theta - \sin^2 \theta$

$= \tan \theta \frac{1}{\tan \theta} - \sin^2 \theta$

$= \frac{\tan \theta}{\tan \theta} - \sin^2 \theta$

$= 1 - \sin^2 \theta$

$= \cos^2 \theta$

5. Sample: Letting a and b be the legs, and c the hypotenuse of a right triangle, the Pythagorean Theorem states that $a^2 + b^2 = c^2$. Dividing both sides by c^2, then $\frac{a^2}{c^2} + \frac{b^2}{c^2} = \left(\frac{a}{c}\right)^2 + \left(\frac{b}{c}\right)^2 = 1$. Calling the angle between a and c θ, then $\sin \theta = \frac{b}{c}$ and $\cos \theta = \frac{a}{c}$. By substitution, $\cos^2 \theta + \sin^2 \theta = 1$.

6. wrong calculation:
$2 - \cos^2 \theta = 2 - (1 - \sin^2 \theta) =$
$2 - 1 + \sin^2 \theta = 1 + \sin^2 \theta$

Practice and Problem-Solving Exercises

A Practice

Guided Practice →

Simplify each trigonometric expression.

◆ **See Problem 1.**

To start, write the expression and use the reciprocal identity $\sec \theta = \frac{1}{\cos \theta}$.

7. $\sin \theta \sec \theta \cot \theta$

$\sin \theta \sec \theta \cot \theta = \sin \theta \cdot \frac{1}{\cos \theta} \cdot \cot \theta$

8. $\tan \theta \cot \theta$ **9.** $1 - \cos^2 \theta$ **10.** $\sec^2 \theta - 1$

11. $1 - \csc^2 \theta$ **12.** $\sin \theta \csc \theta$ **13.** $\sec \theta \cos \theta \sin \theta$

Verify each identity.

◆ **See Problems 2 and 3.**

14. $\cos \theta \cot \theta = \frac{1}{\sin \theta} - \sin \theta$ **15.** $\sin \theta \cot \theta = \cos \theta$ **16.** $\cos \theta \tan \theta = \sin \theta$

17. $\sin \theta \sec \theta = \tan \theta$ **18.** $\cos \theta \sec \theta = 1$ **19.** $\csc \theta - \sin \theta = \cot \theta \cos \theta$

20. $\sec^2 \theta \cot^2 \theta = \csc^2 \theta$ **21.** $\cot \theta = \csc \theta \cos \theta$ **22.** $\sin \theta \tan \theta = \sec \theta - \cos \theta$

B Apply

Simplify each trigonometric expression.

23. $\cos \theta + \sin \theta \tan \theta$ **24.** $\csc \theta \cos \theta \tan \theta$

25. $\tan \theta (\cot \theta + \tan \theta)$ **26.** $\sin \theta (1 + \cot^2 \theta)$

27. $\sin^2 \theta \csc \theta \sec \theta$ **28.** $\sec \theta \cos \theta - \cos^2 \theta$

29. $\csc \theta - \cos \theta \cot \theta$ **30.** $\frac{\csc \theta}{\sin \theta + \cos \theta \cot \theta}$

31. $\frac{\cos \theta \csc \theta}{\cot \theta}$ **32.** $\frac{\sin^2 \theta \csc \theta \sec \theta}{\tan \theta}$

> **Hint**
> You can also use Pythagorean Identities to simplify an expression.

Express the first trigonometric function in terms of the second.

33. $\sin \theta$; $\cos \theta$ **34.** $\tan \theta$; $\cos \theta$ **35.** $\cot \theta$; $\sin \theta$

36. $\csc \theta$; $\cot \theta$ **37.** $\cot \theta$; $\csc \theta$ **38.** $\sec \theta$; $\tan \theta$

39. Error Analysis Find the two errors in the verification of the identity $\frac{\sec^2 \theta - \tan^2 \theta}{\tan^2 \theta} = \cot^2 \theta$ shown at the right. Then verify the identity correctly.

40. Open-Ended Develop your own trigonometric identity. (*Hint:* Start with a simple trigonometric expression and work backward.)

41. Writing Only one of the following equations is an identity. Identify the identity and explain your answer.

$$(x - 1)^2 - 1 = x(x - 2) \qquad (x - 1)^2 = x(x - 1)$$

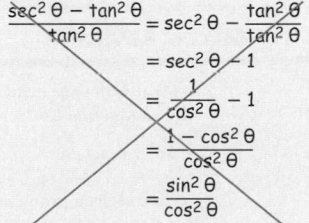

$$\frac{\sec^2 \theta - \tan^2 \theta}{\tan^2 \theta} = \sec^2 \theta - \frac{\tan^2 \theta}{\tan^2 \theta}$$
$$= \sec^2 \theta - 1$$
$$= \frac{1}{\cos^2 \theta} - 1$$
$$= \frac{1 - \cos^2 \theta}{\cos^2 \theta}$$
$$= \frac{\sin^2 \theta}{\cos^2 \theta}$$
$$= \cot^2 \theta$$

Lesson Check

Do you know HOW?   ERROR INTERVENTION

- For Exercises 1–3, encourage students to substitute values for θ after each transformation of an expression. This will help them determine whether their transformation is equivalent to the previous expression.

- If students have difficulty solving Exercise 2, have them review Problem 3. Suggest they start with the more complicated side and rewrite it in terms of sine and cosine. Next, they may choose to use a common denominator to simplify.

Do you UNDERSTAND?

- If students have trouble finding the error in Exercise 6, tell them to rewrite the expression $2 - \cos^2 \theta$ as $1 + 1 - \cos^2 \theta$.

Close

> **Q** How can you simplify $\sin \theta \csc \theta$? Explain.
> **[Rewriting $\csc \theta$ using the reciprocal identity, you have $(\sin \theta)\left(\frac{1}{\sin \theta}\right)$, which is equal to 1, if $\sin \theta \neq 0$.]**

Practice

ASSIGNMENT GUIDE

Basic: 7–22, 39, 40

Average: 7–21 odd, 23–30, 33–47

Standardized Test Prep: 51–56

Mixed Review: 57–64

Reasoning exercises have blue headings.

Applications exercises have red headings.

HOMEWORK QUICK CHECK

To check students' understanding of key skills and concepts, go over Exercises 9, 15, 17, 23, and 40.

Practice and Problem-Solving Exercises

7. 1   **8.** 1   **9.** $\sin^2 \theta$

10. $\tan^2 \theta$ **11.** $-\cot^2 \theta$

12. 1   **13.** $\sin \theta$

14. $\cos \theta \cot \theta$

$$= \cos \theta \left(\frac{\cos \theta}{\sin \theta}\right)$$
$$= \frac{1 - \sin^2 \theta}{\sin \theta}$$
$$= \frac{1}{\sin \theta} - \sin \theta$$

15. $\sin \theta \cot \theta$

$$= \sin \theta \left(\frac{\cos \theta}{\sin \theta}\right) = \cos \theta$$

16. $\cos \theta \tan \theta$

$$= \cos \theta \left(\frac{\sin \theta}{\cos \theta}\right) = \sin \theta$$

17. $\sin \theta \sec \theta$

$$= \sin \theta \left(\frac{1}{\cos \theta}\right) = \frac{\sin \theta}{\cos \theta} = \tan \theta$$

18. $\cos \theta \sec \theta$

$$= \cos \theta \left(\frac{1}{\cos \theta}\right) = 1$$

19. $\csc \theta - \sin \theta$

$$= \frac{1}{\sin \theta} - \sin \theta$$
$$= \frac{1 - \sin^2 \theta}{\sin \theta} = \frac{\cos^2 \theta}{\sin \theta}$$
$$= \frac{\cos \theta}{\sin \theta} \cdot \cos \theta = \cot \theta \cos \theta$$

20. $\sec^2 \theta \cot^2 \theta$

$$= \left(\frac{1}{\cos \theta}\right)^2 \left(\frac{1}{\tan \theta}\right)^2 = \frac{1}{\cos^2 \theta} \cdot \frac{\cos^2 \theta}{\sin^2 \theta}$$
$$= \frac{1}{\sin^2 \theta} = \left(\frac{1}{\sin \theta}\right)^2 = \csc^2 \theta$$

21. $\cot \theta = \frac{\cos \theta}{\sin \theta}$

$$= \left(\frac{1}{\sin \theta}\right)\cos \theta = \csc \theta \cos \theta$$

22. $\sin \theta \tan \theta$

$$= \sin \theta \left(\frac{\sin \theta}{\cos \theta}\right) = \frac{\sin^2 \theta}{\cos \theta}$$
$$= \frac{1 - \cos^2 \theta}{\cos \theta}$$
$$= \frac{1}{\cos \theta} - \frac{\cos^2 \theta}{\cos \theta}$$
$$= \sec \theta - \cos \theta$$

23. $\sec \theta$ **24.** 1   **25.** $\sec^2 \theta$

26. $\csc \theta$ **27.** $\tan \theta$ **28.** $\sin^2 \theta$

29. $\sin \theta$ **30.** 1   **31.** 1   **32.** 1

33. $\pm\sqrt{1 - \cos^2 \theta}$ **34.** $\pm\frac{\sqrt{1 - \cos^2 \theta}}{\cos \theta}$

35. $\pm\frac{\sqrt{1 - \sin^2 \theta}}{\sin \theta}$ **36.** $\pm\sqrt{1 + \cot^2 \theta}$

37. $\pm\sqrt{\csc^2 \theta - 1}$ **38.** $\pm\sqrt{1 + \tan^2 \theta}$

39. First line, incorrect cancellation of $\tan^2 \theta$; last 2 lines, $\frac{\sin^2 \theta}{\cos^2 \theta} = \tan^2 \theta$, not $\cot^2 \theta$. A correct identity verification is:

$$\frac{\sec^2 \theta - \tan^2 \theta}{\tan^2 \theta} = \frac{\frac{1}{\cos^2 \theta} - \frac{\sin^2 \theta}{\cos^2 \theta}}{\frac{\sin^2 \theta}{\cos^2 \theta}}$$

$$= \frac{1 - \sin^2 \theta}{\cos^2 \theta} \cdot \frac{\cos^2 \theta}{\sin^2 \theta} = \frac{1 - \sin^2 \theta}{\sin^2 \theta} = \frac{\cos^2 \theta}{\sin^2 \theta}$$
$$= \cot^2 \theta$$

40–41. See next page.

Answers

Practice and Problem-Solving Exercises (continued)

40. Check students' work.

41. $(x - 1)^2 - 1 = x(x - 2)$ is an identity
since: $(x - 1)^2 - 1 = x^2 - 2x + 1 - 1 =$
$x^2 - 2x = x(x - 2)$. $(x - 1)^2 = x(x - 1)$ is an
eq. since it has a unique solution:
$$(x - 1)^2 = x(x - 1)$$
$$x^2 - 2x + 1 = x^2 - x$$
$$-x = -1$$
$$x = 1$$

42. $\sin^2 \theta \tan^2 \theta = \sin^2 \theta \left(\dfrac{\sin^2 \theta}{\cos^2 \theta}\right)$

$\qquad = (1 - \cos^2 \theta)\left(\dfrac{\sin^2 \theta}{\cos^2 \theta}\right)$

$\qquad = \dfrac{\sin^2 \theta - \sin^2 \theta \cos^2 \theta}{\cos^2 \theta}$

$\qquad = \dfrac{\sin^2 \theta}{\cos^2 \theta} - \dfrac{\sin^2 \theta \cos^2 \theta}{\cos^2 \theta}$

$\qquad = \tan^2 \theta - \sin^2 \theta$

43. $\sec \theta - \sin \theta \tan \theta$

$\qquad = \dfrac{1}{\cos \theta} - \sin \theta \left(\dfrac{\sin \theta}{\cos \theta}\right)$

$\qquad = \dfrac{1}{\cos \theta} - \dfrac{\sin^2 \theta}{\cos \theta} = \dfrac{1 - \sin^2 \theta}{\cos \theta} = \dfrac{\cos^2 \theta}{\cos \theta} = \cos \theta$

44. $\sin \theta \cos \theta(\tan \theta + \cot \theta)$

$\qquad = \sin \theta \cos \theta \left(\dfrac{\sin \theta}{\cos \theta} + \dfrac{\cos \theta}{\sin \theta}\right)$

$\qquad = \dfrac{\sin^2 \theta \cos \theta}{\cos \theta} + \dfrac{\cos^2 \theta \sin \theta}{\sin \theta}$

$\qquad = \sin^2 \theta + \cos^2 \theta = 1$

45. $\dfrac{1 - \sin \theta}{\cos \theta} = \dfrac{1 - \sin \theta}{\cos \theta} \cdot \dfrac{\cos \theta}{\cos \theta}$

$\qquad = \dfrac{(1 - \sin \theta)\cos \theta}{\cos^2 \theta}$

$\qquad = \dfrac{(1 - \sin \theta)\cos \theta}{1 - \sin^2 \theta}$

$\qquad = \dfrac{(1 - \sin \theta)\cos \theta}{(1 - \sin \theta)(1 + \sin \theta)}$

$\qquad = \dfrac{\cos \theta}{1 + \sin \theta}$

46. $\dfrac{\sec \theta}{\cot \theta + \tan \theta}$

$\qquad = \dfrac{\frac{1}{\cos \theta}}{\frac{\cos \theta}{\sin \theta} + \frac{\sin \theta}{\cos \theta}} \cdot \dfrac{\sin \theta \cos \theta}{\sin \theta \cos \theta}$

$\qquad = \dfrac{\sin \theta}{\cos^2 \theta + \sin^2 \theta} = \dfrac{\sin \theta}{1} = \sin \theta$

47. $(\cot \theta + 1)^2 = \cot^2 \theta + 2 \cot \theta + 1$
$\qquad = \cot^2 \theta + 1 + 2 \cot \theta = \csc^2 \theta + 2 \cot \theta$

48. $\dfrac{1 - \sin^2 \theta}{\sin^2 \theta}$

49. $1 - \sin \theta$

Verify each identity.

42. $\sin^2 \theta \tan^2 \theta = \tan^2 \theta - \sin^2 \theta$

43. $\sec \theta - \sin \theta \tan \theta = \cos \theta$

44. $\sin \theta \cos \theta (\tan \theta + \cot \theta) = 1$

45. $\dfrac{1 - \sin \theta}{\cos \theta} = \dfrac{\cos \theta}{1 + \sin \theta}$

46. $\dfrac{\sec \theta}{\cot \theta + \tan \theta} = \sin \theta$

47. $(\cot \theta + 1)^2 = \csc^2 \theta + 2 \cot \theta$

Write each expression in terms of $\sin \theta$.

48. $\cos \theta \csc \theta \cot \theta$

49. $\dfrac{\cos \theta}{\sec \theta + \tan \theta}$

Standardized Test Prep

SAT/ACT

50. Which expression is equivalent to $2 \cot \theta$?
Ⓐ $\dfrac{1}{2 \tan \theta}$ Ⓑ $\dfrac{2}{\cot \theta}$ Ⓒ $\dfrac{2 \cos \theta}{\sin \theta}$ Ⓓ $\dfrac{\sin \theta}{\frac{1}{2} \cos \theta}$

51. Which equation is NOT an identity?
Ⓕ $\cos^2 \theta = 1 - \sin^2 \theta$ Ⓗ $\sin^2 \theta = \cos^2 \theta - 1$
Ⓖ $\cot^2 \theta = \csc^2 \theta - 1$ Ⓘ $\tan^2 \theta = \sec^2 \theta - 1$

52. Which expressions are equivalent?
  I. $(\sin \theta)(\csc \theta - \sin \theta)$ II. $\sin^2 \theta - 1$ III. $\cos^2 \theta$
Ⓐ I and II only Ⓑ II and III only Ⓒ I and III only Ⓓ I, II, and III

53. How can you express $\csc^2 \theta - 2 \cot^2 \theta$ in terms of $\sin \theta$ and $\cos \theta$?
Ⓕ $\dfrac{1 - 2\cos^2 \theta}{\sin^2 \theta}$ Ⓖ $\dfrac{1 - 2\sin^2 \theta}{\sin^2 \theta}$ Ⓗ $\sin^2 \theta - 2\cos^2 \theta$ Ⓘ $\dfrac{1}{\sin^2 \theta} - \dfrac{2}{\tan^2 \theta}$

54. Which expression is equivalent to $\dfrac{\tan \theta}{\cos \theta - \sec \theta}$?
Ⓐ $\csc \theta$ Ⓑ $\sec \theta$ Ⓒ $-\csc \theta$ Ⓓ $\tan^2 \theta$

Short Response

55. Show that $(\sec \theta + 1)(\sec \theta - 1) = \tan^2 \theta$ is an identity.

Mixed Review

Identify the period of each function. Then tell where two asymptotes occur for each function. ◀ See Lesson T-5.

56. $y = \tan 6\theta$ **57.** $y = \tan \dfrac{\theta}{4}$ **58.** $y = \tan 1.5\theta$ **59.** $y = \tan \dfrac{\theta}{6}$

For the given probability of success P on each trial, find the probability of x successes in n trials. ◀ See Lesson 11-8.

60. $x = 4, n = 5, p = 0.2$ **61.** $x = 3, n = 5, p = 0.6$
62. $x = 4, n = 8, p = 0.7$ **63.** $x = 7, n = 8, p = 0.7$

Standardized Test Prep

50. C   **51.** H   **52.** C   **53.** F
54. C
55. [2] By the Difference of Squares
Property and the second
Pythagorean Identity:
$(\sec \theta + 1)(\sec \theta - 1)$
$= \sec^2 \theta - 1 = \tan^2 \theta$
[1] incomplete explanation OR
correct explanation with one
computational error

Mixed Review

56. $\dfrac{\pi}{6}$; $\theta = -\dfrac{\pi}{12}, \dfrac{\pi}{12}$
57. 4π; $\theta = -2\pi, 2\pi$
58. $\dfrac{2\pi}{3}$; $\theta = -\dfrac{\pi}{3}, \dfrac{\pi}{3}$
59. 6π; $\theta = -3\pi, 3\pi$
60. 0.0064   **61.** 0.3456
62. ≈ 0.136 **63.** ≈ 0.198

Lesson Quiz

1. What is a simplified trigonometric expression for $\dfrac{1 - \cos^2 \theta}{\tan \theta}$?
2. Verify the identity $\sin^2 \theta \cot^2 \theta = 1 - \sin^2 \theta$.
3. Verify the identity $(1 - \cos^2 \theta)(\cot \theta) = \sin \theta \cos \theta$.

ANSWERS TO LESSON QUIZ

1. $\sin \theta \cos \theta$

2. $\sin^2 \theta \cot^2 \theta = \sin^2 \theta \dfrac{\cos^2 \theta}{\sin^2 \theta}$
$\qquad = \cos^2 \theta$
$\qquad = 1 - \sin^2 \theta$

3. $(1 - \cos^2 \theta)(\cot \theta) = (\sin^2 \theta)\left(\dfrac{\cos \theta}{\sin \theta}\right)$
$\qquad = \sin \theta \cos \theta$

T Trigonometry Review

Connecting **BIG** ideas and Answering the Essential Questions

1 Function
If you know the value of sin θ, use right triangle trigonometry to find values of the other trigonometric functions.

Right Triangles and Trigonometric Ratios (Lesson T-1)

$$\sin A = \frac{\text{opposite}}{\text{hypotenuse}}$$
$$\cos A = \frac{\text{adjacent}}{\text{hypotenuse}}$$
$$\tan A = \frac{\text{opposite}}{\text{adjacent}}$$

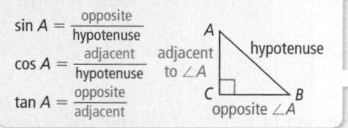

Special Angles (Lesson T-2)

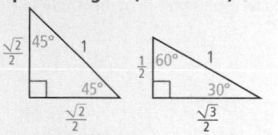

2 Modeling
You can use the sine and cosine functions to model most periodic behavior.

Degrees and Radian Measure (Lesson T-4)
One radian is the measure of a central angle that intercepts an arc of length equal to the radius.

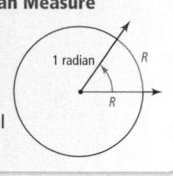

The Unit Circle (Lesson T-3)

$x = \cos \theta$
$\quad = \cos 60° = \frac{1}{2}$
$y = \sin \theta$
$\quad = \sin 60° = \frac{\sqrt{3}}{2}$

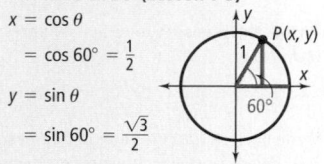

3 Equivalence
To verify that an equation in θ is an identity, show that both of its sides have equal values for each possible replacement for θ.

Basic Identities (Lesson T-6)

$$2 \tan \theta \cos^2 \theta - \frac{2 \sin \theta \cos^2 \theta}{\cos \theta}$$
$$= 2 \sin \theta \cos \theta$$

Graphs of Sine, Cosine, and Tangent Functions (Lesson T-5)

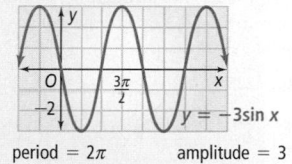

$y = -3\sin x$

period $= 2\pi$ \qquad amplitude $= 3$

Vocabulary

- amplitude (p. 850)
- central angle (p. 841)
- cosine function (p. 848)
- cosine of θ (p. 823)
- cycle (p. 849)
- initial side (p. 834)
- intercepted arc (p. 841)
- period (p. 849)
- periodic function (p. 849)
- radian (p. 841)
- reference angle (p. 835)
- sine function (p. 848)
- sine of θ (p. 823)
- standard position (p. 834)
- tangent function (p. 853)
- tangent of θ (p. 823)
- terminal side (p. 834)
- trigonometric identity (p. 858)
- trigonometric ratios (p. 823)
- unit circle (p. 836)

Choose the correct term to complete each sentence.

1. The __?__ of a periodic function is the length of one cycle.

2. Centered at the origin of the coordinate plane, the __?__ has a radius of 1 unit.

3. An asymptote of the __?__ occurs at $\theta = \frac{\pi}{2}$ and repeats every π units.

4. The six ratios of the lengths of the sides of a right triangle are known as the __?__.

5. A trigonometric equation that is true for all values except those for which the expressions on either side of the equal sign are undefined is a __?__.

BIG idea **Function**

ESSENTIAL QUESTION If you know the value of sin θ, how can you find the values of the other trigonometric ratios?
ANSWER If you know the value of sin θ, use right triangle trigonometry to find values of the other trigonometric functions.

BIG idea **Modeling**

ESSENTIAL QUESTION How can you model periodic behavior?
ANSWER You can use sine and cosine functions to model natural periodic behavior.

BIG idea **Equivalence**

ESSENTIAL QUESTION How do you verify that a trigonometric equation is an identity?
ANSWER If you can transform the expression on the lefthand side of the equation to make it equal the expression on the righthand side, the equation is an identity.

Answers

Trigonometry Review

1. period
2. unit circle
3. tangent function
4. trigonometric ratios.
5. trigonometric identity.

Answers

Trigonometry Test

1. $210°$

2. $-\dfrac{5}{4}$

3. $\dfrac{2\pi}{3}$

4. $150°$

5. $-450°$

6. $-\dfrac{\sqrt{2}}{2}, \dfrac{\sqrt{2}}{2}$

7. $-\dfrac{1}{2}, \dfrac{\sqrt{3}}{2}$

8. $-\dfrac{1}{2}, \dfrac{\sqrt{3}}{2}$

9. $-\dfrac{\sqrt{2}}{2}, -\dfrac{\sqrt{2}}{2}$

10. $\dfrac{10\pi}{3}$, or 10.5

11. $4, \pi$;
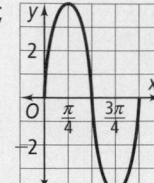

12. $2, \dfrac{\pi}{2}$;
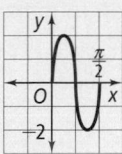

13.
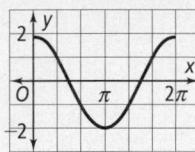

14.
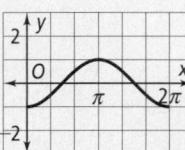

15.
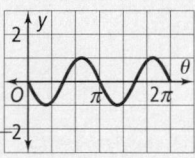

16.
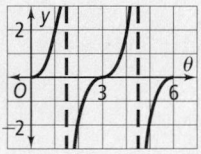

Do you know HOW?

1. Find the measure of the angle in standard position.

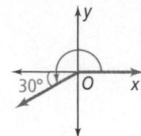

Write each measure in radians. Express your answer in terms of π.

2. $-225°$

3. $120°$

Write each radian measure in degrees. If necessary, round your answer to the nearest degree.

4. $\dfrac{5\pi}{6}$

5. -2.5π

The measure θ of an angle in standard position is given. Find the exact values of $\cos\theta$ and $\sin\theta$ for each angle measure.

6. $-225°$

7. $120°$

8. $-\dfrac{4\pi}{3}$

9. $\dfrac{5\pi}{4}$

10. Find the length of the intercepted arc to the nearest tenth for an arc with a central angle of measure $\theta = \frac{\pi}{3}$ on a circle of radius $r = 10$.

Find the amplitude and period of each function. Then sketch one cycle of the graph of each function.

11. $y = 4\sin(2x)$

12. $y = 2\sin(4x)$

Graph each function in the interval from 0 to 2π.

13. $y = 2\cos x$

14. $y = -\cos x$

15. $y = \sin 2\theta$

16. $y = \tan\frac{\pi}{3}\theta$

Simplify each trigonometric expression.

17. $\sin\theta + \cos\theta\cot\theta$

18. $\csc\theta\cos\theta\tan\theta$

19. $\cot\theta\,(\tan\theta + \cot\theta)$

20. $\sin\theta\cot\theta$

Verify each identity.

21. $\sec\theta\sin\theta\cot\theta = 1$

22. $\csc^2\theta - \cot^2\theta = 1$

23. $\sec\theta\cot\theta = \csc\theta$

24. $\sec^2\theta - 1 = \tan^2\theta$

$\triangle ABC$ has right angle C and $AC = 3$. For the given information, find the missing length.

25. $m\angle A = 60°, AB = \blacksquare$

26. $m\angle B = 60°, BC = \blacksquare$

27. $m\angle A = 45°, AB = \blacksquare$

28. $m\angle A = 30°, AB = \blacksquare$

In $\triangle ABC$, find each value as a fraction and as a decimal. Round to the nearest hundredth.

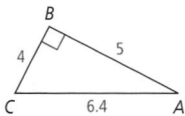

29. $\sin A$

30. $\sec A$

31. $\cot A$

32. $\csc C$

33. $\sec C$

34. $\tan C$

Do you UNDERSTAND?

35. Writing Explain how to convert an angle measure in radians to an angle measure in degrees. Include an example.

36. Physics On each swing, a pendulum 18 inches long travels through an angle of $\frac{3\pi}{4}$ radians. How far does the tip of the pendulum travel in one swing? Round your answer to the nearest inch.

37. Reasoning What are the steps you take to find the asymptotes of the function $y = a\tan bx + c, a \neq 0$?

---

17. $\csc\theta$

18. 1

19. $\csc^2\theta$

20. $\cos\theta$

21. $\sec\theta\sin\theta\cot\theta = \dfrac{1}{\cos\theta} \cdot \dfrac{\sin\theta}{1} \cdot \dfrac{\cos\theta}{\sin\theta}$
$ = \dfrac{\sin\theta\cos\theta}{\cos\theta\sin\theta} = 1$

22. $\csc^2\theta - \cot^2\theta = 1 + \cot^2\theta - \cot^2\theta$
$ = 1$

23. $\sec\theta\cot\theta = \dfrac{1}{\cos\theta} \cdot \dfrac{\cos\theta}{\sin\theta} = \dfrac{1}{\sin\theta}$
$ = \csc\theta$

24. $\sec^2\theta - 1 = 1 + \tan^2\theta - 1$
$ = \tan^2\theta$

25. 6

26. $\sqrt{3}$

27. $3\sqrt{2}$

28. $2\sqrt{3}$

29. $\dfrac{4}{6.4}$, 0.63

30. $\dfrac{6.4}{5}$, 1.28

31. $\dfrac{5}{4}$, 1.25

32. $\dfrac{6.4}{5}$, 1.28

33. $\dfrac{6.4}{4}$, 1.60

34. $\dfrac{5}{4}$, 1.25

35. Answers may vary. Sample:
Multiply the radian measure by $\dfrac{180°}{\pi}$.
Example: $\dfrac{2\pi}{3}$ radians $\cdot \dfrac{180°}{\pi} = 120°$

36. 42 in.

37. The period of $y = a\tan bx + c$ depends only on the value of b. The period is $\frac{\pi}{b}$. Asymptotes appear at the end of the cycle from $-\frac{\pi}{2b}$ to $\frac{\pi}{2b}$, and at the end of each of the other cycles in either direction. Therefore, the asymptotes of $y = a\tan bx + c$ are $\pm\frac{\pi}{2b}, \pm\frac{3\pi}{2b}, \pm\frac{5\pi}{2b}$, and so on.

Skills **Handbook**

Percents and Percent Applications

Percent means "per hundred." Find fraction, decimal, and percent equivalents by replacing one symbol for *hundredths* with another.

Example 1

Write each number as a percent.

a. $0.082 = 8.2\%$

Move the decimal point two places to the right and write a percent sign.

b. $\frac{3}{5} = \frac{60}{100} = 60\%$

Write the fraction as hundredths. Then replace the hundredths with a percent sign.

c. $1\frac{1}{6} = \frac{7}{6} = 1.166\overline{6} = 116.\overline{6}\%$

Divide 7 by 6 to write $1\frac{1}{6}$ as a decimal.

Example 2

Write each percent as a decimal.

a. $50\% = 0.50 = 0.5$

Move the decimal point two places to the left and drop the percent sign.

b. $\frac{1}{2}\% = 0.5\% = 00.5\% = 0.005$

Example 3

Use an equation to solve each percent problem.

a. What is 30% of 12?

$n = 0.3 \times 12$

$n = 3.6$

b. 18 is 0.3% of what?

$18 = 0.003 \times n$

$\frac{18}{0.003} = \frac{0.003n}{0.003}$

$6000 = n$

c. What percent of 60 is 9?

$n \times 60 = 9$

$60n = 9$

$n = \frac{9}{60} = 0.15 = 15\%$

Exercises

Write each decimal as a percent and each percent as a decimal.

1. 0.46   **2.** 1.506   **3.** 0.007   **4.** 8%   **5.** 103.5%   **6.** 3.3%

Write each fraction or mixed number as a percent.

7. $\frac{1}{4}$ **8.** $\frac{3}{8}$ **9.** $\frac{2}{3}$ **10.** $\frac{4}{9}$ **11.** $1\frac{3}{20}$ **12.** $\frac{1}{200}$

Use an equation to solve each percent problem. Round your answer to the nearest tenth, if necessary.

13. What is 25% of 50?   **14.** What percent of 58 is 37?   **15.** 120% of what is 90?

16. 8 is what percent of 40?   **17.** 15 is 75% of what?   **18.** 80% of 58 is what?

Answers

Percents and Percent Applications

1. 46%   **2.** 1150.6%

3. 0.7%   **4.** 0.08

5. 1.035   **6.** 0.033

7. 25%   **8.** 37.5%

9. 66.$\overline{6}$%   **10.** 44.$\overline{4}$%

11. 115%   **12.** 0.5%

13. 12.5   **14.** 63.8%

15. 75   **16.** 20%

17. 20%   **18.** 46.4

Operations With Fractions

To add or subtract fractions, use a common denominator. The common denominator is the least common multiple of the denominators.

Example 1

Simplify $\frac{2}{3} + \frac{3}{5}$.

For 3 and 5, the least common multiple is 15.

Write $\frac{2}{3}$ and $\frac{3}{5}$ as equivalent fractions with denominators of 15.

Add the numerators.

$$\frac{2}{3} + \frac{3}{5} = \frac{2}{3} \cdot \frac{5}{5} + \frac{3}{5} \cdot \frac{3}{3}$$
$$= \frac{10}{15} + \frac{9}{15}$$
$$= \frac{19}{15} \text{ or } 1\frac{4}{15}$$

Example 2

Simplify $5\frac{1}{4} - 3\frac{2}{3}$.

Write equivalent fractions.

Write $5\frac{3}{12}$ as $4\frac{15}{12}$ so you can subtract the fractions.

Subtract the fractions. Then subtract the whole numbers.

$$5\frac{1}{4} - 3\frac{2}{3} = 5\frac{3}{12} - 3\frac{8}{12}$$
$$= 4\frac{15}{12} - 3\frac{8}{12}$$
$$= 1\frac{7}{12}$$

To multiply fractions, multiply the numerators and multiply the denominators. You can simplify by using a greatest common factor.

Example 3

Simplify $\frac{3}{4} \cdot \frac{8}{11}$

Method 1 $\frac{3}{4} \cdot \frac{8}{11} = \frac{24}{44} = \frac{24 \div 4}{44 \div 4} = \frac{6}{11}$

Divide 24 and 44 by 4, their greatest common factor.

Method 2 $\frac{3}{4} \cdot \frac{8\,^{2}}{11} = \frac{6}{11}$

Divide 4 and 8 by 4, their greatest common factor.

To divide fractions, use a reciprocal to change the problem to multiplication.

Example 4

Simplify $3\frac{1}{5} \div 1\frac{1}{2}$

Write mixed numbers as improper fractions.

Multiply by the reciprocal of the divisor.

Simplify.

$$3\frac{1}{5} \div 1\frac{1}{2} = \frac{16}{5} \div \frac{3}{2}$$
$$= \frac{16}{5} \cdot \frac{2}{3}$$
$$= \frac{32}{15} \text{ or } 2\frac{2}{15}$$

Exercises

Perform the indicated operation.

1. $\frac{3}{5} + \frac{4}{5}$
2. $\frac{1}{2} + \frac{2}{3}$
3. $4\frac{1}{2} + 2\frac{1}{3}$
4. $5\frac{3}{4} + 4\frac{2}{5}$
5. $\frac{2}{3} - \frac{3}{7}$
6. $5\frac{1}{2} - 3\frac{2}{5}$
7. $7\frac{3}{4} - 4\frac{4}{5}$
8. $3\frac{4}{5} \cdot 10$
9. $2\frac{1}{2} \cdot 3\frac{1}{5}$
10. $6\frac{3}{4} \cdot 5\frac{2}{3}$
11. $\frac{1}{2} \div \frac{1}{3}$
12. $\frac{6}{5} \div \frac{3}{5}$
13. $8\frac{1}{2} \div 4\frac{1}{4}$
14. $\frac{8}{9} - \frac{2}{3}$
15. $5\frac{1}{4} \cdot 8$

Answers

Operations with Fractions

1. $1\frac{2}{5}$
2. $1\frac{1}{6}$
3. $6\frac{5}{6}$
4. $10\frac{3}{20}$
5. $\frac{5}{21}$
6. $2\frac{1}{10}$
7. $2\frac{19}{20}$
8. 38
9. 8
10. $38\frac{1}{4}$
11. $1\frac{1}{2}$
12. 2
13. 2
14. $\frac{2}{9}$
15. 42

Ratios and Proportions

A *ratio* is a comparison of two quantities by division. You can write *equal ratios* by multiplying or dividing each quantity by the same nonzero number.

Ways to Write a Ratio
$a : b \quad a \text{ to } b \quad \frac{a}{b} \ (b \neq 0)$

Example 1

Write $3\frac{1}{3} : \frac{1}{2}$ as a ratio in simplest form.

In simplest form, both terms should be integers. Multiply by the common denominator, 6.

$$3\frac{1}{3} : \frac{1}{2} \xrightarrow[\times 6]{\times 6} \frac{3\frac{1}{3}}{\frac{1}{2}} = \frac{20}{3} \text{ or } 20 : 3$$

A rate is a ratio that compares different types of quantities. In simplest form for a rate, the second quantity is one unit.

Example 2

Write 247 mi in 5.2 h as a rate in simplest form.

Divide by 5.2 to make the second quantity one unit.

$$\frac{247 \text{ mi}}{5.2 \text{ h}} \xrightarrow[\div 5.2]{\div 5.2} \frac{47.5 \text{ mi}}{1 \text{ h}} \text{ or } 47.5 \text{ mi/h}$$

A proportion is a statement that two ratios are equal. You can find a missing term in a proportion by using the cross products.

Cross Products of a Proportion
$$\frac{a}{b} = \frac{c}{d} \ \rightarrow \ ad = bc$$

Example 3

The Copy Center charges \$2.52 for 63 copies. At that rate, how much will the Copy Center charge for 140 copies?

Set up a proportion. $\quad \begin{array}{l} \text{cost} \rightarrow \\ \text{copies} \rightarrow \end{array} \dfrac{2.52}{63} = \dfrac{c}{140}$

Use cross products. $\quad 2.52 \cdot 140 = 63c$

Solve for c. $\quad c = \dfrac{2.52 \cdot 140}{63}$

Simplify. $\quad = 5.6 \text{ or } \$5.60$

Exercises

Write each ratio or rate in simplest form.

1. 15 to 20   **2.** 85 : 34   **3.** 38 g in 4 oz   **4.** 375 mi in 4.3 h   **5.** $\frac{84}{30}$

Solve each proportion. Round your answer to the nearest tenth, if necessary.

6. $\frac{a}{5} = \frac{12}{15}$ **7.** $\frac{21}{12} = \frac{14}{x}$ **8.** $8 : 15 = n : 25$ **9.** $2.4 : c = 4 : 3$ **10.** $\frac{17}{8} = \frac{n}{20}$

11. $\frac{13}{n} = \frac{20}{3}$ **12.** $5 : 7 = y : 5$ **13.** $\frac{0.4}{3.5} = \frac{5.2}{x}$ **14.** $\frac{4}{x} = \frac{7}{6}$ **15.** $4 : n = n : 9$

16. A canary's heart beats 130 times in 12 s. Use a proportion to find about how many times its heart beats in 50 s.

Ratios and Proportions

1. 3 to 4   **2.** 5 : 2

3. 19 g in 2 oz

4. approximately 87.2 mi in 1 h

5. $\frac{14}{5}$ **6.** 4

7. 8   **8.** $13.\overline{3}$

9. 1.8   **10.** 42.5

11. 1.95   **12.** 3.6

13. 45.5   **14.** 3.4

15. ± 6 **16.** about 542 times

Simplifying Expressions With Integers

To add two numbers with the same sign, *add* their absolute values. The sum has the same sign as the numbers. To add two numbers with different signs, find the *difference* between their absolute values. The sum has the same sign as the number with the greater absolute value.

Example 1

Add.

a. $-8 + (-5) = -13$ **b.** $-8 + 5 = -3$ **c.** $8 + (-5) = 3$

To subtract a number, add its opposite.

Example 2

Subtract.

a. $4 - 7 = 4 + (-7)$ **b.** $-4 - (-7) = -4 + 7$ **c.** $-4 - 7 = -4 + (-7)$
$= -3$ $= 3$ $= -11$

The product or quotient of two numbers with the same sign is positive. The product or quotient of two numbers with different signs is negative.

Example 3

Multiply or divide.

a. $(-3)(-5) = 15$ **b.** $-35 \div 7 = -5$ **c.** $24 \div (-6) = -4$

Example 4

Simplify $2^2 - 3(4 - 6) - 12$.

$$2^2 - 3(4 - 6) - 12 = 2^2 - 3(-2) - 12$$
$$= 4 - 3(-2) - 12$$
$$= 4 - (-6) - 12$$
$$= 4 + 6 - 12 = -2$$

Order of Operations

1. Perform any operation(s) inside grouping symbols.
2. Simplify any terms with exponents.
3. Multiply and divide in order from left to right.
4. Add and subtract in order from left to right.

Exercises

Simplify each expression.

1. $-4 + 5$ **2.** $12 - 12$ **3.** $-15 + (-23)$ **4.** $4 - 17$ **5.** $-5 - 12$

6. $3 - (-5)$ **7.** $-8 - (-12)$ **8.** $-19 + 5$ **9.** $(-7)(-4)$ **10.** $-120 \div 30$

11. $(-3)(4)$ **12.** $75 \div (-3)$ **13.** $(-6)(15)$ **14.** $(18)(-4)$ **15.** $-84 \div (-7)$

16. $-2(1 + 5) + (-3)(2)$ **17.** $-4(-2 - 5) + 3(1 - 4)$ **18.** $20 - (3)(12) + 4^2$

19. $\frac{-15}{-5} - \frac{36}{-12} + \frac{-12}{-4}$ **20.** $5^2 - 6(5 - 9)$ **21.** $(-3 + 2^3)(4 + \frac{-42}{7})$

Answers

Simplifying Expressions with Integers

1. 1   **2.** 0

3. -38 **4.** -13

5. -17 **6.** 8

7. 4   **8.** -14

9. 28   **10.** -4

11. -12 **12.** -25

13. -90 **14.** -72

15. 12   **16.** -18

17. 19   **18.** 0

19. 9   **20.** 49

21. -10

Area and Volume

The *area* of a plane figure is the number of square units contained in the figure.
The *volume* of a space figure is the number of cubic units contained in the figure.
Formulas for area and volume are listed on page 886.

Example 1

Find the area of each figure.

a.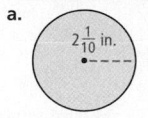

$$A = \pi r^2$$
$$\approx \frac{22}{7} \cdot \left(\frac{21}{10}\right)^2$$
$$= \frac{693}{50} = 13\frac{43}{50} \text{ in.}^2$$

b.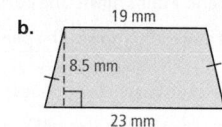

$$A = \frac{1}{2}(b_1 + b_2)h$$
$$= \frac{1}{2}(19 + 23) \cdot 8.5$$
$$= 178.5 \text{ mm}^2$$

Example 2

Find the volume of each figure.

a.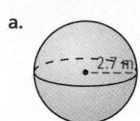

$$V = \frac{4}{3}\pi r^3$$
$$\approx \frac{4}{3} \cdot 3.14 \cdot 2.7^3$$
$$= 82.40616 \approx 82.4 \text{ m}^3$$

b.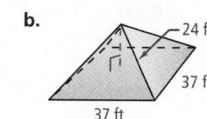

$$V = \frac{1}{3}Bh$$
$$= \frac{1}{3}(37^2) \cdot 24$$
$$= 10,952 \text{ ft}^3$$

Exercises

Find the exact area of each figure.

1.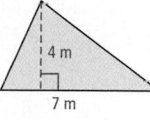
2.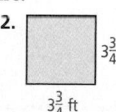
3.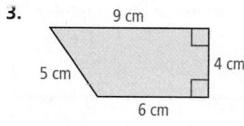
4.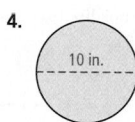

Find the exact volume of each figure.

5.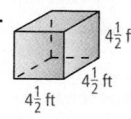
6.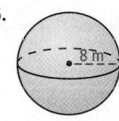
7.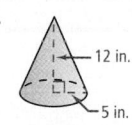
8.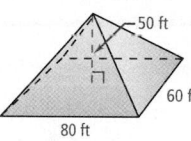

9. Find the area of a triangle with a base of 17 in. and a height of 13 in.

10. Find the volume of a rectangular box 64 cm long, 48 cm wide, and 58 cm high.

11. Find the surface area of the cube in Exercise 5.

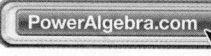
Areas and Volumes

1. 14 m^2
2. $14\frac{1}{16} \text{ ft}^2$
3. 30 cm^2
4. $25\pi \text{ in.}^2$
5. $91\frac{1}{8} \text{ ft}^3$
6. $\frac{2048}{3}\pi \text{ m}^3$
7. $100\pi \text{ in.}^3$
8. $80,000 \text{ ft}^3$
9. 110.5 in.^2
10. $178,176 \text{ cm}^3$
11. $121\frac{1}{2} \text{ ft}^2$

The Coordinate Plane, Slope, and Midpoint

The *coordinate plane* is formed when two perpendicular number lines intersect at a point called the origin, forming four quadrants.

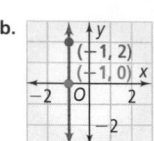

Example 1

In which quadrant would you find each point?

a. $(3, -4)$ Move 3 units right and 4 units down. The point is in Quadrant IV.

b. $(-2, -5)$ Move 2 units left and 5 units down. The point is in Quadrant III.

To find the slope of a line on the coordinate plane, choose two points on the line and use the slope formula.

Example 2

Find the slope of each line.

a.
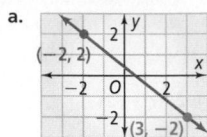

$$m = \frac{y_2 - y_1}{x_2 - x_1}$$
$$= \frac{2 - (-2)}{-2 - 3}$$
$$= \frac{4}{-5} \text{ or } -\frac{4}{5}$$

b.

$$m = \frac{y_2 - y_1}{x_2 - x_1}$$
$$= \frac{2 - 0}{-1 - (-1)} = \frac{2}{0}$$

Since you cannot divide by zero, this line has an undefined slope.

If (x_m, y_m) is the midpoint of the segment joining (x_1, y_1) and (x_2, y_2), then $x_m = \frac{x_1 + x_2}{2}$ and $y_m = \frac{y_1 + y_2}{2}$.

Example 3

Find the coordinates of the midpoint of the segment with endpoints $(-2, 5)$ and $(6, -3)$.

$\frac{-2 + 6}{2} = 2$ and $\frac{5 + (-3)}{2} = 1$ so the midpoint is $(2, 1)$.

Exercises

In which quadrant would you find each point? Graph each point on a coordinate plane.

1. $(3, 2)$ 2. $(-4, 3)$ 3. $(2, -3)$ 4. $(4, -2)$ 5. $(-4, -5)$ 6. $(-1, -3)$

Find the slope of each line.

7.
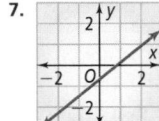

8.
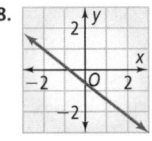

9.
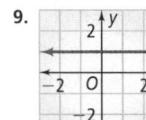

10. the line containing $(-3, 4)$ and $(2, -6)$

11. the line containing $(25, 40)$ and $(100, 55)$

Find the midpoint of the segment with the given endpoints.

12. $(-4, 4), (2, -5)$ 13. $(3, 3), (7, -6)$ 14. $(-1, -8), (0, -3)$ 15. $(3, 4), (2, -6)$

Answers

The Coordinate Plane, Slope, and Midpoint

1. I
2. II
3. IV
4. IV
5. III
6. III
7. $\frac{4}{5}$
8. -1
9. 0
10. -2
11. $\frac{1}{5}$
12. $\left(-1, -\frac{1}{2}\right)$
13. $\left(5, -\frac{3}{2}\right)$
14. $\left(-\frac{1}{2}, -\frac{11}{2}\right)$
15. $\left(\frac{5}{2}, -1\right)$

Operations With Exponents

An exponent indicates how many times a number is used as a factor.

Example 1

Write using exponents.

a. $3 \cdot 3 \cdot 3 \cdot 3 \cdot 3 = 3^5$ b. $a \cdot a \cdot b \cdot b \cdot b \cdot b = a^2 b^4$

$2^n = \blacksquare$	$10^n = \blacksquare$
$2^2 = 4$	$10^2 = 100$
$2^1 = 2$	$10^1 = 10$
$2^0 = 1$	$10^0 = 1$
$2^{-1} = \frac{1}{2}$	$10^{-1} = \frac{1}{10}$
$2^{-2} = \frac{1}{4}$	$10^{-2} = \frac{1}{100}$

The patterns shown at the right indicate that $a^0 = 1$ and that $a^{-n} = \frac{1}{a^n}$.

Example 2

Write each expression so that all exponents are positive.

a. $a^{-2}b^3 = \frac{1}{a^2} \cdot b^3 = \frac{b^3}{a^2}$ b. $x^3 y^0 z^{-1} = x^3 \cdot 1 \cdot \frac{1}{z} = \frac{x^3}{z}$

You can simplify expressions that contain powers with the same base.

Example 3

Simplify each expression.

a. $b^5 \cdot b^3 = b^{5+3}$ Add exponents to multiply
$ = b^8$ powers with the same base.

b. $\frac{x^5}{x^7} = x^{5-7}$ Subtract exponents to divide
$\phantom{\frac{x^5}{x^7}} = x^{-2} = \frac{1}{x^2}$ powers with the same base.

You can simplify expressions that contain parentheses and exponents.

Example 4

Simplify each expression.

a. $\left(\frac{ab}{n}\right)^3 = \frac{a^3 b^3}{n^3}$ Raise each factor in the parentheses to the third power.

b. $(c^2)^4 = c^{2 \cdot 4} = c^8$ Multiply exponents to raise a power to a power.

Exercises

Write each expression using exponents.

1. $x \cdot x \cdot x$ **2.** $x \cdot x \cdot x \cdot y \cdot y$ **3.** $a \cdot a \cdot a \cdot a \cdot b$ **4.** $\frac{a \cdot a \cdot a \cdot a}{b \cdot b}$

Write each expression so that all exponents are positive.

5. c^{-4} **6.** $m^{-2}n^0$ **7.** $x^5 y^{-7} z^{-3}$ **8.** $ab^{-1}c^2$

Simplify each expression. Use positive exponents.

9. $d^2 d^6$ **10.** $\frac{a^5}{a^2}$ **11.** $\frac{c^7}{c}$ **12.** $\frac{n^3}{n^6}$ **13.** $\frac{a^5 b^3}{ab^8}$ **14.** $(3x)^2$

15. $\left(\frac{a}{b}\right)^4$ **16.** $\left(\frac{xz}{y}\right)^6$ **17.** $(c^3)^4$ **18.** $\left(\frac{x^2}{y^5}\right)^3$ **19.** $(u^4 v^2)^3$ **20.** $(p^5)^{-2}$

21. $\frac{(2a^4)(3a^2)}{6a^3}$ **22.** $(x^{-2})^3$ **23.** $(mg^3)^{-1}$ **24.** $g^{-3}g^{-1}$ **25.** $\frac{(3a^3)^2}{18a}$ **26.** $\frac{c^3 d^7}{c^{-3}d^{-1}}$

Operations with Exponents

1. x^3 **2.** $x^3 y^2$

3. $a^4 b$ **4.** $\frac{a^4}{b^2}$

5. $\frac{1}{c^4}$ **6.** $\frac{1}{m^2}$

7. $\frac{x^5}{y^7 z^3}$ **8.** $\frac{ac^2}{b}$

9. d^8 **10.** a^3

11. c^6 **12.** $\frac{1}{n^3}$

13. $\frac{a^4}{b^5}$ **14.** $9x^2$

15. $\frac{a^4}{b^4}$ **16.** $\frac{x^6 z^6}{y^6}$

17. c^{12} **18.** $\frac{x^6}{y^{15}}$

19. $u^{12}v^6$ **20.** $\frac{1}{p^{10}}$

21. a^3 **22.** $\frac{1}{x^6}$

23. $\frac{1}{mg^3}$ **24.** $\frac{1}{g^4}$

25. $\frac{a^5}{2}$ **26.** $c^6 d^8$

Factoring and Operations With Polynomials

Example 1

Perform each operation.

a. $(3y^2 - 4y + 5) + (y^2 + 9y)$

   To add, group like terms. $= (3y^2 + y^2) + (-4y + 9y) + 5$

   Combine like terms. $= 4y^2 + 5y + 5$

b. $(n + 4)(n - 3)$

   Distribute n and 4. $= n(n) + n(-3) + 4(n) + 4(-3)$

   Multiply. $= n^2 - 3n + 4n - 12$

   Combine like terms. $= n^2 + n - 12$

To factor a polynomial, first find the greatest common factor (GCF) of the terms. Then use the distributive property to factor out the GCF.

Example 2

Factor $6x^3 - 12x^2 + 18x$.

List the factors of each term. The GCF is $6x$. $6x^3 = 6 \cdot x \cdot x \cdot x$; $-12x^2 = 6 \cdot (-2) \cdot x \cdot x$; $18x = 6 \cdot 3 \cdot x$

Use the distributive property to factor out $6x$. $6x^3 - 12x^2 + 18x = 6x(x^2) + 6x(-2x) + 6x(3)$

                                                      $= 6x(x^2 - 2x + 3)$

When a polynomial is the product of two binomials, you can work backward to find the factors.

$x^2 + bx + c = (x + \blacksquare)(x + \blacksquare)$

The *sum* of these numbers must equal b.

The *product* of these numbers must equal c.

Example 3

Factor $x^2 - 13x + 36$.

Choose numbers that are factors of 36. Look for a pair with the sum -13.

The numbers -4 and -9 have a product of 36 and a sum of -13. The factors are $(x - 4)$ and $(x - 9)$. So, $x^2 - 13x + 36 = (x - 4)(x - 9)$.

Factors	Sum
$-6 \cdot (-6)$	-12
$-4 \cdot (-9)$	-13

Exercises

Perform the indicated operations.

1. $(x^2 + 3x - 1) + (7x - 4)$ 2. $(5y^2 + 7y) - (3y^2 + 9y - 8)$ 3. $4x^2(3x^2 - 5x + 9)$

4. $-5d(13d^2 + 7d + 8)$ 5. $(x - 5)(x + 3)$ 6. $(n - 7)(n - 2)$

Factor each polynomial.

7. $a^2 - 8a + 12$ 8. $n^2 - 2n - 8$ 9. $x^2 + 5x + 4$ 10. $3m^2 - 9$

11. $y^2 + 5y - 24$ 12. $s^3 + 6s^2 + 11s$ 13. $2x^3 + 4x^2 - 8x$ 14. $y^2 - 10y + 25$

Answers

Factoring and Operations with Polynomials

1. $x^2 + 10x - 5$
2. $2y^2 - 2y + 8$
3. $12x^4 - 20x^3 + 36x^2$
4. $-65d^3 - 35d^2 - 40d$
5. $x^2 - 2x - 15$
6. $n^2 - 9n + 14$
7. $(a - 6)(a - 2)$
8. $(n - 4)(n + 2)$
9. $(x + 4)(x + 1)$

Scientific Notation and Significant Digits

In *scientific notation*, a number has the form $a \times 10^n$, where n is an integer and $1 \leq a < 10$.

Example 1

Write 5.59×10^6 in standard form.

A positive exponent indicates a value greater than 1. $\qquad\qquad 5.59 \times 10^6 = 5\,590\,000 = 5,590,000$
Move the decimal point six places to the right.

Example 2

Write 0.0000318 in scientific notation.

Move the decimal point to create a number between 1 and 10. $\qquad 0.0000318 = 3.18 \times 10^{-5}$
Since the original number is less than 1, use a negative exponent.

When a measurement is in scientific notation, all the digits of the number between 1 and 10 are *significant digits*. When you multiply or divide measurements, your answer should have as many significant digits as the least number of significant digits in any of the numbers involved.

Example 3

Multiply $(6.71 \times 10^8 \, \text{mi/h})$ and $(3.8 \times 10^4 \, \text{h})$.

Rearrange factors. $\qquad\qquad (6.71 \times 10^8 \, \text{mi/h})(3.8 \times 10^4 \, \text{h}) = (6.71 \cdot 3.8)(10^8 \cdot 10^4)$

Add exponents when multiplying powers of 10. $\qquad\qquad\qquad\qquad\qquad\qquad = 25.498 \times 10^{12}$

Write in scientific notation. $\qquad$ three $\qquad$ two $\qquad\qquad\qquad = 2.5498 \times 10^{13}$

Round to two significant digits. $\quad$ significant $\quad$ significant $\qquad\qquad \approx 2.5 \times 10^{13} \text{mi}$
$\qquad\qquad\qquad\qquad\qquad$ digits $\qquad$ digits

Exercises

Change each number to scientific notation or to standard form.

1. 1,340,000 $\qquad$ **2.** 6.88×10^{-2} $\qquad$ **3.** 0.000775 $\qquad$ **4.** 0.0072 $\qquad$ **5.** 1.113×10^5

6. 8.0×10^{-4} $\qquad$ **7.** 1895 $\qquad$ **8.** 2.3×10^3 $\qquad$ **9.** 123,400 $\qquad$ **10.** 7.985×10^4

Write each product or quotient in scientific notation. Round to the appropriate number of significant digits.

11. $(1.6 \times 10^2)(4.0 \times 10^3)$ $\qquad$ **12.** $(2.5 \times 10^{-3})(1.2 \times 10^4)$ $\qquad$ **13.** $(4.237 \times 10^4)(2.01 \times 10^{-2})$

14. $\dfrac{7.0 \times 10^5}{2.89 \times 10^3}$ $\qquad$ **15.** $\dfrac{1.4 \times 10^4}{8.0 \times 10^2}$ $\qquad$ **16.** $\dfrac{6.48 \times 10^6}{3.2 \times 10^5}$

17. $(1.78 \times 10^{-7})(5.03 \times 10^{-5})$ $\qquad$ **18.** $(7.2 \times 10^{11})(5 \times 10^6)$ $\qquad$ **19.** $(8.90 \times 10^8) \div (2.36 \times 10^{-2})$

20. $(3.95 \times 10^4) \div (6.8 \times 10^8)$ $\qquad$ **21.** $(4.9 \times 10^{-8}) \div (2.7 \times 10^{-2})$ $\qquad$ **22.** $(3.972 \times 10^{-5})(4.7 \times 10^{-4})$

10. $3(m^2 - 3)$

11. $(y + 8)(y - 3)$

12. $s(s^2 + 6s + 11)$

13. $2x(x^2 + 2x - 4)$

14. $(y - 5)^2$

Scientific Notation and Significant Figures

1. 1.34×10^6 $\qquad$ **2.** 0.0688

3. 7.75×10^{-4} $\qquad$ **4.** 7.2×10^{-3}

5. 111,300 $\qquad$ **6.** 0.0008

7. 1.895×10^3 $\qquad$ **8.** 2300

9. 1.234×10^5 $\qquad$ **10.** 79,850

11. 6.4×10^5 $\qquad$ **12.** 30

13. 8.52×10^2 $\qquad$ **14.** 2.4×10^2

15. 17.5 $\qquad$ **16.** 20

17. 8.95×10^{-12} $\qquad$ **18.** 3.6×10^{18}

19. 3.77×10^{10} $\qquad$ **20.** 5.8×10^{-5}

21. 1.8×10^{-6} $\qquad$ **22.** 1.9×10^{-8}

The Pythagorean Theorem and the Distance Formula

In a right triangle, the sum of the squares of the lengths of the legs is equal to the square of the length of the hypotenuse. Use this relationship, known as the Pythagorean Theorem, to find the length of a side of a right triangle.

The Pythagorean Theorem

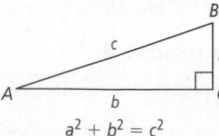

$$a^2 + b^2 = c^2$$

Example 1

Find m in the triangle below, to the nearest tenth.

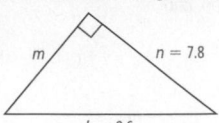

$$m^2 + n^2 = k^2$$
$$m^2 + 7.8^2 = 9.6^2$$
$$m^2 = 9.6^2 - 7.8^2 = 31.32$$
$$m = \sqrt{31.32} \approx 5.6$$

To find the distance between two points on the coordinate plane, use the distance formula.

The distance d between any two points (x_1, y_1) and (x_2, y_2) is

$$d = \sqrt{(x_2 - x_1)^2 + (y_2 - y_1)^2}$$

Example 2

Find the distance between $(-3, 2)$ and $(6, -4)$.

$$d = \sqrt{(6 - (-3))^2 + (-4 - 2)^2}$$
$$= \sqrt{9^2 + (-6)^2}$$
$$= \sqrt{81 + 36}$$
$$= \sqrt{117}$$
$$\approx 10.8$$

Thus, d is about 10.8 units.

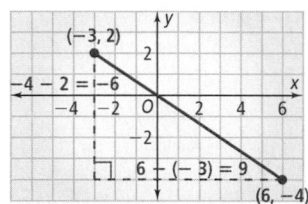

Exercises

In each problem, a and b are the lengths of the legs of a right triangle and c is the length of the hypotenuse. Find each missing length. Round your answer to the nearest tenth.

1. c if $a = 6$ and $b = 8$

2. a if $b = 12$ and $c = 13$

3. b if $a = 8$ and $c = 17$

4. c if $a = 10$ and $b = 3$

5. a if $b = 100$ and $c = 114$

6. b if $a = 12.0$ and $c = 30.1$

Find the distance between each pair of points, to the nearest tenth.

7. $(0, 0), (4, -3)$

8. $(-5, -5), (1, 3)$

9. $(-1, 0), (4, 12)$

10. $(-4, 2), (4, -2)$

11. $(0, 15), (17, 0)$

12. $(-8, 8), (8, 8)$

13. $(-1, 1), (1, -1)$

14. $(-2, 9), (0, 0)$

15. $(-5, 3), (4, 3)$

16. $(2, 1), (3, 4)$

17. $(3, -2), (3, 5)$

18. $(5, 4), (-3, 1)$

Answers

The Pythagorean Theorem and the Distance Formula

1. 10   **2.** 5

3. 15   **4.** 10.4

5. 54.7   **6.** 27.6

7. 5   **8.** 10

9. 13   **10.** 8.9

11. 22.7   **12.** 16

13. 2.8   **14.** 9.2

15. 9   **16.** 3.2

17. 7   **18.** 8.5

Bar and Circle Graphs

Sometimes you can draw different graphs to represent the same data, depending on the information you want to share. A *bar graph* is useful for comparing amounts; a *circle graph* is useful for comparing percents.

Example

Display the 2007 data on immigration to the United States in a bar graph and a circle graph.

To make a circle graph, first find the *percent* of the data in each category. Then express each percent as a decimal and multiply by 360° to find the size of each *central angle*.

$$\text{Africa} \to \frac{89.3}{1003.7} \approx 0.09 \text{ or } 9\%$$

$$0.09 \times 360° \approx 32°$$

Draw a circle and use a protractor to draw each central angle.

Immigration to the United States, 2007

Place of Origin	Immigrants (1000's)
Africa	89.2
Asia	359.4
Europe	120.8
North America	331.7
South America	102.6

SOURCE: Department of Homeland Security

To make a bar graph, place the categories along the bottom axis. Decide on a scale for the side axis. An appropriate scale would be 0–400, marked in intervals of 100. For each data item, draw a bar whose height is equal to the data value.

Immigration to the United States, 2007

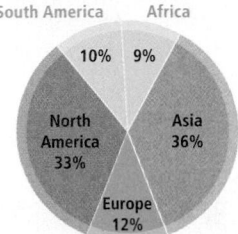

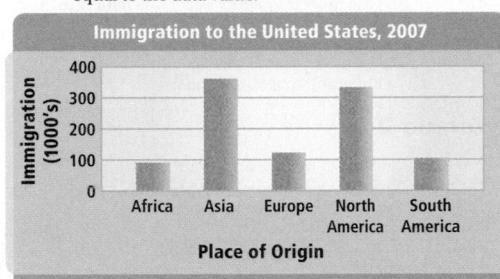

Exercises

Display the data from each table in a bar graph and a circle graph.

1. NASA Space Shuttle Expenses, 2000

Operation	Millions of Dollars
Orbiter, integration	698.8
Propulsion	1,053.1
Mission, launch operations	738.8
Flight operations	244.6
Ground operations	510.3

SOURCE: U.S. National Aeronautics and Space Administration

2. Cable TV Revenue, 2006

	Millions of Dollars
Airtime	4,566
Basic service	42,918
Pay-per-view, premium services	13,322
Installation	729
Other	27,188

SOURCE: U.S. Census Bureau

Bar and Circle Graphs

1.

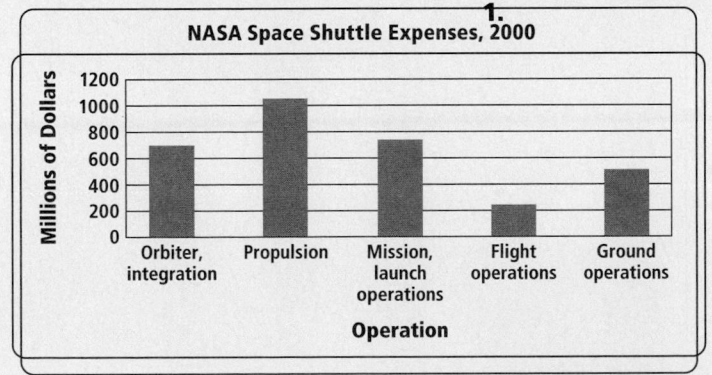

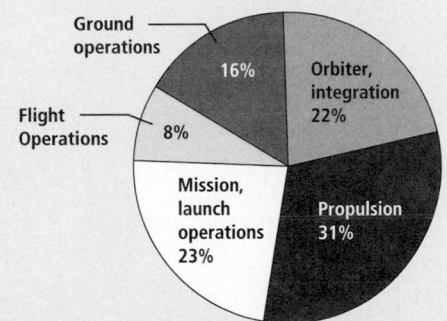

Descriptive Statistics and Histograms

For numerical data, you can find the *mean*, the *median*, and the *mode*.

Mean	The sum of the data values in a data set divided by the number of data values
Median	The middle value of a data set that has been arranged in increasing or decreasing order. If the data set has an even number of values, the median is the mean of the middle two values.
Mode	The most frequently occurring value in a data set

Example 1

Find the mean, median, and mode for the following data set.   5 7 6 3 1 7 9 5 10 7

Mean $\dfrac{5 + 7 + 6 + 3 + 1 + 7 + 9 + 5 + 10 + 7}{10} = 6$

Median   5, 7, 6, 3, 1, 7, 9, 5, 10, 7   Rearrange the numbers from least to greatest.

              1, 3, 5, 5, 6, 7, 7, 7, 9, 10   The median is the mean of the two middle numbers, 6 and 7.

              The median is $\dfrac{6 + 7}{2} = 6.5$.

Mode   The most frequently occurring data value is 7.

The frequency of a data value is the number of times it occurs in a data set.
A *histogram* is a bar graph that shows the frequency of each data value.

Example 2

Use the survey results to make a histogram for the cost of a movie ticket at various theaters.

Survey of Movie Ticket Prices

$7 $8 $7 $9 $8 $9 $8 $10 $8

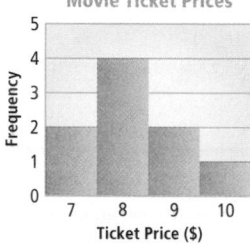

Movie Ticket Prices

Exercises

Find the mean, the median, and the mode of each data set.

1. −3 4 5 5 −2 7 1 8 9

2. 0 0 1 1 2 3 3 5 3 8 7

3. 2.4 2.4 2.3 2.3 2.4 12.0

4. 1 1 1 1 2 2 2 3 3 4

5. 1.2 1.3 1.4 1.5 1.6 1.7 1.8

6. −4 −3 −2 −1 0 1 2 3 4

Make a histogram for each data set.

7. 7 4 8 6 6 8 7 7 5 7

8. 73 75 76 75 74 75 76 74 76 75

Answers

2.

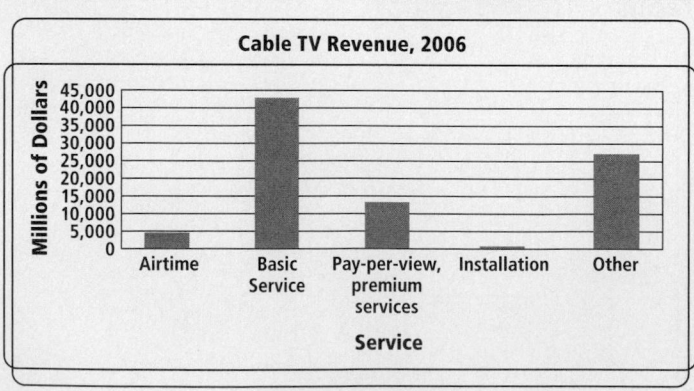

Cable TV Revenue, 2006

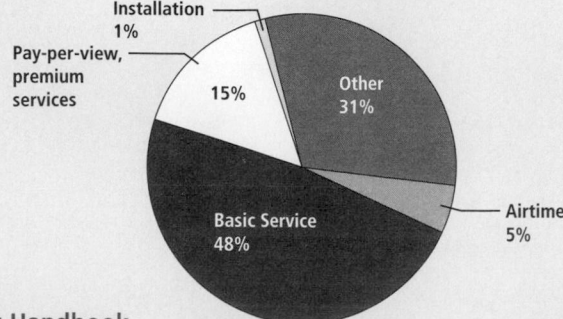

Cable TV Revenue, 2006

Operations With Rational Expressions

A *rational expression* is an expression that can be written in the form $\frac{polynominal}{polynominal}$, where the denominator is not zero. A rational expression is in simplest form if the numerator and denominator have no common factors except 1.

Example 1

Write the expression $\frac{4x + 8}{x + 2}$ in simplest form.

Factor the numerator. $\quad\quad\quad\quad\quad\quad \frac{4x + 8}{x + 2} = \frac{4(x + 2)}{x + 2}$

Divide out the common factor $x + 2$. $\quad\quad\quad\quad = 4$

To add or subtract two rational expressions, use a common denominator.

Example 2

Simplify $\frac{x}{2y} + \frac{x}{3y}$.

The common denominator of 3y and 2y is 6y. $\quad \frac{x}{2y} + \frac{x}{3y} = \frac{x}{2y} \cdot \frac{3}{3} + \frac{x}{3y} \cdot \frac{2}{2}$

Multiply. $\quad\quad\quad\quad\quad\quad\quad\quad\quad\quad = \frac{3x}{6y} + \frac{2x}{6y}$

Add the numerators. $\quad\quad\quad\quad\quad\quad\quad = \frac{5x}{6y}$

To multiply rational expressions, first find and divide out any common factors in the numerators and the denominators. Then multiply the remaining numerators and denominators. To divide rational expressions, first use a reciprocal to change the problem to multiplication.

Example 3

Simplify $\frac{40x^2}{21} \div \frac{5x}{14}$.

Change dividing by $\frac{5x}{14}$ to multiplying by the reciprocal, $\frac{14}{5x}$. $\quad\quad \frac{40x^2}{21} \div \frac{5x}{14} = \frac{40x^2}{21} \cdot \frac{14}{5x}$

Divide out the common factors 5, x, and 7. $\quad\quad\quad\quad\quad\quad = \frac{8}{3}\frac{\cancel{40x^2}1}{\cancel{21}} \times \frac{\cancel{14}2}{\cancel{5x}1}$

Multiply the numerators ($8x \cdot 2$). Multiply the denominators ($3 \cdot 1$). $\quad = \frac{16x}{3}$

Exercises

Write each expression in simplest form.

1. $\frac{4a^2b}{12ab^3}$ **2.** $\frac{5n + 15}{n + 3}$ **3.** $\frac{x - 7}{2x - 14}$ **4.** $\frac{28c^2(d - 3)}{35c(d - 3)}$

Perform the indicated operation.

5. $\frac{3x}{2} + \frac{5x}{2}$ **6.** $\frac{3x}{8} + \frac{5x}{8}$ **7.** $\frac{5}{h} - \frac{3}{h}$ **8.** $\frac{6}{11p} - \frac{9}{11p}$ **9.** $\frac{3x}{5} - \frac{x}{2}$

10. $\frac{13}{2x} - \frac{13}{3x}$ **11.** $\frac{7x}{5} + \frac{5x}{7}$ **12.** $\frac{5a}{b} + \frac{3a}{5b}$ **13.** $\frac{7x}{8} \cdot \frac{32x}{35}$ **14.** $\frac{3x^2}{2} \cdot \frac{6}{x}$

15. $\frac{8x^2}{5} \cdot \frac{10}{x^3}$ **16.** $\frac{7x}{8} \cdot \frac{64}{14x}$ **17.** $\frac{16}{3x} \div \frac{5}{3x}$ **18.** $\frac{4x}{5} \div \frac{16}{15x}$ **19.** $\frac{x^3}{8} \div \frac{x^2}{16}$

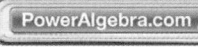
Descriptive Statistics and Histograms

1. $3.\overline{7}$; 5; 5 **2.** 3; 3; 3

3. $3.9\overline{6}$; 2.4; 2.4 **4.** 2; 2; 1

5. 1.5; 1.5; no mode

6. 0; 0; no mode

7.
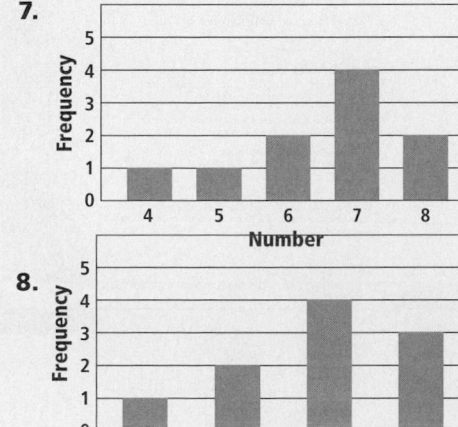

8.

Operations with Rational Expressions

1. $\frac{a}{3b^2}$ **2.** 5

3. $\frac{1}{2}$ **4.** $\frac{4c}{5}$

5. $4x$ **6.** x

7. $\frac{2}{h}$ **8.** $\frac{-3}{11p}$

9. $\frac{x}{10}$ **10.** $\frac{13}{6x}$

11. $\frac{74x}{35}$ **12.** $\frac{28a}{5b}$

13. $\frac{4x^2}{5}$ **14.** $9x$

15. $\frac{16}{x}$ **16.** 4

17. $\frac{16}{5}$ **18.** $\frac{3x^2}{4}$

19. $2x$

Reference

Reference

Table 1 Measures

Reference

	United States Customary	Metric
Length	12 inches (in.) = 1 foot (ft) 36 in. = 1 yard (yd) 3 ft = 1 yard 5280 ft = 1 mile (mi) 1760 yd = 1 mile	10 millimeters (mm) = 1 centimeter (cm) 100 cm = 1 meter (m) 1000 mm = 1 meter 1000 m = 1 kilometer (km)
Area	144 square inches ($in.^2$) = 1 square foot (ft^2) 9 ft^2 = 1 square yard (yd^2) 43,560 ft^2 = 1 acre (a) 4840 yd^2 = 1 acre	100 square millimeters (mm^2) = 1 square centimeter (cm^2) 10,000 cm^2 = 1 square meter (m^2) 10,000 m^2 = 1 hectare (ha)
Volume	1728 cubic inches ($in.^3$) = 1 cubic foot (ft^3) 27 ft^3 = 1 cubic yard (yd^3)	1000 cubic millimeters (mm^3) = 1 cubic centimeter (cm^3) 1,000,000 cm^3 = 1 cubic meter (m^3)
Liquid Capacity	8 fluid ounces (fl oz) = 1 cup (c) 2 c = 1 pint (pt) 2 pt = 1 quart (qt) 4 qt = 1 gallon (gal)	1000 milliliters (mL) = 1 liter (L) 1000 L = 1 kiloliter (kL)
Weight or Mass	16 ounces (oz) = 1 pound (lb) 2000 pounds = 1 ton (t)	1000 milligrams (mg) = 1 gram (g) 1000 g = 1 kilogram (kg) 1000 kg = 1 metric ton
Temperature	32°F = freezing point of water 98.6°F = normal human body temperature 212°F = boiling point of water	0°C = freezing point of water 37°C = normal human body temperature 100°C = boiling point of water

	Customary Units and Metric Units	
Length	1 in. = 2.54 cm 1 ft ≈ 0.305 m 1mi ≈ 1.61 km	1 cm ≈ 0.39 in. 1 m ≈ 3.28 ft 1 km ≈ 0.62 mi
Area	1 acre = 0.40 ha	1 ha = 2.47 acres
Capacity	1 qt ≈ 0.95 L	1 L ≈ 1.06 qt
Weight and Mass	1 oz ≈ 28.4 g 1 lb ≈ 0.45 kg	1 g ≈ 0.035 oz 1 kg ≈ 2.205 lb

Time		
60 seconds (s) = 1 minute (min) 60 minutes = 1 hour (h) 24 hours = 1 day (d) 7 days = 1 week (wk)	4 weeks (approx.) = 1 month (mo) 365 days = 1 year (yr) 52 weeks (approx.) = 1 year	12 months = 1 year 10 years = 1 decade 100 years = 1 century

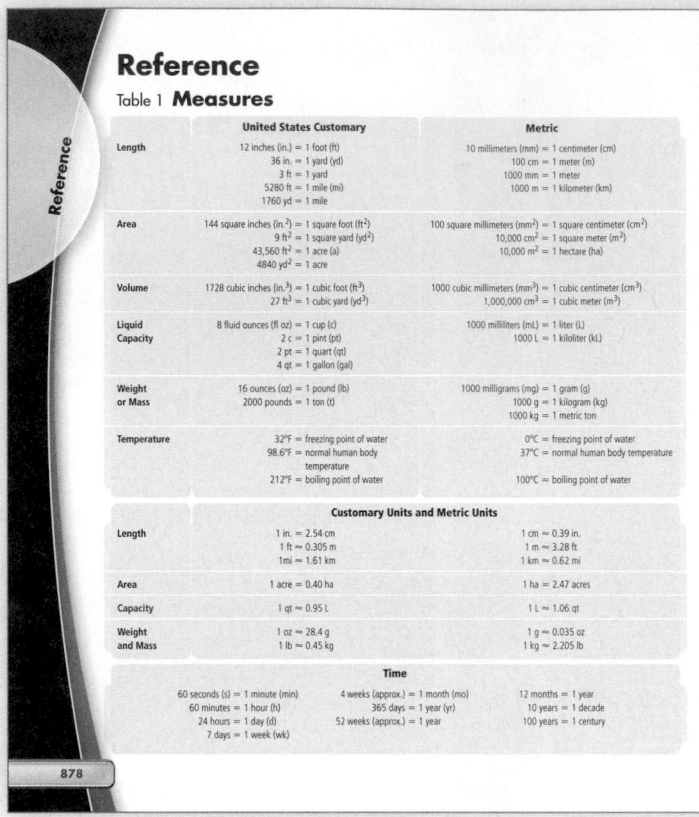

Table 2 Reading Math Symbols

Symbols	Words
$\cdot$, $\times$	multiplication sign, times
$\pm$	plus or minus positive or negative
$=$	equals
$\stackrel{?}{=}$	equals?
$\approx$	is approximately equal to
$\neq$	is not equal to
$<$	is less than
$>$	is greater than
$\leq$	is less than or equal to
$\geq$	is greater than or equal to
$\cong$	is congruent to
$\sim$	is similar to
( )	parentheses for grouping
[ ]	brackets for grouping
{ }	braces for a set
%	percent
$\lvert a \rvert$	absolute value of a
$-a$	opposite of a
$a : b$; $\frac{a}{b}$	ratio of a to b
$\frac{1}{a}$, a^{-1}, $a \neq 0$	reciprocal of a
a^n	nth power of a
a^{-n}	$\frac{1}{a^n}$, $a \neq 0$
$\sqrt{a}$	nonnegative square root of a
$\sqrt[n]{a}$	nth root of a (nonnegative if n even)
° as in $a°$	degree(s)
$\circ$ as in $f \circ g$	composition of functions
π	pi, an irrational number, approximately equal to 3.14
e	an irrational number approximately equal to 2.72
i	the imaginary number $\sqrt{-1}$
$a + bi$, $b \neq 0$	a complex number
∞	infinity
$\sum$	sigma, summation
σ	sigma, standard deviation
σ^2	variance
$\overleftrightarrow{AB}$	line through points A and B

Symbols	Words
$\overline{AB}$	segment with endpoints A and B
AB	length of $\overline{AB}$; distance between points A and B
$\angle A$	angle A
$m\angle A$	measure of angle A
$\triangle ABC$	triangle ABC
(x, y)	ordered pair
$x_1, x_2, \ldots$	specific values of the variable x
$y_1, y_2, \ldots$	specific values of the variable y
$\bar{x}$	mean of data values x_i
$f(x)$	f of x; the function value at x
f^{-1}	function inverse
log	logarithm
$\begin{bmatrix} a & b \\ c & d \end{bmatrix}$	matrix
a_{mn}	element in mth row, nth column of matrix A
A^{-1}	inverse of matrix A
$\begin{vmatrix} a & b \\ c & d \end{vmatrix}$	determinant of a matrix
det A	determinant of matrix A
$n!$	n factorial
${}_nC_r$	combinations of n things chosen r at a time
${}_nP_r$	permutations of n things arranged r at a time
P(event)	probability of an event
$P(A \mid B)$	probability of event A, given event B
sin A	sine of $\angle A$
cos A	cosine of $\angle A$
tan A	tangent of $\angle A$
csc A	cosecant of $\angle A$
sec A	secant of $\angle A$
cot A	cotangent of $\angle A$
^	raised to a power (in a spreadsheet formula)
*	multiply (in a spreadsheet formula)
/	divide (in a spreadsheet formula)
. . .	and so on

Reference

Properties and Formulas

Reference

Order of Operations
1. Perform any operation(s) inside grouping symbols.
2. Simplify any terms with exponents.
3. Multiply and divide in order from left to right.
4. Add and subtract in order from left to right.

The Pythagorean Theorem
In a right triangle, the sum of the squares of the lengths of the legs is equal to the square of the length of the hypotenuse.

$a^2 + b^2 = c^2$

The Distance Formula
The distance d between any two points (x_1, y_1) and (x_2, y_2) is $d = \sqrt{(x_2 - x_1)^2 + (y_2 - y_1)^2}$.

The Midpoint Formula
The midpoint M of a line segment with endpoints $A(x_1, y_1)$ and $B(x_2, y_2)$ is $\left(\frac{x_1 + x_2}{2}, \frac{y_1 + y_2}{2}\right)$.

Chapter 1 Expressions, Equations, and Inequalities

Closure
For all real numbers a and b, $a + b$ and $a \cdot b$ are real numbers.

The Associative Properties
For all real numbers a, b, and c:

$(a + b) + c = a + (b + c)$
$(a \cdot b) \cdot c = a \cdot (b \cdot c)$

The Commutative Properties
For all real numbers a and b:

$a + b = b + a$ and $a \cdot b = b \cdot a$

The Identity Properties
For every real number a:

$a + 0 = a$ and $0 + a = a$ — $a \cdot 1 = a$ and $1 \cdot a = a$
0 is the additive identity. — 1 is the multiplicative identity.

The Inverse Properties
For every real number a:

$a + (-a) = 0$ and $a \cdot \frac{1}{a} = 1 \quad (a \neq 0)$

The Distributive Properties
For all real numbers a, b, and c:

$a(b + c) = ab + ac$ — $(b + c)a = ba + ca$
$a(b - c) = ab - ac$ — $(b - c)a = ba - ca$

Multiplication
Let a represent a real number.
Multiplication by 0: $0 \cdot a = 0$
Multiplication by –1: $-1 \cdot a = -a$

Opposites
Let a and b represent real numbers.
Opposite of a Sum: $-(a + b) = -a + (-b) = -a - b$
Opposite of a Difference: $-(a - b) = -a + b = b - a$
Opposite of a Product: $-(ab) = -a \cdot b = a \cdot (-b)$
Opposite of an Opposite: $-(-a) = a$

Properties of Equality
Assume a, b, and c represent real numbers.
Reflexive: $a = a$
Symmetric: If $a = b$, then $b = a$.
Transitive: If $a = b$ and $b = c$, then $a = c$.
Substitution: If $a = b$, then you can replace a with b and vice versa.
Addition: If $a = b$, then $a + c = b + c$.
Subtraction: If $a = b$, then $a - c = b - c$.
Multiplication: If $a = b$, then $ac = bc$.
Division: If $a = b$ and $c \neq 0$, then $\frac{a}{c} = \frac{b}{c}$.

Properties of Inequality
Let a, b, and c represent real numbers.
Transitive: If $a > b$ and $b > c$, then $a > c$.
Addition: If $a > b$, then $a + c > b + c$.
Subtraction: If $a > b$, then $a - c > b - c$.
Multiplication: If $a > b$ and $c > 0$, then $ac > bc$.
If $a > b$ and $c < 0$, then $ac < bc$.
Division: If $a > b$ and $c > 0$, then $\frac{a}{c} > \frac{b}{c}$.
If $a > b$ and $c < 0$, then $\frac{a}{c} < \frac{b}{c}$.

Chapter 2 Functions, Equations, and Graphs

Direct Variation
$y = kx$ or $\frac{y}{x} = k$, where $k \neq 0$.

Slope of a Line Containing (x_1, y_1) and (x_2, y_2)
slope $= \frac{\text{vertical change (rise)}}{\text{horizontal change (run)}} = \frac{y_2 - y_1}{x_2 - x_1}$,
where $x_2 - x_1 \neq 0$

Point-Slope Equation of a Line
The equation of the line through point (x_1, y_1) with slope m is $y - y_1 = m(x - x_1)$.

Function Families
Assume a, k, and h are positive numbers.
Parent: $y = f(x)$
Reflection in x-axis: $y = -f(x)$
Vertical stretch $(a > 1)$, Vertical shrink $(0 < a < 1)$: $y = af(x)$
Translation
horizontal to left by h: $y = f(x + h)$
horizontal to right by h: $y = f(x - h)$
vertical up by k: $y = f(x) + k$
vertical down by k: $y = f(x) - k$

Chapter 4 Quadratic Functions and Equations

Quadratic Functions
Parent: $y = x^2$
Reflection across x-axis: $y = -x^2$
Stretch $(a > 1)$, Shrink $(0 < a < 1)$: $y = ax^2$
Translation
horizontal by h, vertical by k: $y = (x - h)^2 + k$
Vertex Form: $y = a(x - h)^2 + k$
Standard Form: $y = f(x) = ax^2 + bx + c$
The graph is a parabola that opens up if $a > 0$ and down if $a < 0$.
The vertex is (h, k) (Vertex Form) and $\left(-\frac{b}{2a}, f\left(-\frac{b}{2a}\right)\right)$ (Standard Form).
The axis of symmetry is $x = h$ (Vertex Form) and $x = -\frac{b}{2a}$ (Standard Form).

Factoring Perfect-Square Trinomials
$a^2 + 2ab + b^2 = (a + b)^2$
$a^2 - 2ab + b^2 = (a - b)^2$

Factoring a Difference of Two Squares
$a^2 - b^2 = (a + b)(a - b)$

Multiplication Property of Square Roots
For any numbers $a \geq 0$ and $b \geq 0$, $\sqrt{ab} = \sqrt{a} \cdot \sqrt{b}$.

Division Property of Square Roots
For any numbers $a \geq 0$ and $b > 0$, $\sqrt{\frac{a}{b}} = \frac{\sqrt{a}}{\sqrt{b}}$.

Zero-Product Property
If $ab = 0$, then $a = 0$ or $b = 0$.

The Quadratic Formula
If $ax^2 + bx + c = 0$, then $x = \frac{-b \pm \sqrt{b^2 - 4ac}}{2a}$.

Discriminant
The discriminant of a quadratic equation in the form $ax^2 + bx + c = 0$ is $b^2 - 4ac$.
$b^2 - 4ac > 0 \Rightarrow$ two real solutions
$b^2 - 4ac = 0 \Rightarrow$ one real solution
$b^2 - 4ac < 0 \Rightarrow$ two complex solutions

Square Root of a Negative Real Number
For any positive number a,
$\sqrt{-a} = \sqrt{-1 \cdot a} = \sqrt{-1} \cdot \sqrt{a} = i\sqrt{a}$.
Example: $\sqrt{-5} = i\sqrt{5}$
Note that
$(\sqrt{-5})^2 = (i\sqrt{5})^2 = i^2(\sqrt{5})^2 = -1 \cdot 5 = -5$ (not 5).

Chapter 5 Polynomials and Polynomial Functions

End Behavior of a Polynomial Function
The end behavior of a polynomial function of degree n with leading term ax^n:

a	n	end behavior
positive	even	up and up
positive	odd	down and up
negative	even	down and down
negative	odd	up and down

Factor Theorem
The expression $x - a$ is a linear factor of a polynomial if and only if the value a is a zero of the related polynomial function.

Remainder Theorem
If you divide a polynomial $P(x)$ of degree $n \geq 1$ by $x - a$, then the remainder is $P(a)$.

Factoring a Sum or Difference of Cubes
$a^3 + b^3 = (a + b)(a^2 - ab + b^2)$
$a^3 - b^3 = (a - b)(a^2 + ab + b^2)$

Rational Root Theorem
Let $P(x) = a_nx^n + a_{n-1}x^{n-1} + \cdots + a_1x + a_0$ be a polynomial with integer coefficients.
Integer roots of $P(x) = 0$ must be factors of a_0.
Rational roots have reduced form $\frac{p}{q}$ where p is an integer factor of a_0 and q is an integer factor of a_n.

Conjugate Root Theorems
Suppose $P(x)$ is a polynomial with *rational* coefficients.
If $a + \sqrt{b}$ is an irrational root with a and b rational, then $a - \sqrt{b}$ is also a root.

Suppose $P(x)$ is a polynomial with *real* coefficients.
If $a + bi$ is a complex root with a and b real, then $a - bi$ is also a root.

Reference

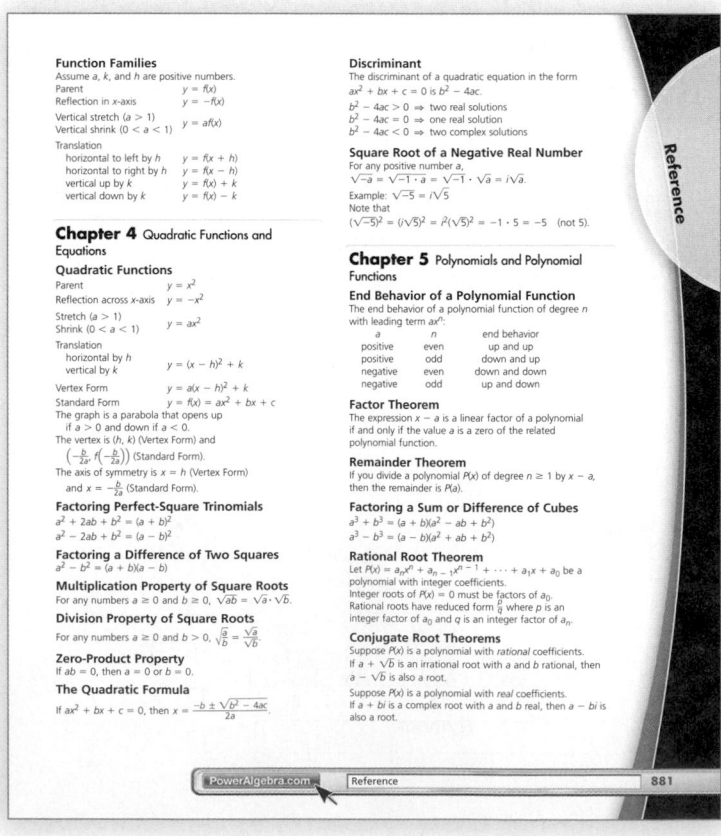

Fundamental Theorem of Algebra
If $P(x)$ is a polynomial of degree $n \geq 1$, then $P(x) = 0$ has exactly n roots, including multiple and complex roots.

Binomial Theorem (Using Pascal's Triangle)
For every positive integer n, $(a + b)^n =$
$P_0 a^n + P_1 a^{n-1}b + P_2 a^{n-2}b^2 + \cdots + P_{n-1}ab^{n-1} + P_n b^n$
where $P_0, P_1, \ldots, P_n$ are the numbers in the nth row of Pascal's Triangle.

Chapter 6 Radical Functions and Rational Exponents

Properties of Exponents
For any nonzero number a and any integers m and n,

$a^0 = 1$ $\qquad (ab)^n = a^n b^n$

$\frac{a^m}{a^n} = a^{m-n}$ $\qquad a^m \cdot a^n = a^{m+n}$

$a^{-n} = \frac{1}{a^n}$ $\qquad (a^m)^n = a^{mn}$

$\left(\frac{a}{b}\right)^n = \frac{a^n}{b^n}$

nth Roots of nth Powers
For any real number a,

$\sqrt[n]{a^n} = \begin{cases} a & \text{if } n \text{ is odd} \\ |a| & \text{if } n \text{ is even} \end{cases}$

Combining Radical Expressions: Products
If $\sqrt[n]{a}$ and $\sqrt[n]{b}$ are real numbers, then $\sqrt[n]{a} \cdot \sqrt[n]{b} = \sqrt[n]{ab}$.

Combining Radical Expressions: Quotients
If $\sqrt[n]{a}$ and $\sqrt[n]{b}$ are real numbers and $b \neq 0$, then $\frac{\sqrt[n]{a}}{\sqrt[n]{b}} = \sqrt[n]{\frac{a}{b}}$.

Properties of Rational Exponents
If the nth root of a is a real number and m is an integer, then $a^{\frac{1}{n}} = \sqrt[n]{a}$ and $a^{\frac{m}{n}} = \sqrt[n]{a^m} = \left(\sqrt[n]{a}\right)^m$. If m is negative, $a \neq 0$.

Composition of Inverse Functions
If f and f^{-1} are inverse functions, then $(f^{-1} \circ f)(x) = x$ and $(f \circ f^{-1})(x) = x$ for x in the domains of f and f^{-1}, respectively.

Radical Functions

	Square Root	nth Root
Parent	$y = \sqrt{x}$	$y = \sqrt[n]{x}$
Reflection in x-axis	$y = -\sqrt{x}$	$y = -\sqrt[n]{x}$
Stretch ($a > 1$) Shrink ($0 < a < 1$)	$y = a\sqrt{x}$	$y = a\sqrt[n]{x}$
Translation horizontal by h vertical by k	$y = \sqrt{x - h} + k$	$y = \sqrt[n]{x - h} + k$

Chapter 7 Exponential and Logarithmic Functions

Exponential Functions
Parent, $b > 0, b \neq 1$	$y = b^x$
Reflection in x-axis	$y = -b^x$
Stretch ($a > 1$) Shrink ($0 < a < 1$)	$y = ab^x$
Translation horizontal by h vertical by k	$y = b^{x-h} + k$

Continuously Compounded Interest
$A(t) = P \cdot e^{rt}$, where $A(t)$ represents the total, P represents the principal, r represents the interest rate, and t represents time in years.

Logarithmic Functions
Base b
Parents, $b > 0, b \neq 1$	$y = \log_b x$
Reflection in x-axis	$y = -\log_b x$
Stretch ($a > 1$) Shrink ($0 < a < 1$)	$y = a \log_b x$
Translation horizontal by h vertical by k	$y = \log_b (x - h) + k$

Properties of Logarithms
For any positive numbers m, n, and b where $b \neq 1$
Product Property: $\log_b mn = \log_b m + \log_b n$
Quotient Property: $\log_b \frac{m}{n} = \log_b m - \log_b n$
Power Property: $\log_b m^n = n\log_b m$

Change of Base Formula
For any positive numbers, m, b, and c, with $b \neq 1$ and $c \neq 1$, $\log_b m = \frac{\log_c m}{\log_c b}$.

Chapter 8 Rational Functions

Inverse Variation
$xy = k$, $y = \frac{k}{x}$, or $x = \frac{k}{y}$, where $k \neq 0$.

Combined Variation
z varies jointly with x and y: $z = kxy$
z varies jointly with x and y and inversely with w: $z = \frac{kxy}{w}$
z varies directly with x and inversely with the product wy: $z = \frac{kx}{wy}$

Reciprocal Functions
Parent	$y = \frac{1}{x}, x \neq 0$
Reflection in x-axis	$y = -\frac{1}{x}, x \neq 0$
Stretch ($a > 1$) Shrink ($0 < a < 1$)	$y = \frac{a}{x}, x \neq 0$
Translation horizontal by h vertical by k	$y = \frac{a}{x-h} + k, x \neq h$
Asymptotes	$y = k$ (horiz.), $x = h$ (vert.)

Chapter 9 Sequences and Series

Arithmetic Mean of Two Numbers
$\frac{x + y}{2}$

Arithmetic Sequence
A recursive definition for an arithmetic sequence with a starting value a and a common difference d has two parts:
$a_1 = a$: initial condition
$a_{n+1} = a_n + d$, for $n \geq 1$: recursive formula
An explicit definition for this sequence is the formula:
$a_n = a + (n - 1)d$ for $n \geq 1$.

Geometric Sequence
A recursive definition for a geometric sequence with a starting value a and a common ratio r has two parts:
$a_1 = a$: initial condition
$a_{n+1} = a_n \cdot r$, for $n \geq 1$: recursive formula
An explicit definition for this sequence is the formula:
$a_n = ar^{n-1}$, for $n \geq 1$.

Sum of a Finite Arithmetic Series
The sum S_n of a finite arithmetic series
$a_1 + a_2 + a_3 + \cdots + a_n$ is $S_n = \frac{n}{2}(a_1 + a_n)$
where a_1 is the first term, a_n is the nth term, and n is the number of terms.

Sum of a Finite Geometric Series
The sum S_n of a finite geometric series
$a_1 + a_1 r + a_1 r^2 + \cdots + a_1 r^{n-1}$ is $S_n = \frac{a_1(1 - r^n)}{1 - r}$
where a_1 is the first term, r is the common ratio, and n is the number of terms.

Sum of an Infinite Geometric Series
An infinite geometric series with $|r| < 1$ converges to the sum S given by the following formula:
$S = \frac{a_1}{1 - r}$

Chapter 10 Quadratic Relations and Conic Sections

Parabolas
	Vertex (0, 0)	Vertex (h, k)
Vertical		
Equation	$y = \frac{1}{4c}x^2$	$y = \frac{1}{4c}(x - h)^2 + k$
Focus	$(0, c)$	$(h, c + k)$
Directrix	$y = -c$	$y = -c + k$
Horizontal		
Equation	$x = \frac{1}{4c}y^2$	$x = \frac{1}{4c}(y - k)^2 + h$
Focus	$(c, 0)$	$(c + h, k)$
Directrix	$x = -c$	$x = -c + h$

Circles, radius = r
	Center (0, 0)	Center (h, k)
Equation	$x^2 + y^2 = r^2$	$(x - h)^2 + (y - k)^2 = r^2$

Ellipses
Horizontal, $a > b$ — Center (0, 0)
Equation: $\frac{x^2}{a^2} + \frac{y^2}{b^2} = 1$
Vertices: $(\pm a, 0)$
Co-Vertices: $(0, \pm b)$
Foci, $c^2 = a^2 - b^2$: $(\pm c, 0)$
Major axis: $y = 0$
Minor axis: $x = 0$

Vertical, $a > b$ — Center (0, 0)
Equation: $\frac{x^2}{b^2} + \frac{y^2}{a^2} = 1$
Vertices: $(0, \pm a)$
Co-Vertices: $(\pm b, 0)$
Foci, $c^2 = a^2 - b^2$: $(0, \pm c)$
Major axis: $x = 0$
Minor axis: $y = 0$

Hyperbolas
Horizontal, $a > b$ — Center (0, 0)
Equation: $\frac{x^2}{a^2} - \frac{y^2}{b^2} = 1$
Vertices: $(\pm a, 0)$
Foci, $c^2 = a^2 + b^2$: $(\pm c, 0)$
Transverse axis: $y = 0$
Asymptotes: $y = \pm\frac{b}{a}x$

Vertical, $a > b$ — Center (0, 0)
Equation: $\frac{y^2}{a^2} - \frac{x^2}{b^2} = 1$
Vertices: $(0, \pm a)$
Foci, $c^2 = a^2 + b^2$: $(0, \pm c)$
Transverse axis: $x = 0$
Asymptotes: $y = \pm\frac{a}{b}x$

Chapter 11 Probability and Statistics

Fundamental Counting Principle
If event M can occur in m ways and is followed by event N that can occur in n ways, then event M followed by event N can occur in $m \cdot n$ ways.

Number of Permutations
The number of permutations of n items of a set arranged r items at a time is
$_nP_r = \frac{n!}{(n-r)!}$ for $0 \leq r \leq n$.

Number of Combinations
The number of combinations of n items of a set chosen r items at a time is
$_nC_r = \frac{n!}{r!(n-r)!}$ for $0 \leq r \leq n$.

Probability of A and B
If A and B are independent events, then
$P(A \text{ and } B) = P(A) \cdot P(B)$.

Probability of A or B
$P(A \text{ or } B) = P(A) + P(B) - P(A \text{ and } B)$
If A and B are mutually exclusive events, then
$P(A \text{ or } B) = P(A) + P(B)$.

Conditional Probability
For any two events A and B with $P(A) \neq 0$, the probability of event B, given event A, is:
$P(B|A) = \frac{P(A \text{ and } B)}{P(A)}$

Mean, Variance, and Standard Deviation
Mean: $\bar{x} = \frac{x_1 + x_2 + x_3 + \cdots + x_n}{n}$
Variance: $\sigma^2 = \frac{\Sigma(x - \bar{x})^2}{n}$
Standard deviation: $\sigma = \sqrt{\frac{\Sigma(x - \bar{x})^2}{n}}$

Binomial Probability
For repeated independent trials, each with a probability of success p and a probability of failure q (with $p + q = 1$), the probability of x successes in n trials is
$P(x) = {_nC_x}p^x q^{n-x}$.

Binomial Theorem (Using Combinations)
For every positive integer n, use the combinations formula $_nC_r$ to expand $(a + b)^n$:
$(a + b)^n = {_nC_0}a^n + {_nC_1}a^{n-1}b + {_nC_2}a^{n-2}b^2 + \cdots + {_nC_{n-1}}ab^{n-1} + {_nC_n}b^n$

Chapter 12 Matrices

Properties of Matrix Addition
If A, B, and C are $m \times n$ matrices, then
Closure Property: $A + B$ is an $m \times n$ matrix
Commutative Property: $A + B = B + A$
Associative Property: $(A + B) + C = A + (B + C)$
Identity Property: There is a unique $m \times n$ matrix O such that $O + A = A + O = A$
Inverse Property: For each A, there is a unique opposite, $-A$, such that $A + (-A) = O$

Properties of Scalar Multiplication
If A and B are $m \times n$ matrices, c and d are scalars, and O is the $m \times n$ zero matrix, then
Closure Property: cA is an $m \times n$ matrix
Associative Property: $(cd)A = c(dA)$
Distributive Property: $c(A + B) = cA + cB$; $(c + d)A = cA + dA$
Identity Property: $1 \cdot A = A$
Property of Zero: $0 \cdot A = O$ and $cO = O$

Properties of Matrix Multiplication
If A, B, and C are $n \times n$ matrices and O is the $n \times n$ zero matrix, then
Closure Property: AB is an $n \times n$ matrix
Associative Property: $(AB)C = A(BC)$
Distributive Property: $A(B + C) = AB + AC$; $(B + C)A = BA + CA$
Property of Zero: $OA = AO = O$

Determinants of 2 × 2 and 3 × 3 Matrices
The determinant of a 2×2 matrix $\begin{bmatrix} a & b \\ c & d \end{bmatrix}$ is $ad - bc$.

The determinant of a 3×3 matrix $\begin{bmatrix} a_1 & b_1 & c_1 \\ a_2 & b_2 & c_2 \\ a_3 & b_3 & c_3 \end{bmatrix}$ is
$(a_1 b_2 c_3 + b_1 c_2 a_3 + c_1 a_2 b_3) - (a_3 b_2 c_1 + b_3 c_2 a_1 + c_3 a_2 b_1)$.

Inverse of a 2 × 2 Matrix
If $A = \begin{bmatrix} a & b \\ c & d \end{bmatrix}$ and det $A \neq 0$,
then the inverse of A is
$A^{-1} = \frac{1}{\det A}\begin{bmatrix} d & -b \\ -c & a \end{bmatrix} = \frac{1}{ad - bc}\begin{bmatrix} d & -b \\ -c & a \end{bmatrix}$.

Chapter T Trigonometry Concepts

Convert Between Radians and Degrees
Use the proportion $\frac{\theta^\circ}{180^\circ} = \frac{t \text{ radians}}{\pi \text{ radians}}$ to convert between radians and degrees.
To convert degrees to radians, multiply by $\frac{\pi \text{ radians}}{180^\circ}$.
To convert radians to degrees, multiply by $\frac{180^\circ}{\pi \text{ radians}}$.

Length of an Intercepted Arc
For a circle of radius r and a central angle of measure θ (in radians), the length s of the intercepted arc is $s = r\theta$.

Sine and Cosine Functions
	Sine	Cosine
Parents	$y = \sin x$	$y = \cos x$
Reflection in x-axis	$y = -\sin x$	$y = -\cos x$
Amplitude $|a|$	$y = a \sin x$	$y = a \cos x$
Period $\frac{2\pi}{b}, b > 0$	$y = \sin bx$	$y = \cos bx$

Tangent Function
Parent: $y = \tan x$
Reflection across x-axis: $y = -\tan x$
Period $\frac{\pi}{b}$: $y = \tan bx$
Asymptotes (tan bx): $x = n\frac{\pi}{2b}$, n odd

Basic Identities
Reciprocal Identities:
$\csc \theta = \frac{1}{\sin \theta}$ $\qquad \sec \theta = \frac{1}{\cos \theta}$ $\qquad \tan \theta = \frac{1}{\cot \theta}$
$\sin \theta = \frac{1}{\csc \theta}$ $\qquad \cos \theta = \frac{1}{\sec \theta}$ $\qquad \cot \theta = \frac{1}{\tan \theta}$
Tangent Identity: $\tan \theta = \frac{\sin \theta}{\cos \theta}$
Cotangent Identity: $\cot \theta = \frac{\cos \theta}{\sin \theta}$

Pythagorean Identities
$\cos^2 \theta + \sin^2 \theta = 1$ $\qquad 1 + \tan^2 \theta = \sec^2 \theta$ $\qquad \cot^2 \theta + 1 = \csc^2 \theta$

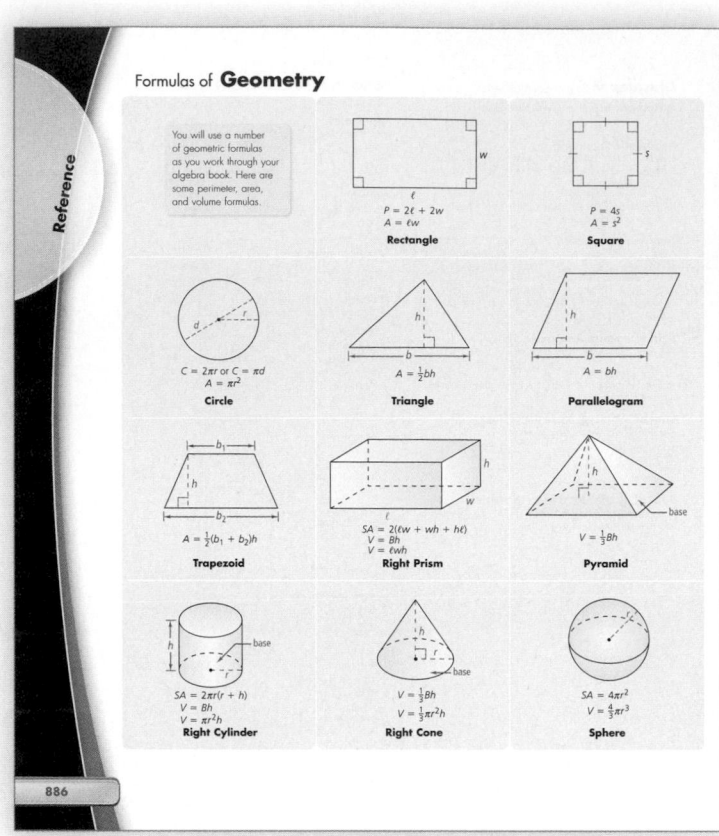

Formulas of **Geometry**

You will use a number of geometric formulas as you work through your algebra book. Here are some perimeter, area, and volume formulas.

Rectangle
$P = 2\ell + 2w$
$A = \ell w$

Square
$P = 4s$
$A = s^2$

Circle
$C = 2\pi r$ or $C = \pi d$
$A = \pi r^2$

Triangle
$A = \frac{1}{2}bh$

Parallelogram
$A = bh$

Trapezoid
$A = \frac{1}{2}(b_1 + b_2)h$

Right Prism
$SA = 2(\ell w + wh + h\ell)$
$V = Bh$
$V = \ell wh$

Pyramid
$V = \frac{1}{3}Bh$

Right Cylinder
$SA = 2\pi r(r + h)$
$V = Bh$
$V = \pi r^2 h$

Right Cone
$V = \frac{1}{3}Bh$
$V = \frac{1}{3}\pi r^2 h$

Sphere
$SA = 4\pi r^3$
$V = \frac{4}{3}\pi r^3$

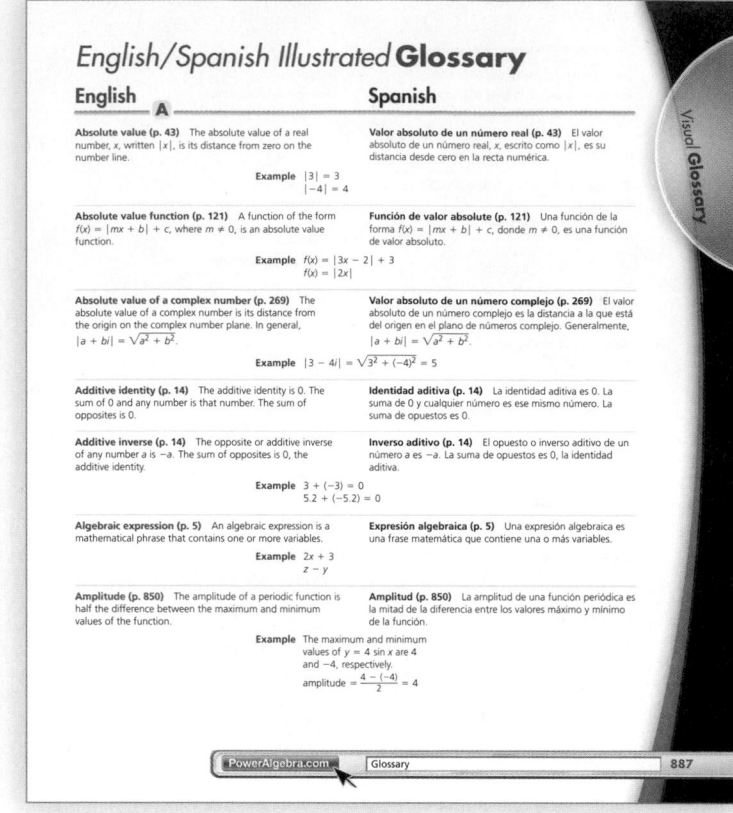

English/Spanish Illustrated **Glossary**

English	Spanish
A	

Absolute value (p. 43) The absolute value of a real number, x, written $|x|$, is its distance from zero on the number line.

Example $|3| = 3$
$|-4| = 4$

Valor absoluto de un número real (p. 43) El valor absoluto de un número real, x, escrito como $|x|$, es su distancia desde cero en la recta numérica.

Absolute value function (p. 121) A function of the form $f(x) = |mx + b| + c$, where $m \neq 0$, is an absolute value function.

Example $f(x) = |3x - 2| + 3$
$f(x) = |2x|$

Función de valor absolute (p. 121) Una función de la forma $f(x) = |mx + b| + c$, donde $m \neq 0$, es una función de valor absoluto.

Absolute value of a complex number (p. 269) The absolute value of a complex number is its distance from the origin on the complex number plane. In general, $|a + bi| = \sqrt{a^2 + b^2}$.

Example $|3 - 4i| = \sqrt{3^2 + (-4)^2} = 5$

Valor absoluto de un número complejo (p. 269) El valor absoluto de un número complejo es la distancia a la que está del origen en el plano de números complejo. Generalmente, $|a + bi| = \sqrt{a^2 + b^2}$.

Additive identity (p. 14) The additive identity is 0. The sum of 0 and any number is that number. The sum of opposites is 0.

Identidad aditiva (p. 14) La identidad aditiva es 0. La suma de 0 y cualquier número es ese mismo número. La suma de opuestos es 0.

Additive inverse (p. 14) The opposite or additive inverse of any number a is $-a$. The sum of opposites is 0, the additive identity.

Example $3 + (-3) = 0$
$5.2 + (-5.2) = 0$

Inverso aditivo (p. 14) El opuesto o inverso aditivo de un número a es $-a$. La suma de opuestos es 0, la identidad aditiva.

Algebraic expression (p. 5) An algebraic expression is a mathematical phrase that contains one or more variables.

Example $2x + 3$
$z - y$

Expresión algebraica (p. 5) Una expresión algebraica es una frase matemática que contiene una o más variables.

Amplitude (p. 850) The amplitude of a periodic function is half the difference between the maximum and minimum values of the function.

Example The maximum and minimum values of $y = 4 \sin x$ are 4 and -4, respectively.
amplitude $= \frac{4 - (-4)}{2} = 4$

Amplitud (p. 850) La amplitud de una función periódica es la mitad de la diferencia entre los valores máximo y mínimo de la función.

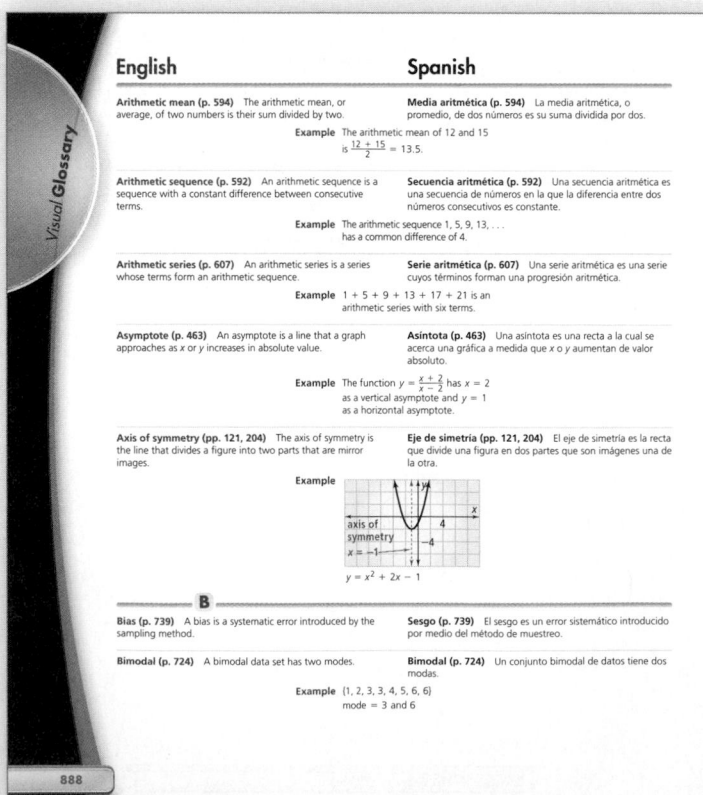

English	Spanish

Arithmetic mean (p. 594) The arithmetic mean, or average, of two numbers is their sum divided by two.

Example The arithmetic mean of 12 and 15 is $\frac{12 + 15}{2} = 13.5$.

Media aritmética (p. 594) La media aritmética, o promedio, de dos números es su suma dividida por dos.

Arithmetic sequence (p. 592) An arithmetic sequence is a sequence with a constant difference between consecutive terms.

Example The arithmetic sequence 1, 5, 9, 13, . . . has a common difference of 4.

Secuencia aritmética (p. 592) Una secuencia aritmética es una secuencia de números en la que la diferencia entre dos números consecutivos es constante.

Arithmetic series (p. 607) An arithmetic series is a series whose terms form an arithmetic sequence.

Example $1 + 5 + 9 + 13 + 17 + 21$ is an arithmetic series with six terms.

Serie aritmética (p. 607) Una serie aritmética es una serie cuyos términos forman una progresión aritmética.

Asymptote (p. 463) An asymptote is a line that a graph approaches as x or y increases in absolute value.

Example The function $y = \frac{x + 2}{x - 2}$ has $x = 2$ as a vertical asymptote and $y = 1$ as a horizontal asymptote.

Asíntota (p. 463) Una asíntota es una recta a la cual se acerca una gráfica a medida que x o y aumentan de valor absoluto.

Axis of symmetry (pp. 121, 204) The axis of symmetry is the line that divides a figure into two parts that are mirror images.

Example
axis of symmetry $x = -1$
$y = x^2 + 2x - 1$

Eje de simetría (pp. 121, 204) El eje de simetría es la recta que divide una figura en dos partes que son imágenes una de la otra.

B		

Bias (p. 739) A bias is a systematic error introduced by the sampling method.

Sesgo (p. 739) El sesgo es un error sistemático introducido por medio del método de muestreo.

Bimodal (p. 724) A bimodal data set has two modes.

Example {1, 2, 3, 3, 4, 5, 6, 6}
mode = 3 and 6

Bimodal (p. 724) Un conjunto bimodal de datos tiene dos modias.

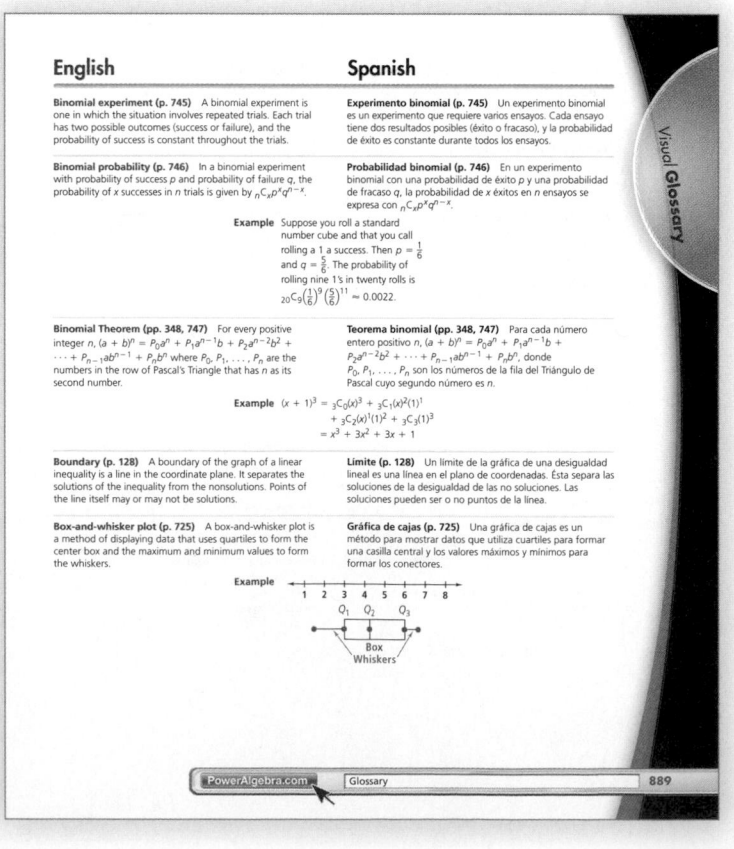

English	Spanish

Binomial experiment (p. 745) A binomial experiment is one in which the situation involves repeated trials. Each trial has two possible outcomes (success or failure), and the probability of success is constant throughout the trials.

Experimento binomial (p. 745) Un experimento binomial es un experimento que requiere varios ensayos. Cada ensayo tiene dos resultados posibles (éxito o fracaso), y la probabilidad de éxito es constante durante todos los ensayos.

Binomial probability (p. 746) In a binomial experiment with probability of success p and probability of failure q, the probability of x successes in n trials is given by ${}_nC_x p^x q^{n-x}$.

Example Suppose you roll a standard number cube and that you call rolling a 1 a success. Then $p = \frac{1}{6}$ and $q = \frac{5}{6}$. The probability of rolling nine 1's in twenty rolls is ${}_{20}C_9 \left(\frac{1}{6}\right)^9 \left(\frac{5}{6}\right)^{11} \approx 0.0022$.

Probabilidad binomial (p. 746) En un experimento binomial con una probabilidad de éxito p y una probabilidad de fracaso q, la probabilidad de x éxitos en n ensayos se expresa con ${}_nC_x p^x q^{n-x}$.

Binomial Theorem (pp. 348, 747) For every positive integer n, $(a + b)^n = P_0 a^n + P_1 a^{n-1}b + P_2 a^{n-2}b^2 + \cdots + P_{n-1} ab^{n-1} + P_n b^n$ where $P_0, P_1, \ldots, P_n$ are the numbers in the row of Pascal's Triangle that has n as its second number.

Example $(x + 1)^3 = {}_3C_0(x)^3 + {}_3C_1(x)^2(1)$
$+ {}_3C_2(x)^1(1)^2 + {}_3C_3(1)^3$
$= x^3 + 3x^2 + 3x + 1$

Teorema binomial (pp. 348, 747) Para cada número entero positivo n, $(a + b)^n = P_0 a^n + P_1 a^{n-1}b + P_2 a^{n-2}b^2 + \cdots + P_{n-1} ab^{n-1} + P_n b^n$, donde $P_0, P_1, \ldots, P_n$ son los números de la fila del Triángulo de Pascal cuyo segundo número es n.

Boundary (p. 128) A boundary of the graph of a linear inequality is a line in the coordinate plane. It separates the solutions of the inequality from the nonsolutions. Points of the line itself may or may not be solutions.

Límite (p. 128) Un límite de la gráfica de una desigualdad lineal es una línea en el plano de coordenadas. Ésta separa las soluciones de la desigualdad de las no soluciones. Las soluciones pueden ser o no puntos de la línea.

Box-and-whisker plot (p. 725) A box-and-whisker plot is a method of displaying data that uses quartiles to form the center box and the maximum and minimum values to form the whiskers.

Example
1 2 3 4 5 6 7 8
Q_1 Q_2 Q_3
Box
Whiskers

Gráfica de cajas (p. 725) Una gráfica de cajas es un método para mostrar datos que utiliza cuartiles para formar una casilla central y los valores máximos y mínimos para formar los conectores.

English | Spanish

Branch (p. 531) Each piece of a discontinuous graph is called a branch.

Rama (p. 531) Cada segmento de una gráfica discontinua se llama rama.

Example
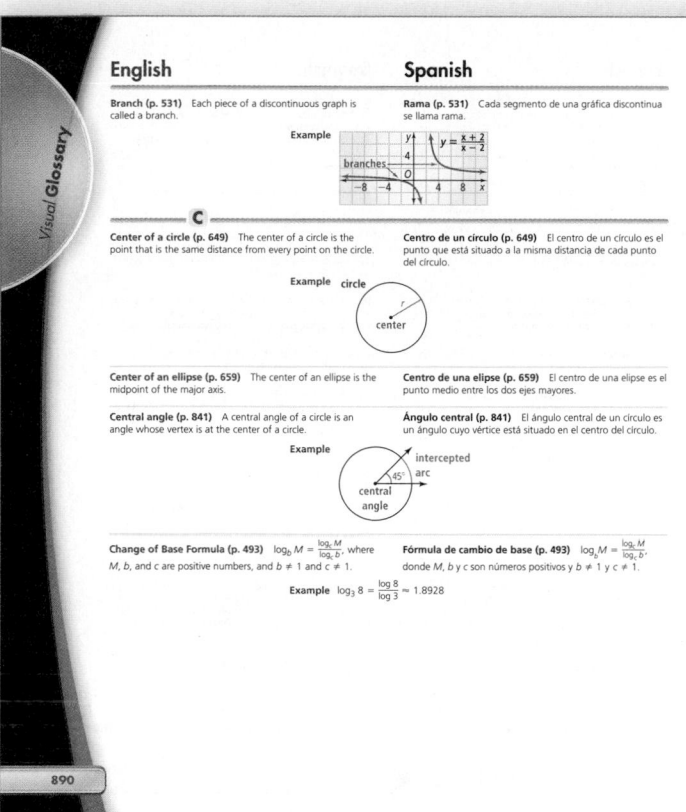

C

Center of a circle (p. 649) The center of a circle is the point that is the same distance from every point on the circle.

Centro de un círculo (p. 649) El centro de un círculo es el punto que está situado a la misma distancia de cada punto del círculo.

Example circle

Center of an ellipse (p. 659) The center of an ellipse is the midpoint of the major axis.

Centro de una elipse (p. 659) El centro de una elipse es el punto medio entre los ejes mayores.

Central angle (p. 841) A central angle of a circle is an angle whose vertex is at the center of a circle.

Ángulo central (p. 841) El ángulo central de un círculo es un ángulo cuyo vértice está situado en el centro del círculo.

Example intercepted arc / central angle

Change of Base Formula (p. 493) $\log_b M = \frac{\log_c M}{\log_c b}$, where M, b, and c are positive numbers, and $b \neq 1$ and $c \neq 1$.

Fórmula de cambio de base (p. 493) $\log_b M = \frac{\log_c M}{\log_c b}$, donde M, b y c son números positivos y $b \neq 1$ y $c \neq 1$.

Example $\log_3 8 = \frac{\log 8}{\log 3} \approx 1.8928$

English | Spanish

Circle (p. 649) A circle is the set of all points in a plane at a distance r from a given point. The standard form of the equation of a circle with center (h, k) and radius r is $(x - h)^2 + (y - k)^2 = r^2$.

Círculo (p. 649) Un círculo es el cojunto de todos los puntos situados en un plano a una distancia r de un punto dado. La forma normal de la ecuación cuyo centro es (h, k) y cuyo radio es r es $(x - h)^2 + (y - k)^2 = r^2$.

Example
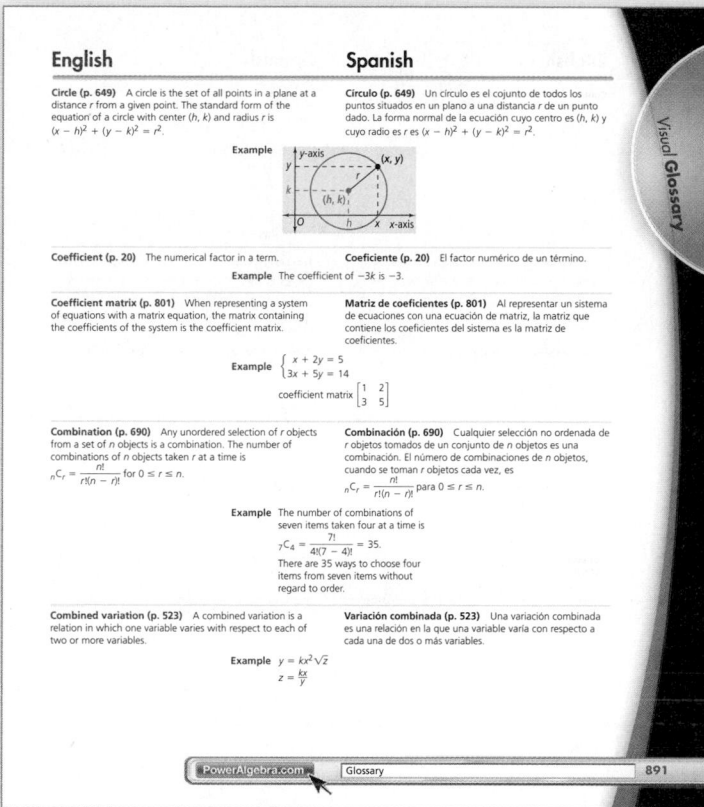

Coefficient (p. 20) The numerical factor in a term.

Coeficiente (p. 20) El factor numérico de un término.

Example The coefficient of $-3k$ is -3.

Coefficient matrix (p. 801) When representing a system of equations with a matrix equation, the matrix containing the coefficients of the system is the coefficient matrix.

Matriz de coeficientes (p. 801) Al representar un sistema de ecuaciones con una ecuación de matriz, la matriz que contiene los coeficientes del sistema es la matriz de coeficientes.

Example $\begin{cases} x + 2y = 5 \\ 3x + 5y = 14 \end{cases}$

coefficient matrix $\begin{bmatrix} 1 & 2 \\ 3 & 5 \end{bmatrix}$

Combination (p. 690) Any unordered selection of r objects from a set of n objects is a combination. The number of combinations of n objects taken r at a time is $_nC_r = \frac{n!}{r!(n-r)!}$ for $0 \leq r \leq n$.

Combinación (p. 690) Cualquier selección no ordenada de r objetos tomados de un conjunto de n objetos es una combinación. El número de combinaciones de n objetos, cuando se toman r objetos cada vez, es $_nC_r = \frac{n!}{r!(n-r)!}$ para $0 \leq r \leq n$.

Example The number of combinations of seven items taken four at a time is
$_7C_4 = \frac{7!}{4!(7-4)!} = 35$.
There are 35 ways to choose four items from seven items without regard to order.

Combined variation (p. 523) A combined variation is a relation in which one variable varies with respect to each of two or more variables.

Variación combinada (p. 523) Una variación combinada es una relación en la que una variable varía con respecto a cada una de dos o más variables.

Example $y = kx^2\sqrt{z}$
$z = \frac{kx}{y}$

English | Spanish

Common difference (p. 592) A common difference is the difference between consecutive terms of an arithmetic sequence.

Diferencia común (p. 592) La diferencia común es la diferencia entre los términos consecutivos de una progresión aritmética.

Example The arithmetic sequence 1, 5, 9, 13, . . . has a common difference of 4.

Common logarithm (p. 482) A common logarithm is a logarithm that uses base 10. You can write the common logarithm $\log_{10} y$ as $\log y$.

Logaritmo común (p. 482) El logaritmo común es un logaritmo de base 10. El logaritmo común $\log_{10} y$ se expresa como $\log y$.

Example $\log 1 = 0$
$\log 10 = 1$
$\log 50 = 1.698970004 \ldots$

Common ratio (p. 600) A common ratio is the ratio of consecutive terms of a geometric sequence.

Razón común (p. 600) Una razón común es la razón de términos consecutivos en una secuencia geométrica.

Example The geometric sequence 2.5, 5, 10, 20, . . . has a common ratio of 2.

Completing the square (p. 255) Completing the square is the process of finding a constant c to add to $x^2 + bx$ so that $x^2 + bx + c$ is the square of a binomial.

Completar el cuadrado (p. 255) Completar un cuadrado es el proceso mediante el cual se halla una constante c que se le pueda sumar a $x^2 + bx$, de manera que $x^2 + bx + c$ sea el cuadrado de un binomio.

Example $x^2 - 12x + \blacksquare$
$x^2 - 12x + \left(\frac{-12}{2}\right)^2$
$x^2 - 12x + 36$

Complex conjugates (p. 272) Number pairs of the form $a + bi$ and $a - bi$ are complex conjugates.

Conjugados complejos (p. 272) Los pares de números de la forma $a + bi$ y $a - bi$ son conjugados complejos.

Example The complex numbers $2 - 3i$ and $2 + 3i$ are complex conjugates.

Complex fraction (p. 559) A complex fraction is a rational expression that has a fraction in its numerator or denominator, or in both its numerator and denominator.

Fracción compleja (p. 559) Una fracción compleja es una expresión racional en la que el numerador, el denominador o ambos son una fracción.

Example $\frac{\frac{2}{3}}{\frac{5}{3}}$

Complex number (p. 269) Complex numbers are the real numbers and the imaginary numbers.

Número complejo (p. 269) Los números complejos son los números reales y los números imaginarios.

Example $6 + i$
$7, 2i$

English | Spanish

Complex number plane (p. 269) The complex number plane is identical to the coordinate plane except each ordered pair (a, b) represents the complex number $a + bi$. The horizontal axis is the Real axis. The vertical axis is the Imaginary axis.

Plano de números complejos (p. 269) El plano de los números complejos es idéntico al plano de coordenadas, a excepción de que cada par ordenado (a, b) representa el número complejo $a + bi$. El eje horizontal es el eje real. El eje vertical es el eje imaginario.

Example
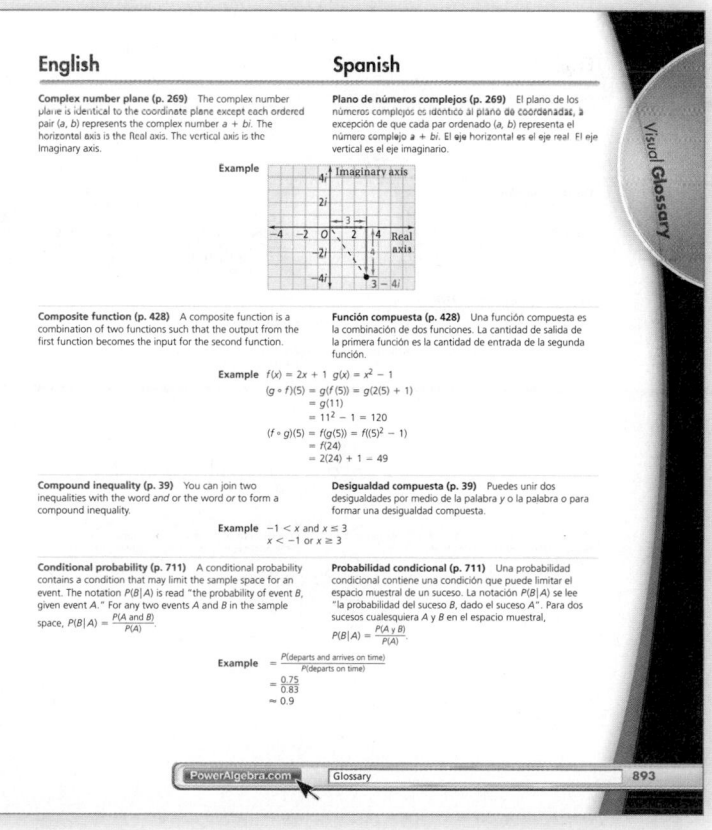

Composite function (p. 428) A composite function is a combination of two functions such that the output from the first function becomes the input for the second function.

Función compuesta (p. 428) Una función compuesta es la combinación de dos funciones. La cantidad de salida de la primera función es la cantidad de entrada de la segunda función.

Example $f(x) = 2x + 1 \quad g(x) = x^2 - 1$
$(g \circ f)(5) = g(f(5)) = g(2(5) + 1)$
$= g(11)$
$= 11^2 - 1 = 120$
$(f \circ g)(5) = f(g(5)) = f(5^2 - 1)$
$= f(24)$
$= 2(24) + 1 = 49$

Compound inequality (p. 39) You can join two inequalities with the word and or the word or to form a compound inequality.

Desigualdad compuesta (p. 39) Puedes unir dos desigualdades por medio de la palabra y o la palabra o para formar una desigualdad compuesta.

Example $-1 < x$ and $x \leq 3$
$x < -1$ or $x \geq 3$

Conditional probability (p. 711) A conditional probability contains a condition that may limit the sample space for an event. The notation $P(B|A)$ is read "the probability of event B, given event A." For any two events A and B in the sample space, $P(B|A) = \frac{P(A \text{ and } B)}{P(A)}$.

Probabilidad condicional (p. 711) Una probabilidad condicional contiene una condición que puede limitar el espacio muestral de un suceso. La notación $P(B|A)$ se lee "la probabilidad del suceso B, dado el suceso A". Para dos sucesos cualesquiera A y B en el espacio muestral, $P(B|A) = \frac{P(A \text{ y } B)}{P(A)}$.

Example $= \frac{P(\text{departs and arrives on time})}{P(\text{departs on time})}$
$= \frac{0.75}{0.83}$
≈ 0.9

Page 894

English	Spanish

Conic section (p. 634) A conic section is a curve formed by the intersection of a plane and a double cone.

Sección cónica (p. 634) Una sección cónica es una curva que se forma por la intersección de un plano con un cono doble.

Example

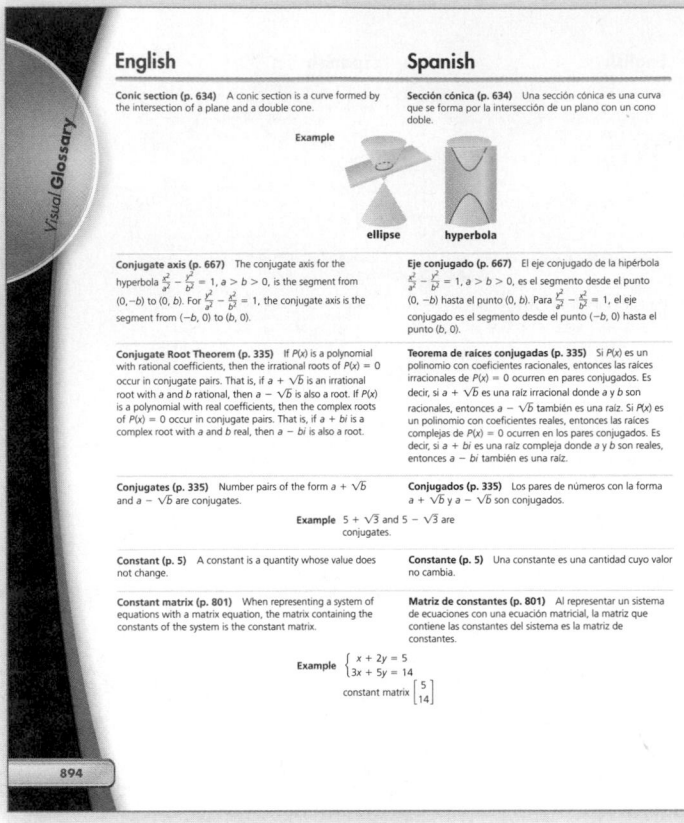

ellipse   hyperbola

Conjugate axis (p. 667) The conjugate axis for the hyperbola $\frac{x^2}{a^2} - \frac{y^2}{b^2} = 1$, $a > b > 0$, is the segment from $(0, -b)$ to $(0, b)$. For $\frac{y^2}{a^2} - \frac{x^2}{b^2} = 1$, the conjugate axis is the segment from $(-b, 0)$ to $(b, 0)$.

Eje conjugado (p. 667) El eje conjugado de la hipérbola $\frac{x^2}{a^2} - \frac{y^2}{b^2} = 1$, $a > b > 0$, es el segmento desde el punto $(0, -b)$ hasta el punto $(0, b)$. Para $\frac{y^2}{a^2} - \frac{x^2}{b^2} = 1$, el eje conjugado es el segmento desde el punto $(-b, 0)$ hasta el punto $(b, 0)$.

Conjugate Root Theorem (p. 335) If $P(x)$ is a polynomial with rational coefficients, then the irrational roots of $P(x) = 0$ occur in conjugate pairs. That is, if $a + \sqrt{b}$ is an irrational root with a and b rational, then $a - \sqrt{b}$ is also a root. If $P(x)$ is a polynomial with real coefficients, then the complex roots of $P(x) = 0$ occur in conjugate pairs. That is, if $a + bi$ is a complex root with a and b real, then $a - bi$ is also a root.

Teorema de raíces conjugadas (p. 335) Si $P(x)$ es un polinomio con coeficientes racionales, entonces las raíces irracionales de $P(x) = 0$ ocurren en pares conjugados. Es decir, si $a + \sqrt{b}$ es una raíz irracional donde a y b son racionales, entonces $a - \sqrt{b}$ también es una raíz. Si $P(x)$ es un polinomio con coeficientes reales, entonces las raíces complejas de $P(x) = 0$ ocurren en los pares conjugados. Es decir, si $a + bi$ es una raíz compleja donde a y b son reales, entonces $a - bi$ también es una raíz.

Conjugates (p. 335) Number pairs of the form $a + \sqrt{b}$ and $a - \sqrt{b}$ are conjugates.

Conjugados (p. 335) Los pares de números con la forma $a + \sqrt{b}$ y $a - \sqrt{b}$ son conjugados.

Example $5 + \sqrt{3}$ and $5 - \sqrt{3}$ are conjugates.

Constant (p. 5) A constant is a quantity whose value does not change.

Constante (p. 5) Una constante es una cantidad cuyo valor no cambia.

Constant matrix (p. 801) When representing a system of equations with a matrix equation, the matrix containing the constants of the system is the constant matrix.

Matriz de constantes (p. 801) Al representar un sistema de ecuaciones con una ecuación matricial, la matriz que contiene las constantes del sistema es la matriz de constantes.

Example $\begin{cases} x + 2y = 5 \\ 3x + 5y = 14 \end{cases}$

constant matrix $\begin{bmatrix} 5 \\ 14 \end{bmatrix}$

Page 895

English	Spanish

Constant of proportionality (p. 363) If $y = ax^b$ describes y as a power function of x, then y varies directly with, or is proportional to, the bth power of x. The constant a is the constant of proportionality.

Constante de proporcionalidad (p. 363) Si $y = ax^b$ describe a y como una potencia de la función de x, entonces y varía directamente con, o es proporcional a, la b^{ma} potencia de x. La constante a es la constante de proporcionalidad.

Constant of variation (p. 74) The constant of variation is the ratio of the two variables in a direct variation and the product of the two variables in an inverse variation.

Constante de variación (p. 74) La constante de variación es la razón de dos variables en una variación directa y el producto de las dos variables en una variación inversa.

Example In $y = 3.5x$, the constant of variation k is 3.5. In $xy = 5$, the constant of variation k is 5.

Constant term (p. 20) A constant term is a term with no variables.

Término constante (p. 20) Un término constante es un término que no tiene variables.

Constraint (p. 169) Constraints are restrictions on the variables of the objective function in a linear programming problem. See **Linear programming**.

Restricción (p. 169) Las restricciones son limitaciones a las variables de una función objetiva en un problema de programación lineal. Ver **Linear programming**.

Continuous graph (p. 539) A graph is continuous if it has no jumps, breaks, or holes.

Gráfica continua (p. 539) Una gráfica es continua si no tiene saltos, interrupciones o huecos.

Continuous probability distribution (p. 752) A continuous probability distribution has as its events any of the infinitely many values in an interval of real numbers.

Distribución de probabilidad continua (p. 752) Una distribución de probabilidad continua tiene como sucesos a cualquiera del número infinito de valores en un intervalo de números reales.

Continuously compounded interest (p. 477) When interest is compounded continuously on principal P, the value A of an account is $A = Pe^{rt}$.

Interés compuesto continuo (p. 477) En un sistema donde el interés es compuesto continuamente sobre el capital P, el valor de A de una cuenta es $A = Pe^{rt}$.

Example Suppose that $P = \$1200$, $r = 0.05$, and $t = 3$. Then
$A = 1200e^{0.05 \cdot 3}$
$= 1200(2.718 \ldots)^{0.15}$
≈ 1394.20

Controlled experiment (p. 739) In a controlled experiment, you divide the sample into two groups. You impose a treatment on one group but not the other "control" group. Then you compare the effect on the treated group to the control group.

Experimento controlado (p. 739) En un experimento controlado, se divide la muestra en dos grupos. Uno de los grupos se manipula y el otro grupo "controlado" se mantiene en su estado original. Luego se comparan el estado del grupo manipulado y el estado del grupo controlado.

Convenience sample (p. 738) In a convenience sample you select any members of the population who are conveniently and readily available.

Muestra de conveniencia (p. 738) En una muestra de conveniencia se selecciona a cualquier miembro de la población que está convenientemente disponible.

Page 896

English	Spanish

Converge (p. 617) An infinite series $a_1 + a_2 + \cdots + a_n + \cdots$ converges if the sum $a_1 + a_2 + \cdots + a_n$ get closer and closer to a real number as n increases.

Convergir (p. 617) Una serie infinita $a_1 + a_2 + \cdots + a_n + \cdots$ es convergente si la suma $a_1 + a_2 + \cdots + a_n$ se aproxima cada vez más a un número real a medida que el valor de n incrementa.

Example $1 + \frac{1}{2} + \frac{1}{4} + \frac{1}{8} + \cdots$ converges.

Correlation (p. 103) A correlation indicates the strength of a relationship between two data sets.

Correlación (p. 103) Una correlación indica la fuerza de una relación entre dos conjuntos de datos.

Correlation coefficient (p. 106) The correlation coefficient, r, indicates the strength of the correlation. The closer r is to 1 or -1, the more closely the data resembles a line and the more accurate your model is likely to be.

Coeficiente de correlación (p. 106) El coeficiente de correlación, r, indica la fuerza de la correlación. Mientras más cerca está r de 1 ó -1, más se parecen los datos a una línea y será más probable que tu modelo sea preciso.

Corresponding elements (p. 772) Corresponding elements are elements in the same position in each matrix.

Elementos correspondientes (p. 772) Los elementos correspondientes son elementos que se encuentran en la misma posición de cada matriz.

Cosine function, Cosine of θ (pp. 823, 848) The cosine function, $y = \cos \theta$, matches the measure θ of an angle in standard position with the x-coordinate of a point on the unit circle. This point is where the terminal side of the angle intersects the unit circle. The x-coordinate is the cosine of θ.

Función coseno, Coseno de θ (pp. 823, 848) La función coseno, $y = \cos \theta$, empareja la medida θ de un ángulo en posición estándar con la x-coordenada de un punto en el círculo unitario. Este es el punto en el que el lado terminal del ángulo interseca al círculo unitario. La coordenada x es el coseno de θ.

Example

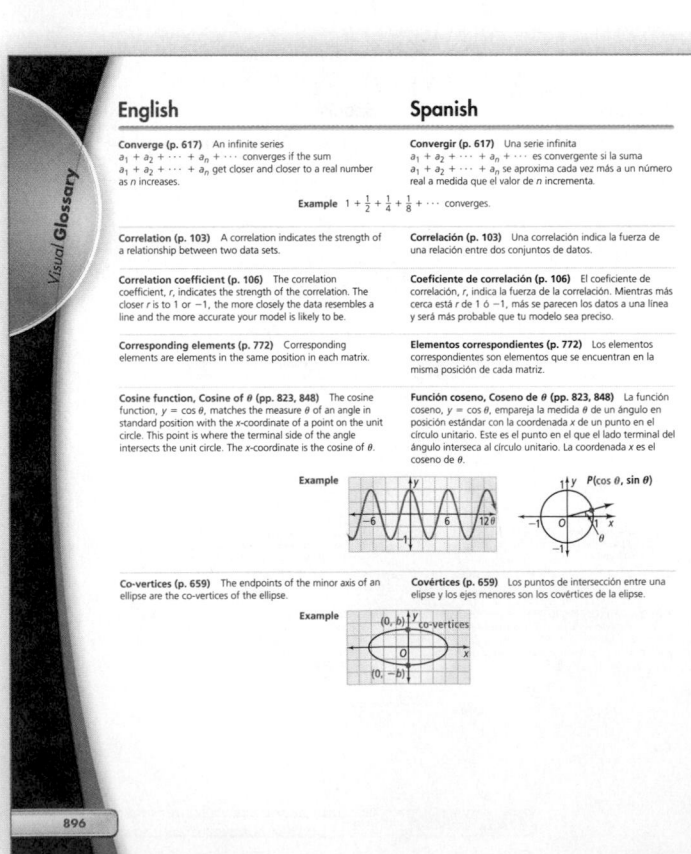

$P(\cos \theta, \sin \theta)$

Co-vertices (p. 659) The endpoints of the minor axis of an ellipse are the co-vertices of the ellipse.

Covértices (p. 659) Los puntos de intersección entre una elipse y sus ejes menores son los covértices de la elipse.

Example

$(0, b)$ co-vertices
$(0, -b)$

Page 897

English	Spanish

Cycle (p. 849) A cycle of a periodic function is an interval of x-values over which the function provides one complete pattern of y-values.

Ciclo (p. 849) El ciclo de una función periódica es un intervalo de valores de x de los cuales la función produce un patrón completo de valores de y.

Example

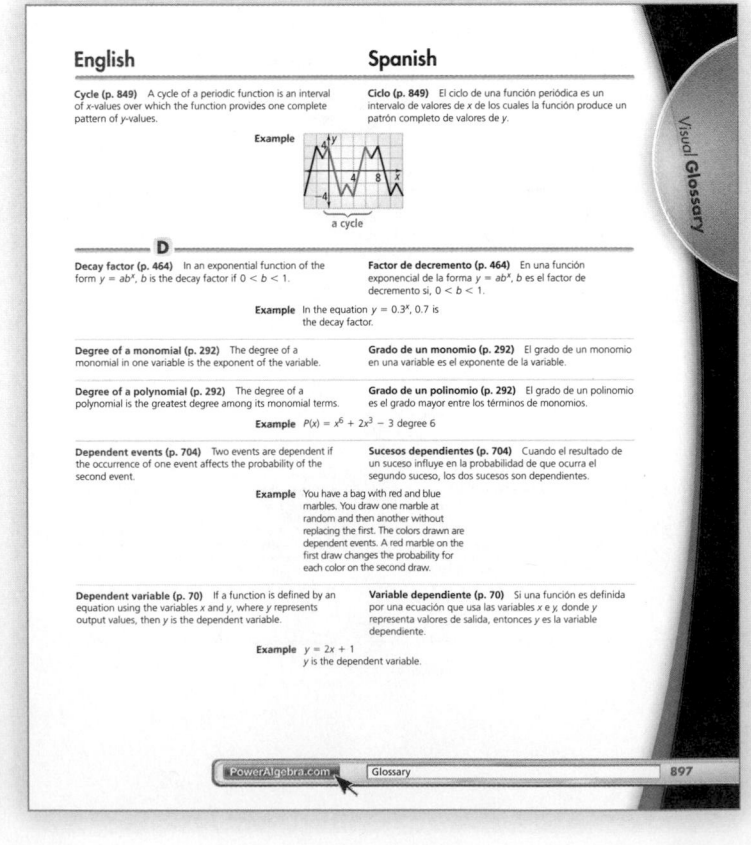

a cycle

D

Decay factor (p. 464) In an exponential function of the form $y = ab^x$, b is the decay factor if $0 < b < 1$.

Factor de decremento (p. 464) En una función exponencial de la forma $y = ab^x$, b es el factor de decremento si, $0 < b < 1$.

Example In the equation $y = 0.3^x$, 0.7 is the decay factor.

Degree of a monomial (p. 292) The degree of a monomial in one variable is the exponent of the variable.

Grado de un monomio (p. 292) El grado de un monomio en una variable es el exponente de la variable.

Degree of a polynomial (p. 292) The degree of a polynomial is the greatest degree among its monomial terms.

Grado de un polinomio (p. 292) El grado de un polinomio es el grado mayor entre los términos de monomios.

Example $P(x) = x^6 + 2x^3 - 3$ degree 6

Dependent events (p. 704) Two events are dependent if the occurrence of one event affects the probability of the second event.

Sucesos dependientes (p. 704) Cuando el resultado de un suceso influye en la probabilidad de que ocurra el segundo suceso, los dos sucesos son dependientes.

Example You have a bag with red and blue marbles. You draw one marble at random and then another without replacing the first. The colors drawn are dependent events. A red marble on the first draw changes the probability for each color on the second draw.

Dependent variable (p. 70) If a function is defined by an equation using the variables x and y, where y represents output values, then y is the dependent variable.

Variable dependiente (p. 70) Si una función es definida por una ecuación que usa las variables x e y, donde y representa valores de salida, entonces y es la variable dependiente.

Example $y = 2x + 1$
y is the dependent variable.

English — Spanish

Descartes' Rule of Signs (p. 336) Let $P(x)$ be a polynomial with real coefficients written in standard form.
– The number of positive real roots of $P(x) = 0$ is either equal to the number of sign changes between consecutive coefficients of $P(x)$ or is less than that by an even number;
– The number of negative real roots of $P(x) = 0$ is either equal to the number of sign changes between consecutive coefficients of $P(-x)$ or is less than that by an even number. (Count multiple roots according to their multiplicity.)

Regla de los signos de Descartes (p. 336) Sea $P(x)$ un polinomio con coeficientes reales escritos en forma normal.
– El número de raíces positivas reales de $P(x) = 0$ es igual al número de cambios de signos entre coeficientes consecutivos de $P(x)$ o es menor que eso en un número par;
– El número de raíces negativas reales de $P(x) = 0$ es igual al número de cambios de signos entre coeficientes consecutivos de $P(-x)$ o es menor que eso en un número par. (Cuenta las raíces múltiples según su multiplicidad.)

Determinant (p. 790) The determinant of a square matrix is a real number that can be computed from its elements according to a specific formula.

Determinante (p. 790) El determinante de una matriz cuadrada es un número real que se puede calcular a partir de sus elementos por medio de una fórmula específica.

Example The determinant of $\begin{bmatrix} 3 & -2 \\ 5 & 6 \end{bmatrix}$ is
$$3(6) - 5(-2) = 28.$$

Difference of cubes (p. 311) A difference of cubes is an expression of the form $a^3 - b^3$. It can be factored as $(a - b)(a^2 + ab + b^2)$.

Diferencia de dos cubos (p. 311) La diferencia de dos cubos es una expresión de la forma $a^3 - b^3$. Se puede factorizar como $(a - b)(a^2 + ab + b^2)$.

Example $x^3 - 27 = (x - 3)(x^2 + 3x + 9)$

Difference of two squares (p. 233) A difference of two squares is an expression of the form $a^2 - b^2$. It can be factored as $(a + b)(a - b)$.

Diferencia de dos cuadrados (p. 233) La diferencia de dos cuadrados es una expresión de la forma $a^2 - b^2$. Se puede factorizar como $(a + b)(a - b)$.

Example $25a^2 - 4 = (5a + 2)(5a - 2)$
$m^6 - 1 = (m^3 + 1)(m^3 - 1)$

Direct variation (p. 74) A linear function defined by an equation of the form $y = kx$, where $k \neq 0$, represents direct variation.

Variación directa (p. 74) Una función lineal definida por una ecuación de la forma $y = kx$, donde $k \neq 0$, representa una variación directa.

Example $y = 3.5x, y = 7x, y = -\frac{1}{2}x$

Directrix (p. 641) The directrix of a parabola is the fixed line used to define a parabola. Each point of the parabola is the same distance from the focus and the directrix.

Directriz (p. 641) La directriz de una parábola es la recta fija con que se define una parábola. Cada punto de la parábola está a la misma distancia del foco y de la directriz.

Example

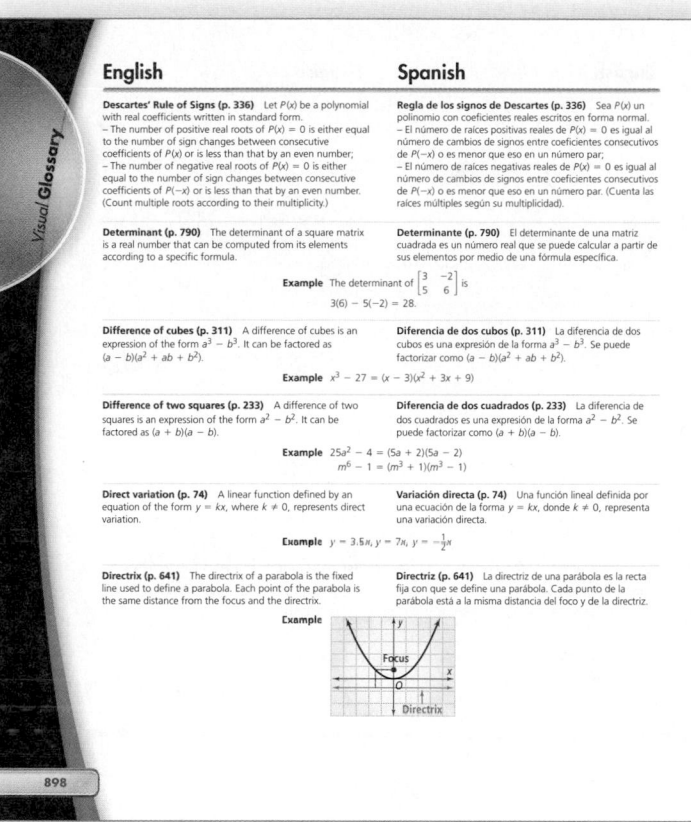

English — Spanish

Discontinuous graph (p. 539) A graph is discontinuous if it has a jump, break, or hole.

Gráfica discontinua (p. 539) Una gráfica es discontinua si tiene un salto, interrupción o hueco.

Discrete probability distribution (p. 752) A discrete probability distribution has a finite number of possible events.

Distribución de probabilidad discreta (p. 752) Una distribución de probabilidad discreta tiene un número finito de sucesos posibles.

Discriminant (p. 262) The discriminant of a quadratic equation in the form $ax^2 + bx + c = 0$ is the value of the expression $b^2 - 4ac$.

Discriminante (p. 262) El discriminante de una ecuación cuadrática en la forma $ax^2 + bx + c = 0$ es el valor de la expresión $b^2 - 4ac$.

Example $3x^2 - 6x + 1$
discriminant $= (-6)^2 - 4(3)(1)$
$= 36 - 12 = 24$

Diverge (p. 617) An infinite series diverges if it does not converge.

Divergir (p. 617) Una serie infinita es divergente si no es convergente.

Example $1 + 2 + 4 + 8 + \cdots$ diverges.

Domain (p. 65) The domain of a relation is the set of all inputs, or x-coordinates, of the ordered pairs.

Dominio (p. 65) El dominio de una relación es el conjunto de todos los valores de entrada, o coordenadas x, de los pares ordenados.

Examples In the relation $\{(0, 1), (0, 2), (0, 3), (0, 4), (1, 3), (1, 4), (2, 1)\}$, the domain is $\{0, 1, 2\}$. In the function $f(x) = x^2 - 10$, the domain is all real numbers.

E

Ellipse (p. 658) An ellipse is the set of points P in a plane such that the sum of the distances from P to two fixed points F_1 and F_2 is a given constant k. The standard form of the equation of an ellipse with its center at the origin is $\frac{x^2}{a^2} + \frac{y^2}{b^2} = 1$ if the major axis is horizontal and $\frac{x^2}{b^2} + \frac{y^2}{a^2} = 1$ if the major axis is vertical, where $a > b$.

Elipse (p. 658) Una elipse es el conjunto de puntos P situados en un plano tal que la suma de las distancias entre P y dos puntos fijos F_1 y F_2 es una constante dada k. La forma normal de la ecuación de una elipse con su centro en el origen es $\frac{x^2}{a^2} + \frac{y^2}{b^2} = 1$ si el eje mayor es horizontal y $\frac{x^2}{b^2} + \frac{y^2}{a^2} = 1$ si el eje mayor es vertical, donde $a > b$.

Example

$$\frac{x^2}{36} + \frac{y^2}{9} = 1$$
$$F_1 = (-3\sqrt{3}, 0), F_2 = (3\sqrt{3}, 0)$$

English — Spanish

End behavior (p. 294) End behavior of the graph of a function describes the directions of the graph as you move to the left and to the right, away from the origin.

Comportamiento extremo (p. 294) El comportamiento extremo de la gráfica de una función describe las direcciones de la gráfica al moverse a la izquierda y a la derecha, apartándose del origen.

Equal matrices (p. 775) Equal matrices are matrices with the same dimensions and equal corresponding elements.

Matrices equivalentes (p. 775) Dos matrices son equivalentes si y sólo si tienen las mismas dimensiones y sus elementos correspondientes son iguales.

Example Matrices A and B are equal.
$$A = \begin{bmatrix} 2 & 6 \\ \frac{9}{3} & 1 \end{bmatrix} \quad B = \begin{bmatrix} 6 & 6 \\ 3 & -13 \end{bmatrix}$$

Equally likely outcomes (p. 698) Equally likely outcomes are events in a sample space that have the same chance of occurring.

Resultados igualmente probables (p. 698) Resultados igualmente probables son sucesos en un espacio muestral con la misma probabilidad de ocurrir.

Equation (p. 26) An equation is a statement that two algebraic expressions are equal.

Ecuación (p. 26) Una ecuación es un enunciado que describe dos expresiones algebraicas iguales.

Equivalent systems (p. 157) Equivalent systems are systems that have the same solution(s).

Sistemas equivalentes (p. 157) Sistemas equivalentes son sistemas que tienen la misma solución o las mismas soluciones.

Evaluate (p. 19) To evaluate an algebraic expression, substitute a number for each variable in the expression. Then simplify using the order of operations.

Evaluar (p. 19) Para evaluar una expresión algebraica, sustituye cada variable de la expresión con un número. Luego, simplifica usando el orden de operaciones.

Example When $x = 2$ and $y = -1$,
$2x + 3y$ evaluates to 1.

Expand (p. 347) To expand the power of a binomial, multiply as needed, then write the polynomial in standard form.

Expandir (p. 347) Para expandir la potencia de un binomio, multiplica como sea necesario. Luego, escribe el polinomio en forma normal.

Example $(x + 4)^3 = (x + 4)(x + 4)^2$
$= (x + 4)(x^2 + 8x + 16)$
$= x^3 + 8x^2 + 16x + 4x^2 + 32x + 64$
$= x^3 + 12x^2 + 48x + 64$

Experimental probability (p. 695) The experimental probability of an event is the ratio $\frac{\text{number of times the event occurs}}{\text{number of trials}}$.

Probabilidad experimental (p. 695) La probabilidad experimental de un suceso es la razón $\frac{\text{number of times the event occurs}}{\text{number of trials}}$.

Example Suppose a basketball player has scored 19 times in 28 attempts at a basket. The experimental probability of the player's scoring is
$P(\text{score}) = \frac{19}{28} \approx 0.68$, or 68%.

English — Spanish

Explicit formula (p. 585) An explicit formula expresses the nth term of a sequence in terms of n.

Fórmula explícita (p. 585) Una fórmula explícita expresa el enésimo término de una progresión en función de n.

Example Let $a_n = 2n + 5$ for positive integers n. If $n = 7$, then
$a_7 = 2(7) + 5 = 19$.

Exponential decay (p. 463) Exponential decay is modeled by a function of the form $y = ab^x$ with $0 < b < 1$.

Decaimiento exponencial (p. 463) El decaimiento exponencial se expresa con una función $y = ab^x$ donde $0 < b < 1$.

Exponential equation (p. 498) An exponential equation contains the form b^{cx}, with the exponent including a variable.

Ecuación exponencial (p. 498) Una ecuación exponencial tiene la forma b^{cx}, y su exponente incluye una variable.

Example $5^{2x} = 270$
$\log 5^{2x} = \log 270$
$2x \log 5 = \log 270$
$2x = \frac{\log 270}{\log 5}$
$2x \approx 3.4785$
$x \approx 1.7392$

Exponential function (p. 462) The general form of an exponential function is $y = ab^x$, where x is a real number, $a \neq 0$, $b > 0$, and $b \neq 1$. When $b > 1$, the function models exponential growth with growth factor b. When $0 < b < 1$, the function models exponential decay with decay factor b.

Función exponencial (p. 462) La forma general de una función exponencial es $y = ab^x$, donde x es un número real, $a \neq 0$, $b > 0$ y $b \neq 1$. Cuando $b > 1$, la función representa un incremento exponencial con factor de incremento b. Cuando $0 < b < 1$, la función representa el decremento exponencial con factor de decremento b.

Example

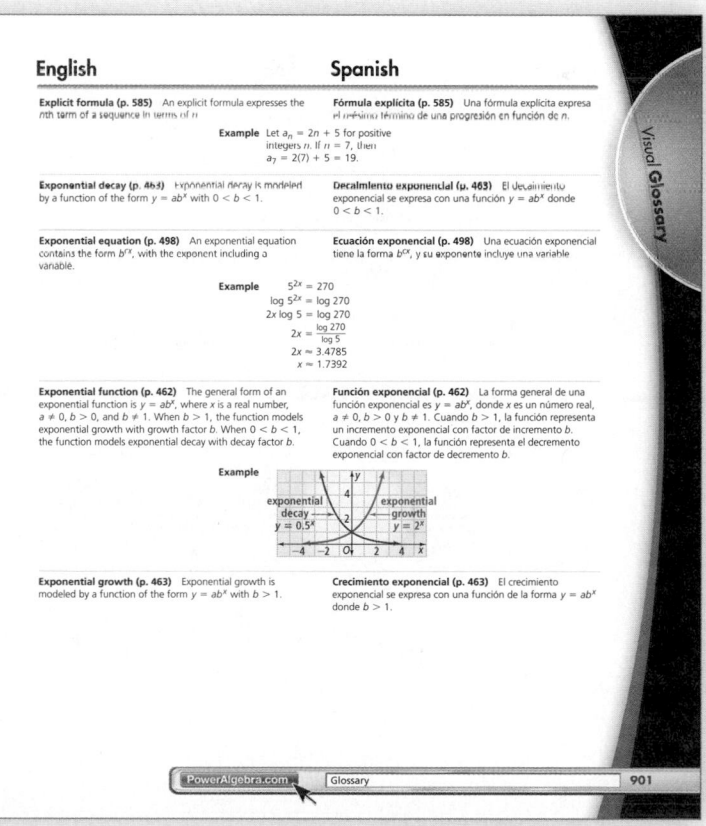

Exponential growth (p. 463) Exponential growth is modeled by a function of the form $y = ab^x$ with $b > 1$.

Crecimiento exponencial (p. 463) El crecimiento exponencial se expresa con una función de la forma $y = ab^x$ donde $b > 1$.

English | Spanish

Extraneous solution (p. 45) An extraneous solution is a solution of an equation derived from an original equation but it is not a solution of the original equation.

Solución extraña (p. 45) Una solución extraña es una solución de una ecuación derivada de una ecuación dada, pero que no satisface la ecuación dada.

Example $\sqrt{x-3} = x - 5$
$$x - 3 = x^2 - 10x + 25$$
$$0 = x^2 - 11x + 28$$
$$0 = (x - 4)(x - 7)$$
$$x = 4 \text{ or } 7$$
The number 7 is a solution, but 4 is not, since $\sqrt{4-3} \neq 4 - 5$.

--- **F** ---

Factor Theorem (p. 302) The expression $x - a$ is a linear factor of a polynomial if and only if the value of a is a root of the related polynomial function.

Teorema de factores (p. 302) La expresión $x - a$ es un factor lineal de un polinomio si y sólo si el valor de a es una raíz de la función polinomial con la que se relaciona.

Example The value 2 makes the polynomial $x^2 + 2x - 8$ equal to zero. So, $x - 2$ is a factor of $x^2 + 2x - 8$.

Factoring (p. 227) Factoring is rewriting an expression as the product of its factors.

Descomposición factorial (p. 227) Descomponer en factores es el proceso de escribir de nuevo una expresión como el producto de sus factores.

Example expanded form   factored form
$x^2 + x - 56$ $(x + 8)(x - 7)$

Feasible region (p. 169) In a linear programming problem, the feasible region contains all the values that satisfy the constraints on the objective function.

Región factible (p. 169) En un problema de programación lineal, la región factible contiene todos los valores que satisfacen las restricciones de la función objetiva.

Finite series (p. 607) A finite series is a series with a finite number of terms.

Serie finita (p. 607) Una serie finita es una serie con un número finito de términos.

Focal length (p. 641) The focal length of a parabola is the distance between the vertex and the focus.

Distancia focal (p. 641) La distancia focal de una parábola es la distancia entre el vértice y el foco.

Focus (plural: foci) of a hyperbola (p. 666) A hyperbola is the set of all points P in a plane such that the difference of the distances from P to two fixed points is constant. Each of the fixed points is a focus of the hyperbola.

Foco de una hipérbola (p. 666) Una hipérbola es el conjunto de puntos P en un plano tal que la diferencia de las distancias desde P hasta dos puntos fijos es constante. Cada uno de los puntos fijos es el foco de la hipérbola.

Focus of a parabola (p. 641) A parabola is the set of all points in a plane that are the same distance from a fixed line and a fixed point not on the line. The fixed point is the focus of the parabola.

Foco de una parabola (p. 641) Una parábola es el conjunto de todos los puntos en un plano con la misma distancia desde una línea fija y un punto fijo que no permanece en la línea. El punto fijo es el foco de la parábola.

English | Spanish

Focus (plural: foci) of an ellipse (p. 658) An ellipse is the set of all points P in a plane such that the sum of the distances from P to two fixed points is constant. Each of the fixed points is a focus of the ellipse.

Foco de una elipse (p. 658) Una elipse es el conjunto de todos los puntos P en un plano en el cual la suma de las distancias desde P hasta dos puntos fijos es constante. Cada uno de estos puntos fijos es un foco de la elipsis.

Frequency table (p. 724) A frequency table is a list of the outcomes in a sample space and the number of times each outcome occurs.

Tabla de frecuencias (p. 724) Una tabla de frecuencias es una lista de los resultados de un espacio muestral y el número de veces que cada resultado ocurre.

Function (p. 66) A function is a relation in which each element of the domain corresponds with exactly one element in the range.

Función (p. 66) Una función es una relación en la que cada elemento del dominio corresponde exactamente con un elemento del rango.

Example The relation $y = 3x^3 - 2x + 3$ is a function. $f(x) = 3x^3 - 2x + 3$ is the same relation written in function notation.

Function notation (p. 70) If f is the name of a function, the function notation $f(x)$ shows the function name f and also represents the range value $f(x)$ for the domain value x. You read the function notation $f(x)$ as "f of x" or "a function of x." Note that $f(x)$ does not mean "f times x."

Notación de una función (p. 70) Si f es el nombre de una función, la notación de la función $f(x)$ indica el nombre de la función y también representa el valor del rango $f(x)$ para el valor del dominio x. La función de la notación $f(x)$ se lee "f de x" o "una función de x." Observa que $f(x)$ no significa "f por x."

Example When the value of x is 3, $f(3)$, read "f of 3," represents the value of the function at 3.

Function rule (p. 70) A function rule represents an output value in terms of an input value.

Regla de función (p. 70) Una regla de función representa un valor de salida en función a un valor de entrada.

Fundamental Counting Principle (p. 686) The Fundamental Counting Principle is a tool that you can use to quickly count the number of ways certain things can happen.

Principio básico de conteo (p. 686) El principio básico de conteo es una herramienta que se puede utilizar para hacer un conteo rápido del número de formas en que pueden ocurrir ciertas cosas.

Fundamental Theorem of Algebra (p. 341) If $P(x)$ is a polynomial of degree $n \geq 1$ with complex coefficients, then $P(x) = 0$ has at least one complex root.

Teorema fundamental de álgebra (p. 341) Si $P(x)$ es un polinomio de grado $n \geq 1$ con coeficientes complejos, entonces $P(x) = 0$ tiene por lo menos una raíz compleja.

Example $P(x) = 3x^3 - 2x + 3$ is of degree 3, so $P(x) = 0$ has at least one complex root.

--- **G** ---

Geometric mean (p. 603) The geometric mean of any two positive numbers is the positive square root of the product of the two numbers.

Media geométrica (p. 603) La media geométrica de dos números positivos es la raíz cuadrada positiva del producto de los dos números.

Example The geometric mean of 12 and 18 is $\sqrt{12 \cdot 18} \approx 14.6969$.

English | Spanish

Geometric sequence (p. 600) A geometric sequence is a sequence with a constant ratio between consecutive terms.

Secuencia geométrica (p. 600) Una secuencia geométrica es una secuencia con una razón constante entre términos consecutivos.

Example The geometric sequence 2.5, 5, 10, 20, 40 . . . , has a common ratio of 2.

Geometric series (p. 614) A geometric series is the sum of the terms in a geometric sequence.

Serie geométrica (p. 614) Una serie geométrica es la suma de términos en una progresión geométrica.

Example One geometric series with five terms is $2.5 + 5 + 10 + 20 + 40$.

Greatest common factor (p. 229) The greatest common factor (GCF) of an expression is the common factor of each term of the expression that has the greatest coefficient and the greatest exponent.

Máximo factor común (p. 229) El máximo factor común de una expresión es el factor común de cada término de la expresión que tiene el mayor coeficiente y el mayor exponente.

Example The GCF of $4x^2 + 20x - 12$ is 4.

Growth factor (p. 464) In an exponential function of the form $y = ab^x$, b is the growth factor if $b > 1$.

Factor de incremento (p. 464) En una función exponencial de la forma $y = ab^x$, b es el factor de incremento si $b > 1$.

Example In the exponential equation $y = 2^x$, 2 is the growth factor.

--- **H** ---

Half-plane (p. 128) A half-plane is the set of points in a coordinate plane that are on one side of the boundary of the graph of a linear inequality.

Semiplano (p. 128) Un semiplano es el conjunto de puntos de un plano de coordenadas que están a un lado del límite de la gráfica de desigualdad lineal.

Hyperbola (p. 666) A hyperbola is a set of points P in a plane such that the difference between the distances from P to the foci F_1 and F_2 is a given constant k. $|PF_1 - PF_2| = k$ The standard form of an equation of a hyperbola centered at $(0, 0)$ is $\frac{x^2}{a^2} - \frac{y^2}{b^2} = 1$ if the transverse axis is horizontal and $\frac{y^2}{a^2} - \frac{x^2}{b^2} = 1$ if the transverse axis is vertical.

Hipérbola (p. 666) Una hipérbola es un conjunto de puntos P en un plano tal que la diferencia entre las distancias de P a los focos F_1 y F_2 es una constante k dada. $|PF_1 - PF_2| = k$ La forma normal de una ecuación de una hipérbola centrada en $(0, 0)$ es $\frac{x^2}{a^2} - \frac{y^2}{b^2} = 1$, si el eje transversal es horizontal, y $\frac{y^2}{a^2} - \frac{x^2}{b^2} = 1$, si el eje transversal es vertical.

Example

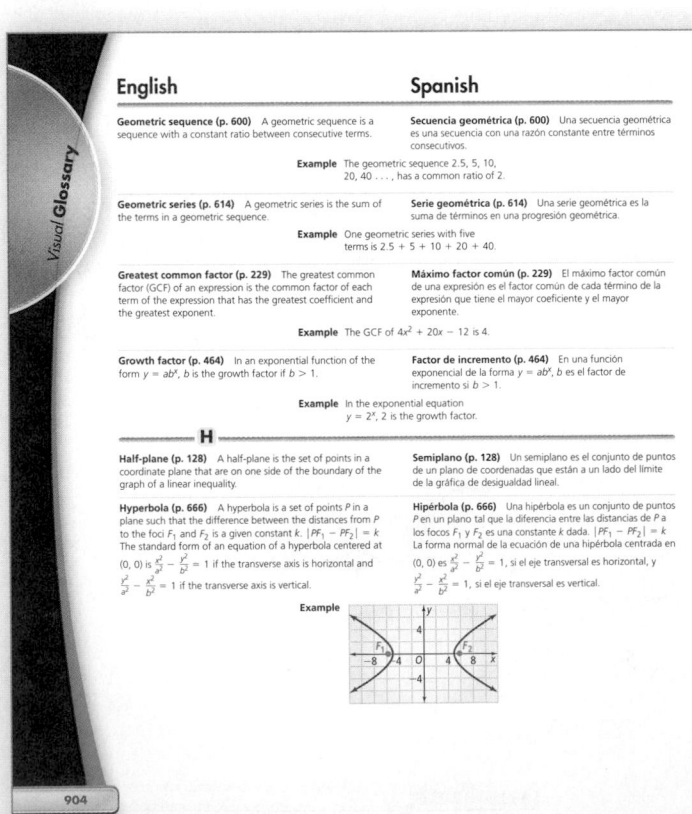

English | Spanish

--- **I** ---

i (p. 268) The imaginary number i is the principal square root of -1.

i (p. 268) El número imaginario i es la raíz principal de -1.

Example $i = \sqrt{-1}$ and $i^2 = -1$.

Identity (p. 29) An equation that is true for every value of the variable is an identity.

Identidad (p. 29) Una ecuación que es verdadera para cada valor de la variable es una identidad.

Imaginary number (p. 269) An imaginary number is any number of the form $a + bi$, where a and b are real numbers and $b \neq 0$.

Número imaginario (p. 269) Un número imaginario es cualquier número de la forma $a + bi$, donde a y b son números reales y $b \neq 0$.

Example $2 + 3i$
$7i$
i

Imaginary unit (p. 268) The imaginary unit i is the complex number whose square is -1.

Unidad imaginaria (p. 268) La unidad imaginaria i es el número complejo cuyo cuadrado es -1.

Independent events (p. 704) When the outcome of one event does not affect the probability of a second event, the two events are independent.

Sucesos independientes (p. 704) Cuando el resultado de un suceso no altera la probabilidad de otro, los dos sucesos son independientes.

Example The results of two rolls of a number cube are independent. Getting a 5 on the first roll does not change the probability of getting a 5 on the second roll.

Independent variable (p. 70) If a function is defined by an equation using the variables x and y, where x represents input values, then x is the independent variable.

Variable independiente (p. 70) Si una función es definida por una ecuación con las variables x e y, donde x representa los valores de entrada, entonces x es la variable independiente.

Example $y = 2x + 1$
x is the independent variable.

Index (p. 382) With a radical sign, the index indicates the degree of the root.

Índice (p. 382) Con un signo de radical, el índice indica el grado de la raíz.

Example index 2   index 3   index 4
$\sqrt{16}$ $\sqrt[3]{16}$ $\sqrt[4]{16}$

Infinite series (p. 607) An infinite series is a series with infinitely many terms.

Serie infinita (p. 607) Una serie infinita es una serie con un número infinito de términos.

English | Spanish

Initial side (p. 834) When an angle is in standard position, the initial side of the angle is given to be on the positive x-axis. The other ray is the terminal side of the angle.

Lado inicial (p. 834) Cuando un ángulo está en posición normal, el lado inicial del ángulo se ubica en el eje positivo de las x. El otro rayo, o semirrecta, forma el lado terminal del ángulo.

Example

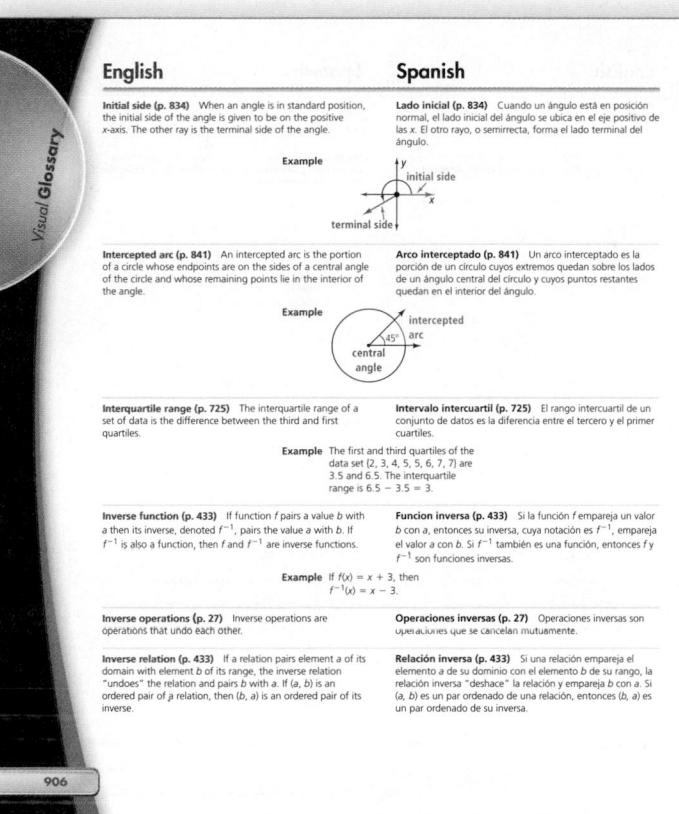

Intercepted arc (p. 841) An intercepted arc is the portion of a circle whose endpoints are on the sides of a central angle of the circle and whose remaining points lie in the interior of the angle.

Arco interceptado (p. 841) Un arco interceptado es la porción de un círculo cuyos extremos quedan sobre los lados de un ángulo central del círculo y cuyos puntos restantes quedan en el interior del ángulo.

Example

Interquartile range (p. 725) The interquartile range of a set of data is the difference between the third and first quartiles.

Intervalo intercuartil (p. 725) El rango intercuartil de un conjunto de datos es la diferencia entre el tercero y el primer cuartiles.

Example The first and third quartiles of the data set {2, 3, 4, 5, 5, 6, 7, 7} are 3.5 and 6.5. The interquartile range is $6.5 - 3.5 = 3$.

Inverse function (p. 433) If function f pairs a value b with a then its inverse, denoted f^{-1}, pairs the value a with b. If f^{-1} is also a function, then f and f^{-1} are inverse functions.

Función inversa (p. 433) Si la función f empareja un valor b con a, entonces su inversa, cuya notación es f^{-1}, empareja el valor a con b. Si f^{-1} también es una función, entonces f y f^{-1} son funciones inversas.

Example If $f(x) = x + 3$, then $f^{-1}(x) = x - 3$.

Inverse operations (p. 27) Inverse operations are operations that undo each other.

Operaciones inversas (p. 27) Operaciones inversas son operaciones que se cancelan mutuamente.

Inverse relation (p. 433) If a relation pairs element a of its domain with element b of its range, the inverse relation "undoes" the relation and pairs b with a. If (a, b) is an ordered pair of a relation, then (b, a) is an ordered pair of its inverse.

Relación inversa (p. 433) Si una relación empareja el elemento a de su dominio con el elemento b de su rango, la relación inversa "deshace" la relación y empareja b con a. Si (a, b) es un par ordenado de una relación, entonces (b, a) es un par ordenado de su inversa.

English | Spanish

Inverse variation (p. 520) An inverse variation is a relation represented by an equation of the form $xy = k$, $y = \frac{k}{x}$, or $x = \frac{k}{y}$, where $k \neq 0$.

Variación inversa (p. 520) Una variación inversa es una relación representada por la ecuación $xy = k$, $y = \frac{k}{x}$, ó $x = \frac{k}{y}$, donde $k \neq 0$.

Example

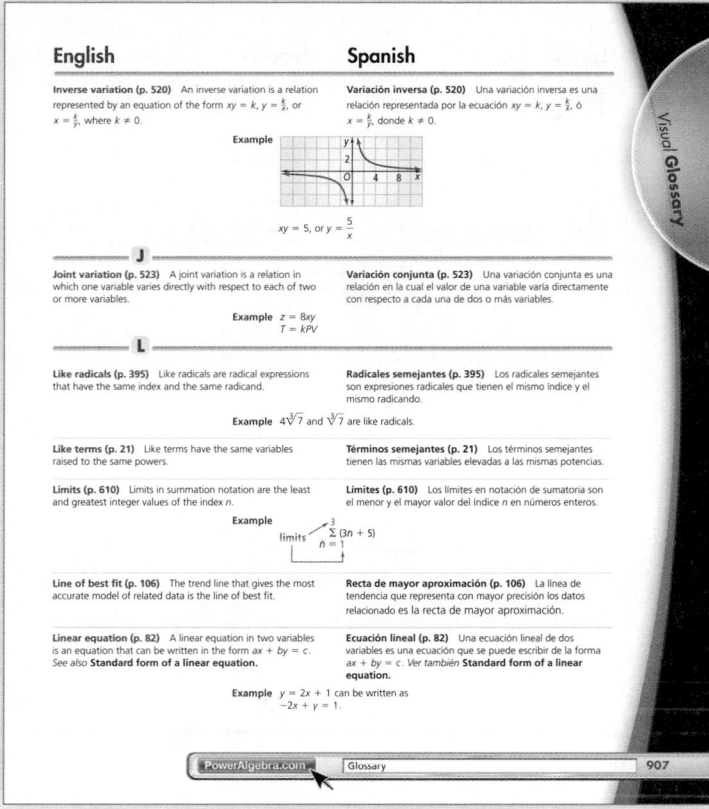

$xy = 5$, or $y = \frac{5}{x}$

J

Joint variation (p. 523) A joint variation is a relation in which one variable varies directly with respect to each of two or more variables.

Variación conjunta (p. 523) Una variación conjunta es una relación en la cual el valor de una variable varía directamente con respecto a cada una de dos o más variables.

Example $z = 8xy$
$T = kPV$

L

Like radicals (p. 395) Like radicals are radical expressions that have the same index and the same radicand.

Radicales semejantes (p. 395) Los radicales semejantes son expresiones radicales que tienen el mismo índice y el mismo radicando.

Example $4\sqrt[3]{7}$ and $\sqrt[3]{7}$ are like radicals.

Like terms (p. 21) Like terms have the same variables raised to the same powers.

Términos semejantes (p. 21) Los términos semejantes tienen las mismas variables elevadas a las mismas potencias.

Limits (p. 610) Limits in summation notation are the least and greatest integer values of the index n.

Límites (p. 610) Los límites en notación de sumatoria son el menor y el mayor valor del índice n en números enteros.

Example $\text{limits} \begin{array}{c} 3 \\ \Sigma (3n + 5) \\ n = 1 \end{array}$

Line of best fit (p. 106) The trend line that gives the most accurate model of related data is the line of best fit.

Recta de mayor aproximación (p. 106) La línea de tendencia que representa con mayor precisión los datos relacionado es la recta de mayor aproximación.

Linear equation (p. 82) A linear equation in two variables is an equation that can be written in the form $ax + by = c$. See also **Standard form of a linear equation.**

Ecuación lineal (p. 82) Una ecuación lineal de dos variables es una ecuación que se puede escribir de la forma $ax + by = c$. Ver también **Standard form of a linear equation.**

Example $y = 2x + 1$ can be written as $-2x + y = 1$.

English | Spanish

Linear function (p. 82) A function whose graph is a line is a linear function. You can represent a linear function with a linear equation.

Función lineal (p. 82) Una función cuya gráfica es una recta es una función lineal. La función lineal se representa con una ecuación lineal.

Example

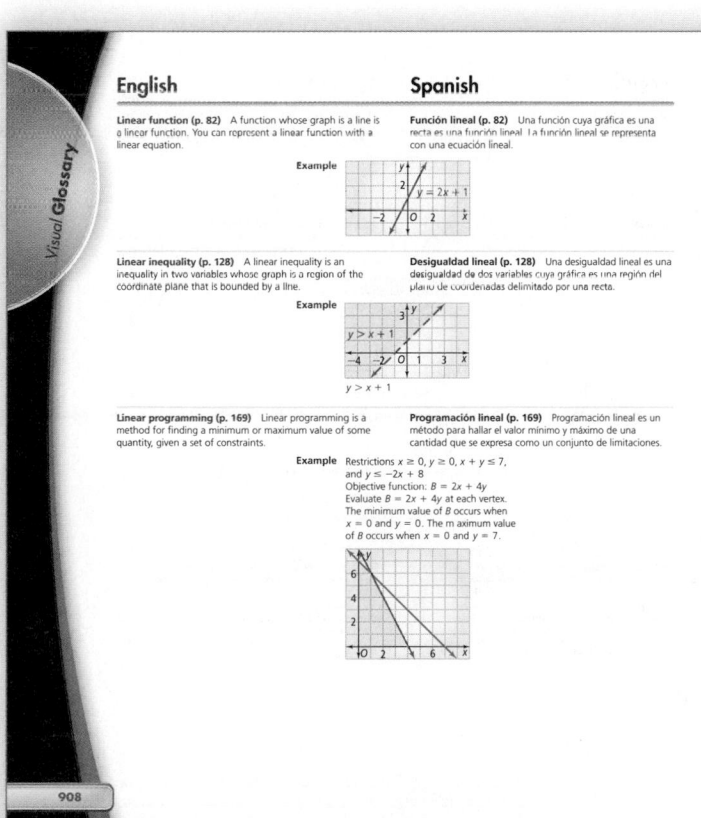

Linear inequality (p. 128) A linear inequality is an inequality in two variables whose graph is a region of the coordinate plane that is bounded by a line.

Desigualdad lineal (p. 128) Una desigualdad lineal es una desigualdad de dos variables cuya gráfica es una región del plano de coordenadas delimitado por una recta.

Example

$y > x + 1$

Linear programming (p. 169) Linear programming is a method for finding a minimum or maximum value of some quantity, given a set of constraints.

Programación lineal (p. 169) Programación lineal es un método para hallar el valor mínimo y máximo de una cantidad que se expresa como un conjunto de limitaciones.

Example Restrictions $x \geq 0$, $y \geq 0$, $x + y \geq 7$, and $y \leq -2x + 8$
Objective function: $B = 2x + 4y$
Evaluate $B = 2x + 4y$ at each vertex.
The minimum value of B occurs when $x = 0$ and $y = 0$. The maximum value of B occurs when $x = 0$ and $y = 7$.

English | Spanish

Linear system (p. 146) A linear system is a set of two or more linear equations that use the same variables.

Sistema lineal (p. 146) Un sistema lineal es un conjunto de dos o más ecuaciones lineales con las mismas variables.

Example

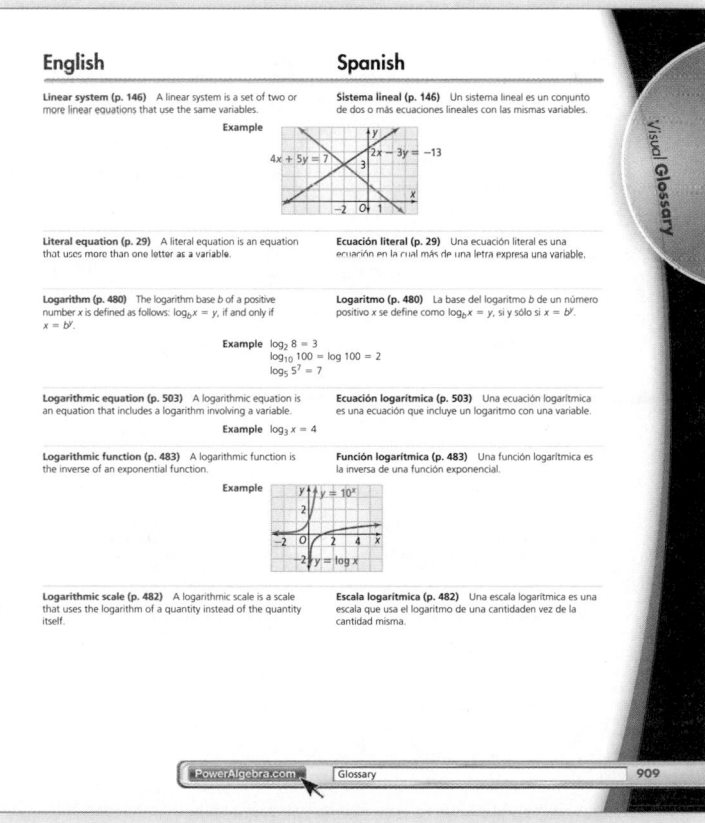

$4x + 5y = 7$ $2x - 3y = -13$

Literal equation (p. 29) A literal equation is an equation that uses more than one letter as a variable.

Ecuación literal (p. 29) Una ecuación literal es una ecuación en la cual más de una letra expresa una variable.

Logarithm (p. 480) The logarithm base b of a positive number x is defined as follows: $\log_b x = y$, if and only if $x = b^y$.

Logaritmo (p. 480) La base del logaritmo b de un número positivo x se define como $\log_b x = y$, si y sólo si $x = b^y$.

Example $\log_2 8 = 3$
$\log_{10} 100 = \log 100 = 2$
$\log_5 5^7 = 7$

Logarithmic equation (p. 503) A logarithmic equation is an equation that includes a logarithm involving a variable.

Ecuación logarítmica (p. 503) Una ecuación logarítmica es una ecuación que incluye un logaritmo con una variable.

Example $\log_3 x = 4$

Logarithmic function (p. 483) A logarithmic function is the inverse of an exponential function.

Función logarítmica (p. 483) Una función logarítmica es la inversa de una función exponencial.

Example

Logarithmic scale (p. 482) A logarithmic scale is a scale that uses the logarithm of a quantity instead of the quantity itself.

Escala logarítmica (p. 482) Una escala logarítmica es una escala que usa el logaritmo de una cantidad en vez de la cantidad misma.

Page 910

English — M

Spanish

Major axis (p. 659) The major axis of an ellipse is the segment that contains the foci of the ellipse and has endpoints on the ellipse.

Eje mayor (p. 659) En una elipsis, el eje mayor es el segmento que contiene los focos de la elipsis y tiene puntos extremos sobre la elipsis.

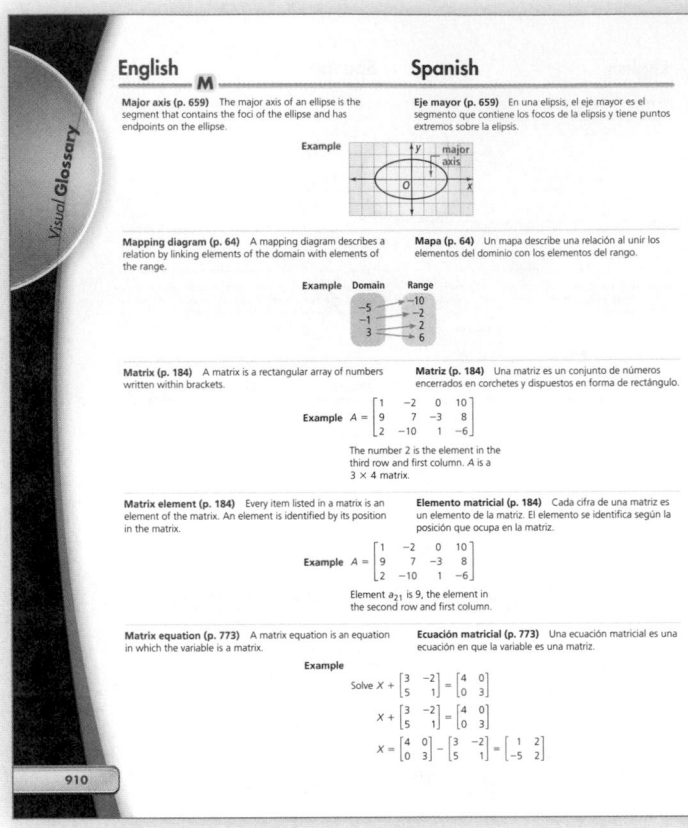

Mapping diagram (p. 64) A mapping diagram describes a relation by linking elements of the domain with elements of the range.

Mapa (p. 64) Un mapa describe una relación al unir los elementos del dominio con los elementos del rango.

Matrix (p. 184) A matrix is a rectangular array of numbers written within brackets.

Matriz (p. 184) Una matriz es un conjunto de números encerrados en corchetes y dispuestos en forma de rectángulo.

Example $A = \begin{bmatrix} 1 & -2 & 0 & 10 \\ 9 & 7 & -3 & 8 \\ 2 & -10 & 1 & -6 \end{bmatrix}$

The number 2 is the element in the third row and first column. A is a 3×4 matrix.

Matrix element (p. 184) Every item listed in a matrix is an element of the matrix. An element is identified by its position in the matrix.

Elemento matricial (p. 184) Cada cifra de una matriz es un elemento de la matriz. El elemento se identifica según la posición que ocupa en la matriz.

Example $A = \begin{bmatrix} 1 & -2 & 0 & 10 \\ 9 & 7 & -3 & 8 \\ 2 & -10 & 1 & -6 \end{bmatrix}$

Element a_{21} is 9, the element in the second row and first column.

Matrix equation (p. 773) A matrix equation is an equation in which the variable is a matrix.

Ecuación matricial (p. 773) Una ecuación matricial es una ecuación en que la variable es una matriz.

Example

Solve $X + \begin{bmatrix} 3 & -2 \\ 5 & 1 \end{bmatrix} = \begin{bmatrix} 4 & 0 \\ 0 & 3 \end{bmatrix}$

$X + \begin{bmatrix} 3 & -2 \\ 5 & 1 \end{bmatrix} = \begin{bmatrix} 4 & 0 \\ 0 & 3 \end{bmatrix}$

$X = \begin{bmatrix} 4 & 0 \\ 0 & 3 \end{bmatrix} - \begin{bmatrix} 3 & -2 \\ 5 & 1 \end{bmatrix} = \begin{bmatrix} 1 & 2 \\ -5 & 2 \end{bmatrix}$

Page 911

English

Spanish

Maximum value (p. 205) The maximum value of a function $y = f(x)$ is the greatest y-value of the function. It is the y-coordinate of the highest point on the graph of f.

Valor máximo (p. 205) El valor máximo de una función $y = f(x)$ es el valor más alto de y de la función. Es la coordenada y del punto más alto de la gráfica de f.

Mean (p. 723) The sum of the data values divided by the number of data values is the mean. *See also* **Arithmetic mean**.

Media (p. 723) La suma de los valores de datos dividida por el número de valores de datos sumados es la media. *Ver también* **Arithmetic mean**.

Example {1, 2, 3, 3, 6, 6}

$\text{mean} = \frac{1 + 2 + 3 + 3 + 6 + 6}{6}$

$= \frac{21}{6} = 3.5$

Measures of central tendency (p. 723) The mean, the median, and the mode are each central values that help describe a set of data. They are called measures of central tendency.

Medidas de tendencia central (p. 723) La media, la mediana y la moda son los valores centrales que facilitan la descripción de un conjunto de datos. A estos valores se les llama medidas de tendencia central.

Example {1, 2, 3, 3, 4, 5, 6, 6}

mean = 3.75
median = 3.5
modes = 3 and 6

Measure of variation (p. 732) Measures of variation, such as the range, the interquartile range, and the standard deviation, describe how the data in a data set are spread out.

Medida de dispersión (p. 732) Las medidas de dispersión, tal como el rango, el intervalo intercuartil y la desviación típica, describen cómo se dispersan los datos en un conjunto de datos.

Median (p. 723) The median is the middle value in a data set. If the data set contains an even number of values, the median is the mean of the two middle values.

Mediana (p. 723) La mediana es el valor situado en el medio en un conjunto de datos. Si el conjunto de datos contiene un número par de valores, la mediana es la media de los dos valores del medio.

Example {1, 2, 3, 3, 4, 5, 6, 6}

$\text{median} = \frac{3 + 4}{2} = \frac{7}{2} = 3.5$

Minimum value (p. 205) The minimum value of a function $y = f(x)$ is the least y-value of the function. It is the y-coordinate of the lowest point on the graph of f.

Valor mínimo (p. 205) El valor mínimo de una función $y = f(x)$ es el valor más bajo de y de la función. Es la coordenada y del punto más bajo de la gráfica de f.

Minor axis (p. 659) The minor axis of an ellipse is the segment that is perpendicular to the major axis at its midpoint and has endpoints on the ellipse.

Eje menor (p. 659) En una elipsis, el eje menor es el segmento perpendicular al eje mayor en su punto medio y que tiene puntos extremos sobre la elipsis.

Example

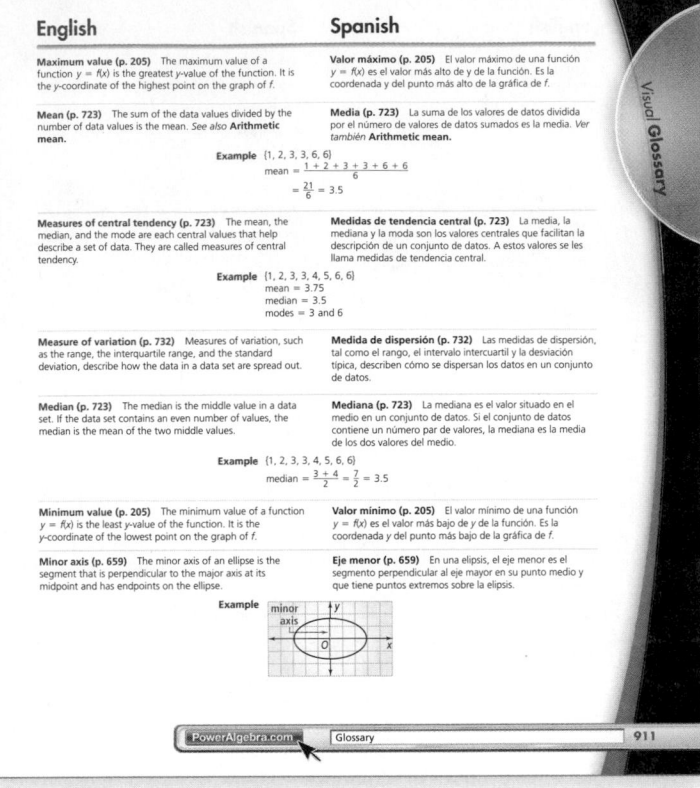

Page 912

English

Spanish

Mode (p. 723) The mode is the most frequently occurring value (or values) in a set of data.

Moda (p. 723) La moda es el valor o valores que ocurren con mayor frecuencia en un conjunto de datos.

Example {1, 2, 3, 3, 4, 5, 6, 6}
The modes are 3 and 6.

Monomial (p. 292) A monomial is either a real number, a variable, or a product of real numbers and variables with whole number exponents.

Monomio (p. 292) Un monomio es un número real, una variable o un producto de números reales y variables cuyos exponentes son números enteros.

Example $1, x, 2z, 4ab^2$

Multiple zero (p. 304) If a linear factor is repeated in the complete factored form of a polynomial, the zero related to that factor is a multiple zero.

Cero múltiplo (p. 304) Si un factor lineal se repite en la forma factorizada completa de un polinomio, el cero relacionado con ese factor es un cero múltiplo.

Example The zeros of the function
$P(x) = 2x(x - 3)^2(x + 1)$ are 0, 3, and −1. Since $(x - 3)$ occurs twice as a factor, 3 is a multiple zero.

Multiplicative identity (p. 14) The multiplicative identity is 1. The product of 1 and any number is that number. The product of reciprocals is 1.

Identidad multiplicativa (p. 14) La identidad multiplicativa es 1. El producto de 1 y cualquier otro número es ese número. El producto del recíproco es 1.

Multiplicative identity matrix (p. 789) For an $n \times n$ square matrix, the multiplicative identity matrix is an $n \times n$ square matrix I, or $I_{n \times n}$, with 1's along the main diagonal and 0's elsewhere.

Matriz de identidad multiplicativa (p. 789) Para una matriz cuadrada $n \times n$, la matriz de identidad multiplicativa es la matriz cuadrada I de $n \times n$, o $I_{n \times n}$, con unos por la diagonal principal y ceros en los demás lugares.

Example $I_{2 \times 2} = \begin{bmatrix} 1 & 0 \\ 0 & 1 \end{bmatrix}$

$I_{3 \times 3} = \begin{bmatrix} 1 & 0 & 0 \\ 0 & 1 & 0 \\ 0 & 0 & 1 \end{bmatrix}$

Multiplicative inverse (p. 14) The reciprocal or multiplicative inverse of any nonzero number a is $\frac{1}{a}$. The product of reciprocals is 1, the multiplicative identity.

Inverso multiplicativo (p. 14) El recíproco o inverso multiplicativo de cualquier número a, que no sea cero, es $\frac{1}{a}$. El producto de recíprocos es 1, la identidad multiplicativa.

Example $5 \times \frac{1}{5} = 1$

Multiplicative inverse of a matrix (p. 789) If A and X are $n \times n$ matrices, and $AX = XA = I$, then X is the multiplicative inverse of A, written A^{-1}.

Inverso multiplicativo de una matriz (p. 789) Si A y X son matrices $n \times n$, y $AX = XA = I$, entonces X es el inverso multiplicativo de A, expresado como A^{-1}.

Example $A = \begin{bmatrix} 2 & 1 \\ 4 & 0 \end{bmatrix}$

$X = \begin{bmatrix} 0 & \frac{1}{4} \\ 1 & -\frac{1}{2} \end{bmatrix}$

$AX = \begin{bmatrix} 1 & 0 \\ 0 & 1 \end{bmatrix} = I$, so $X = A^{-1}$

Page 913

English

Spanish

Multiplicity (p. 304) The multiplicity of a zero of a polynomial function is the number of times the related linear factor is repeated in the factored form of the polynomial.

Multiplicidad (p. 304) La multiplicidad de un cero de una función polinomial es el número de veces que el factor lineal relacionado se repite en la forma factorizada del polinomio.

Example The zeros of the function
$P(x) = 2x(x - 3)^2(x + 1)$ are 0, 3, and −1. Since $(x - 3)$ occurs twice as a factor, the zero 3 has multiplicity 2.

Mutually exclusive events (p. 705) When two events cannot happen at the same time, the events are mutually exclusive. If A and B are mutually exclusive events, then $P(A \text{ or } B) = P(A) + P(B)$.

Sucesos mutuamente excluyentes (p. 705) Cuando dos sucesos no pueden ocurrir al mismo tiempo, son mutuamente excluyentes. Si A y B son sucesos mutuamente excluyentes, entonces $P(A \text{ or } B) = P(A) + P(B)$.

Example Rolling an even number E and rolling a multiple of five M on a standard number cube are mutually exclusive events.

$P(E \text{ or } M) = P(E) + P(M)$

$= \frac{3}{6} + \frac{1}{6}$

$= \frac{4}{6}, \text{ or } \frac{2}{3}$

N

n factorial (n!) (p. 687) For any positive integer n, n factorial is $n(n - 1) \cdots 3 \cdot 2 \cdot 1$. Zero factorial (0!) = 1.

n factorial (n!) (p. 687) Para cualquier entero n, n factorial es $n(n - 1) \cdots 3 \cdot 2 \cdot 1$. El cero factorial (0!) = 1.

Example $4! = 4 \times 3 \times 2 \times 1 = 24$

nth root (p. 381) For any real numbers a and b, and any positive integer n, if $a^n = b$, then a is an nth root of b.

raíz n-ésima (p. 381) Para todos los números reales a y b, y todo número entero positivo n, si $a^n = b$, entonces a es la n-ésima raíz de b.

Example $\sqrt[5]{32} = 2$ because $2^5 = 32$.
$\sqrt[4]{81} = 3$ because $3^4 = 81$.

Natural base exponential function (p. 476) A natural base exponential function is an exponential function with base e.

Función exponencial con base natural (p. 476) Una función exponencial con base natural es una función exponencial con base e.

Non-removable discontinuity (p. 539) A non-removable discontinuity is a point of discontinuity that is not removable. It represents a break in the graph of f where you cannot redefine f to make the graph continuous.

Discontinuidad irremovible (p. 539) Una discontinuidad irremovible es un punto de discontinuidad que no se puede remover. Representa una interrupción en la gráfica f donde no se puede redefinir f para volverla una gráfica continua.

English / Spanish

Normal distribution (p. 752) A normal distribution shows data that vary randomly from the mean in the pattern of a bell-shaped curve.

Distribución normal (p. 752) Una distribución normal muestra, con una curva en forma de campana, datos que varían aleatoriamente respecto de la media.

Example **Distribution of Test Scores**

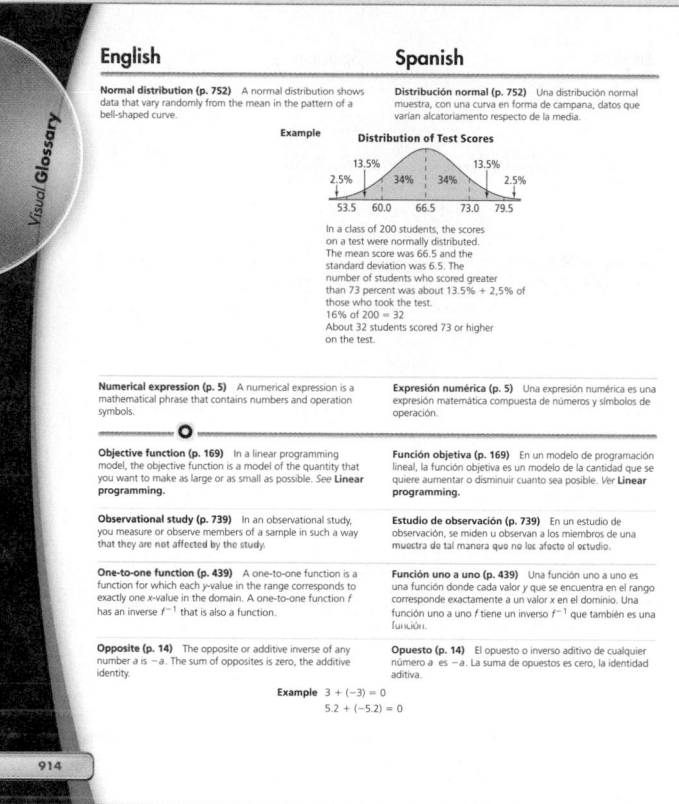

In a class of 200 students, the scores on a test were normally distributed. The mean score was 66.5 and the standard deviation was 6.5. The number of students who scored greater than 73 percent was about 13.5% + 2.5% of those who took the test.
16% of 200 = 32
About 32 students scored 73 or higher on the test.

Numerical expression (p. 5) A numerical expression is a mathematical phrase that contains numbers and operation symbols.

Expresión numérica (p. 5) Una expresión numérica es una expresión matemática compuesta de números y símbolos de operación.

Objective function (p. 169) In a linear programming model, the objective function is a model of the quantity that you want to make as large or as small as possible. See **Linear programming.**

Función objetiva (p. 169) En un modelo de programación lineal, la función objetiva es un modelo de la cantidad que se quiere aumentar o disminuir cuanto sea posible. *Ver* **Linear programming.**

Observational study (p. 739) In an observational study, you measure or observe members of a sample in such a way that they are not affected by the study.

Estudio de observación (p. 739) En un estudio de observación, se miden u observan a los miembros de una muestra de tal manera que no se los afecta el estudio.

One-to-one function (p. 439) A one-to-one function is a function for which each y-value in the range corresponds to exactly one x-value in the domain. A one-to-one function f has an inverse f^{-1} that is also a function.

Función uno a uno (p. 439) Una función uno a uno es una función donde cada valor y que se encuentra en el rango corresponde exactamente a un valor x en el dominio. Una función uno a uno f tiene un inverso f^{-1} que también es una función.

Opposite (p. 14) The opposite or additive inverse of any number a is $-a$. The sum of opposites is zero, the additive identity.

Opuesto (p. 14) El opuesto o inverso aditivo de cualquier número a es $-a$. La suma de opuestos es cero, la identidad aditiva.

Example $3 + (-3) = 0$
$5.2 + (-5.2) = 0$

English / Spanish

Outlier (p. 724) An outlier is a value substantially different from the rest of the data in a set.

Valor extremo (p. 724) Un valor extremo es un valor considerablemente diferente al resto de los datos de un conjunto.

Example The outlier in the data set {56, 64, 73, 59, 98, 65, 59} is 98.

P

Parabola (p. 204) A parabola is the graph of a quadratic function. It is the set of all points P in a plane that are the same distance from a fixed point F, the focus, as they are from a line d, the directrix.

Parábola (p. 204) La parábola es la gráfica de una función cuadrática. Es el conjunto de todos los puntos P situados en un plano a la misma distancia de un punto fijo F, o foco, y de la recta d, o directriz.

Example

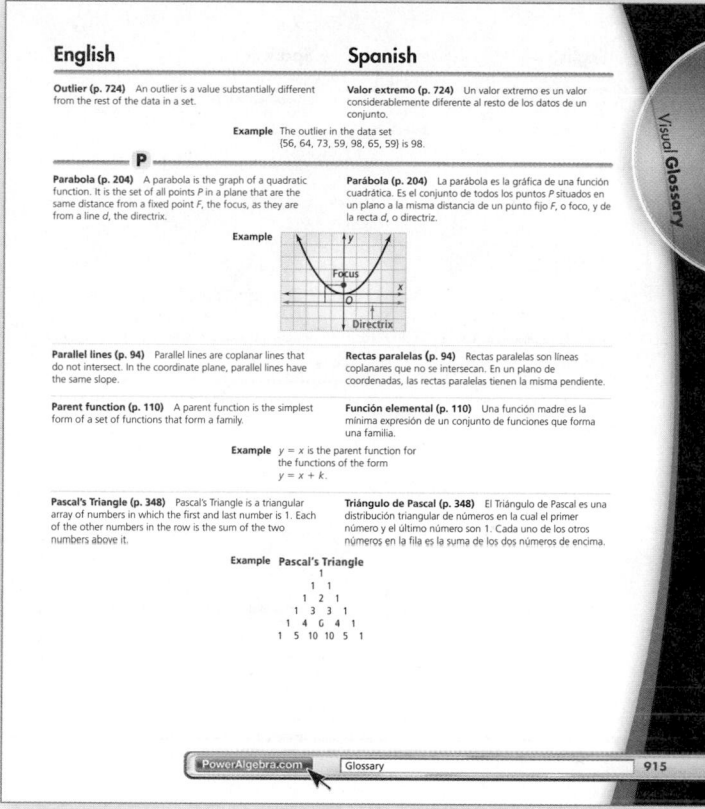

Parallel lines (p. 94) Parallel lines are coplanar lines that do not intersect. In the coordinate plane, parallel lines have the same slope.

Rectas paralelas (p. 94) Rectas paralelas son líneas coplanares que no se intersecan. En un plano de coordenadas, las rectas paralelas tienen la misma pendiente.

Parent function (p. 110) A parent function is the simplest form of a set of functions that form a family.

Función elemental (p. 110) Una función madre es la mínima expresión de un conjunto de funciones que forma una familia.

Example $y = x$ is the parent function for the functions of the form $y = x + k$.

Pascal's Triangle (p. 348) Pascal's Triangle is a triangular array of numbers in which the first and last number is 1. Each of the other numbers in the row is the sum of the two numbers above it.

Triángulo de Pascal (p. 348) El Triángulo de Pascal es una distribución triangular de números en la cual el primer número y el último número son 1. Cada uno de los otros números en la fila es la suma de los dos números de encima.

Example Pascal's Triangle
```
          1
         1 1
        1 2 1
       1 3 3 1
      1 4 6 4 1
    1 5 10 10 5 1
```

English / Spanish

Percentiles (p. 728) A percentile is a number from 0 to 100 that you can associate with a value x from a data set. It shows the percent of the data that are less than or equal to x.

Percentiles (p. 728) Un percentil es un número de 0 a 100 que se puede asociar con un valor x de un conjunto de datos. Éste muestra el porcentaje de los datos que son menores o iguales a x.

Perfect square trinomial (p. 232) A perfect square trinomial is a trinomial that is the square of a binomial.

Trinomio cuadrado perfecto (p. 232) Un trinomio cuadrado perfecto es un trinomio que es el cuadrado de un binomio.

Example perfect square trinomial   binomial square
$16x^2 - 24x + 9 = (4x - 3)^2$

Period (p. 849) The period of a periodic function is the horizontal length of one cycle.

Período (p. 849) El período de una función periódica es el intervalo horizontal de un ciclo.

Example

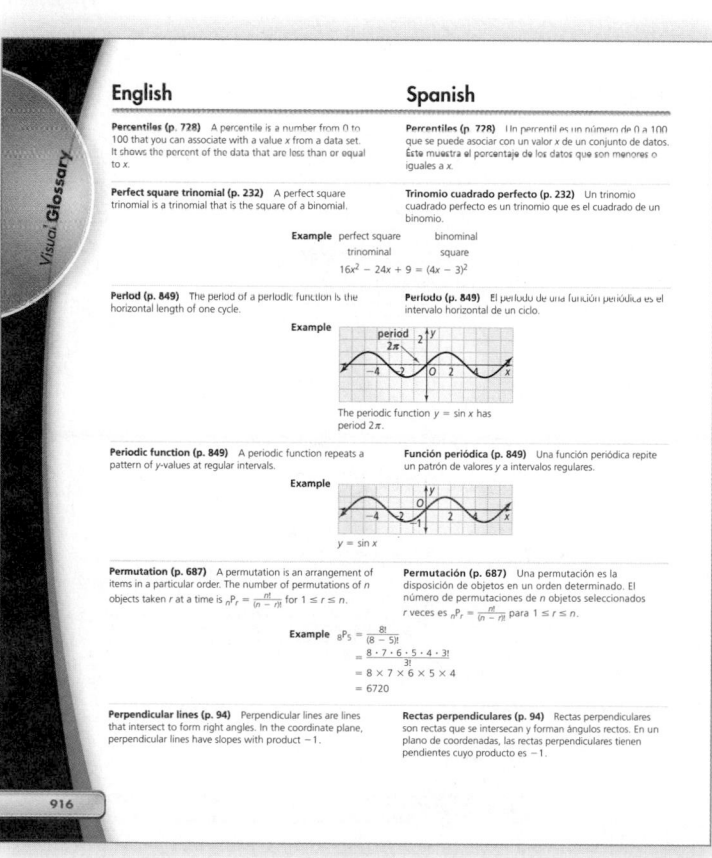

The periodic function $y = \sin x$ has period 2π.

Periodic function (p. 849) A periodic function repeats a pattern of y-values at regular intervals.

Función periódica (p. 849) Una función periódica repite un patrón de valores y a intervalos regulares.

Example
$y = \sin x$

Permutation (p. 687) A permutation is an arrangement of items in a particular order. The number of permutations of n objects taken r at a time is $_nP_r = \frac{n!}{(n-r)!}$ for $1 \le r \le n$.

Permutación (p. 687) Una permutación es la disposición de objetos en un orden determinado. El número de permutaciones de n objetos seleccionados r veces es $_nP_r = \frac{n!}{(n-r)!}$ para $1 \le r \le n$.

Example $_8P_5 = \frac{8!}{(8-5)!}$
$= \frac{8 \cdot 7 \cdot 6 \cdot 5 \cdot 4 \cdot 3!}{3!}$
$= 8 \times 7 \times 6 \times 5 \times 4$
$= 6720$

Perpendicular lines (p. 94) Perpendicular lines are lines that intersect to form right angles. In the coordinate plane, perpendicular lines have slopes with product -1.

Rectas perpendiculares (p. 94) Rectas perpendiculares son rectas que se intersecan y forman ángulos rectos. En un plano de coordenadas, las rectas perpendiculares tienen pendientes cuyo producto es -1.

English / Spanish

Point of discontinuity (p. 539) A point of discontinuity is the x-coordinate of a point where the graph of f(x) is not continuous.

Punto de discontinuidad (p. 539) Un punto de discontinuidad es la coordenada x de un punto donde la gráfica de f(x) no es continua.

Example $f(x) = \frac{2}{x-2}$ has a point of discontinuity at $x = 2$.

Point-slope form (p. 88) The point-slope form of an equation of a line is $y - y_1 = m(x - x_1)$, where m is the slope of the line and (x_1, y_1) is a point on the line.

Forma punto-pendiente (p. 88) La forma punto-pendiente de una ecuación lineal es $y - y_1 = m(x - x_1)$, donde m es la pendiente de la recta y (x_1, y_1) es un punto de la recta.

Example $y - 3 = 2(x - 1)$
$y + 4 = 5(x - 2)$
$y - 2 = 3(x + 2)$

Polynomial (p. 292) A polynomial is a monomial or the sum of monomials.

Polinomio (p. 292) Un polinomio es un monomio o la suma de dos o más monomios.

Example $3x^3 + 4x^2 - 2x + 5$
$8x$
$x^2 + 4x + 2$

Polynomial function (p. 293) A polynomial in the variable x defines a polynomial function of x.

Función polinomial (p. 293) Un polinomio en la variable x define una función polinomial de x.

Example $P(x) = a_n x^n + a_{n-1} x^{n-1} + \cdots + a_1 x + a_0$ is a polynomial function, where n is a nonnegative integer and the coefficients $a_n, \ldots, a_0$ are real numbers.

Population (p. 738) A population is the members of a set.

Población (p. 738) Una población está compuesta por los miembros de un conjunto.

Power function (p. 363) A power function is a function of the form $y = a \cdot x^b$, where a and b are nonzero real numbers.

Función de potencia (p. 363) Una función de potencia es una función de la forma $y = a \cdot x^b$, donde a y b son números reales diferentes de cero.

Principal root (p. 381) When a number has two real roots, the positive root is called the principal root. A radical sign indicates the principal root. The principal root of a negative number a is $i\sqrt{|a|}$.

Raíz principal (p. 381) Cuando un número tiene dos raíces reales, la raíz positiva es la raíz principal. El signo del radical indica la raíz principal. La raíz principal de un número negativo a es $i\sqrt{|a|}$.

Example The number 25 has two square roots, 5 and -5. The principal square root, 5, is indicated by $\sqrt{25}$ or $25^{\frac{1}{2}}$.

Visual Glossary

English | Spanish

Probability distribution (p. 748) A probability distribution is a function that tells the probability of each outcome in a sample space.

Distribución de probabilidades (p. 748) Una distribución de probabilidades es una función que señala la probabilidad de que cada resultado ocurra en un espacio muestral.

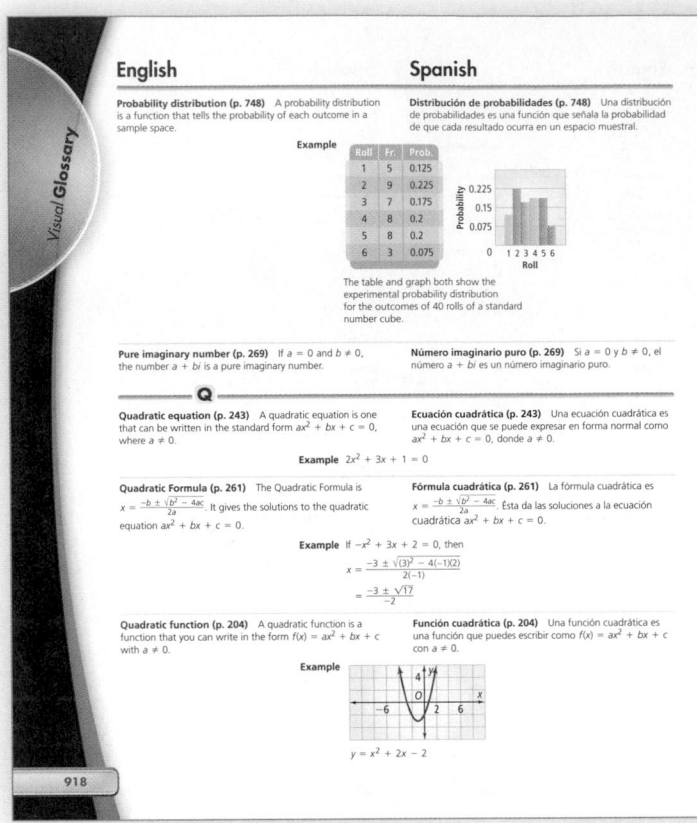

Example

Roll	Fr.	Prob.
1	5	0.125
2	9	0.225
3	7	0.175
4	8	0.2
5	8	0.2
6	3	0.075

The table and graph both show the experimental probability distribution for the outcomes of 40 rolls of a standard number cube.

Pure imaginary number (p. 269) If $a = 0$ and $b \neq 0$, the number $a + bi$ is a pure imaginary number.

Número imaginario puro (p. 269) Si $a = 0$ y $b \neq 0$, el número $a + bi$ es un número imaginario puro.

Q

Quadratic equation (p. 243) A quadratic equation is one that can be written in the standard form $ax^2 + bx + c = 0$, where $a \neq 0$.

Ecuación cuadrática (p. 243) Una ecuación cuadrática es una ecuación que se puede expresar en forma normal como $ax^2 + bx + c = 0$, donde $a \neq 0$.

Example $2x^2 + 3x + 1 = 0$

Quadratic Formula (p. 261) The Quadratic Formula is $x = \frac{-b \pm \sqrt{b^2 - 4ac}}{2a}$. It gives the solutions to the quadratic equation $ax^2 + bx + c = 0$.

Fórmula cuadrática (p. 261) La fórmula cuadrática es $x = \frac{-b \pm \sqrt{b^2 - 4ac}}{2a}$. Ésta da las soluciones a la ecuación cuadrática $ax^2 + bx + c = 0$.

Example If $-x^2 + 3x + 2 = 0$, then
$$x = \frac{-3 \pm \sqrt{(3)^2 - 4(-1)(2)}}{2(-1)}$$
$$= \frac{-3 \pm \sqrt{17}}{-2}$$

Quadratic function (p. 204) A quadratic function is a function that you can write in the form $f(x) = ax^2 + bx + c$ with $a \neq 0$.

Función cuadrática (p. 204) Una función cuadrática es una función que puedes escribir como $f(x) = ax^2 + bx + c$ con $a \neq 0$.

Example

$$y = x^2 + 2x - 2$$

English | Spanish

Quantity (p. 5) A mathematical quantity is anything that can be measured or counted.

Cantidad (p. 5) Una cantidad matemática es cualquier cosa que se puede medir o contar.

Quartile (p. 725) Quartiles are values that separate a finite data set into four equal parts. The second quartile (Q_2) is the median of the data. The first and third quartiles (Q_1 and Q_3) are the medians of the lower half and upper half of the data, respectively.

Cuartil (p. 725) Los cuartiles son valores que separan un conjunto finito de datos en cuatro partes iguales. El segundo cuartil (Q_2) es la mediana de los datos. Los cuartiles primero y tercero (Q_1 y Q_3) son las medianas de la mitad superior e inferior de los datos, respectivamente.

Example {2, 3, 4, 5, 5, 6, 7, 7}
$Q_1 = 3.5$
Q_2 (median) $= 5$
$Q_3 = 6.5$

R

Radian (p. 841) $\frac{d^\circ}{180^\circ} = \frac{r\ radians}{\pi\ radians}$

Radián (p. 841) $\frac{d^\circ}{180^\circ} = \frac{r\ radianes}{\pi\ radianes}$

Example $60^\circ \rightarrow \frac{60}{180} = \frac{x}{\pi}$
$$x = \frac{60\pi}{180}$$
$$= \frac{\pi}{3}$$
Thus, $60^\circ = \frac{\pi}{3}$ radians.

Radical equation (p. 417) A radical equation is an equation that has a variable in a radicand or has a variable with a rational exponent.

Ecuación radical (p. 417) La ecuación radical es una ecuación que contiene una variable en el radicando o una variable con un exponente racional.

Example $(\sqrt{x})^3 + 1 = 65$
$$x^{\frac{1}{2}} + 1 = 65$$

Radical function (p. 445) A radical function is a function that can be written in the form $f(x) = a\sqrt[n]{x - h} + k$, where $a \neq 0$. For even values of n, the domain of a radical function is the real number $x \geq h$. See also **Square root function.**

Función radical (p. 445) Una función radical es una función que puede expresarse como $f(x) = a\sqrt[n]{x - h} + k$, donde $a \neq 0$. Para n par, el dominio de la función radical son los números reales tales que $x \geq h$. Ver también **Square root function.**

Example $f(x) = \sqrt{x - 2}$

Radicand (p. 382) The number under a radical sign is the radicand.

Radicando (p. 382) La expresión que aparece debajo del signo radical es el radicando.

Example The radicand in $3\sqrt[5]{7}$ is 7.

English | Spanish

Radius (p. 649) The radius r of a circle is the distance between the center of the circle and any point on the circumference.

Radio (p. 649) El radio r de un círculo es la distancia entre el centro del círculo y cualquier punto de la circunferencia.

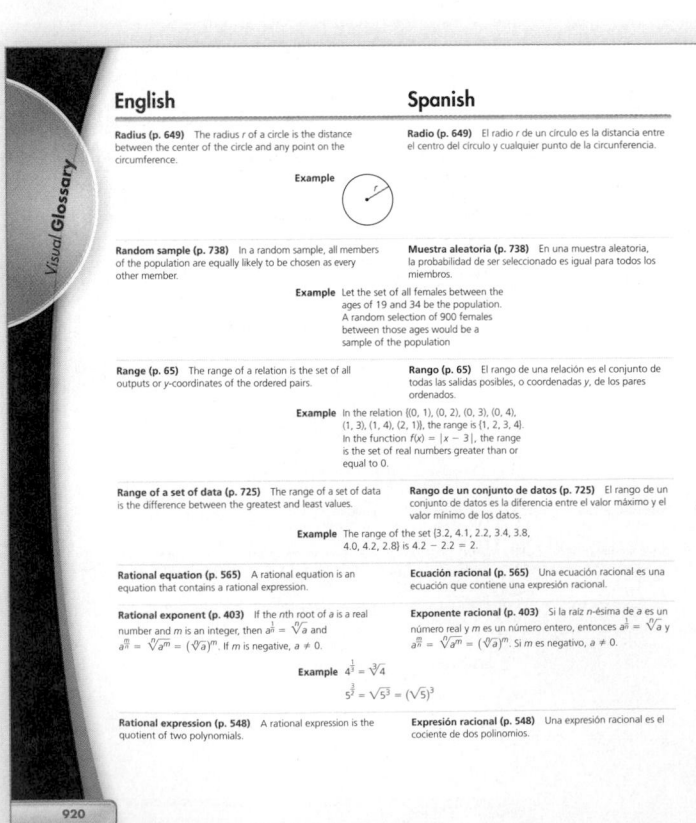

Example

Random sample (p. 738) In a random sample, all members of the population are equally likely to be chosen as every other member.

Muestra aleatoria (p. 738) En una muestra aleatoria, la probabilidad de ser seleccionado es igual para todos los miembros.

Example Let the set of all females between the ages of 19 and 34 be the population. A random selection of 900 females between those ages would be a sample of the population

Range (p. 65) The range of a relation is the set of all outputs or y-coordinates of the ordered pairs.

Rango (p. 65) El rango de una relación es el conjunto de todas las salidas posibles, o coordenadas y, de los pares ordenados.

Example In the relation {(0, 1), (0, 2), (0, 3), (0, 4), (1, 3), (1, 4), (2, 1)}, the range is {1, 2, 3, 4}. In the function $f(x) = |x - 3|$, the range is the set of real numbers greater than or equal to 0.

Range of a set of data (p. 725) The range of a set of data is the difference between the greatest and least values.

Rango de un conjunto de datos (p. 725) El rango de un conjunto de datos es la diferencia entre el valor máximo y el valor mínimo de los datos.

Example The range of the set {3.2, 4.1, 2.2, 3.4, 3.8, 4.0, 4.2, 2.8} is $4.2 - 2.2 = 2$.

Rational equation (p. 565) A rational equation is an equation that contains a rational expression.

Ecuación racional (p. 565) Una ecuación racional es una ecuación que contiene una expresión racional.

Rational exponent (p. 403) If the nth root of a is a real number and m is an integer, then $a^{\frac{1}{n}} = \sqrt[n]{a}$ and $a^{\frac{m}{n}} = \sqrt[n]{a^m} = (\sqrt[n]{a})^m$. If m is negative, $a \neq 0$.

Exponente racional (p. 403) Si la raíz n-ésima de a es un número real y m es un número entero, entonces $a^{\frac{1}{n}} = \sqrt[n]{a}$ y $a^{\frac{m}{n}} = \sqrt[n]{a^m} = (\sqrt[n]{a})^m$. Si m es negativo, $a \neq 0$.

Example $4^{\frac{1}{3}} = \sqrt[3]{4}$
$5^{\frac{3}{2}} = \sqrt{5^3} = (\sqrt{5})^3$

Rational expression (p. 548) A rational expression is the quotient of two polynomials.

Expresión racional (p. 548) Una expresión racional es el cociente de dos polinomios.

English | Spanish

Rational function (p. 538) A rational function $f(x)$ can be written as $f(x) = \frac{P(x)}{Q(x)}$, where $P(x)$ and $Q(x)$ are polynomial functions. The domain of a rational function is all real numbers except those for which $Q(x) = 0$.

Función racional (p. 538) Una función racional $f(x)$ se puede expresar como $f(x) = \frac{P(x)}{Q(x)}$, donde $P(x)$ y $Q(x)$ son funciones de polinomios. El dominio de una función racional son todos los números reales excepto aquéllos para los cuales $Q(x) = 0$.

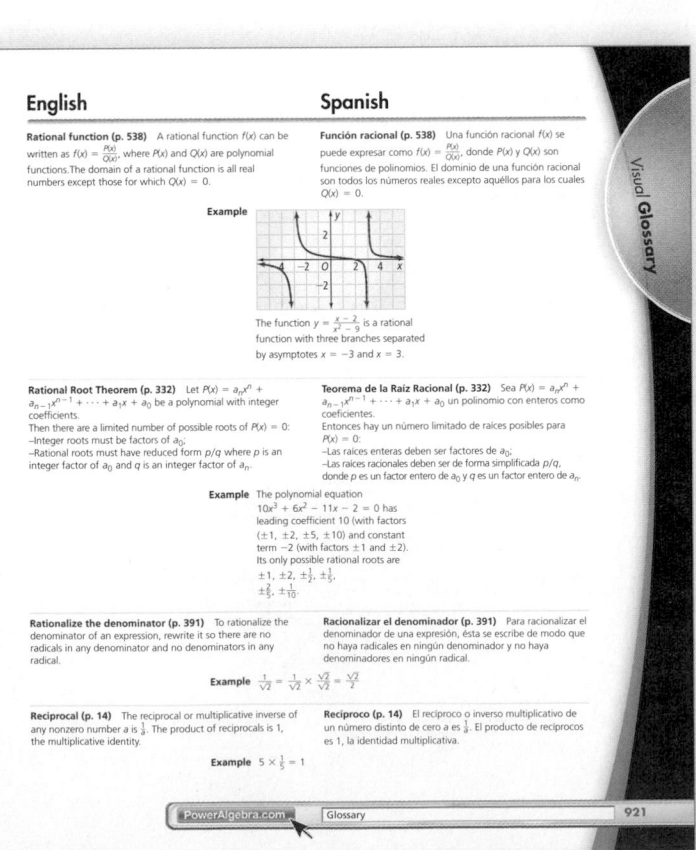

Example

The function $y = \frac{x - 2}{x^2 - 9}$ is a rational function with three branches separated by asymptotes $x = -3$ and $x = 3$.

Rational Root Theorem (p. 332) Let $P(x) = a_n x^n + a_{n-1} x^{n-1} + \cdots + a_1 x + a_0$ be a polynomial with integer coefficients. Then there are a limited number of possible roots of $P(x) = 0$:
–Integer roots must be factors of a_0;
–Rational roots must have reduced form p/q where p is an integer factor of a_0 and q is an integer factor of a_n.

Teorema de la Raíz Racional (p. 332) Sea $P(x) = a_n x^n + a_{n-1} x^{n-1} + \cdots + a_1 x + a_0$ un polinomio con enteros como coeficientes. Entonces hay un número limitado de raíces posibles para $P(x) = 0$:
–Las raíces enteras deben ser factores de a_0;
–Las raíces racionales deben ser de forma simplificada p/q, donde p es un factor entero de a_0 y q es un factor entero de a_n.

Example The polynomial equation $10x^3 + 6x^2 - 11x - 2 = 0$ has leading coefficient 10 (with factors $\pm1, \pm2, \pm5, \pm10$) and constant term -2 (with factors ±1 and ±2). Its only possible rational roots are $\pm1, \pm2, \pm\frac{1}{2}, \pm\frac{1}{5}, \pm\frac{2}{5}, \pm\frac{1}{10}$.

Rationalize the denominator (p. 391) To rationalize the denominator of an expression, rewrite it so there are no radicals in any denominator and no denominators in any radical.

Racionalizar el denominador (p. 391) Para racionalizar el denominador de una expresión, ésta se escribe de modo que no haya radicales en ningún denominador y no haya denominadores en ningún radical.

Example $\frac{1}{\sqrt{2}} = \frac{1}{\sqrt{2}} \times \frac{\sqrt{2}}{\sqrt{2}} = \frac{\sqrt{2}}{2}$

Reciprocal (p. 14) The reciprocal or multiplicative inverse of any nonzero number a is $\frac{1}{a}$. The product of reciprocals is 1, the multiplicative identity.

Recíproco (p. 14) El recíproco o inverso multiplicativo de un número distinto de cero es $\frac{1}{a}$. El producto de recíprocos es 1, la identidad multiplicativa.

Example $5 \times \frac{1}{5} = 1$

English / Spanish

Reciprocal function (p. 530) A reciprocal function belongs to the family whose parent function is $f(x) = \frac{1}{x}$ where $x \neq 0$. You can write a reciprocal function in the form $f(x) = \left(\frac{a}{x} - h\right) + k$, where $a \neq 0$ and $x \neq h$.

Función recíproca (p. 530) Una función recíproca pertenece a la familia cuya función madre es $f(x) = \frac{1}{x}$ donde $x \neq 0$. Se puede escribir una función recíproca como $f(x) = \left(\frac{a}{x} - h\right) + k$, donde $a \neq 0$ y $x \neq h$.

Example $f(x) = \frac{1}{2x + 5}$
$p(x) = \frac{1}{x} + 5$

Recursive formula (p. 586) A recursive formula defines the terms in a sequence by relating each term to the ones before it.

Fórmula recursiva (p. 586) Una fórmula recursiva define los términos de una secuencia al relacionar cada término con los términos que lo anteceden.

Example Let $a_n = 2.5a_{n-1} + 3a_{n-2}$.
If $a_3 = 3$ and $a_4 = 7.5$, then
$a_6 = 2.5(3) + 3(7.5) = 30.$

Reduced row echelon form (p. 188) A matrix that represents the solution of a system is in reduced row echelon form. The leading 1 in each row has 0's elsewhere in its column.

Forma reducida fila-escalón (p. 188) Una matriz que representa la solución de un sistema está en forma reducida fila-escalón. El 1 principal en cada fila tiene ceros en otras partes de la columna.

Reference angle (p. 835) The reference angle is the acute angle formed by the terminal side of an angle in standard position and the x-axis.

Ángulo de referencia (p. 835) El ángulo de referencia es el ángulo agudo formado por el lado terminal de un ángulo en posición estándar y el eje x.

Example

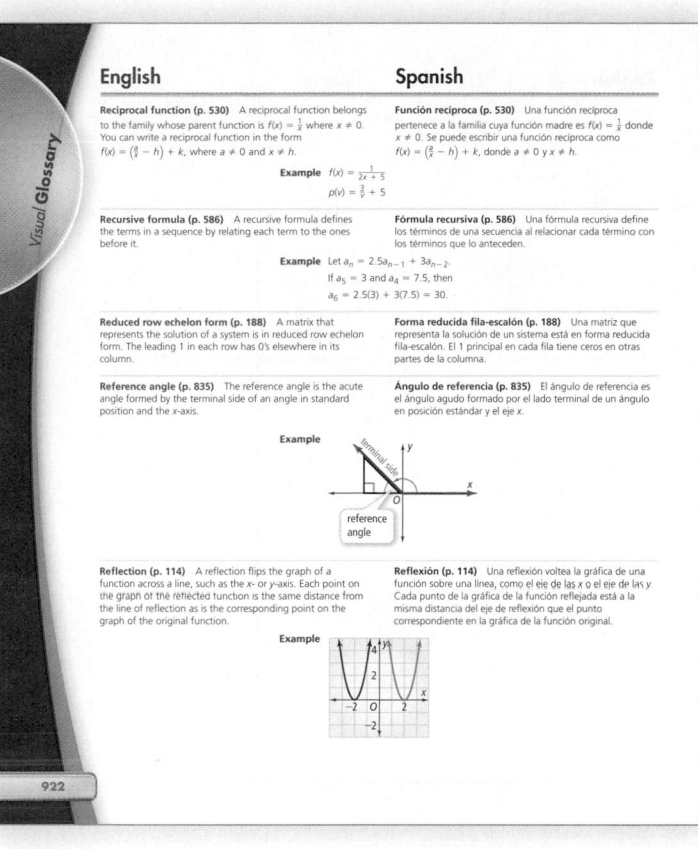

Reflection (p. 114) A reflection flips the graph of a function across a line, such as the x- or y-axis. Each point on the graph of the reflected function is the same distance from the line of reflection as is the corresponding point on the graph of the original function.

Reflexión (p. 114) Una reflexión voltea la gráfica de una función sobre una línea, como el eje de las x o el eje de las y. Cada punto de la gráfica de la función reflejada está a la misma distancia del eje de reflexión que el punto correspondiente en la gráfica de la función original.

Example

922

English / Spanish

Relation (p. 64) A relation is a set of ordered pairs.

Relación (p. 64) Una relación es un conjunto de pares ordenados.

Example $\{(0, 1), (0, 2), (0, 3), (0, 4), (1, 3)\}$

Relative maximum (minimum) (p. 305) A relative maximum (minimum) is the value of the function at an up-to-down (down-to-up) turning point.

Máximo (mínimo) relativo (p. 305) El máximo (mínimo) relativo es el valor de la función en un punto de giro de arriba hacia abajo (de abajo hacia arriba).

Example

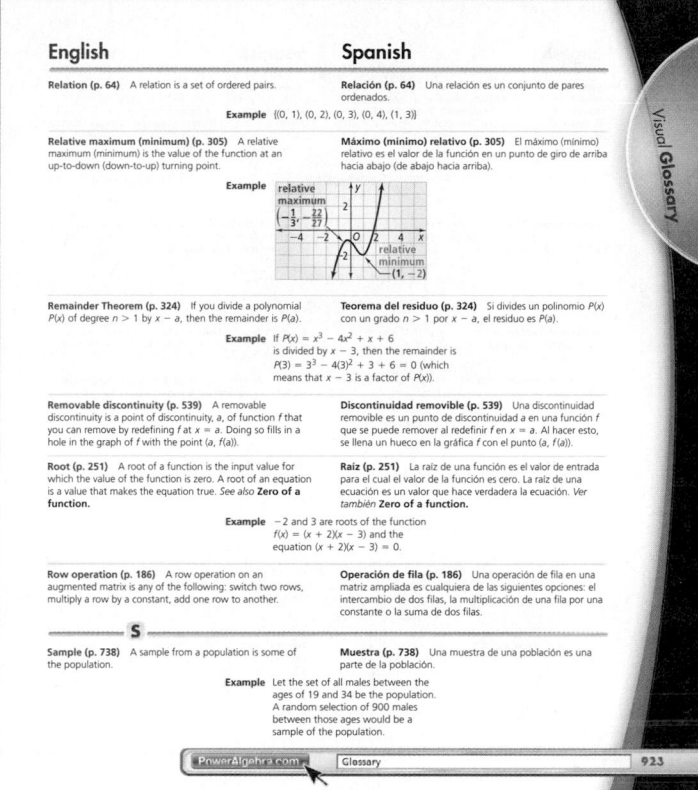

Remainder Theorem (p. 324) If you divide a polynomial $P(x)$ of degree $n > 1$ by $x - a$, then the remainder is $P(a)$.

Teorema del residuo (p. 324) Si divides un polinomio $P(x)$ con un grado $n > 1$ por $x - a$, el residuo es $P(a)$.

Example If $P(x) = x^3 - 4x^2 + x + 6$
is divided by $x - 3$, then the remainder is
$P(3) = 3^3 - 4(3)^2 + 3 + 6 = 0$ (which means that $x - 3$ is a factor of $P(x)$).

Removable discontinuity (p. 539) A removable discontinuity is a point of discontinuity, a, of function f that you can remove by redefining f at $x = a$. Doing so fills in a hole in the graph of f with the point $(a, f(a))$.

Discontinuidad removible (p. 539) Una discontinuidad removible es un punto de discontinuidad a en una función f que se puede remover al redefinir f en $x = a$. Al hacer esto, se llena un hueco en la gráfica f con el punto $(a, f(a))$.

Root (p. 251) A root of a function is the input value for which the value of the function is zero. A root of an equation is a value that makes the equation true. *See also* **Zero of a function.**

Raíz (p. 251) La raíz de una función es el valor de entrada para el cual el valor de la función es cero. La raíz de una ecuación es un valor que hace verdadera la ecuación. *Ver también* **Zero of a function.**

Example -2 and 3 are roots of the function
$f(x) = (x + 2)(x - 3)$ and the
equation $(x + 2)(x - 3) = 0$.

Row operation (p. 186) A row operation on an augmented matrix is any of the following: switch two rows, multiply a row by a constant, add one row to another.

Operación de fila (p. 186) Una operación de fila en una matriz ampliada es cualquiera de las siguientes opciones: el intercambio de dos filas, la multiplicación de una fila por una constante o la suma de dos filas.

S

Sample (p. 738) A sample from a population is some of the population.

Muestra (p. 738) Una muestra de una población es una parte de la población.

Example Let the set of all males between the ages of 19 and 34 be the population. A random selection of 900 males between those ages would be a sample of the population.

PowerAlgebra.com Glossary

923

English / Spanish

Sample space (p. 698) The set of all possible outcomes of an experiment is called the sample space.

Espacio muestral (p. 698) El espacio muestral es el conjunto de todos los resultados posibles de un suceso.

Example When you roll a number cube, the sample space is $\{1, 2, 3, 4, 5, 6\}$.

Scalar (p. 781) A scalar is a real number factor in a special product.

Escalar (p. 781) Un escalar es un factor que es un número real en un producto especial.

Example $2.5\begin{bmatrix} 1 & 0 \\ -2 & 3 \end{bmatrix} = \begin{bmatrix} 2.5(1) & 2.5(0) \\ 2.5(-2) & 2.5(3) \end{bmatrix}$
$= \begin{bmatrix} 2.5 & 0 \\ -5 & 7.5 \end{bmatrix}$

Scalar multiplication (p. 781) Scalar multiplication is an operation that multiplies a matrix A by a scalar c. To find the resulting matrix cA, multiply each element of A by c.

Multiplicación escalar (p. 781) La multiplicación escalar es la que multiplica una matriz A por un número escalar c. Para hallar la matriz cA resultante, multiplica cada elemento de A por c.

Example $2.5\begin{bmatrix} 1 & 0 \\ -2 & 3 \end{bmatrix} = \begin{bmatrix} 2.5(1) & 2.5(0) \\ 2.5(-2) & 2.5(3) \end{bmatrix}$
$= \begin{bmatrix} 2.5 & 0 \\ -5 & 7.5 \end{bmatrix}$

Scatter plot (p. 103) A scatter plot is a graph that relates two different sets of data by plotting the data as ordered pairs. You can use a scatter plot to determine a relationship between the data sets.

Diagrama de puntos (p. 103) Un diagrama de puntos es una gráfica que relaciona dos conjuntos de datos presentando los datos como pares ordenados. El diagrama de puntos sirve para definir la relación entre conjuntos de datos.

Example

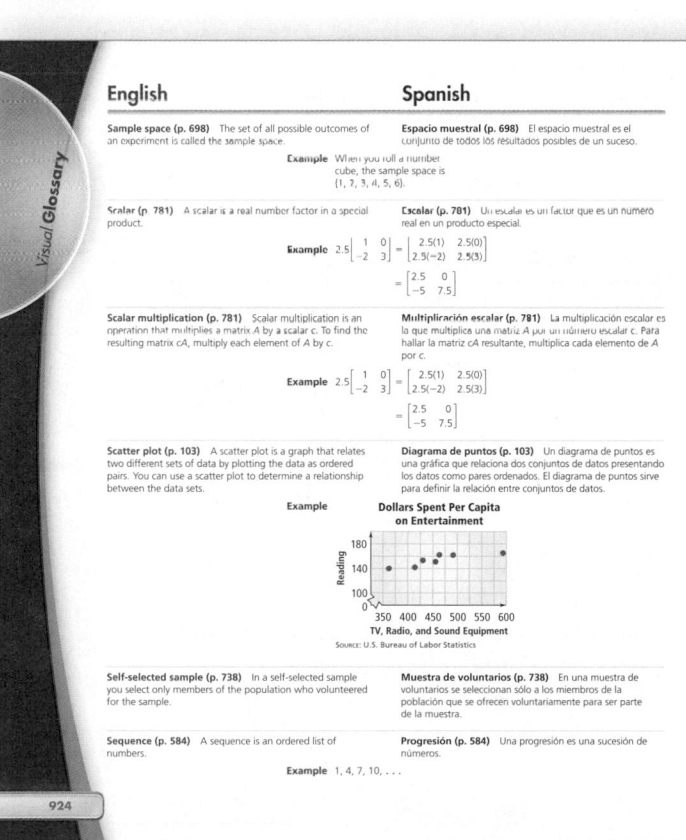

Dollars Spent Per Capita on Entertainment
TV, Radio, and Sound Equipment
Source: U.S. Bureau of Labor Statistics

Self-selected sample (p. 738) In a self-selected sample you select only members of the population who volunteered for the sample.

Muestra de voluntarios (p. 738) En una muestra de voluntarios se seleccionan sólo a los miembros de la población que se ofrecen voluntariamente para ser parte de la muestra.

Sequence (p. 584) A sequence is an ordered list of numbers.

Progresión (p. 584) Una progresión es una sucesión de números.

Example 1, 4, 7, 10, . . .

924

English / Spanish

Series (p. 607) A series is the sum of the terms of a sequence.

Serie (p. 607) Una serie es la suma de los términos de una secuencia.

Example The series $3 + 6 + 9 + 12 + 15$ corresponds to the sequence 3, 6, 9, 12, 15. The sum of the series is 45.

Simplest form of a radical expression (p. 388) A radical expression with index n is in simplest form if there are no radicals in any denominator, no denominators in any radical, and any radicand has no nth power factors.

Mínima expresión de una expresión radical (p. 388) Una expresión radical con índice n está en su mínima expresión si no tiene radicales en ningún denominador ni denominadores en ningún radical y los radicandos no tienen factores de potencia.

Simplest form of a rational expression (p. 548) A rational expression is in simplest form if its numerator and denominator are polynomials that have no common divisor other than 1.

Forma simplificada de una expresión racional (p. 548) Una expresión racional se encuentra en su mínima expresión si su numerador y su denominador son polinomios que no tienen otro divisor aparte de 1.

Example $\frac{x^2 - 7x + 12}{x^2 - 9} = \frac{(x - 4)(x - 3)}{(x + 3)(x - 3)} = \frac{x - 4}{x + 3}$,
where $x \neq -3$

Simulation (p. 696) A simulation is a model that imitates one or more events.

Simulación (p. 696) Una simulación es un modelo que imita uno o más sucesos.

Example Suppose a weather forecaster predicts a 50% chance of rain for the next three days. You can use three coins landing heads up to simulate three days in a row of rain.

Sine function, Sine of θ (pp. 823, 848) The sine function, $y = \sin \theta$, matches the measure θ of an angle in standard position with the y-coordinate of a point on the unit circle. This point is where the terminal side of the angle intersects the unit circle. The y-coordinate is the sine of θ.

Función seno, Seno de θ (pp. 823, 848) La función seno, $y = \sin \theta$, empareja la medida θ de un ángulo en posición estándar con la coordenada y de un punto en el círculo unitario. Este es el punto en el que el lado terminal del ángulo interseca al círculo unitario. La coordenada y es el seno de θ.

Example

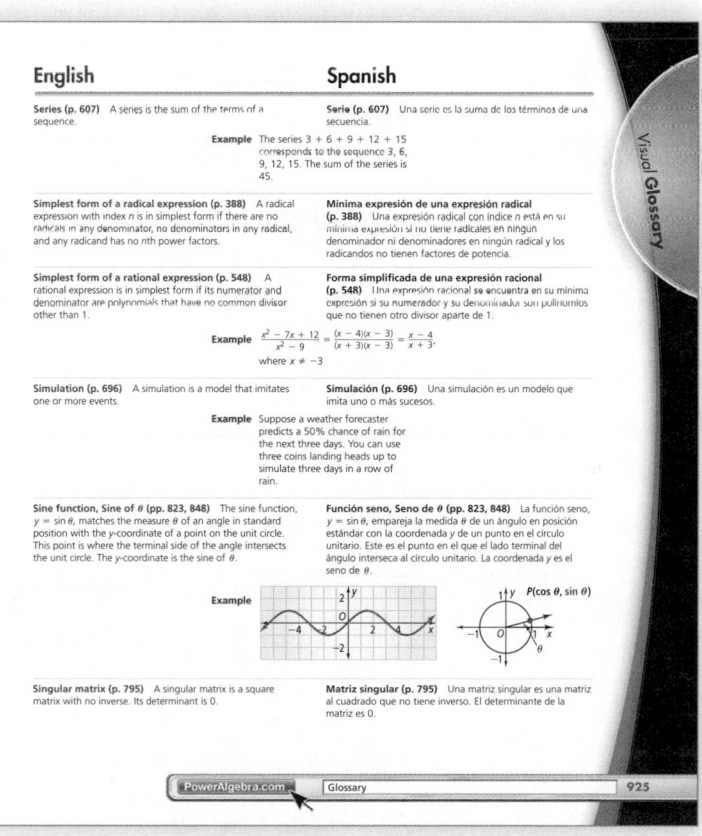

$P(\cos \theta, \sin \theta)$

Singular matrix (p. 795) A singular matrix is a square matrix with no inverse. Its determinant is 0.

Matriz singular (p. 795) Una matriz singular es una matriz al cuadrado que no tiene inverso. El determinante de la matriz es 0.

PowerAlgebra.com Glossary

925

English / Spanish

Slope (p. 81) The slope of a non-vertical line is the ratio of the vertical change to the horizontal change between points. You can calculate slope by finding the ratio of the difference in the y-coordinates to the difference in the x-coordinates for any two points on the line. The slope of a vertical line is undefined.

Pendiente (p. 81) La pendiente de una línea no vertical es la razón del cambio vertical al cambio horizontal entre puntos. Puedes calcular la pendiente al hallar la razón de la diferencia de la coordenada y a la diferencia de la coordenada x para dos puntos cualesquiera de la línea. La pendiente de una línea vertical es indefinida.

Example The slope of the line through points $(-1, -1)$ and $(1, -2)$ is
$$\frac{-2 - (-1)}{1 - (-1)} = \frac{-1}{2} = -\frac{1}{2}$$

Slope-intercept form (p. 83) The slope-intercept form of an equation of a line is $y = mx + b$, where m is the slope and b is the y-intercept.

Forma pendiente-intercepto (p. 83) La forma pendiente-intercepto de una ecuación lineal es $y = mx + b$, donde m es la pendiente y b es el intercepto en y.

Example $y = 8x + 2$
$y = -x + 1$
$y = -\frac{1}{3}x - 14$

Solution of a system (p. 146) A solution of a system is a set of values for the variables that makes all the equations true.

Solución de un sistema (p. 146) Una solución de un sistema es un conjunto de valores para las variables que hace que todas las ecuaciones sean verdaderas.

Solution of an equation (p. 27) A solution of an equation is a number that makes the equation true.

Solución de una ecuación (p. 27) Una solución de una ecuación es cualquier número que haga verdadera la ecuación.

Example The solution of $2x - 7 = -12$ is $x = -2.5$.

Square matrix (p. 789) A square matrix is a matrix with the same number of columns as rows.

Matriz cuadrada (p. 789) Una matriz cuadrada es la que tiene la misma cantidad de columnas y filas.

Example Matrix A is a square matrix.
$$A = \begin{bmatrix} 1 & 2 & 0 \\ -1 & 0 & -2 \\ 1 & 2 & 3 \end{bmatrix}$$

Square root equation (p. 417) A square root equation is a radical equation in which the radical has index 2.

Ecuación de raíz cuadrada (p. 417) Una ecuación de raíz cuadrada es una ecuación radical en la cual el radical tiene índice 2.

Example $\sqrt{x} = 4$

Square root function (p. 445) A square root function is a function that can be written in the form $f(x) = a\sqrt{x - h} + k$, where $a \neq 0$. The domain of a square root function is all real numbers $x \geq h$.

Función de raíz cuadrada (p. 445) Una función de raíz cuadrada es una función que puede ser expresada como $f(x) = a\sqrt{x - h} + k$, donde $a \neq 0$. El dominio de una función de raíz cuadrada son todos los números reales tales que $x \geq h$.

Example $f(x) = 2\sqrt{x - 3} + 4$

English / Spanish

Standard deviation (p. 732) Standard deviation is a measure of how much the values in a data set vary, or deviate, from the mean, $\bar{x}$. To find the standard deviation, follow five steps:
- Find the mean of the data set.
- Find the difference between each data value and the mean.
- Square each difference.
- Find the mean of the squares.
- Take the square root of the mean of the squares. This is the standard deviation.

Desviación típica (p. 732) La desviación típica denota cuánto los valores de un conjunto de datos varían, o se desvían, de la media, $\bar{x}$. Para hallar la desviación típica, se siguen cinco pasos:
- Se halla la media del conjunto de datos.
- Se calcula la diferencia entre cada valor de datos y la media.
- Se eleva al cuadrado cada diferencia.
- Se halla la media de los cuadrados.
- Se calcula la raíz cuadrada de la media de los cuadrados. Ésa es la desviación típica.

Example $\{0, 2, 3, 4, 6, 7, 8, 9, 10, 11\}$
$\bar{x} = 6$
standard deviation $= \sqrt{12} \approx 3.46$

Standard form of a circle (p. 650) *See Circle.*

Forma normal de un círculo (p. 650) *Ver Circle.*

Example $(x - 3)^2 + (y - 4)^2 = 4$

Standard form of a linear equation (p. 89) The standard form of a linear equation is $Ax + By = C$, where A, B, and C are real numbers, and A and B are not *both* zero.

Forma normal de una ecuación lineal (p. 89) La forma normal de una ecuación lineal es $Ax + By = C$, donde A, B y C son números reales, y A y B no son cero ambos.

Example In standard form, the equation
$y = \frac{4}{3}x - 1$ is
$4x + (-3)y = 3$.

Standard form of a polynomial function (p. 293) The standard form of a polynomial function arranges the terms by degree in descending numerical order. A polynomial function, $P(x)$, in standard form is $P(x) = a_n x^n + a_{n-1}x^{n-1} + \cdots + a_1 x + a_0$, where n is a nonnegative integer and $a_n, \ldots, a_0$ are real numbers.

Forma normal de una función polinomial (p. 293) La forma normal de una función polinomial organiza los términos por grado en orden numérico descendiente. Una función polinomial, $P(x)$, en forma normal es $P(x) = a_n x^n + a_{n-1}x^{n-1} + \cdots + a_1 x + a_0$, donde n es un número entero no negativo y $a_n, \ldots, a_0$ son números reales.

Example $2x^3 - 5x^2 - 2x + 5$

Standard form of a quadratic function (p. 212) The standard form of a quadratic function is $f(x) = ax^2 + bx + c$ with $a \neq 0$.

Forma normal de una función cuadrática (p. 212) La forma normal de una función cuadrática es $f(x) = ax^2 + bx + c$ con $a \neq 0$.

Example $f(x) = 2x^2 + 5x + 2$

English / Spanish

Standard normal curve (p. 752) The standard normal curve is a normal distribution centered on the y-axis. The mean of the standard normal curve is 0. The standard deviation is 1.

Curva normal en posición normal (p. 752) La curva normal es la distribución normal centrada en el eje y. La media de la curva normal es 0. La desviación normal es 1.

Example

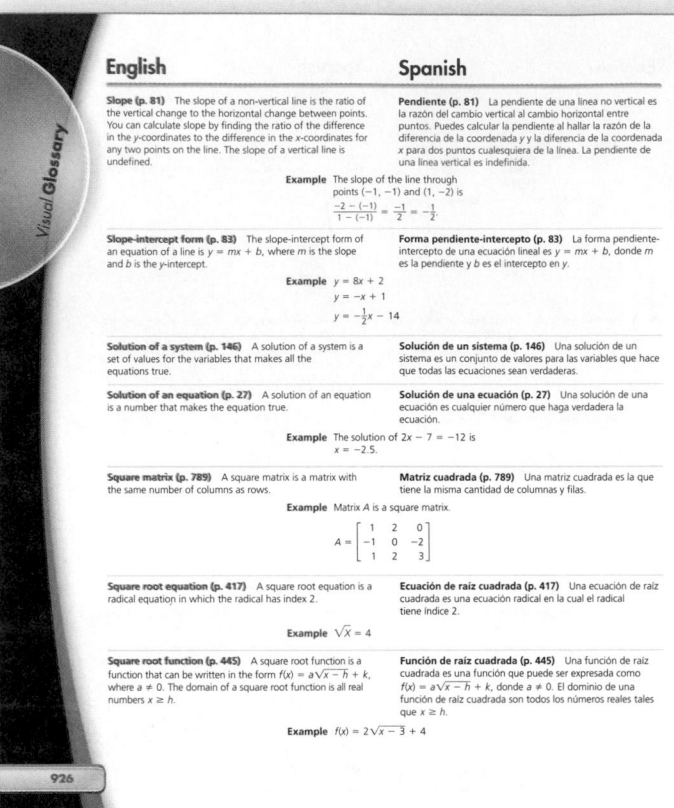

Standard position (p. 834) An angle in the coordinate plane is in **standard position** when the vertex is at the origin and one ray is on the positive x-axis.

Posición estándar (p. 834) Un ángulo en el plano de coordenadas se encuentra en **posición estándar** si el vértice se encuentra en el origen y una semirrecta se encuentra en el eje x positivo.

Example

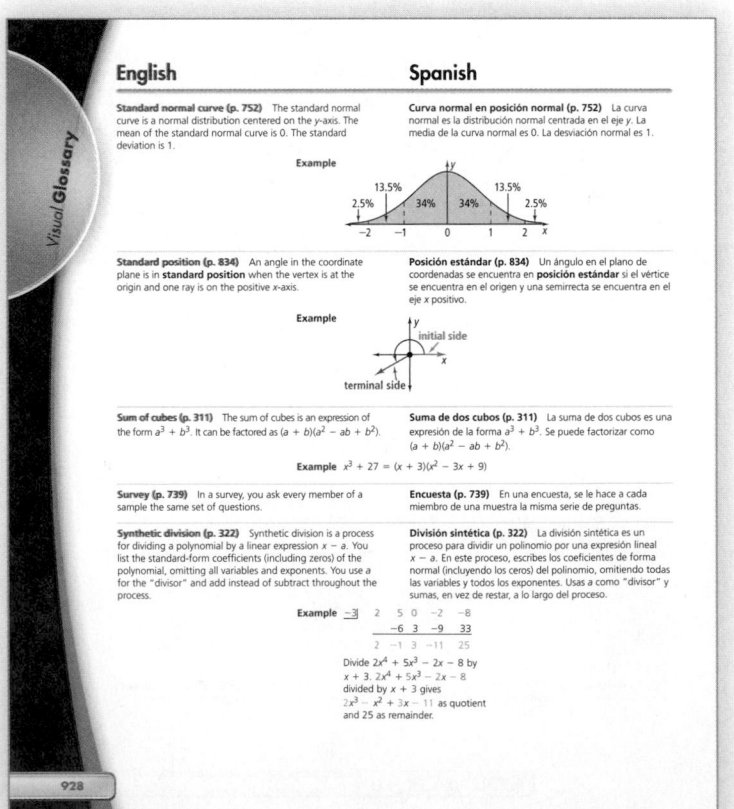

Sum of cubes (p. 311) The sum of cubes is an expression of the form $a^3 + b^3$. It can be factored as $(a + b)(a^2 - ab + b^2)$.

Suma de dos cubos (p. 311) La suma de dos cubos es una expresión de la forma $a^3 + b^3$. Se puede factorizar como $(a + b)(a^2 - ab + b^2)$.

Example $x^3 + 27 = (x + 3)(x^2 - 3x + 9)$

Survey (p. 739) In a survey, you ask every member of a sample the same set of questions.

Encuesta (p. 739) En una encuesta, se le hace a cada miembro de una muestra la misma serie de preguntas.

Synthetic division (p. 322) Synthetic division is a process for dividing a polynomial by a linear expression $x - a$. You list the standard-form coefficients (including zeros) of the polynomial, omitting all variables and exponents. You use a for the "divisor" and add instead of subtract throughout the process.

División sintética (p. 322) La división sintética es un proceso para dividir un polinomio por una expresión lineal $x - a$. En este proceso, escribes los coeficientes de forma normal (incluyendo los ceros) del polinomio, omitiendo todas las variables y todos los exponentes. Usas a como "divisor" y sumas, en vez de restar, a lo largo del proceso.

Example
$$\begin{array}{r|rrrr} -3 & 2 & 5 & 0 & -2 & -8 \\ & & -6 & 3 & -9 & 33 \\ \hline & 2 & -1 & 3 & -11 & 33 \end{array}$$
Divide $2x^4 + 5x^3 - 2x - 8$ by $x + 3$. $2x^4 + 5x^3 - 2x - 8$ divided by $x + 3$ gives $2x^3 - x^2 + 3x - 11$ as quotient and 25 as remainder.

English / Spanish

System of equations (p. 146) A system of equations is a set of two or more equations using the same variables.

Sistema de ecuaciones (p. 146) Un sistema de ecuaciones es un conjunto de dos o más ecuaciones que contienen las mismas variables.

Example $\begin{cases} 2x - 3y = -13 \\ 4x + 5y = 7 \end{cases}$

Systematic sample (p. 738) In a systematic sample you order the population in some way, and then select from it at regular intervals.

Muestra sistemática (p. 738) En una muestra sistemática se ordena la población de cierta manera y luego se selecciona una muestra de esa población a intervalos regulares.

T

Tangent function, Tangent of θ (pp. 823, 853) The tangent function, $y = \tan \theta$, matches the measure θ, of an angle in standard position with the y/x ratio of the (x, y) coordinates of a point on the unit circle. This point is where the terminal side of the angle intersects the unit circle. y/x is the tangent of θ.

Función tangente, Tangente de θ (pp. 823, 853) La función tangente, $y = \tan \theta$, empareja la medida θ, de un ángulo en posición estándar con la razón y/x de las coordenadas (x, y) de un punto en el círculo unitario. Este es el punto en el que el lado terminal del ángulo interseca al círculo unitario. y/x es la tangente de θ.

Example

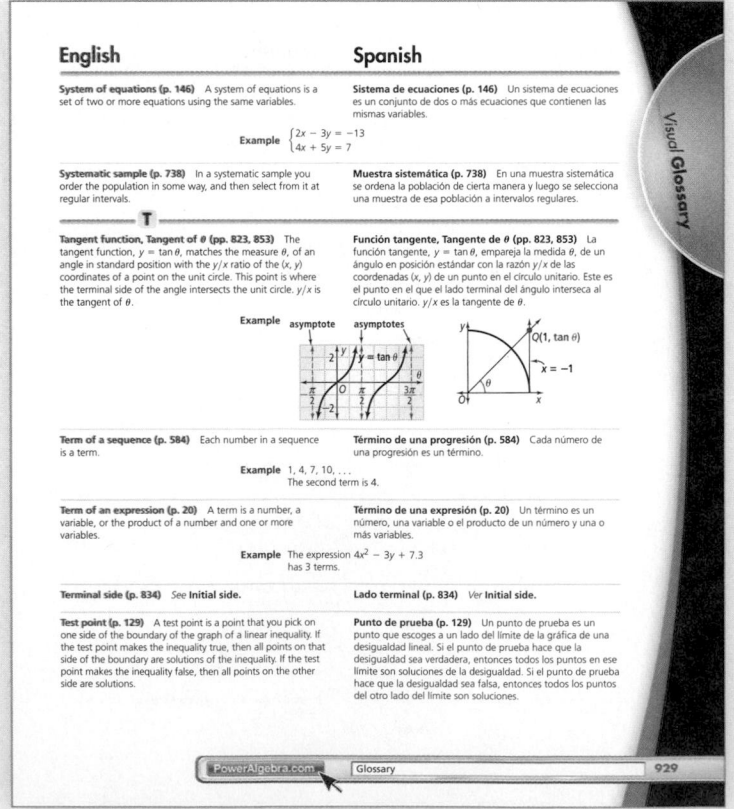

Term of a sequence (p. 584) Each number in a sequence is a term.

Término de una progresión (p. 584) Cada número de una progresión es un término.

Example $1, 4, 7, 10, \ldots$
The second term is 4.

Term of an expression (p. 20) A term is a number, a variable, or the product of a number and one or more variables.

Término de una expresión (p. 20) Un término es un número, una variable o el producto de un número y una o más variables.

Example The expression $4x^2 - 3y + 7.3$ has 3 terms.

Terminal side (p. 834) *See Initial side.*

Lado terminal (p. 834) *Ver Initial side.*

Test point (p. 129) A test point is a point that you pick on one side of the boundary of the graph of a linear inequality. If the test point makes the inequality true, then all points on that side of the boundary are solutions of the inequality. If the test point makes the inequality false, then all points on the other side are solutions.

Punto de prueba (p. 129) Un punto de prueba es un punto que escoges a un lado del límite de la gráfica de una desigualdad lineal. Si el punto de prueba hace que la desigualdad sea verdadera, entonces todos los puntos en ese límite son soluciones de la desigualdad. Si el punto de prueba hace que la desigualdad sea falsa, entonces todos los puntos del otro lado del límite son soluciones.

Page 930

English

Spanish

Theoretical probability (p. 698) If a sample space has n equally likely outcomes, and an event A occurs in m of these outcomes, then the theoretical probability of event A is $P(A) = \frac{m}{n}$.

Probabilidad teórica (p. 698) Si un espacio muestral tiene n resultados con la misma probabilidad de ocurrir, y ocurre un suceso A en m de estos resultados, entonces la probabilidad teórica del suceso A es $P(A) = \frac{m}{n}$.

Example Use the set {1, 4, 9, 16, 25, 36, 49, 64, 81, 100}. The probability that a number selected at random is greater than 50 is $P(A) = \frac{3}{10} = 0.3$.

Tolerance (p. 48) The difference between a desired measurement and its maximum and minimum allowable values is the tolerance. The tolerance equals one half of the difference between the maximum and minimum values.

Tolerancia (p. 48) La diferencia entre una medida deseada y sus valores máximo y mínimo permitidos es la tolerancia. La tolerancia equivale a la mitad de la diferencia entre los valores máximo y mínimo.

Example A manufacturing specification calls for a dimension d of 10 cm with a tolerance of 0.1 cm. The allowable difference between d and 10 is less than or equal to 0.1.

Transformation (p. 110) A transformation of a function $y = af(x - h) + k$ is a change made to at least one of the values a, h, and k. The four types of transformations are dilations, reflections, rotations, and translations.

Transformación (p. 110) Una transformación de una función $y = af(x - h) + k$ es un cambio que se le hace a por lo menos uno de los valores a, h y k. Hay cuatro tipos de transformaciones: dilataciones, reflexiones, rotaciones y traslaciones.

Example $g(x) = 2(x - 3)^2$ is a transformation of $f(x) = x^2$.

Translation (p. 110) A translation shifts the graph of the parent function horizontally, vertically, or both without changing its shape or orientation.

Traslación (p. 110) Una traslación desplaza la gráfica de la función madre horizontalmente, verticalmente o en ambas direcciones, sin cambiar su forma u orientación.

Example

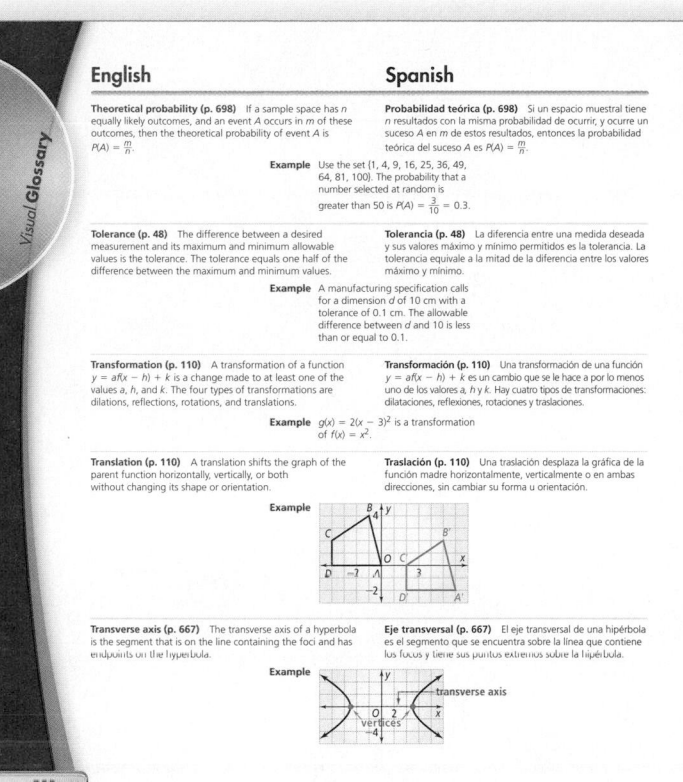

Transverse axis (p. 667) The transverse axis of a hyperbola is the segment that is on the line containing the foci and has endpoints on the hyperbola.

Eje transversal (p. 667) El eje transversal de una hipérbola es el segmento que se encuentra sobre la línea que contiene los focos y tiene sus puntos extremos sobre la hipérbola.

Example

Page 931

English

Spanish

Trend line (p. 104) A trend line is a line that approximates the relationship between two variables, or data sets, of a scatter plot.

Línea de tendencia (p. 104) Una línea de tendencia es una línea que aproxima la relación entre dos variables o conjuntos de datos de un diagrama de dispersión.

Example

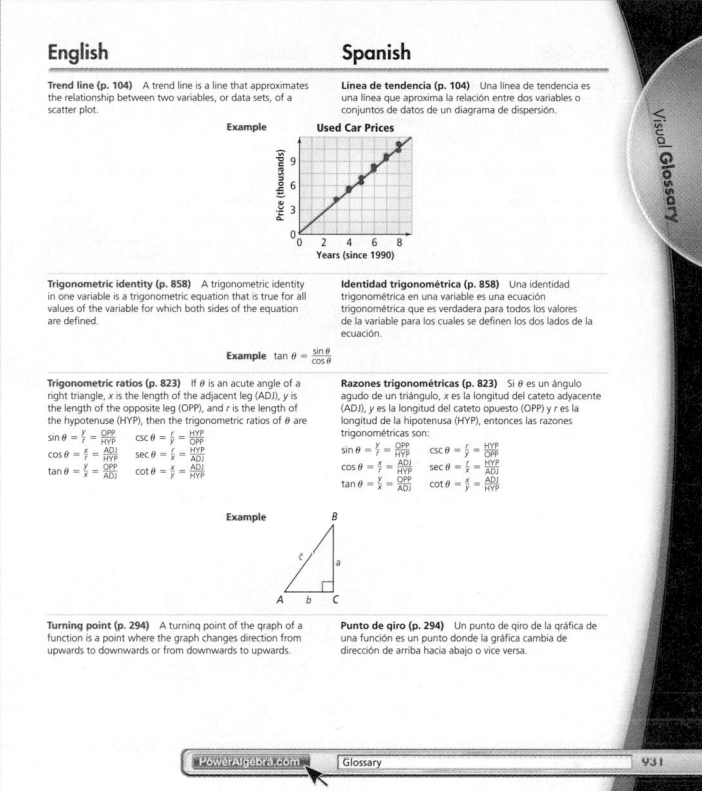

Trigonometric identity (p. 858) A trigonometric identity in one variable is a trigonometric equation that is true for all values of the variable for which both sides of the equation are defined.

Identidad trigonométrica (p. 858) Una identidad trigonométrica en una variable es una ecuación trigonométrica que es verdadera para todos los valores de la variable para los cuales se definen los dos lados de la ecuación.

Example $\tan \theta = \frac{\sin \theta}{\cos \theta}$

Trigonometric ratios (p. 823) If θ is an acute angle of a right triangle, x is the length of the adjacent leg (ADJ), y is the length of the opposite leg (OPP), and r is the length of the hypotenuse (HYP), then the trigonometric ratios of θ are

$\sin \theta = \frac{y}{r} = \frac{\text{OPP}}{\text{HYP}}$ $\csc \theta = \frac{r}{y} = \frac{\text{HYP}}{\text{OPP}}$

$\cos \theta = \frac{x}{r} = \frac{\text{ADJ}}{\text{HYP}}$ $\sec \theta = \frac{r}{x} = \frac{\text{HYP}}{\text{ADJ}}$

$\tan \theta = \frac{y}{x} = \frac{\text{OPP}}{\text{ADJ}}$ $\cot \theta = \frac{x}{y} = \frac{\text{ADJ}}{\text{OPP}}$

Razones trigonométricas (p. 823) Si θ es un ángulo agudo de un triángulo, x es la longitud del cateto adyacente (ADJ), y es la longitud del cateto opuesto (OPP) y r es la longitud de la hipotenusa (HYP), entonces las razones trigonométricas son:

$\sin \theta = \frac{y}{r} = \frac{\text{OPP}}{\text{HYP}}$ $\csc \theta = \frac{r}{y} = \frac{\text{HYP}}{\text{OPP}}$

$\cos \theta = \frac{x}{r} = \frac{\text{ADJ}}{\text{HYP}}$ $\sec \theta = \frac{r}{x} = \frac{\text{HYP}}{\text{ADJ}}$

$\tan \theta = \frac{y}{x} = \frac{\text{OPP}}{\text{ADJ}}$ $\cot \theta = \frac{x}{y} = \frac{\text{ADJ}}{\text{OPP}}$

Example

Turning point (p. 294) A turning point of the graph of a function is a point where the graph changes direction from upwards to downwards or from downwards to upwards.

Punto de giro (p. 294) Un punto de giro de la gráfica de una función es un punto donde la gráfica cambia de dirección de arriba hacia abajo o vice versa.

Page 932

English

U

Spanish

Unit circle (p. 836) The unit circle has a radius of 1 unit and its center is at the origin of the coordinate plane.

Círculo unitario (p. 836) El círculo unitario tiene un radio de 1 unidad y su centro está situado en el origen del plano de coordenadas.

Example

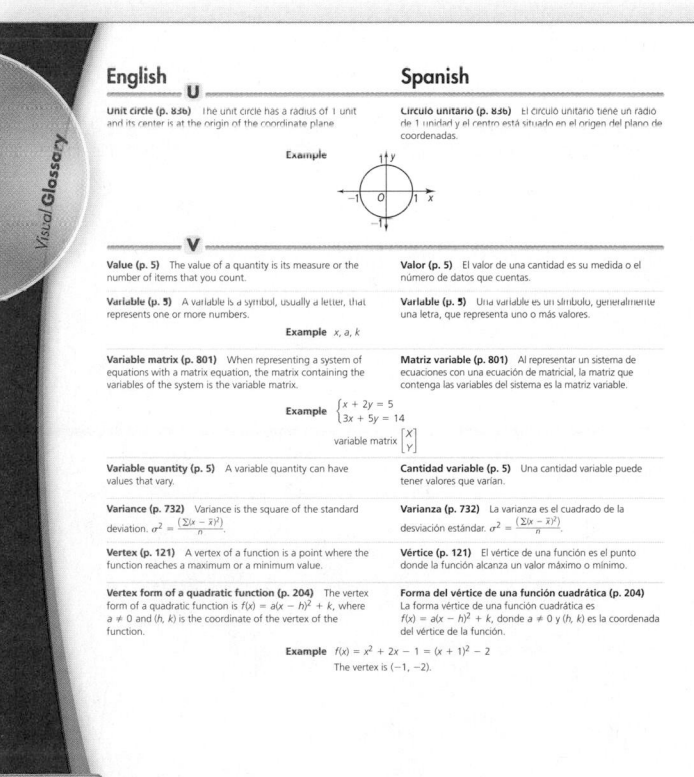

V

Value (p. 5) The value of a quantity is its measure or the number of items that you count.

Valor (p. 5) El valor de una cantidad es su medida o el número de datos que cuentas.

Variable (p. 5) A variable is a symbol, usually a letter, that represents one or more numbers.

Variable (p. 5) Una variable es un símbolo, generalmente una letra, que representa uno o más valores.

Example x, a, k

Variable matrix (p. 801) When representing a system of equations with a matrix equation, the matrix containing the variables of the system is the variable matrix.

Matriz variable (p. 801) Al representar un sistema de ecuaciones con una ecuación de matricial, la matriz que contenga las variables del sistema es la matriz variable.

Example $\begin{cases} x + 2y = 5 \\ 3x + 5y = 14 \end{cases}$

variable matrix $\begin{bmatrix} x \\ y \end{bmatrix}$

Variable quantity (p. 5) A variable quantity can have values that vary.

Cantidad variable (p. 5) Una cantidad variable puede tener valores que varían.

Variance (p. 732) Variance is the square of the standard deviation. $\sigma^2 = \frac{(\Sigma(x - \bar{x})^2)}{n}$

Varianza (p. 732) La varianza es el cuadrado de la desviación estándar. $\sigma^2 = \frac{(\Sigma(x - \bar{x})^2)}{n}$

Vertex (p. 121) A vertex of a function is a point where the function reaches a maximum or a minimum value.

Vértice (p. 121) El vértice de una función es el punto donde la función alcanza un valor máximo o mínimo.

Vertex form of a quadratic function (p. 204) The vertex form of a quadratic function is $f(x) = a(x - h)^2 + k$, where $a \neq 0$ and (h, k) is the coordinate of the vertex of the function.

Forma del vértice de una función cuadrática (p. 204) La forma vértice de una función cuadrática es $f(x) = a(x - h)^2 + k$, donde $a \neq 0$ y (h, k) es la coordenada del vértice de la función.

Example $f(x) = x^2 + 2x - 1 = (x + 1)^2 - 2$ The vertex is $(-1, -2)$.

Page 933

English

Spanish

Vertex of a parabola (p. 204) The vertex of a parabola is the point where the function for the parabola reaches a maximum or a minimum value. The parabola intersects its axis of symmetry at the vertex.

Vértice de una parábola (p. 204) El vértice de una parábola es el punto donde la función de la parábola alcanza un valor máximo o mínimo. La parábola y su eje de simetría se intersecan en el vértice.

Example

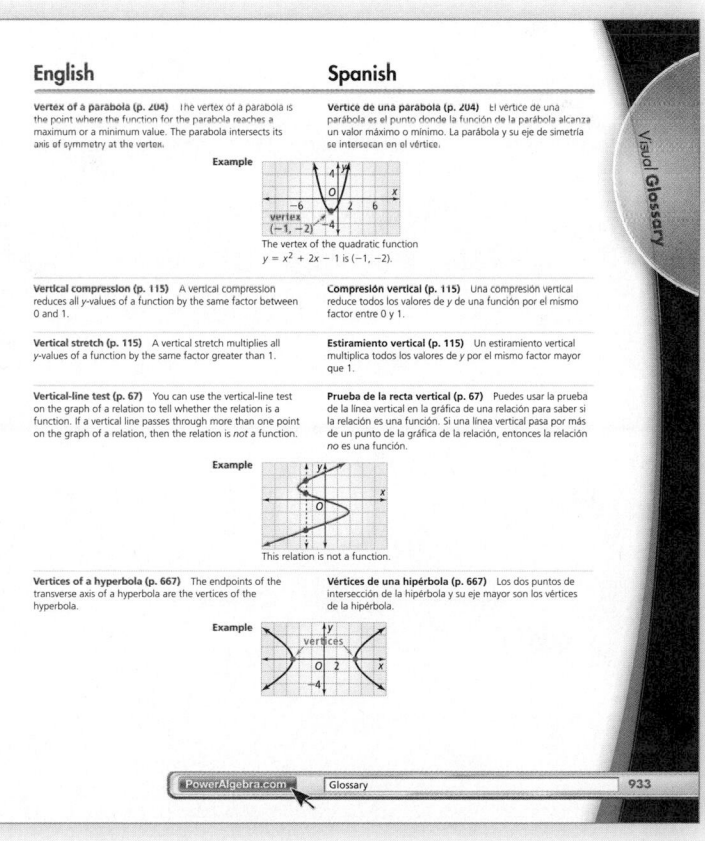

The vertex of the quadratic function $y = x^2 + 2x - 1$ is $(-1, -2)$.

Vertical compression (p. 115) A vertical compression reduces all y-values of a function by the same factor between 0 and 1.

Compresión vertical (p. 115) Una compresión vertical reduce todos los valores de y de una función por el mismo factor entre 0 y 1.

Vertical stretch (p. 115) A vertical stretch multiplies all y-values of a function by the same factor greater than 1.

Estiramiento vertical (p. 115) Un estiramiento vertical multiplica todos los valores de y por el mismo factor mayor que 1.

Vertical-line test (p. 67) You can use the vertical-line test on the graph of a relation to tell whether the relation is a function. If a vertical line passes through more than one point on the graph of a relation, then the relation is not a function.

Prueba de la recta vertical (p. 67) Puedes usar la prueba de la línea vertical en la gráfica de una relación para saber si la relación es una función. Si una línea vertical pasa por más de un punto de la gráfica de la relación, entonces la relación no es una función.

Example

This relation is not a function.

Vertices of a hyperbola (p. 667) The endpoints of the transverse axis of a hyperbola are the vertices of the hyperbola.

Vértices de una hipérbola (p. 667) Los dos puntos de intersección de la hipérbola y su eje mayor son los vértices de la hipérbola.

Example

English

Spanish

Vertices of an ellipse (p. 659) The endpoints of the major axis of an ellipse are the vertices of the ellipse.

Vértices de una elipse (p. 659) Los dos puntos de intersección de la elipse y su eje mayor son los vértices de la elipse.

Example

X

x-intercept, y-intercept (p. 83) The point at which a line crosses the x-axis (or the x-coordinate of that point) is an x-intercept. The point at which a line crosses the y-axis (or the y-coordinate of that point) is a y-intercept.

Intercepto en x, intercepto en y (p. 83) El punto donde una recta corta el eje x (o la coordenada x de ese punto) es el intercepto en x. El punto donde una recta cruza el eje y (o la coordenada y de ese punto) es el intercepto en y.

Example

The x-intercept of $y = 2x + 1$ is $\left(-\frac{1}{2}, 0\right)$ or $-\frac{1}{2}$.

The y-intercept of $y = 2x + 1$ is $(0, 1)$ or 1.

Z

Zero matrix (p. 775) The zero matrix O, or $O_{m \times n}$, is the $m \times n$ matrix whose elements are all zeros. It is the additive identity matrix for the set of all $m \times n$ matrices.

Matriz cero (p. 775) La matriz cero, O, o $O_{m \times n}$, es la matriz $m \times n$ cuyos elementos son todos ceros. Es la matriz de identidad aditiva para el conjunto de todas las matrices $m \times n$.

Example $\begin{bmatrix} 1 & 4 \\ 2 & -3 \end{bmatrix} + O = \begin{bmatrix} 1 & 4 \\ 2 & -3 \end{bmatrix}$

Zero of a function (p. 243) A zero of a function $f(x)$ is any value of x for which $f(x) = 0$.

Cero de una función (p. 243) Un cero de una función $f(x)$ es cualquier valor de x para el cual $f(x) = 0$.

Example

The zeros of the function are $x = -1$, $x = 0$, and $x = 3$.

Zero-Product Property (p. 243) If the product of two or more factors is zero, then one of the factors must be zero.

Propiedad del cero del producto (p. 243) Si el producto de dos o más factores es cero, entonces uno de los factores debe ser cero.

Example $(x - 3)(2x - 5) = 0$
$x - 3 = 0$ or $2x - 5 = 0$

Selected **Answers**

Chapter 1

Get Ready! p. 1

1. 0 **2.** −2 **3.** −2.09 **4.** 8.05 **5.** −$\frac{3}{4}$ **6.** $\frac{11}{12}$
7. $10\frac{7}{10}$ **8.** $3\frac{1}{2}$ **9.** −42 **10.** 72 **11.** 9 **12.** −9.8
13. −$3\frac{1}{3}$ **14.** −$5\frac{1}{2}$ **15.** −$4\frac{2}{3}$ **16.** −$\frac{3}{4}$ **17.** −21
18. 7.35 **19.** −$\frac{1}{8}$ **20.** −$\frac{3}{5}$ **21.** −20 **22.** 8 **23.** 0.97
24. −5 **25.** 55 **26.** 3 **27.** because the placement of the parentheses changes the order of operations **28.** 3
29. 3 terms **30.** Calculate the answer numerically.
31. $\frac{n}{n-3}$

Lesson 1-1 pp. 4–10

Got It? 1. The pattern shows a center square and a yellow square added to each side with the number of squares per side increasing by one.

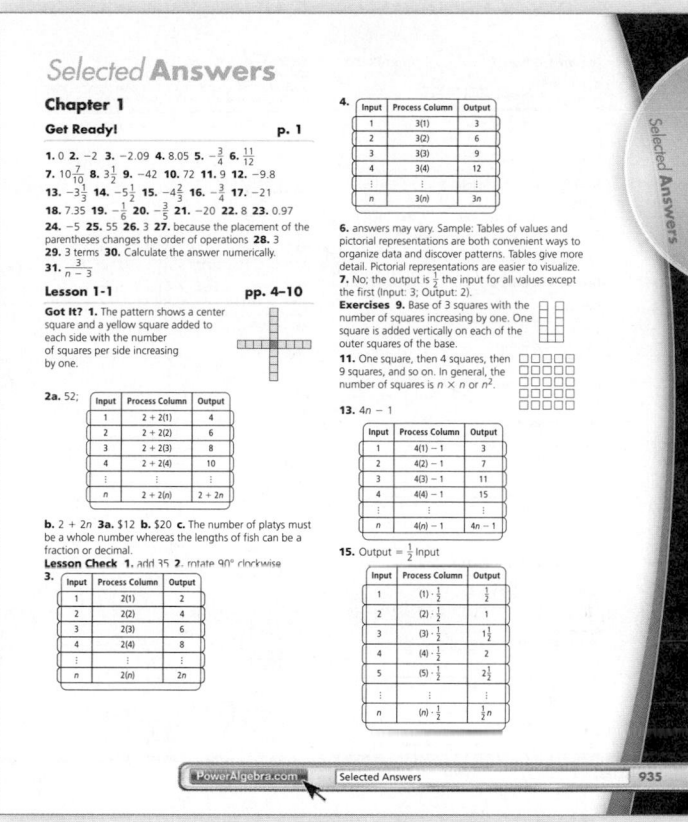

2a. 52;

Input	Process Column	Output
1	2 + 2(1)	4
2	2 + 2(2)	6
3	2 + 2(3)	8
4	2 + 2(4)	10
⋮	⋮	⋮
n	2 + 2(n)	2 + 2n

b. 2 + 2n **3a.** $12 **b.** $20 **c.** The number of platys must be a whole number whereas the lengths of fish can be a fraction or decimal.
Lesson Check 1. add 35 **2.** rotate 90° clockwise
3.

Input	Process Column	Output
1	2(1)	2
2	2(2)	4
3	2(3)	6
4	2(4)	8
⋮	⋮	⋮
n	2(n)	2n

4.

Input	Process Column	Output
1	3(1)	3
2	3(2)	6
3	3(3)	9
4	3(4)	12
⋮	⋮	⋮
n	3(n)	3n

6. answers may vary. Sample: Tables of values and pictorial representations are both convenient ways to organize data and discover patterns. Tables give more detail. Pictorial representations are easier to visualize.
7. No; the output is $\frac{1}{2}$ the input for all values except the first (Input: 3; Output: 2).
Exercises 9. Base of 3 squares with the number of squares increasing by one. One square is added vertically on each of the outer squares of the base.
11. One square, then 4 squares, then 9 squares, and so on. In general, the number of squares is $n \times n$ or n^2.
13. 4n − 1

Input	Process Column	Output
1	4(1) − 1	3
2	4(2) − 1	7
3	4(3) − 1	11
4	4(4) − 1	15
⋮	⋮	⋮
n	4(n) − 1	4n − 1

15. Output = $\frac{1}{2}$ Input

Input	Process Column	Output
1	(1) · $\frac{1}{2}$	$\frac{1}{2}$
2	(2) · $\frac{1}{2}$	1
3	(3) · $\frac{1}{2}$	1$\frac{1}{2}$
4	(4) · $\frac{1}{2}$	2
5	(5) · $\frac{1}{2}$	2$\frac{1}{2}$
⋮	⋮	⋮
n	(n) · $\frac{1}{2}$	$\frac{1}{2}n$

---

17. 10 **19.** 2n **21.** add 3 and then subtract 1; 8, 7, 10 **23.** add 4; 18, 22, 26 **25.** multiply by 5; 2500, 12,500, 62,500
27a.

Input	Output
1	3
2	6
3	9
4	12
5	15
⋮	⋮
n	3n

b. 18; 21; 24

29a.

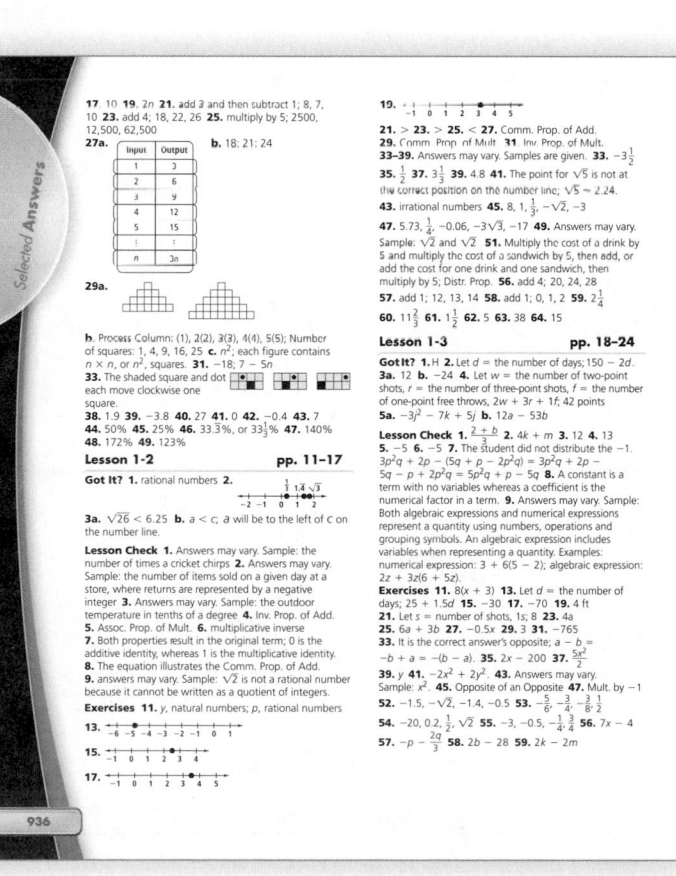

b. Process Column: (1), 2(2), 3(3), 4(4), 5(5); Number of squares: 1, 4, 9, 16, 25 **c.** n^2; each figure contains $n \times n$, or n^2, squares. **31.** −18; 7 − 5n
33. The shaded square and dot each move clockwise one square.
38. 1.9 **39.** −3.8 **40.** 27 **41.** 0 **42.** −0.4 **43.** 7 **44.** 50% **45.** 25% **46.** 33.3%, or 33$\frac{1}{3}$% **47.** 140% **48.** 172% **49.** 123%

Lesson 1-2 pp. 11–17

Got It? 1. rational numbers **2.**

3a. $\sqrt{26}$ < 6.25 **b.** a < c; a will be to the left of c on the number line.

Lesson Check 1. Answers may vary. Sample: the number of times a cricket chirps **2.** Answers may vary. Sample: the number of items sold on a given day at a store, where returns are represented by a negative integer **3.** Answers may vary. Sample: the outdoor temperature in tenths of a degree **4.** Inv. Prop. of Add. **5.** Assoc. Prop. of Mult. **6.** multiplicative inverse **7.** Both properties result in the original term; 0 is the additive identity, whereas 1 is the multiplicative identity. **8.** The equation illustrates the Comm. Prop. of Add. **9.** answers may vary. Sample: $\sqrt{2}$ is not a rational number because it cannot be written as a quotient of integers.
Exercises 11. y, natural numbers; p, rational numbers

13.

15.

17.

19.

21. > **23.** > **25.** < **27.** Comm. Prop. of Add. **29.** Comm. Prop. of Mult. **31.** Inv. Prop. of Mult.
33–39. Answers may vary. Samples are given. **33.** −3$\frac{1}{2}$
35. 1$\frac{1}{2}$ **37.** 3$\frac{1}{3}$ **39.** 4.8 **41.** The point for $\sqrt{5}$ is not at the correct position on the number line; $\sqrt{5}$ ≈ 2.24.
43. irrational numbers **45.** 8, 1, $\frac{1}{3}$, −$\sqrt{2}$, −3
47. 5.73, $\frac{1}{2}$, −0.06, −3$\sqrt{3}$, −17 **49.** Answers may vary. Sample: $\sqrt{2}$ and $\sqrt{2}$ **51.** Multiply the cost of a drink by 5 and multiply the cost of a sandwich by 5, then add, or add the cost for one drink and one sandwich, then multiply by 5; Distr. Prop. **56.** add 4; 20, 24, 28 **57.** add 1; 12, 13, 14 **58.** add 1; 0, 1, 2 **59.** 2$\frac{1}{4}$
60. 11$\frac{2}{9}$ **61.** 1$\frac{1}{2}$ **62.** 5 **63.** 38 **64.** 15

Lesson 1-3 pp. 18–24

Got It? 1. H **2.** Let d = the number of days; 150 − 2d.
3a. 12 **b.** −24 **4.** Let w = the number of two-point shots, r = the number of three-point shots, f = the number of one-point free throws, 2w + 3r + 1f; 42 points
5a. −3j² − 7k + 5j **b.** 12a − 53b
Lesson Check 1. $\frac{2+b}{3}$ **2.** 4k + m **3.** 12 **4.** 13
5. −5 **6.** −5 **7.** The student did not distribute the −1. 3p²q + 2p − (5q + p − 2p²q) = 3p²q + 2p − 5q − p + 2p²q = 5p²q + p − 5q **8.** A constant is a term with no variables whereas a coefficient is the numerical factor in a term. **9.** Answers may vary. Sample: Both algebraic expressions and numerical expressions represent a quantity using numbers, operations and grouping symbols. An algebraic expression includes variables when representing a quantity. Examples: numerical expression: 3 + 6(5 − 2); algebraic expression: 2z + 3z(6 + 5z).
Exercises 11. 8(x + 3) **13.** Let d = the number of days; 25 + 1.5d **15.** −30 **17.** −70 **19.** 4 ft
21. Let s = number of shots, 1s; 8 **23.** 4a
25. 6a + 3b **27.** −0.5x **29.** 3 **31.** −765
33. It is the correct answer's opposite; a − b = −b + a = −(b − a). **35.** 2x − 200 **37.** $\frac{5r}{2}$
39. y **41.** −2x² + 2y². **43.** Answers may vary. Sample: x² **45.** Opposite of an Opposite **47.** Mult. by −1
52. −1.5, −$\sqrt{2}$, −1.4, −0.5 **53.** −$\frac{5}{6}$, −$\frac{3}{4}$, −$\frac{3}{2}$
54. −20, 0.2, $\frac{1}{2}$, $\sqrt{2}$ **55.** −3, −0.5, −$\frac{1}{4}$, $\frac{1}{2}$ **56.** 7x − 4
57. −p − $\frac{2q}{3}$ **58.** 2b − 28 **59.** 2k − 2m

Lesson 1-4 pp. 26–32

Got It? 1. $\frac{3}{2}$ **2.** −1 **3.** 40 m × 120 m **4a.** never
b. always **5a.** C = K − 273 **b.** always
Lesson Check 1. 23.2 **2.** −90 **3.** 12
4. K = $\frac{1}{3}$(r − 15) **5.** K = $\frac{1}{3}$(r + 6)
6. K = −($\frac{1}{2}$)(h + 14) **7.** To find a solution of an equation means to find a value of the variable that makes the equation true. **8.** Four buses are not enough. The number of buses must be a whole number, so round the number of buses to 5. **9.** 2nd line incorrect; subtract 10 from both sides; 12x = −12, x = −1
Exercises 11. −81 **13.** 23 **15.** −5 **17.** $\frac{3}{2}$ **19.** 2
21. 300 mi/h; 600 mi/h **23.** sometimes **25.** sometimes
27. h = $\frac{2A}{b}$ **29.** w = $\frac{V}{\ell h}$ **31.** x = a(b + 5), a ≠ 0
33. $\frac{23}{3}$, or 7$\frac{2}{3}$ **35.** 34° and 56° **37.** b₂ = $\frac{2A}{h}$ − b₁
39. h = $\frac{S − 2\pi r^2}{2\pi r}$ **41.** 43, 45, 47, and 49 **43.** first stage, 90 s; second stage, 62 s **48.** −7 **49.** −$\frac{16}{9}$ **50.** −20
51. −$\frac{1}{2}$ **52.** x + 5 **53.** 16x **54.** 3(12 − x) **55.** true
56. false **57.** true

Lesson 1-5 Part 1 pp. 33–38

Got It? 1. $\frac{x}{5}$ ≤ 15
2a. x ≤ −4;

b. x > −1;

3. at least 33 songs **4a.** always **b.** sometimes **c.** never
Lesson Check 1. R ≥ J **2.** x + 5 < −7
3. x ≤ −$\frac{1}{2}$

4. x ≤ −2

5. Answers may vary. Sample: 5 < 6, but −5 > −6.
6. The transitive, addition, and subtraction properties of inequalities are similar to the properties of equality. The multiplication and division properties differ. Multiplying or dividing each side of an inequality by a negative quantity reverses the direction of the inequality symbol.
Exercises 7. 8x ≥ 25 **9.** $\frac{x}{12}$ = 6

11. t ≤ 11

13. y ≤ −6

15. n > 8

17. The width is less than 11.5 in., and the length is 3 in. greater than the width. **19.** The smaller number is an integer greater than or equal to 8. **21.** always **23.** never

25. never **27.** z ≥ 6

29. x ≥ −48

31. The classmate reversed the direction of the ≥ symbol to ≤ incorrectly. The correct answer is y ≤ −20.
33. Distr. Prop.; simplify; Subtr. Prop. of Inequality; Mult. Prop. of Inequality

Lesson 1-5 Part 2 pp. 39–42

Got It? 5a. 2 ≤ x < 6

b. sometimes; Sample: The compound inequality is true when x = 5 and not true when x = 7.
6a. w < −3 or w > $\frac{8}{7}$

b. x < −1 or x > 3

Lesson Check 1. 40 ≤ w < 74 **2.** a < 12 or a > 60
3. 1 < x < $\frac{9}{4}$

4. x ≤ 0 or x > 3

5. x < 8 or x > 8; All real numbers are solutions except x = 8.

6. No; Answers may vary. Sample: 2x < x + 1 and x + 1 > 3
Exercises 7. −5 < x < 2

9. −4 ≤ x < 6

11. 2 ≤ x < 6

13. all real numbers

15. x ≤ −3 or x ≥ 9

17. 98 **19.** 2 < AB < 6
21. −1 < x < 8

25. All real numbers

31. 7a + 5 **32.** −2x + 14y **33.** $\frac{b}{12}$ + 1
34. 1.61 − 0.1k **35.** 4 **36.** no solution **37.** $\frac{9}{10}$
38. −20

Lesson 1-6 Part 1   pp. 43–46

Got It? 1. $\frac{2}{3}$, -2 [number line]
2. -7, -11 [number line]
3. -1
Lesson Check 1. -4, 4 **2.** -12, 4 **3.** $-\frac{6}{5}$
4. A solution of an eq. is extraneous if it is a solution to a derived eq., but is not a solution to the original eq.
5. when the number is positive or 0
Exercises 7. -6, 6 **9.** $-\frac{5}{3}$, 3 **11.** no solution
13. -7, 17 **15.** $-\frac{3}{2}$ **17.** $\frac{3}{2}$ **19.** -1, $\frac{3}{2}$ **21.** 1
23. $-\frac{3}{4}$, 1 **25.** $-\frac{1}{3}$ **27.** $\frac{5}{2}$ **29.** $-\frac{71}{36}$ **31.** $|x - 1| = 1$
33. sometimes; when $x \neq 0$

Lesson 1-6 Part 2   pp. 47–52

Got It? 4. $-\frac{4}{3} \le x \le 4$ [number line]
5a. $x < -5$ or $x > 1$ [number line]
b. The graph will have two closed circles with an arrow extending to the left of one and to the right of the other.
6. $|h - 52.5| \le .5$
Lesson Check 1. $-11 < x < 9$ [number line]
2. $x \le -1$ or $x \ge 4$ [number line]
3. $-3\frac{1}{2} \le w \le \frac{1}{2}$ [number line]
4. Answers may vary. Sample: $d < -5$ and $5d > 25$
5. Answers may vary. Sample: An absolute value equation or inequality represents two equations or inequalities; each equation or inequality is solved in the same manner as a linear equation or inequality.
Exercises 7. $-2\frac{2}{5} < y < 3\frac{1}{5}$
9. $x < -12$ or $x > 6$
11. $x \le -3$ or $x \ge 13$
13. $-3\frac{1}{2} \le w \le \frac{1}{2}$
15. $x \le -3$ or $x \ge 4$

17. $|h - 1.4| \le 0.1$ **19.** $|b - 52.5| \le 2.5$
21. $|d - 0.11885| \le 0.00015$ **23.** $|x| < 4$ **25.** The graph of $|x| < a$ is the set of all points on the number line that lie between a and $-a$. The graph of $|x| > a$ has two parts; the left part consists of the points to the left of $-a$, and the right part consists of the points to the right of a.
27. $-6 \le x \le 8\frac{1}{2}$ [number line]
29. all real numbers [number line]
31. all real numbers [number line]
33. $x \le -8.4$ or $x \ge 9.6$ [number line]
35. $|t - 350| \le 5$ **37.** $|t - 15| \le 30$ **39.** always; if $x > 0$, then $|x| + |x| = 2x$; if $x < 0$, then $|x| + |x| > 2x$.
41. The "3" in the second set of inequalities should be "-3".
$-4x + 1 < -3$
$-4x < -4$
$x > 1$, not $x > -\frac{1}{2}$
43. $|x - 9.55| \le 0.02$; $9.53 \le x \le 9.57$
49. $y < 6$ [number line]
50. $s < \frac{2}{15}$ [number line]
51. $a > 4$ [number line]
52. Each figure has 4 more squares than the previous figure, with one square added at both ends of each row.
53. Each figure has n more circles than the previous figure, with the new row of circles at the top.
54. 55. 56. 57.

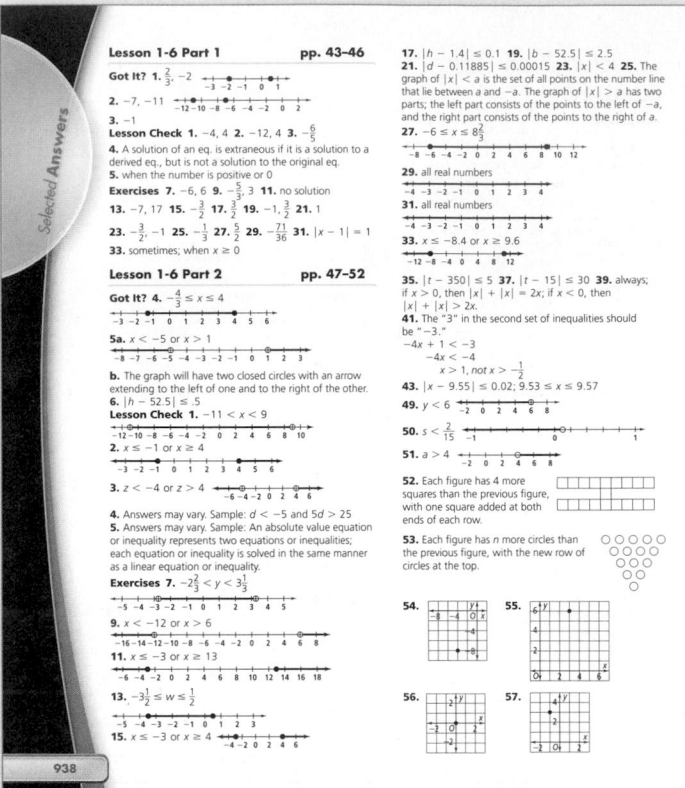

Chapter Review   pp. 54–56

1. solution of an equation **2.** absolute value
3. Reciprocal **4.** compound inequality **5.** add 5; 25, 30, 35
6. add 1; 7, 8, 9 **7.** 12; $n +$ **8.** 76; 19n **9.** $20n
10. irrational numbers **11.** rational numbers, integers
12. rational numbers, integers, whole numbers, natural numbers **13.** rational numbers **14.** $-\sqrt{60} > -8$
15. $5 < \sqrt{32}$ **16.** Inv. Prop. of Mult. **17.** Assoc. Prop. of Mult. **18.** 114 **19.** 5b **20.** 11 **21.** 6
22. $z \le \frac{5}{2}$ [number line]
23. $x > 2$ [number line]
24. no solution
25. $x \le \frac{3}{2}$ or $x > 6$ [number line]
26. 10 cm, 6 cm **27.** 1 **28.** no solution **29.** $x = -8$ or $x = -12$ **30.** no solution
31. $-\frac{1}{3} \le x \le \frac{5}{2}$ [number line]
32. $y < 0$ or $y > 18$ [number line]
33. $-\frac{18}{5} \le x \le \frac{18}{5}$ [number line]
34. $x < -14$ or $x > 10$ [number line]
35. $|x - 43.6| \le 0.1$

Chapter 2

Get Ready!   p. 61

1. 6s **2.** $4a + b$ **3.** $xy - y + x$ **4.** 1.5g **5.** 0
6. $3b - 2c - 2$ **7.** $6f - 5d$ **8.** $3h + 3g$ **9.** $-2z + 5$
10. $2g - 4dg - 12d$ **11.** $8v - 6$ **12.** $7t - 3st - 5s$
13. -56 **14.** 80 **15.** -10 **16.** -24 **17.** 1075 **18.** 5
19. -1.75 **20.** 1.5 **21.** 20 **22.** 2 **23.** 5 **24.** 4
25. $-2 < x < 8$ [number line]
26. $a \le 0$ [number line]
27. $x > -1$ [number line]
28. $x < -4$ or $x > \frac{10}{3}$ [number line]
29. $\frac{3}{2} \le a \le \frac{25}{4}$ [number line]
30. $-24 \le t \le 18$ [number line]
31. Answers may vary. Sample: the Civil War, the Great Depression, the Louisiana Purchase **32.** Answers may vary. Sample: From 1 to 2 years of age; a person has usually stopped growing by age 30, but a baby is still growing at age 1. **33.** Answers may vary. Sample:

The image is a reflection, left to right, of what other people see; the size is the same. **34.** Answers may vary. Sample: An inequality determines the limit of a value, or a boundary, for the solutions on the number line.

Lesson 2-1 Part 1   pp. 64–69

Got It? 1. Let Jan = 1, Feb = 2, Mar = 3, and Apr = 4.

$\{(1, 69), (2, 70), (3, 75), (4, 78)\}$

2a. domain: $\{-3, -2, 4, 5\}$; range: $\{-3, 2, 4, 8\}$
b. domain: $\{-3, 0, 2, 4, 9\}$; range: $\{-2, 3, 7, 9, 12\}$
3a. no **b.** yes **c.** In a mapping diagram for a relation that is not a function, there is at least one element in the domain that has more than one arrow originating from it. In a mapping diagram for a function, each element in the domain has one arrow originating from it. **4.** b and c
Lesson Check 1. domain: $\{0, 3, 4\}$, range: $\{-2, 1, 2, 4\}$ **2.** domain: $\{-4, -3, 0, 4\}$, range: $\{-4, -3, 0, 4\}$ **3.** no **4.** yes **5.** Yes; a relation is any set of pairs of input and output values. No; a relation is a relation in which each element of the domain is paired with exactly one element of the range. **6.** Every vertical line does not need to intersect a function. No; a function, every vertical line must intersect the graph in at most one point." **7.** A horizontal-line test checks the pairing of one element of the range with one or more elements of the domain. A function can have a pairing of one element of the range with one or more elements of the domain. A horizontal-line test cannot determine whether a relation is a function.
Exercises 9. domain: $\{1, 2, 3, 4, 5, 6\}$, range: $\{6, 7, 8, 9, 11\}$ **11.** yes **13.** yes **15.** yes **17.** yes **19.** no **21.** domain: $-3 \le x \le 3$, range: $-1 \le y \le 1$; no **23.** domain: $\{-3, -1, 1, 2, 4\}$, range: $\{0, 1, 2, 3\}$; no

Lesson 2-1 Part 2   pp. 70–73

Got It? 5a. 1 **b.** 0.25 **c.** -8 **6.** Let $x =$ number of bottles purchased and $C =$ total cost; $C(x) = 1.19x$; $17.85

Lesson Check 1. 14 **2.** -4 **3.** 55 **4.** 19 **5.** range
6. The friend who said the output is 49 is correct. Substitute 9 for x: $5(9) + 4 = 45 + 4 = 49$.
Exercises 7. 3; $(-5, 3)$ **9.** -15; $(9, -15)$ **11.** -2; $(3, -2)$ **13.** $-\frac{5}{2}$; $(9, -\frac{5}{2})$ **15.** $C(m) = 3.12 + 0.18m$; $34.62 **17.** 13.5 cm² **19.** 11 **21.** 7 **23.** 4
25. ≈ 4849 cm³ **27a.** into **b.** into **c.** onto **d.** into
32. $\frac{2}{3}$, $-\frac{20}{3}$ **33.** -13, 15 **34.** $x > -35$ **35.** $x \le \frac{3}{2}$
36. $-\frac{3}{2} < x < \frac{3}{2}$ **37.** $x \ge -3$ **38.** $\frac{1}{4}x$ **39.** $-\frac{1}{2}x$
40. 20x

Lesson 2-2   pp. 74–80

Got It? 1a. yes; -7, $y = -7x$ **b.** no **2a.** yes; $-\frac{5}{2}$
b. yes; $\frac{1}{2}$ **3.** 60 **4a.** 280 **b.** No; if $y^2 = kx^2$ then $y = \pm\sqrt{k}\,x$. So $\frac{y}{x}$ could be $+\sqrt{k}$ for one pair of values and $-\sqrt{k}$ for another pair. Then y would not vary directly with x.
5a. [graph] **b.** [graph]
Lesson Check 1. $y = -\frac{1}{2}x$ **2.** $\frac{1}{3}$ **3.** $\frac{2}{5}$ **4.** Answers may vary. Sample: Two variables are directly related when the ratio of the output to the input is a constant value. **5.** For a direct variation, $y = kx$ where k is the constant of variation. If $x = 0$, then $y = 0$ and the graph of $y = kx$ passes through the origin.
Exercises 7. no **9.** yes; $\frac{5}{2}$ **11.** yes; 12 **13.** no
15. yes; 6 **17.** -3 **19.** $\frac{6}{5}$ **21.** 21 **23.** 13.5 min
25.

x	y
-1	-3
0	-9
2	-18

27. no **29.** no
31. $y = 2x$ **33.** $y = -4.5x$ **35.** $y = \frac{3}{5}x$ [graphs]
37. 0.625 **39.** 0.225 **41.** Every direct variation includes the point (0, 0), so k cannot be determined because k could be any value.

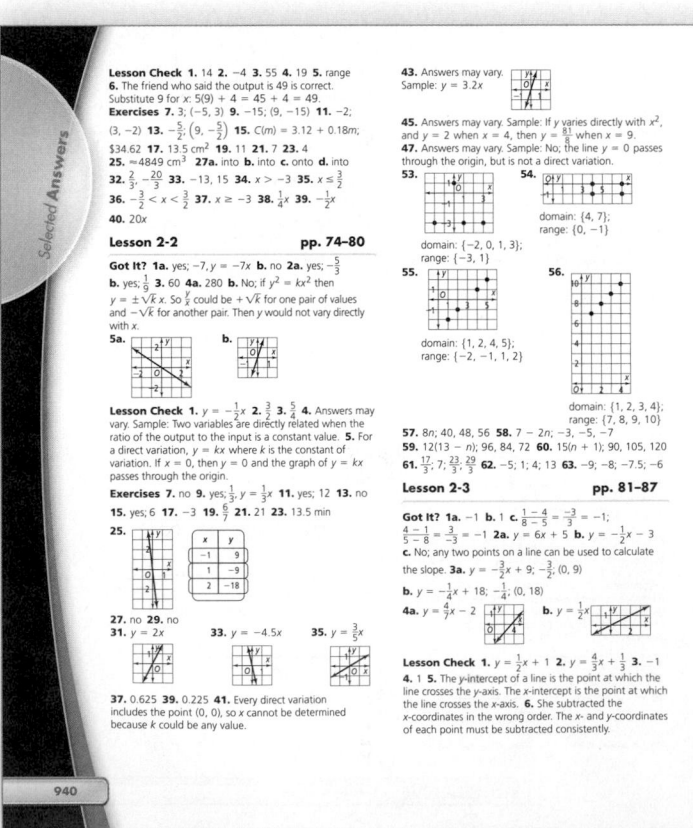

43. Answers may vary. Sample: $y = 3.2x$ [graph]
45. Answers may vary. Sample: If y varies directly with x^2, and $y = 2$ when $x = 4$, then $y = \frac{81}{8}$ when $x = 9$.
47. Answers may vary. Sample: No; the line $y = 0$ passes through the origin, but is not a direct variation.
53. [graph] domain: $\{-2, 0, 1, 3\}$; range: $\{-3, 1\}$
54. [graph] domain: $\{4, 7\}$; range: $\{0, -1\}$
55. [graph] domain: $\{1, 2, 4, 5\}$; range: $\{-2, -1, 1, 2\}$
56. [graph] domain: $\{1, 2, 3, 4\}$; range: $\{7, 8, 9, 10\}$
57. 8n; 40, 48, 56 **58.** $7 - 2n$; -3, -5, -7
59. $12(13 - n)$; 96, 84, 72 **60.** $15(n + 1)$; 90, 105, 120
61. $\frac{17}{3}$, 7; $\frac{23}{3}$, $\frac{29}{3}$ **62.** -5; 1; 4; 13 **63.** -9; -8; -7.5; -6

Lesson 2-3   pp. 81–87

Got It? 1a. -1 **b.** $\frac{1}{5}$ **c.** $\frac{1-8}{8-5} = \frac{-3}{3} = -1$; $\frac{4-1}{5-8} = \frac{3}{-3} = -1$ **2a.** $y = 6x + 5$ **b.** $y = -\frac{1}{2}x - 3$
c. No; any two points on a line can be used to calculate the slope. **3a.** $y = -\frac{3}{4}x + 9$; $-\frac{3}{4}$, (0, 9)
b. $y = -\frac{1}{4}x + 18$; $-\frac{1}{4}$, (0, 18)
4a. $y = \frac{4}{7}x - 2$ [graph] **b.** $y = \frac{1}{2}x$ [graph]
Lesson Check 1. $y = \frac{1}{2}x + 1$ **2.** $y = \frac{4}{3}x + \frac{1}{3}$ **3.** -1
4. 1 **5.** The y-intercept of a line is the point at which the line crosses the y-axis. The x-intercept is the point at which the line crosses the x-axis. **6.** She subtracted the x-coordinates in the wrong order. The x- and y-coordinates of each point must be subtracted consistently.

Exercises 7. -1 **9.** 3 **11.** 1 **13.** 0 **15.** $y = -5x - 7$
17. $y = 2x + 1$ **19.** $y = -\frac{1}{2}x - \frac{3}{4} - \frac{1}{2}$, $(0, -\frac{3}{4})$
21. $y = 7$; 0, (0, 7)
23. [graph] **25.** [graph]
27. [graph] **29.** [graph]
31. [graph] **33.** [graph]
35. 0; (0, 3) **37a.** the rate at which you walk; the slope is the same as the change in distance divided by the change in time, which is the rate at which you walk.
b. towards your home; the slope is negative and the distance (y-value) decreases as the time (x-value) increases.
39. He did not isolate y first and then find the coefficient of x. The slope is $\frac{2}{3}$. **41.** $\frac{2}{3}$ **43.** -0.8; (0, 0.4) **45.** 0; (0, 0)
47. $\frac{4}{8}$; $(0, -\frac{8}{3})$ **48.** $B \neq 0$ **53.** domain: $\{-2, 1, 2, 3, 4\}$, range: $\{-2, -1, 2, 3\}$; no **54.** domain: all real numbers, range ≥ -2; no **55.** domain: $\{-5, 0, 2, 9\}$, range: $\{-3, -1, 5, 15\}$; no **56.** 2 **57.** 8 **58.** 13

Lesson 2-4 Part 1   pp. 88–91

Got It? 1. $y + 1 = -3(x - 7)$ **2a.** $y - 7 = \frac{7}{4}x$
b. $y = \frac{7}{6}(x + 5)$; Either point can be used to put the equation of the line in point-slope form. **3a.** $-4x + 6y = 1$ **b.** $-91x + 10y = 36$
Lesson Check 1. $y = -3x - 1$ **2.** $y = \frac{1}{2}x + 2$
3. $x + 4y = 20$ **4.** $-2x + 10y = -17$ **5a.** point-slope **b.** slope-intercept **c.** standard **d.** point-slope **6.** Point-slope form; since the x-intercept is the point where y is zero, you know the point on the line, $(x, 0)$, and you know the slope.
Exercises 7. $y - 5 = 3(x - 1)$ **9.** $y + 2 = 0$
11. $y - 3 = -(x + 10)$ or $y + 5 = -(x + 2)$
13. $y - 10 = -\frac{5}{2}(x + 4)$ or $y - 15 = -\frac{5}{2}(x + 6)$
15. $-x + 2y = -4$ **17.** $3x + 5y = 15$
19. $y - \frac{1}{3} = -\frac{5}{13}(x + \frac{2}{3})$ or $y + \frac{1}{2} = -\frac{5}{13}(x - \frac{2}{3})$

21. $y - \frac{1}{2} = -\frac{7}{10}x$ or $y = -\frac{7}{10}(x - \frac{5}{2})$
23. The equation should have $-3x$ instead of $3x$.

Lesson 2-4 Part 2   pp. 92–97

Got It? 4. $(0, -2)$, $(4, 0)$ [graph]
5a.

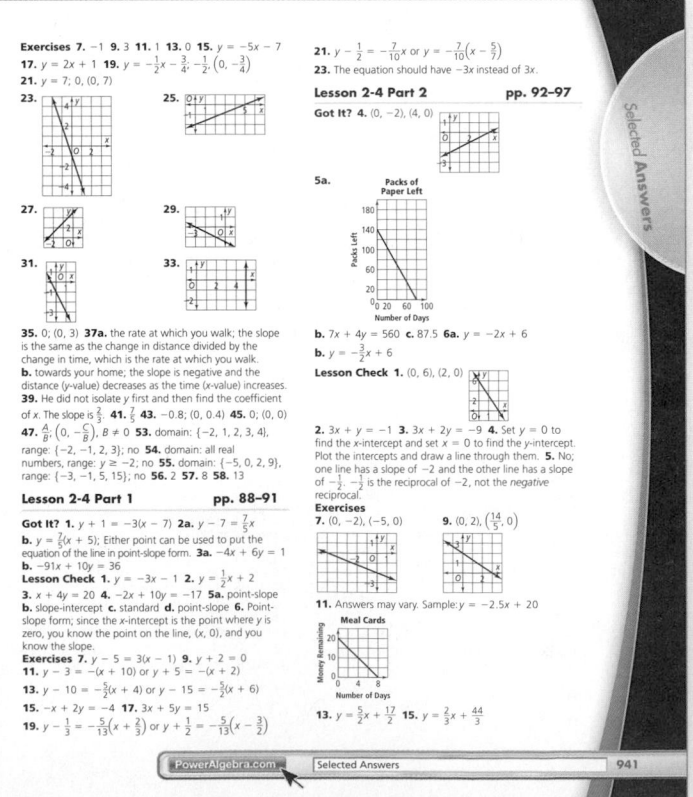

Packs of Paper Left

b. $7x + 4y = 560$ **c.** 87.5 **6a.** $y = -2x + 6$
b. $y = -\frac{3}{2}x + 6$
Lesson Check 1. $(0, 6)$, $(2, 0)$ [graph]
2. $3x + y = -1$ **3.** $3x + 2y = -9$ **4.** Set $y = 0$ to find the x-intercept and set $x = 0$ to find the y-intercept. Plot the intercepts and draw a line through them. **5.** No; one line has a slope of -2 and the other line has a slope of $-\frac{1}{2}$, $-\frac{1}{2}$ is the reciprocal of -2, not the negative reciprocal.
Exercises
7. $(0, -2)$, $(-5, 0)$ **9.** $(0, 2)$, $(\frac{14}{5}, 0)$ [graphs]
11. Answers may vary. Sample: $y = -2.5x + 20$
Meal Cards
13. $y = \frac{5}{2}x + \frac{17}{2}$ **15.** $y = \frac{2}{3}x + \frac{44}{3}$

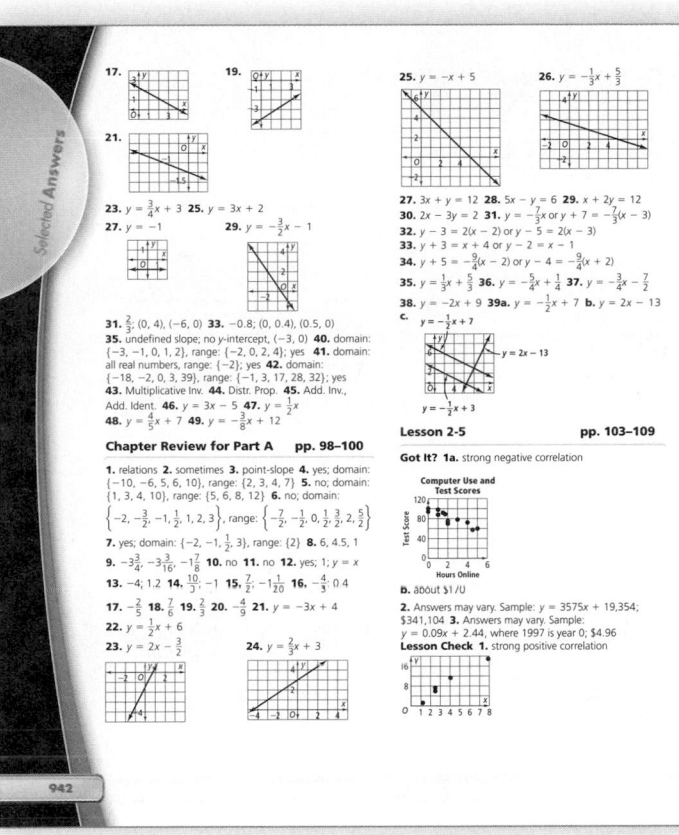

17. (graph) 19. (graph) 25. $y = -x + 5$ 26. $y = -\frac{1}{3}x + \frac{5}{3}$

21. (graph)

23. $y = \frac{3}{2}x + 3$ 25. $y = 3x + 2$

27. $y = -1$ 29. $y = -\frac{3}{2}x - 1$ (graph)

27. $3x + y = 12$ 28. $5x - y = 6$ 29. $x + 2y = 12$
30. $2x - 3y = 21$ 31. $y = -\frac{7}{2}x$ or $y + 7 = -\frac{7}{2}(x - 3)$
32. $y - 3 = 2(x - 2)$ or $y - 5 = 2(x - 3)$
33. $y - 3 = x + 4$ or $y - 2 = x - 1$
34. $y + 5 = -\frac{9}{4}(x - 2)$ or $y - 4 = -\frac{9}{4}(x + 2)$
35. $y = \frac{1}{3}x + \frac{5}{3}$ 36. $y = -\frac{5}{4}x + \frac{1}{4}$ 37. $y = -\frac{3}{4}x - 7$
38. $y = -2x + 9$ 39a. $y = -\frac{1}{2}x + 7$ b. $y = 2x - 13$
c. $y = -\frac{1}{2}x + 7$
(graph) $y = 2x - 13$, $y = -\frac{1}{2}x + 3$

31. $\frac{2}{3}$; (0, 4), (−6, 0) 33. −0.8; (0, 0.4), (0.5, 0)
35. undefined slope; no y-intercept, (−3, 0) 40. domain: {−3, −1, 0, 1, 2}, range: {−2, 0, 2, 4}; yes 41. domain: all real numbers, range: {−2}; yes 42. domain: {−18, −2, 0, 3, 39}, range: {−1, 3, 17, 28, 32}; yes
43. Multiplicative Inv. 44. Distr. Prop. 45. Add. Inv., Add. Ident. 46. $y = 3x - 5$ 47. $y = \frac{1}{3}x$
48. $y = \frac{4}{5}x + 7$ 49. $y = -\frac{3}{8}x + 12$

Chapter Review for Part A   pp. 98–100

1. relations 2. sometimes 3. point-slope 4. yes; domain: {−10, −6, 5, 6, 10}, range: {2, 3, 4, 7} 5. no; domain: {1, 3, 4, 10}, range: {5, 6, 8, 12} 6. no; domain: $\left\{-2, -\frac{3}{2}, -1, \frac{1}{2}, 1, 2, 3\right\}$, range: $\left\{-\frac{7}{2}, -\frac{1}{2}, 0, \frac{1}{2}, \frac{3}{2}, 2, \frac{5}{2}\right\}$
7. yes; domain: $\{-2, -1, \frac{1}{2}, 3\}$, range: {2} 8. 6, 4.5, 1
9. $-3\frac{3}{4}, -3\frac{7}{16}, 1$ 10. no 11. no 12. yes; 1; $y = x$
13. −4; 1.2 14. $\frac{10}{3}$; −1 15. $\frac{7}{2}$; $-1\frac{1}{20}$ 16. $-\frac{4}{3}$; 0.4
17. $-\frac{5}{3}$ 18. $\frac{7}{6}$ 19. $\frac{2}{3}$ 20. $-\frac{4}{9}$ 21. $y = -3x + 4$
22. $y = \frac{1}{2}x + 6$
23. $y = 2x - \frac{3}{2}$ 24. $y = \frac{2}{3}x + 3$
(graphs)

Lesson 2-5   pp. 103–109

Got It? 1a. strong negative correlation

Computer Use and Test Scores (graph)

b. about $170
2. Answers may vary. Sample: $y = 3575x + 19{,}354$; $341,104 3. Answers may vary. Sample: $y = 0.09x + 2.44$, where 1997 is year 0; $4.96
Lesson Check 1. strong positive correlation
(graph)

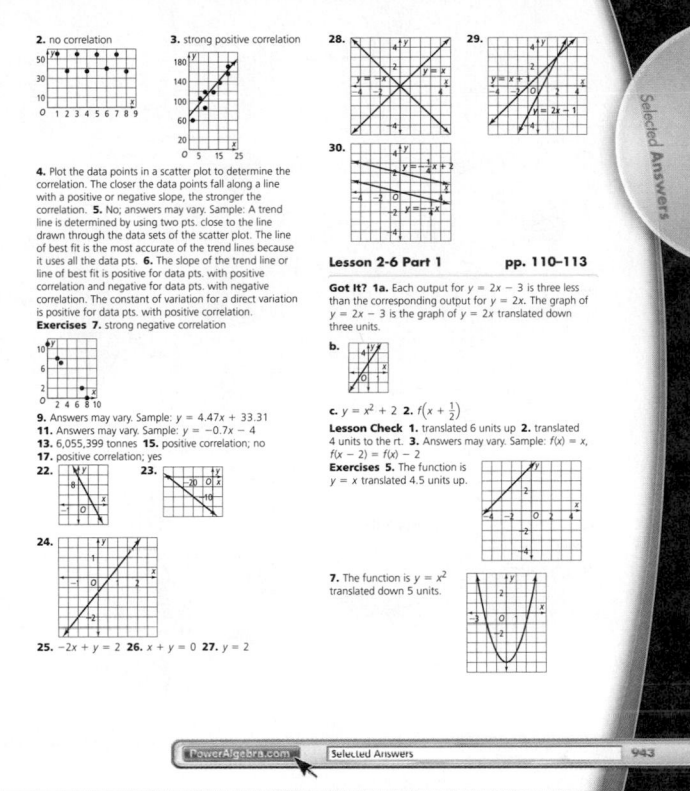

2. no correlation (graph) 3. strong positive correlation (graph)

4. Plot the data points in a scatter plot to determine the correlation. The closer the data points fall along a line with a positive or negative slope, the stronger the correlation. 5. No; answers may vary. Sample: A trend line is determined by using two pts. close to the line drawn through the data sets of the scatter plot. The line of best fit is the most accurate of the trend lines because it uses all the data pts. 6. The slope of the trend line or line of best fit is positive for data pts. with positive correlation and negative for data pts. with negative correlation. The constant of variation for a direct variation is positive for data pts. with positive correlation.
Exercises 7. strong negative correlation
9. Answers may vary. Sample: $y = 4.47x + 33.31$
11. Answers may vary. Sample: $y = -0.7x - 4$
13. 6,055,399 tonnes 15. positive correlation; no
17. positive correlation; yes
22. (graph) 23. (graph)
24. (graph)
25. $-2x + y = 2$ 26. $x + y = 0$ 27. $y = 2$

28. (graph) 29. (graph)
30. (graph)

Lesson 2-6 Part 1   pp. 110–113

Got It? 1a. Each output for $y = 2x - 3$ is three less than the corresponding output for $y = 2x$. The graph of $y = 2x - 3$ is the graph of $y = 2x$ translated down three units.
b. (graph)
c. $y = x^2 + 2$ 2. $f\left(x + \frac{1}{2}\right)$
Lesson Check 1. translated 6 units up 2. translated 4 units to the rt. 3. Answers may vary. Sample: $f(x) = x$, $f(x - 2) = f(x) - 2$
Exercises 5. The function is $y = x$ translated 4.5 units up. (graph)
7. The function is $y = x^2$ translated down 5 units. (graph)

PowerAlgebra.com

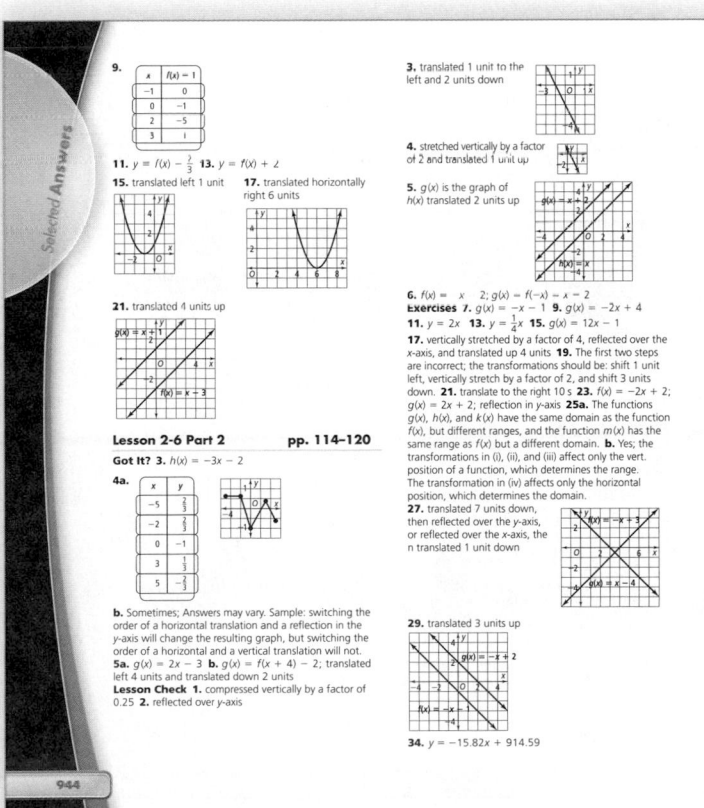

9.

x	f(x) = 1
−1	3
0	−1
2	−5
3	1

11. $y = f(x) - \frac{7}{3}$ 13. $y = f(x) + 2$
15. translated left 1 unit 17. translated horizontally right 6 units
(graphs)
21. translated 4 units up
(graph)

Lesson 2-6 Part 2   pp. 114–120

Got It? 3. $h(x) = -3x - 2$
4a.

x	y
−5	$\frac{2}{3}$
−2	2
0	−1
3	$\frac{1}{3}$
5	1

(graph)
b. Sometimes; Answers may vary. Sample: switching the order of a horizontal translation and a reflection in the y-axis will change the resulting graph, but switching the order of a horizontal and a vertical translation will not.
5a. $g(x) = 2x - 3$ b. $g(x) = f(x + 4) - 2$; translated left 4 units and translated down 2 units
Lesson Check 1. compressed vertically by a factor of 0.25 2. reflected over y-axis

3. translated 1 unit to the left and 2 units down (graph)
4. stretched vertically by a factor of 2 and translated 1 unit up (graph)
5. g(x) is the graph of h(x) translated 2 units up (graph)
6. $f(x) = x - 2$; $g(x) = f(-x) - x - 2$
Exercises 7. $g(x) = -x - 1$ 9. $g(x) = -2x + 4$
11. $y = 2x$ 13. $y = \frac{1}{4}x$ 15. $g(x) = 12x - 1$
17. vertically stretched by a factor of 4, reflected over the x-axis, and translated up 4 units 19. The first two steps are incorrect; the transformations should be: shift 1 unit left, vertically stretch by a factor of 2, and shift 3 units down. 21. translate to the right 10 s 23. $f(x) = -2x + 2$; $g(x) = 2x + 2$; reflection in y-axis 25a. The functions g(x), h(x), and k(x) have the same domain as the function f(x), but different ranges, and the function m(x) has the same range as f(x) but a different domain. b. Yes; the transformations in (i), (ii), and (iii) affect only the vert. position of a function, which determines the range. The transformation in (iv) affects only the horizontal position, which determines the domain.
27. translated 7 units down, then reflected over the y-axis, or reflected over the x-axis, then translated 1 unit down (graph)
29. translated 3 units up (graph)
34. $y = -15.82x + 914.59$

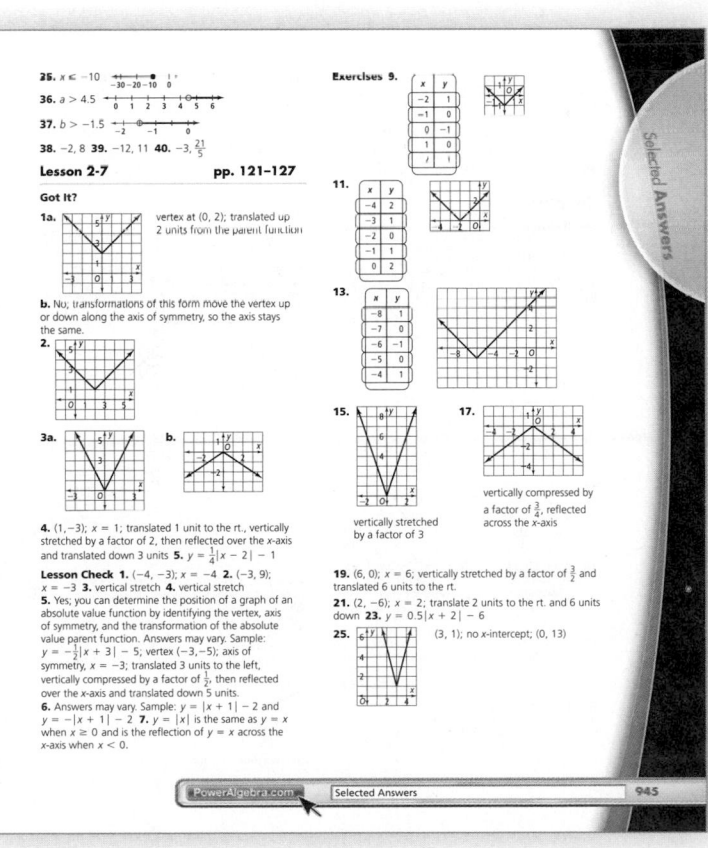

25. $x \le -10$ (number line)
36. $a > 4.5$ (number line)
37. $b > -1.5$ (number line)
38. −2, 8 39. −12, 11 40. $-3, \frac{21}{5}$

Lesson 2-7   pp. 121–127

Got It?
1a. (graph) vertex at (0, 2); translated up 2 units from the parent function
b. No; transformations of this form move the vertex up or down along the axis of symmetry, so the axis stays the same.
2. (graph)
3a. (graph) b. (graph)
4. (1, −3); $x = 1$; translated 1 unit to the rt., vertically stretched by a factor of 2, then reflected over the x-axis and translated down 3 units 5. $y = \frac{1}{4}|x - 2| - 1$
Lesson Check 1. (−4, −3); $x = -4$ 2. (−3, 9); $x = -3$ 3. vertical stretch 4. vertical stretch 5. Yes; you can determine the position of a graph of an absolute value function by identifying the vertex, axis of symmetry, and the transformation of the absolute value parent function. Answers may vary. Sample: $y = -\frac{1}{2}|x + 3| - 5$; vertex (−3, −5); axis of symmetry, $x = -3$; translated 3 units to the left, vertically compressed by a factor of $\frac{1}{2}$, then reflected over the x-axis and translated down 5 units.
6. Answers may vary. Sample: $y = |x + 1| - 2$ and $y = -|x + 1| - 2$ 7. $y = |x|$ is the same as $y = x$ when $x \ge 0$ and is the reflection of $y = x$ across the x-axis when $x < 0$.

Exercises 9.

x	y
−2	3
−1	1
0	−1
1	1

(graph)

11.

x	y
−4	2
−3	1
−2	0
−1	1
0	2

(graph)

13.

x	y
−8	−1
−7	0
−6	−1
−5	0

(graph)

15. (graph) vertically stretched by a factor of 3
17. (graph) vertically compressed by a factor of $\frac{3}{4}$, reflected across the x-axis
19. (6, 0); $x = 6$; vertically stretched by a factor of $\frac{3}{2}$ and translated 6 units to the rt.
21. (2, −6); $x = 2$; translate 2 units to the rt. and 6 units down 23. $y = 0.5|x + 2| - 6$
25. (graph) (3, 1); no x-intercept; (0, 13)

PowerAlgebra.com

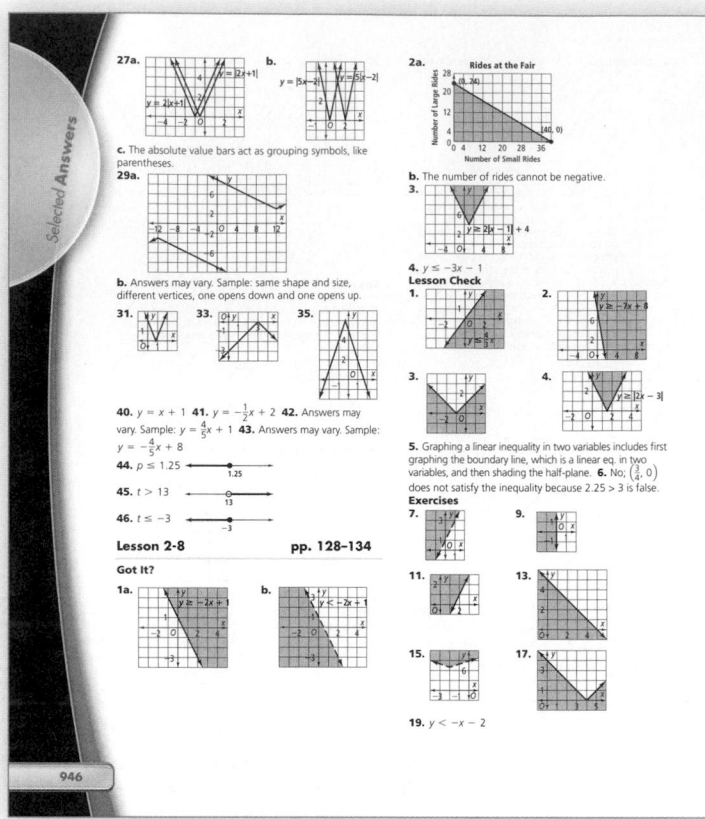

27a. [graphs] b.

c. The absolute value bars act as grouping symbols, like parentheses.

29a.

b. Answers may vary. Sample: same shape and size, different vertices, one opens down and one opens up.

31. 33. 35.

40. $y = x + 1$ 41. $y = -\frac{1}{3}x + 2$ 42. Answers may vary. Sample: $y = \frac{4}{5}x + 1$ 43. Answers may vary. Sample: $y = -\frac{4}{5}x + 8$

44. $p \le 1.25$

45. $t > 13$

46. $t \le -3$

Lesson 2-8 pp. 128–134

Got It?
1a. b.

2a. Rides at the Fair

b. The number of rides cannot be negative.
3.
4. $y \le -3x - 1$

Lesson Check
1. 2.
3. 4.

5. Graphing a linear inequality in two variables includes first graphing the boundary line, which is a linear eq. in two variables, and then shading the half-plane. 6. No; $\left(\frac{1}{4}, 0\right)$ does not satisfy the inequality because $2.25 > 3$ is false.

Exercises
7. 9.
11. 13.
15. 17.
19. $y < -x - 2$

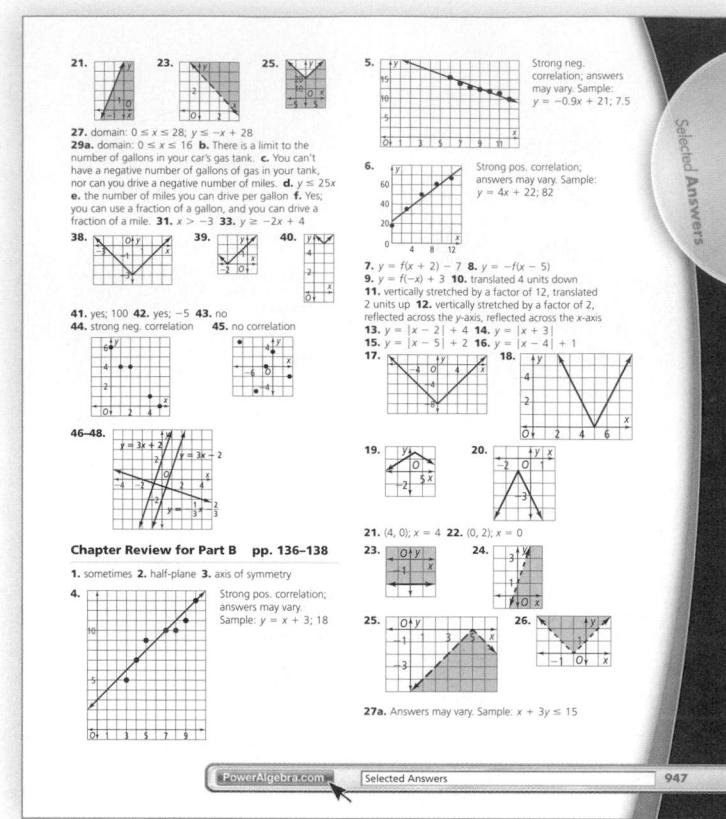

21. 23. 25. 5. Strong neg. correlation; answers may vary. Sample: $y = -0.9x + 21$; 7.5

27. domain: $0 \le x \le 28$; $y \le -x + 28$
29a. domain: $0 \le x \le 16$ b. There is a limit to the number of gallons in your car's gas tank. c. You can't have a negative number of gallons of gas in your tank, nor can you drive a negative number of miles. d. $y \le 25x$
e. the number of miles you can drive per gallon f. Yes; you can use a fraction of a gallon, and you can drive a fraction of a mile. 31. $x > -3$ 33. $y \ge -2x + 4$

6. Strong pos. correlation; answers may vary. Sample: $y = 4x + 22$; 82

38. 39. 40.
41. yes; 100 42. yes; -5 43. no
44. strong neg. correlation 45. no correlation
46–48.

7. $y = f(x + 2) - 7$ 8. $y = -f(x - 5)$
9. $y = f(-x) + 3$ 10. translated 4 units down
11. vertically stretched by a factor of 12, translated 2 units up 12. vertically stretched by a factor of 2, reflected across the y-axis, reflected across the x-axis
13. $y = |x - 2| + 4$ 14. $y = |x + 3|$
15. $y = |x - 5| + 2$ 16. $y = |x - 4| + 1$
17. 18.
19. 20.
21. $(4, 0)$; $x = 4$ 22. $(0, 2)$; $x = 0$
23. 24.

Chapter Review for Part B pp. 136–138

1. sometimes 2. half-plane 3. axis of symmetry
4. Strong pos. correlation; answers may vary. Sample: $y = x + 3$; 18

25. 26.

27a. Answers may vary. Sample: $x + 3y \le 15$

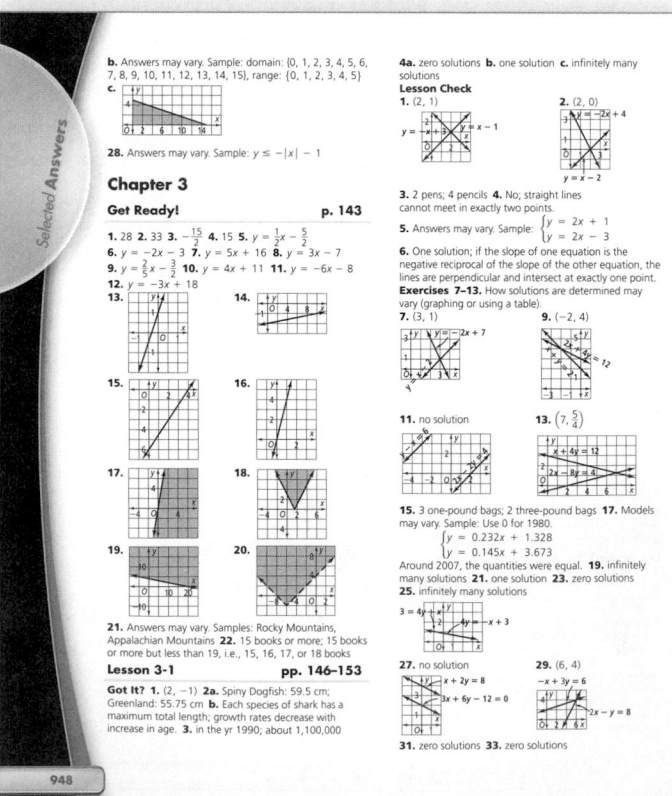

b. Answers may vary. Sample: domain: {0, 1, 2, 3, 4, 5, 6, 7, 8, 9, 10, 11, 12, 13, 14, 15}, range: {0, 1, 2, 3, 4, 5}
c.

28. Answers may vary. Sample: $y \le -|x| - 1$

Chapter 3

Get Ready! p. 143
1. 28 2. 33 3. $-\frac{15}{2}$ 4. 15 5. $y = \frac{1}{3}x - \frac{5}{2}$
6. $y = -2x - 3$ 7. $y = 5x + 16$ 8. $y = 3x - 7$
9. $y = \frac{5}{2}x - \frac{3}{2}$ 10. $y = 4x + 11$ 11. $y = -6x - 4$
12. $y = -3x + 18$
13. 14.
15. 16.
17. 18.
19. 20.

21. Answers may vary. Samples: Rocky Mountains, Appalachian Mountains 22. 15 books or more; 15 books or more but less than 19, i.e., 15, 16, 17, or 18 books

Lesson 3-1 pp. 146–153
Got It? 1. $(2, -1)$ 2a. Spiny Dogfish: 59.5 cm; Greenland: 55.75 cm b. Each species of shark has a maximum total length; growth rates decrease with increase in age. 3. in the yr 1990; about 1,100,000

4a. zero solutions b. one solution c. infinitely many solutions

Lesson Check
1. $(2, 1)$ 2. $(2, 0)$

3. 2 pens; 4 pencils 4. No; straight lines cannot meet in exactly two points.

5. Answers may vary. Sample: $\begin{cases} y = 2x + 1 \\ y = 2x - 3 \end{cases}$

6. One solution; if the slope of one equation is the negative reciprocal of the slope of the other equation, the lines are perpendicular and intersect at exactly one point.

Exercises 7–13. How solutions are determined may vary (graphing or using a table).
7. $(3, 1)$ 9. $(-2, 4)$

11. no solution 13. $\left(7, \frac{5}{4}\right)$

15. 3 one-pound bags; 2 three-pound bags 17. Models may vary. Sample: Use 0 for 1980. $\begin{cases} y = 0.232x + 1.328 \\ y = 0.145x + 3.673 \end{cases}$ Around 2007, the quantities were equal. 19. infinitely many solutions 21. one solution 23. zero solutions 25. infinitely many solutions

27. no solution 29. $(6, 4)$

31. zero solutions 33. zero solutions

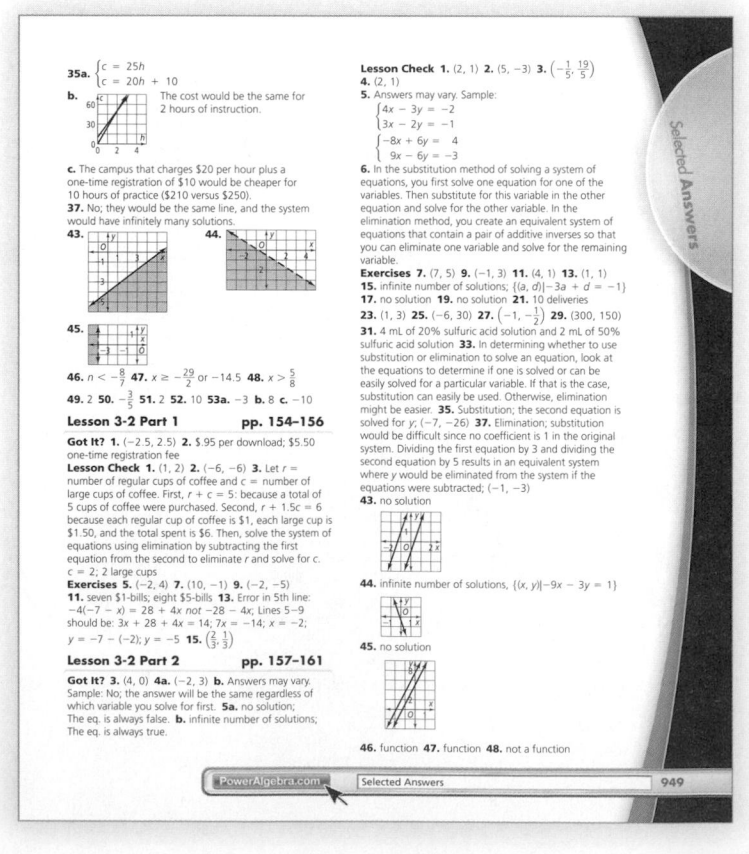

35a. $\begin{cases} c = 25h \\ c = 20h + 10 \end{cases}$

b. The cost would be the same for 2 hours of instruction.

c. The campus that charges $20 per hour plus a one-time registration of $10 would be cheaper for 10 hours of practice ($210 versus $250).
37. No; they would be the same line, and the system would have infinitely many solutions.

43. 44.
45.
46. $n < -\frac{8}{7}$ 47. $x \ge -\frac{29}{2}$ or -14.5 48. $x > \frac{5}{8}$
49. 2 50. $-\frac{3}{5}$ 51. 2 52. 10 53a. -3 b. 8 c. -10

Lesson 3-2 Part 1 pp. 154–156
Got It? 1. $(-2.5, 2.5)$ 2. $.95 per download; $5.50 one-time registration fee
Lesson Check 1. $(1, 2)$ 2. $(-6, -6)$ 3. Let $r =$ number of regular cups of coffee and $c =$ number of large cups of coffee. First, $r + c = 5$ because a total of 5 cups of coffee were purchased. Second, $r + 1.5c = 6$ because each regular cup of coffee is $1, each large cup is $1.50, and the total spent is $6. Then, solve the system of equations using elimination by subtracting the first equation from the second to eliminate r and solve for c. $c = 2$; 2 large cups
Exercises 5. $(-2, 4)$ 7. $(10, -1)$ 9. $(-2, -5)$
11. seven $1-bills; eight $5-bills 13. Error in 5th line: $-4(-7 - x) = 28 + 4x$ not $-28 - 4x$; Lines 5–9 should be: $3x + 28 + 4x = 14$; $7x = -14$; $x = -2$; $y = -7 - (-2)$; $y = -5$ 15. $\left(\frac{2}{3}, \frac{1}{3}\right)$

Lesson 3-2 Part 2 pp. 157–161
Got It? 3. $(4, 0)$ 4a. $(-2, 3)$ b. Answers may vary. Sample: No; the answer will be the same regardless of which variable you solve for first. 5a. no solution; The eq. is always false. b. infinite number of solutions; The eq. is always true.

Lesson Check 1. $(2, 1)$ 2. $(5, -3)$ 3. $\left(-\frac{1}{5}, \frac{19}{5}\right)$
4. $(2, 1)$
5. Answers may vary. Sample:
$\begin{cases} 4x - 3y = -2 \\ 3x - 2y = -1 \end{cases}$
$\begin{cases} -8x + 6y = 4 \\ 9x - 6y = -3 \end{cases}$
6. In the substitution method of solving a system of equations, you first solve one equation for one of the variables. Then substitute for this variable in the other equation and solve for the other variable. In the elimination method, you create an equivalent system of equations that contain a pair of additive inverses so that you can eliminate one variable and solve for the remaining variable.
Exercises 7. $(7, 5)$ 9. $(-1, 3)$ 11. $(4, 1)$ 13. $(1, 1)$
15. infinite number of solutions; $\{(a, d)|-3a + d = -1\}$ 17. no solution 19. no solution 21. 10 deliveries
23. $(1, 3)$ 25. $(-6, 30)$ 27. $\left(-1, -\frac{1}{2}\right)$ 29. $(300, 150)$
31. 4 mL of 20% sulfuric acid solution and 2 mL of 50% sulfuric acid solution 33. In determining whether to use substitution or elimination to solve an equation, look at the equations to determine if one is solved or can be easily solved for a particular variable. If that is the case, substitution can easily be used. Otherwise, elimination might be easier. 35. Substitution; the second equation is solved for y; $(-7, -26)$ 37. Elimination; substitution would be difficult since no coefficient is 1 in the original system. Dividing the first equation by 3 and dividing the second equation by 5 results in an equivalent system where y would be eliminated from the system if the equations were subtracted; $(-1, -3)$
43. no solution
44. infinite number of solutions; $\{(x, y)|-9x - 3y = 1\}$
45. no solution
46. function 47. function 48. not a function

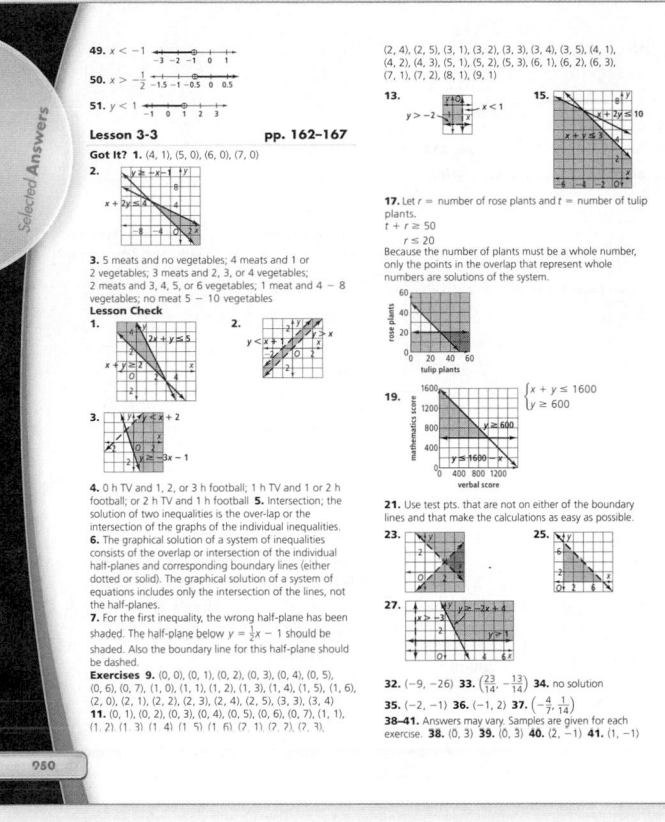

49. $x < -1$ [number line]
50. $x > -\frac{1}{2}$ [number line]
51. $y < 1$ [number line]

Lesson 3-3   pp. 162–167
Got It? 1. (4, 1), (5, 0), (6, 0), (7, 0)
2. [graph] $y \ge -x + 1$, $x + 2y \le 4$

3. 5 meats and no vegetables; 4 meats and 1 or 2 vegetables; 3 meats and 2, 3, or 4 vegetables; 2 meats and 3, 4, 5, or 6 vegetables; 1 meat and 4 – 8 vegetables; no meat 5 – 10 vegetables
Lesson Check
1. [graph] $2x + y \le 5$
2. [graph] $y < 2x$, $y > x$
3. [graph] $y < x + 2$, $y \ge -3x - 1$

4. 0 h TV and 1, 2, or 3 h football; 1 h TV and 1 or 2 h football; or 2 h TV and 1 h football **5.** Intersection; the solution of two inequalities is the over-lap or the intersection of the graphs of the individual inequalities. **6.** The graphical solution of a system of inequalities consists of the overlap or intersection of the individual half-planes and corresponding boundary lines (either dotted or solid). The graphical solution of a system of equations includes only the intersection of the lines, not the half-planes. **7.** For the first inequality, the wrong half-plane has been shaded. The half-plane below $y = \frac{1}{2}x - 1$ should be shaded. Also the boundary line for this half-plane should be dashed.
Exercises 9. (0, 0), (0, 1), (0, 2), (0, 3), (0, 4), (0, 5), (0, 6), (0, 7), (1, 0), (1, 1), (1, 2), (1, 3), (1, 4), (1, 5), (1, 6), (2, 0), (2, 1), (2, 2), (2, 3), (2, 4), (2, 5), (3, 3), (3, 4)
11. (0, 1), (0, 2), (0, 3), (0, 4), (0, 5), (0, 6), (0, 7), (1, 1), (1, 2), (1, 3), (1, 4), (1, 5), (1, 6), (2, 1), (2, 2), (2, 3), (2, 4), (2, 5), (3, 1), (3, 2), (3, 3), (3, 4), (3, 5), (4, 1), (4, 2), (4, 3), (5, 1), (5, 2), (5, 3), (6, 1), (6, 2), (6, 3), (7, 1), (7, 2), (8, 1), (9, 1)
13. [graph] $y > -2$, $x < 1$ **15.** [graph] $x + 2y \le 10$, $x + y \le 8$

17. Let r = number of rose plants and t = number of tulip plants.
$t + r \ge 50$
$r \ge 20$
Because the number of plants must be a whole number, only the points in the overlap that represent whole numbers are solutions of the system.
[graph: rose plants / tulip plants]

19. [graph: mathematics score / verbal score] $\begin{cases} x + y \ge 1600 \\ y \ge 600 \end{cases}$

21. Use test pts. that are not on either of the boundary lines and that make the calculations as easy as possible.
23. [graph]   **25.** [graph]
27. [graph] $y \ge -2x + 4$

32. (−9, −26) **33.** $\left(\frac{23}{14}, -\frac{13}{14}\right)$ **34.** no solution
35. (−2, −1) **36.** (−1, 2) **37.** $\left(-\frac{4}{7}, \frac{1}{14}\right)$
38–41. Answers may vary. Samples are given for each exercise. **38.** (0, 3) **39.** (0, 3) **40.** (2, −1) **41.** (1, −1)

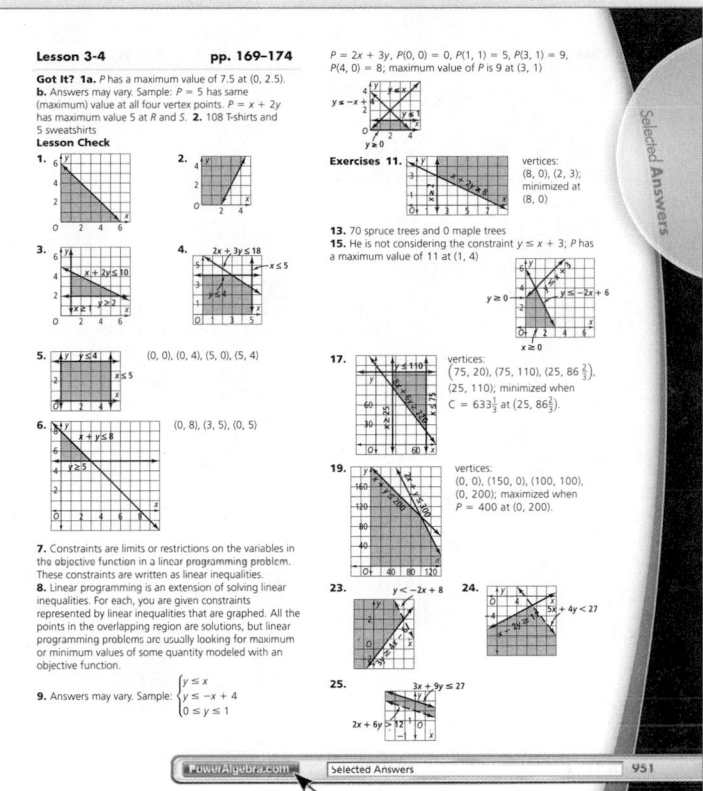

Lesson 3-4   pp. 169–174
Got It? 1a. P has a maximum value of 7.5 at (0, 2.5).
b. Answers may vary. Sample: $P = 5$ has same (maximum) value at all four vertex points. $P = x + 2y$ has maximum value 5 at R and S. **2.** 108 T-shirts and 5 sweatshirts
Lesson Check
1. [graph]   **2.** [graph]
3. [graph] $x + 2y \le 10$ **4.** [graph] $2x + 3y \le 18$, $x \le 5$
5. [graph] $y \le 4$, $x \le 5$ (0, 0), (0, 4), (5, 0), (5, 4)
6. [graph] $x + y \le 8$, $x \ge 5$ (0, 8), (3, 5), (5, 0), (5, 5)

7. Constraints are limits or restrictions on the variables in the objective function in a linear programming problem. These constraints are written as linear inequalities.
8. Linear programming is an extension of solving linear inequalities. For each, you are given constraints represented by linear inequalities that are graphed. All the points in the overlapping region are solutions, but linear programming problems are usually looking for maximum or minimum values of some quantity modeled with an objective function.
9. Answers may vary. Sample: $\begin{cases} y \le x \\ y \le -x + 4 \\ 0 \le y \le 1 \end{cases}$

$P = 2x + 3y$, $P(0, 0) = 0$, $P(1, 1) = 5$, $P(3, 1) = 9$, $P(4, 0) = 8$; maximum value of P is 9 at (3, 1)
[graph] $y \le -x + 3$

Exercises 11. [graph] vertices: (8, 0), (2, 3); minimized at (8, 0)
13. 70 spruce trees and 0 maple trees
15. He is not considering the constraint $y \le x + 3$; P has a maximum value of 11 at (1, 4) [graph] $y \ge 0$, $y \le -2x + 6$
17. [graph] vertices: $\left(75, 20\right)$, (75, 110), $\left(25, 86\frac{2}{3}\right)$, (25, 110); minimized when $C = 633\frac{1}{3}$ at $\left(25, 86\frac{2}{3}\right)$.
19. [graph] vertices: (0, 0), (150, 0), (100, 100), (0, 200); maximized when $P = 400$ at (0, 200).
23. [graph] $y < -2x + 8$ **24.** [graph] $5x + 4y < 27$
25. [graph] $3x + 9y \le 27$, $2x + 6y \ge 12$

26. 1 **27.** 24 **28.** 65 **29.** (0, 6), (−3, 0) **30.** (0, 4), (18, 0) **31.** (0, −1), (1, 0)

Lesson 3-5   pp. 176–183
Got It? 1. (4, 2, −3) **2a.** (4, −1, 7) **b.** Answers may vary. Sample: Yes; you can choose to eliminate either x, y, or z resulting in a system of equations in 2 variables.
3a. (2, 1, −4) **b.** No; in Step 1 we solved for x in terms of y only. Therefore, once we found the value of y we could have substituted that value into the equation we wrote in Step 1 and solved for x without ever finding the z-value. **4.** 50 T-shirts, 50 polo shirts, and 100 rugby shirts
Lesson Check 1. (5, −3, −2) **2.** (6, 0, −2) **3.** (0, 3, 4)
4. Answers may vary. Sample: Substitution is the best method to use when one of the equations can be solved easily for one variable. **5.** Answers may vary. Sample: (0, 0, 0) is a unique solution to a system of three variables. The planes intersect at one common point. When a system has no solution, no point lies in all three planes. **6.** infinitely many solutions
Exercises 7. (4, 2, −3) **9.** (2, 1, −5) **11.** (0, 3, −2) **13.** (2, −1, 1) **15.** (8, −4, 2) **17.** (0, 1, 7) **19.** (1, −1, 2) **21.** Machine A: 112 bolts per hour; Machine B: 90 bolts per hour; Machine C: 85 bolts per hour **23.** Section A has 24,500 seats, Section B has 14,400 seats, and Section C has 10,100 seats.
25. (8, 1, 3) **27.** $\left(\frac{1}{2}, 2, -3\right)$ **29.** (−2, −1, 12)
35. P has a maximum value of 12 at (0, 4).
36. $x \ge -\frac{3}{2}$; [number line]
37. $x \le -18$; [number line]
38. $x < -1$; [number line]
39. $\left(7, \frac{5}{4}\right)$
40. infinite number of solutions, $\left\{(x, y) \mid y = -\frac{1}{2}x - \frac{3}{4}\right\}$
41. no solution

Lesson 3-6   pp. 184–191
Got It? 1a. 17 **b.** −3
2a. $\begin{bmatrix} -4 & -2 & | & 7 \\ 3 & 1 & | & -5 \end{bmatrix}$ **b.** $\begin{bmatrix} 4 & -1 & 2 & | & 1 \\ 0 & 1 & 5 & | & 20 \\ 2 & 1 & 0 & | & 7 \end{bmatrix}$
3. $\begin{cases} 2x = 6 \\ 5x - 2y = 1 \end{cases}$
4a. (1, 2) **b.** elimination; you use the same steps to solve
5. $\left(1, \frac{1}{2}, 3\right)$

Lesson Check 1. 2 × 1 **2.** 2 × 4
3. $\begin{bmatrix} 3 & 5 & 0 \\ 1 & 1 & 7 \end{bmatrix}$ **4.** $\begin{bmatrix} 1 & -3 & 1 & 2 \\ 1 & 0 & 2 & 8 \\ 0 & 2 & -1 & 1 \end{bmatrix}$
5. 16 **6.** a_{21} is 0, the element in row 2, column 1. a_{12} is −9, the element in row 1 and column 2. **7.** Answers may vary. Sample: The entry fee to a school play is $2 for adults. Jamie paid for 4 student entry fees and 2 adult entry fees. What is the student entry fee?
Exercises 9. 1 **11.** 8
13. $\begin{bmatrix} 1 & 2 & | & 11 \\ 2 & 3 & | & 18 \end{bmatrix}$ **15.** $\begin{bmatrix} -3 & 1 & | & -7 \\ 1 & 0 & | & 1 \end{bmatrix}$
17. $\begin{cases} 5x + y = -3 \\ -2x + 2y = 4 \end{cases}$
19. (2, 1) **21.** (4, 6) **23.** (2, 3)
25. $10,000 at 4% and $15,000 at 6%
Let x = amount invested at 4% and y = amount invested at 6%.
$\begin{cases} x + y = 25{,}000 \\ 0.04x + 0.06y = 1300 \end{cases}$
$\begin{bmatrix} 1 & 1 & | & 25000 \\ 0.04 & 0.06 & | & 1300 \end{bmatrix} = \begin{bmatrix} 1 & 0 & | & 10000 \\ 0 & 1 & | & 15000 \end{bmatrix}$
27. (2, 3) **29.** 1 qt. of red paint: $7.75; 1 qt. of yellow paint: $5.75
33. $x \le -\frac{3}{2}$; [number line]
34. $x \ge -35$; [number line]
35. $x \ge 4$; [number line]
36. $\frac{15}{2}, -\frac{9}{2}$ **37.** 10, −10 **38.** 10, −6 **39.** $y = 2x$
40. $y = \frac{1}{3}x$

Chapter Review   pp. 193–196
1. solution of a system **2.** Linear programming; constraints
3. row operations; matrix
4. one solution; (−1, −4) [graph]
5. infinitely many solutions **6.** zero solutions
7. infinitely many solutions

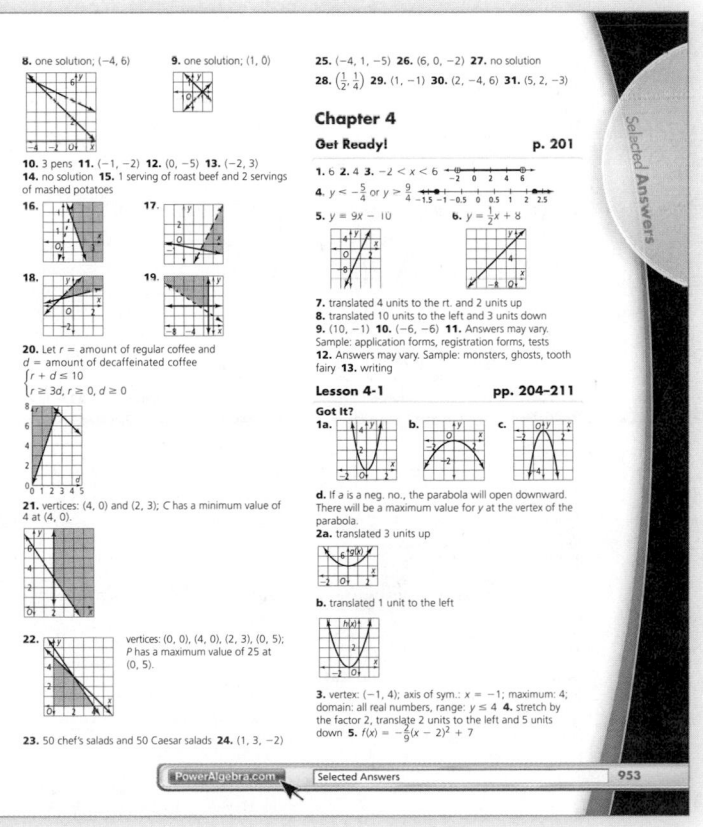

8. one solution; (−4, 6) [graph]   **9.** one solution; (1, 0) [graph]
10. 3 pens **11.** (−1, −2) **12.** (0, −5) **13.** (−2, 3)
14. no solution **15.** 1 serving of roast beef and 2 servings of mashed potatoes
16. [graph]   **17.** [graph]
18. [graph]   **19.** [graph]
20. Let r = amount of regular coffee and d = amount of decaffeinated coffee
$\begin{cases} r + d \le 10 \\ r \ge 3d, r \ge 0, d \ge 0 \end{cases}$
[graph]
21. vertices: (4, 0) and (2, 3); C has a minimum value of 4 at (4, 0).
22. [graph] vertices: (0, 0), (4, 0), (2, 3), (0, 5); P has a maximum value of 25 at (0, 5).
23. 50 chef's salads and 50 Caesar salads **24.** (1, 3, −2)

25. (−4, 1, −5) **26.** (6, 0, −2) **27.** no solution
28. $\left(\frac{1}{2}, \frac{1}{4}\right)$ **29.** (1, −1) **30.** (−2, −4, 6) **31.** (5, 2, −3)

Chapter 4
Get Ready!   p. 201
1. 6 **2.** 4 **3.** $-4 < x < 6$ [number line]
4. $y < -\frac{5}{4}$ or $y \ge \frac{9}{4}$ [number line]
5. $y = 9x - 10$ **6.** $y = \frac{1}{2}x + 8$
7. translated 4 units to the rt. and 2 units up
8. translated 10 units to the left and 3 units down
9. (10, −1) **10.** (−6, −6) **11.** Answers may vary. Sample: application forms, registration forms, tests
12. Answers may vary. Sample: monsters, ghosts, tooth fairy **13.** writing

Lesson 4-1   pp. 204–211
Got It?
1a. [graph] **b.** [graph] **c.** [graph]
d. If a is a neg. no., the parabola will open downward. There will be a maximum value for y at the vertex of the parabola.
2a. translated 3 units up
b. translated 1 unit to the left
3. vertex: (−1, 4); axis of sym.: $x = -1$; maximum: 4; domain: all real numbers, range: $y \le 4$. stretch by the factor 2, translate 2 units to the left and 5 units down **5.** $f(x) = -\frac{4}{9}(x - 2)^2 + 7$

Lesson Check

1. 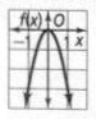

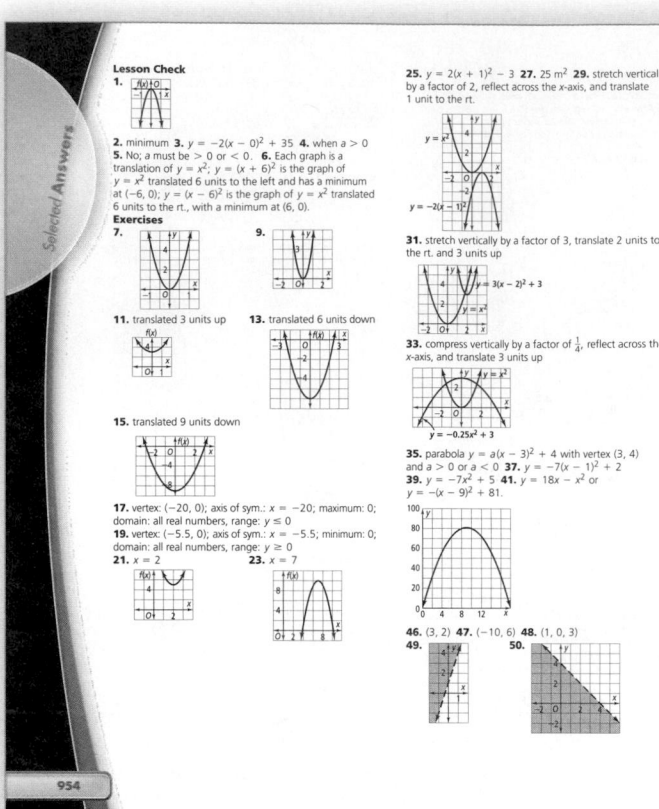

2. minimum **3.** $y = -2(x - 0)^2 + 35$ **4.** when $a > 0$ **5.** No; a must be > 0 or < 0. **6.** Each graph is a translation of $y = x^2$; $y = (x + 6)^2$ is the graph of $y = x^2$ translated 6 units to the left and has a minimum at $(-6, 0)$; $y = (x - 6)^2$ is the graph of $y = x^2$ translated 6 units to the rt., with a minimum at $(6, 0)$.

Exercises

7. 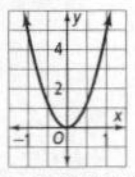

9. 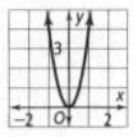

11. translated 3 units up

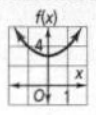

13. translated 6 units down

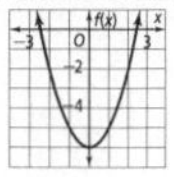

15. translated 9 units down

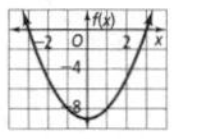

17. vertex: $(-20, 0)$; axis of sym.: $x = -20$; maximum: 0; domain: all real numbers, range: $y \le 0$
19. vertex: $(-5.5, 0)$; axis of sym.: $x = -5.5$; minimum: 0; domain: all real numbers, range: $y \ge 0$
21. $x = 2$

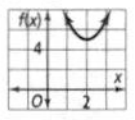

23. $x = 7$

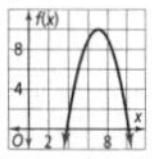

25. $y = 2(x + 1)^2 - 3$ **27.** 25 m^2 **29.** stretch vertically by a factor of 2, reflect across the x-axis, and translate 1 unit to the rt.

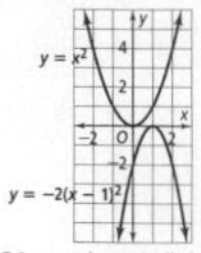

31. stretch vertically by a factor of 3, translate 2 units to the rt. and 3 units up

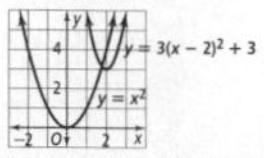

33. compress vertically by a factor of $\frac{1}{4}$, reflect across the x-axis, and translate 3 units up

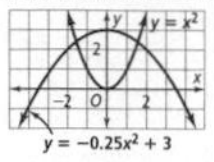

35. parabola $y = a(x - 3)^2 + 4$ with vertex $(3, 4)$ and $a > 0$ or $a < 0$ **37.** $y = -7(x - 1)^2 + 2$
39. $y = -7x^2 + 5$ **41.** $y = 18x - x^2$ or $y = -(x - 9)^2 + 81$.

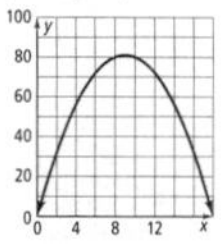

46. (3, 2) **47.** (−10, 6) **48.** (1, 0, 3)

49. 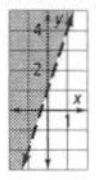

50. 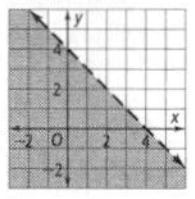

51. 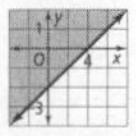

52. yes **53.** no **54.** no **55.** (0, 0) **56.** (−1, 0)
57. (5, 0)

Lesson 4-2 Part 1 pp. 212–215

Got It? 1. vertex: $\left(-\frac{2}{3}, 7\frac{1}{3}\right)$; axis of symmetry: $x = -\frac{2}{3}$; maximum: $7\frac{1}{3}$; range: $y \le 7\frac{1}{3}$

2. 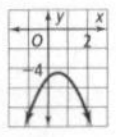

Lesson Check 1. vertex: $(0, -4)$; axis of sym.: $x = 0$; minimum: −4

2. 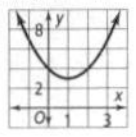

3. 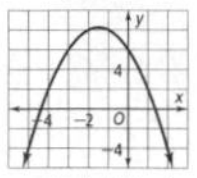

4. Error in calculation of x. The correct calculation is:

$$x = \frac{-(-4)}{2(2)} = 1$$
$$y = 2(1) - 4(1) - 3$$
$$= 2 - 4 - 3$$
$$= -5$$

Vertex: (1, −5)

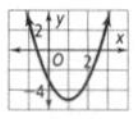

Exercises 5. vertex: $(-2, -3)$; axis of sym.: $x = -2$; minimum: 3; range: $y \ge -3$ **7.** vertex: $(1, 2)$; axis of sym.: $x = 1$; maximum: 2; range: $y \le 2$

9. vertex: $\left(-\frac{3}{4}, 5\frac{1}{8}\right)$; axis of sym.: $x = -\frac{3}{4}$; maximum: $5\frac{1}{8}$; range: $y \le 5\frac{1}{8}$ **11.** vertex: $(0, 5)$; axis of sym.: $x = 0$; minimum: 5; range: $y \ge 5$

13. 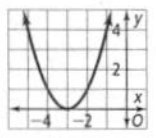

15. 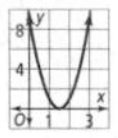

17. 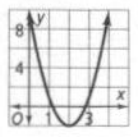

19. 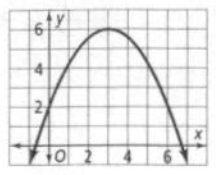

21. 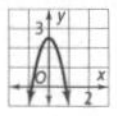

23. $y = \left(-\frac{1}{10}\right)x^2 + 10$

Lesson 4-2 Part 2 pp. 216–219

Got It? 3. $y = -(x - 2)^2 - 1$ **4a.** about 3.84 feet **b.** because the y-intercept is (0, 0)
Lesson Check 1. $y = (x - 1)^2 + 8$
2. $y = -\left(x - \frac{3}{2}\right)^2 + \frac{5}{4}$ **3.** The vertex of a function written in vertex form can easily be determined. It is (h, k) where $f(x) = a(x - h)^2 + k$. The vertex of a function in standard form is $\left(\frac{-b}{2a}, f\left(\frac{-b}{2a}\right)\right)$ where $f(x) = ax^2 + bx + c$.
Exercises 5. $y = (x + 1)^2 + 4$
7. $y = 2\left(x - \frac{5}{4}\right)^2 + \frac{71}{8}$ **9.** \$100; \$25,000 **11.** $b = -6$; $c = 5$ **13.** $a = 1$; $c = -2$ **15.** 2 s; 64 ft **19.** (0, −16)
24. $\frac{1}{4}$ **25.** −2.5 **26.** (7, −1); elimination **27.** Explanations may vary. Sample: Substitution because the first equation is already solved for y; (27, 15) **28.** (3, 2); elimination **29.** vertex: (1, 3); axis of sym.: $x = 1$; maximum at (1, 3); domain: all real numbers, range: $y \le 3$ **30.** vertex: (−4, 0); axis of sym.: $x = -4$; minimum at (−4, 0); domain: all real numbers, range: $y \ge 0$ **31.** vertex: (4, 6); axis of sym.: $x = 4$; maximum at (4, 6); domain: all real numbers, range: $y \le 6$

Lesson 4-3 pp. 220–225

Got It? 1. $y = -3x^2 + x$ **2a.** No; the ball will only reach a height of 5 when $x = 5$, which is lower than the top of the wall at (5, 6). The ball will hit the wall on its way down. **b.** domain: $0 \le x \le 7$, range: $0 \le y \le 6\frac{1}{8}$
3. $y = -0.329x^2 + 9.798x + 15.571$; 88.5°F at 2:53 P.M. (although the meteorologist's prediction is 89° at 3 P.M.)
Lesson Check 1. $y = -2x^2 + 3x - 1$
2. $y = 2x^2 + 6x + 7.5$ **3.** $y = -2x^2 + 10x - 13.5$
4. Answers may vary. Sample: A rough plot of the data will indicate whether the data are collinear (linear regression) or non-collinear where the data follow a curve (quadratic regression). **5.** Answers may vary.

Sample: A rough plot will show that the four pts. do ***not*** lie on a single parabola.
6. y is not a function of x since for one value of x, "3," there are 2 values of y, "4" and "0."
Exercises 7. $y = -x^2 + 3x - 4$ **9.** $y = x^2 + 2x - 2$ **11.** $y = -x^2 - 4x + 5$ **13a.** $y = -16x^2 + 33x + 46$, where x is the number of seconds after release and y is the height in ft **b.** 28.5 ft **c.** about 63 ft **15.** yes; $y = -2x^2 + 3x + 5$ **17.** yes; $y = 0.625x^2 - 1.75x + 1$
19. B **21.** Answers may vary. Sample: $y = -\frac{1}{25}x^2$, $y = \frac{1}{25}x^2 - \frac{2}{5}x$, $y = \frac{1}{5}x^2 - \frac{6}{5}x$

27. 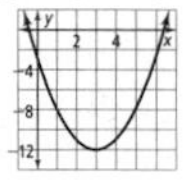

28. 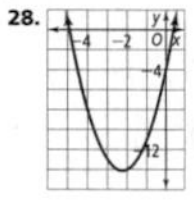

29. 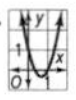

30. (2, 5) **31.** (5, 8) **32.** (−1, −1) **33.** $\frac{4}{5}$ **34.** $-\frac{7}{2}$
35. $x^2 + 5x - 1$ **36.** $6x^2 - 10x - 3$ **37.** $4x^2 - x - 10$

Lesson 4-4 Part 1 pp. 227–230

Got It? 1a. $(x + 10)(x + 4)$ **b.** $(x - 5)(x - 6)$ **c.** $-(x + 2)(x - 16)$ **2a.** $7(n^2 - 3)$ **b.** $9(x + 2)(x - 1)$ **c.** $4(x^2 + 2x + 3)$
Lesson Check 1. $(x + 4)(x + 2)$ **2.** $(x - 12)(x - 1)$ **3.** $5x$ **4.** $4a^2$ **5.** 6 **6.** $7h$ **7.** x is also a factor common to both terms. $27x^2 + 21x = 3x(9x + 7)$, so the GCF is $3x$.
8. 61, 32, 23, 19, 17, 16
Exercises 9. $(x + 2)(x + 3)$ **11.** $(x + 2)(x + 5)$ **13.** $(y + 3)(y + 12)$ **15.** $(x - 1)(x - 2)$ **17.** $(x - 4)(x - 6)$ **19.** 3; $3(a^2 + 3)$ **21.** $5b$; $5b(5b - 4)$ **23.** 5; $5(t + 1)(t - 2)$ **25.** 9; $9(3p^2 - p + 2)$ **27.** $(x - 7)(x + 2)$ **29.** $-(x - 8)(x + 5)$ **31.** $-(t - 11)(t + 4)$ **33.** b; $b(ab - 1)$ **35.** $3t$; $3t(t - 8)$ **37.** xy; $xy(xy + 1)$ **39.** To factor $5x^2 + 5x - 60$ completely, first factor the GCF, 5, from the terms to get $5(x^2 + x - 12)$. Then look for numbers whose product is −12 and whose sum is 1. The numbers −3 and 4 work. The complete factorization is $5(x - 3)(x + 4)$; To factor $-5x - 5x + 60$ completely, factor out −5 to get $-5(x^2 + x - 12)$ and proceed as above.

Lesson 4-4 Part 2 pp. 231–236

Got It? 3a. $(x + 1)(4x + 3)$ **b.** $(x - 2)(2x - 3)$ **c.** No; $2x^2 + 2x + 2 = 2(x^2 + x + 1)$, there are no real factors of a and c whose product is 1 and whose sum is 1. **4.** $(8x - 1)^2$ **5.** $(4x - 9)(4x + 9)$

Lesson Check 1. $(x - 9)(x + 9)$ **2.** $(5y - 6)(5y + 6)$ **3.** $(y - 3)^2$ **4.** $(2x - 1)^2$ **5.** No; the middle term is not twice the product of the square root of the end terms. **6.** For $a \ne 1$, look for two factors whose sum is b and whose product is ac. For $a = 1$, look for two factors whose sum is b and whose product is c.
Exercises 7. $(3x + 2)(x + 3)$ **9.** $(x - 8)(2x - 3)$ **11.** $(m - 3)(2m - 5)$ **13.** $(x - 2)(7x + 6)$ **15.** $(x + 4)(3x - 4)$ **17.** $(t - 7)^2$ **19.** $(k - 9)^2$ **21.** $(3x + 8)^2$ **23.** $(c - 8)(c + 8)$ **25.** $(5x - 1)$ cm by $(5x - 1)$ cm **27.** $2(3z + 2)(3z - 2)$ **29.** $2(a - 4)^2$ **31.** $3(2x + 3)^2$ **33.** $3(x + 1)(x - 9)$ **35.** $-(x - 1)(x - 4)$ **37.** $(x - y)(x + y)$ **39.** $-6(z^2 + 100)$ **41.** $(3x - 1)(3x + 1)$ **43.** The third line should be $x(2x - 5) - (2x - 5)$, and the final line should be $(x - 1)(2x - 5)$. **45.** $\pi h(R + r)(R - r)$
52. $y = -0.149x^2 + 5.171x + 16.971$ **53.** penny: 2.5 g, nickel: 5 g, dime: 2.3 g

54. 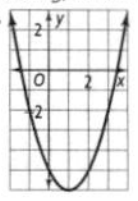

55. 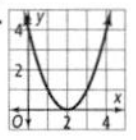

56. 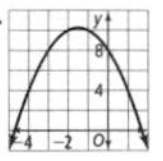

Chapter Review for Part A pp. 237–239

1. standard **2.** axis of symmetry **3.** maximum value **4.** vertex: $(-2, -6)$; axis of sym.: $x = -2$; minimum: −6; domain: all real numbers, range: $y \ge -6$ **5.** vertex: (3, 2); axis of sym.: $x = 3$; maximum: 2; domain: all real numbers, range: $y \le 2$ **6.** vertex: (1, 5); axis of sym.: $x = 1$; minimum: 5; domain: all real numbers, range: $y \ge 5$ **7.** vertex: (−9, −4); axis of sym.: $x = -9$; minimum: −4; domain: all real numbers, range: $y \ge -4$

8. 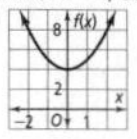 translation 4 units up

9. 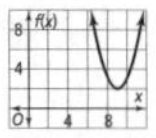 translation 9 units to the rt. and 2 units up

10. 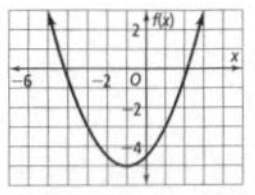 vert. compression by a factor of $\frac{1}{2}$, translation 1 unit to the left and 5 units down

11. 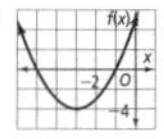

12. 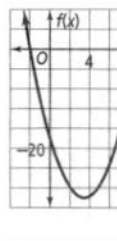

13. 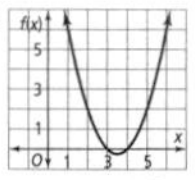

14. 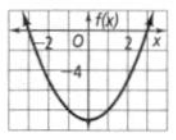

15. $f(x) = 4(x - 1)^2 - 2$ **16.** $f(x) = (x - 4)^2 - 4$
17. $f(x) = 8\left(x + \frac{1}{2}\right)^2 - 14$ **18.** $f(x) = -2\left(x + \frac{3}{2}\right)^2 + \frac{29}{2}$
19. 1 s; 25 ft **20.** $y = x^2 - 6x + 5$
21. $y = -2x^2 + 8x - 8$ **22.** $y = x^2 + 3x - 18$
23. $y = -0.5x^2 + 2.5x - 7$
24. $y = -0.0043x^2 + 0.3521x + 0.3691$
25. $(x - 6)(x - 2)$ **26.** $(3x - 4)(x + 5)$
27. $-2(2x - 1)(x - 3)$ **28.** $(x + 10)(x + 4)$
29. $(x - 7)^2$ **30.** $(3x + 5)^2$ **31.** $4(3x - 2)(3x + 2)$
32. $(5x - 2)(5x + 2)$ **33.** $6x$; $6x(x - 4)$
34. −7; $-7(2x^2 + 7)$

Review p. 242

1. $3\sqrt{2}$ **3.** $-4\sqrt{2}$ **5.** $\frac{-\sqrt{91}}{13}$ **7.** $-10\sqrt{2}$ **9.** 108
11. $|xy|$ **13.** $\frac{-|x|\sqrt{35}}{5}$ **15.** $\frac{5\sqrt{14}}{7}$

Lesson 4-5 Part 1 pp. 243–245

Got It? 1a. 3, 4 **b.** −3, 6 **2.** 3, $\frac{1}{4}$
Lesson Check 1. 3, −3 **2.** −4, −9 **3.** $-\frac{2}{3}$, 1 **4.** −1; since $y = 0$ when $x = 5$, substitute these values into the eq. to find b. **5.** One solution: when the table's range consists of zero and all pos. numbers or zero and all neg. numbers No solution: when the table does not include zero and the y-values are either all pos. or all neg. numbers
Exercises 7. 3, 6 **9.** 5 **11.** 0, 4 **13.** 3, 8 **15.** −1.32, 8.32 **17.** 1, −0.75 **19.** 0.5, 0.6 **21.** Answers may vary. Samples are given: **a.** $x^2 - 8x + 15 = 0$ **b.** $x^2 + x - 6 = 0$ **c.** $x^2 + 7x + 6 = 0$ **23.** (0, −2), (2, 2)

Lesson 4-5 Part 2 pp. 246–250

Got It? 3. −6, 4 **4a.** $53\frac{1}{3}$ m; $21\frac{1}{3}$ m; answers may vary. Sample: domain: $0 \le x \le 60$, range: $0 \le y \le 30$ **b.** No; domains and ranges are constrained by real-world limits.

Lesson Check 1. 4.372, −1.372 **2.** 2.608, −2.108 **3.** when the coefficients are not integers or no recognizable factoring pattern is evident
Exercises 5. −0.59, 2.26 **7.** −5.53, 0.36 **9.** −5.16, 1.16 **11a.** about 6.61 s **b.** about 6.89 s **c.** domain: $0 \le t \le 10.4$, range: $0 \le h \le 1700$ **13.** 3 in. **15.** about 3.6 ft **17.** $-\frac{3}{2}, -\frac{2}{3}$ **19.** −4, $\frac{5}{2}$ **21.** −1, 4 **23.** −4, 0 **25.** 4.37, −1.37 **27.** −1, $\frac{10}{3}$ **29.** The solutions of $x^2 - 10x + 24 = (x - 4)(x - 6) = 0$ are 4 and 6. Average 4 and 6 to get 5. This is the x-coordinate of the vertex. Substitute 5 in for x in $x^2 - 10x + 24$ to find that −1 is the y-coordinate of the vertex. So, the vertex is (5, −1). **34.** $(4x - 1)(4x + 1)$ **35.** $(5x - 1)(x - 5)$ **36.** $(2x - 1)(x + 7)$ **37.** (2, 0, −2) **38.** (−2, 1, 5) **39.** (7, 1, −1) **40.** vertex: (−9, 4); axis of sym.: $x = -9$; translation 9 units to the left and 4 units up **41.** vertex: $\left(\frac{7}{2}, 0\right)$; axis of sym.: $x = \frac{7}{2}$; stretch by a factor of 2, translation $3\frac{1}{2}$ units to the rt. **42.** vertex: (0, −1); axis of sym.: $x = 0$; compression by a factor of $\frac{3}{4}$, translation 1 unit down **43.** $x^2 + 8x + 13$ **44.** $4x^2 - 4x + 1$ **45.** $x^2 - 6x + 9$

Lesson 4-6 Part 1 pp. 252–254

Got It? 1a. $\sqrt{5}, -\sqrt{5}$ **b.** $\sqrt{2}, -\sqrt{2}$ **2.** 42 in. × 67.2 in. **3.** 2, 12
Lesson Check 1. 6, −6 **2.** 3, −3 **3.** First, factor the perfect square trinomial: $(x + 4)^2 = 36$. Then find the square root of each side of the equation: $x + 4 = \pm 6$. Rewrite as two equations and solve: $x + 4 = -6$ or $x + 4 = 6$. The solutions are −10 and 2.
Exercises 5. 2, −2 **7.** $2\sqrt{2}, -2\sqrt{2}$ **9.** −4, −2 **11.** −1, 3 **13.** 1, 11 **15.** $-\frac{10}{3}, \frac{2}{3}$ **17.** 20, −20 **19.** 16, −16 **21.** 10, −10 **23.** 12, −12

Lesson 4-6 Part 2 pp. 255–259

Got It? 4. 9 **5.** $\frac{1}{2} \pm \frac{\sqrt{13}}{2}$
6. $y = \left(x + \frac{3}{2}\right)^2 - \frac{33}{4}$; vertex: $\left(-\frac{3}{2}, -\frac{33}{4}\right)$; y-intercept: (0, −6)
Lesson Check 1. 1 **2.** 25 **3.** 4 **4.** 36 **5.** 2500 **6.** 256
7.

$x^2 + 12x + 5 = 3$	
$x^2 + 12x = -2$	Rewrite to get all terms with x on one side of the eq.
$\left(\frac{12}{2}\right)^2 = 6^2 = 36$	Find $\left(\frac{b}{2}\right)^2 = 36$.
$x^2 + 12x + 36 = -2 + 36$	Add 36 to each side.
$(x + 6)^2 = 34$	Factor the trinomial.

8. Your friend should also have subtracted 49; $(x^2 - 14x + 49) + 36 - 49 = (x - 7)^2 - 13$

Exercises 9. 81 **11.** 144 **13.** $\frac{9}{4}$ **15.** $-3 \pm 2\sqrt{3}$ **17.** $-2 \pm \sqrt{2}$ **19.** $5 \pm \sqrt{13}$ **21.** $3 \pm \sqrt{11}$ **23.** $-\frac{5}{4} \pm \frac{1}{4}\sqrt{37}$ **25.** $y = (x + 2)^2 - 3$ **27.** $y = -(x + 1)^2 + 4$ **29.** 8 in. **31.** $\frac{-5 \pm \sqrt{37}}{2}$ **33.** $\frac{2 \pm \sqrt{10}}{3}$ **35.** $\frac{-3 + \sqrt{41}}{8}$ **37.** $\frac{1}{3}, -\frac{2}{3}$ **39.** $-3 \pm \sqrt{7}$ **44.** $\frac{1}{2}$, 1 **45.** −4, 1 **46.** 8, $-\frac{2}{3}$ **47.** yes; $y = \frac{1}{2}x^2 + \frac{7}{2}x + 9$ **48.** yes; $y = -\frac{1}{2}x^2 + x + 2$ **49.** yes; $y = 3x^2 - 5x + 2$ **50.** (2, 0) **51.** (3, 1) **52.** (3, 1) **53.** 24 **54.** 84

Lesson 4-7 pp. 260–267

Got It? 1a. −2 **b.** $-2 \pm \sqrt{7}$ **2a.** \$10.74 **b.** Yes; a neg. profit means more money was spent than earned. **3a.** no real solutions **b.** two real solutions **4.** Yes; $b^2 - 4ac = (85)^2 - 4(-16)\left(-109\frac{11}{12}\right) = -190\frac{1}{3}$. The discriminant is positive. So the eq. has two real solutions.
Lesson Check 1. $\frac{5 \pm \sqrt{53}}{2}$ **2.** $\frac{-3 \pm \sqrt{61}}{2}$ **3.** 3, $-\frac{1}{2}$ **4.** no real solutions **5.** −32; no real solutions **6.** 273; two real solutions **7.** 0; one real solution **8.** $k = \pm 6$ for one real solution; $k > 6$ or $k < -6$ for two real solutions **9.** Answers may vary. Sample: The discriminants of eqs. with one real solution are all zero and thus equal, but the solutions may or may not be equal. An example is $x^2 - 8x + 16$ and $x^2 - 4x + 4$. Each has a discriminant of zero, but the solutions are 4 and 2. **10.** Yes; the eqs. can share common factors such as for $x^2 + 2x - 8$ where the discriminant is 36 and the solutions are 2 and −4, and $x^2 - 4x + 4$ where the discriminant is zero and the solution is 2.
Exercises 11. 1, 3 **13.** $-\frac{7}{2}$, 1 **15.** $\frac{3 \pm \sqrt{5}}{2}$ **17.** 1, 4 **19.** \$.86 **21.** 36; two **23.** −223; no real solutions **25.** 0; one **27.** −35; no real solutions **29.** no **31.** 2.29 in. × 15.71 in. **33.** $-\frac{1}{6}$, 1 **35.** −2.90, 1.90 **37.** 1, 10 **39.** −3.45, 1.45 **41.** 1.47, −7.47 **43.** two **45.** two **47.** two **49.** about 1.89 s **51a.** II **b.** III **c.** I **56.** −2, 10 **57.** $\frac{2 \pm \sqrt{2}}{2}$ **58.** $\frac{3 \pm \sqrt{41}}{2}$ **59.** $9z^2 + 3z$ **60.** $4x + k$ **61.** $2y - 8x$ **62.** $2\sqrt{17}$ **63.** 5 **64.** 13

Lesson 4-8 Part 1 pp. 268–273

Got It? 1a. $2i\sqrt{3}$ **b.** $5i$ **c.** $i\sqrt{7}$ **d.** $8i \neq -8$
2a. 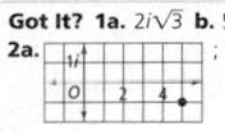 ; $\sqrt{26}$ **b.** 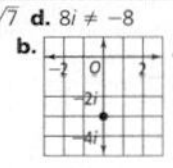 ; 3
c.  ; $\sqrt{17}$ **d.** 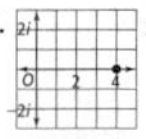 ; 4

3a. $4 - i$ **b.** $-2 + 7i$ **c.** $12i$ **d.** $18i$ **4a.** −21 **b.** $23 - 2i$ **c.** 41 **5a.** $\frac{7}{25} - \frac{26}{25}i$ **b.** $-\frac{1}{6} - \frac{2}{3}i$ **c.** $\frac{15}{113} - \frac{112}{113}i$
Lesson Check 1. $5i\sqrt{3}$ **2.** 5 **3.** $7 - 3i$ **4.** $13 - 6i$ **5.** The add. inv. of a complex no., $a + bi$, is the opposite of the complex no., or $-a - bi$. The complex conjugate of a complex no., $a + bi$, is the real part plus the opposite of the imaginary part of the complex no., or $a - bi$.
6. error in the sign of the last term of the first line, which carries through to the end of the calculation; the line should be: "… $= 16 + 28i - 28i - 49i^2$
$= 16 + 49$
$= 65$."
Exercises 7. $2i$ **9.** $i\sqrt{15}$
11. 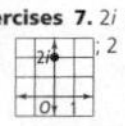 ; 2 **13.** 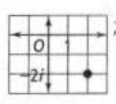 ; $2\sqrt{2}$
15. $6 + 3i$ **17.** $10 + 6i$ **19.** $9 + 58i$ **21.** $65 + 72i$ **23.** $\frac{8}{17} + \frac{19}{17}i$ **25.** $\frac{8}{13} + \frac{12}{13}i$ **27.** $-1 + 5i$ **29.** $8 - 2i$ **31.** $10 + 11i$

Lesson 4-8 Part 2 pp. 274–277

Got It? 6a. $\pm 2i$ **b.** $\pm i\sqrt{15}$ **7a.** $\frac{1 \pm i\sqrt{23}}{6}$ **b.** $2 \pm i$
Lesson Check 1. $\pm 4i$ **2.** $\pm i\sqrt{7}$ **3.** $\pm 6i$ **4.** The graph does not intersect the x-axis, which means that there are no real solutions to the related equation. The complex solutions are $3 \pm i$.
Exercises 5. $\pm 5i$ **7.** $\pm 8i\frac{\sqrt{3}}{3}$ **9.** $-1 \pm i\sqrt{2}$ **11.** $1 \pm i\frac{\sqrt{10}}{2}$ **13.** $2 \pm i$ **15.** $-\frac{5}{2} \pm \frac{\sqrt{15}}{2}i$ **17.** −5, 5 **19.** trapezoid **21.** $\frac{1}{26} + \frac{3}{52}i$ **23.** $x = -7, y = 3$ **25.** $x = -7, y = -3$ **27.** sum: $-\frac{2}{5}$, product: $\frac{1}{5}$ **29.** Answers may vary. Sample: $x^2 + 36 = 0$ **31.** Answers may vary. Sample: $x^2 - 8x + 25 = 0$ **36.** $\frac{-3 \pm \sqrt{41}}{4}$ **37.** $\frac{-1 \pm \sqrt{17}}{8}$ **38.** $\frac{-7 \pm \sqrt{17}}{2}$
39. 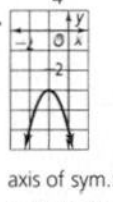 axis of sym.: $x = -1$
40. 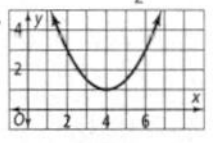 axis of sym.: $x = 4$
41. 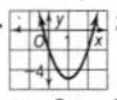 ; axis of sym.: $x = 1$
42. $y = 3x - 4$ **43.** $y = -0.5x - 2$ **44.** $y = -7x + 10$ **45.** $y = 2x + 8$ **46.** 11q **47.** $ab^2 + 2a^2b$ **48.** $-y^2 + 2y$

Chapter Review for Part B pp. 282–284

1. Formula **2.** discriminant **3.** complex **4.** −2, 6 **5.** −2, $\frac{7}{2}$ **6.** −4, 2 **7.** −9, 2
8. 1, −2.6; 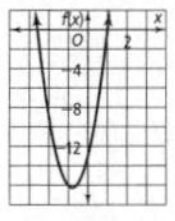
9. 1.345, −3.345; 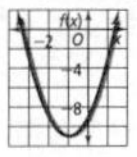
10. 1.618, −0.618; 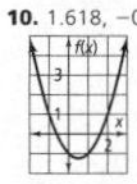
11. 3.236, −1.236; 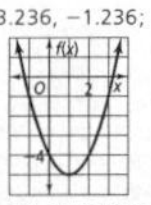
12. 2, 4 **13.** no real solution **14.** 4.56, 0.44 **15.** 2, 4 **16.** ±2 **17.** $\pm\sqrt{5}$ **18.** ±3 **19.** $\pm 2\sqrt{3}$ **20.** 9 **21.** $\frac{9}{4}$ **22.** $-4 \pm \sqrt{10}$ **23.** $5 \pm \sqrt{38}$ **24.** −1, $\frac{1}{3}$ **25.** $1 \pm i\sqrt{3}$ **26.** $\frac{-3 \pm i\sqrt{91}}{2}$ **27.** 1, $-\frac{3}{4}$ **28.** 1, $-\frac{8}{3}$ **29.** 3 **30.** 4, −1 **31.** 1.744, −0.344 **32.** 164; two **33.** −3; none **34.** 0; one **35.** 233; two **36.** 10.27 ft × 16.55 ft **37.** $2i\sqrt{6}$ **38.** $-3 + i\sqrt{2}$ **39.** $-50 + 40i$ **40.** $6 + 4i\sqrt{6}$ **41.** $3 + 9i$ **42.** $13 + 20i$ **43.** $21 - 25i$ **44.** $-12 - 15i$ **45.** $-3 - 2i$ **46.** $-\frac{1}{2} - \frac{1}{2}i$ **47.** $\pm 3i$ **48.** $\frac{1}{5} \pm \frac{2}{5}i$ **49.** $2 \pm i\sqrt{6}$ **50.** $\frac{-4 \pm i\sqrt{26}}{7}$

Chapter 5

Get Ready! p. 289

1. 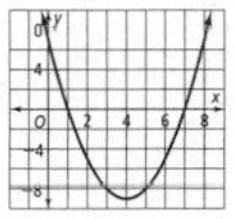 **2.** 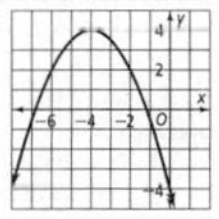
3. 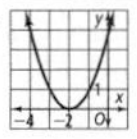

4. $y = x^2 + 3x - 4$ **5.** $y = x^2 - 2x + 1$ **6.** $y = -x^2 - x + 12$ **7.** 0.25, −1 **8.** −6.39, 4.39 **9.** −6.38, 0.38 **10.** −4, 5 **11.** −9, 3 **12.** 1, 2 **13.** 24; two real solutions **14.** 0; one real solution **15.** 0; one real solution **16.** south **17.** The highest pt. in Maine may be lower than the highest pt. in the United States. The relative maximum of a graph for a given region is the maximum for that region only, whereas the maximum of the graph may be greater than or equal to the relative maximum for the region. **18.** $4x^2 + 4x + 1$

Lesson 5-1 pp. 292–299

Got It? 1a. $5x^4 + 3x^3 - x$; quartic trinomial **b.** $-4x^5 + 2x^2 + 13$; quintic trinomial **2.** up and down
3a. end behavior: up and down; two turning pts. 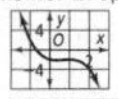
b. end behavior: down and up; no turning pts. 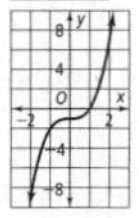
4a. degree: 4 **b.** Answers may vary. Sample: $y = x^5$
Lesson Check 1. cubic monomial **2.** quadratic trinomial **3.** $5x^2 + 7x + 3$ **4.** $9x - 3$ **5.** up and down **6.** Yes; the graph of a linear binomial or linear monomial is a straight line. Sample: $y = 2x + 1$. **7.** The graph of $y = 4x^3 + 4$ has no turning pts., *not* one turning point.
Exercises 9. $10x + 5$; linear binomial **11.** $x^4 - x^3 + x$; quartic trinomial **13.** $3a^3 + 5a^2 + 1$; cubic trinomial **15.** $12x^4 + 3$; quartic binomial **17.** $5x^2 + 4x + 8$; quadratic trinomial **19.** up and up **21.** down and up **23.** up and up **25.** end behavior: up and down; two turning pts. **27.** end behavior: down and up; no turning pts. **29.** 3 **31.** $-4a^4 + a^3 + a^2$; quartic trinomial **33.** $2a^3 - 5a^2 - 2a + 5$; cubic polynomial of 4 terms **35a.** $\pi r^2 h$ **b.** $\frac{2}{3}\pi r^3$ **c.** $\pi r^2\left(h + \frac{2}{3}r\right)$, or $\frac{2}{3}\pi r^3 + \pi r^2 h$ **37.** neg.; 3 **39.** pos.; 4 **45.** $-4 + 3i$ **46.** $7 + 7i$ **47.** $3 + 3i$ **48.** $35x - 5y = -2$ **49.** $6x + 2y = -5$ **50.** $2x + 7y = 28$ **51.** $(x + 4)(x + 3)$ **52.** $(x + 10)(x - 2)$ **53.** $(x - 12)(x - 2)$

Lesson 5-2 Part 1 pp. 300–303

Got It? 1. $x(x - 4)(x + 3)$
2. 0, 3, −5; 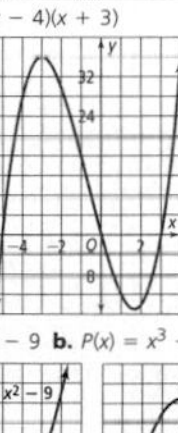
3. a. $f(x) = x^2 - 9$ **b.** $P(x) = x^3 - 3x^2 - 9x + 27$
c. 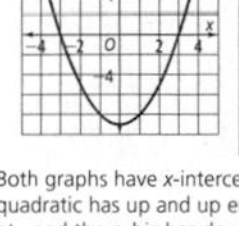

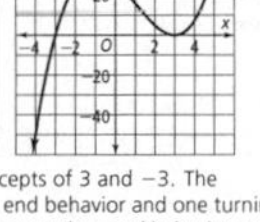

Both graphs have x-intercepts of 3 and −3. The quadratic has up and up end behavior and one turning pt., and the cubic has down and up end behavior and two turning pts.
Lesson Check 1. 0, 6 **2.** −4, 5 **3.** −12, 7, 9 **4.** $f(x) = x^3 - x$ **5.** Error in writing the factors: a function that has zeros at 3 and −1 has factors of $x - 3$ and $x + 1$, *not* $x + 3$ and $x - 1$, so $f(x) = x^2 - 2x - 3$, *not* $x^2 + 2x - 3$.
Exercises 7. $x(x - 3)(x + 2)$ **9.** $x(x - 7)(x + 3)$ **11.** $x(x + 4)^2$
13. 1, −2; 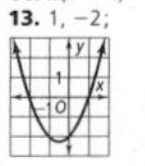
15. 0, −5, 8; 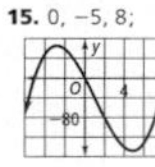
17. −1, 1, 2; 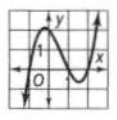
19. $y = x^3 + x^2 - 2x$ **21.** $y = x^3 + 9x^2 + 15x - 25$ **23.** $y = x^3 + 2x^2 - x - 2$ **25.** $y = x^4 - 5x^3 + 6x^2$ **27.** $y = -2x(x + 5)(x - 4)$ **29.** B

Lesson 5-2 Part 2 pp. 304–309

Got It? 4. 0 is a zero of multiplicity 1, and the graph looks close to linear at $x = 0$; 2 is a zero of multiplicity 2, and the graph looks close to quadratic at $x = 2$. **5.** relative maximum: (−0.86, 3.13), relative minimum: (0.64, −2) **6.** 2.28 in.^{3}
Lesson Check 1. 2 **2.** 1 **3.** 3 **4.** relative maximum (−2.737, 48.517), relative minimum (2.070, −7.035) **5.** $h(x) = x^4 + 4x^3 - 26x^2 - 60x + 225$ **6.** No; Explanations may vary. Sample: A cubic function has either 0 or 2 turning points. Of the two possible turning points, one must be an up-to-down turning point and the other a down-to-up turning point. Relative maximums occur only at up-to-down turning points.
Exercises 7. 0, 1 (multiplicity 3) **9.** −1, 0, 1 **11.** 1, 2 (multiplicity 2) **13.** −1 (multiplicity 2), 1, 2 **15.** relative maximum: (2.15, 12.32), relative minimum: (−0.15, −12.32) **17a.** $\ell = 16 - 2x$; $w = 12 - 2x$; $h = x$ **b.** $V = x(16 - 2x)(12 - 2x)$
c. 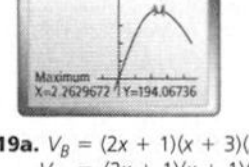

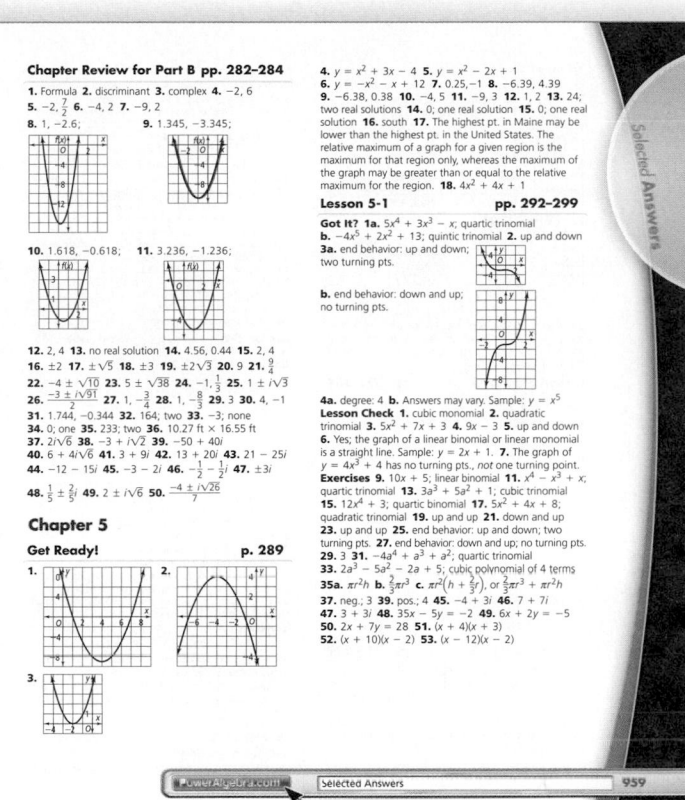

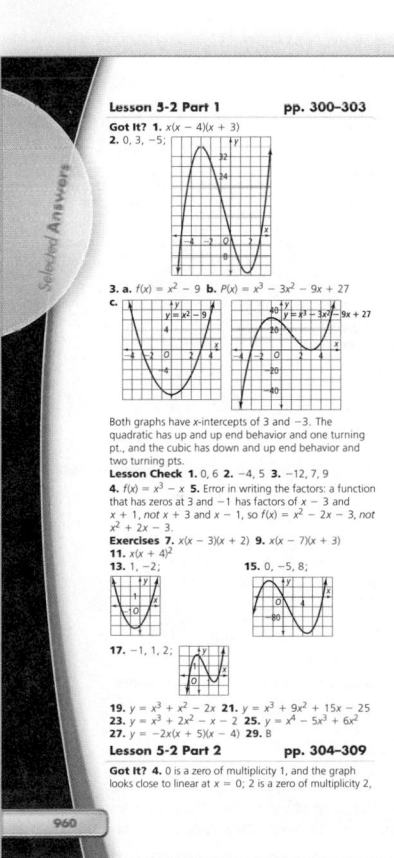

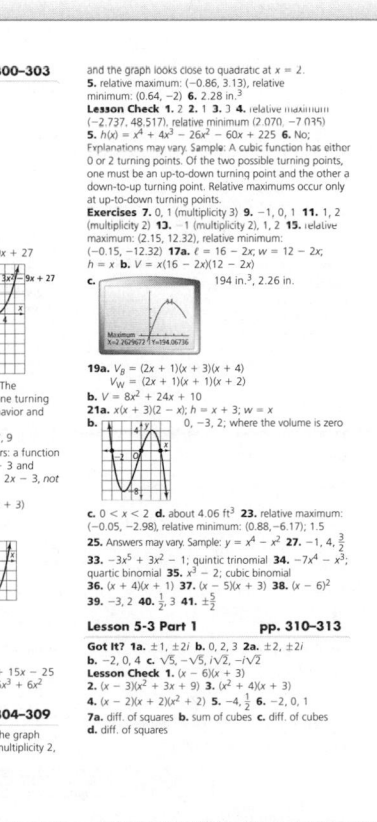

194 in.^{3}, 2.26 in.
19a. $V_B = (2x + 1)(x + 3)(x + 4)$
$V_W = (2x + 1)(x + 1)(x + 2)$
b. $V = 8x^2 + 24x + 10$
21a. $x(x + 3)(2 - x)$; $h = x + 3$; $w = x$
b. 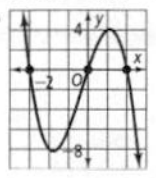 0, −3, 2; where the volume is zero
c. $0 < x < 2$ **d.** about 4.06 ft^3 **23.** relative maximum: (−0.05, −2.98), relative minimum: (0.88, −6.17); 1.5 **25.** Answers may vary. Sample: $y = x^4 - x^2$ **27.** −1, 4, $\frac{3}{2}$ **33.** $-3x^5 + 3x^2 - 1$; quintic trinomial **34.** $-7x^4 - x^3$; quartic binomial **35.** $x^3 - 2$; cubic binomial **36.** $(x + 4)(x + 1)$ **37.** $(x - 5)(x + 3)$ **38.** $(x - 6)^2$ **39.** −3, 2 **40.** $\frac{1}{2}$, 3 **41.** $\pm\frac{5}{2}$

Lesson 5-3 Part 1 pp. 310–313

Got It? 1a. ±1, ±2*i* **b.** 0, 2, 3 **2a.** ±2, ±2*i* **b.** −2, 0, 4 **c.** $\sqrt{5}, -\sqrt{5}, i\sqrt{2}, -i\sqrt{2}$
Lesson Check 1. $(x - 6)(x + 3)$ **2.** $(x - 3)(x^2 + 3x + 9)$ **3.** $(x^2 + 4)(x + 3)$ **4.** $(x - 2)(x + 2)(x^2 + 2)$ **5.** −4, $\frac{1}{2}$ **6.** −2, 0, 1 **7a.** diff. of squares **b.** sum of cubes **c.** diff. of cubes **d.** diff. of squares

8. Method 1: Graph $y = x^6 - x^2$. Find the zeros for the real solutions. 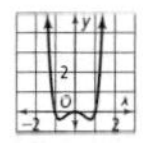
Method 2: Factor and solve $x^6 - x^2 = 0$ for x.
$x^2(x^4 - 1) = x^2(x^2 - 1)(x^2 + 1)$
$= x^2(x - 1)(x + 1)(x^2 + 1)$
$x = 0, \pm 1$
Exercises 9. $-4, 2 \pm 2i\sqrt{3}$ **11.** $\frac{3}{5}, \frac{-3 \pm 3i\sqrt{3}}{10}$ **13.** $-2, \pm i\sqrt{5}$ **15.** $3, \frac{-3 \pm 3i\sqrt{3}}{2}$ **17.** $\frac{1}{2}, \frac{-1 \pm i\sqrt{3}}{4}$ $\frac{1 \pm i\sqrt{3}}{4}$ **19.** −4, 0, 2 **21.** ±2 **23.** $\pm\sqrt{2}, \pm 3i$ **25.** $-\frac{6}{5}, \frac{3 \pm 3i\sqrt{3}}{5}$ **27.** $\pm 2\sqrt{2}, \pm 2i\sqrt{2}$ **29.** 0, ±1, ±2 **31.** C

Lesson 5-3 Part 2 pp. 314–317

Got It? 3. −1.84 **4.** 7, 8, 9
Lesson Check 1. 0, 1.536, 8.464 **2.** 0, 1.268, 4.732 **3.** −1.036, 0, 6.036 **4.** Graphing; imaginary numbers don't exist on the x-axis. **5.** 3.13 is the y-value of the intersection point. The solution is the x-value, −1.13.
Exercises 7. −1, 0, 3 **9.** 0, 8 **11.** 0, −3.5, 1 **13.** −0.5, 0, 3 **15.** −2, 5
17. 5, 6, 7; $x(x + 1)(x + 2) = 210$; 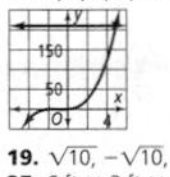
19. $\sqrt{10}, -\sqrt{10}, i\sqrt{10}, -i\sqrt{10}$ **21.** 1, $\pm i$ **23.** −1, 1 **25.** 6 ft × 3 ft × 2 ft
27. $-\frac{5}{2}$, 1; $y = (2x + 5)(x - 1)$; 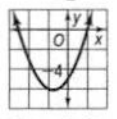
29. −1, 2; $y = (x + 1)(x - 2)^2$; 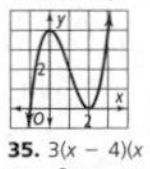
35. $3(x - 4)(x - 2)$ **36.** $2x(x + 3)^2(x - 3)$ **37.** $x^2(x - 5)(x + 1)$ **38.** −2, 6 **39.** ±6 **40.** $-\frac{1}{2}$, 3 **41.** 12 **42.** $-\frac{1}{5}$

Lesson 5-4 Part 1 pp. 318–321

Got It? 1. $3x - 8$, R 0 **2a.** yes; $P(x) = (x + 5)(x^4 - 1)$ **b.** $(x + 2)(3x + 1)$
Lesson Check 1. $2x + 3$, R 5 **2.** $9x^2 + 12x + 40$, R120 **3.** $x - a$ is a factor of $P(x)$ by the Factor Theorem.
Exercises 5. $3x - 5$ **7.** $2x^2 + 5x + 2$ **9.** $9x - 12$, R −32 **11.** no **13.** yes **15.** $5x^3 - 22x^2 - 3x - 53$ **17.** $x + 4$ **19.** no **21.** yes

Lesson 5-4 Part 2 pp. 322–326

Got It? 3. $x^2 + 7x - 8$, R 0 **4.** width: $(x + 1)$ in.; height: $(x + 2)$ in., length: $(x + 3)$ in. **5.** 0
Lesson Check 1. $x^2 + 2x + 5$ **2.** $x^2 + x - 2$ **3.** $4x^2 + x - 6$, R 6 **4.** The polynomials need to be written in standard form since the leading coefficient of both polynomials determines the leading term of the quotient.
Exercises 7. $x^2 - 2x + 2$ **9.** $x^2 + 2x + 5$ **11.** $3x^2 + 8x - 3$ **13.** $y = (x + 1)(x + 3)(x - 2)$ **15.** length = $x + 3$; height = $x - 2$ **17.** 0 **19.** 168 **21.** yes **23.** no **25.** $x^3 - x^2 + 1$ **27.** $x^3 - 3x^2 + 12x - 35$, R 109 **29.** There are two errors. The constant term of the dividend is missing and the divisor is −1 *not* 1: $x^3 - x^2 - 2x = (x + 1)(x^2 - 2x) = x(x + 1)(x - 2)$. **35.** 0, −1 **36.** 0, 1 **37.** −5, 0, 5 **38.** $\frac{-3 \pm \sqrt{17}}{2}$ **39.** $-1 \pm \sqrt{3}$ **40.** 1, $-\frac{5}{7}$ **41.** $\frac{5 \pm \sqrt{5}}{2}$ **42.** $3 \pm \sqrt{2}$ **43.** $\frac{-7 \pm \sqrt{5}}{2}$
44. 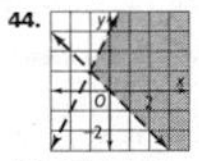 **45.** 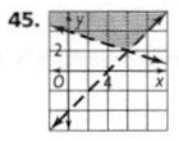
46. 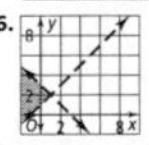
47. 24 **48.** 5 **49.** $23 - 11i$

Chapter Review for Part A pp. 327–329

1. relative minimum **2.** degree **3.** standard form of a polynomial function **4.** synthetic division **5.** multiplicity **6.** $y = -x^4 + 12$; quartic binomial; down and down **7.** $y = x^2 - x + 7$; quadratic trinomial; up and up **8.** $y = -x^4 + 2x^3 + 3x^2 - 6x + 12$; quartic polynomial of five terms; down and down **9.** $y = x^3 + 2x^2 - 4x + 8$; cubic polynomial of four terms; down and up **10.** $y = x^4 - 3x^3 + 3x^2 + 10$; quartic polynomial of four terms; up and up **11.** 3 **12.** If n is even, there are an odd no. of turning pts.; if n is odd, there are an even no. of turning pts. **13.** $f(x) = x^3 - 4x^2 - 11x - 6$ **14.** $f(x) = x^3 - x^2 - 2x$ **15.** $f(x) = x^3 - 6x^2 + 11x - 6$

16. $f(x) = x^3 - 3x^2 - 6x + 8$ **17.** 0, −2 (multiplicity 3) **18.** 2 (multiplicity 2), −2 (multiplicity 2) **19.** 0, $-\frac{1}{2}$, 1 **20.** 5, −2 (multiplicity 2) **21.** relative maximum: (0.8672, −1.9351), relative minimums: (0, −3), (2.8828, −12.1704); zeros: $x \approx -0.5992$, $x \approx 3.7115$ **22.** relative maximum: (−0.8441, 9.3023), relative minimum: (0.7108, −0.0964); zeros: $x = -1.6180$, $x \approx 0.6180$, $x \approx 0.8$ **23.** relative minimum: (1, −4); zeros: $x \approx -0.2490$, $x \approx 1.6633$ **24.** relative maximum: (−0.4142, −3.3431), relative minimum: (2.4142, −14.6569); zero: $x = 4$ **25.** 3, 8 **26.** $-\frac{1}{2}$ **27.** 0, $\frac{-1 \pm \sqrt{37}}{2}$ **28.** $\frac{2 \pm i\sqrt{2}}{2}$

29. no real roots;

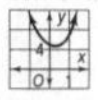

30. 2.3949;

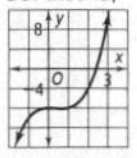

31. 4.87 in. × 2.87 in. × 2.87 in. **32.** $x^2 + 6x + 9$ **33.** $2x^2 + x - 3$, R 1 **34.** yes **35.** no **36.** $x^2 - 1$ **37.** $2x^2 - 6x + 2$, R −20 **38.** $5x^2 + 18x + 36$, R 12 **39.** −14 **40.** 2

Lesson 5-5 Part 1 pp. 332–334

Got It? 1. $\frac{2}{3}$ **2.** 2, −1, $-\frac{3}{2}$
Lesson Check 1. ±1, ±2 **2.** ±1, ±2, ±3, ±6, $\pm\frac{1}{2}$, $\pm\frac{3}{2}$ **3.** ±1, ±2, ±3, ±4, ±6, ±12, $\pm\frac{1}{3}$, $\pm\frac{2}{3}$, $\pm\frac{4}{3}$ **4a.** never; 5 is not a factor of 8. **b.** always; −2 is a factor of 8.
Exercises 5. ±1, ±2, ±4, $\pm\frac{1}{2}$; no rational roots **7.** ±1, ±3, ±9; no rational roots **9.** ±1, ±2, ±3, ±6, $\pm\frac{1}{3}$, $\pm\frac{2}{3}$; no rational roots **11.** ±1, ±2, ±3, ±6, ±9, ±18, $\pm\frac{1}{6}$, $\pm\frac{1}{3}$, $\pm\frac{1}{2}$, $\pm\frac{3}{2}$, $\pm\frac{2}{3}$, $\pm\frac{9}{2}$; no rational roots **13.** ±1, $\pm\frac{1}{8}$, $\pm\frac{1}{4}$, $\pm\frac{1}{2}$; −1, $\frac{1}{4}$, $\frac{1}{2}$ **15.** no rational roots **17.** no rational roots **19.** no rational roots **21.** The roots were written as the factors of the leading coefficients over the factors of the constant term. The possible roots should list the factors of the constant term over the factors of the leading coefficient.

Lesson 5-5 Part 2 pp. 335–339

Got It? 3. $3 + 2i$ **4.** $P(x) = x^4 - 14x^3 + 69x^2 - 194x + 208$ **5a.** There are three or one pos. real roots and one neg. real root. The graph confirms one neg. and one pos. real root. **b.** Real roots can be confirmed graphically because they are x-intercepts. Complex roots cannot be confirmed graphically because they have an imaginary component.

Lesson Check 1. $P(x) = x^2 - 14x + 45$ **2.** $P(x) = x^3 + 4x^2 + 4x + 16$ **3.** Answers may vary. Samples: $1 + 2i$ and $1 - 2i$; $1 + \sqrt{2}$ and $1 - \sqrt{2}$ **4.** Complex number roots come in pairs if the equation has real coefficients; if $-4i$ is a root, so is $4i$.
Exercises 5. $2i$, $-\sqrt{10}$ **7.** $-i$, $7 - 8i$ **9.** $P(x) = x^2 + 100$ **11.** $P(x) = x^2 + 24x + 135$ **13.** $P(x) = x^4 - 22x^3 + 466x^2 - 7368x + 23{,}168$ **15.** $P(x) = x^4 - 38x^3 + 710x^2 - 7126x + 29{,}125$ **17.** two or no pos. real roots; one neg. real root **19.** ≈5.67 cm **21.** $P(x) = x^4 - 8x^3 + 75x^2 - 512x + 704$ **23.** Error in second line, sign of second term; the line should be: $P(-x) = -x^3 + x^2 - x + 1$. Since there are three sign changes in $P(-x)$, there are three or one neg. real roots. **25.** height: 5 ft; bases: 10 ft, 14 ft **32.** $x^2 + 6x + 6$, R 3 **33.** $7x - 3$, R 2 **34.** $8x^2 - 36x + 216$, R −1289 **35.** $\pm 3i$ **36.** $\pm 9i$ **37.** $\pm 12i$ **38.** $-5x^4 + 6x^2 + 9x + 11$; quartic polynomial of four terms **39.** $-4x^5 + 7x^3 + 13x + 2$; quintic polynomial of four terms

Lesson 5-6 pp. 340–345

Got It? 1. 0, 1, −5, 2 **2a.** −1, 2, $\frac{1 \pm i\sqrt{23}}{4}$
b. i. A 5th degree polynomial function has four, two, or zero turning pts. Three turning pts. are visible, so there must be a fourth one. This will turn the graph back across the x-axis. **ii.** The Fundamental Thm. of Algebra states there will be five roots, and the Conjugate Root Thm. requires pairs of irrational or complex roots. Only two zeros appear in the graph, so there are three zeros remaining. Of the remaining roots, either there are three real roots, or one real and two complex roots. Either way, there is at least one real root that does not appear as a real zero in the graph.
Lesson Check 1. four roots **2.** fourteen roots **3.** 5, $\pm 4i$ **4.** 0, 2, $\pm i$ **5.** By the Fundamental Thm. of Algebra, a polynomial equation of degree n has exactly n complex roots. **6.** Answers may vary. Sample: $y = x^4 + 8x^2 + 16$ **7.** Use synthetic division to test for and factor out linear factors until a quadratic factor is obtained. Then use the Quadratic Formula if the quadratic factor cannot be factored further.
Exercises 9. −3, −2, 1 **11.** −3, −1, $\pm 2i$ **13.** −1, $\frac{1 \pm i\sqrt{7}}{4}$ **15.** 2, $\pm\sqrt{3}$ **17.** ±2, $\pm i$ **19.** −6, $\pm i$ **21.** five complex roots; one, three, or five real roots; possible rational roots: ±1, ±2, ±3, ±6, ±9, ±18 **23.** six complex roots; zero, two, four, or six real roots; possible rational roots: $\pm\frac{1}{4}$, $\pm\frac{1}{2}$, $\pm\frac{3}{4}$, ±1, $\pm\frac{3}{2}$, ±2, ±3, ±4, ±6, ±8, ±12, ±24 **25.** −2, $-\frac{1}{2}$, 4 **27.** 3, $-1 \pm i\sqrt{2}$ **29.** 3 bridges **31.** No; a 4th degree polynomial has four complex roots. If $5 - i$

is a root, then by the Conjugate Root Thm. $5 + i$ must also be a root. Likewise, if $4 + i$ is a root, then $4 - i$ must also be a root. This would result in five roots, which is impossible. **33.** always **35.** Maurice is incorrect. Although every function of degree 1 has exactly one zero, $y = 2$ is a function of degree 0 but is still a linear function. So linear functions with degree zero may have no zero or x-intercept. Therefore, $y = 2$ has no zero or x-intercept. **40.** $x^4 + 6x^3 + 14x^2 + 24x + 40 = 0$ **41.** $3 \pm 2\sqrt{2}$ **42.** $\frac{-5 \pm i\sqrt{47}}{4}$ **43.** $\frac{3 \pm i\sqrt{23}}{4}$ **44.** $f(x) = -x^2 + 2x + 3$ **45.** $f(x) = 2x^2 + 24x + 75$ **46.** $x^3 + 3x^2 + 3x + 1$ **47.** $x^3 - 9x^2 + 27x - 27$ **48.** $x^3 + 15x^2 + 75x + 125$

Lesson 5-7 pp. 347–352

Got It? 1. $a^8 + 8a^7b + 28a^6b^2 + 56a^5b^3 + 70a^4b^4 + 56a^3b^5 + 28a^2b^6 + 8ab^7 + b^8$ **2a.** $16x^4 - 96x^3 + 216x^2 - 216x + 81$ **b.** If you express 11 as (10 + 1) and calculate the powers of (10 + 1) using Pascal's Triangle, the result is the indicated pattern.
Lesson Check 1. $x^3 + 3x^2a + 3xa^2 + a^3$ **2.** $x^5 - 10x^4 + 40x^3 - 80x^2 + 80x - 32$ **3.** $4x^2 + 16x + 16$ **4.** $27a^3 - 54a^2 + 36a - 8$ **5a.** yes **b.** yes **c.** no **6.** The coefficients for the expansion of $(a + b)^n$ are equal to the numbers in the nth row of Pascal's Triangle, respectively.
Exercises 7. $a^4 + 8a^3 + 24a^2 + 32a + 16$ **9.** $46{,}656 + 46{,}656a + 19{,}440a^2 + 4320a^3 + 540a^4 + 36a^5 + a^6$ **11.** $y^8 + 8y^7 + 28y^6 + 56y^5 + 70y^4 + 56y^3 + 28y^2 + 8y + 1$ **13.** $128x^7 - 448x^6y + 672x^5y^2 - 560x^4y^3 + 280x^3y^4 - 84x^2y^5 + 14xy^6 - y^7$ **15.** $4096x^6 + 12{,}288x^5 + 15{,}360x^4 + 10{,}240x^3 + 3840x^2 + 768x + 64$ **17.** $16x^2 + 40x + 25$ **19.** $81y^4 - 1188y^3 + 6534y^2 - 15{,}972y + 14{,}641$ **21a.** 6 **b.** 489,888 **23.** $135x^4$ **25.** $625b^8$ **27.** The challenge of the Binomial Thm. occurs when there is a coefficient with the x. However, it is much more efficient to use the Binomial Thm. than FOIL when expanding a binomial that is raised to a high power. **29.** $x^{12} + 24x^{10} + 240x^8 + 1280x^6 + 3840x^4 + 6144x^2 + 4096$ **31.** $a^5 - 5a^4b^2 + 10a^3b^4 - 10a^2b^6 + 5ab^8 - b^{10}$ **33.** $256x^4 - 1792x^3y + 4704x^2y^2 - 5488xy^3 + 2401y^4$ **35.** $4096x^{18} + 12{,}288x^{15}y^2 + 15{,}360x^{12}y^4 + 10{,}240x^9y^6 + 3840x^6y^8 + 768x^3y^{10} + 64y^{12}$ **37.** $125a^3 + 150a^2b + 60ab^2 + 8b^3$ **39.** $-32y^{10} + 80y^8x - 80y^6x^2 + 40y^4x^3 - 10y^2x^4 + x^5$ **41.** Answers may vary. Sample: One of the terms is neg. $(-y)$ and it is alternately raised to odd and even powers; the term is neg. when raised to an odd power and pos. when raised to an even power. **48.** −3, −1, $\frac{-3 \pm i\sqrt{11}}{2}$ **49.** 1, $\pm i$, $\pm 3i$ **50.** −4, $\frac{-3 \pm i\sqrt{7}}{4}$

51. 1, $\frac{-1 \pm 3i\sqrt{3}}{2}$ **52.** $-18 + 43i$ **53.** −2 **54.** $2x^3 + 5x^2 - x + 9$; cubic polynomial of 4 terms **55.** $-7x^2 + 4x + 1$; quadratic trinomial

Lesson 5-8 pp. 353–360

Got It? 1. $y = 1.667x^3 - 4.667x + 5$ **2.** about 22.7 billion lb **3.** Answers may vary. Sample: The cubic model would fit the data better than the linear model because of the $(n + 1)$ Pt. Principle. Both models have down and up end behavior and increasing growth. The cubic shows slowing growth followed by rapidly increasing growth.
4a. $y = 0.269867411x - 3.919692952$

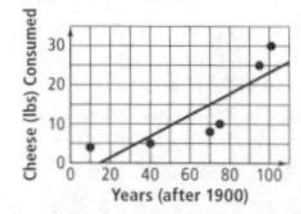

b. 1980: 17.67 lb; 2000: 23.07 lb; 2012: 26.31 lb; most confident for the year 1980, since it is within the domain of the data set; least confident for the year 2012, since it is outside of the domain of the data set
Lesson Check 1. linear **2.** quadratic **3.** cubic **4.** quartic **5.** interpolation since the data pt. is within the domain of the data set **6.** yes; $y = -x^3 - 3x^2 - 3x$ **7.** cubic model; the closer R^2 is to 1, the better the fit.
Exercises 9. $y = -9x + 5$ **11.** $y = x^2 - 6x + 1$ **13.** (where x = yrs after 1900) linear: $y = 49.238x - 2614.286$, cubic: $y = 0.028x^3 - 6.711x^2 + 578.194x - 16{,}226.666$; cubic; linear **15.** (where x = yrs after 1900) linear: $y = 5.8x - 379.667$, quadratic: $y = 0.8x^2 - 146.2x + 6827$; quadratic; linear **17.** 1990: \$1700 billion; 2010: \$3141 billion **19.** 1985: \$180,000; 1999: \$194,000; 2020: \$803,000 **21.** cubic: $y = 0.922x^3 - 1.462x^2 + 7.978x + 4.681$; quartic: $y = -\frac{1}{3}x^4 + \frac{5}{3}x^3 + \frac{1}{3}x^2 + \frac{16}{3}x + 3$; quartic, $(R^2 = 1)$ **23.** $y = 0.000508x^4 - 0.00234x^3 - 0.0349x^2 + 0.293x - 1$ **25.** Sample: 405.7 ppm; not very confident because 2022 is outside the domain of the data **27.** $y = -0.0288800705x^3 - 0.469356261x^2 - 7.401675485x + 3.038800705$; $R^2 = 1$; good fit **29.** Sample: A quadratic model would be more appropriate, given the real-world context. According to the cubic model, there would be a neg. no. of Americans in the year 2024. **36.** $32x^5 + 240x^4 + 720x^3 + 1080x^2 + 810x + 243$ **37.** $1331x^3 - 363x^2 + 33x - 1$ **38.** $4096 - 6144x + 3456x^2 - 864x^3 + 81x^4$ **39.** $|x - 8| < 1$ **40.** $|y - 2.8| < 1.1$ **41.** $|t - 750| < 250$ **42.** $s = \sqrt{A}$ **43.** $\ell = \frac{P}{2} - w$

44. $r = \frac{C}{2\pi}$

45.

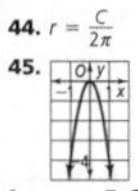

46.

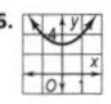

47.

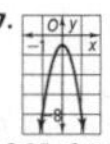

Lesson 5-9 pp. 361–367

Got It? 1. $y = 2(x + 3)^3 - 4$ **2.** $1 - \sqrt[3]{2}$ **3a.** Answers may vary. Sample: $y = x^4 - 6x^3 + x^2 - 6x$ **b.** Yes; $-f(x)$ is the function reflected across the x-axis, so the zeros will stay the same. **4.** 972.2 kW
Lesson Check 1. −2 **2.** 3 **3.** $\frac{1}{3}$ **4.** No; a power function is of the form $y = ax^b$, where y varies directly with the bth power of x. **5.** Both $y = x^3$ and $y = 4x^3$ have the same end behavior of down and up and no turning pts. $y = 4x^3$ is $y = x^3$ stretched vertically by a factor of 4.
Exercises 7. $y = 2(x + 3)^3 + 4$ **9.** $y = -3\left(x + \frac{1}{2}\right)^3 + \frac{3}{4}$ **11.** $\frac{8}{3}$ **13.** $-\frac{2}{15}$ **15.** $1 - \frac{1}{2}\sqrt[3]{20}$ **17.** Answers may vary. Sample: $x^4 - x^3 - x^2 - x - 2$ **19.** Answers may vary. Sample: $x^4 - 2x^3 - 2x^2 - 2x - 3$ **21.** Answers may vary. Sample: $x^4 + x^3 - 5x^2 + x - 6$ **23.** 17,155.9 ft³ **25.** Yes; using parent function $y = x^3$, stretch vertically by a factor of 3. **27.** no **29.** Yes; using parent function $y = x^4$, translate 2 units to the left. **31.** translation 4 units up and 1 unit to the left **33.** vert. stretch by a factor of 5, translation 1 unit up and 1 unit to the rt. **35.** 40 lb·ft²/s² **37.** Error in (2) "a transformation of $y = x^2$." Some polynomials do not contain an x^2 term. **42.** $y = -2x^3 + 3x^2 - x - 2$ **43.** $y = 3x^3 - 5x - 3$ **44.** $y = -\frac{4}{5}x + \frac{16}{5}$ **45.** $y = -3x + 5$ **46.** yes **47.** no **48.** $x^2(x^8 + 1)$ **49.** $(x - y)(x + y)(x^2 + y^2)$ **50.** $9x^3y^6(9x^3y^6 - 1)$

Chapter Review for Part B pp. 369–372

1. D **2.** B **3.** C **4.** A **5.** ±1, ±2, ±3, ±6 **6.** ±1, ±2, $\pm\frac{1}{3}$, $\pm\frac{2}{3}$ **7.** ±1, ±2, ±3, ±4, ±6, ±12, $\pm\frac{1}{4}$, $\pm\frac{1}{2}$, $\pm\frac{3}{4}$, $\pm\frac{3}{2}$ **8.** ±1, ±7, $\pm\frac{1}{3}$, $\pm\frac{7}{3}$ **9.** −3 **10.** −5 **11.** 1, −4, $-\frac{1}{2}$ **12.** 1, −2, $-\frac{2}{3}$ **13.** $1 + i$ **14.** $5 - \sqrt{3}$, $\sqrt{2}$ **15.** $3i$, $-7i$ **16.** $-2 - \sqrt{11}$, $-4 + 6i$ **17.** $y = x^2 - 17x + 70$ **18.** $y = x^3 + 3x^2 + 25x + 75$ **19.** $y = x^2 - 12x + 37$ **20.** $y = x^4 - 4x^3 - 10x^2 + 68x - 80$ **21.** one pos. real zero; two or no neg. real zeros **22.** two or no pos. real zeros; one neg. real zero **23.** four, two, or no pos. real zeros; no neg. real zeros **24.** two or no pos. real zeros; two or no neg. real zeros **25.** 3 **26.** 5 **27.** 6 **28.** 1, $-3 \pm \sqrt{7}$ **29.** 2, $\pm\sqrt{5}$ **30.** −3, 6, $\frac{1 \pm \sqrt{5}}{2}$ **31.** 9 **32.** 1, 8, 28, 56, 70, 56, 28, 8, 1

33. $x^3 + 27x^2 + 243x + 729$ **34.** $b^4 + 8b^3 + 24b^2 + 32b + 16$ **35.** $27a^3 + 27a^2 + 9a + 1$ **36.** $x^3 - 15x^2 + 75x - 125$ **37.** $x^3 - 6x^2y + 12xy^2 - 8y^3$ **38.** $243a^5 + 1620a^4b + 4320a^3b^2 + 5760a^2b^3 + 3840ab^4 + 1024b^5$ **39.** $x^6 + 6x^5 + 15x^4 + 20x^3 + 15x^2 + 6x + 1$ **40.** $64x^6 - 192x^5 + 240x^4 - 160x^3 + 60x^2 - 12x + 1$ **41.** 108 **42.** $6a^2c^2$ **43.** $y = 3.5x^2 - 4.5x + 5$ **44.** $y = 2.082999x - 2.475234$; $y = 0.086232x^2 + 0.008929x + 5.963724$; $y = -0.002554x^3 + 0.178307x^2 - 0.913645x + 8.205128$; cubic is best fit since $R^2 = 1$. **45.** $y = -5.8667x^3 + 120.5333x^2 - 629.2667x + 1421$; 1097.3 ≈ 1097 **46.** $y = -(x - 2)^3 + 1$ **47.** $y = 6(x + 3)^3$ **48.** Answers may vary. Sample: $y = x^4 - 10x^3 + 25x^2 - 10x + 24$ **49.** $y = 0.3x^5 + 3$

Chapter 6

Get Ready! p. 377

1. domain: {1, 2, 3, 4}, range: {2, 3, 4, 5} **2.** domain: {1, 2, 3, 4}, range: {2} **3.** domain: all real numbers, range: $y \geq -8$ **4.** domain: all real numbers, range: $y \geq 3$

5.

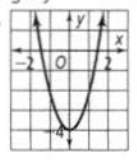

6.

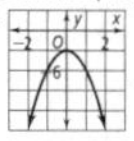

7.

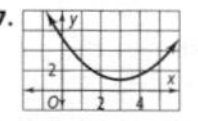

8. $3y^2 - 14y + 8$ **9.** $49a^2 - 100$ **10.** $x^3 + 4x^2 - 15x - 18$ **11.** −2, 7 **12.** $\frac{5}{2}$, 3 **13.** −4, $\frac{2}{3}$ **14.** $\frac{1}{2}$ **15.** $\pm\frac{7}{2}$ **16.** $\pm\sqrt{7}$ **17.** Yes; it is a better deal to first take 50% off the shirt and then use the \$10 coupon. **18.** A "one-to-one function" is a function where there is exact correspondence of every element of the domain with exactly one element of the range. **19.** the nonnegative root

Lesson 6-1 pp. 381–386

Got It? 1a. 0; −1; 2 **b.** ±0.1; no real square root; $\pm\frac{6}{11}$ **c.** Any negative number multiplied by itself an even number of times will always be positive. Therefore, there can be no real nth roots (where n is even) for a negative number b. **2a.** −3 **b.** no real root **c.** 7 **d.** no real root **3a.** $9x^2$ **b.** a^4b^5 **c.** $|x^3|y^4$ **4.** 0; 100
Lesson Check 1. ±5 **2.** ±0.4 **3.** no real square roots **4.** $3|b|$ **5.** $a^4|b^9|$ **6.** $-5a$ **7.** 16 has two real

fourth roots, 2 and −2. **8.** The real roots of a number are the positive and negative (but not imaginary) roots of the number; the principal root of a number is the nonnegative root of the number. **9.** n is odd.
Exercises 11. ±0.07 **13.** −4 **15.** $-\frac{1}{2}$ **17.** 6 **19.** −3 **21.** $3y^2$ **23.** $2y^2$ **25.** ±10 **27.** ±0.5 **29.** about 0.8 in. **31.** 0.5 **33.** 0.2 **35.** Answers may vary. Sample: $\sqrt[3]{-8x^6}$, $-\sqrt[4]{16x^8}$, $\sqrt[5]{-32x^{10}}$ **37.** sometimes; they are equal for $x \geq 0$ **43.** $y = (x + 2)^3 + 3$ **44.** $y = \frac{1}{2}x^3 - 2$ **45.** 1, $\frac{3}{4}$ **46.** $\frac{5 \pm i\sqrt{11}}{6}$ **47.** $\frac{11}{6}$ **48.** $2x^3y^3$ **49.** $\frac{ac}{3}$ **50.** $\frac{4}{x^2}$

Lesson 6-2 Part 1 pp. 387–389

Got It? 1a. Yes; $\sqrt[4]{60}$ **b.** No; the indexes are different. **c.** Yes; $\sqrt[5]{10}$ **2.** $4x^2\sqrt[3]{2x}$ **3.** $10x^3y^3\sqrt{3y}$
Lesson Check 1. $\sqrt{10}$ **2.** $-3\sqrt[3]{4}$ **3.** Cannot be simplified; the indexes are different. **4.** No real solutions; $\sqrt{-4}$ is not a real number. **5.** $x \leq 0$; for $x \leq 0$, $-4x^3 \geq 0$ and $\sqrt{-4x^3}$ is real. **6.** A product of two square roots can be simplified in this way only if the square roots are real numbers. $\sqrt{-2}$ and $\sqrt{-8}$ are not real numbers.
Exercises 7. 16 **9.** −9 **11.** $2x\sqrt{5x}$ **13.** $10|a^3|b^3\sqrt{2b}$ **15.** $2\sqrt[3]{12}$ **17.** $40x|y|\sqrt{3}$ **19.** $-2x^2y\sqrt[3]{30x}$ **21.** $5\sqrt{10}$ **23.** $10 + 7\sqrt{2}$ **25.** sometimes **27.** $20\sqrt{22}$ cm²

Lesson 6-2 Part 2 pp. 390–394

Got It? 4a. $5|x|$ **b.** yes; $\frac{3x^2\sqrt{2x}}{x\sqrt{2x}} = 3x$ **5a.** $\frac{\sqrt[3]{175xy}}{5y}$ **b.** D; there is no y in the expression.
Lesson Check 1. $\sqrt[3]{3x}$ **2.** $x^2\sqrt{3x}$ **3.** Write the root of the quotient as the quotient of roots: $\sqrt[3]{\frac{3y}{20xy^2}} = \frac{\sqrt[3]{3y}}{\sqrt[3]{20xy^2}} = \frac{\sqrt[3]{3y}}{\sqrt[3]{2^2 \cdot 5xy^2}}$. Then rationalize the denominator by multiplying by $\frac{\sqrt[3]{2 \cdot 5^2x^2y}}{\sqrt[3]{2 \cdot 5^2x^2y}}$ to get $\frac{\sqrt[3]{2 \cdot 3 \cdot 5^2x^2y^2}}{\sqrt[3]{(2 \cdot 5xy)^3}} = \frac{\sqrt[3]{150x^2y^2}}{2 \cdot 5xy}$
Exercises 5. $\frac{4x}{y}$ **7.** $5x\sqrt[3]{x^2y^2}$ **9.** $\frac{2\sqrt{a}}{3ab}$ **11.** $\frac{\sqrt{2x}}{2}$ **13.** $\frac{\sqrt[3]{45x^2}}{3x}$ **15.** $5x^2\sqrt{5}$ **17.** $\frac{\sqrt[3]{150ab^2c}}{5a}$ **19.** 6 cm² **21.** about 212 mi/h **23.** $\frac{5\sqrt{14x}}{21x}$ **25.** error in line 1: $\frac{\sqrt[7]{x^5}}{\sqrt[4]{x^2}} \neq \sqrt[7-4]{\frac{x^5}{x^2}}$ **33.** $11|a^{45}|$ **34.** $9c^{24}d^{32}$ **35.** $4a^{27}$ **36.** $y^2 - 4y + 16$, R −128 **37.** $6a^2 - 5a + 4$

38. 25 **39.** 25 **40.** $\frac{121}{4}$ **41.** $\frac{3}{5} + \frac{1}{5}i$ **42.** $\frac{10}{13} - \frac{15}{13}i$ **43.** $\frac{16}{17} - \frac{4}{17}i$ **44.** $\frac{-7}{74} - \frac{5}{74}i$

Lesson 6-3 pp. 395–401

Got It? 1a. The indexes are different. You cannot combine the expressions. **b.** $7x\sqrt{xy}$ **c.** $2\sqrt[5]{3x^2}$ **2a.** about 84.9 in. **b.** The length of the diagonal of a square of side 6 can be found using the Pythagorean Thm. to be $\sqrt{6^2 + 6^2} = \sqrt{72}$. Using this information you can calculate the perimeter of the window and simplify the expression at the end. **3.** $6\sqrt[3]{2}$ **4.** $46 + 16\sqrt{5}$ **5a.** 24 **b.** 1 **6a.** $-\sqrt{21} - \sqrt{35}$ **b.** $\frac{1}{3}(12x + 4x\sqrt{6})$ **c.** after rationalizing; When the numerator is multiplied by the conjugate of the denominator, it is more convenient if $\sqrt{8}$ is not yet simplified.
Lesson Check 1. $12\sqrt{6}$ **2.** cannot combine **3.** $3\sqrt{3x}$ **4.** $7\sqrt{3}$ **5.** 13 **6.** $75 + 34\sqrt{5}$ **7.** $-16 - 3\sqrt{2}$ **8.** −166 **9a.** not like radicals **b.** like radicals; $9\sqrt{3xy}$ **c.** not like radicals **10.** They are alike in that you can also use the Distr. Prop. to multiply binomial radical expressions; they are different in that you cannot multiply radicands together if they do not have the same index.
Exercises 11. $6\sqrt{6}$ **13.** cannot combine **15.** $90\sqrt{2}$ in., or about 127.3 in. **17.** $13\sqrt{5}$ **19.** $2\sqrt[4]{2} + 2\sqrt[4]{3}$ **21.** $23 + 7\sqrt{7}$ **23.** $8 + 2\sqrt{15}$ **25.** $38 + 12\sqrt{10}$ **27.** 4 **29.** −2 **31.** $13 + 7\sqrt{3}$ **33.** 140.3 in.² **35.** $8\sqrt{3}$ **37.** $5\sqrt{3} - 4\sqrt{2}$ **39.** $-2\sqrt[3]{2}$ **41.** $-11 + \sqrt{21}$ **43.** $4x\sqrt{3}$ s **45.** $\frac{\sqrt{2} - 1}{\sqrt{2} + 1} = \frac{6 - \sqrt{32}}{2} = 3 - 2\sqrt{2}$ **47.** $\frac{89 + 42\sqrt{3}}{-239}$ **49.** $\frac{1}{2}(\sqrt{3} - \sqrt{7})$ **51.** $1 + 2\sqrt[3]{4}$ **58.** $3\sqrt[3]{2}$ **59.** $\frac{2\sqrt[3]{x^2}}{x}$ **60.** 4 **61.** $2x$ **62.** $7x^2\sqrt{2}$ **63.** $x\sqrt{15}$ **64.** 2, $-1 \pm i\sqrt{3}$ **65.** −10, $5 \pm 5i\sqrt{3}$ **66.** $\frac{1}{5}$, $\frac{-1 \pm i\sqrt{3}}{10}$ **67.** $\sqrt{7}$ (multiplicity 2), $-\sqrt{7}$ (multiplicity 2) **68.** $\frac{2\sqrt{5}}{5}$ (multiplicity 2), $-\frac{2\sqrt{5}}{5}$ (multiplicity 2) **69.** $\pm\frac{1}{3}$, $\pm\frac{1}{3}i$ **70.** x^6 **71.** p^5q^5 **72.** 2^9, or 512

Lesson 6-4 Part 1 pp. 402–405

Got It? 1a. 8 **b.** 11 **c.** 6 **2a.** $\frac{\sqrt[8]{w^3}}{w}$, $\sqrt[5]{x}$ **b.** $x^{\frac{1}{4}}$, $z^{\frac{4}{5}}$ **c.** If m is negative, a is in the denominator and $\frac{1}{a}$ is undefined when $a = 0$. **3a.** about 0.61 Earth years **b.** about 12.76 Earth years
Lesson Check 1. 5 **2.** 5 **3.** $\frac{1}{128}$ **4.** $(-64)^{\frac{1}{3}} = \sqrt[3]{-64} = -4$ and $-64^{\frac{1}{3}} = -\sqrt[3]{64} = -4$;

$(-64)^{\frac{1}{2}} = \sqrt{-64}$, which is not a real number, but $-64^{\frac{1}{2}} = -\sqrt{64} = -8$, which is a real number.
Exercises **5.** 6 **7.** 7 **9.** $7\sqrt{3}$ **11.** $\frac{1}{\sqrt[8]{y^9}}$ or $\frac{1}{(\sqrt[8]{y})^9}$ **13.** $\sqrt[7]{x^2}$ or $(\sqrt[7]{x})^2$ **15.** $\frac{1}{\sqrt[4]{t^3}}$ or $\frac{1}{(\sqrt[4]{t})^3}$ **17.** $\sqrt[5]{y^6}$ or $(\sqrt[5]{y})^6$ **19.** $(7x)^{\frac{3}{2}}$ **21.** $a^{\frac{2}{3}}$ **23.** $c^{\frac{1}{2}}$ **25.** ≈7.9 m **27.** −7 **29.** 64 **31.** 1,000,000,000 or 10^9
33a. $4^{\frac{1}{2}} \times 4^{\frac{1}{2}} = 4^1 = 4$ **b.** $4^{\frac{1}{2}} \times 4^{\frac{1}{2}} = 2 \times 2 = 4$ **c.** $\sqrt{4} \times \sqrt{4} = \sqrt{16} = 4$

Lesson 6-4 Part 2 pp. 406–411

Got It? 4a. $\sqrt[6]{x^5}$ **b.** $\sqrt[4]{27}$ **5a.** $\frac{1}{8}$ **b.** 8 **c.** $\frac{1}{2187}$ **6a.** $\frac{1}{2x^5}$ **b.** $27x\sqrt[8]{x^4y^3}$
Lesson Check 1. $\sqrt[4]{11^3}$ **2.** $\frac{\sqrt{x}}{x}$ **3.** error in third line, second term; $5(5^{\frac{1}{2}}) = 5^{\frac{3}{2}}$. The third and fourth lines should be:
$20 - 5^{\frac{3}{2}}$
$20 - 5\sqrt{5}$
4. $(1 + \sqrt{2})$ or any nonzero rational number times $(1 + \sqrt{2})$
Exercises 5. $\sqrt[12]{6^7}$ **7.** $\sqrt[10]{5^7}$ **9.** $\frac{\sqrt[6]{16}}{2}$ **11.** $\frac{\sqrt[6]{7776}}{6}$ **13.** 16 **15.** 64 **17.** 8 **19.** $\frac{1}{x^2}$ **21.** $\frac{\sqrt[3]{x}}{3x}$ **23.** $-\frac{3}{x^3}$ **25.** $\frac{y^4}{x^3}$ **27.** $\frac{1}{x}$ **29.** about 251,000,000 in., or 3961 mi **31.** $y^{\frac{4}{5}}$ **33.** $x^{\frac{1}{6}}y^{\frac{1}{4}}$ **35.** $\frac{2x^2}{3y^3}$ **37a.** $\sqrt{x} \cdot \sqrt{x} \cdot \sqrt{x} \cdot \sqrt{x} = x \cdot x = x^2$ so $\sqrt[4]{x^2} = \sqrt{x}$ **b.** $\sqrt[4]{x^2} = (x^2)^{\frac{1}{4}} = x^{\frac{2}{4}} = x^{\frac{1}{2}} = \sqrt{x}$
43. $4\sqrt[3]{3}$ **44.** $21\sqrt{2}$ **45.** $1 + 3\sqrt{5}$ **46.** −7 **47.** $-8\sqrt{3}$ **48.** $9\sqrt[4]{2}$ **49.** $4x(x^2 - 2x + 4)$ **50.** $(x + 2)^2$ **51.** $(x - 9)^2$ **52.** $(4a - 3b)(4a + 3b)$ **53.** $(5x - 4y)^2$ **54.** $(3x + 8)^2$ **55.** −3, 2 **56.** 7, −2 **57.** $-\frac{3}{2}$, 1 **58.** $-\frac{1}{3}$, 2 **59.** $-\frac{5}{2}, \frac{1}{2}$ **60.** $-\frac{2}{3}, \frac{3}{2}$

Chapter Review for Part A pp. 412–414

1. radicand **2.** rational exponent **3.** are not **4.** 5 **5.** 0.7 **6.** −2 **7.** −2 **8.** $9|x|$ **9.** $4x^2$ **10.** $2|x^3|$ **11.** $0.2x$ **12.** $\frac{x^2}{2}$ **13.** $5x^2y^3$ **14.** 3 **15.** −7 **16.** 4 **17.** $4x^2$ **18.** $30y$ **19.** 4 **20.** $3xy$ **21.** $\frac{3|x|}{y^2}$ **22.** $\frac{2\sqrt{3}}{3}$ **23.** $\frac{\sqrt{3x}}{8}$ **24.** $\frac{y\sqrt[3]{150x}}{10x^2}$ **25.** $22\sqrt{3}$ **26.** $26\sqrt{5x}$ **27.** $x\sqrt[3]{2}$ **28.** $14 + 7\sqrt{2}$ **29.** −6 **30.** $100 + 10\sqrt{6} - 10\sqrt{3} - 3\sqrt{2}$ **31.** $\frac{5 + 2\sqrt{5}}{5}$ **32.** $\frac{9 + 3\sqrt{2}}{7}$ **33.** 5 **34.** 3 **35.** 4 **36.** 25 **37.** x **38.** $-2y^3$ **39.** $81x^2y^4$ **40.** $\frac{1}{x^3y^6}$ **41.** $\frac{1}{x}$ **42.** x^3y^6

Lesson 6-5 Part 1 pp. 417–420

Got It? 1. 6 **2a.** 5, −11 **b.** 93 **3.** 37,500,000 m^3
Lesson Check 1. 12 **2.** 27 **3.** Solving square root equations is different from solving absolute value equations in that you use a different technique to isolate the variable. In square root equations, you square each side. In absolute value equations, you write two new equations and solve both. Solving square root equations is similar to solving absolute value equations in that both can introduce extraneous solutions.
Exercises 5. 1 **7.** 15 **9.** 4 **11.** 3, −13 **13.** 18 **15.** 8 **17.** about 25.8 ft **19.** 5 **21.** 8 **23.** 5

Lesson 6-5 Part 2 pp. 421–425

Got It? 4a. 10 **b.** when you raise each side of an equation to a power **5.** 9
Lesson Check 1. $\frac{1}{25}$ **2.** 4 **3.** 1 **4.** 512 **5.** 3; The solution of 3 yields a negative value for the left side of the equation, but the right side of the equation $(\sqrt{3(3)})$ cannot be negative.
Exercises 7. 1 **9.** 1, 4 **11.** 1 **13.** 3 **15.** 1 **17.** 6 **19.** 8 **21.** −1, 2 **23.** $36\sqrt{2} - 36$ **25.** $x = 4$ is a solution, but $x = 1$ is an extraneous solution. **27.** Answers may vary. Sample: $\sqrt{x - 3} = \sqrt{3x + 5}$ **29.** 1 **31.** 9, −7 **33.** 9 **39.** 3 **40.** 16 **41.** 625 **42.** 512 **43.** $\frac{1}{1000}$ **44.** $6\sqrt{2}$ **45.** 3, 4 **46.** 3, 5 **47.** −5, −4 **48.** $-2, -\frac{2}{3}$ **49.** $-\frac{1}{3}, -\frac{4}{3}$ **50.** $-2, -\frac{3}{4}$ **51.** domain: {0, 2, 4}, range: {−5, −3, −1}; yes **52.** domain: {−1, 0, 1}, range: {2, 0, 1}; yes **53.** domain: {−2, 0, 1}, range: {−2, 0, 1}; yes **54.** domain: {3, 4, 5}, range: {−1}; yes **55.** domain: {0, 1, 2}, range: {0, 1, 2}; no **56.** domain: {0}, range: {−2, 0, 2}; no

Lesson 6-6 pp. 426–432

Got It? 1. $(f + g)(x) = 2x^2 + x + 5$, domain: all real numbers $(f - g)(x) = 2x^2 - x + 11$, domain: all real numbers **2.** $(f \cdot g)(x) = 9x^3 - 30x^2 - 23x - 4$, domain: all real numbers; $(\frac{f}{g})(x) = x - 4$, domain: all real numbers except $x = -\frac{1}{3}$ **3.** 4 **4.** Let $D(x)$ = cost after applying the 15% store discount, $E(x)$ = cost after applying the 20% employee discount, and x = cost of items. Then $D(x) = 0.85x$ and $E(x) = 0.80x$. **a.** $(E \circ D)(x) = 0.68x$ **b.** $(D \circ E)(x) = 0.68x$ **c.** The total discounts are the same.
Lesson Check 1. $3x^3 - 2x^2 + 3x - 2$ **2.** $-x^2 + 3x - 3$ **3.** $3x^2 + 1$ **4.** $x^2 + 3x - 1$ **5.** $x^2 - 3x + 3$ **6.** $-x^2 + 3x - 3$ **7.** Answers may vary. Sample: $f(x) = 3x^2 + 1$, $g(x) = 2x + 1$; $(f \circ g) = 12x^2 + 12x + 4$; $(g \circ f) = 6x^2 + 3$ **8.** Answers may vary.

Sample: $f(x) = 2x$, $g(x) = 0.5x$; $f(g(x)) = x$
Exercises 9. $x^2 + 7x + 5$; domain: all real numbers **11.** $7x^3 + 5x^2$; domain: all real numbers **13.** $\frac{x^2}{7x + 5}$; domain: all real numbers except $x = -\frac{5}{7}$ **15.** $\frac{1}{x} + x - 2$; domain: all real numbers except $x = 0$ **17.** $2x - x^2$; domain: all real numbers except $x = 0$ **19.** 20 **21.** 8 **23.** 25 **25.** 9 **27.** 0.25 **29a.** $(g \circ f)(x) = 2.1105x$ **b.** 31.6575 pesos **31.** $x^2 - x + 7$; domain: all real numbers **33.** $-2x^2 + 8x + 1$; domain: all real numbers **35.** $2x^2 + 2x + 24$; domain: all real numbers **37.** $-6x^3 + 3x^2 + 33x - 30$; domain: all real numbers **39.** $\frac{10x + 25}{x^2 - 3x + 2}$; domain: all real numbers except $x = 1$ and 2 **41a.** $g(x)$ is the bonus earned when x is the amount of sales over \$5000. $h(x)$ is the excess sales over \$5000. **b.** $(g \circ h)(x)$; you first need to find the excess sales over \$5000 to calculate the bonus. **43.** −4 **45.** 17 **47.** $-\frac{8}{9}$ **49.** $12x^2 + 2$; $6x^2 + 4$ **55.** 1 **56.** −3 **57.** 4 **58.** 3 **59.** 2 **60.** 3 **61.** $x^6 + 6x^5y + 15x^4y^2 + 20x^3y^3 + 15x^2y^4 + 6xy^5 + y^6$ **62.** $16x^4 - 32x^3y + 24x^2y^2 - 8xy^3 + y^4$ **63.** $59{,}049 - 65{,}610x + 29{,}160x^2 - 6480x^3 + 720x^4 - 32x^5$ **64.** $1024x^5 - 1280x^4y + 640x^3y^2 - 160x^2y^3 + 20xy^4 - y^5$ **65.** $x^8 + 4x^7 + 6x^6 + 4x^5 + x^4$ **66.** $x^{12} + 12x^{10}y^3 + 60x^8y^6 + 160x^6y^9 + 240x^4y^{12} + 192x^2y^{15} + 64y^{18}$
67. no solution

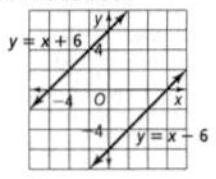

68. (2, 2)

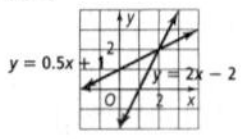

69. (1, 1)

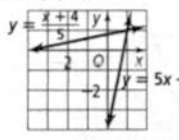

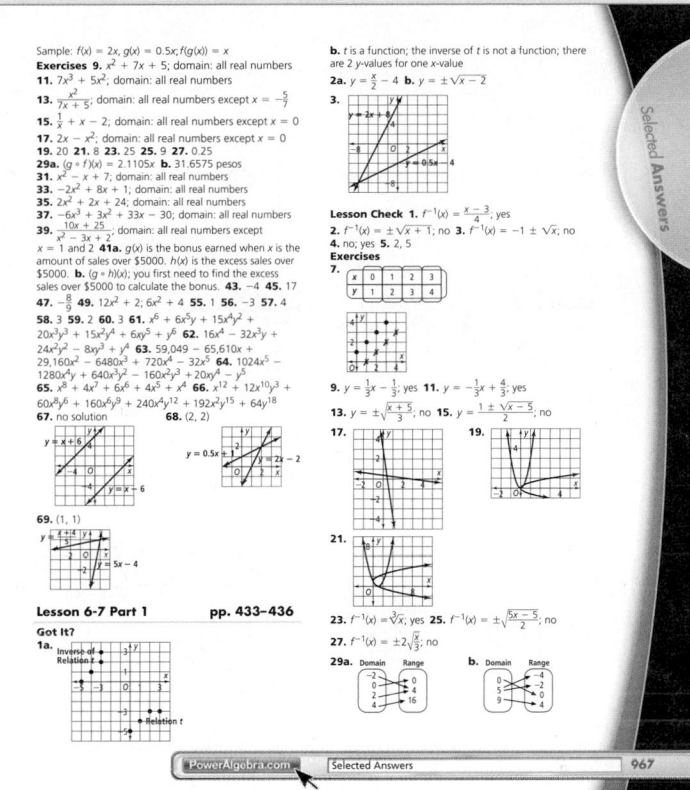

Lesson 6-7 Part 1 pp. 433–436

Got It?
1a.

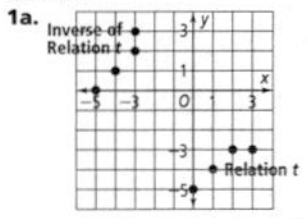

b. t is a function; the inverse of t is not a function; there are 2 y-values for one x-value
2a. $y = \frac{x}{2} - 4$ **b.** $y = \pm\sqrt{x - 2}$
3.

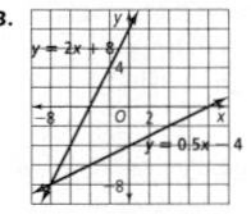

Lesson Check 1. $f^{-1}(x) = \frac{x - 3}{4}$; yes **2.** $f^{-1}(x) = \pm\sqrt{x + 1}$; no **3.** $f^{-1}(x) = -1 \pm \sqrt{x}$; no **4.** no; yes **5.** 2, 5
Exercises
7.

x	0	1	2	3
y	1	2	3	4

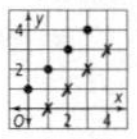

9. $y = \frac{1}{3}x - \frac{1}{3}$; yes **11.** $y = -\frac{1}{3}x + \frac{4}{3}$; yes **13.** $y = \pm\sqrt{\frac{x + 5}{3}}$; no **15.** $y = \frac{1 \pm \sqrt{x - 5}}{2}$; no
17.

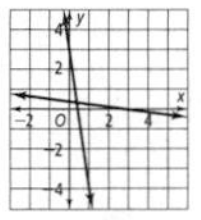

19.

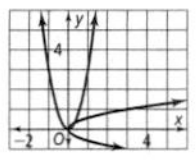

21.

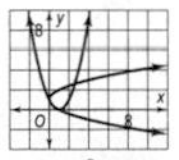

23. $f^{-1}(x) = \sqrt[3]{x}$; yes **25.** $f^{-1}(x) = \pm\sqrt{\frac{5x - 5}{2}}$; no **27.** $f^{-1}(x) = \pm 2\sqrt{\frac{x}{3}}$; no
29a.

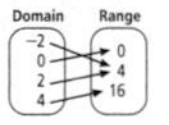

b.

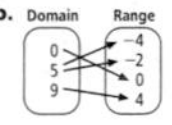

Lesson 6-7 Part 2 pp. 437–442

Got It? 4a. domain: all real numbers; range: all real numbers **b.** $g^{-1}(x) = \frac{1}{4}x + \frac{3}{2}$ **c.** domain: all real numbers; range: all real numbers **d.** Yes; for each x in the domain of g^{-1}, there is only one value of y in the range. **5.** $v = \sqrt{19.6d}$; about 21.7 m/s **6a.** $g^{-1}(x) = \frac{4 - 2x}{x}$ **b.** 0 is not in the domain of g^{-1} so $(g \circ g^{-1})(0)$ does not exist. **c.** 0
Lesson Check 1a. $h^{-1}(x) = -\frac{1}{x} - 2$ **b.** −2.25 **c.** 0 **2.** Answers may vary. Samples: $f(x) = 2x + 1$ and $g(x) = x - 2$; $f(x) = x^2$ and $g(x) = x + 1$
Exercises 3. $f^{-1}(x) = \frac{x - 4}{3}$, domain of f: all real numbers, range of f: all real numbers, domain of f^{-1}: all real numbers, range of f^{-1}: all real numbers; f^{-1} is a function. **5.** $f^{-1}(x) = x^2 + 5$, domain of f: $x \geq 5$, range of f: $y \geq 0$, domain of f^{-1}: $x \geq 0$, range of f^{-1}: $y \geq 5$; f^{-1} is a function **7.** $f^{-1}(x) = \frac{3 - x^2}{2}$, domain of f: $x \leq \frac{3}{2}$, range of f: $y \geq 0$, domain of f^{-1}: $x \geq 0$, range of f^{-1}: $y \leq \frac{3}{2}$; f^{-1} is a function. **9.** $f^{-1}(x) = \pm\sqrt{1 - x}$, domain of f: all real numbers, range of f: $y \leq 1$, domain of f^{-1}: $x \leq 1$, range of f^{-1}: all real numbers; f^{-1} is not a function. **11a.** $r = \sqrt[3]{\frac{3V}{4\pi}}$; yes **b.** about 20.29 ft **13.** −10 **15.** *d* **17.** −1 **19.** $f^{-1}(x) = x^2$, domain of f: $x \geq 0$, range of f: $y \leq 0$, domain of f^{-1}: $x \leq 0$, range of f^{-1}: $y \geq 0$; f^{-1} is a function. **21.** $f^{-1}(x) = 3 - x^2$, domain of f: $x \leq 3$, range of f: $y \geq 0$, domain of f^{-1}: $x \geq 0$, range of f^{-1}: $y \leq 3$; f^{-1} is a function. **23.** $f^{-1}(x) = \pm\sqrt{2x}$, domain of f: all real numbers, range of f: $y \geq 0$, domain of f^{-1}: $x \geq 0$, range of f^{-1}: all real numbers; f^{-1} is not a function. **25.** $f^{-1}(x) = \pm\sqrt{x} + 4$, domain of f: all real numbers, range of f: $y \geq 0$, domain of f^{-1}: $x \geq 0$, range of f^{-1}: all real numbers; f^{-1} is not a function. **27.** $f^{-1}(x) = \pm\frac{1}{\sqrt{x}} - 1$, domain of f: $x \neq -1$, range of f: $y > 0$, domain of f^{-1}: $x > 0$, range of f^{-1}: $y \neq -1$; f^{-1} is not a function. **29.** $f^{-1}(x) = \left(\frac{3}{x}\right)^2$, domain of f: $x > 0$, range of f: $y > 0$, domain of f^{-1}: $x > 0$, range of f^{-1}: $y > 0$; f^{-1} is a function.
31. r is not a function because there are two y-values for one x-value. r^{-1} is a function because each of its x-values has one y-value. **33.** Answers may vary. Sample: $f(x) = \sqrt{-(x + 1)} - 2$
38. $2x + 7$ **39.** $-x - 10$ **40.** $-\frac{3}{2}x + 11$ **41.** $2x^2 + 28x$ **42.** 32 **43.** $2x + 28$ **44.** −2 **45.** no real root **46.** 3 **47.** −3 **48.** −3 **49.** 0.4
50.

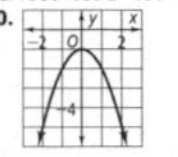

51.

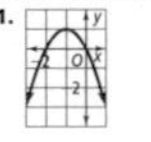

52.

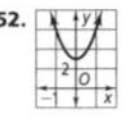

Lesson 6-8 pp. 444–450

Got It?
1.

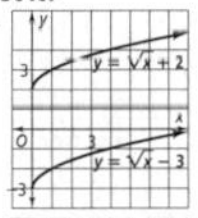

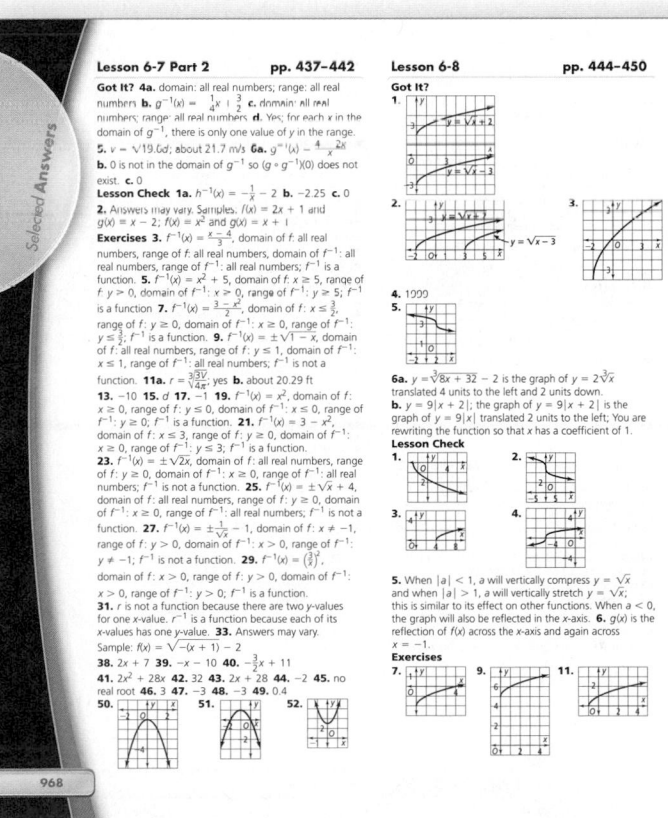

2.

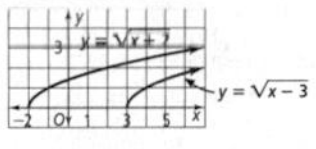

3.

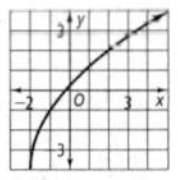

4. 1999
5.

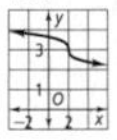

6a. $y = \sqrt[3]{8x + 32} - 2$ is the graph of $y = 2\sqrt[3]{x}$ translated 4 units to the left and 2 units down.
b. $y = 9|x + 2|$; the graph of $y = 9|x + 2|$ is the graph of $y = 9|x|$ translated 2 units to the left; You are rewriting the function so that x has a coefficient of 1.
Lesson Check
1.

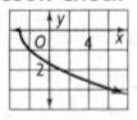

2.

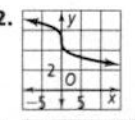

3.

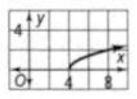

4.

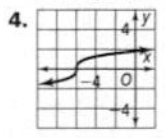

5. When $|a| < 1$, a will vertically compress $y = \sqrt{x}$ and when $|a| > 1$, a will vertically stretch $y = \sqrt{x}$; this is similar to its effect on other functions. When $a < 0$, the graph will also be reflected in the x-axis. **6.** $g(x)$ is the reflection of $f(x)$ across the x-axis and again across $x = -1$.
Exercises
7.

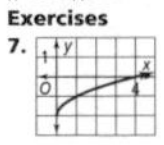

9.

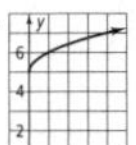

11.

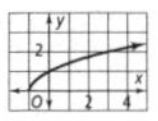

13.

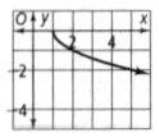

15.

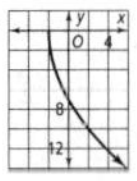

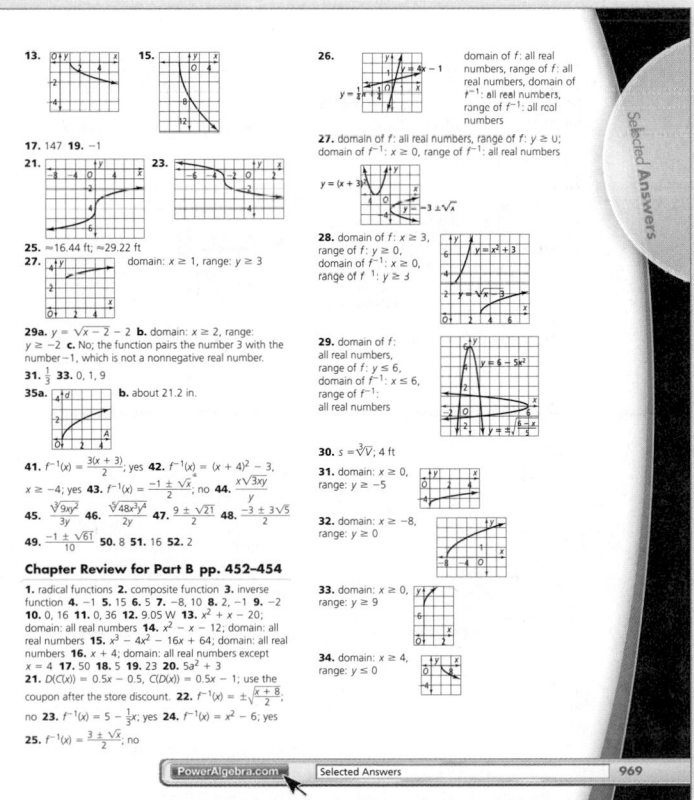

17. 147 **19.** −1
21.

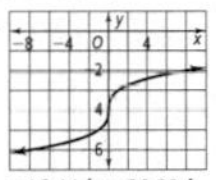

23.

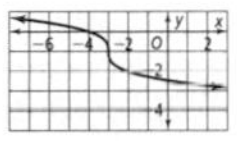

25. ≈16.44 ft; ≈29.22 ft
27.

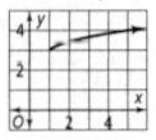

domain: $x \geq 1$, range: $y \geq 3$
29a. $y = \sqrt{x - 2} - 2$ **b.** domain: $x \geq 2$, range: $y \geq -2$ **c.** No; the function pairs the number 3 with the number −1, which is not a nonnegative real number.
31. $\frac{1}{3}$ **33.** 0, 1, 9
35a.

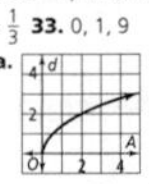

b. about 21.2 in.
41. $f^{-1}(x) = \frac{3(x + 3)}{2}$; yes **42.** $f^{-1}(x) = (x + 4)^2 - 3$, $x \geq -4$; yes **43.** $f^{-1}(x) = \frac{-1 \pm \sqrt{x}}{2}$; no **44.** $\frac{x\sqrt{3xy}}{y}$ **45.** $\frac{\sqrt[3]{9xy^2}}{3y}$ **46.** $\frac{\sqrt[5]{48x^3y^4}}{2y}$ **47.** $\frac{9 \pm \sqrt{21}}{2}$ **48.** $\frac{-3 \pm 3\sqrt{5}}{2}$ **49.** $\frac{-1 \pm \sqrt{61}}{10}$ **50.** 8 **51.** 16 **52.** 2

Chapter Review for Part B pp. 452–454

1. radical functions **2.** composite function **3.** inverse function **4.** −1 **5.** 15 **6.** 5 **7.** −8, 10 **8.** 2, −1 **9.** −2 **10.** 0, 16 **11.** 0, 36 **12.** 9.05 W **13.** $x^2 + x - 20$; domain: all real numbers **14.** $x^2 - x - 12$; domain: all real numbers **15.** $x^3 - 4x^2 - 16x + 64$; domain: all real numbers **16.** $x + 4$; domain: all real numbers except $x = 4$ **17.** 50 **18.** 5 **19.** 23 **20.** $5a^2 + 3$ **21.** $D(C(x)) = 0.5x - 0.5$, $C(D(x)) = 0.5x - 1$; use the coupon after the store discount. **22.** $f^{-1}(x) = \pm\sqrt{\frac{x + 8}{2}}$; no **23.** $f^{-1}(x) = 5 - \frac{1}{3}x$; yes **24.** $f^{-1}(x) = x^2 - 6$; yes **25.** $f^{-1}(x) = \frac{3 \pm \sqrt{x}}{2}$; no
26.

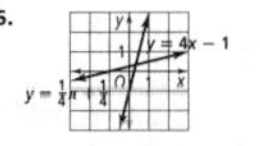

domain of f: all real numbers, range of f: all real numbers, domain of f^{-1}: all real numbers, range of f^{-1}: all real numbers
27. domain of f: all real numbers, range of f: $y \geq 0$; domain of f^{-1}: $x \geq 0$, range of f^{-1}: all real numbers

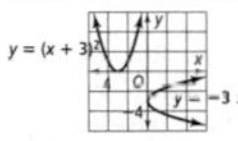

28. domain of f: $x \geq 3$, range of f: $y \geq 0$, domain of f^{-1}: $x \geq 0$, range of f^{-1}: $y \geq 3$

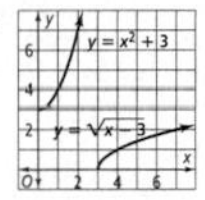

29. domain of f: all real numbers, range of f: $y \leq 6$, domain of f^{-1}: $x \leq 6$, range of f^{-1}: all real numbers

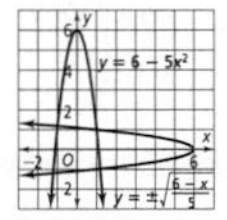

30. $s = \sqrt[3]{V}$; 4 ft
31. domain: $x \geq 0$, range: $y \geq -5$

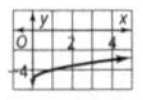

32. domain: $x \geq -8$, range: $y \geq 0$

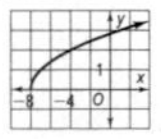

33. domain: $x \geq 0$, range: $y \geq 9$

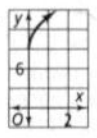

34. domain: $x \geq 4$, range: $y \leq 0$

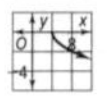

35. domain: all real numbers, range: all real numbers

36. domain: all real numbers, range: all real numbers

37. no solution 38. 6

Chapter 7

Get Ready! p. 459

1. 0.1; 10; 1000 2. $\frac{4}{9}$; 1; $\frac{9}{4}$ 3. $-\frac{1}{625}$; $-\frac{1}{25}$; -1
4. $-\frac{1}{3}$; -1; -3
5. ; $y = 2x + 2$
6. ; $y = 25x + 25$
7. $y = x^2$ 8. $y = x^3$

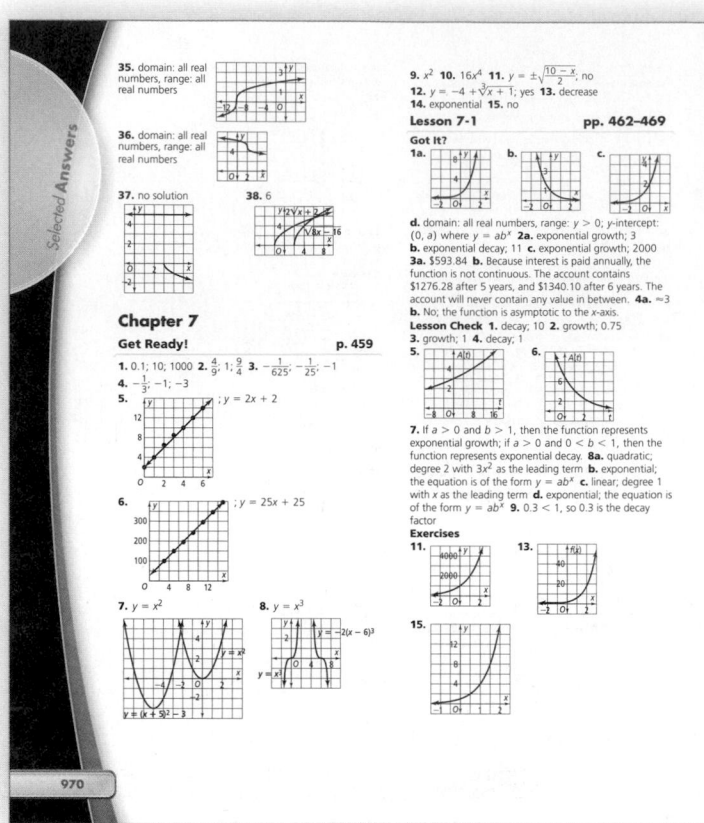

9. x^2 10. $16x^4$ 11. $y = \pm\sqrt{\frac{10-x}{2}}$; no
12. $y = -4 + \sqrt[3]{x + 1}$; yes 13. decrease
14. exponential 15. no

Lesson 7-1 pp. 462-469

Got It?
1a. b. c.
d. domain: all real numbers, range: $y > 0$; y-intercept: $(0, a)$ where $y = ab^x$ 2a. exponential growth; 3
b. exponential decay; 11 c. exponential growth; 2000
3a. $593.84 b. Because interest is paid annually, the function is not continuous. The account contains $1276.28 after 5 years, and $1340.10 after 6 years. The account will never contain any value in between. 4a. ≈3
b. No; the function is asymptotic to the x-axis.
Lesson Check 1. decay; 10 **2.** growth; 0.75
3. growth; 1 **4.** decay; 1
5. 6.
7. If $a > 0$ and $b > 1$, then the function represents exponential growth; if $a > 0$ and $0 < b < 1$, then the function represents exponential decay. **8a.** quadratic; degree 2 with $3x^2$ as the leading term. **b.** exponential; the equation is of the form $y = ab^x$ **c.** linear; degree 1 with x as the leading term. **d.** exponential; the equation is of the form $y = ab^x$ **9.** $0.3 < 1$, so 0.3 is the decay factor
Exercises
11. 13.
15.

17. exponential decay; 2 19. exponential decay; 0.8
21. exponential growth; $\frac{1}{100}$ 23a. $2249.73
b. $4051.63 c. 6 yrs d. 11 yrs
25. $y = 1{,}860{,}000(0.985)^x$; 1,551,485 27. $262.48
29. 0.25 31. 0.999 33. 2
35a. $y = 80(0.965)^x$
b.

about 47 yrs
42. 43.
44.
45. $(2 + 3x)(4 - 6x + 9x^2)$ 46. $(3x - 1)(x + 4)$
47. $(4x - 5)(4x - 5)$ 48. $(1, -1)$ 49. $(0, 0)$
50. $(1.2, 0.6)$
51. 52.
53.

Lesson 7-2 Part 1 pp. 470-475

Got It? 1a. Stretches by a factor of 2
21. As the value of b approaches 1, the graph comes closer to being a straight line.

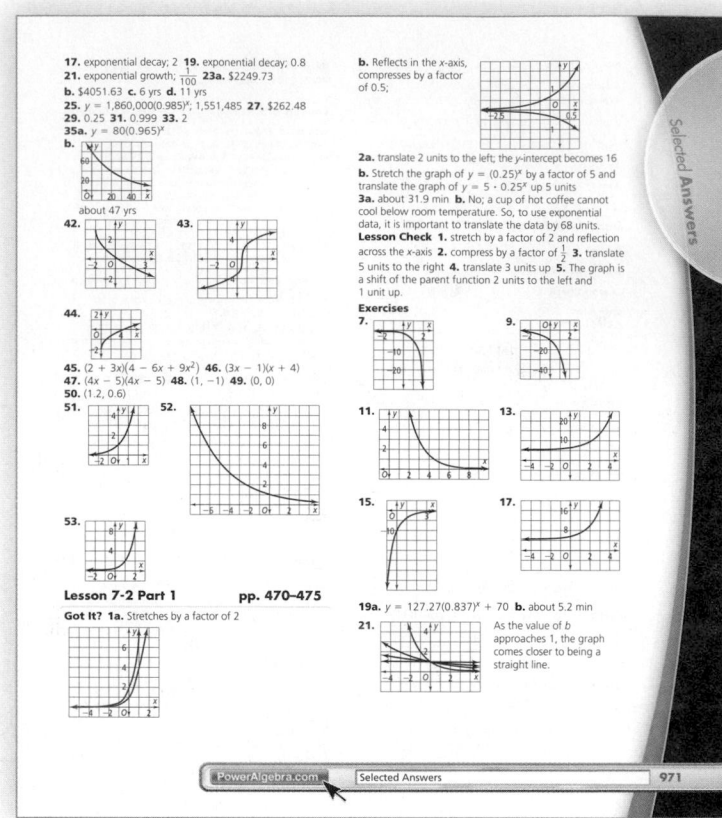

b. Reflects in the x-axis, compresses by a factor of 0.5;
2a. translate 2 units to the left; the y-intercept becomes 16
b. Stretch the graph of $y = (0.25)^x$ by a factor of 5 and translate the graph of $y = 5 \cdot 0.25^x$ up 5 units
3a. about 31.9 min b. No; a cup of hot coffee cannot cool below room temperature. So, to use exponential data, it is important to translate the data by 68 units.
Lesson Check 1. stretch by a factor of 2 and reflection across the x-axis **2.** compress by a factor of $\frac{1}{2}$ **3.** translate 5 units to the right **4.** translate 3 units up **5.** The graph is a shift of the parent function 2 units to the left and 1 unit up.
Exercises
7. 9.
11. 13.
15. 17.
19a. $y = 127.27(0.837)^x + 70$ b. about 5.2 min

23. $y = -3^x$; $y = -3^{x-8} + 2$ 25. $-3\left(\frac{1}{3}\right)^x$;
$y = -3\left(\frac{1}{3}\right)^{x+15} - 1$

Lesson 7-2 Part 2 pp. 476-479

Got It? 4. $e^8 \approx 2980.957987$; two methods: use the e^x key and let $x = 8$; graph $y = e^x$ and trace to $x = 8$. **5.** about $4475
Lesson Check 1. 403.4288 **2.** 0.3679 **3.** 22,026.4658
4. no; $2000e^{0.05t} \neq 1000(e^{0.04t} + e^{0.06t})$
Exercises 5. 0.1353 **7.** 15.1543 **9.** $448.30
11. $6168.41 13. $y = 50\left(\frac{1}{2}\right)^{t/3}$; 0.85 mg
15. ≈61.4 pascals 22. exponential growth; 23
23. exponential growth; 3 24. exponential decay; 2
25. $6\sqrt{5}$ 26. $-\sqrt[3]{4}$ 27. $5(\sqrt{3} + \sqrt{5})$ 28. $2(\sqrt[3]{2} + \sqrt[3]{8})$
29. $\sqrt{3}$ 30. $11\sqrt{7}$ 31. $f^{-1}(x) = \frac{x+1}{4}$; yes
32. $f^{-1}(x) = x^{\frac{1}{3}}$; yes 33. $f^{-1}(x) = \left(\frac{x-1}{5}\right)^{\frac{1}{3}}$; yes

Lesson 7-3 pp. 480-487

Got It? 1a. $\log_6 36 = 2$ **b.** $\log_3 1 = 0$
c. $\log_2 \frac{8}{27} = 3$ **2a.** 3 **b.** $\frac{5}{2}$ **c.** $-\frac{2}{3}$ **3.** ≈16 times
4a. domain: $x > 0$; range: all numbers; no y-intercept; vertical asymptote: $x = 0$
b.

x	$2^x = x$	y
-1	$2^y = -1$	undefined
0	$2^y = 0$	undefined
1	$2^y = 1$	0
2	$2^y = 2$	1

5a. translates the graph of the parent function 3 units to the right and 4 units up; The asymptote changes from $x = 0$ to $x = 3$. The domain changes from $x > 0$ to $x > 3$. The range remains all real numbers. **b.** stretches the graph of the parent function by a factor of 5; The asymptote, domain, and the range remain the same.
Lesson Check 1. $\log_5 25 = 2$ **2.** $\log_4 64 = 3$
3. $\log_3 243 = 5$ **4.** $\log_5 25 = 2$ **5.** 3 **6.** 1 **7.** 2 **8.** -2
9a. no **b.** yes **c.** yes **d.** no **10.** Choose a few points on

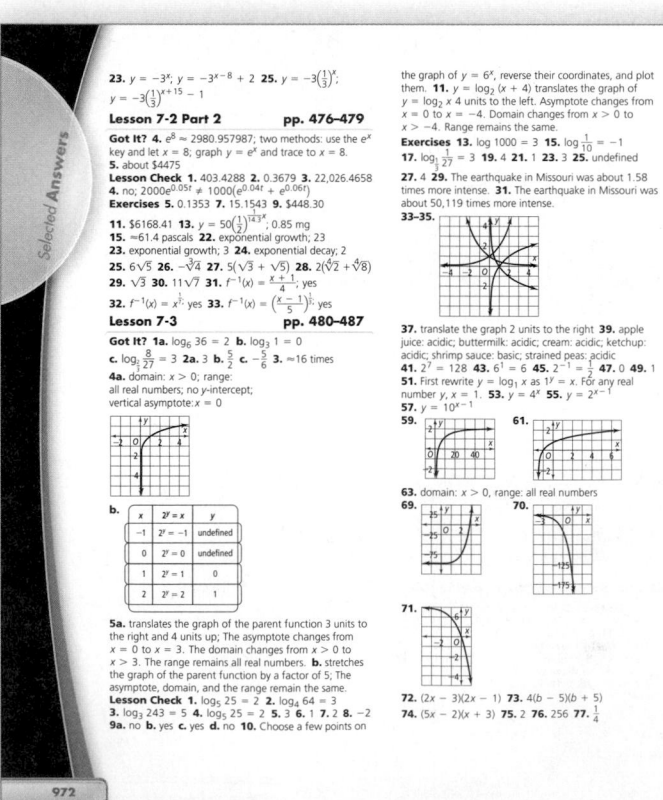

the graph of $y = 6^x$, reverse their coordinates, and plot them. **11.** $y = \log_2 (x + 4)$ translates the graph of $y = \log_2 x$ 4 units to the left. Asymptote changes from $x = 0$ to $x = -4$. Domain changes from $x > 0$ to $x > -4$. Range remains the same.
Exercises 13. $\log 1000 = 3$ **15.** $\log \frac{1}{10} = -1$
17. $\log_3 \frac{1}{27} = 3$ **19.** 4 **21.** 1 **23.** 3 **25.** undefined
27. 4 **29.** The earthquake in Missouri was about 1.58 times more intense. **31.** The earthquake in Missouri was about 50,119 times more intense.
33-35.
37. translate the graph 2 units to the right 39. apple juice: acidic; buttermilk: acidic; cream: acidic; ketchup: acidic; shrimp sauce: basic; strained peas: acidic
41. $2^7 = 128$ 43. $6^1 = 6$ 45. $2^{-1} = \frac{1}{2}$ 47. 0 49. 1
51. First rewrite $y = \log_1 x$ as $1^y = x$. For any real number y, $1^y = 1$. 53. $y = 4^x$ 55. $y = 2^{x-1}$
57. $y = 10^{x-1}$
59. 61.
63. domain: $x > 0$, range: all real numbers
69.
71.
72. $(2x - 3)(2x - 1)$ 73. $4(b - 5)(b + 5)$
74. $(5x - 2)(x + 3)$ 75. 2 76. 256 77. $\frac{1}{4}$

Lesson 7-4 pp. 491-497

Got It? 1a. $\log_4 15x^2$ **b.** 1
2a. $\log_3 2 + 3\log_3 5 - \log_3 37$ **b.** $2 + 5 \log_3 x$
3a. $\frac{5}{2}$ **b.** -2.085 **4.** Substance 8; $\log 2$; $-\log[H^+_B] + \log[H^+_B] = \log 2$
Lesson Check 1. $\log_6 16$ **2.** $\log_6 3$ **3.** $\log_3 x - \log_3 y$
4. $2 \log m + 5 \log n$ **5.** $\frac{1}{2}\log_2 x$ **6a.** Product Prop. and Power Prop. **b.** Quotient Prop. **7.** 0.00001 **8.** Answers may vary. Sample: $\log 150 = \log 25 + \log 6$
Exercises 9. $\log_3 3$ **11.** $\log 972$ **13.** $3 \log x + 5 \log y$
15. $\log_2 7 + 2\log_2 (2x - 3)$ **17.** ≈3.17 **19.** ≈1.75
21. ≈3.63 **23.** 12 **25.** about 3 dB **27.** 1 **29.** 2
31. false; $\frac{1}{3} \log_3 3 = \log_3 3^{\frac{1}{3}}$, not $\log_3 \frac{3}{3}$ 33. false;
$(\log x)^2 = (\log x) \cdot (\log x) \neq \log_4 x^2$ 35. $\log_4 \frac{m^r n^j}{p}$
37. No, the expression $(2x + 1)$ is a sum, so it is not covered by the Product, Quotient, or Power Props. 39. $\frac{1}{2}\log 2 + \frac{1}{3}\log x - \frac{1}{2}\log y$ 41. $3 \log 2 + \frac{2}{3}\log x - 3 \log 5$
43. $3\log 2 + \frac{1}{2}\log - \log s$ 45. $\frac{\log 2}{\log 7}$ 47. $\frac{\log 3x}{\log 4}$
49. Capella is about 1.02 times brighter than Rigel.
54. $\log_7 49 = 2$ 55. $\log_4 \frac{1}{4} = -\frac{5}{2}$ 56. $-3 = \log_5 \frac{1}{125}$
57. ± 8 58. $\frac{64}{5}$ 59. 2 60. $f(x) = x^3 + 5x^2 - 3x - 15$
61. $f(x) = x^4 + 17x^2 + 16$
62. $f(x) = x^4 - 3x^2 - 2x^2 + 14x - 35$
63. 2 64. 3 65. $\frac{1}{3}$

Lesson 7-5 Part 1 pp. 498-502

Got It? 1. $\frac{4}{3}$ **2a.** ≈1.5122 **b.** because the terms cannot be written with a common base **3a.** ≈0.8588
b. ≈1.2114 **4.** ≈13.51 yrs
Lesson Check 1. 2 **2.** 3 **3.** ≈3.6439 **4.** yes; $5^x = 0$ has no solution.
Exercises 5. $\frac{3}{2}$ **7.** -1 **9.** -1 **11.** $\frac{2}{5}$ **13.** 2.1240
15. 3.4650 **17.** 0.2720 **19.** 0.5690 **21.** 4.7027
23. 4.89 **25.** about the yr 2012 **27.** ≈7.6 yrs **29.** 3
31. $-\frac{1}{3}$ **33a.** 13 yrs after July 2007 **b.** 35 yrs after July 2007 **c.** 25 yrs after July 2007 **35.** 0.8505 **37.** 1
39. 3.0389

Lesson 7-5 Part 2 pp. 503-506

Got It? 5. 1.45 **6.** 200
Lesson Check 1. 25 **2.** 2000 **3.** $\frac{\sqrt{10}}{10}$ or about ≈0.3162

4. The log bases are not equal.
$\log_2 x = 2 \log_3 9$
$\log_2 x = \log_3 9^2$
$\log_2 x = 4$
$x = 16$
Exercises 5. 0.05 **7.** 10,000 **9.** $\sqrt{10}$ or ≈3.1623
11. 2 **13.** 20 **15.** 5 **17.** ≈1357.2 **19.** 5.8 **21a.** 1 W/m²; 10^6 W/m² **b.** 10,000 times as intense **23.** 625 **25.** 1.5
27. 500 **29.** $\frac{7}{2}$ **31.** $\frac{1}{3}$ **33.** Answers may vary. Sample: $\log x = 1.6$; $x \approx 39.81$ **40.** $\log 2 = 9 \log x - 2 \log y$
41. $\log_3 x - \log_3 y$ **42.** $1 + \frac{1}{3}\log_3 x$ **43.** $x^2 - 3x - 1$
44. $3x^2 - 3$ **45.** $9x^2 - 1$ **46.** $1, \pm i$ **47.** $\pm 2, \pm 2i$
48. $\pm\sqrt{3}, \pm\sqrt{2}$ **49.** 10 **50.** 15

Chapter Review pp. 509-512

1. exponential decay; exponential growth 2. asymptote
3. exponential function; natural base exponential function
4. continuously compounded interest 5. common logarithm 6. exponential growth; (0, 1) 7. exponential growth; (0, 2) 8. exponential growth; (0, 0.2)
9. exponential decay; (0, 3) 10. exponential growth; $\left(0, \frac{7}{3}\right)$ 11. exponential growth; (0, 0.0015)
12. exponential decay; (0, 2.25) 13. exponential decay; (0, 0.5) 14. $y = 12{,}500(0.91)^x$; $7800
15. $y = 50(1.03)^x$; $58 16. The parent graph $y = 2^x$ is stretched by a factor of 5, translated 1 unit to the left, and 3 units up. 17. The parent graph $y = \left(\frac{1}{3}\right)^x$ is reflected across the x-axis, stretched by a factor of 2, and translated 2 units to the right. 18. $1100.76
19. $291.91 20. ≈0.0498 21. 0.3679 22. 148.4132
23. 0.6065 24. $2 = \log_6 36$ 25. $-3 = \log_3 0.125$
26. $3 = \log_3 27$ 27. $-3 = \log 0.001$ 28. 6 29. -2
30. -5 31. 0
32. 33.
34. 35.

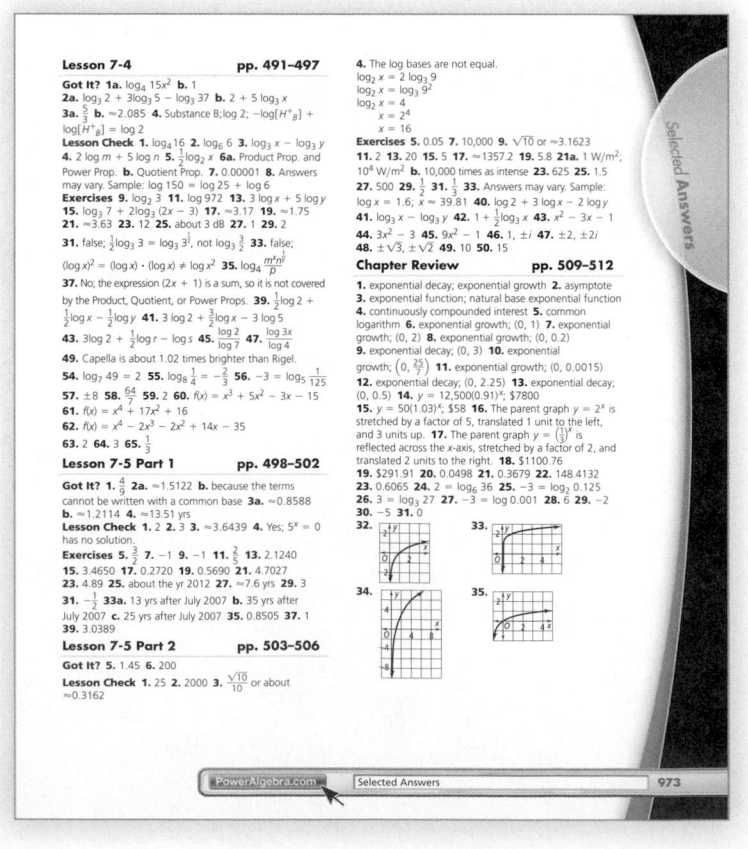

36. The parent graph $y = \log_4 x$ is stretched by a factor of 3 and translated 1 unit to the left. **37.** The parent graph $y = \log_3 x$ is translated 5 units right and 3 units up. **38.** $\log 24$; Product Prop. **39.** $\log_2 \frac{3}{2}$; Quotient Prop. **40.** 0 Power and Product Prop. **41.** $\log \frac{6}{5}$; Quotient Prop. **42.** $\log \frac{5}{3}$; Power and Quotient Prop. **43.** $\log_4 x^5$; Power and Product Prop. **44.** $2\log_4 x + 3\log_4 y$; Product and Power Prop. **45.** $\log 4 + 4\log s + \log t$; Product and Power Prop. **46.** $\log 2 - \log 3 x$; Quotient Prop. **47.** $2\log(x + 3)$; Power Prop. **48.** $3\log_2 2 + 3\log_2 (y - 2)$; Power and Product Prop. **49.** $2\log z - \log 5$; Power and Quotient Prop. **50.** ≈2.8 **51.** ≈2.1 **52.** 0.75 **53.** 3.2619 **54.** 4.6542 **55.** 1.3652 **56.** 3.3333 **57.** 8 **58.** 50 **59.** 15.5885 **60.** 0.9307 **61.** 0.6599 **62.** 0.6658 **63.** 3.0589 **64.** ≈18.2 h

Chapter 8

Get Ready!   p. 517

1. $\frac{4}{3}$, −4 **2.** $-\frac{2}{3}$, 2 **3.** $-\frac{10}{3}$; 10 **4.** $-\frac{16}{7}$; $\frac{48}{7}$ **5.** $(x + 3)(x − 2)$ **6.** $(4x + 5)(x + 3)$ **7.** $(3x − 5)(3x + 5)$ **8.** $(x − 6)^2$ **9.** $(3x + 4)(x + 2)$ **10.** $(x − 3)(x − 2)$ **11.** 1, −8 **12.** −6, −8 **13.** 4, 2 **14.** 0, $-\frac{5}{2}$ **15.** 8, $\frac{1}{2}$ **16.** 15, −2 **17.** Answers may vary. Sample: Inverse is used when one quantity increases as the other quantity decreases.

18. Answers may vary. Sample:

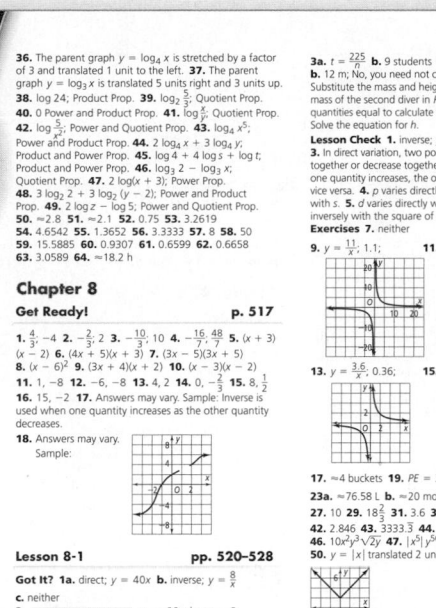

Lesson 8-1   pp. 520–528

Got It? 1a. direct; $y = 40x$ **b.** inverse; $y = \frac{8}{x}$ **c.** neither

2.

$y = −28$ when $x = 2$.

3a. $t = \frac{225}{5}$ **b.** 9 students **4.** 23 bags **5a.** 4018 joules **b.** 12 m; No, you need not calculate P to find the height. Substitute the mass and height of the first diver, and the mass of the second diver in $P = mgh$ and set the two quantities equal to calculate the height of the second diver. Solve the equation for h.

Lesson Check 1. inverse; $y = \frac{6}{x}$ **2.** direct; $y = 5x$ **3.** In direct variation, two positive quantities either increase together or decrease together. In an inverse variation, as one quantity increases, the other quantity decreases and vice versa. **4.** p varies directly with q, r, and t and inversely with s. **5.** d varies directly with the cube root of r and inversely with the square of t.

Exercises 7. neither

9. $y = \frac{11}{x}$; 1.1; **11.** $y = \frac{1}{x}$; $\frac{1}{10}$;

13. $y = \frac{3.6}{x}$; 0.36; **15.** $y = -\frac{5}{3x}$; $-\frac{1}{6}$;

17. ≈4 buckets **19.** $PE = 2gh$ **21.** $F = \frac{km}{d^2}$ **23a.** ≈76.58 L **b.** ≈20 moles **25.** $z = 10xy$; 360 **27.** 10 **29.** $18\frac{2}{3}$ **31.** 3.6 **33.** 2.5 **35.** 2.625 **41.** 4 **42.** 2.846 **43.** $3333.\overline{3}$ **44.** −90x^2 **45.** $84x^2$ **46.** $10x^2y^3\sqrt{2y}$ **47.** $|x^5|y^{50}$ **48.** −4ab^2 **49.** $2m^2|n|\sqrt[5]{4}$ **50.** $y = |x|$ translated 2 units up;

51. $y = |x|$ translated 2 units to the left;

52. $y = |x|$ translated 3 units down;

53. $y = |x|$ translated 3 units to the rt.;

54. $y = |x|$ translated 4 units to the left and 5 units down;

55. $y = |x|$ translated 10 units to the rt. and 7 units up;

Lesson 8-2   pp. 530–537

Got It?
1a. no x- or y-intercept; horizontal asymptote: $y = 0$; vertical asymptote: $x = 0$; domain: all real numbers except $x = 0$, range: all real numbers except $y = 0$

b. Yes; they have similar graphs.
2a. $y = \frac{1}{2x}$ is a shrink of the graph of $y = \frac{1}{x}$ by a factor of $\frac{1}{2}$. **b.** $y = \frac{2}{x}$ is a stretch of the graph of $y = \frac{1}{x}$ by a factor of 2. **c.** $y = -\frac{1}{2x}$ is a reflection across the x-axis and a shrink of the graph of $y = \frac{1}{x}$ by a factor of $\frac{1}{2}$.
3. domain: all real numbers except $x = 2$, range: all real numbers except $y = 4$

4. $y = \frac{2}{x − 1} − 4$ **5a.** $C = \frac{1200}{x}$, **b.** domain: whole numbers from 1 to 312; **c.** 160 students

Lesson Check
1.

2. $y = \frac{1}{x}$ translated 5 units up **3.** $y = \frac{1}{x}$ reflected across the x-axis and stretched by a factor of 4 **4.** horizontal asymptote: $y = −7$, vertical asymptote: $x = −2$ **5.** shrink of the graph of $y = \frac{1}{x}$ by a factor of $\frac{1}{2}$ **6.** Answers may vary. Sample: $y = -\frac{a}{x}$; for $y = \frac{a}{x}$: stretch if $|a| > 1$ and compression if $0 < |a| < 1$

Exercises
9. no x- or y-intercept; horizontal asymptote: $x = 0$; domain: all real numbers except $x = 0$, range: all real numbers except $y = 0$

11. no x- or y-intercept; horizontal asymptote: $y = 0$, vertical asymptote: $x = 0$; domain: all real numbers except $x = 0$, range: all real numbers except $y = 0$

13. reflection across the x-axis and a stretch by a factor of 4

13. compression by a factor of 0.75

17. domain: all real numbers except $x = 0$, range: all real numbers except $y = −3$

19. domain: all real numbers except $x = 3$, range: all real numbers except $y = 4$

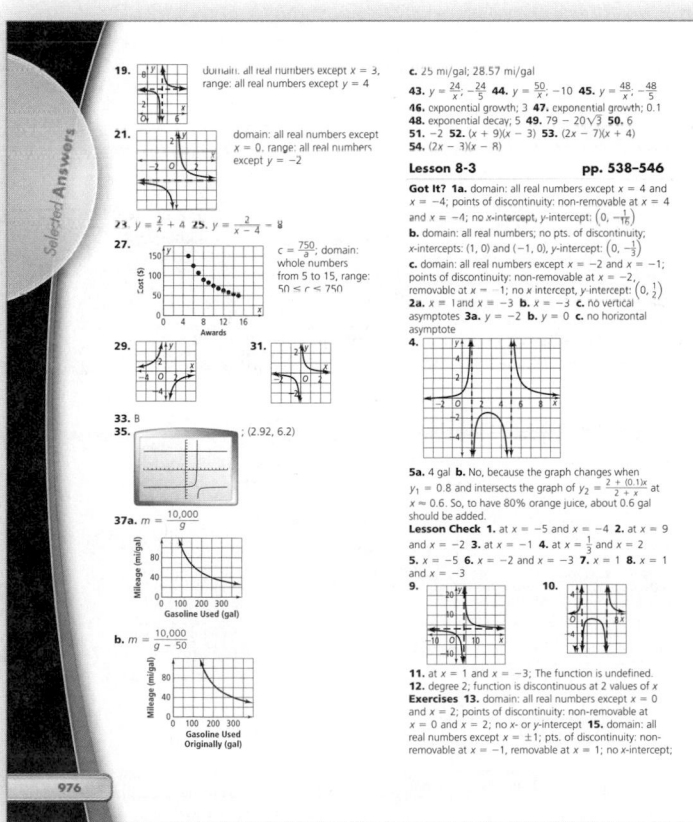

21. domain: all real numbers except $x = 0$, range: all real numbers except $y = −2$

23. $y = \frac{2}{x} + 4$ **25.** $y = \frac{2}{x − 4} − 4$

27. $c = \frac{750}{x}$; domain: whole numbers from 5 to 15, range: $50 \le c \le 750$

29.

31.

33. B

35. ; (2.92, 6.2)

37a. $m = \frac{10,000}{g}$

b. $m = \frac{10,000}{g − 50}$

c. 25 mi/gal; 28.57 mi/gal
43. $y = \frac{24}{x}$, $-\frac{24}{5}$ **44.** $y = \frac{50}{x}$, −10 **45.** $y = \frac{48}{x}$, $-\frac{48}{5}$
46. exponential growth; 3 **47.** exponential growth; 0.1 **48.** exponential decay; 5 **49.** $79 − 20\sqrt{3}$ **50.** 6 **51.** −2 **52.** $(x + 9)(x − 3)$ **53.** $(2x − 7)(x + 4)$ **54.** $(2x − 3)(x − R)$

Lesson 8-3   pp. 538–546

Got It? 1a. domain: all real numbers except $x = 4$ and $x = −4$; points of discontinuity: non-removable at $x = 4$ and at $x = −4$; no x-intercept, y-intercept: $\left(0, -\frac{1}{16}\right)$ **b.** domain: all real numbers; no pts. of discontinuity; x-intercepts: (1, 0) and (−1, 0), y-intercept: $\left(0, -\frac{1}{3}\right)$ **c.** domain: all real numbers except $x = −2$ and $x = −1$; points of discontinuity: non-removable at $x = −2$, removable at $x = −1$; no x intercept, y-intercept: $\left(0, \frac{1}{2}\right)$ **2a.** $x = 1$ and $x = −3$ **b.** $x = −3$ **c.** no vertical asymptotes **3a.** $y = −2$ **b.** $y = 0$ **c.** no horizontal asymptote

4.

5a. 4 gal **b.** No, because the graph changes when $y_1 = 0.8$ and intersects the graph of $y_2 = \frac{2 + (0.1)x}{2 + x}$ at $x = 0.6$. So, to have 80% orange juice, about 0.6 gal should be added.

Lesson Check 1. at $x = −5$ and $x = −4$ **2.** at $x = 9$ and at $x = −2$ **3.** at $x = −1$, at $x = \frac{1}{3}$ and $x = 2$ **5.** $x = −5$ **6.** $x = −2$ and $x = −3$ **7.** $x = 1$ **8.** $x = 1$ and $x = −3$

9. **10.**

11. at $x = 1$ and $x = −3$; The function is undefined. **12.** degree 2; function is discontinuous at 2 values of x

Exercises 13. domain: all real numbers except $x = 0$ and $x = 2$; points of discontinuity: non-removable at $x = 0$ and $x = 2$ **15.** domain: all real numbers except $x = \pm 1$; pts. of discontinuity: non-removable at $x = −1$, removable at $x = 1$; no x-intercept;

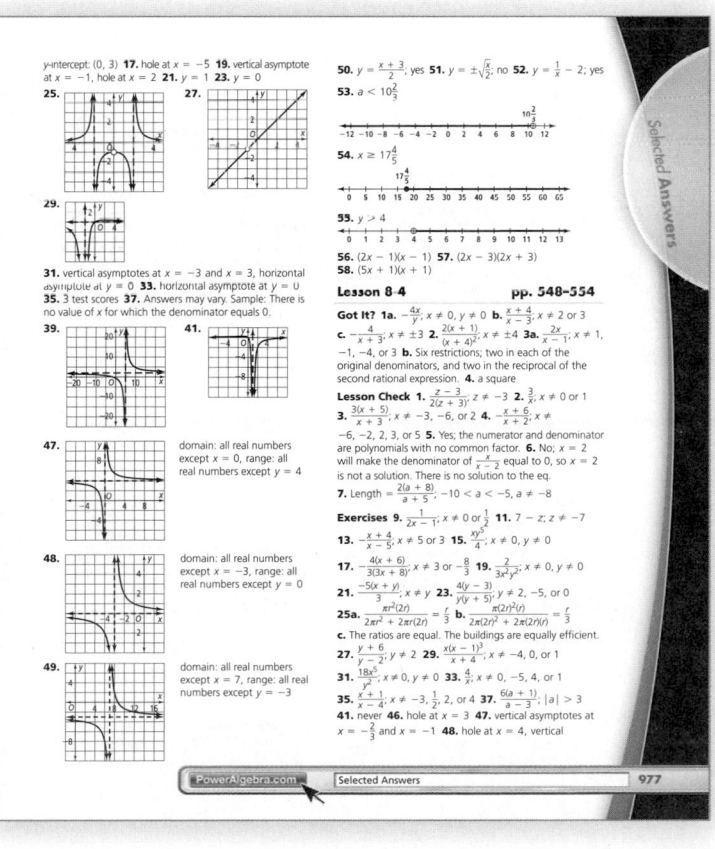

y-intercept: (0, 3) **17.** hole at $x = −5$ **19.** vertical asymptote at $x = −1$, hole at $x = 2$ **21.** $y = 1$ **23.** $y = 0$

25. **27.**

29.

31. vertical asymptotes at $x = −3$ and $x = 3$, horizontal asymptote at $y = 0$ **33.** horizontal asymptote at $y = 0$ **35.** test scores **37.** Answers may vary. Sample: There is no value of x for which the denominator equals 0.

39. **41.**

47. domain: all real numbers except $x = 0$, range: all real numbers except $y = 0$

48. domain: all real numbers except $x = −3$, range: all real numbers except $y = 0$

49. domain: all real numbers except $x = 7$, range: all real numbers except $y = −3$

50. $y = \frac{x + 3}{2}$; yes **51.** $y = \pm\sqrt{\frac{x}{2}}$; no **52.** $y = \frac{1}{x} − 2$; yes **53.** $a < 10\frac{2}{3}$

54. $x \ge 17\frac{4}{5}$

55. $y > 4$

56. $(2x − 1)(x − 1)$ **57.** $(2x − 3)(2x + 3)$ **58.** $(5x + 1)(x + 1)$

Lesson 8-4   pp. 548–554

Got It? 1a. $-\frac{4x}{y}$; $x \ne 0$, $y \ne 0$ **b.** $\frac{x + 4}{x − 3}$; $x \ne 2$ or 3 **c.** $-\frac{4}{x + 3}$; $x \ne \pm 3$ **2.** $\frac{2(x + 1)}{(x + 4)^2}$; $x \ne \pm 4$ **3a.** $-\frac{2x}{x − 1}$; $x \ne 1$, −1, −4, or 3 **b.** Six restrictions; two in each of the original denominators, and two in the reciprocal of the second rational expression. **4.** a square

Lesson Check 1. $\frac{z − 3}{2(z + 3)}$; $z \ne −3$ **2.** $\frac{3}{x}$; $x \ne 0$ or 1 **3.** $\frac{3(x + 5)}{x + 3}$; $x \ne −3$, −6, or 3 **4.** $-\frac{x + 6}{x + 2}$; $x \ne −6$, −2, 2, 3, or 5 **5.** Yes; the numerator and denominator are polynomials with no common factor. **6.** No; $x = 2$ will make the denominator of $\frac{x}{x − 2}$ equal to 0, so $x = 2$ is not a solution. There is no solution to the eq. **7.** Length = $\frac{2(a + 8)}{a + 5}$, −10 < a < −5, $a \ne −8$

Exercises 9. $\frac{1}{2x − 1}$; $x \ne 0$ or $\frac{1}{2}$ **11.** $7 − z$; $z \ne −7$ **13.** $-\frac{x + 4}{x − 5}$; $x \ne 5$ or 3 **15.** $\frac{xy^5}{4}$; $x \ne 0$, $y \ne 0$ **17.** $-\frac{4(x + 6)}{3(3x + 8)}$; $x \ne 3$ or $-\frac{8}{3}$ **19.** $\frac{2}{3x^4y^2}$; $x \ne 0$, $y \ne 0$ **21.** $\frac{-5(x + y)}{3}$; $x \ne y$ **23.** $\frac{4(y − 3)}{y(y + 5)}$; $y \ne 2$, −5, or 0 **25a.** $\frac{\pi r^2(2r)}{2\pi r^2 + 2\pi r(2r)} = \frac{r}{3}$ **b.** $\frac{\pi(2r)^2(r)}{2\pi(2r)^2 + 2\pi(2r)(r)} = \frac{r}{3}$ **c.** The ratios are equal. The buildings are equally efficient. **27.** $\frac{y + 6}{y}$; $y \ne 2$ **29.** $\frac{x(x − 1)^3}{x + 4}$; $x \ne −4$, 0, or 1 **31.** $\frac{18x^5}{y^2}$; $x \ne 0$, $y \ne 0$ **33.** $\frac{4}{x}$; $x \ne 0$, −5, 4, or 1 **35.** $\frac{x + 1}{4}$; $x \ne −3$, $\frac{1}{2}$, 2, or 4 **37.** $\frac{6(a + 1)}{a − 3}$; $|a| > 3$ **41.** never **46.** hole at $x = 3$ **47.** vertical asymptotes at $x = -\frac{5}{2}$ and $x = −1$ **48.** hole at $x = 4$, vertical asymptote at $x = -3$ **49.** 3 **50.** −5 **51.** $\frac{3}{4}$ **52.** 49 **53.** 168 **54.** 2 **55.** $\frac{17}{38}$ **56.** $\frac{11}{72}$ **57.** $\frac{137}{180}$

Lesson 8-5 Part 1 — pp. 555–558

Got It? 1a. $2(x + 2)(x - 3)$ **b.** $(x - 1)(x - 2)^2(x + 4)$ **2a.** $\frac{x+2}{x}$, $x \neq 1$ or 0 **b.** $\frac{2(x-1)}{x^2-4}$; $x \neq \pm 2$ **c.** Yes, however the denominator would have to be factored more and there could be additional, incorrect limitations on x. **3a.** $\frac{x-2}{x-1}$, $x \neq 1$ or 2 **b.** $\frac{x^2-x-4}{x^2+6x+5}$; $x \neq -5$ or −1
Lesson Check 1. $\frac{2a-10}{3a-5}$; $a \neq \frac{5}{3}$ **2.** $\frac{6x-11}{x^2-4}$; $x \neq \pm 2$ **3.** $\frac{-11m}{3m+6}$; $m \neq -2$ **4.** $\frac{-4(2b-5)}{(b-4)(b+4)(b-2)}$; $b \neq 2$ or ± 4 **5.** Answers may vary. Sample: $\frac{x^2-1}{x^2-6x+5}$, $\frac{x^2+6x+5}{x^2-25}$ **6.** Factor the polynomials completely. Then identify the greatest power of each factor that occurs in either expression. The least common multiple is the product of those factors.
Exercises 7. $9(x + 2)(2x - 1)$ **9.** $2(x + 5)(x^2 - 32x - 10)$ **11.** $\frac{2(d-2)}{2d+1}$; $d \neq -\frac{1}{2}$ **13.** $\frac{-3(2y+1)}{2y-1}$; $y \neq \frac{1}{2}$ **15.** $\frac{y-6}{2(y+2)}$; $y \neq -2$ **17.** $\frac{3x-8}{4x^2}$; $x \neq 0$ **19.** $\frac{7x-17}{(x-3)(x+3)}$; $x \neq \pm 3$ **21.** $\frac{x(3x^2+x-1)}{x^2-2}$; $x \neq \pm\sqrt{2}$

Lesson 8-5 Part 2 — pp. 559–564

Got It? 4a. $\frac{x^2y}{x+y}$ **b.** $\frac{(x-1)^2}{2x}$ **c.** Answers may vary. Samples: Method 1; it requires fewer steps. Method 2; it is easier to simplify the numerator and denominator separately. **5.** Option 1 still gives the better combined mpg since Option 3 gives 18.46 mpg.
Lesson Check 1. $\frac{y}{2x}$ **2.** $\frac{b}{9}$
3. error in dividing by the denominator:

$$\frac{1+\frac{1}{x}}{\frac{3}{x}} = \frac{\frac{x+1}{x}}{\frac{3}{x}} = \frac{x+1}{x}\cdot\frac{x}{3} = \frac{x+1}{3}$$

Exercises 5. $\frac{2}{3(x+y)}$ **7.** $\frac{y}{x+y}$ **9.** $\frac{2}{5}$ **11.** $\frac{-3x}{5+xy}$ **13.** $\frac{2(x+5)}{x+7}$ **15.** 3.84 in. **17.** $\frac{-x+6}{(x-3)(x+3)}$; $x \neq \pm 3$ **19.** $\frac{-2x(x+3)}{(x-2)(x-1)(x+1)}$; $x \neq \pm 1$ or 2 **21.** $\frac{3x+2y}{7x-5y}$

23. x **30.** $\frac{12x}{x+3}$; $x \neq 2$ or ± 3 **31.** $\frac{3(x+2)}{4(x-3)}$; $x \neq \pm 2$ or 3 **32.** $\frac{3(x+1)}{2(x+3)}$; $x \neq \pm 1$ or −3 **33.** $\log_3 yt^4$ **34.** $\log p^7q^2$ **35.** $\log_5 \frac{x}{\sqrt[5]{y}}$ **36.** 30 **37.** 82 **38.** $\frac{15}{4}$ **39.** $-\frac{4}{5}$ **40.** 21 **41.** 18

Lesson 8-6 — pp. 565–571

Got It? 1a. 1 **b.** 0 **2a.** ≈ 4.47 mi/h **b.** The direction of wind affects the speed (rate) of the bike. Since the speed is inversely related to time, change in speed will lead to change in time. Since there is no wind, the speed of the bike will remain same to and from the store, hence the time to and from the store will remain the same. **3.** $0.\overline{27}$
Lesson Check 1. 5 **2.** −1 **3.** −2 **4.** 310 mi/h
5. LCD was not found; the correct answer is

$$\frac{35+9x}{7x} = \frac{28(7)}{7x},\ x \neq 0$$
$$9x = 161$$
$$x = \frac{161}{9} = 17.\overline{8}.$$

6. Answers may vary. Sample: $\frac{2}{x-3} + \frac{1}{x+3} = \frac{5x}{x^2-9}$ **7.** Answers may vary. Sample: (1) Substitute the solution into the original equation. (2) Check to see if the solution is in the domain of the graph of the original equation.
Exercises 9. $\frac{2}{9}$ **11.** −1, 2 **13.** 1 **15a.** $\frac{35}{18}$ h **b.** 90 mi/h **17.** 1.5 **19.** ±2 **21.** 1.69, −0.44 **23.** $E = mc^2$ **25.** $c = \pm\sqrt{a^2 - b^2}$ **27.** $B = \pm\sqrt{\frac{2Vm}{r^2q}}$ **29.** $1\frac{5}{7}$ h **31.** 4 test scores **33a.** \$2250 **b.** $\frac{15{,}000}{24+x}(3.60)$ **c.** $2250 - \frac{15{,}000}{24+x}(3.60)$ **d.** ≈32.7 mpg **35.** no solution **37.** 30 **39.** −4 **41.** −1 **48.** $\frac{-y-13}{4(y+1)}$ **49.** $\frac{5xy-12}{2y(y+2)}$ **50.** $\frac{x^2+3}{2(x-1)(x+3)}$ **51.** $x = -3$ **52.** $x = -1$ **53.** $x = -0.875$ **54.** $y = \frac{5-x}{2}$; yes **55.** $y = \pm\sqrt{x-1}$; no **56.** $y = \sqrt[3]{x+4}$; yes **57.** add 2; 9, 11, 13 **58.** subtract 2; −10, −12, −14 **59.** multiply by 5; 625, 3125, 15625 **60.** subtract 5; 30, 25, 20 **61.** multiply by 2; 128, 256, 512 **62.** subtract 4; −19, −23, −27

Chapter Review — pp. 573–576

1. simplest form **2.** combined variation **3.** complex fraction **4.** point of discontinuity **5.** branch **6.** 12 **7.** $y = \frac{72}{x}$ **8.** $y = 6x$ **9.** $z = \frac{7}{4}xy$; 56 **10.** $z = \frac{4x}{y}$; 2
11.
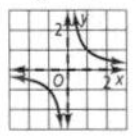
no x- or y-intercept; vert. asymptote: $x = 0$, horizontal asymptote: $y = 0$

12.
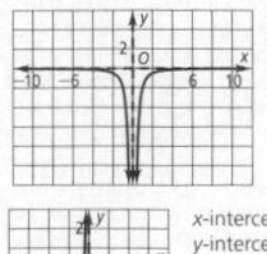
no x- or y-intercept; vert. asymptote: $x = 0$, horizontal asymptote: $y = 0$

13.
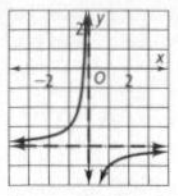
x-intercept: (−0.25, 0), no y-intercept; vert. asymptote: $x = 0$, horizontal asymptote: $y = -4$

14.
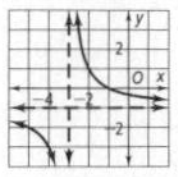
x-intercept: (−1, 0), y-intercept: $(0, -\frac{1}{3})$; vert. asymptote: $x = -3$, horizontal asymptote: $y = -1$

15. $y = \frac{4}{x} + 3$ **16.** $y = \frac{4}{x-2} + 2$ **17.** $y = \frac{4}{x+3} - 4$ **18.** $y = \frac{4}{x-4} - 3$
19. pts. of discontinuity: $x = -2, 1$;
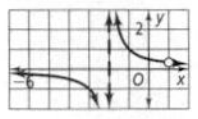
vert. asymptote: $x = -2$, horizontal asymptote: $y = 0$; hole at $x = 1$

20. pts. of discontinuity: $x = 1, -1$
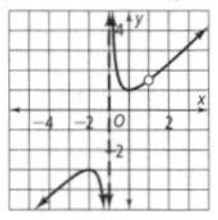
vert. asymptote: $x = -1$; hole at $x = 1$

21. no pts. of discontinuity
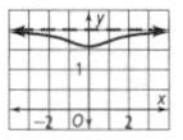
horizontal asymptote: $y = 2$

22.
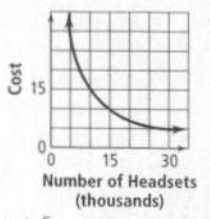
Cost
Number of Headsets (thousands)
≈31,056 headsets

23. $\frac{x+5}{x+4}$; $x \neq -4$ or −5 **24.** $\frac{(x-1)(x+1)}{x+3}$; $x \neq -4, -3$, or 6 **25.** $\frac{(2x-1)(x+1)}{x+4}$; $x \neq -4, -1$, or 0 **26.** $\frac{r}{3}$, where r is the radius **27.** $\frac{3(3x-4)}{(x-2)(x+2)}$; $x \neq \pm 2$ **28.** $\frac{-x^2+3x+2}{x(x+1)(x-1)(x+3)}$; $x \neq \pm 1$, 0, or −3 **29.** $\frac{2(x-1)}{3x-1}$ **30.** $\frac{1}{4(x+y)}$ **31.** −1 **32.** no solution **33.** −12, 9 **34.** you: 10 mi/h friend: 8 mi/h

Chapter 9

Get Ready! — p. 581

1. 9, 11, 13, 15 **2.** 1, 6, 11, 16 **3.** 0.9, 1.1, 1.3, 1.5 **4.** −2, −7, −12, −17 **5.** $3\frac{1}{3}$, $7\frac{1}{3}$, $11\frac{1}{3}$, $15\frac{1}{3}$ **6.** −12, −15, −18, −21 **7.** subtract 5; −11, −16, −21 **8.** mult. by 2; 16, 32, 64 **9.** alternate subtract 9 and add 1; −7, −6, −15 **10.** add 3; 19, 22, 25 **11.** $\frac{4}{3}$ **12.** $\frac{3}{4}$ **13.** $\frac{5}{3}$ **14.** $\frac{5}{18}$ **15.** Answers may vary. Sample: $f(x) = 2x - 1$; 1, 3, 5, 7, 9 **16.** Answers may vary. Sample: $g(x) = 1 - 2x$; −1, −3, −5, −7, −9; yes; common difference: −2 **17.** Answers may vary. Sample: $h(x) = 5(2)^x$; 10, 20, 40, 80, 160; yes; common ratio: 2

Lesson 9-1 — pp. 584–591

Got It? 1. 147 **2a.** $a_1 = 1$ and $a_n = na_{n-1}$ **b.** $a_1 = 1$ and $a_n = a_{n-1} + n^2$ **3a.** $a_n = n^2 - 1$; 399 **b.** To find the nth term using an explicit formula, you simply substitute for n in the formula. To find the nth term using a recursive definition may require many iterations. **4.** 18 months
Lesson Check 1. 2, 7, 12, 17, 22 **2.** −1, 0, 3, 8, 15 **3.** $a_1 = 3$ and $a_n = 2a_{n-1}$ **4.** $a_n = 2 + 3n$ **5.** A recursive formula defines the terms in a sequence by relating each term after the first term to the one before it and requires that the previous term be known to find a given term. An example of a recursive formula for the sequence 8, 4, 2, 1, . . . is $a_1 = 8$ and $a_n = \frac{1}{2}a_{n-1}$. An explicit formula describes the nth term of a sequence using the variable n and only requires the number of the term to be known. An example of an explicit formula for

the sequence 1, 3, 5, 7, . . . is $a_n = 2n - 1$. **6.** The "+1" in $a_n = 3n + 1$ is incorrect for the sequence 1, 4, 7, 10, . . . The correct explicit formula is $a_n = -2 + 3n$.
Exercises 7. −4, −9, −14, −19, −24, −29 **9.** 2, 5, 10, 17, 26, 37 **11.** 1, 3, 7, 15, 31, 63 **13.** −3, 9, −27, 81, −243, 729 **15.** $a_1 = 4$ and $a_n = 2a_{n-1}$ **17.** $a_1 = 1$ and $a_n = a_{n-1} + 3$ **19.** $a_1 = \frac{1}{2}$ and $a_n = \frac{1}{2}a_{n-1}$ **21.** $a_n = n + 3$; 13 **23.** $a_n = \frac{n-6}{2}$; 2 **25.** $a_n = \frac{1}{n+1}$; $\frac{1}{11}$ **27.** 5 **29.** $\frac{5}{16}$ **31.** $\frac{1}{256}$ **33.** 13.8 mi **35.** explicit; −24, −21, −16, −9, 0 **37.** explicit; −6, −18, −38, −66, −102 **39.** 15; 26; 40 **41.** 96, 192; $a_n = 3 \cdot 2^{n-1}$, explicit OR $a_n = 2a_{n-1}$, $a_1 = 3$, recursive **43.** 4096, 16,384; $a_n = 4^n$, explicit OR $a_n = 4a_{n-1}$, $a_1 = 4$, recursive **45.** −1, 1; $a_n = (-1)^n$, explicit OR $a_n = -1(a_{n-1})$, $a_1 = -1$, recursive **47.** −47, −40; $a_n = -82 + 7n$, explicit OR $a_n = a_{n-1} + 7$, $a_1 = -75$, recursive **49a.** 25 boxes **b.** 110 boxes **c.** 9 levels **51.** $\frac{16}{5}, \frac{25}{6}, \frac{36}{7}, \frac{49}{8}$ **53.** Answers may vary. Sample: **a.** 1, −2, 4, −8, . . . **b.** $a_n = -2(a_{n-1})$, and $a_1 = 1$; $a_n = (-2)^{n-1}$ **c.** −524,288 **59.** 2 **60.** 4 **61.** −5 **62.** −1 **63.** 1 **64.** 2 **65.** subtract 2; −2, −4, −6 **66.** add 17; 185, 202, 219 **67.** add $\frac{3}{7}$; $\frac{17}{7}, \frac{20}{7}, \frac{23}{7}$

Lesson 9-2 — pp. 592–598

Got It? 1a. no **b.** yes **2a.** 93 **b.** 95, 110 **3a.** 115 **b.** yes, use the formula for arithmetic mean and solve for a_7, $a_7 = 2a_6 - a_5$ **4.** 65 seats
Lesson Check 1. 56 **2.** 87 **3.** 13 **4.** 39 **5.** In an arithmetic sequence, the diff. between any two consecutive terms is always the same number. **6.** Answers may vary. Sample: 2, 4, 8, 16, 32, . . .
Exercises 7. yes; 10 **9.** yes; 3 **11.** yes; 4 **13.** 127 **15.** −59 **17.** −146 **19.** 12.5 **21.** 21 **23.** −8 **25.** 7.5 **27.** \$135 **29.** 18 **31.** 36 **33.** 2 **35.** 4 **37.** −20 **39.** 1.1 **41.** The student multiplied the third term by 2 instead of adding 2. The correct answer is 6. **43.** $a_n = -5 + 1(n - 1)$; $a_n = a_{n-1} + 1$, $a_1 = -5$ **45.** $a_n = -5 + 1.5(n - 1)$; $a_n = a_{n-1} + 1.5$, $a_1 = -5$ **47.** $a_n = 27 - 12(n - 1)$; $a_n = a_{n-1} - 12$, $a_1 = 27$ **49.** Answers may vary. Sample: An advantage of a recursive formula is that only the preceding term must be known to find the next term; a disadvantage is that many calculations may be required to find a term. An advantage of an explicit formula is that it is easy to find any term. Use the recursive formula when the previous term and common diff. are known. Use the explicit formula when the term number and common diff. are known. **51.** −4, −10, −16 **53.** −8, −17, −26 **55.** 17, 17, 17 **57.** \$5055 **59a.** Answers may vary. Sample: 25, 18, 11, 4, −3, −10, . . . ; to find the 6th term, multiply 5 times (−7) and add to a_1; to find the 8th term, multiply 7 times (−7) and add to a_1; to find the 20th term, multiply 19 times (−7) and add to a_1. **b.** Answers may vary. Sample: Start with the first term and continue to subtract 7 for each term. For each term, you subtract 7 · (term number − 1) from the first term. **63.** recursive; −2, −7, −12, −17, −22 **64.** explicit; 6, 18, 36, 60, 90 **65.** explicit; 0, 3, 8, 15, 24 **66.** $y - 3 = \frac{8}{3}x$ or $y - 11 = \frac{8}{3}(x - 3)$ **67.** $y - 6 = 4(x - 4)$ or $y - 30 = 4(x - 10)$ **68.** $y - 10 = 8(x - 1)$ or $y - 42 = 8(x - 5)$ **69.** $r = \frac{\sqrt[3]{6\pi^2 V}}{2\pi}$ **70.** 32 **71.** 625 **72.** −81

Lesson 9-3 — pp. 600–606

Got It? 1a. yes; $a_1 = 2$, $r = 2$ **b.** no **c.** yes; $a_1 = 2^3$, $r = 2^4$ **2a.** 156,250 **b.** 60; 30 **3a.** explicit; it is easier to use because only one calculation is needed. **b.** about 16.8 cm, about 4 cm **4.** ±60
Lesson Check 1. no **2.** yes; 2 **3.** 729 **4.** 0.0064 **5.** The third term would be the geometric mean of 5 and 80 which is 20. Since a is pos. and r^2 is always pos., the third term, ar^2, cannot be neg. **6.** For both the arithmetic mean and the geometric mean, the middle term of any three consecutive terms can be determined using the first and last of the three terms. The arithmetic mean is the sum of the first and last terms divided by 2, whereas the geometric mean is the square root (or its opposite) of the product of the first and the last terms.
Exercises 7. yes; 2 **9.** yes; −2 **11.** yes; 0.1 **13.** 6561 **15.** $\frac{-3}{2048}$ **17.** about 656.1 g; about 182.5 g; about 96.2 g **19.** $\pm\frac{4}{15}$ **21.** ±3.75 **23.** $a_n = 100(-20)^{n-1}$; 100, −2000, 40,000, −800,000, 16,000,000 **25.** $a_n = 1024(0.5)^{n-1}$; 1024, 512, 256, 128, 64 **27.** $a_n = 10(-1)^{n-1}$; 10, −10, 10, −10, 10 **29.** arithmetic; 125, 150 **31.** geometric; −80, 160 **33.** neither; 25, 36 **35.** 7.5, 22.5, 67.5 or −7.5, 22.5, −67.5 **37.** −6.64, −11.02, −18.30 or 6.64, −11.02, 18.30 **39.** about 74.3 mi **41.** 3×4^{16}, or 12,884,901,888 **43.** $3(4^{n-1})$ **45.** 2.5 **47.** Both the common diff. and the common ratio are used to find the next term in a sequence, but a common diff. is added and a common ratio is multiplied. **52.** $a_n = -3 + 3(n - 1)$; $a_n = a_{n-1} + 3$, $a_1 = -3$ **53.** $a_n = 17 - 9(n - 1)$; $a_n = a_{n-1} - 9$, $a_1 = 17$ **54.** $a_n = -2 - 11(n - 1)$; $a_n = a_{n-1} - 11$, $a_1 = -2$ **55.** $a^4 + 20a^3 + 150a^2 + 500a + 625$ **56.** $x^3 - 27x^2 + 243x - 729$ **57.** $32x^5 + 80x^4y + 80x^3y^2 + 40x^2y^3 + 10xy^4 + y^5$ **58.** $b^{12} - 18b^{10} + 135b^8 - 540b^6 + 1215b^4 - 1458b^2 + 729$ **59.** vert. asymptote: $x = -3$ **60.** vert. asymptote: $x = -1$ **61.** vert. asymptotes: $x = 0, 1$ **62.** vert. asymptote: $x = 3$; hole at $x = -3$ **63.** $a_n = a_{n-1} + n$, $a_1 = 1$ **64.** $a_n = a_{n-1} + (2n - 1)$, $a_1 = 1$ **65.** $a_n = a_{n-1} + n^2$, $a_1 = 1$

Lesson 9-4 — pp. 607–613

Got It? 1a. 2500 **b.** 1863 **c.** Yes; no; the sum of any number of even numbers is always even. The sum of an odd number of odd numbers is odd, but the sum of an even number of odd numbers is even. **2.** 59 sales; 1725 sales **3a.** $\sum_{n=1}^{40}(7n - 12)$ **b.** $\sum_{n=1}^{50}(510 - 10n)$
Lesson Check 1. 91 **2.** 780 **3.** $\sum_{n=1}^{7}3n$ **4.** $\sum_{n=1}^{12}(4n - 3)$ **5.** An arithmetic sequence is a list of numbers for which successive numbers have a common difference. An arithmetic series is an expression for the sum of the terms of an arithmetic sequence. **6.** The lower limit should not be 3, it should be zero. The correct summation notation is $\sum_{n=0}^{8}(3 + 5n)$. **7.** Yes; $44 = 2(a_1 + a_4)$, so any combination of a_1 and a_4 with a sum of 22 is a possible series.
Exercises 9. 56 **11.** 840 **13.** −165 **15a.** 95 **b.** 510 **17.** $\sum_{n=1}^{8}(2n + 5)$ **19.** $\sum_{n=1}^{10}(110 - 10n)$ **21.** sequence; infinite **23.** series; infinite **25.** 32 **27.** 264 **29.** 4292 **31a.** $\sum_{n=1}^{20}(3n + 15)$, or 18 + 21 + 24 + · · · + 75 **b.** 930 seats **c.** \$46,950 **33.** 110 **41.** $a_n = 2^{n-1}$; 1, 2, 4 **42.** $a_n = -1(-1)^{n-1}$; −1, 1, −1 **43.** $a_n = 3\left(\frac{3}{2}\right)^{n-1}$; 3, $\frac{9}{2}$, $\frac{27}{4}$ **44.** $\frac{x+3}{x-4}$; $x \neq 4$, $x \neq -1$ **45.** $\frac{c-2}{c-5}$; $c \neq 5$, $c \neq 6$ **46.** $\frac{z^2+12z+20}{z-1}$; $z \neq 1$, $z \neq 0$ **47.** $-\frac{1}{3}$ **48.** $\frac{3}{4}$ **49.** $-\frac{1}{2}$

Lesson 9-5 — pp. 614–621

Got It? 1a. 315 **b.** −1705 **2.** about \$2138.43 **3a.** diverges **b.** converges; $\frac{1}{4}$ **c.** Yes; if $|r| < 1$, the series converges. If $|r| \geq 1$, the series diverges.
Lesson Check 1. $\frac{31}{80}$ **2.** $\frac{55}{9}$ **3.** converges **4.** diverges **5.** Since $r = 1.1 > 1$, the series diverges and does not have a sum. **6.** An infinite geometric series has a sum only when $|r| < 1$. **7.** The sum of a finite arithmetic series is $S_n = \frac{n}{2}(a_1 + a_n)$. The sum of finite geometric series is $S_n = \frac{a_1(1 - r^n)}{1 - r}$. The formulas are similar in that each sum requires the first term and the number of terms in the series. The formulas are different in that the sum of a finite arithmetic series needs the last term, while the sum of a finite geometric series needs the common ratio.
Exercises 9. 1456 **11.** −5115 **13.** no; \$133.76 **15.** converges; $\frac{2}{3}$ **17.** diverges **19.** converges; −81 **21.** $1.\overline{2}$ **23.** $\frac{9}{5}$ **25.** geometric; 2046 **27.** geometric; −1,627,605 **29.** arithmetic; 500,500

31a.
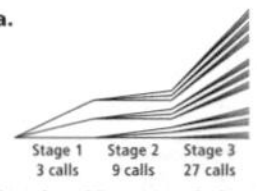
Stage 1
3 calls
Stage 2
9 calls
Stage 3
27 calls

b. 3 + 9 + 27 + 81 + 243 + 729 **c.** 1092 **35.** choice (b); (a) yields \$26,000; using the formula for finding the sum of a finite geometric series, (b) yields \$1,342,177.26. **42.** 140 **43.** −825 **44.** $\frac{7c-4}{2c^2}$ **45.** $\frac{10(2y+3)}{(y+3)(y-3)}$ **46.** $\frac{x^2+6x+4}{(x+6)(x-6)}$ **47.** 0 **48.** 2 **49.** 1

Chapter Review — pp. 623–626

1. limits **2.** sequence **3.** converges **4.** common ratio **5.** explicit formula **6.** 1, −1, −3, −5, −7 **7.** 1, 0, −3, −8, −15 **8.** 2, 3, 5, 9, 17 **9.** 20, 10, 5, 2.5, 1.25 **10.** $a_n = a_{n-1} + 17$, $a_1 = 5$ **11.** $a_n = a_{n-1} + 9$, $a_1 = -2$ **12.** $a_n = 3n - 2$ **13.** $a_n = 6.5 - 2.5n$ **14.** no **15.** yes; $d = 15$, $a_{32} = 468$ **16.** yes; $d = 3$, $a_{32} = 100$ **17.** no **18.** 5 **19.** 101.5 **20.** 5 **21.** −4.9 **22.** −10.5, −8, −5.5 **23.** 1.4, 0.8, 0.2 **24.** $a_n = -2 + 9(n - 1)$ **25.** $a_n = 62 - 3(n - 1)$ **26.** yes; $r = \frac{1}{2}$; $\frac{1}{16}, \frac{1}{32}$ **27.** no **28.** yes; $r = 1.2$; 6.2208, 7.46496 **29.** ±6 **30.** ±0.04 **31.** ±10, −5, ±2.5 **32.** $a_n = 2^{n-1}$ **33.** $a_n = 25\left(\frac{1}{5}\right)^{n-1}$ **34.** 2560 **35.** 1536 **36.** $\sum_{n=1}^{5}(13 - 3n)$; 20 **37.** $\sum_{n=1}^{7}(45 + 5n)$; 455 **38.** $\sum_{n=1}^{11}(4.6 + 1.4n)$; 143 **39.** $\sum_{n=1}^{8}(23 - 2n)$; 112 **40.** 31 **41.** $53\frac{1}{8}$ **42.** $14\frac{7}{18}$ **43.** converges; $S = 187.5$ **44.** diverges **45.** diverges **46.** converges; $S = 2$

Chapter 10

Get Ready! — p. 631

1.
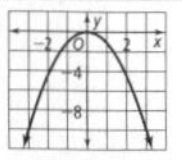
2.
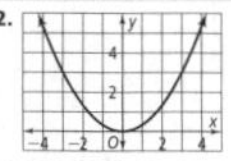
3.
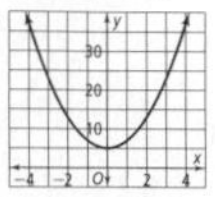
4.
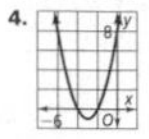

5. quadratic; $-x^2$, $6x$, 1 **6.** linear; none, $-12x$, -18
7. linear; none, x, $-\frac{13}{2}$ **8.** quadratic; $-8x^2$, $28x$, none
9. quadratic; $-2x^2$, $-3x$, 6 **10.** linear; none, $-x$, -10
11. 16 **12.** $\frac{25}{4}$ **13.** 49
14. $y = (x + 3)^2 - 2$

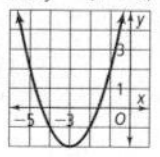

15. $y = 2(x - 1)^2 + 8$

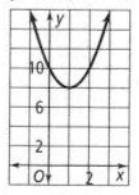

16. $y = -3\left(x - \frac{1}{6}\right)^2 + \frac{1}{12}$

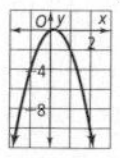

17.

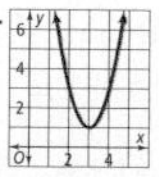

18.

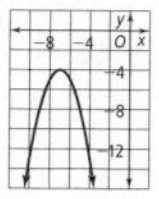

19.

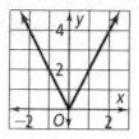

20.

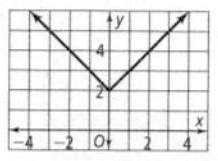

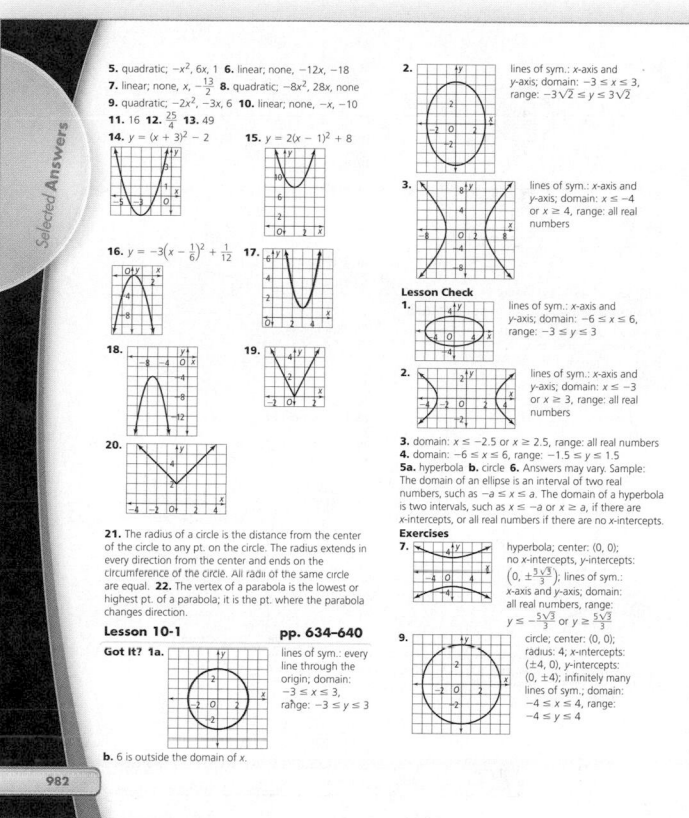

21. The radius of a circle is the distance from the center of the circle to any pt. on the circle. The radius extends in every direction from the center and ends on the circumference of the circle. All radii of the same circle are equal. **22.** The vertex of a parabola is the lowest or highest pt. of a parabola; it is the pt. where the parabola changes direction.

Lesson 10-1 pp. 634–640

Got It? 1a.

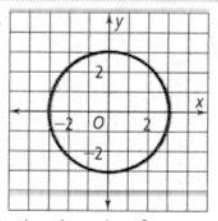

lines of sym.: every line through the origin; domain: $-3 \le x \le 3$, range: $-3 \le y \le 3$

b. 6 is outside the domain of x.

2.

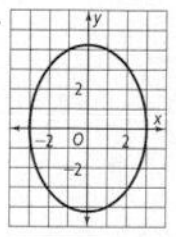

lines of sym.: x-axis and y-axis; domain: $-3 \le x \le 3$, range: $-3\sqrt{2} \le y \le 3\sqrt{2}$

3.

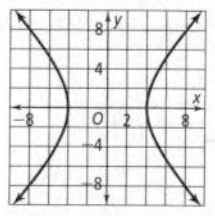

lines of sym.: x-axis and y-axis; domain: $x \le -4$ or $x \ge 4$, range: all real numbers

Lesson Check

1.

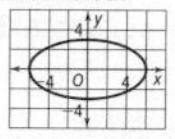

lines of sym.: x-axis and y-axis; domain: $-6 \le x \le 6$, range: $-3 \le y \le 3$

2.

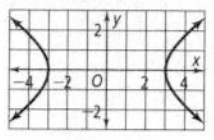

lines of sym.: x-axis and y-axis; domain: $x \le -3$ or $x \ge 3$, range: all real numbers

3. domain: $x \le -2.5$ or $x \ge 2.5$, range: all real numbers
4. domain: $-6 \le x \le 6$, range: $-1.5 \le y \le 1.5$
5a. hyperbola **b.** circle **6.** Answers may vary. Sample: The domain of an ellipse is an interval of two real numbers, such as $-a \le x \le a$. The domain of a hyperbola is two intervals, such as $x \le -a$ or $x \ge a$, if there are x-intercepts, or all real numbers if there are no x-intercepts.

Exercises

7.

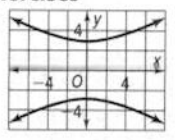

hyperbola; center: (0, 0); no x-intercepts, y-intercepts: $\left(0, \pm\frac{5\sqrt{3}}{3}\right)$; lines of sym.: x-axis and y-axis; domain: all real numbers, range: $y \le -\frac{5\sqrt{3}}{3}$ or $y \ge \frac{5\sqrt{3}}{3}$

9.

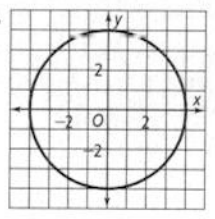

circle; center: (0, 0); radius: 4; x-intercepts: $(\pm 4, 0)$, y-intercepts: $(0, \pm 4)$; infinitely many lines of sym.; domain: $-4 \le x \le 4$, range: $-4 \le y \le 4$

11.

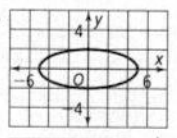

ellipse; center: (0, 0); x-intercepts: $(\pm 5, 0)$, y-intercepts: $(0, \pm 2)$; lines of sym.: x-axis and y-axis; domain: $-5 \le x \le 5$, range: $-2 \le y \le 2$

13.

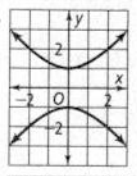

hyperbola; center: (0, 0); no x-intercepts, y-intercepts: $(0, \pm 1)$; lines of sym.: x-axis and y-axis; domain: all real numbers, range: $y \le -1$ or $y \ge 1$

15.

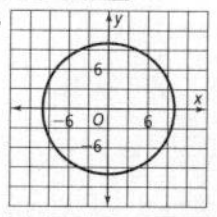

circle; center: (0, 0); radius: 10; x-intercepts: $(\pm 10, 0)$, y-intercepts: $(0, \pm 10)$; infinitely many lines of sym.; domain: $-10 \le x \le 10$, range: $-10 \le y \le 10$

17.

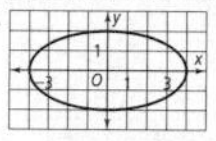

ellipse; center: (0, 0); x-intercepts: $(\pm 4, 0)$, y-intercepts: $(0, \pm 2)$; lines of sym.: x-axis and y-axis; domain: $-4 \le x \le 4$, range: $-2 \le y \le 2$

19.

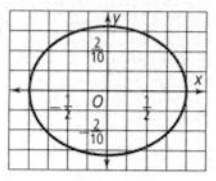

ellipse; center: (0, 0); x-intercepts: $(\pm 1, 0)$, y-intercepts: $\left(0, \pm\frac{1}{3}\right)$; lines of sym.: x-axis and y-axis; domain: $-1 \le x \le 1$, range: $-\frac{1}{3} \le y \le \frac{1}{3}$

21.

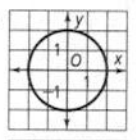

circle; center: (0, 0); radius: 2; x-intercepts: $(\pm 2, 0)$, y-intercepts: $(0, \pm 2)$; infinitely many lines of sym.; domain: $-2 \le x \le 2$, range: $-2 \le y \le 2$

23.

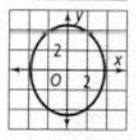

ellipse; center: (0, 0); x-intercepts: $\left(\pm\frac{8\sqrt{5}}{5}, 0\right)$, y-intercepts: $(0, \pm 2\sqrt{5})$; lines of sym.: x-axis and y-axis; domain: $-\frac{8\sqrt{5}}{5} \le x \le \frac{8\sqrt{5}}{5}$, range: $-2\sqrt{5} \le y \le 2\sqrt{5}$

25a. All lines in the plane that pass through the center of a circle are axes of sym. of the circle. **b.** The axes of sym. of an ellipse intersect at the center of the ellipse. The same is true for a hyperbola. This can be confirmed using, for example, $4x^2 + 9y^2 = 36$ and $4x^2 - 9y^2 = 36$.

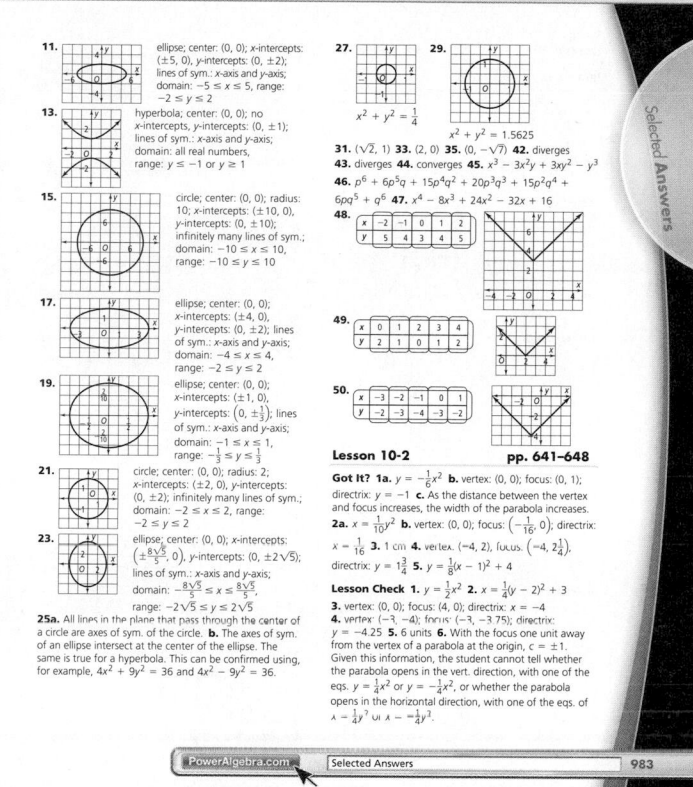

27. **29.**

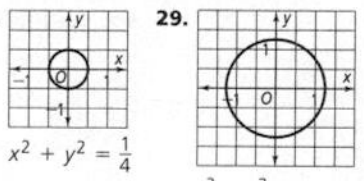

$x^2 + y^2 = \frac{1}{4}$ $x^2 + y^2 = 1.5625$

31. $(\sqrt{2}, 1)$ **33.** (2, 0) **35.** $(0, -\sqrt{7})$ **42.** diverges **43.** diverges **44.** converges **45.** $x^3 - 3x^2y + 3xy^2 - y^3$ **46.** $p^6 + 6p^5q + 15p^4q^2 + 20p^3q^3 + 15p^2q^4 + 6pq^5 + q^6$ **47.** $x^4 - 8x^3 + 24x^2 - 32x + 16$

48.

x	−2	−1	0	1	2
y	5	4	3	4	5

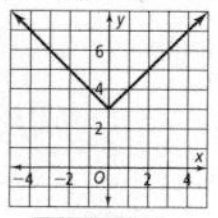

49.

x	0	1	2	3	4
y	2	1	0	1	2

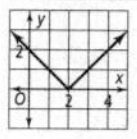

50.

x	−3	−2	−1	0	1
y	−2	−3	−4	−3	−2

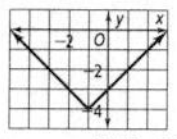

Lesson 10-2 pp. 641–648

Got It? 1a. $y = -\frac{1}{6}x^2$ **b.** vertex: (0, 0); focus: (0, 1); directrix: $y = -1$ **c.** As the distance between the vertex and focus increases, the width of the parabola increases. **2a.** $x = \frac{1}{10}y^2$ **b.** vertex: (0, 0); focus: $\left(-\frac{1}{16}, 0\right)$; directrix: $x = \frac{1}{16}$ **3.** 1 cm **4.** vertex: (−4, 2), focus: $\left(-4, 2\frac{1}{4}\right)$, directrix: $y = 1\frac{3}{4}$ **5.** $y = \frac{1}{8}(x - 1)^2 + 4$

Lesson Check 1. $y = \frac{1}{2}x^2$ **2.** $x = \frac{1}{4}(y - 2)^2 + 3$
3. vertex: (0, 0); focus: (4, 0); directrix: $x = -4$
4. vertex: (−3, −4); focus: (−3, −3.75); directrix: $y = -4.25$ **5.** 6 units **6.** With the focus one unit away from the vertex of a parabola at the origin, $c = \pm 1$. Given this information, the student cannot tell whether the parabola opens in the vert. direction, with one of the eqs. $y = \frac{1}{4}x^2$ or $y = -\frac{1}{4}x^2$, or whether the parabola opens in the horizontal direction, with one of the eqs. of $x = \frac{1}{4}y^2$ or $x = -\frac{1}{4}y^2$.

Exercises 7. $x = \frac{1}{24}y^2$ **9.** $x = -\frac{1}{4}y^2$

11. vertex: (0, 0); focus: $\left(0, \frac{1}{16}\right)$; directrix: $y = -\frac{1}{16}$

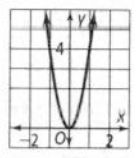

13. vertex: (0, 0); focus: $\left(\frac{1}{2}, 0\right)$; directrix: $x = -\frac{1}{2}$

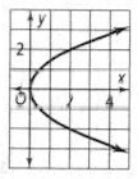

15. $y = -\frac{1}{20}x^2$ **17.** Answers may vary. Sample: $y = x^2$. The light produced by the bulb will reflect off the parabolic mirror in parallel rays.

19. vertex: (3, 2); focus: $\left(3, \frac{9}{4}\right)$; directrix: $y = \frac{7}{4}$

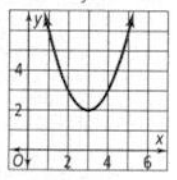

21. vertex: (−1, −4); focus: $\left(-1, -3\frac{7}{8}\right)$; directrix: $y = -4\frac{1}{8}$

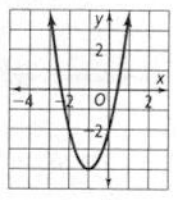

23. $x = -\frac{1}{32}(y - 3)^2$ **25.** $y = -\frac{1}{16}(x - 7)^2 + 2$
27. 3.5 in.

29. vertex: (0, 0); focus: (0, −1); directrix: $y = 1$

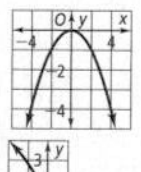

31. vertex: (0, 0); focus: (−2, 0); directrix: $x = 2$

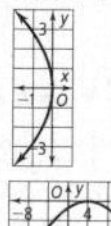

33. vertex: (4, 0); focus: (4, −6); directrix: $y = 6$

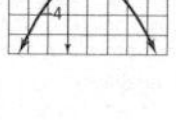

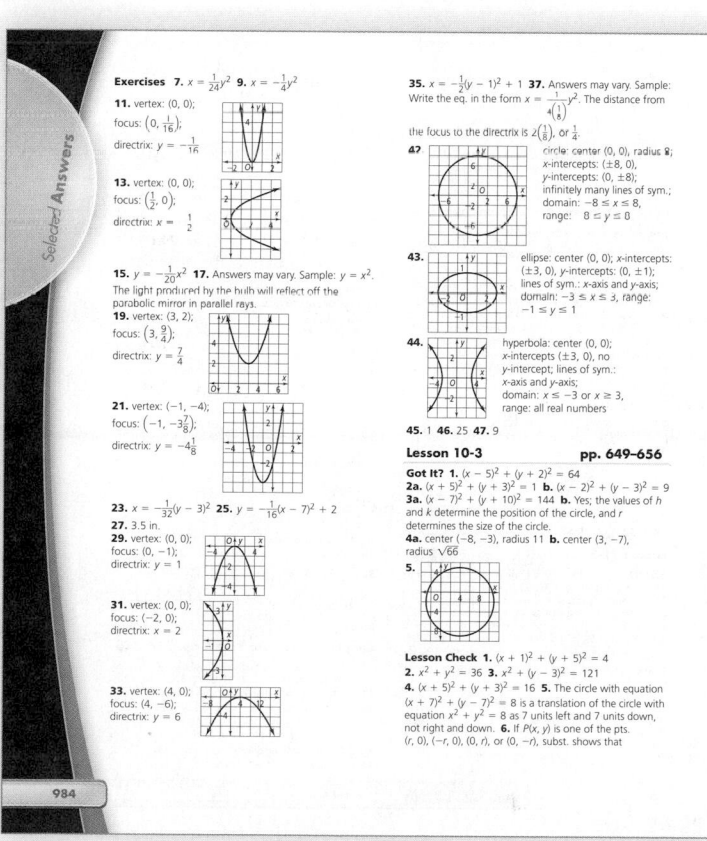

35. $x = -\frac{1}{2}(y - 1)^2 + 1$ **37.** Answers may vary. Sample: Write the eq. in the form $x = \frac{1}{4\left(\frac{1}{8}\right)}y^2$. The distance from the focus to the directrix is $2\left(\frac{1}{8}\right)$, or $\frac{1}{4}$.

42.

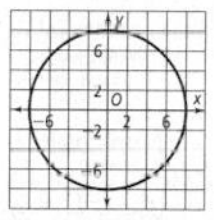

circle: center (0, 0), radius 8; x-intercepts: $(\pm 8, 0)$, y-intercepts: $(0, \pm 8)$; infinitely many lines of sym.; domain: $-8 \le x \le 8$, range: $8 \le y \le 8$

43.

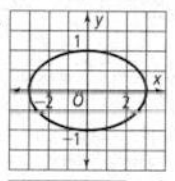

ellipse: center (0, 0); x-intercepts: $(\pm 3, 0)$, y-intercepts: $(0, \pm 1)$; lines of sym.: x-axis and y-axis; domain: $-3 \le x \le 3$, range: $-1 \le y \le 1$

44.

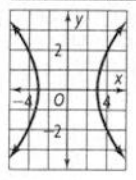

hyperbola: center (0, 0); x-intercepts $(\pm 3, 0)$, no y-intercept; lines of sym.: x-axis and y-axis; domain: $x \le -3$ or $x \ge 3$, range: all real numbers

45. 1 **46.** 25 **47.** 9

Lesson 10-3 pp. 649–656

Got It? 1. $(x - 5)^2 + (y + 2)^2 = 64$
2a. $(x + 5)^2 + (y + 3)^2 = 1$ **b.** $(x - 2)^2 + (y - 3)^2 = 9$
3a. $(x - 7)^2 + (y + 10)^2 = 144$ **b.** Yes; the values of h and k determine the position of the circle, and r determines the size of the circle.
4a. center (−8, −3), radius 11 **b.** center (3, −7), radius $\sqrt{66}$

5.

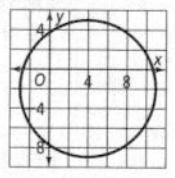

Lesson Check 1. $(x + 1)^2 + (y + 5)^2 = 4$
2. $x^2 + y^2 = 36$ **3.** $x^2 + (y - 3)^2 = 121$
4. $(x + 5)^2 + (y + 3)^2 = 16$ **5.** The circle with equation $(x + 7)^2 + (y - 7)^2 = 8$ is a translation of the circle with equation $x^2 + y^2 = 8$ as 7 units left and 7 units down, not right and down. **6.** If $P(x, y)$ is one of the pts. $(r, 0)$, $(-r, 0)$, $(0, r)$, or $(0, -r)$, subst. shows that

$x^2 + y^2 = r^2$. If $P(x, y)$ is any other pt. on the circle, drop a perpendicular $\overline{PK}$ from P to K on the x-axis. $\triangle OPK$ is a rt. triangle with legs of lengths $|x|$ and $|y|$ and with hypotenuse of length r. By the Pythagorean Thm., $|x|^2 + |y|^2 = r^2$, so $x^2 + y^2 = r^2$.

Exercises 7. $x^2 + y^2 = 100$ **9.** $(x - 2)^2 + (y - 3)^2 = 20.25$ **11.** $(x - 1)^2 + (y + 3)^2 = 100$ **13.** $(x + 1)^2 + (y - 3)^2 = 81$ **15.** $(x - 2)^2 + (y + 4)^2 = 25$ **17.** $(x - 3)^2 + (y - 2)^2 = 49$ **19.** $(x - 2)^2 + (y + 6)^2 = 16$ **21.** center (1, 1), radius 1 **23.** center (0, −3), radius 5

25. **27.**

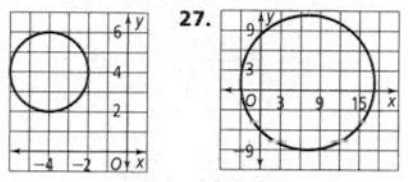

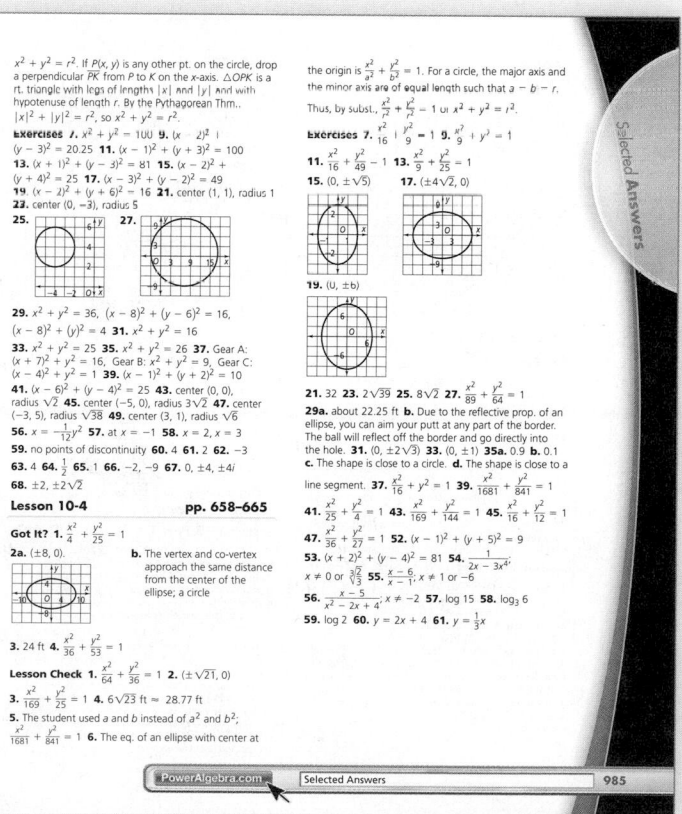

29. $x^2 + y^2 = 36$, $(x - 8)^2 + (y - 6)^2 = 16$, $(x - 8)^2 + (y)^2 = 4$ **31.** $x^2 + y^2 = 16$
33. $x^2 + y^2 = 25$ **35.** $x^2 + y^2 = 26$ **37.** Gear A: $(x + 7)^2 + y^2 = 16$, Gear B: $x^2 + y^2 = 9$, Gear C: $(x - 4)^2 + y^2 = 1$ **39.** $(x - 1)^2 + (y + 2)^2 = 10$
41. $(x - 6)^2 + (y - 4)^2 = 25$ **43.** center (0, 0), radius $\sqrt{2}$ **45.** center (−5, 0), radius $3\sqrt{2}$ **47.** center (−3, 5), radius $\sqrt{38}$ **49.** center (3, 1), radius $\sqrt{6}$
56. $x = -\frac{1}{12}y^2$ **57.** at $x = -1$ **58.** $x = 2$, $x = 3$
59. no points of discontinuity **60.** 4 **61.** 2 **62.** −3
63. 4 **64.** $\frac{1}{2}$ **65.** 1 **66.** −2, −9 **67.** 0, ±4, ±4i
68. ± 2, $\pm 2\sqrt{2}$

Lesson 10-4 pp. 658–665

Got It? 1. $\frac{x^2}{4} + \frac{y^2}{25} = 1$

2a. (±8, 0).

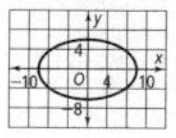

b. The vertex and co-vertex approach the same distance from the center of the ellipse; a circle

3. 24 ft **4.** $\frac{x^2}{36} + \frac{y^2}{53} = 1$

Lesson Check 1. $\frac{x^2}{64} + \frac{y^2}{36} = 1$ **2.** $(\pm\sqrt{21}, 0)$
3. $\frac{x^2}{169} + \frac{y^2}{25} = 1$ **4.** $6\sqrt{23}$ ft ≈ 28.77 ft
5. The student used a and b instead of a^2 and b^2; $\frac{x^2}{1681} + \frac{y^2}{841} = 1$ **6.** The eq. of an ellipse with center at the origin is $\frac{x^2}{a^2} + \frac{y^2}{b^2} = 1$. For a circle, the major axis and the minor axis are of equal length such that $a = b = r$. Thus, by subst., $\frac{x^2}{r^2} + \frac{y^2}{r^2} = 1$ or $x^2 + y^2 = r^2$.

Exercises 7. $\frac{x^2}{16} + \frac{y^2}{9} = 1$ **9.** $\frac{x^2}{9} + y^2 = 1$
11. $\frac{x^2}{16} + \frac{y^2}{49} = 1$ **13.** $\frac{x^2}{9} + \frac{y^2}{25} = 1$
15. $(0, \pm\sqrt{5})$ **17.** $(\pm 4\sqrt{2}, 0)$

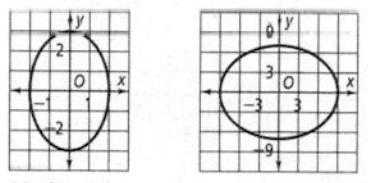

19. (0, ±6)

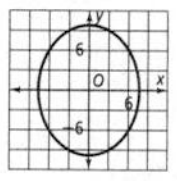

21. 32 **23.** $2\sqrt{39}$ **25.** $8\sqrt{2}$ **27.** $\frac{x^2}{89} + \frac{y^2}{64} = 1$
29a. about 22.25 ft **b.** Due to the reflective prop. of an ellipse, you can aim your putt at any part of the border. The ball will reflect off the border and go directly into the hole. **31.** $(0, \pm 2\sqrt{3})$ **33.** (0, ±1) **35a.** 0.9 **b.** 0.1 **c.** The shape is close to a circle. **d.** The shape is close to a line segment. **37.** $\frac{x^2}{16} + y^2 = 1$ **39.** $\frac{x^2}{1681} + \frac{y^2}{841} = 1$
41. $\frac{x^2}{25} + \frac{y^2}{4} = 1$ **43.** $\frac{x^2}{169} + \frac{y^2}{144} = 1$ **45.** $\frac{x^2}{16} + \frac{y^2}{12} = 1$
47. $\frac{x^2}{36} + \frac{y^2}{27} = 1$ **52.** $(x - 1)^2 + (y + 5)^2 = 9$
53. $(x + 2)^2 + (y - 4)^2 = 81$ **54.** $\frac{1}{2x - 3x^4}$; $x \ne 0$ or $\sqrt[3]{\frac{2}{3}}$ **55.** $\frac{x - 6}{x - 1}$; $x \ne 1$ or -6
56. $\frac{x - 5}{x^2 - 2x + 4}$; $x \ne -2$ **57.** log 15 **58.** $\log_3 6$
59. log 2 **60.** $y = 2x + 4$ **61.** $y = \frac{1}{3}x$

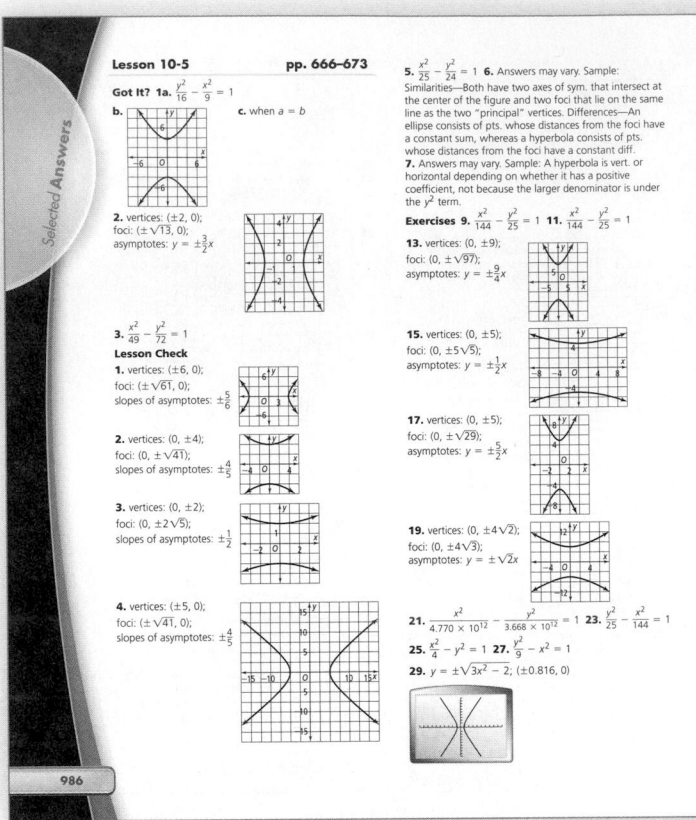

Lesson 10-5 pp. 666–673

Got It? 1a. $\frac{y^2}{16} - \frac{x^2}{9} = 1$

b.

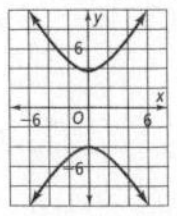

c. when $a = b$

2. vertices: $(\pm 2, 0)$; foci: $(\pm\sqrt{13}, 0)$; asymptotes: $y = \pm\frac{3}{2}x$

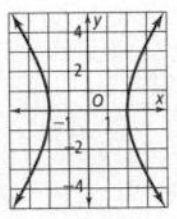

3. $\frac{x^2}{49} - \frac{y^2}{72} = 1$

Lesson Check

1. vertices: $(\pm 6, 0)$; foci: $(\pm\sqrt{61}, 0)$; slopes of asymptotes: $\pm\frac{5}{6}$

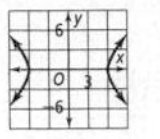

2. vertices: $(0, \pm 4)$; foci: $(0, \pm\sqrt{41})$; slopes of asymptotes: $\pm\frac{4}{5}$

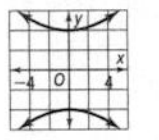

3. vertices: $(0, \pm 2)$; foci: $(0, \pm 2\sqrt{5})$; slopes of asymptotes: $\pm\frac{1}{2}$

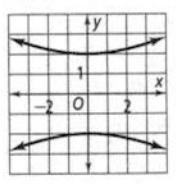

4. vertices: $(\pm 5, 0)$; foci: $(\pm\sqrt{41}, 0)$; slopes of asymptotes: $\pm\frac{4}{5}$

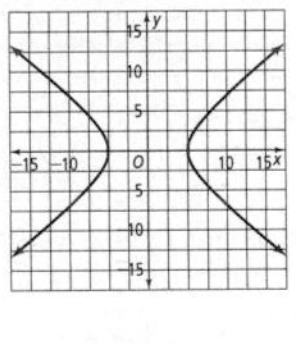

5. $\frac{x^2}{25} - \frac{y^2}{24} = 1$ **6.** Answers may vary. Sample: Similarities—Both have two axes of sym. that intersect at the center of the figure and two foci that lie on the same line as the two "principal" vertices. Differences—An ellipse consists of pts. whose distances from the foci have a constant sum, whereas a hyperbola consists of pts. whose distances from the foci have a constant diff.
7. Answers may vary. Sample: A hyperbola is vert. or horizontal depending on whether it has a positive coefficient, not because the larger denominator is under the y^2 term.

Exercises 9. $\frac{x^2}{144} - \frac{y^2}{25} = 1$ **11.** $\frac{x^2}{144} - \frac{y^2}{25} = 1$

13. vertices: $(0, \pm 9)$; foci: $(0, \pm\sqrt{97})$; asymptotes: $y = \pm\frac{9}{4}x$

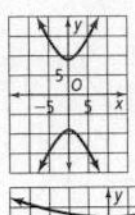

15. vertices: $(0, \pm 5)$; foci: $(0, \pm 5\sqrt{5})$; asymptotes: $y = \pm\frac{1}{2}x$

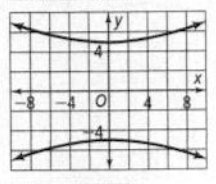

17. vertices: $(0, \pm 5)$; foci: $(0, \pm\sqrt{29})$; asymptotes: $y = \pm\frac{5}{2}x$

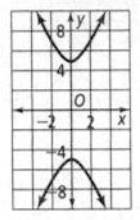

19. vertices: $(0, \pm 4\sqrt{2})$; foci: $(0, \pm 4\sqrt{3})$; asymptotes: $y = \pm\sqrt{2}x$

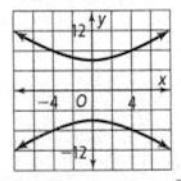

21. $\frac{x^2}{4.770 \times 10^{12}} - \frac{y^2}{3.668 \times 10^{12}} = 1$ **23.** $\frac{y^2}{25} - \frac{x^2}{144} = 1$

25. $\frac{x^2}{4} - y^2 = 1$ **27.** $\frac{y^2}{9} - x^2 = 1$

29. $y = \pm\sqrt{3x^2 - 2}$; $(\pm 0.816, 0)$

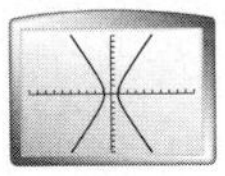

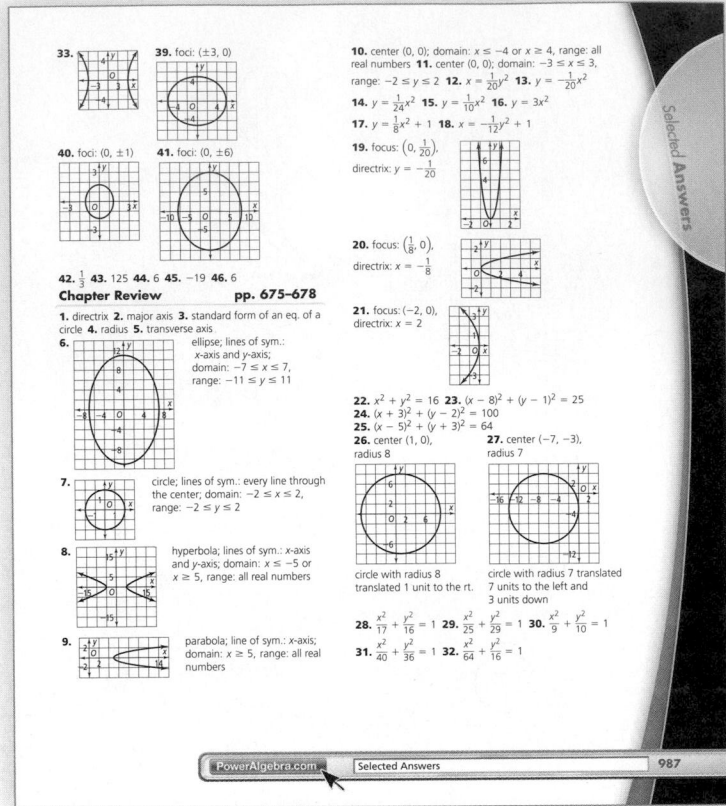

33.

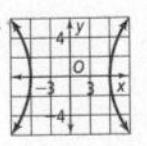

39. foci: $(\pm 3, 0)$

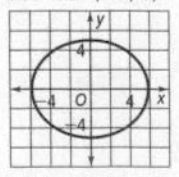

40. foci: $(0, \pm 1)$

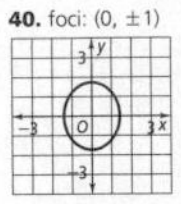

41. foci: $(0, \pm 6)$

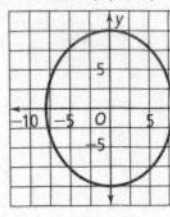

42. $\frac{1}{3}$ **43.** 125 **44.** 6 **45.** −19 **46.** 6

Chapter Review pp. 675–678

1. directrix **2.** major axis **3.** standard form of an eq. of a circle **4.** radius **5.** transverse axis

6.

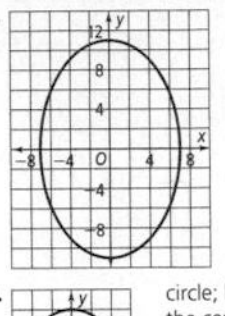

ellipse; lines of sym.: x-axis and y-axis; domain: $-7 \le x \le 7$, range: $-11 \le y \le 11$

7.

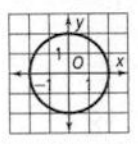

circle; lines of sym.: every line through the center; domain: $-2 \le x \le 2$, range: $-2 \le y \le 2$

8.

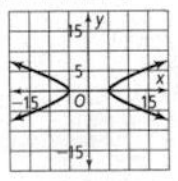

hyperbola; lines of sym.: x-axis and y-axis; domain: $x \le -5$ or $x \ge 5$, range: all real numbers

9.

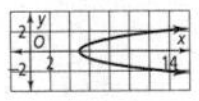

parabola; line of sym.: x-axis; domain: $x \ge 5$, range: all real numbers

10. center (0, 0); domain: $x \le -4$ or $x \ge 4$, range: all real numbers **11.** center (0, 0); domain: $-3 \le x \le 3$, range: $-2 \le y \le 2$ **12.** $x = \frac{1}{20}y^2$ **13.** $y = -\frac{1}{20}x^2$

14. $y = \frac{1}{24}x^2$ **15.** $y = \frac{1}{10}x^2$ **16.** $y = 3x^2$

17. $y = \frac{1}{8}x^2 + 1$ **18.** $x = -\frac{1}{12}y^2 + 1$

19. focus: $\left(0, \frac{1}{20}\right)$, directrix: $y = -\frac{1}{20}$

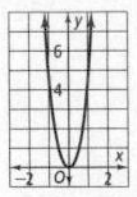

20. focus: $\left(\frac{1}{8}, 0\right)$, directrix: $x = -\frac{1}{8}$

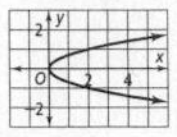

21. focus: $(-2, 0)$, directrix: $x = 2$

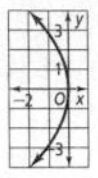

22. $x^2 + y^2 = 16$ **23.** $(x - 8)^2 + (y - 1)^2 = 25$
24. $(x + 3)^2 + (y - 2)^2 = 100$
25. $(x - 5)^2 + (y + 3)^2 = 64$

26. center (1, 0), radius 8

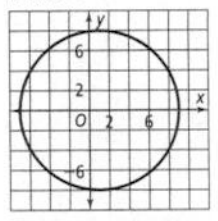

circle with radius 8 translated 1 unit to the rt.

27. center (−7, −3), radius 7

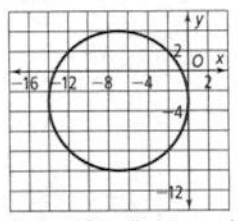

circle with radius 7 translated 7 units to the left and 3 units down

28. $\frac{x^2}{17} + \frac{y^2}{16} = 1$ **29.** $\frac{x^2}{25} + \frac{y^2}{29} = 1$ **30.** $\frac{x^2}{9} + \frac{y^2}{10} = 1$

31. $\frac{x^2}{40} + \frac{y^2}{36} = 1$ **32.** $\frac{x^2}{64} + \frac{y^2}{16} = 1$

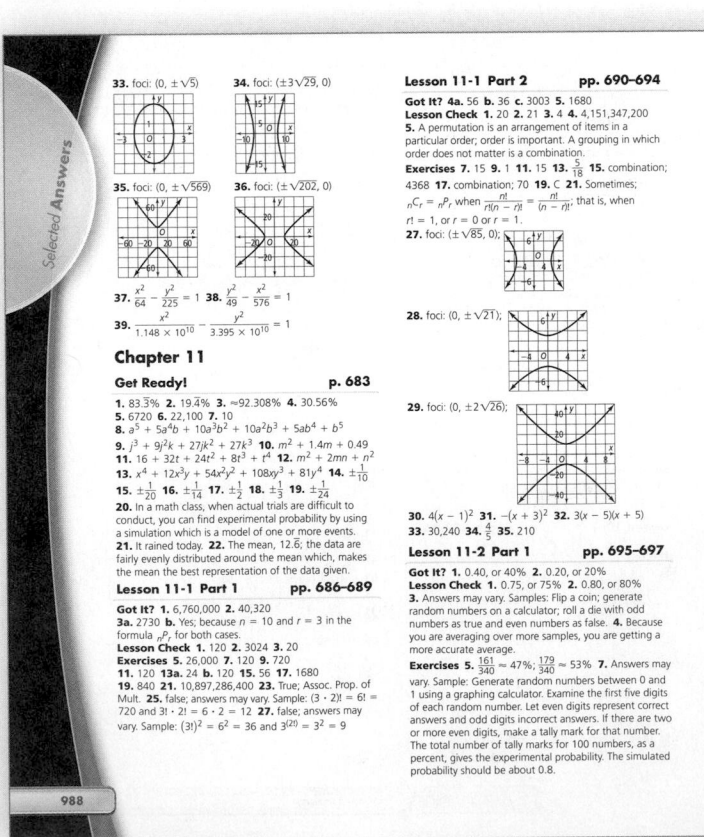

33. foci: $(0, \pm\sqrt{5})$

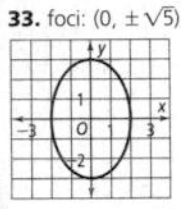

34. foci: $(\pm 3\sqrt{29}, 0)$

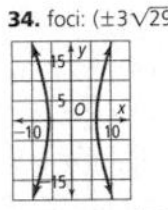

35. foci: $(0, \pm\sqrt{569})$

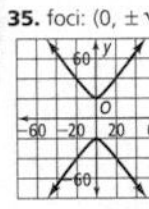

36. foci: $(\pm\sqrt{202}, 0)$

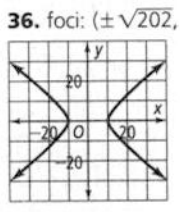

37. $\frac{x^2}{64} - \frac{y^2}{225} = 1$ **38.** $\frac{y^2}{49} - \frac{x^2}{576} = 1$

39. $\frac{x^2}{1.148 \times 10^{10}} - \frac{y^2}{3.395 \times 10^{10}} = 1$

Chapter 11

Get Ready! p. 683

1. $83.\overline{3}\%$ **2.** $19.\overline{4}\%$ **3.** ≈92.308% **4.** 30.56%
5. 6720 **6.** 22,100 **7.** 10
8. $a^5 + 5a^4b + 10a^3b^2 + 10a^2b^3 + 5ab^4 + b^5$
9. $j^3 + 9j^2k + 27jk^2 + 27k^3$ **10.** $m^2 + 1.4m + 0.49$
11. $16 + 32t + 24t^2 + 8t^3 + t^4$ **12.** $m^2 + 2mn + n^2$
13. $x^4 + 12x^3y + 54x^2y^2 + 108xy^3 + 81y^4$ **14.** $\pm\frac{1}{10}$
15. $\pm\frac{1}{20}$ **16.** $\pm\frac{1}{14}$ **17.** $\pm\frac{1}{2}$ **18.** $\pm\frac{1}{3}$ **19.** $\pm\frac{1}{24}$
20. In a math class, when actual trials are difficult to conduct, you can find experimental probability by using a simulation which is a model of one or more events.
21. It rained today. **22.** The mean, $12.\overline{6}$; the data are fairly evenly distributed around the mean which, makes the mean the best representation of the data given.

Lesson 11-1 Part 1 pp. 686–689

Got It? 1. 6,760,000 **2.** 40,320
3a. 2730 **b.** Yes; because $n = 10$ and $r = 3$ in the formula ${}_nP_r$ for both cases.
Lesson Check 1. 120 **2.** 3024 **3.** 20
Exercises 5. 26,000 **7.** 120 **9.** 720
11. 120 **13a.** 24 **b.** 120 **15.** 56 **17.** 1680
19. 840 **21.** 10,897,286,400 **23.** True; Assoc. Prop. of Mult. **25.** false; answers may vary. Sample: $(3 \cdot 2)! = 6! = 720$ and $3! \cdot 2! = 6 \cdot 2 = 12$ **27.** false; answers may vary. Sample: $(3!)^2 = 6^2 = 36$ and $3^{(2!)} = 3^2 = 9$

Lesson 11-1 Part 2 pp. 690–694

Got It? 4a. 56 **b.** 36 **c.** 3003 **5.** 1680
Lesson Check 1. 20 **2.** 21 **3.** 4 **4.** 4,151,347,200
5. A permutation is an arrangement of items in a particular order; order is important. A grouping in which order does not matter is a combination.
Exercises 7. 15 **9.** 1 **11.** 15 **13.** $\frac{5}{18}$ **15.** combination; 4368 **17.** combination; 70 **19.** C **21.** Sometimes; ${}_nC_r = {}_nP_r$ when $\frac{n!}{r!(n-r)!} = \frac{n!}{(n-r)!}$; that is, when $r! = 1$, or $r = 0$ or $r = 1$.

27. foci: $(\pm\sqrt{85}, 0)$;

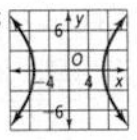

28. foci: $(0, \pm\sqrt{21})$;

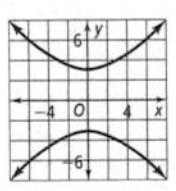

29. foci: $(0, \pm 2\sqrt{26})$;

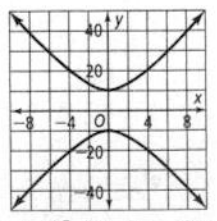

30. $4(x - 1)^2$ **31.** $-(x + 3)^2$ **32.** $3(x - 5)(x + 5)$
33. 30,240 **34.** $\frac{4}{5}$ **35.** 210

Lesson 11-2 Part 1 pp. 695–697

Got It? 1. 0.40, or 40% **2.** 0.20, or 20%
Lesson Check 1. 0.75, or 75% **2.** 0.80, or 80%
3. Answers may vary. Samples: Flip a coin; generate random numbers on a calculator; roll a die with odd numbers as true and even numbers as false. **4.** Because you are averaging over more samples, you are getting a more accurate average.
Exercises 5. $\frac{161}{340} \approx 47\%$; $\frac{179}{340} \approx 53\%$ **7.** Answers may vary. Sample: Generate random numbers between 0 and 1 using a graphing calculator. Examine the first five digits of each random number. Let even digits represent correct answers and odd digits incorrect answers. If there are two or more even digits, make a tally mark for that number. The total number of tally marks for 100 numbers, as a percent, gives the experimental probability. The simulated probability should be about 0.8.

9. Answers may vary. Sample: Randomly generate a 1, 2, 3, 4, or 5 five times. Let 1 represent a correct guess and 2–5 represent incorrect guesses. Tally the recorded numbers with exactly one digit that represents a correct answer. Tally the recorded numbers with exactly two digits that represent correct answers. Tally the recorded numbers with exactly three digits that represent correct answers. The tally totals, as percents, give the experimental probabilities. They should be in the neighborhood of 40%, 20%, and 5%, respectively.

Lesson 11-2 Part 2 pp. 698–703

Got It? 3a. $\frac{1}{2}$ **b.** The likelihoods of getting an even or odd are the same, i.e. $\frac{1}{2}$. **4.** $\frac{48}{2{,}598{,}960}$ or 0.0000184689 or ≈0.00185% **5.** 0.05 or 5%

Lesson Check 1. $\frac{1}{6}$ **2.** $\frac{1}{3}$ **3.** Experimental probabilities are calculated on the basis of data from an experiment, actual or simulated. Given equally likely outcomes, the basis for calculating theoretical probability is being able to determine the no. of ways that an event can occur within these outcomes. Comparisons of measures such as length and area are the basis of geometric probability. **4.** $\frac{3}{10}$, or 30% **5.** $\frac{1}{2}$, or 50% **6.** $\frac{1}{2}$, or 50%

Exercises 7. $\frac{4}{5}$, or 80% **9.** $\frac{48}{125}$, or 38.4%
11. $\frac{103}{125}$, or 82.4% **13.** $\frac{77}{125}$, or 61.6%
15. $\frac{{}_{30}C_3 \cdot {}_{120}C_6}{{}_{150}C_9} \approx 0.17879 \approx 17.9\%$ **17.** $\frac{5}{8}$, or 62.5%
19. $\frac{3}{4}$, or 75% **21.** $\frac{116}{147} \approx 78.9\%$ **23.** $\frac{43}{147} \approx 29.3\%$
25. 1 chance in 2,869,685 or ≈0.00003485% **32.** 20
33. 840 **34.** 10 **35.** 45 **36.** $\frac{25b - 7a^3}{5a^2b^2}$ **37.** $\frac{3q + 7p}{pq}$
38. 0 **39.** $\frac{7}{36} = 19.\overline{4}\%$ **40.** $\frac{25}{36} \approx 69.\overline{4}\%$ **41.** $\frac{1}{2}$, or 50%

Lesson 11-3 pp. 704–710

Got It? 1. Independent; the number of coins is the same after the coin is replaced. **2.** 0.20, or 20%
3a. Not mutually exclusive; 2 is a prime number and an even number. **b.** Mutually exclusive; there is no even number less than 2 in the roll of a number cube.
4a. 0.61, or 61% **b.** Yes; the percentage of students tells which language is chosen by more students. **5a.** $\frac{5}{9}$ **b.** $\frac{5}{9}$
Lesson Check 1. $\frac{1}{15}$ or $6.\overline{6}\%$ **2.** $\frac{27}{80}$ or 33.75% **3.** 1
4. $\frac{7}{8}$ or 87.5% **5.** $\frac{5}{8}$ or 62.5% **6.** Events A and B are independent if the outcomes of A do not affect the outcomes of B. The events are mutually exclusive if A and B cannot occur at the same time. For independent events, $P(A \text{ and } B) = P(A) \cdot P(B)$. For mutually exclusive events, $P(A \text{ and } B) = 0$. For any events, $P(A \text{ or } B) = P(A) + P(B) - P(A \text{ and } B)$. **7.** Since these are not mutually exclusive events, $P(A \text{ and } B) \neq 0$. The student should have calculated $P(A \text{ or } B) = P(A) + P(B) - P(A \text{ and } B)$, which is 0.79, or 79%.
Exercises 9. independent **11.** dependent **13.** $\frac{9}{34}$
15. $\frac{9}{25}$ **17.** mutually exclusive; if the numbers are equal, then the sum is even **19.** $\frac{14}{15}$ **21.** 47% **23.** $\frac{5}{6}$ **25.** $\frac{2}{3}$
27. $\frac{2}{5}$ **29.** 38% **31.** $\frac{4}{15}$ **33.** $\frac{8}{15}$ **35.** not mutually exclusive **43.** $\frac{1}{6}$ **44.** $\frac{1}{2}$ **45.** $\frac{1}{2}$ **46.** $\frac{3}{7}$ **47.** $-\frac{3}{2}$, 2 **48.** $\frac{1}{6}$
49. 500 **50.** 500,000 **51.** ±100 **52.** $\frac{1}{16}$ **53.** $\frac{1}{16}$ **54.** $\frac{3}{16}$

Lesson 11-4 pp. 711–717

Got It? 1a. ≈0.57355 or ≈57.355% **b.** Female; there are more females enrolled. **2a.** ≈0.026448 or ≈2.64% **b.** ≈0.040302 or ≈4.03% **3.** 0.2 **4.** 9%
Lesson Check 1. $\frac{1}{2}$ **2.** $\frac{1}{13}$, or 7.7% **3.** 0% **4.** 50%
5. The sum of the probability of an event happening and the probability of an event not happening is 1. Each branch represents either the event happening or the event not happening. **7.** Answers may vary. Sample: Tree diagrams apply to cases in which more than one event occurs in a sequence. The Fundamental Counting Principle applies to situations in which there are multiple outcomes of a single event. With a tree diagram, but not with the Fundamental Counting Principle, you can determine probabilities of dependent events, or conditional probabilities.
Exercises 9. 0.6 **11.** ≈0.682 **13.** ≈0.709 **15.** ≈23%
17.

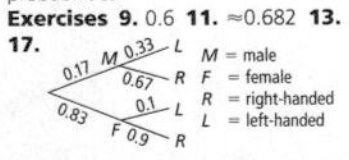

$P(L|F) = 10\%$; $P(M \text{ and } R) \approx 8.3\%$
19. 75% **21.** $P(R|W)$ **23.** 0.08, or 8% **25.** 0.84
30. $\frac{1}{3} = 33.\overline{3}\%$ **31.** $\frac{17}{76} \approx 0.22368 \approx 22.37\%$
32. $x = \frac{1}{4}(y - 2)^2 + 5$ **33.** $y = \frac{1}{12}(x + 2)^2 + 3$
44. 0.2, 0.3, 0.6, 0.7, 0.8, 0.9, 1.2; 0.7
45. 11, 15, 17, 18, 21, 21, 23; 18

Chapter Review for Part A pp. 718–720

1. permutation **2.** Conditional **3.** simulation **4.** mutually exclusive **5.** 6 **6.** 362,880 **7.** 12 **8.** 30 **9.** 21 **10.** 10 **11.** 30 **12.** 744 **13.** 220; 84; 20; 1 **14.** 3.315312×10^9 **15.** 216 **16.** $\frac{47}{70}$ **17.** 0 **18.** $\frac{2}{5}$ **19.** Not necessarily; you may pick a 5 zero times, one time, or more than once. Each time you pick, the prob. that it will be a 5 is $\frac{1}{20}$.
20. dependent **21.** independent **22.** 0.21 **23.** 0.79
24. 0.3 **25.** 0.7 **26.** $\frac{1}{4}$ **27.** $\frac{1}{5}$ **28.** $\frac{1}{8}$

Lesson 11-5 pp. 723–731

Got It? 1. mean: 5.25, median: 5, mode: 5 **2a.** Yes; it is unlikely that the water temperature of a lake would change by 25 degrees. **b.** No; 98 would represent the busiest night of the week, and it may relate to a weekly event. **3.** Dauphin Island: mean: $69.08\overline{3}$, mode: 84, range: 33, $Q_1 = 58$, median: 71, $Q_3 = 81$, interquartile range: 23; Grand Isle: mean: $73.41\overline{6}$, modes: 61, 70, 77, 83, 85, range: 24, $Q_1 = 64.5$, median: 73.5, $Q_3 = 83$, interquartile range: 18.5; The range and the interquartile range show the temperatures varying less at Grand Isle than at Dauphin Island. Also, the temperatures at Grand Isle are generally higher. **4a.** Use STAT PLOT, select a box-and-whisker plot. Enter data for the three remaining Gulf Coast sites. Enter the window values. Draw the box-and-whisker plots. Use TRACE on the plot to find quartiles Q_1, Q_2, and Q_3.

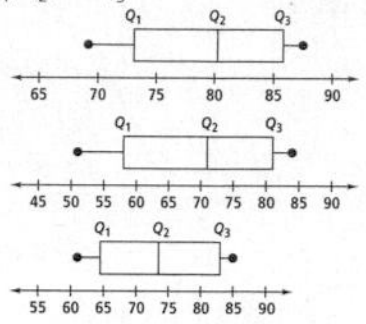

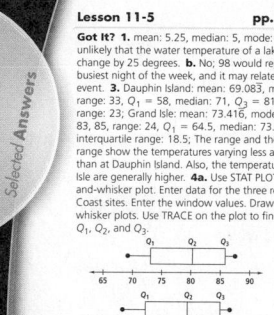

b. Yes, a box-and-whisker plot uses minimum and maximum values, the median, and the first and third quartiles to display the variability in a data set.
5a. 79 **b.** 98
Lesson Check 1. outlier: 54; outlier included: mean: 22.8, median: 19.5, mode: 18; outlier not included: mean: $19.\overline{3}$, median: 19, mode: 18 **2.** outlier: 40; outlier included: mean: $92.\overline{6}$, median: 98, mode: 90; outlier not included: mean: 99.25, median: 99, mode: 90 **3.** 40%: 49 and below; 80%: 58 and below **4.** The error is in how to calculate the median. The median is the middle value, or the 11th value, which is 90.
Exercises 5. mean: $112.\overline{3}$, median: 95, mode: none **7.** 9.8 **9.** Jacksonville: mean: $67.991\overline{6}$, mode: none, range: 29.2, $Q_1 = 58.15$, median: 68.4, $Q_3 = 78.6$, interquartile range: 20.45; Austin: mean: $68.58\overline{3}$, mode: none, range: 36, $Q_1 = 56.85$, median: 70.5, $Q_3 = 80.75$, interquartile range: 23.9; the range and the interquartile range show the temperatures varying less at Jacksonville than at Austin.

11.

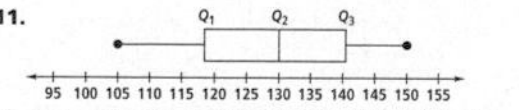

13. 5; 17 **15.** outliers: 22.2 and 99.9; outliers included: mean: ≈60.74, median: 58, mode: none; both outliers not included: mean: $60.6\overline{81}$, median: 58, mode: none

17a.

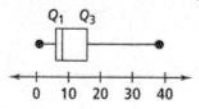

b.

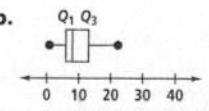

c. The main effect of removing the outlier is a shortening of the long whisker. The median decreases from 8.5 to 8. **19.** 65th **21a.** mean: \$1047.88, median: \$1049.50, mode: \$695 **b.** mode; it gives the lowest price **c.** median; when extreme values (outliers) are involved (\$695 and \$1499), the median gives a more accurate measure of central tendency **27.** ≈0.20 **28.** ≈0.56 **29.** yes; −9 **30.** yes; 17 **31.** no **32.** ±16 **33.** ±0.09 **34.** $\pm\frac{11}{4}$

Lesson 11-6 pp. 732–737

Got It? 1. $\bar{x} = 69.8\overline{3}$, $\sigma^2 \approx 115.1389$, $\sigma \approx 10.7303$ **2.** $\bar{x} = 7.2\overline{6}$, $\sigma \approx 3.214$ **3a.** within 3 standard deviations of the mean **b.** FEMA can expect that the no. of hurricanes for a 15-year period will fall within 3 standard deviations of the mean.
Lesson Check 1. $\bar{x} = 10$, $\sigma^2 = 19.8$, $\sigma \approx 4.45$ **2.** within 2 standard deviations of the mean **3.** Measures of central tendency are specific data pts. which give a summary of the middle of the data set, whereas the measures of variation give a summary of the variation of the data set within the range of distribution. **4.** Standard deviation measures how widely spread the data values are. If the data pts. are close to the mean, the standard deviation is small; if the data pts. are far from the mean, the standard deviation is large. The data pts. of Set B are closer to the mean of 70 than the data pts. of Sets A and C; likewise, the data pts. of Set A are closer to 70 than the data pts. of Set C.
Exercises 5. $\bar{x} \approx 258.6$, $\sigma^2 \approx 52{,}136.8$, $\sigma \approx 228.3$ **7.** $\bar{x} = 5.5$, $\sigma^2 \approx 10.9$, $\sigma \approx 3.3$ **9.** $\bar{x} = 1992.\overline{3}$, $\sigma \approx 61.85$ **11.** 2 standard deviations **13.** $\bar{x} = 53.8$, $\sigma \approx 3.4$; 1σ: 7; 2σ: 9; 3σ: 10 **15.** Overall farm income increased slightly, but there was less variability among the states in 2002. The income in 2001 clustered more tightly around the mean. (2001: $\sigma \approx 2679$, 2002: $\sigma \approx 2758$)
17a. $\bar{x} = 82.3$, $\sigma \approx 4.3$ **b.** 1σ: 7; 2σ: 9; 3σ: 10

23.

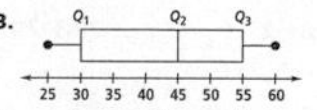

24.

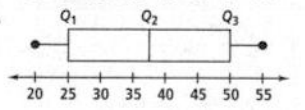

25. center (2, −1); radius 6 **26.** center (1, 1); radius 2 **27.** $\frac{1}{2}$ **28.** $-\frac{1}{3}$ **29.** $\frac{1}{6}$

Lesson 11-7 pp. 738–743

Got It? 1a. convenience sample; yes; since the location is at the food court in the mall, the sample may over represent food court or fast food supporters. **b.** Answers may vary. Sample: population data for the US census **2a.** Yes; the question asks about two issues, nutrition and taste. **b.** Yes; the question is "loaded," suggesting the student council is "highly effective" and that you want a particular answer. **3a.** Answers may vary. Sample: Have pictures of five well known figures, the swimmer and four others who are not sports figures, such as an actor, the president, etc. Ask a member in every fifth house in your neighborhood to identify the five figures. **b.** Explanations may vary. Sample: The sampling method is not appropriate because the members of a swim team are more likely than a person not on a swim team to know the name of a famous swimmer. Also, the question is not appropriate as it identifies that the person in the photograph is a swimmer.
Lesson Check 1a. convenience sample **b.** Yes; since the location is near the exit of a history museum, the sample may overrepresent people who enjoy learning history and the results will have a bias. **2.** Yes; the question is leading and loaded. It suggests the person wants a particular answer. **3.** All members of the set are the population. A sample is a subset of the population. Answers may vary. Sample: population: students in a high school; sample: students who like to snowboard. **4.** It is important to have as little error as poss. in a sample, thus giving an unbiased sample. An unbiased sample is more representative of an entire population. **5.** A large sample size would give a better estimate. The size of the sample is important to the reliability of the sample.
Exercises 7. systematic sampling; no **9.** The question asks about two issues, academic homework and household chores. **11.** The question is leading. It suggests you want a certain answer, that the wrestling team doesn't get enough coverage in the school newspaper. **13.** Answers may vary. Sample: Convenience sampling; interview students at a local high school. **15.** Answers may vary. Sample: Self-selected sampling; a newspaper article invites females over the age of 21 to call the paper and express their opinions. **17.** self-selected sampling; biased because only those who spend time online will respond. **19.** Answers may vary. Sample: Do you think career opportunitites will decrease if Congress considers additional unemployment control laws? **21.** Answers may vary. Sampling: Do you think opening more colleges and encouraging students to complete their education will help provide careers to financially challenged people? **23.** systematic sampling; This sample may have a bias since people with no strong interest in any leisure-time activity may choose not to respond.
25. ≈±0.019988, or ±1.9988% **30.** $\bar{x} \approx 2.83$, $\sigma \approx 2.54$ **31.** $\bar{x} \approx 5.62$, $\sigma \approx 3.67$ **32.** $y = \frac{1}{2}(x - 5)$; yes **33.** $y = \pm\sqrt{x}$; no **34.** $y = \frac{x^2}{9}, x \geq 0$; yes **35.** 6 **36.** 1 **37.** 10

Lesson 11-8 pp. 745–751

Got It? 1. $P(0) = 0.07776$; $P(1) = 0.2592$; $P(2) = 0.3456$; $P(3) = 0.2304$; $P(5) = 0.01024$ **2.** $81x^4 + 108x^3y + 54x^2y^2 + 12xy^3 + y^4$ **3.** ≈0.1035, or about 10.4%
Lesson Check 1. ≈0.3110, or ≈31.10% **2.** ≈0.1641, or ≈16.41% **3.** $20c^3d^3$ **4.** $-10x^4y$ **5.** 0.2646, or 26.46% **6.** Answers may vary. Sample: A binomial experiment has three important features: a. The situation involves repeated trials; flipping a coin 10 times has 10 trials. b. Each trial has two possible outcomes; in this case, heads or tails. c. The probability of success is constant throughout the trials; the trials of flipping a coin, are independent. **7.** The student wrote "5" instead of "4". It should be: ${}_nC_{(5-1)}a^{n-4}b^4 = {}_7C_4 j^3(-k)^4 = 35j^3k^4$
Exercises 9. ≈0.2461, or ≈24.61% **11.** 0.6561, or 65.61% **13.** $256c^4 - 256c^3d + 96c^2d^2 - 16cd^3 + d^4$ **15.** $5xy^4$ **17.** $P(0) \approx 0.1176$, $P(1) \approx 0.3025$, $P(2) \approx 0.3241$, $P(3) \approx 0.1852$, $P(4) \approx 0.0595$, $P(5) \approx 0.0102$, $P(6) \approx 0.0007$ **19.** 0.99328 **21.** ≈0.2824 **23.** ≈ 0.2461 **25.** ≈0.6230 **27a.** 0.0914 **b.** The probability that three boxes would be underweight is 0.0001. You can conclude that there might be a malfunction in the machinery or that the company's claim may be false. **29.** Answers may vary. Sample: 60% of the summer days in Eastport are sunny. What is the probability of a week containing exactly two sunny days? **36.** loaded and leading question by the use of the words "beautiful" and "Do you agree" **37.** not enough information about the amendments to make a decision **38.** vertices: (0, ±7); foci: $(0, \pm\sqrt{74})$; asymptotes: $y = \pm\frac{7}{5}x$ **39.** vertices: (0, ±3); foci: $(0, \pm\sqrt{13})$; asymptotes: $y = \pm\frac{3}{2}x$ **40.** vertices: (0, ±3); foci: (0, ±5); asymptotes: $y = \pm\frac{3}{4}x$ **41.** $\frac{2}{3}$ **42.** $\frac{1}{2}$ **43.** $\frac{2}{3}$ **44.** $\bar{x} = 24.4$, $\sigma \approx 5.04$ **45.** $\bar{x} = 81.8$, $\sigma \approx 4.77$ **46.** $\bar{x} = 8.6$, $\sigma \approx 0.47$ **47.** $\bar{x} \approx 24.74$, $\sigma \approx 2.046$

Lesson 11-9 pp. 752–759

Got It? 1a. 71% **b.** 88%
2.

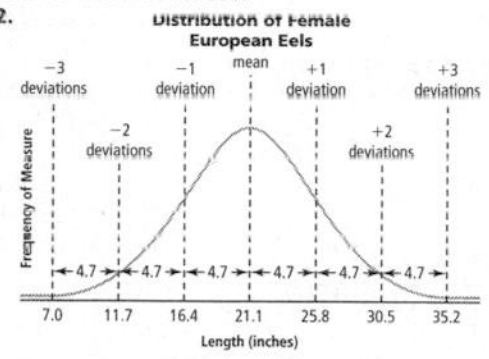

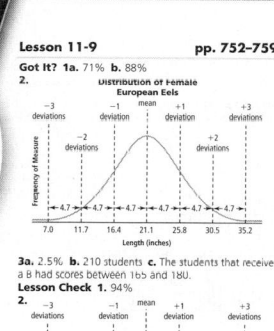

3a. 2.5% **b.** 210 students **c.** The students that received a B had scores between 165 and 180.
Lesson Check 1. 94%
2.

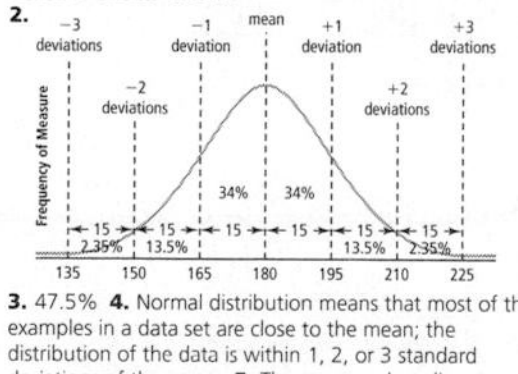

3. 47.5% **4.** Normal distribution means that most of the examples in a data set are close to the mean; the distribution of the data is within 1, 2, or 3 standard deviations of the mean. **5.** The mean and median are equivalent in a normal distribution. **6.** mean increases by 10: the bell curve is translated 10 units to the rt.
Exercises 7. ≈43% **9.** ≈43 men
11.

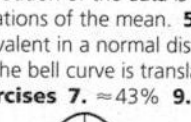

13.

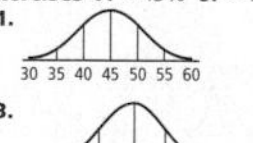

15. 97.5%
17a. Set 2
b-c.

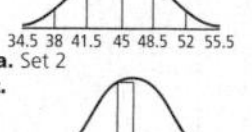

19. Yes; 99% of all grades are expected to be within 3 standard deviations of the mean, and this score is 4.4 standard deviations above the mean. **21.** 47.5%

23. 84%
25a.

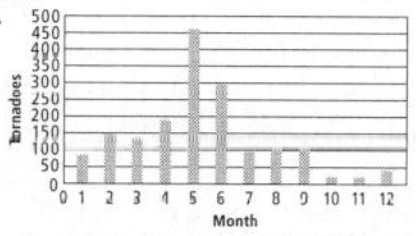

b. Yes; the curve is skewed to the left. **27.** Yes; Elena scored within the top 10% of her group. Her score is 2.75 standard deviations above the mean, which places her in the top 1%. Jake did not score in the top 10%. His score is 1.16 standard deviations above the mean, or at the 88th percentile. **32.** 0.02867 **33.** 0.1612 **34.** 0.03676
35.

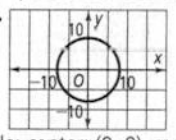

circle; center: (0, 0), radius: 8; lines of sym.: all lines through the center; domain: $-8 \leq x \leq 8$, range: $-8 \leq y \leq 8$
36.

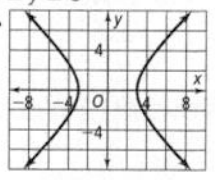

hyperbola; center: (0, 0), foci: $(\pm 3\sqrt{2}, 0)$; lines of sym.: $x = 0$, $y = 0$; domain: $x \leq -3$ or $x \geq 3$; range: all real numbers
37.

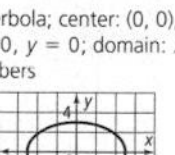

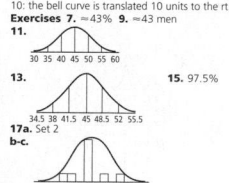

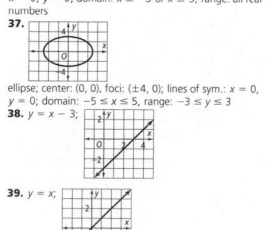

ellipse; center: (0, 0), foci: (±4, 0); lines of sym.: $x = 0$, $y = 0$; domain: $-5 \leq x \leq 5$, range: $-3 \leq y \leq 3$
38. $y = x - 3$;

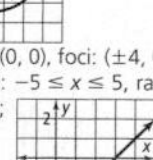

39. $y = x$;

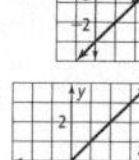

40. $y = x - \frac{5}{4}$;

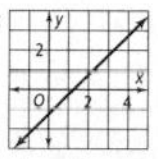

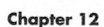

Chapter Review for Part B pp. 761–764

1. sample **2.** outlier **3.** probability distribution **4.** range of a set of data **5.** 9 **6.** mean: 6, median: 6, mode: 9 **7.** mean: $10.\overline{6}$, median: 7, modes: 3 and 7 **8.** mean: 15, median: 15, mode: 18 **9.** mean: 9.5, median: 9.5, mode: none **10.** range: 35; $Q_1 = 30$; $Q_3 = 55$ **11.** range: 35; $Q_1 = 25$; $Q_3 = 50$ **12.** range: 65; $Q_1 = 42$; $Q_3 = 87$ **13.** heights of 3 ppl. **14.** ages of thirty college students **15.** gas mileage of 18 automobiles of various types **16.** $\bar{x} \approx 6.64$, $\sigma \approx 5.12$ **17.** $\bar{x} \approx 17.14$, $\sigma \approx 3.52$ **18.** $\bar{x} = 7.5$, $\sigma \approx 2.67$ **19.** not a random sample; they will all begin with the letter "a" **20.** not a random sample; the lawyers will choose jurors that are likely to support their side **21.** random sample; all students have an equal chance to be chosen **22.** not a random sample; the five with the largest (or smallest) circulation size will be picked **23.** not a random sample; people at the bus station may be less likely to own a car and therefore less likely to be in favor of a new garage. **24.** $\frac{1}{2}$ **25.** $\frac{1}{3}$ **26.** ≈0.14 **27.** ≈0.0710 **28.** ≈0.2066 **29.** ≈0.1766 **30.** $21a^5b^2$ **31.** $56a^3b^5$ **32.** continuous **33.** discrete **34.** discrete **35.** continuous **36.** 16%; 2.5%

Chapter 12

Get Ready! p. 769

1. 6 **2.** $\frac{1}{3}$ **3.** $-\frac{3}{8}$ **4.** $\frac{7}{72}$ **5.** −9 **6.** 11 **7.** 3 **8.** $\left(\frac{1}{2}, -4\right)$ **9.** $\left(-\frac{2}{3}, -\frac{2}{3}\right)$ **10.** $\left(\frac{3}{4}, \frac{11}{4}\right)$ **11.** (7, 9, −6) **12.** (0, 0, 8) **13.** (7, 5, 0)

Lesson 12-1 pp. 772–779

Got It? 1a. $\begin{bmatrix} -15 & 25 \\ -1 & 1 \\ -2 & 15 \end{bmatrix}$ **b.** $\begin{bmatrix} -9 & 23 \\ -5 & 9 \\ 0 & 5 \end{bmatrix}$
c. Yes; it does not matter in which order you add matrices.
2. $A = \begin{bmatrix} 3 & 6 & -1 \\ 1 & 3 & 7 \\ 1 & 1 & 3 \end{bmatrix}$ **3a.** $\begin{bmatrix} 0 & 0 \\ 0 & 0 \end{bmatrix}$ **b.** $\begin{bmatrix} -1 & 10 & -5 \\ 0 & 2 & -3 \end{bmatrix}$
4a. $x = 6, y = -6$ **b.** $x = 4, y = -3$
Lesson Check 1. $\begin{bmatrix} 1 & 1 \\ -2 & 8 \end{bmatrix}$ **2.** $\begin{bmatrix} 1 & -9 & 8 \\ -3 & -1 & 8 \end{bmatrix}$ **3.** $\begin{bmatrix} -3 & 4 \\ -5 & 11 \end{bmatrix}$ **4.** Yes; the elements in each of the corresponding positions are equal. **5.** The elements were not subtracted. The correct answer is $\begin{bmatrix} 6 \\ 5 \end{bmatrix} - \begin{bmatrix} 3 \\ 7 \end{bmatrix} = \begin{bmatrix} 3 \\ -2 \end{bmatrix}$
Exercises 7. $\begin{bmatrix} 2.9 & -2.2 \\ -0.6 & 9.1 \end{bmatrix}$ **9.** $\begin{bmatrix} 6 & 2 \\ -1 & 3 \end{bmatrix}$ **11.** $\begin{bmatrix} -9 & -7 & 12 \\ -15 & 11 & -7 \end{bmatrix}$ **13.** $\begin{bmatrix} 0 & 0 \\ 0 & 0 \end{bmatrix}$ **15.** $x = 2, t = \frac{1}{10}$
17. B and D cannot be added because they do not have the same dimensions.
19.

Plant 1: $\begin{matrix} & \text{Plastic} & \text{Rubber} \\ \text{1-color} & 1000 & 1400 \\ \text{3-color} & 2600 & 3800 \end{matrix}$ Plant 2: $\begin{matrix} & \text{Plastic} & \text{Rubber} \\ \text{1-color} & 1200 & 3600 \\ \text{3-color} & 1800 & 4800 \end{matrix}$

Plant 1 − Plant 2 = $\begin{bmatrix} -200 & -2200 \\ 800 & -1000 \end{bmatrix}$, where the top row represents 1-color balls and the bottom represents 3-color balls. **21.** $c = \frac{5}{2}, d = \frac{2}{5}, f = 7, g = 5, h = -1$
23a. $\begin{bmatrix} 124.6 \\ 113.3 \\ 71.6 \\ 87.2 \end{bmatrix}$ **b.** $\begin{bmatrix} -6.2 \\ -4.7 \\ 9.4 \\ 3.6 \end{bmatrix}$
c. Yes; order matters because subtraction is not comm. **29.** 68% **30.** 97.5% **31.** 47.5% **32.** 2, −6 **33.** $\frac{2}{3}$, 2 **34.** 5, 0 **35.** $\begin{bmatrix} 9 & 15 \\ 6 & 24 \end{bmatrix}$ **36.** $\begin{bmatrix} -20 \\ 35 \end{bmatrix}$

Lesson 12-2 pp. 781–788

Got It? 1. $\begin{bmatrix} 8 & 24 & -19 \\ -3 & 9 & 10 \end{bmatrix}$ **2.** $\begin{bmatrix} 5 & -1 \\ \frac{7}{3} & 0 \end{bmatrix}$ **3a.** $\begin{bmatrix} -6 & 0 \\ -9 & 11 \end{bmatrix}$ **b.** $\begin{bmatrix} -3 & 7 \\ 6 & 8 \end{bmatrix}$ **c.** No; explanations may vary. Sample: For the matrices in parts (a) and (b), $AB = \begin{bmatrix} -6 & 0 \\ -9 & 11 \end{bmatrix}$ and $BA = \begin{bmatrix} -3 & 7 \\ 6 & 8 \end{bmatrix}$, so $AB \neq BA$.
4. player from 1994: 100 pts., player from 2006: 81 pts. **5a.** no **b.** yes **c.** yes **d.** no **e.** yes
Lesson Check 1. $\begin{bmatrix} 6 & -2 \\ 4 & 0 \end{bmatrix}$ **2.** $\begin{bmatrix} -3 & 11 \\ -10 & 6 \end{bmatrix}$ **3.** $\begin{bmatrix} 5 & 7 \\ 2 & 6 \end{bmatrix}$ **4.** $\begin{bmatrix} 9 & -1 \\ -2 & 2 \end{bmatrix}$
5. Scalar; repeated matrix addition is repeated addition of each element of the matrix, which is the same as scalar multiplication of the matrix. **6.** The product of two matrices A and B exists only if the number of columns of A is equal to the number of rows of B. Since A is a 2×4

matrix with 4 columns and B is a 3×6 matrix with 3 rows and $4 \neq 3$, the product AB does not exist. Likewise, since $6 \neq 2$, the product BA does not exist.

Exercises 7. $\begin{bmatrix} 9 & 12 \\ 18 & -6 \\ 3 & 0 \end{bmatrix}$ **9.** $\begin{bmatrix} -5 & -1 \\ 0 & -2 \end{bmatrix}$ **11.** $\begin{bmatrix} 19 & 11 \\ -12 & 10 \end{bmatrix}$

13. $\begin{bmatrix} -1 & 2 \\ 3 & -4 \end{bmatrix}$ **15.** $\begin{bmatrix} -4 & 8 \\ -22 & 2 \end{bmatrix}$ **17.** $\begin{bmatrix} -3 & 4 \\ -21 & 2 \end{bmatrix}$ **19.** [34]

21. [0 34]

23a.

	Lilies	Carnations	Daisies
Arrangement 1	3	0	0
Arrangement 2	3	4	0
Arrangement 3	0	3	4

b.

	Cost
Lilies	\$2.15
Carnations	\$0.90
Daisies	\$1.30

c.

	Cost
Arrangement 1	\$6.45
Arrangement 2	\$10.05
Arrangement 3	\$7.90

25. yes **27.** yes **29a.** River's Edge: 99 pts.; West River: 97 pts. **b.** West River

31. $\begin{bmatrix} 1 & -6 & -5 \\ 6 & 1 & -5 \\ -3 & -12 & 0 \end{bmatrix}$ **33.** $\begin{bmatrix} 17 & -24 \\ -33 & -7 \\ 69 & -18 \end{bmatrix}$

35. $\begin{bmatrix} 34 & -1 \\ 6 & -13 \\ -7 & 16 \end{bmatrix}$ **42.** $\begin{bmatrix} -33 & -12 \\ -6 & 27 \end{bmatrix}$

43. $\begin{bmatrix} 9 & -6 & 12 \\ 2 & 20 & 12 \end{bmatrix}$ **44a.** 12 **b.** 12 **c.** 0

45a. −12 **b.** −12 **c.** 0

Lesson 12-3 Part 1 pp. 789–792

Got It? 1a. yes **b.** yes **c.** No; no matrix that is multiplied by the zero matrix will give an identity matrix. **2a.** 3 **b.** −48

Lesson Check 1. 16 **2.** 7

3. The student added $ad + bc$ instead of subtracting $ad - bc$.

$\det\begin{bmatrix} 2 & 5 \\ -3 & 1 \end{bmatrix} = (2)(1) - (-3)(5) = 2 - (-15)$
$= 2 + 15 = 17$

Exercises 5. yes **7.** no **9.** 0 **11.** 11 **13.** −5 **15.** 36 **17.** 25 **19a.** 0 **b.** 0 **c.** 0 **d.** 0 Answers may vary. Sample: When the top row and bottom row are identical and the middle row has the same numbers as both rows, then the determinant is zero.

Lesson 12-3 Part 2 pp. 793–798

Got It? 3a. 12 units^2 **b.** 28 units^2

4a. yes; $\begin{bmatrix} 1 & -1 \\ -\frac{3}{2} & 2 \end{bmatrix}$ **b.** no **c.** yes; $\begin{bmatrix} 3 & -4 \\ -5 & 7 \end{bmatrix}$

5a. 88, 68, 84, 60, 12, 32, 52, 72, 28, 30, 14, 18, 2, 8, 14, 20 **b.** Multiply the coded information by the inverse of the coding matrix and get the following:
$\begin{bmatrix} 4 & 1 & 7 & 3 & 1 & 2 & 3 & 4 \\ 9 & 8 & 7 & 6 & 1 & 3 & 5 & 7 \end{bmatrix}$

Lesson Check 1. does not exist **2.** $\begin{bmatrix} 3 & -2 \\ -7 & 5 \end{bmatrix}$

3. Multiplicative inverses are only defined for square matrices because a pair of square matrices can be multiplied in either order, and can therefore be defined as multiplicative inverses of each other.

Exercises 5. yes; $\begin{bmatrix} 0 & 1 \\ -1 & 2 \end{bmatrix}$ **7.** yes; $\begin{bmatrix} 2 & -1.5 \\ -1 & 1 \end{bmatrix}$ **9.** no

11. 44 units^2 **13.** 34 units^2 **15.** 0 **17.** −30

19. yes; $\begin{bmatrix} -3 & 4 \\ 1 & -1 \end{bmatrix}$ **21.** yes; $\begin{bmatrix} 0.5 & 0 \\ 0 & 0.5 \end{bmatrix}$

23. yes; $\begin{bmatrix} 0.4 & 0.4 & 0.2 \\ -0.6 & -0.6 & 0.2 \\ -0.2 & 0.8 & 0.4 \end{bmatrix}$ **25.** 6 **31.** $\begin{bmatrix} 2 & 5 \\ 1 & 1 \end{bmatrix}$

32. $\begin{bmatrix} -10 & 19 \\ -20 & 7 \end{bmatrix}$ **33.** 720 **34.** 362,880

35. $1.08972864 \times 10^{10}$ **36.** 110,880

37. no solution **38.** (6, 0, −3)

Lesson 12-4 Part 1 pp. 799–802

Got It? 1a. $\begin{bmatrix} -8 \\ 9 \end{bmatrix}$ **b.** $\begin{bmatrix} -14 & -20 \\ 19 & 28 \end{bmatrix}$

c. Since matrix A has no inverse, the eq. has no solution.

2a. $\begin{bmatrix} 3 & -7 \\ 5 & 1 \end{bmatrix}\begin{bmatrix} x \\ y \end{bmatrix} = \begin{bmatrix} 8 \\ -2 \end{bmatrix}$

b. $\begin{bmatrix} 1 & 3 & 5 \\ -2 & 1 & -4 \\ 7 & -2 & 0 \end{bmatrix}\begin{bmatrix} x \\ y \\ z \end{bmatrix} = \begin{bmatrix} 12 \\ -2 \\ 7 \end{bmatrix}$

c. $\begin{bmatrix} 2 & -8 \\ -1 & 1 \end{bmatrix}\begin{bmatrix} x \\ y \end{bmatrix} = \begin{bmatrix} -3 \\ -4 \end{bmatrix}$

Lesson Check 1. $\begin{bmatrix} -6 & 3 \\ 4 & -2 \end{bmatrix}\begin{bmatrix} x \\ y \end{bmatrix} = \begin{bmatrix} 8 \\ 10 \end{bmatrix}$

2. $\begin{bmatrix} 2 & 3 & 0 \\ 1 & -2 & 1 \\ 0 & 6 & -4 \end{bmatrix}\begin{bmatrix} x \\ y \\ z \end{bmatrix} = \begin{bmatrix} 12 \\ 9 \\ 8 \end{bmatrix}$

3. Use matrix multiplication to combine the coefficient matrix and the variable matrix into a product matrix. Then set the first element in the product matrix equal to the first element in the constant matrix and set the second element in the product matrix equal to the second

element in the constant matrix. The result will be a system of equations:
$-2p + 3q = 2$
$4p + q = -5$

Exercises

5. $\begin{bmatrix} \frac{29}{31} \\ -\frac{66}{217} \\ \frac{34}{217} \end{bmatrix}$ **7.** $\begin{bmatrix} \frac{2487}{253} \\ \frac{1192}{253} \\ -\frac{430}{253} \end{bmatrix}$

9. $\begin{bmatrix} -3 & 1 \\ 1 & 0 \end{bmatrix}\begin{bmatrix} x \\ y \end{bmatrix} = \begin{bmatrix} -7 \\ 2 \end{bmatrix}$; coefficient matrix: $\begin{bmatrix} -3 & 1 \\ 1 & 0 \end{bmatrix}$, variable matrix: $\begin{bmatrix} x \\ y \end{bmatrix}$, constant matrix: $\begin{bmatrix} -7 \\ 2 \end{bmatrix}$

11. (6, 2) **13.** (16, −22)

Lesson 12-4 Part 2 pp. 804–808

Got It? 3a. (5, −21) **b.** no solution **4.** run: 32 min; jog: 8 min

Lesson Check 1. (5, 3) **2.** (−6, −6) **3.** The student did not separate the coefficient matrix and the variable matrix. The matrix eq. should be written as $\begin{bmatrix} 2 & 3 \\ -4 & 5 \end{bmatrix}\begin{bmatrix} x \\ y \end{bmatrix} = \begin{bmatrix} 5 \\ 1 \end{bmatrix}$.

Exercises 5. $\left(\frac{1}{2}, 20\right)$ **7.** (3, 2) **9.** (2, −1, 3) **11.** about 22 min at 11 mph and about 38 min at 15 mph **13.** 1 lb of almonds, 1 lb of peanuts, and 1 lb of raisins **15.** (2, 4) **17.** (5, 0, 1) **19.** (2, −1, 3) **21.** length = 280 ft, width = 140 ft **23.** (2, 40) **25.** (12.5, 1187.5) **27.** no unique solution **33.** −44 **34.** 4913 **35.** −218 **36.** $34.\overline{4}$; 30.9; 5.56 **37.** 4.17; 1.32; 1.15 **38.** $19.\overline{6}$ m; $22.\overline{2}$ m; 4.7 m **39.** 57.4 mi; 345.44 mi^2; 18.6 mi **40.** 4 **41.** 21 **42.** 52.5

Chapter Review pp. 810–812

1. equal matrices **2.** zero matrix **3.** matrix equation **4.** square matrix

5. $\begin{bmatrix} -1 & 9 & -8 \\ 4 & 0 & 6 \end{bmatrix}$ **6.** $\begin{bmatrix} 5 & -4 \\ 5 & 0 \end{bmatrix}$ **7.** [1 −8 12]

8. $\begin{bmatrix} -3 & 10 \\ -3 & 3 \end{bmatrix}$ **9.** $x = -2, w = 8, r = 4, t = -1$

10. $t = -4, y = \frac{11}{2}, r = 4, w = 4$

11. $\begin{bmatrix} 18 & 3 & 0 & 24 \\ -12 & 9 & 21 & 33 \end{bmatrix}$ **12.** undefined **13.** undefined

14. $\begin{bmatrix} -6 & 10 & 21 & 41 \\ -28 & 10 & 28 & 28 \end{bmatrix}$ **15.** $\begin{bmatrix} -14 & -2 \\ 43 & -7 \end{bmatrix}$

16. $\begin{bmatrix} -11 & 18 \\ -17 & -2 \end{bmatrix}$ **17.** 24; $\begin{bmatrix} \frac{1}{6} & -\frac{1}{24} \\ 0 & \frac{1}{4} \end{bmatrix}$

18. 0; does not exist **19.** 42; $\begin{bmatrix} \frac{5}{42} & -\frac{1}{42} \\ -\frac{4}{21} & \frac{5}{21} \end{bmatrix}$

20. 6; $\begin{bmatrix} \frac{1}{3} & -\frac{2}{3} & 0 \\ -\frac{1}{6} & \frac{1}{3} & -\frac{1}{2} \\ \frac{1}{3} & \frac{1}{3} & 0 \end{bmatrix}$ **21.** $\begin{bmatrix} 1 & 2 \\ -1 & 0 \end{bmatrix}$ **22.** (−4, −7)

23. $\begin{bmatrix} 2 \\ 2 \end{bmatrix}$ **24.** $\begin{bmatrix} 2 & 1 \\ 3 & 2 \end{bmatrix}$ **25.** no unique solution

26. no unique solution

Chapter T

T-1 pp. 823–827

Got It? 1. a. $\frac{4}{5}$ **b.** $\frac{5}{3}$ **c.** $\frac{4}{3}$ **2.** $\sin E = \frac{3}{5}$, $\sec F = \frac{5}{3}$

3a. 27.1 m b. 32.2 m

Lesson Check 1. $\sin 57° = \frac{b}{c}$, $\cos 57° = \frac{a}{c}$, $\tan 57° = \frac{b}{a}$ **2.** 15.4 **3.** $\sin 33° = \frac{a}{c} = 0.5$, $\cos 33° = \frac{b}{c} = 0.8$, $\tan 33° = \frac{a}{b} = 0.6$ **4.** The cotangent is $\frac{\text{adjacent}}{\text{opposite}}$ and he used $\frac{\text{opposite}}{\text{adjacent}}$. So $\cot Q = \frac{p}{q}$. **5.** Answers may vary. Sample: Use the inverse of sine to find the measure of the angle opposite the shortest side, $\theta = \sin^{-1}\frac{3}{5} \approx 36.9°$. Then find the tangent of the angle opposite the shortest side, $\tan 36.9° \approx 0.75$.

Exercises 7. $\frac{17}{8} \approx 2.13$ **9.** $\frac{17}{8} \approx 2.13$ **11.** $\frac{8}{15} \approx 0.53$

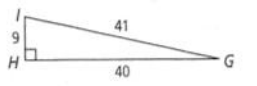

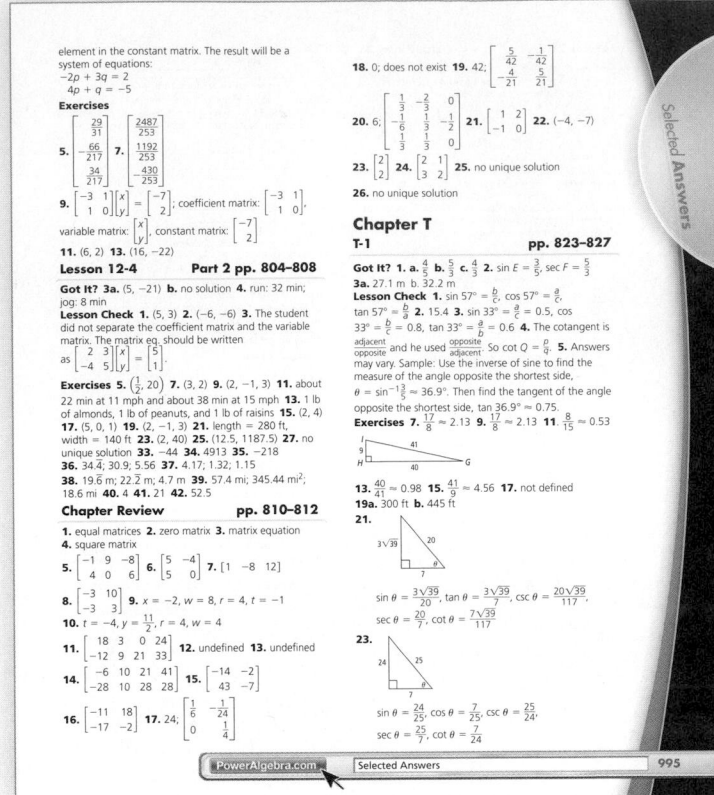

13. $\frac{40}{41} \approx 0.98$ **15.** $\frac{41}{9} \approx 4.56$ **17.** not defined

19a. 300 ft **b.** 445 ft

21.

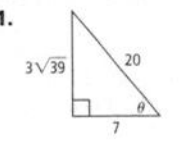

$\sin\theta = \frac{3\sqrt{39}}{20}$, $\tan\theta = \frac{3\sqrt{39}}{7}$, $\csc\theta = \frac{20\sqrt{39}}{117}$,
$\sec\theta = \frac{20}{7}$, $\cot\theta = \frac{7\sqrt{39}}{117}$

23.

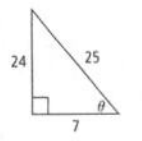

$\sin\theta = \frac{24}{25}$, $\cos\theta = \frac{7}{25}$, $\csc\theta = \frac{25}{24}$,
$\sec\theta = \frac{25}{7}$, $\cot\theta = \frac{7}{24}$

25.

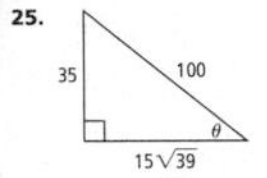

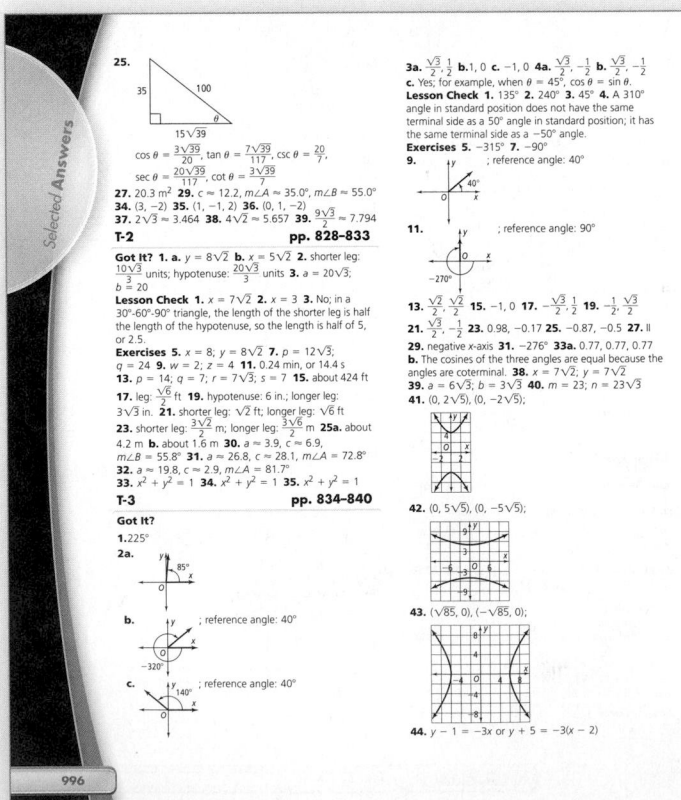

$\cos\theta = \frac{3\sqrt{39}}{20}$, $\tan\theta = \frac{7\sqrt{39}}{117}$, $\csc\theta = \frac{20}{7}$,
$\sec\theta = \frac{20\sqrt{39}}{117}$, $\cot\theta = \frac{3\sqrt{39}}{7}$

27. 20.3 m^2 **29.** $c \approx 12.2$, $m\angle A \approx 35.0°$, $m\angle B \approx 55.0°$ **34.** (3, −2) **35.** (1, −1, 2) **36.** (0, 1, −2) **37.** $2\sqrt{3} \approx 3.464$ **38.** $4\sqrt{2} \approx 5.657$ **39.** $\frac{9\sqrt{3}}{2} \approx 7.794$

T-2 pp. 828–833

Got It? 1. a. $y = 8\sqrt{2}$ **b.** $x = 5\sqrt{2}$ **2.** shorter leg: $\frac{10\sqrt{3}}{3}$ units; hypotenuse: $\frac{20\sqrt{3}}{3}$ units **3.** $a = 20\sqrt{3}$; $b = 20$

Lesson Check 1. $x = 7\sqrt{2}$ **2.** $x = 3$ **3.** No; in a 30°-60°-90° triangle, the length of the shorter leg is half the length of the hypotenuse, so the length is half of 5, or 2.5.

Exercises 5. $x = 8$; $y = 8\sqrt{2}$ **7.** $p = 12\sqrt{3}$; $q = 24$ **9.** $w = 2$; $z = 4$ **11.** 0.24 min, or 14.4 s **13.** $p = 14$; $q = 7$; $r = 7\sqrt{3}$; $s = 7$ **15.** about 424 ft **17.** leg: $\frac{\sqrt{6}}{2}$ ft **19.** hypotenuse: 6 in.; longer leg: $3\sqrt{3}$ in. **21.** shorter leg: $\sqrt{2}$ ft; longer leg: $\sqrt{6}$ ft **23.** shorter leg: $\frac{3\sqrt{2}}{2}$ m; longer leg: $\frac{3\sqrt{6}}{2}$ m **25a.** about 4.2 m **b.** about 1.6 m **30.** $a \approx 3.9$, $c \approx 6.9$, $m\angle B = 55.8°$ **31.** $a \approx 26.8$, $c \approx 28.1$, $m\angle A = 72.8°$ **32.** $a \approx 19.8$, $c \approx 2.9$, $m\angle A = 81.7°$ **33.** $x^2 + y^2 = 1$ **34.** $x^2 + y^2 = 1$ **35.** $x^2 + y^2 = 1$

T-3 pp. 834–840

Got It?

1. 225°

2a.

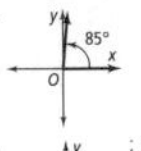

b. ; reference angle: 40°

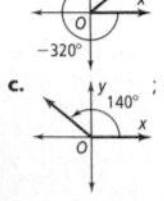

c. ; reference angle: 40°

3a. $\frac{\sqrt{3}}{2}, \frac{1}{2}$ **b.** 1, 0 **c.** −1, 0 **4a.** $\frac{\sqrt{3}}{2}, -\frac{1}{2}$ **b.** $\frac{\sqrt{3}}{2}, -\frac{1}{2}$ **c.** Yes; for example, when $\theta = 45°$, $\cos\theta = \sin\theta$.

Lesson Check 1. 135° **2.** 240° **3.** 45° **4.** A 310° angle in standard position does not have the same terminal side as a 50° angle in standard position; it has the same terminal side as a −50° angle.

Exercises 5. −315° **7.** −90°

9. ; reference angle: 40°

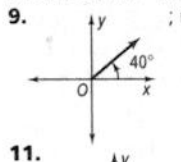

11. ; reference angle: 90°

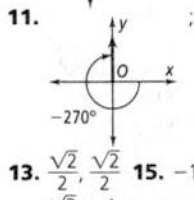

13. $\frac{\sqrt{2}}{2}, \frac{\sqrt{2}}{2}$ **15.** −1, 0 **17.** $-\frac{\sqrt{3}}{2}, \frac{1}{2}$ **19.** $-\frac{1}{2}, \frac{\sqrt{3}}{2}$ **21.** $\frac{\sqrt{3}}{2}, -\frac{1}{2}$ **23.** 0.98, −0.17 **25.** −0.87, −0.5 **27.** II **29.** negative x-axis **31.** −276° **33a.** 0.77, 0.77, 0.77 **b.** The cosines of the three angles are equal because the angles are coterminal. **38.** $x = 7\sqrt{2}$; $y = 7\sqrt{2}$ **39.** $a = 6\sqrt{3}$; $b = 3\sqrt{3}$ **40.** $m = 23$; $n = 23\sqrt{3}$

41. $(0, 2\sqrt{5}), (0, -2\sqrt{5})$;

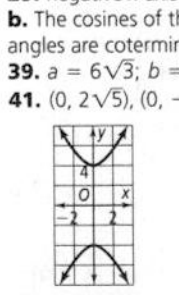

42. $(0, 5\sqrt{5}), (0, -5\sqrt{5})$;

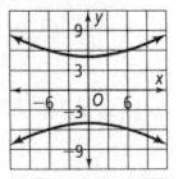

43. $(\sqrt{85}, 0), (-\sqrt{85}, 0)$;

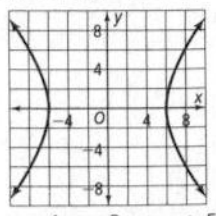

44. $y - 1 = -3x$ or $y + 5 = -3(x - 2)$

45. $y + 4 = -\frac{7}{5}(x + 4)$ or $y - 3 = -\frac{7}{5}(x + 9)$ **46.** $y - 2 = -(x - 7)$ or $y - 8 = -(x - 1)$ **47.** 50.24 in.^{2} **48.** 200.96 mi^2 **49.** 9.0746 ft^2

T-4 pp. 841–847

Got It? 1a. 90° **b.** $\frac{5\pi}{4}$ radians **c.** $\frac{360°}{\pi} \approx 114.59°$ **d.** $\frac{5\pi}{6}$ radians **2.** $-\frac{\sqrt{3}}{2}, -\frac{1}{2}$ **3a.** 6.3 in. **b.** arc length would also double. **4.** ≈15,708 km

Lesson Check 1. $\frac{5\pi}{3}$ radians ≈ 5.24 radians **2.** 135° **3.** $\frac{20\pi}{3} \approx 20.94$ in. **4.** 1 radian **5.** 6 "perfect" slices

Exercises 7. $\frac{5\pi}{6}$, 2.62 **9.** $\frac{\pi}{9}$, 0.35 **11.** 198° **13.** −172° **15.** $\frac{1}{2}, \frac{\sqrt{3}}{2}$ **17.** $-\frac{1}{2}, \frac{\sqrt{3}}{2}$ **19.** $-\frac{\sqrt{3}}{2}, -\frac{1}{2}$ **21.** 51.8 ft **23.** ≈746 ft **25a.** ≈11,048 km, ≈33,144 km, ≈27,620 km, ≈276,198 km **b.** 18.1 h **27a.** 15°, $\frac{\pi}{12}$ **b.** ≈1036.7 mi **c.** ≈413.6 mi **29.** II

31. 0.71, −0.71

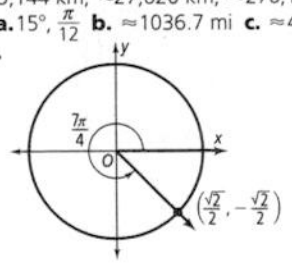

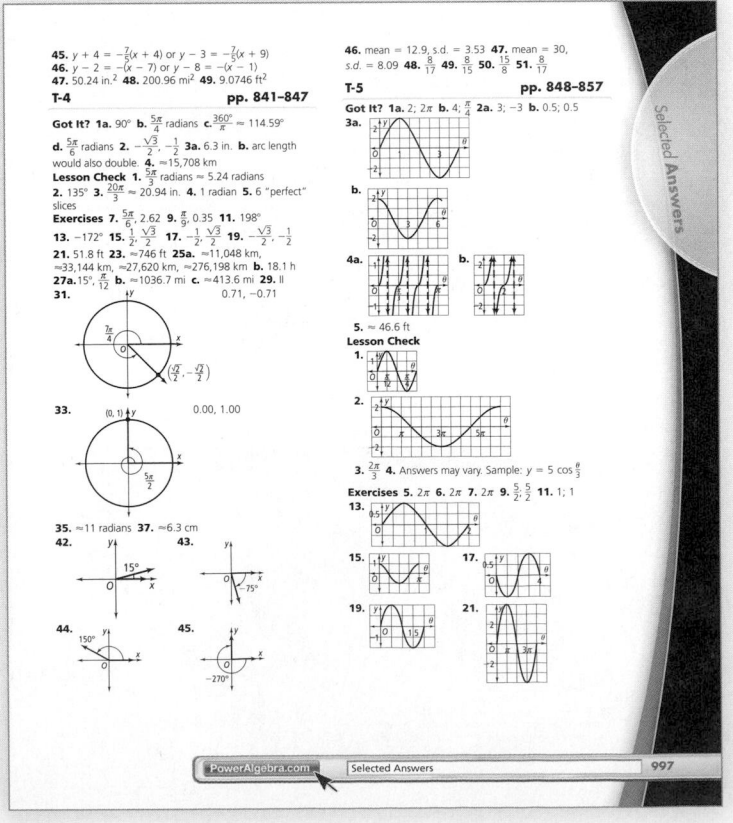

33. 0.00, 1.00

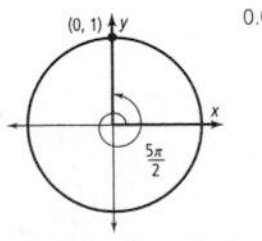

35. ≈11 radians **37.** ≈6.3 cm

42.

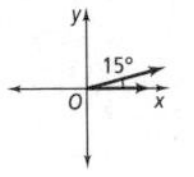

43.

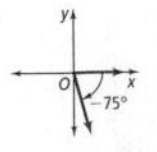

44.

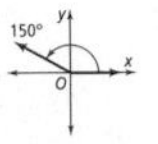

45.

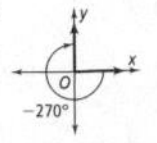

46. mean = 12.9, s.d. = 3.53 **47.** mean = 30, s.d. = 8.09 **48.** $\frac{8}{17}$ **49.** $\frac{8}{15}$ **50.** $\frac{15}{8}$ **51.** $\frac{8}{17}$

T-5 pp. 848–857

Got It? 1a. 2; 2π **b.** 4; $\frac{\pi}{4}$ **2a.** 3; −3 **b.** 0.5; 0.5

3a.

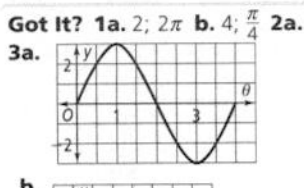

b.

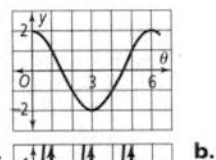

4a.

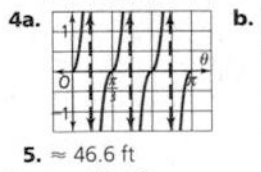

b.

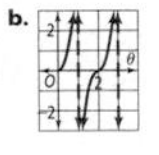

5. ≈ 46.6 ft

Lesson Check

1.

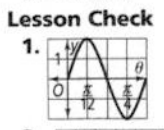

2.

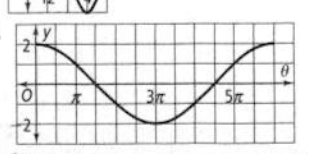

3. $\frac{2\pi}{3}$ **4.** Answers may vary. Sample: $y = 5\cos\frac{\theta}{3}$

Exercises 5. 2π **6.** 2π **7.** 2π **9.** $\frac{5}{2}, \frac{5}{2}$ **11.** 1; 1

13.

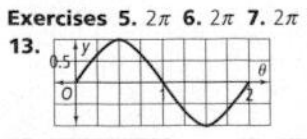

15.

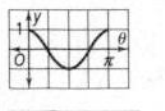

17.

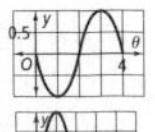

19.

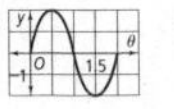

21.

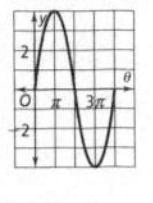

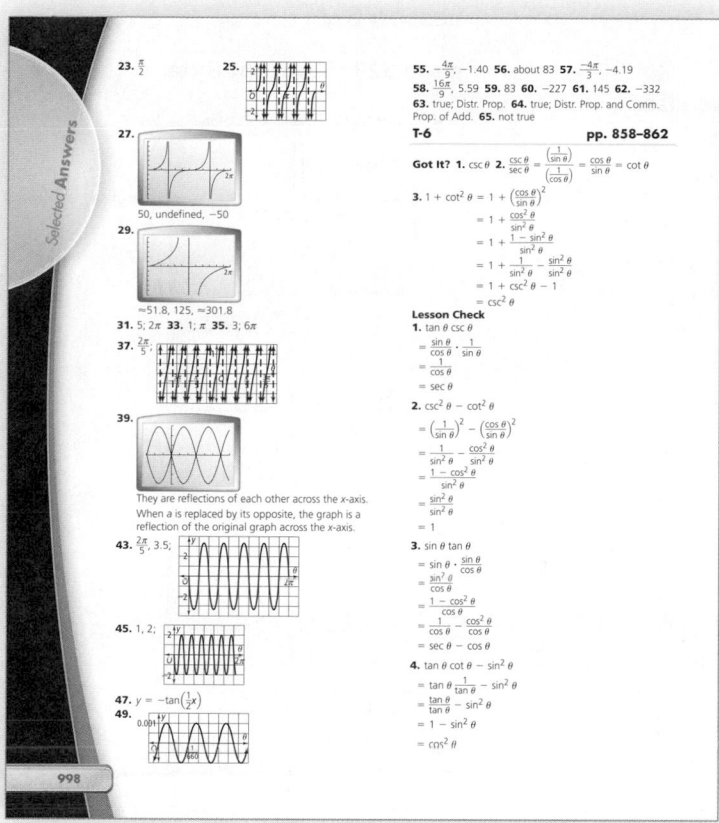

23. $\frac{\pi}{2}$ 25. [graph]

27. [graph]
50, undefined, −50

29. [graph]
≈51.8, 125, ≈301.8

31. 5; 2π 33. 1; π 35. 3; 6π
37. $\frac{2\pi}{5}$; [graph]

39. [graph]
They are reflections of each other across the x-axis. When a is replaced by its opposite, the graph is a reflection of the original graph across the x-axis.

43. $\frac{2\pi}{5}$; 3.5; [graph]
45. 1; 2; [graph]
47. $y = -\tan\left(\frac{1}{2}x\right)$
49. 0.00; [graph]

55. $-\frac{4\pi}{9}$; −1.40 56. about 83 57. $\frac{-4\pi}{3}$; −4.19
58. $\frac{16\pi}{9}$; 5.59 59. 83 60. −227 61. 145 62. −332
63. true; Distr. Prop. 64. true; Distr. Prop. and Comm. Prop. of Add. 65. not true

T-6 pp. 858–862

Got It? 1. $\csc\theta$ **2.** $\dfrac{\csc\theta}{\sec\theta} = \dfrac{\left(\frac{1}{\sin\theta}\right)}{\left(\frac{1}{\cos\theta}\right)} = \dfrac{\cos\theta}{\sin\theta} = \cot\theta$

3. $1 + \cot^2\theta = 1 + \left(\dfrac{\cos\theta}{\sin\theta}\right)^2$
$= 1 + \dfrac{\cos^2\theta}{\sin^2\theta}$
$= 1 + \dfrac{1 - \sin^2\theta}{\sin^2\theta}$
$= 1 + \dfrac{1}{\sin^2\theta} - \dfrac{\sin^2\theta}{\sin^2\theta}$
$= 1 + \csc^2\theta - 1$
$= \csc^2\theta$

Lesson Check
1. $\sin\theta \cdot \csc\theta$
$= \dfrac{\sin\theta}{1} \cdot \dfrac{1}{\sin\theta}$
$= \dfrac{1}{\cos\theta}$
$= \sec\theta$

2. $\csc^2\theta - \cot^2\theta$
$= \left(\dfrac{1}{\sin\theta}\right)^2 - \left(\dfrac{\cos\theta}{\sin\theta}\right)^2$
$= \dfrac{1}{\sin^2\theta} - \dfrac{\cos^2\theta}{\sin^2\theta}$
$= \dfrac{1 - \cos^2\theta}{\sin^2\theta}$
$= \dfrac{\sin^2\theta}{\sin^2\theta}$
$= 1$

3. $\sin\theta + \tan\theta$
$= \sin\theta + \dfrac{\sin\theta}{\cos\theta}$
$= \dfrac{1}{\cos\theta} - \cos\theta$
$= \dfrac{1}{\cos\theta} - \dfrac{\cos^2\theta}{\cos\theta}$
$= \sec\theta - \cos\theta$

4. $\tan\theta\cot\theta - \sin^2\theta$
$= \tan\theta\,\dfrac{1}{\tan\theta} - \sin^2\theta$
$= 1 - \sin^2\theta$
$= \cos^2\theta$

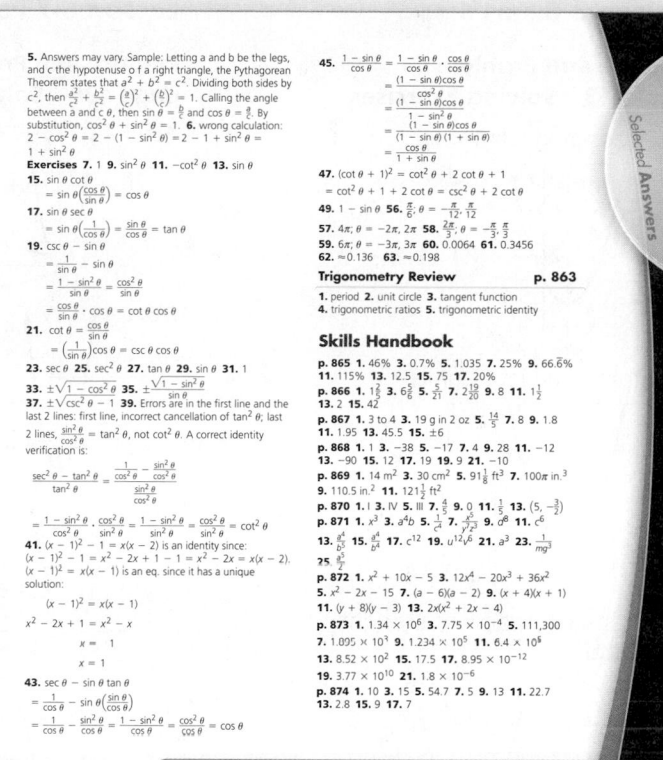

5. Answers may vary. Sample: Letting a and b be the legs, and c the hypotenuse of a right triangle, the Pythagorean Theorem states that $a^2 + b^2 = c^2$. Dividing both sides by c^2, then $\frac{a^2}{c^2} + \frac{b^2}{c^2} = \left(\frac{a}{c}\right)^2 + \left(\frac{b}{c}\right)^2 = 1$. Calling the angle between a and c θ, then $\sin\theta = \frac{b}{c}$ and $\cos\theta = \frac{a}{c}$. By substitution, $\cos^2\theta + \sin^2\theta = 1$. **6.** wrong calculation: $2 - \cos^2\theta = 2 - (1 - \sin^2\theta) = 2 - 1 + \sin^2\theta = 1 + \sin^2\theta$

Exercises 7. 1 **9.** $\sin^2\theta$ **11.** $-\cot^2\theta$ **13.** $\sin\theta$
15. $\sin\theta\cot\theta$
$= \sin\theta\left(\dfrac{\cos\theta}{\sin\theta}\right) = \cos\theta$
17. $\sin\theta\sec\theta$
$= \sin\theta\left(\dfrac{1}{\cos\theta}\right) = \dfrac{\sin\theta}{\cos\theta} = \tan\theta$
19. $\csc\theta - \sin\theta$
$= \dfrac{1}{\sin\theta} - \sin\theta$
$= \dfrac{1 - \sin^2\theta}{\sin\theta}$
$= \dfrac{\cos^2\theta}{\sin\theta}$
$= \dfrac{\cos\theta}{\sin\theta} \cdot \cos\theta = \cot\theta\cos\theta$
21. $\cot\theta$
$= \left(\dfrac{1}{\sin\theta}\right)\cos\theta = \csc\theta\cos\theta$
23. $\sec\theta$ **25.** $\sec^2\theta$ **27.** $\tan\theta$ **29.** $\sin\theta$ **31.** 1
33. $\pm\sqrt{1 - \cos^2\theta}$ **35.** $\dfrac{\pm\sqrt{1 - \sin^2\theta}}{\sin\theta}$
37. $\pm\sqrt{\csc^2\theta - 1}$ **39.** Errors are in the first line and the last 2 lines: first line, incorrect cancellation of $\tan^2\theta$; last 2 lines, $\frac{\sin^2\theta}{\cos^2\theta} = \tan^2\theta$, not $\cot^2\theta$. A correct identity verification is:

$\dfrac{\sec^2\theta - \tan^2\theta}{\tan^2\theta} = \dfrac{\frac{1}{\cos^2\theta} - \frac{\sin^2\theta}{\cos^2\theta}}{\frac{\sin^2\theta}{\cos^2\theta}}$

$= \dfrac{1 - \sin^2\theta}{\cos^2\theta} \cdot \dfrac{\cos^2\theta}{\sin^2\theta} = \dfrac{1 - \sin^2\theta}{\sin^2\theta} = \dfrac{\cos^2\theta}{\sin^2\theta} = \cot^2\theta$

41. $(x - 1)^2 - 1 = x(x - 2)$ is an identity since:
$(x - 1)^2 - 1 = x^2 - 2x + 1 - 1 = x^2 - 2x = x(x - 2)$.
$(x - 1)^2 = x(x - 1)$ is an eq. since it has a unique solution:
$(x - 1)^2 = x(x - 1)$
$x^2 - 2x + 1 = x^2 - x$
$x = 1$
$x = 1$

43. $\sec\theta - \sin\theta\tan\theta$
$= \dfrac{1}{\cos\theta} - \sin\theta\left(\dfrac{\sin\theta}{\cos\theta}\right)$
$= \dfrac{1}{\cos\theta} - \dfrac{\sin^2\theta}{\cos\theta} = \dfrac{1 - \sin^2\theta}{\cos\theta} = \dfrac{\cos^2\theta}{\cos\theta} = \cos\theta$

45. $\dfrac{1 - \sin\theta}{\cos\theta} = \dfrac{1 - \sin\theta}{\cos\theta} \cdot \dfrac{\cos\theta}{\cos\theta}$
$= \dfrac{(1 - \sin\theta)\cos\theta}{\cos^2\theta}$
$= \dfrac{(1 - \sin\theta)\cos\theta}{1 - \sin^2\theta}$
$= \dfrac{(1 - \sin\theta)\cos\theta}{(1 - \sin\theta)(1 + \sin\theta)}$
$= \dfrac{\cos\theta}{1 + \sin\theta}$

47. $(\cot\theta + 1)^2 = \cot^2\theta + 2\cot\theta + 1$
$= \cot^2\theta + 1 + 2\cot\theta = \csc^2\theta + 2\cot\theta$
49. $1 - \sin\theta$ **56.** $\frac{\pi}{6}$; $\theta = -\frac{\pi}{6}$; $\frac{\pi}{12}$; $\frac{\pi}{12}$
57. 4π; $\theta = -2\pi, 2\pi$ **58.** $\frac{2\pi}{3}$; $\theta = -\frac{\pi}{12}$; $\frac{\pi}{3}$
59. 6π; $\theta = -3\pi, 3\pi$ **60.** 0.0064 **61.** 0.3456
62. ≈0.136 **63.** ≈0.198

Trigonometry Review p. 863
1. period **2.** unit circle **3.** tangent function
4. trigonometric ratios **5.** trigonometric identity

Skills Handbook

p. 865 **1.** 46% **3.** 0.7% **5.** 1.035 **7.** 25% **9.** $66.\overline{6}\%$
11. 115% **13.** 12.5 **15.** 75 **17.** 20%
p. 866 **1.** $1\frac{1}{5}$ **3.** $6\frac{2}{3}$ **5.** $\frac{2}{7}$ **7.** $2\frac{10}{21}$ **9.** 8 **11.** $1\frac{1}{2}$
13. 2 **15.** 42
p. 867 **1.** 3 to 4 **3.** 19 g in 2 oz **5.** $\frac{14}{5}$ **7.** 8 **9.** 1.8
11. 1.95 **13.** 45.5 **15.** ±6
p. 868 **1.** 1 **3.** −38 **5.** −17 **7.** 4 **9.** 28 **11.** −12
13. −90 **15.** 12 **17.** 19 **19.** 9 **21.** −10
p. 869 **1.** 14 m² **3.** 30 cm² **5.** $91\frac{1}{8}$ ft³ **7.** 100π in.³
9. 110.5 in.² **11.** $121\frac{1}{2}$ ft²
p. 870 **1.** I **3.** IV **5.** III **7.** $\frac{4}{9}$ **9.** 0 **11.** $\frac{1}{2}$ **13.** $\left(5, -\frac{3}{2}\right)$
p. 871 **1.** x^3 **3.** a^4b **5.** $\frac{1}{c^4}$ **7.** $\frac{x^4}{y^{23}}$ **9.** 0^6 **11.** c^6
13. $\frac{x^4}{b^5}$ **15.** $\frac{a^4}{b^4}$ **17.** c^{12} **19.** $u^{12}v^6$ **21.** a^3 **23.** $\frac{1}{mg^3}$
25. $\frac{b^9}{a^9}$

p. 872 **1.** $x^2 + 10x - 5$ **3.** $12x^4 - 20x^3 + 36x^2$
5. $x^2 - 2x - 15$ **7.** $(a - 6)(a - 2)$ **9.** $(x + 4)(x + 1)$
11. $(y + 8)(y - 3)$ **13.** $2x(x^2 + 2x - 4)$
p. 873 **1.** 1.34×10^6 **3.** 7.75×10^{-4} **5.** 111,300
7. 1.095×10^9 **9.** 1.234×10^5 **11.** 6.4×10^6
13. 8.52×10^2 **15.** 17.5 **17.** 8.95×10^{-12}
19. 3.77×10^{10} **21.** 1.8×10^{-6}
p. 874 **1.** 10 **3.** 15 **5.** 54.7 **7.** 5 **9.** 13 **11.** 22.7
13. 2.8 **15.** 9 **17.** 7

---

p. 875
1.
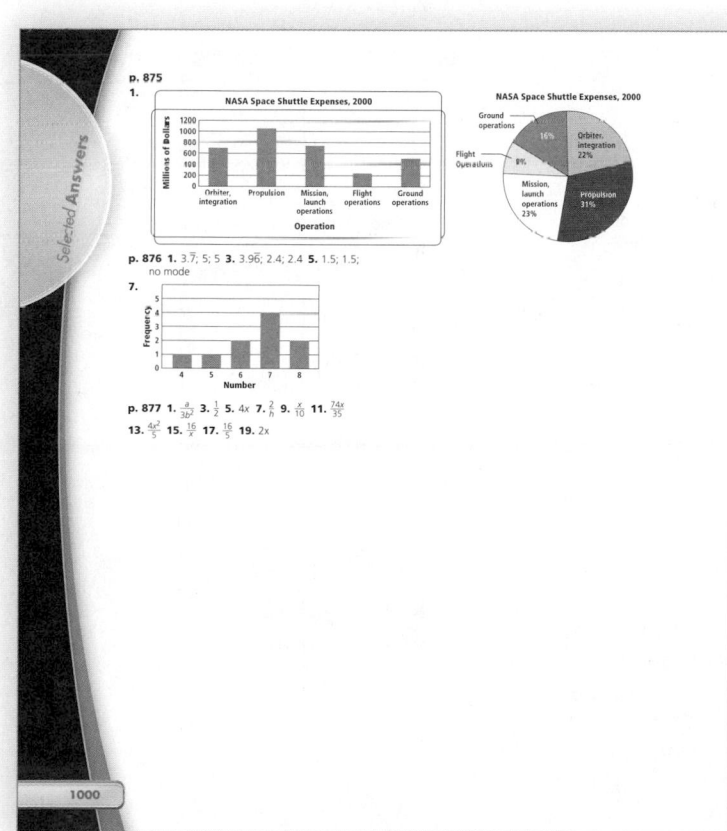
NASA Space Shuttle Expenses, 2000

p. 876 **1.** $3.\overline{7}$; 5; 5 **3.** $3.9\overline{6}$; 2.4; 2.4 **5.** 1.5; 1.5; no mode
7. [histogram]

p. 877 **1.** $\frac{a}{3b^2}$ **3.** $\frac{1}{2}$ **5.** $4x$ **7.** $\frac{2}{h}$ **9.** $\frac{x}{10}$ **11.** $\frac{74x}{35}$
13. $\frac{4x^2}{5}$ **15.** $\frac{16}{x}$ **17.** $\frac{16}{5}$ **19.** $2x$

Additional Answers

Chapter 2

Lesson 2-6 Part 1

Practice and Problem
page 113   Solving Exercises

15. translated left 1 unit

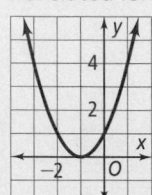

16. translated left 3 units

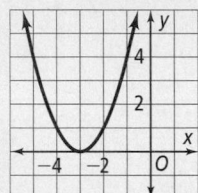

17. translated horizontally right 6 units

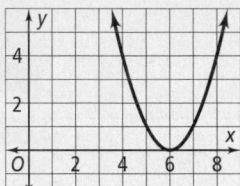

18. a.

x	f(x)
2	0
3	2
5	3.5
6	0

x	f(x + 3)
−1	0
0	2
2	3.5
3	0

b.

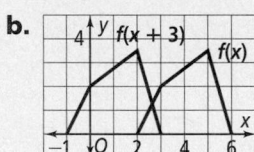

19. Check students' work.

20. translated 6 units down

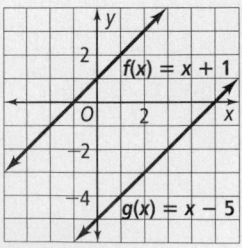

21. translated 4 units up

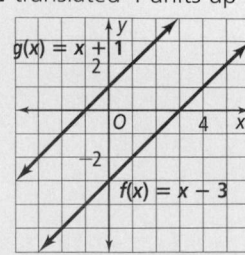

Chapter 6

Lesson 6-7 Part 1

Practice and Problem
page 436   Solving Exercises

19.

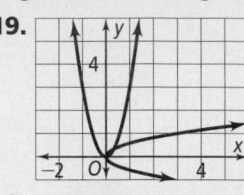

20.

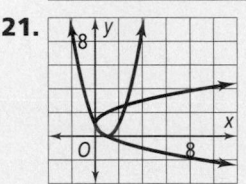

21.

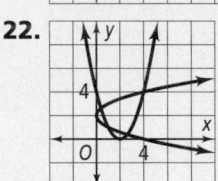

22.

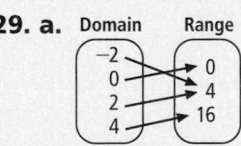

23. $f^{-1}(x) = \sqrt[3]{x}$; yes

24. $f^{-1}(x) = \pm\sqrt[4]{x}$; no

25. $f^{-1}(x) = \pm\sqrt{\dfrac{5x - 5}{2}}$; no

26. $f^{-1}(x) = \pm\sqrt{\dfrac{2x + 8}{3}}$; no

27. $f^{-1}(x) = \pm 2\sqrt{\dfrac{x}{3}}$; no

28. $f^{-1}(x) = \dfrac{x^2 - 6x + 10}{2}$; yes

29. a.
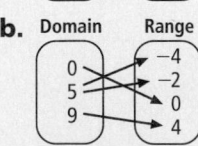

Domain: −2, 0, 2, 4
Range: 0, 4, 16

b.

Domain: 0, 5, 9
Range: −4, −2, 0, 4

30. a. The horizontal line test tells you if there is more than one x-value for every y-value. Since the graph of f^{-1} interchanges the x and y values of f, if f passes the horizontal line test, f^{-1} will pass the vertical line test and it will be a function.

b. no

Chapter 8

Lesson 8-2

page 529   Concept Byte

5.

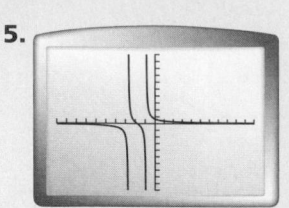

6.

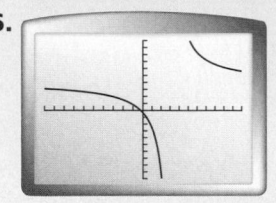

7.

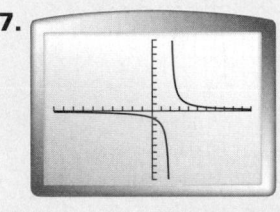

8.

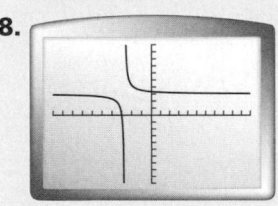

9.

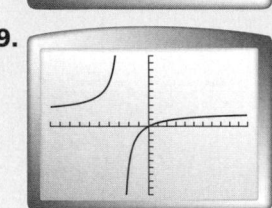

10.

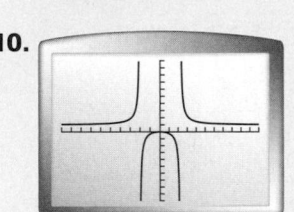

11.

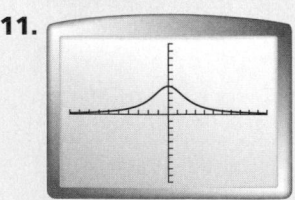

Chapter 10

Get Ready

page 631 Get Ready!

15. $y = 2(x - 1)^2 + 8$

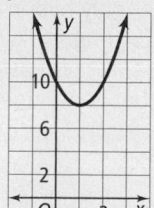

16. $y = -3\left(x - \frac{1}{6}\right)^2 + \frac{1}{12}$

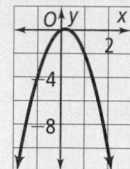

17.

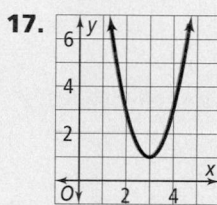

18.

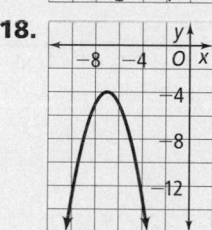

19.

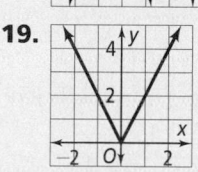

20.

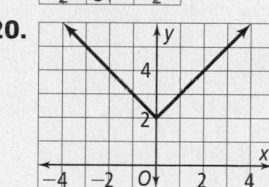

21. The radius of a circle is the distance from the center of the circle to any pt. on the circle. The radius extends in every direction from the center and ends on the circumference of the circle. All radii of the same circle are equal.

22. The vertex of a parabola is the lowest or highest pt. of a parabola; it is the pt. where the parabola changes direction.

Lesson 10-1

Practice and Problem
page 638   Solving Exercises

13.

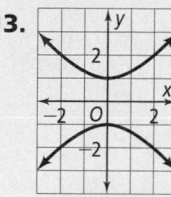

hyperbola; center: (0, 0); no x-intercepts, y-intercepts: (0, ±1); lines of sym.: x-axis and y-axis; domain: all real numbers, range: $y \le -1$ or $y \ge 1$

14.

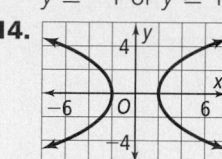

hyperbola; center: (0, 0); x-intercepts: (±2, 0), no y-intercepts; lines of sym.: x-axis and y-axis; domain: $x \le -2$ or $x \ge 2$, range: all real numbers

15.

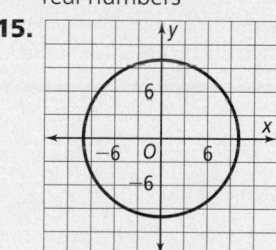

circle; center: (0, 0); radius: 10; x-intercepts: (±10, 0), y-intercepts: (0, ±10); infinitely many lines of sym.; domain: $-10 \le x \le 10$, range: $-10 \le y \le 10$

16.

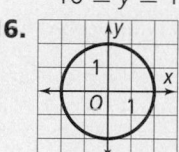

circle; center: (0, 0); radius: 2; x-intercepts: (±2, 0), y-intercepts: (0, ±2); infinitely many lines of sym.; domain: $-2 \le x \le 2$, range: $-2 \le y \le 2$

17.

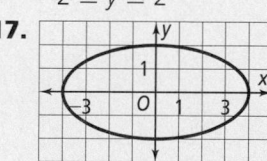

ellipse; center: (0, 0); x-intercepts: (±4, 0), y-intercepts: (0, ±2); lines of sym.: x-axis and y-axis; domain: $-4 \le x \le 4$, range: $-2 \le y \le 2$

18.

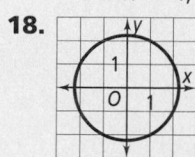

circle; center: (0, 0); radius: $\sqrt{5}$; x-intercepts: (±$\sqrt{5}$, 0), y-intercepts:

(0, ±$\sqrt{5}$); infinitely many lines of sym.; domain: $-\sqrt{5} \le x \le \sqrt{5}$, range: $-\sqrt{5} \le y \le \sqrt{5}$

19.

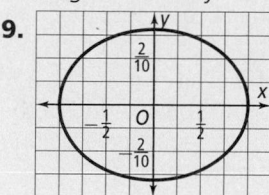

ellipse; center: (0, 0); x-intercepts: (±1, 0), y-intercepts: $\left(0, \pm\frac{1}{3}\right)$; lines of sym.: x-axis and y-axis; domain: $-1 \le x \le 1$, range: $-\frac{1}{3} \le y \le \frac{1}{3}$

20.

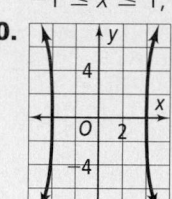

hyperbola; center: (0, 0); x-intercepts: (±4, 0), no y-intercepts; lines of sym.: x-axis and y-axis; domain: $x \le -4$ or $x \ge 4$, range: all real numbers

21.

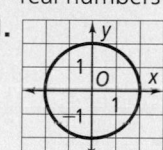

circle; center: (0, 0); radius: 2; x-intercepts: (±2, 0), y-intercepts: (0, ±2); infinitely many lines of sym.; domain: $-2 \le x \le 2$, range: $-2 \le y \le 2$

22.

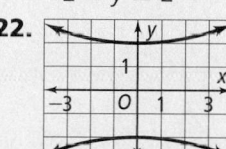

hyperbola; center: (0, 0); no x-intercepts, y-intercepts: (0, ±2); lines of sym.: x-axis and y-axis; domain: all real numbers, range: $y \le -2$ or $y \ge 2$

23.

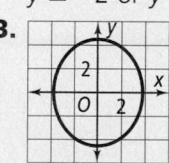

ellipse; center: (0, 0); x-intercepts: $\left(\pm\frac{8\sqrt{5}}{5}, 0\right)$, y-intercepts: (0, ±2$\sqrt{5}$); lines of sym.: x-axis and y-axis; domain: $-\frac{8\sqrt{5}}{5} \le x \le \frac{8\sqrt{5}}{5}$, range: $-2\sqrt{5} \le y \le 2\sqrt{5}$

24. parabola: Hold the lamp so that the edge of the shade furthest from the wall is parallel to the plane of the wall.

circle: Hold the lamp so that the circular top rim of the shade is parallel to the wall.

hyperbola: Let the lamp sit in a normal, upright position, but close enough to the wall for the bottom rim of the shade to almost touch the wall.

ellipse: Hold the lamp at an angle so that the light from the top of the shade gives a closed, curved oblong area of light on the wall.

25. a. All lines in the plane that pass through the center of a circle are axes of sym. of the circle.

b. The axes of sym. of an ellipse intersect at the center of the ellipse. The same is true for a hyperbola. This can be confirmed using, for example, $4x^2 + 9y^2 = 36$ and $4x^2 - 9y^2 = 36$.

26.

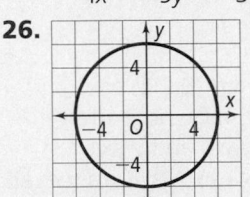

$x^2 + y^2 = 36$

27.

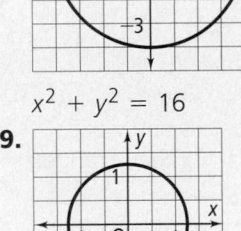

$x^2 + y^2 = \frac{1}{4}$

28.

$x^2 + y^2 = 16$

29.

$x^2 + y^2 = 1.5625$

page 640   Concept Byte

7. a.

x-intercepts: $(\pm 4.5, 0)$, y-intercepts: $(0, \pm 4.5)$

c. Check students' work.

d. circle with center at the origin and radius 4.5

8.

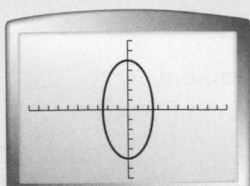

x-intercepts: $(\pm 2.5, 0)$, y-intercepts: $(0, \pm 5)$

9.

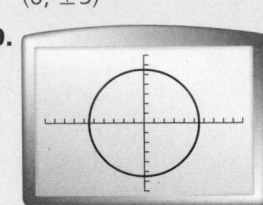

x-intercepts: $(\pm \sqrt{30}, 0)$, y-intercepts: $(0, \pm \sqrt{30})$

10. .

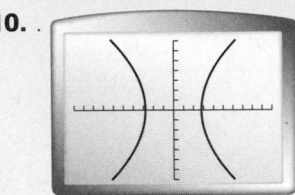

x-intercepts: $(\pm 2\sqrt{2}, 0)$, no y-intercepts

11. Parabolas with a vert. axis of sym.; other conic sections have the x-axis as a line of sym., so they fail the vert. line test.

Chapter Test

page 679   Chapter Test

20. foci: $(0, \pm 4\sqrt{3})$

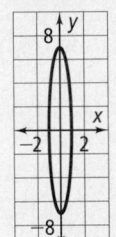

21. foci: $(0, \pm \sqrt{3})$

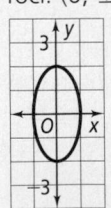

22. foci: $(\pm 2\sqrt{17}, 0)$

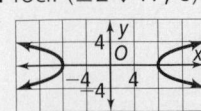

23. foci: $(0, \pm \sqrt{226})$

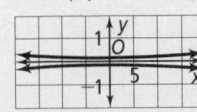

24. $\frac{x^2}{16} + \frac{y^2}{9} = 1$

25. $\frac{x^2}{25} + \frac{y^2}{36} = 1$

26. $\frac{x^2}{9} - \frac{y^2}{16} = 1$

27. $\frac{y^2}{25} - \frac{x^2}{24} = 1$

28. hyperbola; the only conic sections that have two foci are ellipses and hyperbolas. Of these, only hyperbolas can have a domain or range of all real numbers (ellipses always have domain and range that is bounded).

29. circle

30. Check students' work.

Chapter 12

Lesson 12-4

Practice and Problem page 802   Solving Exercises

8. $\begin{bmatrix} 1 & 1 \\ 1 & -2 \end{bmatrix}\begin{bmatrix} x \\ y \end{bmatrix} = \begin{bmatrix} 5 \\ -4 \end{bmatrix}$; coefficient matrix: $\begin{bmatrix} 1 & 1 \\ 1 & -2 \end{bmatrix}$, variable matrix: $\begin{bmatrix} x \\ y \end{bmatrix}$, constant matrix: $\begin{bmatrix} 5 \\ -4 \end{bmatrix}$

9. $\begin{bmatrix} -3 & 1 \\ 1 & 0 \end{bmatrix}\begin{bmatrix} x \\ y \end{bmatrix} = \begin{bmatrix} -7 \\ 2 \end{bmatrix}$; coefficient matrix: $\begin{bmatrix} -3 & 1 \\ 1 & 0 \end{bmatrix}$, variable matrix: $\begin{bmatrix} x \\ y \end{bmatrix}$, constant matrix: $\begin{bmatrix} -7 \\ 2 \end{bmatrix}$

10. $\begin{bmatrix} 1 & 3 & -1 \\ 1 & 0 & 2 \\ 0 & 2 & -1 \end{bmatrix}\begin{bmatrix} x \\ y \\ z \end{bmatrix} = \begin{bmatrix} 2 \\ 8 \\ 1 \end{bmatrix}$; coefficient matrix: $\begin{bmatrix} 1 & 3 & -1 \\ 1 & 0 & 2 \\ 0 & 2 & -1 \end{bmatrix}$, variable matrix: $\begin{bmatrix} x \\ y \\ z \end{bmatrix}$, constant matrix: $\begin{bmatrix} 2 \\ 8 \\ 1 \end{bmatrix}$

11. $(6, 2)$

12. no unique solution

13. $(16, -22)$

Index

A

absolute value
  defined, 43
  equations, 43–52
  inequalities, 43–52, 61, 131
  of algebraic expressions, 56
  of complex numbers, 269
  of real numbers, 43
  symbols, 45

absolute value function(s)
  compression, 123
  defined, 138
  family of, 122, 137
  general form of, 124
  graphing, 122, 138
  stretching, 123
  writing, 124

Absolute Value Parent function, 121

*Activities, Games, and Puzzles
    worksheets,* 10B, 17B, 24B, 32B, 42B,
    52B, 73B, 80B, 87B, 97B, 109B, 120B,
    127B, 134B, 153B, 161B, 167B, 174B,
    183B, 191B, 211B, 219B, 225B, 236B,
    250B, 259B, 267B, 277B, 299B, 309B,
    317B, 326B, 339B, 345B, 32B, 360B,
    367B, 386B, 394B, 401B, 411B, 425B,
    432B, 442B, 450B, 469B, 479B, 487B,
    479B, 506B, 528B, 537B, 546B, 554B,
    564B, 571B, 591B, 598B, 606B, 613B,
    621B, 639B, 648B, 656B, 665B, 673B,
    694B, 703B, 710B, 717B, 731B, 737B,
    743B, 751B, 759B, 779B, 788B, 798B,
    808B

Activity
  Dynamic. *See* Dynamic Activities
  Graphing Inverses, 443
  Linear Programming, 175
  Quadratic Inequalities, 279–280
  Using Logarithms for Exponential Models,
    507
  Writing Equations From Roots, 251

addition. *See also* summation
  inverse operation to, 27
  of complex numbers, 271
  of function, 426, 427
  of matrices, 772–776
  of radical expressions, 395–401
  of rational expressions, 555, 556, 576

Additional Problems, 6, 13, 20, 28, 35, 40,
    48, 66, 71, 76, 83, 90, 94, 105, 112,
    116, 123, 130, 148, 155, 158, 164, 171,
    178, 186, 206, 214, 217, 222, 229, 233,
    244, 247, 253, 256, 262, 270, 275, 294,
    302, 306, 312, 315, 320, 323, 333, 337,
    342, 349, 355, 363, 383, 389, 391, 397,
    404, 408, 419, 423, 428, 435, 439, 446,
    464, 472, 477, 482, 493, 500, 504, 522,
    532, 540, 550, 557, 561, 567, 586, 594,
    602, 609, 616, 636, 643, 651, 660, 668,
    688, 691, 696, 699, 706, 713, 725, 734,
    740, 747, 754, 774, 783, 791, 795, 801,
    804

Addition Property
  of Equality, 27
  of Inequality, 34

additive identity, 13, 14

additive inverse
  defined, 14
  matrices, 775
  opposites, 14

algebraic expressions, 18–24
  defined, 5
  dividing, 21
  evaluating, 19, 56
  modeling words with, 18–19
  representing patterns using, 5, 55
  simplifying, 21, 56, 61
  subtracting, 21

angle
  central, 841
  reference, 835
  tangent of, 852–854

applications
  academics, 384
  acoustics, 505
  advertising, 730
  aerodynamics, 664
  agriculture, 235, 758
  air pollution, 266
  air quality, 173
  air travel, 359
  aircraft, 567, 569
  airline tickets, 765
  aquarium, 6
  athletics, 605
  automobiles, 49, 764, 846
  aviation, 31
  awards, 693
  bacteria growth, 173
  baking, 265, 475
  banking, 19, 57
  basketball, 221
  battery life, 749
  boat building, 385
  bonus, 609
  bridges, 58, 214, 217, 344
  bus travel, 31
  car racing, 49
  career, 724
  carpentry, 308
  class project, 23
  climate, 51, 856
  clubs, 534
  collecting, 9
  college enrollment, 166
  comets, 672
  communications, 156, 223, 620, 670
  competition, 247
  computer use, 104
  concerts, 120
  conservation, 78
  construction, 41, 58, 496, 536, 551, 827
  consumer issues, 693
  cooking, 51, 173, 365
  crafts, 323, 490
  data collection, 742
  decorations, 166
  demographics, 148
  depreciation, 490
  design, 854
  discounts, 453
  distance, 78
  earthquakes, 482, 486, 505
  education, 712, 714
  electricity, 16, 59
  electronics, 449
  endangered species, 466
  energy, 736, 742
  entertainment, 35, 130, 247, 590, 742
  estimation, 224
  exercise, 589, 805
  financial planning, 19, 23, 57, 182, 619
  fitness, 806

  flight, 567
  flower carpets, 28
  food, 17, 106
  food production, 108, 355
  fuel economy, 561, 570
  fundraising, 164, 265, 526
  games, 701
  gardening, 28, 166, 339
  gasoline mileage, 536
  geometry, 31, 41, 59, 72, 190, 308, 317,
    325, 326, 351, 389, 393, 400, 440, 590,
    598, 700, 702, 797
  grades, 41, 385, 545, 570, 611
  grocery, 612
  harmony, 563
  health, 526
  home prices, 105
  hydraulics, 420
  income, 597, 736
  investing/investment, 23, 197, 478, 490,
    513, 599
  land, 794
  landscaping, 219, 249, 448, 523
  languages, 706
  long distance phone calls, 79
  lottery, 702
  machinery, 655
  manufacturing, 59, 60, 108, 182, 210,
    553, 748
  market research, 713
  marketing, 750
  measurement, 308, 455
  metalwork, 308
  mileage, 536, 561, 570
  miniature golf, 663
  money, 19, 23, 57, 156
  motor vehicles, 687
  movie rentals, 35
  movie tickets, 101
  musical, 57, 120, 155, 563, 847, 857
  nature, 208
  navigation, 567
  nutrition, 807
  optics, 563
  optimal height, 405
  packaging design, 298
  paint/painting, 191, 526
  pharmacology, 545
  planetary motion, 404
  population, 148, 467, 468, 708
  postage/postal rates, 224
  potential energy, 526
  projectile motion, 264
  public opinion, 739
  quality control, 750
  reading, 708
  recreation, 139, 832
  resource management, 500
  restaurant, 17
  road safety, 224
  sales, 76, 197, 262, 431, 813
  satellite dish, 672
  satellites, 393
  savings, 19, 57, 465, 467, 596
  scheduling, 689
  science, 135, 410, 604
  security, 693
  shopping, 192, 813
  sky diving, 65
  snacks, 190
  solar reflector, 644
  sound, 639, 648, 661, 856
  space, 846

Index

Index

Acknowledgments

Staff Credits

The people who made up the High School Mathematics team—representing composition services, core design digital and multimedia production services, digital product development, editorial, editorial services, manufacturing, marketing, and production management—are listed below.

Dan Anderson, Scott Andrews, Christopher Anton, Carolyn Artin, Michael Avidon, Margaret Banker, Charlie Bink, Niki Birbilis, Suzanne Biron, Beth Blumberg, Kyla Brown, Rebekah Brown, Judith Buice, Sylvia Bullock, Stacie Cartwright, Carolyn Chappo, Christia Clarke, Tom Columbus, Andrew Coppola, AnnMarie Coyne, Bob Craton, Nicholas Cronin, Patrick Culleton, Damaris Curran, Steven Cushing, Sheila DeFazio, Cathie Dillender, Emily Dumas, Patty Fagan, Frederick Fellows, Jorgensen Fernandez, Mandy Figueroa, Suzanne Finn, Sara Freund, Matt Frueh, Jon Fuhrer, Andy Gaus, Mark Geyer, Mircea Goia, Andrew Gorlin, Shelby Gragg, Ellen Granter, Jay Grasso, Lisa Gustafson, Toni Haluga, Greg Ham, Marc Hamilton, Chris Handorf, Angie Hanks, Scott Harris, Cynthia Harvey, Phil Hazur, Thane Heninger, Aun Holland, Amanda House, Chuck Jann, Linda Johnson, Blair Jones, Marian Jones, Tim Jones, Gillian Kahn, Brian Keegan, Jonathan Kier, Jennifer King, Tamara King, Elizabeth Krieble, Meytal Kotik, Brian Kubota, Roshni Kutty, Mary Landry, Christopher Langley, Christine Lee, Sara Levendusky, Lisa Lin, Wendy Marberry, Dominique Mariano, Clay Martin, Rich McMahon, Eve Melnechuk, Cynthia Metallides, Hope Morley, Christine Nevola, Michael O'Donnell, Michael Oster, Ameer Padshah, Jeffrey Paulhus, Jonathan Penyack, Valerie Perkins, Brian Reardon, Wendy Rock, Marcy Rose, Carol Roy, Irene Rubin, Hugh Rutledge, Vicky Shen, Jewel Simmons, Ted Smykal, Emily Soltanoff, William Speiser, Jayne Stevenson, Richard Sullivan, Dan Tanguay, Dennis Tarwood, Susan Tauer, Tiffany Taylor-Sullivan, Catherine Terwilliger, Mark Tricca, Maria Torti, Leonid Tunik, Ilana Van Veen, Lauren Van Wart, John Vaughan, Laura Vivenzio, Samuel Voigt, Kathy Warfel, Don Weide, Laura Wheel, Eric Whitfield, Sequoia Wild, Joseph Will, Kristin Winters, Allison Wyss, Dina Zolotusky

Additional Credits: Michele Cardin, Robert Carlson, Kate Dalton-Hoffman, Dana Guterman, Narae Maybeth, Carolyn McGuire, Manjula Nair, Rachel Terino, Steve Thomas

Illustration

Stephen Durke: 574; **Phil Guzy:** 596, 597; **Rob Schuster:** 4, 5, 11, 18, 26, 33, 39, 41, 48, 60, 68, 74, 81, 84, 99, 107, 114, 116, 134, 142, 143, 149, 157, 165, 166, 168, 171, 174, 194, 202, 207, 216, 226, 233, 240, 258, 280, 288, 294, 296, 303, 308, 312, 325, 326, 331, 367, 374, 375, 381, 390, 395, 398, 405, 414, 429, 434, 449, 451, 469, 498, 515, 522, 527, 534, 542, 547, 564, 566, 567, 570, 571, 572, 580, 587, 595, 609, 614, 617, 619, 630, 639, 641, 649, 687; **Pronk&Associates:** 12, 362, 399, 462, 589; **XNR Productions:** 797

Technical Illustration

GGS Book Services

Photography

All photographs not listed are the property of Pearson Education

Back Cover: Klein J.-L & Hube/Biosphoto

Page 3, ©Franck Seguin/Corbis; **28,** ©BL Images Ltd/Alamy; **41,** ©Richard Wahlstrom/JupiterImages; **49,** ©UPI Photo/Roger Williams/Newscom; **63,** ©Joe McBride/Getty Images; **65,** ©JUPITERIMAGES/Brand X/Alamy; **65,** ©JUPITERIMAGES/Brand X/Alamy; **65,** ©JUPITERIMAGES/Brand X/Alamy; **65,** ©Roberto Mettifogo/Getty Images; **93,** ©www.indepthexposure.com; **93,** ©Zen Shui/SuperStock; **145,** ©Hisham Ibrahim/Getty Images; **147,** ©Doug Perrine/Peter Arnold Inc.; **147,** ©PAUL NICKLEN/National Geographic Stock; **171,** ©Andy Crawford/Dorling Kindersley; **171,** ©Thomas Northcut/Photodisc/Getty Images; **171,** ©Steve Gorton/Dorling Kindersley; **203,** ©Atlantide Phototravel/Corbis; **208,** ©Stuart Westmorland/Getty Images; **217,** Jeff Greenberg/PhotoEdit Inc.; **221,** ©Thomas Barwick/Getty Images; **247,** ©Andy Harmer/Photo Researchers, Inc.; **247,** ©Harvey Lloyd/Getty Images; **253,** ©Rolf Hicker Photography/Alamy; **291,** ©Claudius/zefa/Corbis; **323,** ©James Baigrie/Botanica/Jupiterimages; **355,** ©D. Hurst/Alamy; **355,** ©Peter Cade/Getty Images; **355,** ©D. Hurst/Alamy; **355,** ©FOOD DRINK AND DIET/MARK SYKES/Alamy; **355,** ©Andre Gallant/Getty Images; **364,** ©Ed Darack/Getty Images; **379,** ©Jake Norton/Getty Images; **396,** ©Panoramic Images/Getty Images; **404,** ©Detlev van Ravenswaay/Photo Researchers, Inc.; **419,** ©Bob Llewellyn/Jupiterimages; **438,** ©Bob Krist/CORBIS; **461,** ©Peter Mason/Getty Images; **466,** ©Jose B. Ruiz/npl/Minden Pictures; **482,** ©Earth Imaging/Getty Images; **496,** ©Jerry Lodriguss/Photo Researchers, Inc; **519,** ©Stephen Dalton/Minden Pictures; **524,** ©Corbis Super RF/Alamy; **524,** ©Chase Jarvis/Photolibrary; **536,** ©NASA-HQ-GRIN; **567,** ©NASA - JPL; **583,** ©Yu Xiangquan/Xinhua Press/Corbis; **638,** ©B.A.E. Inc./Alamy; **661,** ©Museum of Science and Industry; **673,** Photolibrary; **675,** Ron Chapple Stock/Corbis; **684,** Koji Aoki/Aflo/Getty Images; **755,** Jim Sanborn; **767 both,** Jason Lugo/iStockphoto; **795,** Wolfgang Spunbarg/PhotoEdit; **819,** Ron Watts/Getty Images; **839 t,** Steve Gorton/Dorling Kindersley; **839 b,** European Space/Photo Researchers; **881,** Demetrio Carrasco/Dorling Kindersley; **895,** AFP PHOTO/Fabrice/Newscom; **913,** age footstock/SuperStock, **923,** mediacolor's/Alamy.